Addison-Wesley

Geometry

Teacher's Edition

Stanley R. Clemens
Phares G. O'Daffer
Thomas J. Cooney
John A. Dossey

Teacher's Edition
Freddie Lee Renfro

▲▼ **ADDISON-WESLEY PUBLISHING COMPANY**
Menlo Park, California · Reading, Massachusetts · New York
Don Mills, Ontario · Wokingham, England · Amsterdam · Bonn
Sydney · Singapore · Tokyo · Madrid · San Juan

Editorial Staff: Mary Fraser, Project Editor;
    Joe Todaro, Tony Watkins
Photo Editor: Margee Huntzicker

Cover photograph: © Ken Graham / AllStock

ISBN 0-201-81261-4

1 2 3 4 5 6 7 8 9 10-VH-96 95 94 93

Authors

Stanley R. Clemens is Professor of Mathematics at Bluffton College. He received a B.A. from Bluffton College, an M.A. from Indiana University, and a Ph.D. in Mathematics from the University of North Carolina. Dr. Clemens has written several journal articles and co-authored *Laboratory Investigations in Geometry* and *Geometry: An Investigative Approach,* both published by Addison-Wesley.

Phares G. O'Daffer is Professor Emeritus of Mathematics at Illinois State University. He received a B.A. and an M.A. in mathematics from Illinois State University, and a Ph.D. in Mathematics Education from the University of Illinois. Formerly a high school teacher, Dr. O'Daffer is the author or co-author of numerous articles and textbooks, including *Experiences With Geometry, Laboratory Investigations in Geometry,* and *Geometry: An Investigative Approach,* all published by Addison Wesley. He has also served as president of the Illinois Council of Teachers of Mathematics.

Thomas J. Cooney is Professor of Mathematics Education at the University of Georgia. A former high school mathematics teacher who taught geometry for six years, he received a B.A. and an M.A. from the University of Toledo and a Ph.D. in Mathematics Education from the University of Illinois. Dr. Cooney is a member of the Evaluation Working Group for the development of the Curriculum and Evaluation Standards for the National Council of Mathematics Teachers, and is Issue Editor for the 1990 NCTM yearbook. He has numerous publications on teaching mathematics and is a frequent speaker at national and international meetings.

John A. Dossey is Professor of Mathematics at Illinois State University, where he received a B.A. and an M.A; he received a Ph.D. from the University of Illinois. He has taught at every level from grade 7 through graduate school and has been a K–12 supervisor of mathematics. During 1986–88, Dr. Dossey served as President of NCTM. He has also served on the Mathematics Science Education Board, the National Research Council, and the Mathematical Association of America's Board of Governors. He is co-author of *Addison Wesley Essentials of Mathematics.*

Teacher's Edition Author

Freddie Lee Renfro is a K–12 Mathematics Coordinator at LaPorte Independent School District, LaPorte, Texas. She received a B.A. and an M.A. from Lamar University and Texas Southern University, respectively. Ms. Renfro also served as a consultant on *Addison-Wesley Pre-Algebra.*

Consultants

Paul J. Hartle, Edgewater High School, Orlando, Florida

Barry L. Kauffman, Penn Manor School District, Millersville, Pennsylvania

Brenda Blakemore Morrow, Goose Creek High School, Goose Creek, South Carolina

Carol A. Smith, California State Polytechnic University, Pomona, California

Donald Swanson, Evergreen High School, Seattle, Washington

Bruce A. Thornquist, Downers Grove South High School, Downers Grove, Illinois

Reviewers

Debbie Alford, Miami Southridge Senior High School, Miami, Florida

Donald Ault, West Orange High School, Winter Garden, Florida

Eva Gates, Pasadena Independent School District, Pasadena, Texas

Gerry Greer, Broward County School System, Fort Lauderdale, Florida

Nadine Harrison, Bines High School, Plano, Texas

Arthur C. Howard, Aldine Independent School District, Houston, Texas

Richard E. Neiman, Dover High School, Dover, Delaware

Barbara E. Pohla, Elsik High School, Alief, Texas

Elizabeth Ann Przybysz, Dr. Phillips High School, Orlando, Florida

Jack R. Sorteberg, Burnsville High School, Burnsville, Minnesota

Herbert Wills III, Florida State University, Tallahassee, Florida

Contents

1 Basic Ideas of Geometry

2 Introduction to Proof

5   Using Congruent Triangles

6   Similarity

7 Right Triangles

8 Circles

9 Constructions and Loci

10 Area and Perimeter of Polygons

11 Surface Area and Volume

12 Coordinate Geometry

13 Transformations

Appendix

Teacher's Resource Packages

Your deep-pocket resource for management and instruction comes to you as a set of ten supplements, each addressing a different daily teaching challenge.

Five instruction supplements provide a treasury of help, motivation, and creative stimulus for every student in your class.

Five management aids support you from student placement to final evaluation.

Lesson Plan Book

Detailed one-page lesson plans with objectives and NCTM Standards correlations.

First Five Minutes Transparency Masters

Fast class starters from the FIRST FIVE MINUTES feature in your Teacher's Edition.

Active Learning

Management guide for using the program materials in a student-directed setting with suggestions for cooperative learning.

Assessment

Quizzes and cumulative tests, choice of three levels for chapter tests; placement test.

Teacher's Overhead Manipulative Kit

Includes transparent geoboard, protractor, tangrams, and geometry template.

Skills Practice and Mixed Review

Includes arithmetic and geometry review as well as lesson-correlated practice.

Technology

Calculator activities and BASIC computer projects.

Lab Manual (with Teaching Guide)

Alternative hands-on approaches to topics in the student text, with optional materials such as miras, geoboards, or investigative software.

Enrichment Using Manipulatives

Bonus topics for all students. Includes additional exploratory activities, work with manipulatives, and teaching tools.

SAT Practice

For use with 1993 PSAT and 1994 SAT, includes "grid-in" practice.

Connections/Explorations
Encourage Students to Reach a Higher Level of Mathematical Understanding

✔ Connections
The text helps students to connect
- Geometry to everyday experiences
- Geometry to algebra
- Different geometric approaches

In every lesson, algebra and applications are connected to geometry.

Special features encourage students to solve problems by interacting among synthetic, coordinate, and transformational geometry. See page 422.

You'll also find connections to discrete mathematics. See pages 199, 248.

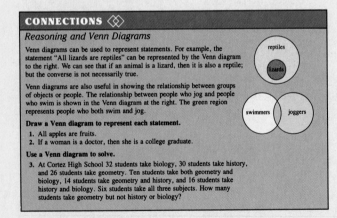

CONNECTIONS ◈◈

Reasoning and Venn Diagrams

Venn diagrams can be used to represent statements. For example, the statement "All lizards are reptiles" can be represented by the Venn diagram to the right. We can see that if an animal is a lizard, then it is also a reptile; but the converse is not necessarily true.

Venn diagrams are also useful in showing the relationship between groups of objects or people. The relationship between people who jog and people who swim is shown in the Venn diagram at the right. The green region represents people who both swim and jog.

Draw a Venn diagram to represent each statement.
1. All apples are fruits.
2. If a woman is a doctor, then she is a college graduate.

Use a Venn diagram to solve.
3. At Cortez High School 32 students take biology, 30 students take history, and 26 students take geometry. Ten students take both geometry and biology, 14 students take geometry and history, and 16 students take history and biology. Six students take all three subjects. How many students take geometry but not history or biology?

✔ Explore
Explore activities provide informal, hands-on experiences. See pages 111, 153.

✔ Computer Activity

✔ Calculator Investigation
Please see the next page for more information about Computer Activity and Calculator Investigation.

Problem Solving/Critical Thinking
Promotes Critical Thinking in a Broad Range of Situations

✔ Problem Solving Strategies
Special one-page features that reinforce students' skills using problem-solving strategies. See page 339.

✔ Math Contest Problems
Challenges students to solve problems like those appearing in math contests. See page 91.

✔ Preparing for College Entrance Exams
These pages promote success with standardized tests. See pages 103, 575.

✔ Critical Thinking Problems
In every exercise set, there are critical thinking problems designed for all levels of students. See pages 19, 110.

✔ Critical Thinking Feature
In every chapter, there is a critical thinking feature to help students develop their thinking skills. See pages 51, 527.

CRITICAL THINKING

Common Errors in Everyday Reasoning

These situations will help you discover or review some common reasoning errors.

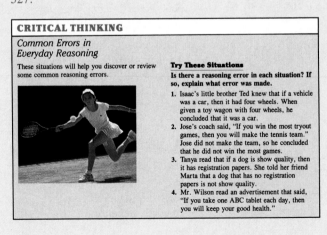

Try These Situations

Is there a reasoning error in each situation? If so, explain what error was made.

1. Isaac's little brother Ted knew that if a vehicle was a car, then it had four wheels. When given a toy wagon with four wheels, he concluded that it was a car.
2. Jose's coach said, "If you win the most tryout games, then you will make the tennis team." Jose did not make the team, so he concluded that he did not win the most games.
3. Tanya read that if a dog is show quality, then it has registration papers. She told her friend Marta that a dog that has no registration papers is not show quality.
4. Mr. Wilson read an advertisement that said, "If you take one ABC tablet each day, then you will keep your good health."

nineties by preparing students for the twenty-first century

Technology
Motivates Students to Explore Geometry

✔ Computer Activity

Students can use software to test cases and make generalizations. See page 110.

✔ Calculator Investigation

This special feature at the end of lessons helps students to explore concepts by using the calculator. See page 500.

Several calculator packages to accompany **Addison-Wesley Geometry** are available for purchase. Please see your Addison-Wesley catalog for more details.

✔ Computer Explorations

Students use software to investigate geometry and form conjectures. See page 634.

✔ References to Software

References to software for use with specific lessons are given in the Teacher's Edition margin. The following software is suggested.

Euclid's Toolbox. Heartland Software, 2025 S. 26th Street, Lincoln, NE 68502, 1990. Macintosh Plus, SE, or II.

The Geometric Supposer: Triangles, Quadrilaterals, Circles. Sunburst Communications, 1987. Apple II, IBM, Macintosh. 1-800-628-8897

GeoDraw: IBM Geometry Series, IBM Corporation, 1987. 1-800-426-2468.

Logo Math Tools and Games, Henri Picciotto. Portland, ME: Terrapin Software, Inc., 1990. Apple IIe, IIgs, Macintosh, IBM. 1-203-878-8200.

Applications
Help Students Learn to Apply Mathematics

✔ Chapter Openers

A question or statement relating to geometry provides a springboard for discussion. See page 104.

✔ Careers

Special pages show how geometry applies to particular careers. See pages 19, 235.

Careers

Surveyor

A surveyor is involved in the construction of buildings, roads, and bridges. One of the surveyor's responsibilities is to establish exact land boundaries by measuring distances and angles accurately. The transit, an instrument invented in the 16th century, is a surveyor's most valuable tool. It is used at the site to measure both distances and angles. Later, at the office, the surveyor uses these measurements and various geometric properties to create a map or drawing of the surveyed land.

✔ Integrated Applications

Applications are connected to geometry throughout the lesson development, and in every exercise set. See pages 270–273.

Addison-Wesley Geometry's clear, consistent lesson structure

BEFORE THE CHAPTER . . .

Chapter Openers The chapter begins with a question or statement relating to Geometry that provides a springboard for discussion.

DURING THE CHAPTER . . .

Objective

The objective for each section appears on the student page.

Lesson Openers

Select lessons in each chapter begin with a special Explore activity that gives students an informal, hands-on experience.

OBJECTIVE: *Apply relationships in 45°–45°–90° and 30°–60°–90° right triangles.*

7-4 Special Right Triangles

EXPLORE Construct three squares and three equilateral triangles of different sizes. Label each as shown.

Measure segments to the nearest millimeter. Find the ratios $\frac{c}{a}$ for each square. Find the ratios $\frac{c}{a}$ and $\frac{b}{a}$ for each triangle.

Recall that $\sqrt{2} \approx 1.414$ and $\sqrt{3} \approx 1.732$. What conjectures can you make about the two special triangles shown above in blue?

Certain special right triangles are frequently involved in applications of mathematics. One of these, an isosceles right triangle, has two 45° angles and is called a **45°–45°–90° triangle.** It is often necessary to find the length of the hypotenuse of a 45°–45°–90° triangle when the length of a leg is known. Theorem 7.7, proved using the Pythagorean Theorem, gives an efficient way to do this.

◆ **THEOREM 7.7** 45°–45°–90° Triangle Theorem
The length of the hypotenuse of a 45°–45°–90° triangle is $\sqrt{2}$ times the length of a leg.

Given: △ABC is a 45°–45°–90° triangle.
Prove: $c = a\sqrt{2}$.

Proof △ABC is a 45°–45°–90° triangle. Using the Pythagorean Theorem, $a^2 + a^2 = c^2$ Simplifying, it follows that $c^2 = 2a^2$, $c = \sqrt{2a^2}$, and $c = a\sqrt{2}$.

Examples

Students' understanding is enhanced by fully worked examples.

Try This Exercises

Following the examples, the Try This exercises provide students with immediate reinforcement of concepts and skills and help teachers diagnose student difficulties.

Example 1
Find the value of c.

Solution
$c = a\sqrt{2}$ *Theorem 7.7*
$c = 5\sqrt{2}$ *Substitute 5 for a.*

Try This
Find the length of the diagonal of a square with side length 12 cm.

Chapter 7 Right Triangles

makes rigorous content accessible to every student

Class Exercises

These exercises consist of Short Answer, Sample Exercises, and Discussion Exercises and are ideal for open discussion or for use with cooperative learning groups.

A Exercises

Students can use the A exercises to reinforce their understanding of the lesson.

B Exercises

By using the B exercises, students discover connections and integrate their understanding of concepts.

C Exercises

Challenge exercises motivate students to use their acquired knowledge creatively.

Critical Thinking Problems

Designed for students of all abilities, a unique set of critical thinking problems is included in every exercise set.

Mixed Review or Algebra Review

Through daily review, students maintain their previously learned skills.

Class Exercises

Short Answer

1. To find the length of the hypotenuse of a 45°–45°–90° triangle, multiply the length of one of the legs by ___ .

Sample Exercises

Find the value of x.

2.

3.

4.

Discussion

5. Draw a 45°–45°–90° triangle and explain how to use variable expressions to give the relative lengths of the sides in terms of x.

Exercises

A

D and E are midpoints of the sides of $\triangle ABC$. **Complete each statement.**

1. If $AB = 8$, then $DE =$ ___ .   2. If $AC = 9$, then $AD =$ ___ .   3. If $BE = 5$, then $BC =$ ___ .

B

4. The perimeter of a square is 36. Find the length of the diagonal of the square.

C

5. The figure is a pyramid with a regular hexagonal base with center C. $DB = 4$, $AB = 17$ Find the height h of the hexagonal pyramid.

Critical Thinking

6. Devise a formula for finding (a) the length of the altitude of an equilateral triangle with side length s, and (b) the area of an equilateral triangle with side length s.

Mixed Review

Use $\square JKLM$ to determine whether each statement is always, sometimes, or never true.

1. $\overline{MN} \cong \overline{NK}$ 2. $\overline{JL} \perp \overline{MK}$

AFTER THE CHAPTER . . .

Chapter Summary   Contains a vocabulary list and a list of key points from the chapter.

Chapter Review   Contains review problems for each section.

Chapter Test   Provides three test items per objective so you can test students' mastery of the objectives.

Addison-Wesley Geometry Teacher's Edition provides tools

BEFORE THE CHAPTER . . .
Four special chapter planning guide pages provide for planning, assignment, and assessment.

DURING THE CHAPTER . . .

Chapter Overview Provides a quick summary of the chapter's content.
Chapter Objectives List all objectives for the chapter.
Teaching Guide Provides suggestions for cooperative learning, alternative assessment, and communication ideas for each chapter. A multicultural note and

possible investigations or projects are also included.
Multi-Level Management Guide Helps teachers adjust plans appropriately for different level classes. The guides include suggestions for planning each lesson and utilize all of the supplementary materials.

First Five Minutes

Provides a quiz on the previous lesson.

Lesson Opener

Suggests ways the teacher can introduce the lesson—sometimes includes an Explore activity.

Materials

Lists the materials needed for the lesson.

Teaching Notes

Notes and suggestions are provided to help teach the lesson content.

When appropriate, the **Teaching Notes** include
• **Key questions** to stimulate class discussion
• **Error Analysis** to help guide students to avoid error patterns
• **Enrichment Activities** to provide extensions to the lesson
• **Key Terms** list

First Five Minutes

(Quiz on previous lesson)

1. If M is the midpoint of $\overline{PS}$, $PM = 5x + 3$, and $MS = 33$, find the value of x. 6
2. The statement $m\angle MPV = m\angle MST$ is equivalent to the statement ___?___ .
$\angle MPV \cong \angle MST$

Lesson Opener

To demonstrate the rigidity of the triangle, have students work in small groups to join together at the endpoints three strips of tagboard that have the following measurements:
a. 12 cm, 16 cm, 26 cm
b. 8 cm, 12 cm, 26 cm

Materials

student notebooks
tagboard
paper fasteners

Teaching Notes

Point out that triangles are classified by their sides (scalene, isosceles, equilateral) and by their angles (acute, obtuse, right, equiangular).

Key Questions

1. Are triangles formed in every situation above?
2. Can a generalization or rule be made when it is not possible to form a triangle given the measures of its three sides?

Key Terms

triangle   right triangle
vertex   scalene
hypotenuse   isosceles

OBJECTIVE: *Identify triangles and classify them according to the number of congruent sides and types of angles. Apply the Distance Formula.*

1-5 Triangles

Since triangles are used so often in geometry and its applications, it is important to be able to define triangles and to classify the different types of triangles.

▪ **DEFINITION**
A **triangle** is a figure formed by three segments joining three noncollinear points.

We can name triangle ABC by writing $\triangle ABC$, $\triangle BCA$, $\triangle ACB$, $\triangle CBA$, $\triangle CAB$, or $\triangle BAC$. In the figure, A, B, and C are the **vertices**; $\overline{AB}$, $\overline{BC}$, and $\overline{AC}$ are the **sides**; and $\angle A$, $\angle B$, and $\angle C$ are the **angles of the triangle.** Every triangle has *three* vertices, *three* sides, and *three* angles.

The words *opposite* and *included* are used to talk about relationships between sides and angles of a triangle. In $\triangle ABC$, for example,
$\overline{AB}$ is *opposite* $\angle C$ and $\angle C$ is *opposite* $\overline{AB}$;
$\angle C$ is *included* between side $\overline{BC}$ and side $\overline{AC}$;
$\overline{AB}$ is *included* between $\angle A$ and $\angle B$.

Triangles can be classified according to the types of angles they have, as shown in the figures below.

Acute triangle | **Right** triangle | **Obtuse** triangle | **Equiangular** triangle

All acute angles—
$\angle A$, $\angle B$, and $\angle C$
are all acute.

One right angle
$\angle G$ is a right
angle.

One obtuse angle
$\angle D$ is obtuse.

All angles congruent
$\angle J \cong \angle K \cong \angle L$

In a right triangle, the side opposite the right angle is called the **hypotenuse**. The other two sides are called the **legs**.

Example 1
Name an equiangular triangle.
Solution
$\triangle PQS$

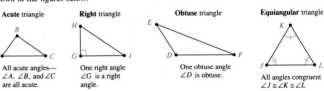

Try This
Name two right triangles.

for heightening teaching effectiveness

Another way of classifying triangles is by the number of congruent sides they have as shown in the figures below.

Scalene triangle

No sides congruent

Isosceles triangle

At least 2 sides congruent
$\overline{EF} \cong \overline{FG}$

Equilateral triangle

All sides congruent
$\overline{HI} \cong \overline{IJ} \cong \overline{JH}$

Example 2

Name an isosceles triangle and give its congruent sides.

Solution

$\triangle STV$ is isosceles.
$\overline{ST} \cong \overline{SV}$

Try This

Name an equilateral triangle and give its congruent sides.

A coordinate grid is useful for exploring side length relationships in triangles and other figures.

In algebra, you learned that the length of $\overline{AB}$ on a coordinate grid—where A has coordinates (x_1, y_1) and B has coordinates (x_2, y_2)—can be found using the following.

Distance Formula $\quad AB = \sqrt{(x_2 - x_1)^2 + (y_2 - y_1)^2}$

This formula will be used to explore relationships and solve problems throughout the book and will be proved in Chapter 12. The following example illustrates its use.

Example 3

Find the length of $\overline{AB}$ in $\triangle ABC$ on the coordinate grid above.

Solution

$AB = \sqrt{(x_2 - x_1)^2 + (y_2 - y_1)^2}$ *Use the Distance Formula with*
$AB = \sqrt{(5 - 2)^2 + (3 - 1)^2}$ $A(2, 1)$ *and* $B(5, 3)$.
$AB = \sqrt{3^2 + 2^2}$ $x_2 = 5,\ x_1 = 2,\ y_2 = 3,$ *and*
$AB = \sqrt{9 + 4}$ $y_1 = 1$
$AB = \sqrt{13} \approx 3.6$

Try This

Find the length of $\overline{AC}$ in $\triangle ABC$ on the coordinate grid above and decide if $\triangle ABC$ is an isosceles triangle.

Guided Practice

Chalkboard Examples

1. Name a right triangle. $\triangle BCD$

Answer to **Try This** $\triangle PRS,\ \triangle STQ$

Class Exercise Answers

1. K, L, M 2. $\overline{KL},\ \overline{LM},\ \overline{KM}$
3. $\triangle MLK,\ \triangle MKL,\ \triangle KML,\ \triangle LMK,$

Assignment Guide
Minimum: 1–37 e/o, 43, 44, MR
Regular: 1–37 e/o, 38, 39, 43, MR
Advanced: 1–37 e/o, 38–44, MR

Applications
Exercises 26, 38

Constructions
Exercises 41, 42

Coordinate Geometry
Class Exercises 15, 17
Exercises 24, 25, 39, 40

Lesson Closure

Ask students to name the different triangles discussed in the lesson.

Teacher's Resource Materials
Practice Master 5

Exercise Answers

1. $\triangle AEC,\ \triangle CED,\ \triangle BED,\ \triangle AEB$
2. $\triangle ACE,\ \triangle EAC,\ \triangle ECA,\ \triangle CAE,$
$\triangle CEA$ 3. $\overline{BE},\ \overline{EA},\ \overline{AB}$

Guided Practice

Consists of
• **Chalkboard Examples**—additional examples with their accompanying answers,
• **Class Exercise Answers**,
• A brief **Assignment Guide**,
• A list of all **Application, Algebra, Coordinate Geometry,** or **Construction exercises** in the lesson exercise set

Lesson Closure

Suggests ways to summarize the lesson.

Teacher's Resource Materials

Lists supplements and software appropriate for use with the lesson.

Answers

Answers for all exercises, quizzes, activities, and special feature exercises are provided either in the Teacher Edition margin or in the Student Edition odd-numbered answers.

Tips for Teachers

The teacher's role in creating an atmosphere conducive to producing successful geometry students cannot be overemphasized.

• Be enthusiastic about the geometry experience; explore geometry along with students. "Think aloud" as you examine and make generalizations and encourage students to do the same.

• Relate geometry to experience in everyday life whenever possible. Encourage different approaches to solving a problem or proving a theorem.

• Have students analyze their own solutions and proofs; show that verification and interpretion are part of the answer process.

Using Cooperative Learning Groups

Students benefit in several ways from small-group instruction. Working in small groups helps reduce the anxiety associated with geometry and proofs. Group work also demonstrates that there is more than one way to solve a mathematical problem—one of the most important ideas students can learn.

Algebra

This text assumes one year of high school algebra and some familiarity with the geometry taught in junior high and middle schools. So that students will not forget algebra as they study geometry, algebra is integrated throughout the text and algebra reviews follow about half the lessons. Also an entire section in the appendix reviews algebraic concepts and provides skills practice.

Proof

The understanding of proof and the ability to write proofs are major goals in the study of geometry. Since logic is an integral part of planning a proof, several lessons on logic are presented before the introduction of any postulates or theorems. The first proofs, which appear in the last lesson of Chapter 1, are algebraic proofs. Proof is then developed step by step in Chapter 2.

Alternate Approaches

The basic Euclidean approach to the study of geometry is integrated with other methods of proof using coordinate geometry or transformational geometry. Certain theorems, for example, are proved by more than one method. Intuition and a hands-on approach are used throughout the text in the Explore features, which encourage students to make generalizations based on observations made using concrete materials.

Using the Assignment Guide

Assignment schedules are provided for three levels of courses—minimum, regular, and advanced. All three levels provide for 170 teaching days and include review and testing days. The Management Guide prior to each chapter gives daily assignments and optional supplementary assignments. Lesson assignments and a list of supplementary material to go with the lesson are also provided in the teacher's margin notes.

Minimum Course

The minimum course is for students who need extra practice and frequent review in order to master concepts. The suggested daily assignments include the A-level Exercises, Critical Thinking, and Mixed Review/Algebra Review. Since these students tend to learn best with a hands-on approach, the supplement *Enrichment Using Manipulatives* provides discovery learning. The overhead transparencies and accompanying worksheets are recommended as you develop the concepts. Minimum-level chapter tests are provided for this course.

Regular Course

The regular course is for students who need skills practice and review, yet can apply these skills to higher-level thinking. The suggested lesson assignments include both A- and B-level exercises, Critical Thinking, and Mixed Review/Algebra Review. Regular-level chapter tests are provided.

Advanced Course

The advanced course is intended for students who can master concepts quickly. The suggested lesson assignments include some A-level, but mostly B- and C-level exercises, Critical Thinking, and Mixed Review/Algebra Review. If the use of computers is available, students may further explore concepts using the software that has been referenced in the teacher's margin notes. Advanced-level tests are provided .

The following chart summarizes the number of days allocated to each chapter for the three levels of ability, including chapter reviews and tests.

Chapter	Semester 1							Semester 2					
	1	2	3	4	5	6	7	8	9	10	11	12	13
Minimum Course	13	12	12	12	13	12	12	15	14	14	15	13	13
Regular Course	13	12	12	12	13	12	12	15	14	14	15	13	13
Advanced Course	13	12	12	12	13	12	12	15	14	14	15	13	13

Using the Computer Explorations

The Computer Explorations on pages 634–661 focus on the process of formulating and supporting conjectures—an integral part of the inquiry approach to discovering geometric relationships. A discussion of this process is recommended before students begin the activities. The process of mathematical thinking is: exploration, conjecture, and proof. A conjecture is a statement that one believes to be true. It is an educated guess, based on exploration and data gathering, that goes beyond what is known for certain. In most cases, the conjecture should be based upon several sets of supporting data. It is important to note whether data was collected from special cases, and to take this into account when stating the conjecture. For example, a conjecture based on data obtained from equilateral triangles might be valid when stated for equilateral triangles, but invalid when stated for all triangles.

Most of the Computer Explorations involve the discovery of theorems, corollaries, or other material presented in a lesson. Thus, most should be used before the related lesson. The teacher's margin notes indicate when each activity is best used.

Classes could approach the gathering of data in various ways. All students could collect data on the same figures and make their own conjectures, then discuss them as a class. Individuals could collect data on certain figures, then share their data with a small group and make conjectures with the group. Or, small groups could collect data on certain figures, then share their data with the full class and come to a conjecture together.

With some software, the labeling of figures given in the student text may not match the labeling on the computer screen. For example, for a right triangle, shown with right angle BCA, the 90° angle on the computer screen may be labeled $\angle ABC$. Data called for in the Computer Exploration data charts is coordinated with the labeling of the figures in the text. Caution students about labeling differences. Have them compare labels on the figures they create with the computer to the figures in the text. If the labeling differs and cannot be changed on the screen, students should change the labels on their charts to make sure they find the lengths, measures, or ratios required.

Many of the activities require students to do computations on the data they collect. In some cases, columns are provided in the chart for recording the results of all necessary computations. This, of course, tells students what computations to perform. In other cases, columns are not provided for all necessary computations. Not providing a column for every computation forces students to think and to become more active learners. This can make them feel that they are discovering or developing (perhaps their own) mathematics.

When students do calculations to formulate a conjecture, they may need a calculator. Encourage students to use a calculator in conjunction with the computer.

Addison-Wesley

Geometry

Stanley R. Clemens
Phares G. O'Daffer
Thomas J. Cooney
John A. Dossey

ADDISON-WESLEY PUBLISHING COMPANY

Menlo Park, California · Reading, Massachusetts · New York
Don Mills, Ontario · Wokingham, England · Amsterdam · Bonn
Sydney · Singapore · Tokyo · Madrid · San Juan

Basic Ideas of Geometry

Chapter Overview

This chapter is primarily concerned with the introduction of basic concepts. Concepts are introduced using a threefold approach: relating the concept to the world outside the classroom, providing an intuitive meaning of the concept through a hands-on approach, and stating a definition of the concept. The intent of the chapter is to introduce basic geometric concepts in such a way that the student can relate geometry to the everyday world.

Objectives

1-1 ▪ Name, describe, and draw models for points, lines, and planes and use these terms to define some basic relationships.

1-2 ▪ Use absolute value to find the distance between two points on a line. Apply the Segment Addition Postulate.

1-3 ▪ Name angles and find their measure.

1-4 ▪ Use the definition of congruent segments and angles to define midpoint of a segment, segment bisector, and angle bisector.

1-5 ▪ Identify triangles and classify them according to the number of congruent sides and types of angles.
Apply the Distance Formula.

1-6 ▪ Given a statement, change it to a conditional or biconditional and state its converse, inverse, or contrapositive.

1-7 ▪ Use definitions, postulates, and other true statements to draw and support conclusions.

1-8 ▪ Use properties of equality and deductive reasoning to draw conclusions about properties of congruence.

TEACHING CHAPTER 1

Cooperative Learning Opportunities

You are probably accustomed to having students do the **Class Exercises** orally. This is an excellent way to check for comprehension needed to do the homework. But, you might try a cooperative learning arrangement for the class exercises. This gets everyone actively involved. The following are a few places in Chapter 1 where you can try such an approach.

For the **Class Exercises** in Lesson 1-3, page 16, assign students to pairs. Give them about 10 minutes to complete the first 21 **Class Exercises**. Have one student in a pair do the odd exercises, and the other the even exercises. After a student writes down an answer, the other student reads it and says whether s/he agrees. If not, they discuss the exercise and try to reach agreement.

In a similar way, the **Class Exercises** for Lesson 1-4, page 22, can be done in pairs. Students should learn that there is a big difference between working together and copying.

Multicultural Note: *Euclid—Postulates and Common Notions*

Students should not pass through the first few chapters without at least a brief discussion of Euclid. He lived at about 300 B.C. and taught in Alexandria, the great cultural center, in northern Egypt. His book, the *Elements,* synthesized previous mathematical work and is undoubtedly the most influential textbook ever written.

Euclid distinguished between postulates and common notions. He viewed postulates as unproved assertions specific to geometry. An example of a postulate is: It is possible to draw a straight line from any point to any point.

Common notions were general statements applicable to many sciences. Some of his common notions are:

1. Things which are equal to the same thing are also equal to one another.
2. If equals be added to equals, the results are equal.

You may wish to discuss with students the difference between postulates and common notions.

Alternative Assessment and Communication Ideas

Chapter 1 introduces a large number of terms. Some of these will be familiar to students; others will be new. The **Vocabulary** list on page 52 contains 45 words. Students should know these and be able to use them. This vocabulary can form the basis for several different forms of alternative assessments.

One approach is to have a contest in which two teams line up on opposite sides of the room. You ask for the meaning of a word and a student must give a definition or explanation acceptable to you. A student is seated after one (or 2) misses. Last one up wins for the team. You may wish to promote group coaching to promote team spirit.

Another approach is to make flash cards and spend a few minutes each day on an oral drill. Finally, you might give a written test based on the vocabulary list. Some students will welcome this because they will know what to expect.

Investigations and Projects

You can help students gain an appreciation and understanding of how postulates build a system by working with a finite deductive system.

Give students the following postulates about a system, *S.*

1. Each point in *S* lies on exactly two lines.
2. Each pair of lines in *S* has exactly one point in common.
3. *S* contains exactly four lines.

Explain that in the system, *S,* each line does not contain infinitely many points but only those points satisfying

the postulates. Have students draw a set of lines that satisfy the postulates and ask what other conclusions they can draw.

One conclusion is that *S* contains exactly 6 points. Another is that each line contains 3 points.

Lesson	PACING CHART (DAYS)			Opening Activity	Cooperative Activity	Seat or Group Work
	1-Year Minimum	1-Year Regular	1-Year Advanced			
1-1	2	2	2	Chapter Opener: **TE** p. 2; Lesson Opener: **TE** p. 3	Lab Worksheet 1-1A: *Laboratory Manual* p. 1; Lab Worksheet 1-1B: *Laboratory Manual* p. 2	Try This Exercise
1-2	1	1	1	First Five Minutes 1-2: *FFM Transparency Masters* p. 1 or **TE** p. 8; Lesson Opener: **TE** p. 8	Explore: **SE** p. 8; ✂ Lab Worksheet 1-2A: *Laboratory Manual* p. 4; ✂ Lab Worksheet 1-2B: *Laboratory Manual* p. 5	Try This Exercises
1-3	2	2	2	First Five Minutes 1-3: *FFM Transparency Masters* p. 1 or **TE** p. 13; Lesson Opener: **TE** p. 13	✂ Lab Worksheet 1-3A: *Laboratory Manual* p. 7; ✂ Lab Worksheet 1-3B: *Laboratory Manual* p. 8	Try This Exercises
1-4	1	1	1	First Five Minutes 1-4: *FFM Transparency Masters* p. 2 or **TE** p. 20; Lesson Opener: **TE** p. 20	Explore: **SE** p. 20; ✂ Lab Worksheet 1-4A: *Laboratory Manual* p. 10; ✂ Lab Worksheet 1-4B: *Laboratory Manual* p. 11: ✂ Lab Worksheet 1-4C: *Laboratory Manual* p. 12	Try This Exercises
1-5	1	1	1	First Five Minutes 1-5: *FFM Transparency Masters* p. 2 or **TE** p. 26; Lesson Opener: **TE** p. 26	✂ Lab Worksheet 1-5: *Laboratory Manual* p. 14	Try This Exercises
1-6	1	1	1	First Five Minutes 1-6: *FFM Transparency Masters* p. 3 or **TE** p. 32; Lesson Opener: **TE** p. 32	Connections: **SE** p. 38	Try This Exercises
1-7	2	2	2	First Five Minutes 1-7: *FFM Transparency Masters* p. 3 or **TE** p. 39; Lesson Opener: **TE** p. 39	Enrichment: **TE** p. 44	Try This Exercises
1-8	1	1	1	First Five Minutes 1-8: *FFM Transparency Masters* p. 4 or **TE** p. 45; Lesson Opener: **TE** p. 45	Algebra Review: **SE** p. 622	Try This Exercises
Review	1	1	1			
Test	1	1	1			

FFM = First Five Minutes

Enrichment	Review/Assess	Reteach	Technology	Lesson
Study Skills: **SE** p. 7; ✂ Enrichment Using Manipulatives 1-1: **Enrichment** p. 1; BASIC 1-1: **Technology** p. B1; ✂ Lab Worksheet 1-1C: **Laboratory Manual** p. 3	Class Exercises: **SE** p. 5; Algebra Review: **SE** p. 7	Practice Worksheet 1-1: **Practice and Mixed Review** p. 1	BASIC 1-1: **Technology** p. B1	1-1
Computer Activity: **SE** p. 12; ✂ Enrichment Using Manipulatives 1-2: **Enrichment** p. 2; BASIC 1-2: **Technology** p. B3	Class Exercises: **SE** p. 10; Algebra Review: **SE** p. 12	Practice Worksheet 1-2: **Practice and Mixed Review** p. 2	Computer Activity: **SE** p. 12; BASIC 1-2: **Technology** p. B3	1-2
Careers: **SE** p. 19; ✂ Enrichment Using Manipulatives 1-3: **Enrichment** p. 3; ✂ Lab Worksheet 1-3C: **Laboratory Manual** p. 9	Class Exercises: **SE** p. 16; Mixed Review: **SE** p. 19	Practice Worksheet 1-3: **Practice and Mixed Review** p. 3		1-3
Calculator Investigation: **SE** p. 25; ✂ Enrichment Using Manipulatives 1-4: **Enrichment** p. 4; BASIC 1-4: **Technology** p. B4; ✂ Lab Worksheet 1-4D: **Laboratory Manual** p. 13	Class Exercises: **SE** p. 22; Algebra Review **SE** p. 25; Quiz: **Assessment** p. 79	Practice Worksheet 1-4: **Practice and Mixed Review** p. 4	Calculator Investigation: **SE** p. 25; BASIC 1-4: **Technology** p. B4	1-4
Comparing Approaches in Geometry: **SE** p. 31; ✂ Enrichment Using Manipulatives 1-5: **Enrichment** p. 5	Class Exercises: **SE** p. 28; Mixed Review: **SE** p. 30; Quiz: **SE** p. 30	Practice Worksheet 1-5: **Practice and Mixed Review** p. 5	Calculator Worksheet 1-5: **Technology** p. CL1; BASIC 1-5: **Technology** p. B6	1-5
Connections: **SE** p. 38	Class Exercises: **SE** p. 34; Mixed Review: **SE** p. 38	Practice Worksheet 1-6: **Practice and Mixed Review** p. 6		1-6
Enrichment: **SE** p. 44	Class Exercises: **SE** p. 40; Algebra Review: **SE** p. 43	Practice Worksheet 1-7: **Practice and Mixed Review** p. 7		1-7
✂ Enrichment Using Manipulatives 1-8: **Enrichment** p. 6	Class Exercises: **SE** p. 48; Mixed Review: **SE** p. 50; Quiz: **SE** p. 50; Quiz: **Assessment** p. 80	Practice Worksheet 1-8: **Practice and Mixed Review** p. 8		1-8
Critical Thinking: **SE** p. 51	Summary & Review: **SE** p. 52–53	Mixed Review: **Practice and Mixed Review** p. 102		Review
Problem Solving: **SE** p. 55	Chapter 1 Test: **SE** p. 54; Chapter 1 Tests: **Assessment** p. 1–6; **MathTest**			Test

Chapter Opener

The photo illustrates how often geometry occurs in the world around us. Ask students to find examples of geometric concepts in the classroom.

Answer

Answers may vary. Some geometric concepts shown in the photo include rectangular traffic signs, parallel and perpendicular lines on the street, and circular wheels and lights.

1

Basic Ideas of Geometry

What concepts of geometry can you find in this street scene?

DEFINITIONS AND POSTULATES

OBJECTIVE: *Name, describe, and draw models for points, lines, and planes and use these terms to define some basic relationships.*

1-1 Points, Lines, Planes, and Space

As you learn about geometry, you will see that it is useful in many occupations and can help you develop your ability to discover, organize, and reason carefully. To begin your study of geometry, you need to understand the meaning of three basic terms—point, line, and plane.

Think of a **point** as a location, such as a dot on a map or on a computer. A point has no size but can be represented by a dot labeled with a capital letter. Point *A*, point *B*, point *C* are shown below.

A •

      • *B*   • *C*

Some computers use a string of very small dots, or "bits," to show lines. This suggests the idea that a line is a set of points.

A **line,** like all geometric figures, is an infinite set of points. This idea is understood by thinking of straightness as suggested by the string of very small dots on the computer screen. A line has no thickness. A line is named by a lower-case letter or by any two points on the line. The double arrow indicates that the line continues without end in both directions.

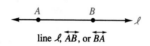

line ℓ, $\overrightarrow{AB}$, or $\overrightarrow{BA}$

A **plane** is also an infinite set of points. This idea is understood by thinking of flatness as suggested by a table top extending in all directions without bound. A plane has no thickness and is named by a capital letter or three points not in a straight line. *Point, line,* and *plane* are called undefined terms in geometry. Some relationships between points, lines, and planes are also described using terms that are not defined, such as those in italics below.

plane *P* or plane *ABC*

Point *A* is *on* line ℓ.
A, B, and *C,* are *in* line ℓ.
ℓ *contains* *A, B,* and *C.*
ℓ *passes through* *A, B,* and *C.*
B is *between* *A* and *C.*

Point *C* and line *n* are *in* plane *R.*
Plane *R contains C* and *n.*

It is important to understand that for a point to be *between* two other points as described above, all three points must be on the same line.

Definitions use undefined terms, previously defined terms, and ordinary words to give clear meaning to terms used in geometry. For example, the undefined term "point" is used to define space: **space** is the set of all points.

The following definitions describe other relationships with points, lines, and planes.

Lesson Opener

Begin with a discussion on the geometry of ancient Egypt. Some 6000 years ago, geometry was the study of the size, shape, and position of plots of land and was used to measure land, construct buildings, and erect pyramids. (See page 62: Historical Note—The Beginnings of Geometry.)

Then discuss how geometry is used today in constructing buildings and bridges. The study of geometry in this course demonstrates the usefulness of geometry not only in everyday life, but also as a mathematical system that can help develop a student's ability to discover, organize, and reason logically.

Key Questions

1. Name an aspect of geometry you have experienced in your everyday life.
2. Name an occupation that requires some knowledge of geometry.

Materials

student notebooks

Teaching Notes

In order to begin the study of any mathematical system, a few basic statements, words, and ideas are agreed to and are not defined. In geometry, the terms *point, line,* and *plane* are accepted as intuitive ideas and are called undefined terms. These three terms will be used to define other terms.

Remind students that the flat surface of their desk or a line drawn with a pencil are just physical models.

Collinear points are points all in one line. Points that are not in one line are called **noncollinear points.**

Coplanar points are points all in one plane. Points that are not in the same plane are called **noncoplanar points.** Similarly, **coplanar lines** are lines all in one plane. These ideas are illustrated in this figure.

The **intersection** of two figures is the set of points both figures have in common.

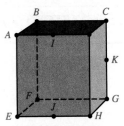

A, I, and D are collinear.
A, B, and C are noncollinear.
E, F, G, and H are coplanar.
A, B, D, and E are noncoplanar.
$\overleftrightarrow{AB}$ and $\overleftrightarrow{AD}$ are coplanar.

Example

Use symbols to describe the intersection of planes P and Q.

> **Solution**
> The intersection of planes P and Q is $\overleftrightarrow{CD}$.

Try This

Use symbols to describe the intersection of $\overleftrightarrow{AB}$ and $\overleftrightarrow{CD}$.

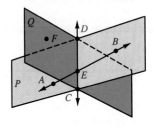

A **postulate** is a statement that is accepted as true without proof. The following postulates give some basic relationships among points, lines, planes, and space. Note that "two points (lines, planes)" means "two *different* points (lines, planes)."

● **POSTULATE 1**

A line, a plane, and space each contain an infinite number of points. Some points in a plane are noncollinear. Some points in space are noncoplanar.

● **POSTULATE 2**

For any two points, there is exactly one line containing them.

● **POSTULATE 3**

For any three noncollinear points, there is exactly one plane containing them.

● **POSTULATE 4**

If two points are in a plane, then the line containing them is in the plane.

● **POSTULATE 5**

If two planes intersect, then they intersect in exactly one line.

The following is a **convincing argument** that two lines cannot intersect in more than one point.

Two lines, ℓ and m, cannot intersect in two or more points. If they could, you would have two points that have more than one line containing them. This contradicts Postulate 2.

Class Exercises

Short Answer

1. Name real-world objects that suggest points, lines, and planes.
2. Give five different names for this line.
3. Two lines that have a point in common are called __?__ lines.
4. Three points that are all on a line are __?__ points.
5. Four points that are not in the same plane are __?__ points.

Sample Exercises

6. Name four sets of three collinear points.
7. Name two sets of three noncollinear points.
8. Name three pairs of intersecting lines. Give the points of intersection.
9. Name two points between K and P. Why is point L not between points K and P?

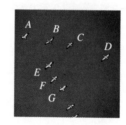

10. Name three sets of four points that are coplanar.
11. Name two coplanar lines.
12. Use three points in each plane to name a pair of intersecting planes. Name the line of intersection.

13. Draw and label a diagram showing four coplanar points, G, H, I, and J.
14. State the postulate that asserts that this statement is true. You can name as many points as you wish on a line.

Discussion

15. Think of this formation of geese flying south in the winter as a set of points. Use the words collinear, noncollinear, coplanar, and noncoplanar to describe the situation.
16. Use the postulates to give a convincing argument that the existence of a line and a point not on the line is enough to establish the existence of an infinite number of lines.

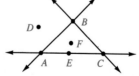

Exercises

A

Write each of the following using symbols.

1. the line containing points A and B
2. a point not on $\overleftrightarrow{AC}$
3. a pair of lines that intersect at point A
4. a point on $\overleftrightarrow{AC}$ but not on $\overleftrightarrow{BC}$
5. a point between A and C

Draw and label each figure.

6. two points, J and K
7. three noncollinear points: R, S, and T
8. $\overleftrightarrow{GH}$
9. line ℓ containing points M, N, and Q
10. plane R containing points A and B
11. $\overrightarrow{CD}$ and $\overrightarrow{EF}$, intersecting at point Z
12. three collinear points: C, D, and E
13. point L between points S and T

Exercise Answers

1. $\overleftrightarrow{AB}$ **2.** F   **3.** $\overleftrightarrow{AB}$ and $\overleftrightarrow{AC}$
4. E   **5.** E   **6.** ·J ·K
7.   •S
     •R   •T

8.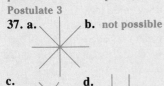
     G   H

9. ◄—•——•—•——► ℓ
       M N Q

10.
         •B
      •A   •R

11.   E   Z   D
            C   F

12. ◄—•——•——•——►
         C D E

13. ◄—•——•——•——►
         S L T

14. true   **15.** true
16. true   **17.** false   **18.** L
19. $\overrightarrow{TU}$ **20.** $\overrightarrow{MK}$
21. Postulate 2
22. Postulate 5
23. Postulate 4
24. Postulate 3
25. Postulate 2   **26.** true
27. false

28. true   **29.** true
30. true   **31.** true
32. Postulate 5
33. Postulate 2
34. Postulate 3
35. Postulate 4   **36.** Three points determine a plane; Postulate 3
37. a.   **b.** not possible

c.   **d.**

Determine whether each statement is true or false.

14. Points E, J, and G are collinear.
15. Points A, F, and H are coplanar.
16. Plane ABC intersects plane AIJ in $\overleftrightarrow{AC}$.
17. $\overleftrightarrow{IJ}$ intersects $\overleftrightarrow{EG}$ at point I.

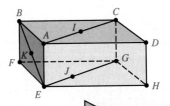

Complete each statement.

18. The intersection of $\overrightarrow{MK}$ and $\overrightarrow{NP}$ is ___ .
19. The intersection of plane R and plane S is ___ .
20. Line ___ intersects plane S in only one point.

State the postulate that asserts that each statement is true.

21. Point A and B are on $\overleftrightarrow{AB}$ and are not both on any other line.
22. When planes P and Q have line ℓ in common, they have no other line in common.
23. When points A and B are in plane R, $\overleftrightarrow{AB}$ is also in plane R.
24. When three noncollinear points A, B, and C are in plane P, all three are in no other plane.
25. A carpenter often needs to make a straight line. To do this, he stretches a taut chalkline from point A to point B and snaps the string to form a straight line. Which postulate does this suggest?

B

Determine whether each statement is true or false. If false, explain why.

26. Three collinear points are always coplanar.
27. Three coplanar points are always collinear.
28. Any three points are coplanar.
29. When A is between C and D, the three points are collinear.
30. It is possible to have four coplanar points, no three of which are collinear.
31. Space may contain more, but not less, than four noncoplanar points.

Given the first statement, state the postulate that allows you to conclude that the second statement is true.

32. Two planes, M and N, both contain line ℓ. Therefore it is impossible for planes M and N both to contain another line, m.
33. Two lines, ℓ and m, both contain point A. Therefore it is impossible for lines ℓ and m both to contain another point, B.
34. Three noncollinear points A, B, and C are contained in plane M. Therefore points A, B, and C cannot all be contained in another plane, N.
35. A and B are points in plane M. Therefore, every point of $\overleftrightarrow{AB}$ is in plane M.

36. A photographer uses a tripod to hold a camera. Explain why a tripod has three legs instead of four. Which postulate applies to this situation?

C

37. Make drawings, when possible, to show that four coplanar lines can be drawn to intersect in only

a. 1 point   **b.** 2 points   **c.** 3 points   **d.** 4 points   **e.** 5 points   **f.** 6 points

38. List 12 different sets of four coplanar points for this cube. List the letters in each set alphabetically.

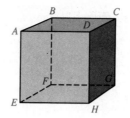

Critical Thinking

39. Points U, V, W, X, and Y are collinear. How many line segments are determined?

40. When one line is drawn through each pair of points, three points determine at most three lines. Give a convincing argument that n points determine at most $\dfrac{n(n-1)}{2}$ lines.

Algebra Review

Simplify.

1. $|3|$
2. $|-6|$
3. $|7.5|$
4. $|-10|$
5. $|0|$
6. $|7-3|$
7. $|4-9|$
8. $|-3-4|$
9. $|5-(-2)|$
10. $|-1-1|$
11. $|-2-(-4)|$
12. $|6-6|$

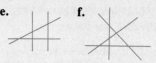

e.   **f.**

38. A,B,C,D; A,B,E,F; E,F,G,H; C,D,G,H; A,D,E,H; B,C,F,G; B,D,F,H; A,C,E,G; C,D,E,F; A,B,G,H; A,D,F,G; B,C,E,H

39. 10

40.

$n = 3$
3 lines
$\dfrac{3(2)}{2} = 3$

$n = 4$
6 lines
$\dfrac{4(3)}{2} = 6$

$n = 5$
10 lines
$\dfrac{5(4)}{2} = 10$

Thus, n points determine $\dfrac{n(n-1)}{2}$ lines.

Algebra Review Answers

1. 3
2. 6
3. 7.5
4. 10
5. 0
6. 4
7. 5
8. 7
9. 7
10. 2
11. 2
12. 0

(Quiz on previous lesson)
Draw and label a figure.

1. Plane M and $\overleftrightarrow{CD}$ intersect at P.

2. P is on $\overrightarrow{AB}$.

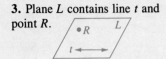

3. Plane L contains line t and point R.

4. $\overleftrightarrow{AB}$ and $\overleftrightarrow{CD}$ intersect at R.

5. A, B, and C lie on line m but D does not lie on line m.

Lesson Opener

The concept of distance is a very basic and important one in geometry—and in everyday life. Ask students to give examples of their most recent experience in finding distances.

Materials

rulers
student notebooks

Teaching Notes

To illustrate ways of finding the distance between two points, mark two points, P and Q, on the chalkboard. Discuss how to find the distance between points P and Q, with and without laying one end of the ruler on P as shown in the Explore.

OBJECTIVE: *Use absolute value to find the distance between two points on a line. Apply the Segment Addition Postulate.*

1-2 Distance and Segment Measure

EXPLORE

Mark a pair of points on a sheet of paper. Find the distance between the points without laying one end of the ruler on a point. Try this with several pairs of points.

Can you state a generalization for finding the distance?

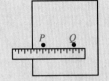

In algebra, you learned that the points on a line can be matched one-to-one with real numbers. A number that corresponds to a point on the line is the **coordinate** of that point. For example, the coordinate of point C below is -3.

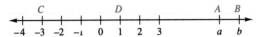

In geometry, you can use these ideas to understand distance. As you may have discovered in the Explore, the **distance** AB between any two points A and B with coordinates a and b on a number line is found as follows.

$$AB = |a - b| \quad \text{or} \quad AB = |b - a|$$

For example, on the number line above,

$$CD = |-3 - 1| = |-4| = 4 \quad \text{or} \quad CD = |1 - (-3)| = |4| = 4$$

The following postulate summarizes these ideas about distance.

● **POSTULATE 6** Ruler Postulate

The points on a line can be matched one-to-one with real-number coordinates so that

a. for any two points there corresponds a unique positive number, called the distance between the two points;
b. the distance between any two points is the absolute value of the difference of their coordinates.

Example 1
Find the distance between R and S.

Solution
$$RS = |-1.5 - 2| = |-3.5| = 3.5$$

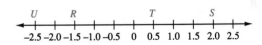

Try This
Find the distance between T and U.

A **segment** is a set of points consisting of two points, called **endpoints,** and all the points between these points.

A segment is named by its endpoints. Write $\overline{AB}$ or $\overline{BA}$ to name the segment with endpoints A and B. The **length of a segment** is the positive real number that is the distance between its endpoints. The length of $\overline{AB}$ is written as AB.

The following postulate ensures that the lengths of parts of a segment can be added to give the length of the whole segment.

● **POSTULATE 7** Segment Addition Postulate
If Q is between P and R, then $PQ + QR = PR$.

Example 2

Q is between P and R.   Find PQ.

Solution

$$
\begin{aligned}
2x + (x + 9) &= 30 \\
3x + 9 &= 30 \\
3x &= 21 \\
x &= 7 \\
PQ = 2x = 2(7) &= 14
\end{aligned}
$$

Use the Segment Addition Postulate
$(PQ + QR = PR)$ to write the equation.

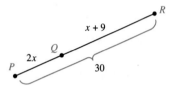

Try This

Find QR and check to see if $PQ + QR = PR$.

You have used a single real-number coordinate to describe the location of a point on a line. An ordered pair (x, y) of numbers, called **coordinates,** can be used to describe the location of a point in the plane. For example, a horizontal **x-axis** and a vertical **y-axis** have been used here to graph $\overline{AB}$. The coordinates of the endpoints of $\overline{AB}$ are (2, 1) and (4, 3).

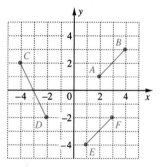

Example 3

Give the coordinates of the endpoints of $\overline{CD}$ and the coordinates of a point between C and D.

Solution

The coordinates of C are $(-4, 2)$; the coordinates of D are $(-2, -2)$; the point with coordinates $(-3, 0)$ is between C and D.

Try This

Give the coordinates of the endpoints of $\overline{EF}$ and the coordinates of a point between E and F.

Remind students to focus on the *meaning* of the Segment Addition Postulate rather than on memorizing the statement.

Point out that a linear coordinate system is not sufficient to show the relationships of lines. Therefore, a rectangular coordinate system is needed.

Key Questions

1. Can you find a general rule for finding the distance between two points? Subtract their coordinates.
2. Given the coordinates of two points, is it always necessary to subtract the smaller coordinate from the larger? If not, what must occur to get a positive distance? Use absolute value.

Common Errors

Stress that AB is the symbol for the distance between points A and B, but $\overline{AB}$ is the symbol for a line segment with endpoints A and B.

Guided Practice

Chalkboard Examples

1. Find the distance between U and S. 4.5

Answer to **Try This** 3

2. Point Q is between P and R. If $PQ = 3x$, $QR = x - 6$, and $PR = 30$, find PQ and QR.
$PQ = 27$, $QR = 3$

Answer to **Try This**
$QR = 16$, $PQ + QR = 14 + 16 = 30 = PR$

3. Give the coordinates of a point between the points with coordinates $(-5, -4)$ and $(-3, -2)$. $(-4, -3)$

Answer to **Try This** $E(1, -4)$, $F(3, -2)$; $(2, 3)$ is between E and F.

Class Exercises

Short Answer

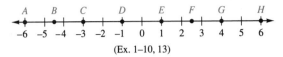
(Ex. 1–10, 13)

Give the coordinate of each of the following.

1. point *G*   2. point *F*   3. point *A*

Name the point with the given coordinate.

4. −1   5. 6   6. −4½
7. Complete the following to find *AE*. |−6 − ?| = ?
8. The distance between points *D* and *H* is ___ .
9. Between which two points is the point with coordinate −1.73?
10. Give three numbers that are coordinates for points between *G* and *H*.

11. A segment is a set of __?__ . The length of a segment is a __?__ .
12. Which postulate allows us to say that *DF* = 9?

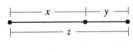

Sample Exercises

13. Find *BG* on the number line used in Exercises 1–10.

Find the distance between each pair of points with the given coordinates.

14. 17, 32   15. −9, 13   16. −6.2, −8.7   17. 7¾, −4½

18. *F* is between *T* and *R*. *TF* = 3*x*, *FR* = 4*x* − 2, *TR* = 54
    Find *TF* and *FR*.

19. If *PQ* + *QR* = *PR*, which of the points *P*, *Q*, or *R* is between the
    other two?
20. Use the Segment Addition Postulate to give an addition equation and two
    subtraction equations that are true about the lengths *x*, *y*, and *z* of
    segments in this figure.

Discussion

21. Describe the difference in meaning between $\overline{AB}$, $\overleftrightarrow{AB}$, and *AB*.
22. A student claimed that the Ruler Postulate makes every line in
    the plane a "number line ruler." Do you think this is true? If so,
    give a convincing argument why or why not.
23. Find the lengths of the four segments shown. Can you give a
    rule for finding the length of a horizontal segment with endpoint
    coordinates (*a*, *c*) and (*b*, *c*)? a vertical segment with endpoint
    coordinates (*w*, *s*) and (*w*, *t*)?

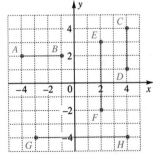

10   *Chapter 1   Basic Ideas of Geometry*

Exercises

A

Find each distance on the number line.

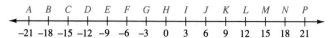

A B C D E F G H I J K L M N P
-21 -18 -15 -12 -9 -6 -3 0 3 6 9 12 15 18 21

1. *KN*   2. *PH*   3. *FJ*   4. *DI*   5. *DA*
6. *AF*   7. *BN*   8. *IC*   9. *CP*   10. *DK*

Find the distance between each pair of points with the given coordinates.

11. 15, 12   12. 14, 28   13. 33, 12   14. 17, 0   15. 13, 21
16. −15, 13   17. 19, −12   18. −13, −17   19. $-5\frac{1}{2}, 8\frac{3}{4}$ 20. 7.26, −8.7

Write and solve an equation to find the length of each segment.

21. $AB = x$, $BC = 2x$, $AC = 18$ Find *AB* and *BC*.
22. $AB = y - 2$, $BC = y$, $AC = 22$ Find *AB* and *BC*.
23. $EB = x$, $BD = 30$, $ED = 4x + 6$ Find *EB* and *ED*.
24. $BD = t + 9$, $EB = t$, $ED = 31$ Find *BD* and *EB*.
25. *B* is between *A* and *C*. $AB = 2x$, $BC = 3x - 1$, $AC = 14$
    Find *AB* and *BC*.
26. *T* is between *R* and *S*. $RT = 2x$, $TS = 4$, $RS = 3x - 1$
    Find *RS* and *RT*.
27. A basketball coach is interested in measuring a player's vertical jumping
    ability. While standing and reaching up, the player's hand reaches the
    4-in. mark on the scale. When jumping, the player can reach the 19-in.
    mark. What is the player's vertical jumping ability?

B

Use the segment lengths in the figure to evaluate each expression.

28. $AC + BD$ 29. $AD - AB$
30. $(AD - CD) + AC$ 31. $(AC - BD) + BC$

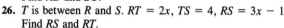

A   B   C   D
   6   13   4

**Points A, B, and C are collinear. The lengths of certain segments
are given. Which point is between the other two?**

32. $AC = 4$, $CB = 8$, $AB = 12$ 33. $BA = 9$, $BC = 12$, $AC = 3$
34. $AC = 26$, $BC = 19$ Find the coordinates *a* and *b*.

35. $DE = EF$ Find *e*.

A   B   C
a   b   54

D   E   F
-7   e   13

A, B, and C are collinear points with coordinates a, b, and c.

36. If $b = -10$, $c = 4$, and $BA = 287$, find *BC* and *CA*. Give two possible
    answers. How many answers are possible?
37. *C* is between *A* and *B*. $AC = CB$, $CB = 10$, $c = 14$
    Give two possible coordinates for *A*.
38. *B* is between *A* and *C*. $AB = \frac{1}{5}BC$, $AC = 18$ Find *AB* and *BC*.
39. *A* is between *B* and *C*. $AB = \frac{1}{6}BC$, $AC = 25$ Find *AB* and *BC*.

1-2 Distance and Segment Measure   **11**

Teacher's Resource Materials

Manipulatives 2   Practice 2
BASIC 2   Software 2

Exercise Answers

1. 9   2. 21   3. 12
4. 15   5. 9   6. 15
7. 36   8. 18   9. 36
10. 21   11. 3   12. 14
13. 21   14. 17   15. 8
16. 28   17. 31   18. 4
19. $14\frac{1}{4}$ 20. 15.96
21. $AB = 6$, $BC = 12$
22. $AB = 10$, $BC = 12$
23. $EB = 8$, $ED = 38$
24. $BD = 20$, $EB = 11$
25. $AB = 6$, $BC = 8$
26. $RS = 14$, $RT = 10$
27. 15 in.   28. 36
29. 17   30. 38   31. 15
32. *C*   33. *A*   34. $a = 28$, $b = 35$
35. $e = 3$ 36. $BC = 14$, $CA = 301$, $BC = 14$, $CA = 273$
37. $A = 4$, $A = 24$
38. $AB = 3$, $BC = 15$
39. $AB = 5$, $BC = 30$

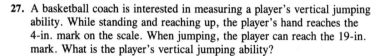

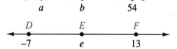

40. $x = 8$ **41.** $x = \pm 4$
42. $x = 4$ **43.** $GH = 5$,
$IJ = 9$, $KL = 7$, $MN = 8$
44. $8x + 5x + 3x = 48$,
$16x = 48$, $x = 3$; $AB = 8x = 24$,
$BD = BC + CD = 5x + 3x =$
$8x = 24$ **45.**

C B A   D   E

E D   A B C

They are reflections of each
other.   **46.** True; $\frac{a + b}{2}$ is the
average of a and b, so it lies between them.

Algebra Review
Answers

1. 7   **2.** 4   **3.** 13   **4.** 1

Computer Activity
Answers

1. 17
2. 10 REM FIND SEGMENT
LENGTHS ON A NUMBER LINE
20 INPUT "ENTER THE COORDI-
NATES OF THE TWO END-
POINTS "; A,B
30 PRINT "THE LENGTH OF THE
SEGMENT JOINING "A" AND "B"
IS "ABS(A − B)
40 INPUT "WOULD YOU LIKE TO
FIND ANOTHER SEGMENT
LENGTH (Y/N)? ";A$
50 IF A$ = "Y" THEN PRINT:
GOTO 20
60 END
3. to ensure a positive length
4. 10 REM FIND SEGMENT
LENGTH ON A NUMBER LINE
20 INPUT "ENTER THE COORDI-
NATES OF THE TWO END-
POINTS ";A,B
30 IF A > B THEN LET
L = A − B: GOTO 50
40 LET L = B − A
50 PRINT "THE LENGTH OF THE
SEGMENT JOINING "A" AND "B"
IS "L
60 END

C

Find the value of the variable.

40. $AB = 3x - 4$, $AC = 40$, $AB = BC$
41. $BC = 2x^2$, $AC = 64$, $AB = BC$
42. $FE = 2x$, $EC = x^2$, $FC = 24$

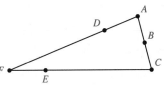

43. Find the length of $\overline{GH}$, $\overline{IJ}$, $\overline{KL}$, and $\overline{MN}$.

44. Points B and C divide $\overline{AD}$ in the ratio 8:5:3. $AD = 48$
Show that $AB = BD$. (HINT: Let $AB = 8x$.)

A   B   C   D

Critical Thinking

45. Draw two different figures, each of which satisfies all these
conditions. How are the figures related?
a. There are five points A, B, C, D, and E all collinear.
b. $CA = AD$.   **c.** $AB = BC$ **d.** $AD = DE$
e. E is not between C and D.

46. Give the coordinates, a and b, of two points that are close together on
the number line. A student claimed that no matter how close together a
pair of points are chosen, the point with coordinate $\frac{(a + b)}{2}$ would be
between them. Try some examples. Do you think the student's claim is
true? Give a convincing argument to support your conclusion.

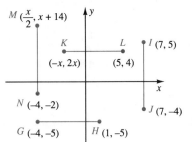

Algebra Review

Solve for x.

1. $5x + 2x = 49$ **2.** $3x - 2 + x = 14$
3. $12x - (7x - 1) = 66$ **4.** $8x + 1 - (4x + 2) = 3x$

Computer Activity

This BASIC program finds the length of a segment on the number line given
the coordinates of its endpoints.

```
10 REM FIND SEGMENT LENGTH ON A NUMBER LINE
20 INPUT "ENTER TWO COORDINATES  "; A,B
30 PRINT " THE LENGTH OF THE SEGMENT IS  "; ABS(A−B)
40 END
```

1. Run the program to find the length of the segment with endpoint
   coordinates −6 and 11.
2. Change the program so that the user can find the lengths of as many
   segments as desired without rerunning the program.
3. Why is the ABS function used in line 30?
4. Rewrite the program without using the ABS function.

OBJECTIVE: *Name angles and find their measures.*

1-3 Rays, Angles, and Angle Measure

You can use what you have learned about lines to understand rays. Then the definition of a ray can be used to define an angle. Looking at the golf iron suggests that it is useful to be able to measure angles.

A **ray**, $\overrightarrow{AB}$, is the part of $\overleftrightarrow{AB}$ that contains the point A and all the points on the same side of A as B. The single arrowhead indicates that the ray continues without end in one direction. Point A is the endpoint of $\overrightarrow{AB}$.

Ray AB or $\overrightarrow{AB}$

When the points of two rays all lie on the same line, the rays are **collinear rays.** Otherwise, they are **noncollinear rays.**

An **angle** is a figure consisting of two noncollinear rays with a common endpoint. $\overrightarrow{AB}$ and $\overrightarrow{AC}$ are **sides** of the angle. Point A is the **vertex** of the angle.

The angle can be named using three letters, either $\angle BAC$ or $\angle CAB$. Notice that the vertex is always written in the middle. Sometimes an angle is named using only the vertex letter or a number, as long as no confusion results. For example, the angle above could be named $\angle A$ or $\angle 1$.

In geometry, you will usually measure angles using a unit called a **degree(°).** The figure below shows a $1°$ angle.

A protractor marked in degree units can be used as follows to find the measure of an angle.

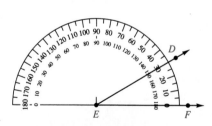

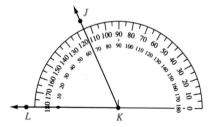

Read the outer scale.
The degree measure of $\angle DEF$ is 30.
Write: $m\angle DEF = 30$

Read the inner scale.
$m\angle JKL = 65$

5 iron

Angles are measured in many everyday situations, including sports. For example, the angles of golf irons vary from $18°$ to $58°$.

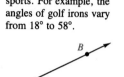

Stress that the first letter used to name a ray must be its endpoint. For example, $\overrightarrow{AB}$ and $\overrightarrow{AC}$ are names for the same ray.

$\overrightarrow{AB}$ and $\overrightarrow{BA}$ are names for different rays.

Point out that since all angle measures in this text are understood to be in degrees, the degree symbol (°) is not necessary in the expression $m\angle ABC = 50$ (read, "the measure of $\angle ABC$ is 50").
Correct: $m\angle B = 70$
Incorrect: $m\angle B = 70°$
Point out that the small square in a figure indicates a right angle.

Sometimes a straight line is called a "straight angle" having a measure of 180. However, in this text, angles will have measures between 0 and 180.

Suggest that students concentrate on the meaning of the Angle Addition Postulate rather than on memorizing the statement.
NOTE: The Angle Addition Postulate refers to angles, whereas the Segment Addition Postulate refers to segments.

Key Terms

ray
angle
degree
acute/obtuse/right angle
interior/exterior of an angle

This procedure for measuring angles is justified by the following postulate.

● **POSTULATE 8** Protractor Postulate

Given any line AB in a plane with point O between A and B; $\overrightarrow{OA}$, $\overrightarrow{OB}$, and all the rays from point O on one side of $\overleftrightarrow{AB}$ can be matched one-to-one with the real numbers from 0 through 180 so that

a. $\overrightarrow{OA}$ is matched with 0
b. $\overrightarrow{OB}$ is matched with 180
c. if $\overrightarrow{OR}$ is matched with r and $\overrightarrow{OS}$ is matched with s, then
$m\angle ROS = |r - s| = |s - r|$

The Protractor Postulate ensures that every angle has a unique number between 0 and 180 called its measure. This picture will help you understand the postulate.

Angles are classified according to their measures as shown below.

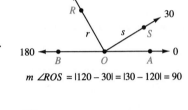

$m\angle ROS = |120 - 30| = |30 - 120| = 90$

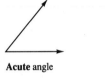

Acute angle

Measure between 0 and 90 degrees

This mark is often used to indicate a right angle.

Right angle

Measure 90 degrees

Obtuse angle

Measure between 90 and 180 degrees

Example 1

Find the measure of $\angle JFI$.
Classify it as an acute, right, or obtuse angle.

Solution

$m\angle JFI = |160 - 110| = |50| = 50$

Since $m\angle JFI$ is less than 90, it is acute.

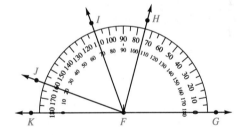

Try This

Find the measure of $\angle JFH$. Classify it as an acute, right, or obtuse angle.

An angle in the plane separates the plane into three parts—the points in the **interior** of the angle, the points of the angle, and the points in the **exterior** of the angle.

Point F is in the interior of $\angle D$.
Point P is in the exterior of $\angle D$.
Point C is on $\angle D$.

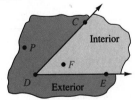

The following postulate, like the Segment Addition Postulate, describes an important property of angles.

● **POSTULATE 9**   Angle Addition Postulate

If F is in the interior of $\angle CDE$, then
$m\angle CDF + m\angle FDE = m\angle CDE$.

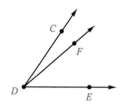

Example 2 shows how the Angle Addition Postulate may be used to find the measure of angles.

Example 2
$m\angle BOD = 45$, $m\angle BOC = 132$
Find $m\angle DOC$.

Solution

$$m\angle BOD + m\angle DOC = m\angle BOC \qquad \text{Angle Addition Postulate}$$
$$45 + m\angle DOC = 132$$
$$m\angle DOC = 132 - 45$$
$$m\angle DOC = 87$$

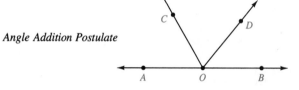

Try This
$m\angle BOD = 37$, $m\angle DOC = 54$
Find $m\angle BOC$.

The Angle Addition Postulate also applies when algebraic expressions represent angle measures. This idea is illustrated in the following example.

Example 3
$m\angle BAC = 46$
Find $m\angle BAD$ and $m\angle DAC$.

Solution

$$m\angle BAD + m\angle DAC = m\angle BAC$$
$$(4x - 3) + 3x = 46 \qquad \text{Angle Addition Postulate}$$
$$7x - 3 = 46$$
$$7x = 49$$
$$x = 7$$
$$m\angle BAD = 4x - 3 = 4(7) - 3 = 25$$
$$m\angle DAC = 3x = 3(7) = 21$$

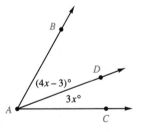

Try This
Suppose $m\angle BAC = 9x$, $m\angle DAC = 2x + 16$, and $m\angle BAD = 40$.
Find $m\angle BAC$ and $m\angle DAC$.

1-3 *Rays, Angles, and Angle Measure*   **15**

Guided Practice

Chalkboard Examples

1. Find the measure of $\angle IFH$. **35** Classify it as an acute, right, or abtuse angle. **acute**

Answer to **Try This** **85°, acute**

2. $m\angle BOC = 143$,
$m\angle BOD = 48$
Find $m\angle DOC$. **95**

Answer to **Try This** **91**

3. $m\angle DAC = 24$,
$m\angle BAD = 3x + 7$,
$m\angle BAC = 6x + 1$
Find $m\angle BAD$ and $m\angle BAC$.
37,61

Answer to **Try This** **72, 32**

Class Exercise Answers

1. endpoint   **2.** Q
3. ∠CQB, ∠1   **4.** degree
5. 65   **6.** 65   **7.** ∠BQC,
∠CQD, ∠DQE, ∠EQF
8. ∠BQF, ∠BQE, ∠AQD, ∠AQC
9. interior: C, exterior: F
10. 35   **11.** 95   **12.** 30
13. 145   **14.** 30   **15.** 30
16. 85   **17.** 30   **18.** 60
19.

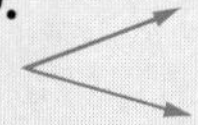

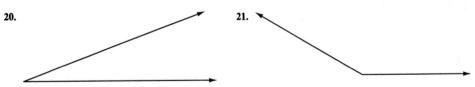

20. 20°   **21.** 150°
22. segments: no, $\overline{AB}$ is same as
$\overline{BA}$; rays: yes, $\overrightarrow{AB}$ and $\overrightarrow{BA}$ have
different endpoints; angles: yes,
∠ABC and ∠BAC have different
vertices.   **23.** Yes; every ray
with its endpoint on the line can
be matched with a number and
this number can be used to
measure angles.

Assignment Guide

Minimum: 1–44 e/o, 52, MR
Regular: 1–51 e.o, 52, MR
Advanced: 9–40 e/o, 41–52, MR

Applications

Exercises 20, 44, 51

Algebra

Exercises 15–19, 33–36

Lesson Closure

As a summary, have students
define and illustrate the key
terms of the lesson.

Teacher's Resource Materials

Manipulatives 3
Practice 3   Transparency 2

Class Exercises

Short Answer

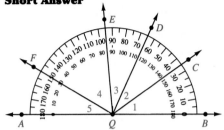

Complete each statement.

1. Point Q is called the ___ of $\overrightarrow{QD}$.
2. The vertex of ∠BQC is point ___ .
3. Two other names for ∠BQC are ___ and ___ .
4. The unit of angle measure is called a ___ .
5. $m∠BQD$ = ___
6. $m∠1 + m∠2$ = ___

7. Use symbols to name four acute angles.
8. Use symbols to name four obtuse angles.
9. Name a point in the interior and a point in the exterior of ∠BQE.

Sample Exercises

Find the measure of each angle.

10. ∠BQC   **11.** ∠BQE   **12.** ∠AQF
13. ∠AQC   **14.** ∠CQD   **15.** ∠EQD

Find each angle measure.

16. $m∠4 + m∠3$ **17.** $m∠AQE − m∠4$ **18.** $m∠BQE − m∠BQC$

19. Use a protractor to draw a 35° angle.

First estimate each angle. Then measure to check your estimate.

20.   **21.**

Discussion

22. Does the order in which the letters are written matter when naming a
segment? Does it matter when naming a ray? an angle? Explain.
23. A student claimed that the Protractor Postulate "places a protractor"
along side of every line in the plane. Is this a good description? Give a
convincing argument to support your conclusion.

16   *Chapter 1   Basic Ideas of Geometry*

Exercises

A

Find the measure of each angle.

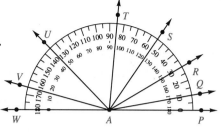

1. $m \angle QAP$
2. $m \angle WAS$
3. $m \angle PAT$
4. $m \angle PAV$
5. $m \angle SAU$
6. $m \angle VAR$

7. Write four different names for the angle below.

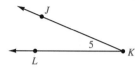

For each angle below, (a) visually classify as acute, right, or obtuse, (b) estimate the actual measure, and (c) use a protractor to find the actual measure.

8. $\angle CBD$
9. $\angle EBC$
10. $\angle FBC$
11. $\angle GBD$
12. $\angle FBD$
13. $\angle GBF$

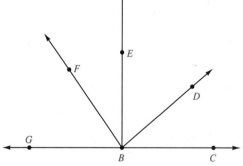

14. Use a protractor to draw a 125° angle.

Write and solve an equation to find the measure of each angle.

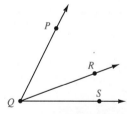

15. $m \angle PQS = 45$, $m \angle SQR = 26$
Find $m \angle PQR$.
16. $m \angle PQS = 80$, $m \angle RQP = 37$
Find $m \angle SQR$.
17. $m \angle PQS = 4x$, $m \angle SQR = 2x$, $m \angle RQP = 24$
Find $m \angle SQR$ and $m \angle PQS$.
18. $m \angle SQR = 3x - 2$, $m \angle SQP = 5x$, $m \angle PQR = 34$
Find $m \angle SQR$ and $m \angle PQS$.
19. $m \angle PQS = 6x$, $m \angle PQR = 3x + 2$, $m \angle SQR = 22$
Find $m \angle PQS$ and $m \angle PQR$.

20. A source of light, such as a flashlight, is said to emit rays. Give another example of rays.

1-3 Rays, Angles, and Angle Measure **17**

21. false

22. false

23. true   **24.** true

25. false

26. false

27. 70   **28.** 35   **29.** 20
30. 70   **31.** 160
32. 140   **33.** 56
34. 60   **35.** 50   **36.** 36
37. 36   **38.** 11 or 85
39.

40.

41.

42.

43.

44. 90, Angle Addition Postulate
45. Sometimes; true when *C* is in the interior of ∠*ABD*.
46. Sometimes; true when *R*, *S*, and *T* are collinear, with *S* and *T* on the same side of *R*.
47. never, different vertices
48. sometimes

49. always
50. Sometimes; true when the average of the measures of the angles is greater than 45.
51. 120, 130
52. 66

Determine whether each statement is true or false. If false, draw a figure to justify your answer.

21. $\overrightarrow{AB}$ is the same ray as $\overrightarrow{BA}$.
22. Any figure made up of two rays is an angle.
23. ∠*JKL* is the same angle as ∠*LKJ*.
24. Every angle is either acute, right, or obtuse.
25. A point in the plane that is not in the interior of an angle must be in the exterior of the angle.
26. When *D* is in the interior of ∠*ABC*, the Angle Addition Postulate allows you to conclude that $m\angle ABC + m\angle DBC = m\angle ABD$.

B

∠*IKF* **is a right angle.** $m\angle HKI = 20$, $m\angle HKG = m\angle FKG$, $m\angle DKE = m\angle HKI$ **Find the measure of each angle.**

27. $m\angle HKF$ **28.** $m\angle HKG$ **29.** $m\angle DKE$
30. $m\angle EKF$ **31.** $m\angle IKE$ **32.** $m\angle EKH$

$m\angle BPD = m\angle DPE$ **Find the measure of each angle.**

33. $m\angle APC = 90$, $m\angle 1 = 3x + 5$, $m\angle 2 = 2x$ Find $m\angle 1$.
34. $m\angle 4 = 4x + 12$, $m\angle BPE = 10x$ Find $m\angle 4$.
35. $m\angle 4 = x + 30$, $m\angle BPD = 3x - 10$ Find $m\angle 4$.
36. $m\angle 2 = 3x$, $m\angle 3 = 3x + 9$, $m\angle BPD = 7x$ Find $m\angle 3$.
37. $m\angle 4 = 72$, $m\angle 2 = m\angle 3$ Find $m\angle 2$.
38. $m\angle LMN = 37$, $m\angle LMQ = 48$
Find $m\angle NMQ$. (Find two possible answers.)

Draw each figure. Use a protractor if needed.

39. two angles with equal measures that each have $\overrightarrow{AB}$ as a side
40. two angles in which the vertex of each is in the interior of the other
41. two angles that intersect in exactly one point
42. two rays that intersect in a segment
43. three rays that form an obtuse angle, a right angle, and an acute angle

44. Two sides of a picture frame are glued together to form a corner. Each side is cut at a 45° angle. What is the measure of the corner of the frame? Which postulate or definition is being used?

C

Determine whether each statement is always, sometimes, or never true. Give a reason for your answer.

45. $m\angle ABC + m\angle CBD = m\angle ABD$
46. $\overrightarrow{RS}$ and $\overrightarrow{RT}$ are the same ray.
47. ∠*ABC* and ∠*CAB* are the same angle.
48. ∠*ABC* and ∠*EBF* are the same angle.
49. If *E* is between *D* and *F*, then $\overrightarrow{ED}$ and $\overrightarrow{EF}$ make up $\overleftrightarrow{DF}$.
50. The sum of two acute angles is an obtuse angle.

51. Without using a protractor, find the measure of the angle formed by the hands of a clock when it is 8:00 and when it is 8:20.

Critical Thinking

52. How many different angles are formed when ten distinct rays are drawn in the interior of the angle?

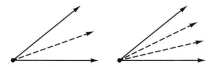

When *one* ray is drawn, *three* angles are formed.
When *two* rays are drawn, *six* angles are formed.

Complete this table and discover a pattern to help you predict the number of angles formed when ten rays are drawn.

Number of rays	1	2	3	4	5	$\cdots$
Number of angles	3	6				$\cdots$

Mixed Review

Complete each statement.

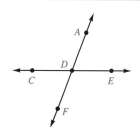

1. $\overleftrightarrow{CE}$ and $\overrightarrow{AF}$ intersect at point ___ .
2. $AD + $ ___ $ = AF$
3. Points C, D, and E are ___ .
4. If $AF = 28$ and $DF = 15$, then $AD = $ ___ .
5. If $CD = 4x + 1$, $DE = 2x - 5$, and $CE = 14$, then $CD = $ ___ .
6. If $m \angle CDF = 65$, then it is a(n) ___ angle.

Careers
Surveyor

A surveyor is involved in the construction of buildings, roads, and bridges. One of the surveyor's responsibilities is to establish exact land boundaries by measuring distances and angles accurately. The transit, an instrument invented in the 16th century, is a surveyor's most valuable tool. It is used at the site to measure both distances and angles. Later, at the office, the surveyor uses these measurements and various geometric properties to create a map or drawing of the surveyed land.

1-3   Rays, Angles, and Angle Measure   **19**

First Five Minutes

(Quiz on previous lesson)

1. Name all the points in the interior of ∠SNA; exterior of ∠MNS. *B,E;D,T*

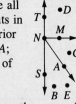

2. Give another name for ∠MNA. *∠ANM*

3. Name the sides and vertex of ∠TNM. *NT, NM, N*

4. If ∠MNS is a right angle and $m\angle ANS = 23$, find $m\angle MNA$. *67*

Lesson Opener

In geometry, figures that have the same size and shape are called congruent. In everyday life, this concept is used on assembly lines by automobile manufacturers and by draftsmen in constructing buildings. Many objects, such as toothpicks, are identical in size and shape. Discuss other objects in the classroom that have the same size and shape.

Materials

compasses and straightedges and/or investigative software
student notebooks

OBJECTIVE: *Use the definitions of congruent segments and angles to define midpoint of a segment, segment bisector, and angle bisector.*

1-4 Congruent Segments and Angles

EXPLORE

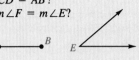

How could you use these tools to construct

a. a segment $\overline{CD}$ so that $CD = AB$?

b. an angle ∠F, so that $m\angle F = m\angle E$?

compass straightedge (no marks)

In the Explore, you may have been able to construct an "exact" copy of a segment and an angle. This suggests the idea of congruence as defined below.

■ DEFINITION

Congruent segments are segments that have the same length.

You write $\overline{CD} \cong \overline{EF}$ and say, "$\overline{CD}$ is congruent to $\overline{EF}$."
Statements such as $\overline{CD} \cong \overline{EF}$ are equivalent to statements such as $CD = EF$, so you will see these types of statements used interchangeably.

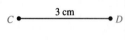

■ DEFINITION

The **midpoint of a segment** is the point that divides the segment into two congruent segments.

M is the midpoint of $\overline{RS}$, since $\overline{RM} \cong \overline{MS}$ (or $RM = MS$). The two segments are marked to show that they are congruent.

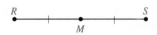

■ DEFINITION

The **bisector of a segment** is any point, line, part of a line, or plane that divides the segment into two congruent segments.
Since $\overline{GM} \cong \overline{MH}$, point M, line ℓ, $\overline{FM}$, and plane S are all bisectors of $\overline{GH}$.

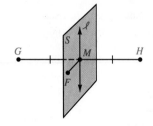

● **POSTULATE 10**   Midpoint Postulate

A segment has exactly one midpoint.

Example 1

V is the midpoint of $\overline{UW}$. Find UW.

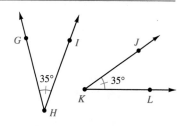

$$U \quad 3a + 5 \quad V \quad 5a - 7 \quad W$$

Solution

$UV = VW$	*Since V is the midpoint of segment $\overline{UW}$, the lengths*
$3a + 5 = 5a - 7$	*of $\overline{UV}$ and $\overline{VW}$ are equal.*
$2a = 12$	
$a = 6$	

$UV = 3a + 5 = 3(6) + 5 = 23 \quad UW = 2UV = 46$

Try This

Suppose that $UV = \frac{x}{4} + 3$ and $VW = \frac{2x}{5}$.   Find UW.

■ **DEFINITION**

Congruent angles are angles that have the same measure.

You write $\angle GHI \cong \angle JKL$. Note the marks that are used to show that $\angle GHI$ is congruent to $\angle JKL$.

Statements such as $\angle GHI \cong \angle JKL$ are equivalent to statements such as $m \angle GHI = m \angle JKL$, so these two types of statements will be used interchangeably from now on. The idea of congruent angles is used in the following important definition.

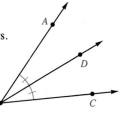

■ **DEFINITION**

The **bisector of an angle** is a ray in the interior of the angle that divides the angle into two congruent angles.

$\overrightarrow{BD}$ is the bisector of $\angle ABC$, since $\angle ABD \cong \angle DBC$.

It is natural to think that an angle could not have two or more bisectors. The following postulate states that this is true.

● **POSTULATE 11**   Angle Bisector Postulate

An angle has exactly one bisector.

Teaching Notes

Although Chapter 9 deals with constructions, a brief review of some basic constructions could be done at the same time, since many students are already familiar with them. Have students follow while each construction is demonstrated at the board or with investigative software.

Construction 1—Construct a segment congruent to a given segment.
Construction 2—Construct an angle congruent to a given angle.
Construction 3—Bisect a segment.
Construction 4—Bisect an angle.
Emphasize that the concept of congruence relates to figures and not to numbers, i.e., $\overline{AB} \cong \overline{BC}$, not $AB \cong BC$.

Point out the difference between $\overline{CD} \cong \overline{EF}$ and $CD = EF$. $\overline{CD} \cong \overline{EF}$ is used when referring to congruent segments. When reference is made to the length of a segment, the bar is not used. Thus, $CD = EF$ means that the length of $\overline{CD}$ is equal to the length of $\overline{EF}$.

Also, emphasize the difference between $\angle GHI \cong \angle JKL$ and $m \angle GHI = m \angle JKL$.

Key Terms

congruent segments
congruent angles
midpoint of a segment
bisector of an angle

Common Errors

Incorrect: $\overline{CD} = \overline{EF}$, $CD \cong EF$
Correct: $\overline{CD} \cong \overline{EF}$, $CD = EF$

Incorrect: $\angle GHI = \angle JKL$, $m \angle GHI \cong m \angle JKL$
Correct: $\angle GHI \cong \angle JKL$, $m \angle GHI = m \angle JKL$

Chalkboard Examples

1. *V* is the midpoint of $\overline{UW}$.
$UV = 3x - 5$, $VW = x + 27$
Find *UW*. **86**

Answer to **Try This** **16**

2. $\overline{YP}$ bisects $\angle XYZ$,
$m\angle XYZ = 138$ Find $m\angle XYP$
and $m\angle ZYP$. **69**

Answer to **Try This** **64**

Class Exercise Answers

1. length **2.** $EF = GH$
3. congruent **4.** 9 cm
5. $\overline{CE} \cong \overline{EF}$ **6.** 32
7. 6 **8.** $\angle QPR \cong \angle RPS$,
$\angle QPV \cong \angle VPU$ **9.** 25
10. 70 **11.** No; they have
infinite length. **12.** *F*, *G*, and
H are not collinear. **13.** *E* is
not in the interior of $\angle FGH$.
14. Endpoint 1: $A(1, 5)$, $C(3, 4)$,
$E(1, -2)$, $G(-6, 1)$, $I(-4, 1)$,
$K(1, -5)$, $W(6, 5)$ Endpoint 2:
$B(3, 1)$, $D(5, 2)$, $F(5, -4)$,
$H(-2, 5)$, $J(-2, -5)$, $L(5, -5)$,
$U(6, 0)$ Midpoint: $M(2, 3)$,
$N(4, 3)$, $P(3, -3)$, $Q(-4, 3)$,
$R(-3, -2)$, $S(3, -5)$, $V(6, 2.5)$
General rule: midpoint of (a, b)
and (c, d) is $\left(\frac{a + c}{2}, \frac{b + d}{2}\right)$.

Assignment Guide

Minimum: 1–40 e/o, 49, AR
Regular: 1–51 e/o, AR
Advanced: 13–40 e/o, 41–51, AR

Applications

Exercises 23, 40, 51

Constructions

Exercise 50

Coordinate Geometry

Class Exercise 14
Exercises 6, 7, 41, 42, 47, 49

Algebra

Class Exercises 9, 10
Exercises 8–11, 19–22, 29–31,
   AR

Example 2

$\overrightarrow{YP}$ bisects $\angle XYZ$. $m\angle XYP = 4n - 9$, $m\angle PYZ = 2n + 25$ Find $m\angle PYZ$.

Solution

$m\angle XYP = m\angle PYZ$ *Since $\overrightarrow{YP}$ bisects $\angle XYZ$, we know that the*
$4n - 9 = 2n + 25$ *measures of the two angles formed are equal.*
$\quad\quad 2n = 34$
$\quad\quad\ \ n = 17$
$m\angle PYZ = 2n + 25 = 2(17) + 25 = 59$

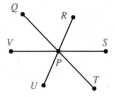

Try This

$\overrightarrow{YP}$ bisects $\angle XYZ$. $m\angle PYZ = 4x$, $m\angle XYZ = 9x - 8$ Find $m\angle XYZ$.

Class Exercises

Short Answer

Complete each statement.

1. Two segments are congruent if they have the same ___.
2. The statement $\overline{EF} \cong \overline{GH}$ is equivalent to the statement ___.
3. Two angles that have the same measure are ___.
4. *H* is the midpoint of $\overline{CD}$ and $HD = 9$ cm. $CH =$ ___
5. $CE = 8$ cm and $EF = 8$ cm, so ___.
6. $\overrightarrow{CF}$ is the bisector of $\angle DCG$ and $m\angle FCG = 32$. $m\angle FCD =$ ___
7. $\overline{EF}$ is a bisector of $\overline{CG}$. $CG = 12$, $EG =$ ___

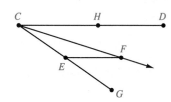

Sample Exercises

8. $\overrightarrow{PR}$ bisects $\angle QPS$. $\overrightarrow{PV}$ bisects $\angle QPU$. Name two pairs of congruent angles.
9. $\overline{UR}$ bisects $\overline{VS}$. $VP = 2x + 5$, $VS = 5x$ Find *PS*.
10. $\overrightarrow{PR}$ bisects $\angle QPS$. $m\angle QPR = 3p + 10$, $m\angle QPS = 7p$ Find $m\angle RPS$.

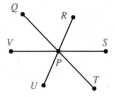

Discussion

11. Does it make sense to say that a line or a ray has a midpoint? Explain why or why not.
12. Given that $FG = GH$, why is *G* not the midpoint of $\overline{FH}$?
13. Given that $\angle 1 \cong \angle 2$, why is $\overrightarrow{GE}$ not the bisector of $\angle FGH$?
14. How could you find the midpoint of each segment on the graph?
   Complete a table like the following.

Endpoint 1	Endpoint 2	Midpoint
$A(1, 5)$	$B(3, 1)$	$M(2, 3)$

   Can you discover a rule for finding the coordinates of the midpoint of a segment with endpoints (a, b) and (c, d)?

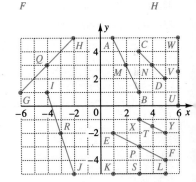

Exercises

A

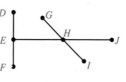

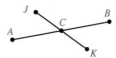

1. H is the midpoint of $\overline{GI}$. $\overline{GI}$ bisects $\overline{EJ}$. $DE = EF$
   Name the congruent segments formed.
2. The midpoint of $\overline{ST}$ is R. Name the congruent segments formed.
3. Line ℓ bisects $\overline{GH}$ at point S. Name the congruent segments formed.
4. $\overline{JK}$ and $\overline{AB}$ bisect each other. What other true statements can you make about this situation?
5. Name two pairs of segments on the number line that have the same length. Use the symbol $\cong$ to write a statement about each pair of segments.

Give the coordinate of the midpoint for each segment.

6. $\overline{DE}$ 7. $\overline{AD}$

M is the midpoint of $\overline{AB}$.   Find AM, MB, and AB.

8. $AM = 2x + 9$, $MB = 4x - 5$ 9. $AM = 2z + 6$, $MB = \frac{5z}{2}$
10. $AM = 2x^2 + 16$, $AB = 6x^2$ 11. $AM = \frac{x + 8}{3}$, $MB = \frac{x - 1}{2}$
12. $\overrightarrow{YT}$ is the bisector of $\angle XYZ$. Name the congruent angles that are formed.

$\angle TRV$ **is a right angle.** $\angle URS$ **is a right angle.**
$\overrightarrow{RU}$ **bisects** $\angle TRV$.
$\overrightarrow{TR}$ **bisects** $\angle QRU$.
$\overrightarrow{RV}$ **bisects** $\angle SRU$.
Find the measure of each angle.

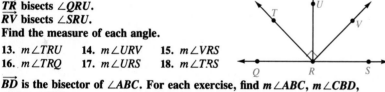

13. $m\angle TRU$ 14. $m\angle URV$ 15. $m\angle VRS$
16. $m\angle TRQ$ 17. $m\angle URS$ 18. $m\angle TRS$

$\overrightarrow{BD}$ **is the bisector of** $\angle ABC$. **For each exercise, find** $m\angle ABC$, $m\angle CBD$, **and** $m\angle DBA$.

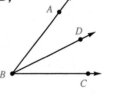

19. $m\angle ABD = 2y - 3$, $m\angle DBC = y + 12$
20. $m\angle ABD = 5(x - 8)$, $m\angle DBC = \frac{5x}{3}$
21. $m\angle ABD = 7x + 2$, $m\angle DBC = 2(46 - x)$
22. $m\angle ABD = 2x^2$, $m\angle ABC = 64$

23. Assuming there is an equal amount of weight on each end, a lever will balance when the fulcrum is located at the midpoint. How long is the lever $\overline{AC}$ if $AB = 5$ ft and the lever is balanced?

Determine whether each statement is true or false. Give a definition or a postulate to support your answer.

24. A segment can have more than one midpoint.
25. Any pair of segments that are congruent have the same length and any pair of segments that have the same length are congruent.
26. The bisector of an angle is sometimes in the exterior of the angle.
27. An angle cannot have two or more bisectors.
28. The bisector of an obtuse angle forms two obtuse angles.

1-4 Congruent Segments and Angles   **23**

29. no **30.** yes **31.** no
32. yes **33.** no **34.** true
35. true **36.** false
37. false **38.** true
39. true **40.** 70 **41.** 32
42. 2.7 **43.** 45 **44.** 45
45. 15 **46.** 30 **47.** $D(2.5, 4.5)$, $E(5, 4.5)$; $AB = 5$, $DE = 2.5$, $DE = \frac{1}{2}AB$; yes
48.

$CA = 28$, $AB = 16$, $BD = 12$; A is the midpoint of $\overline{CD}$.

B

29. $PS = 3x + 2$, $SQ = 4x - 5$, $PQ = 39$ Is S the midpoint of $\overline{PQ}$?
30. $PQ = 36$, $PS = 4b + 2$, $SQ = 6b - 6$ Does ℓ bisect $\overline{PQ}$ at S?
31. $PQ = 72$, $PS = 5h + 3$, $SQ = 8h - 9$ Is S the midpoint of $\overline{PQ}$?

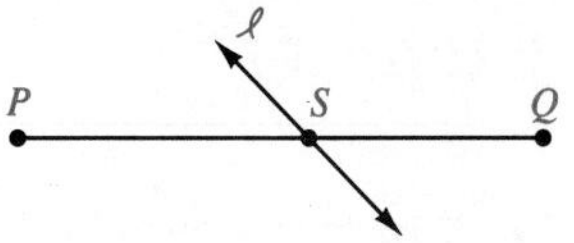

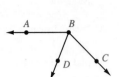

32. $\angle WXY$ is a right angle.
$m\angle WXZ = 5t + 5$
$m\angle YXZ = 6t - 3$
Is $\overrightarrow{XZ}$ the bisector of $\angle WXY$?

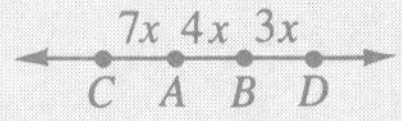

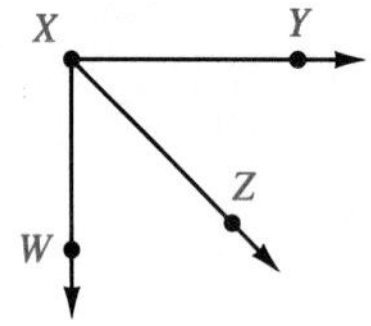

33. $m\angle ABC = 130$
$m\angle ABD = 3x + 4$
$m\angle CBD = 4x - 14$
Is $\overrightarrow{BD}$ the bisector of $\angle ABC$?

R is the midpoint of $\overline{ST}$. $\overline{PQ}$ bisects $\overline{RT}$.
$\overline{ST} \cong \overline{SQ}$, $\overline{PV} \cong \overline{VQ}$, $\overline{SQ} \cong \overline{PQ}$
Write *true*, *false*, or *no conclusion* for each statement.

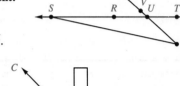

34. $\overline{SR} \cong \overline{RT}$
35. $\overline{RU} \cong \overline{UT}$
36. $\overline{PU} \cong \overline{UQ}$
37. $\overleftrightarrow{ST}$ is a bisector of $\overline{PQ}$.
38. $\overline{PQ}$ intersects $\overline{ST}$.
39. V is the midpoint of $\overline{PQ}$.

40. When a beam of light reflects off a mirror, the angle of incidence is equal to the angle of the reflection. If the angle of incidence is 35°, find $m\angle ABC$.

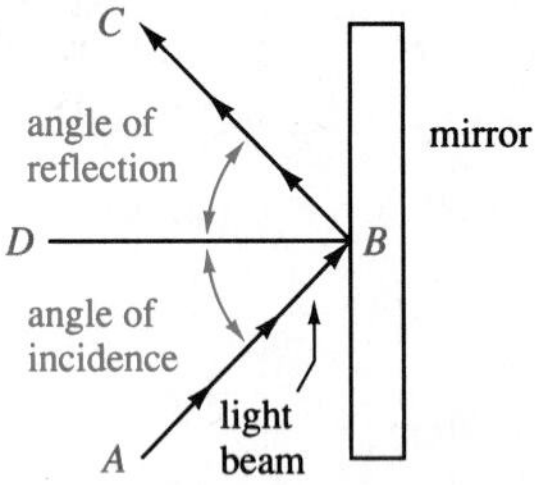

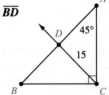

C

41. The numbers r, s, and t are coordinates of points R, S, and T on a number line. If $r = -12$, $s = 10$, and S is the midpoint of $\overline{RT}$, find t.
42. F is the midpoint of $\overline{EG}$. The coordinate of F is $f = 5.3$. The coordinate of G is $g = 7.9$. Find the coordinate of E.

$\overrightarrow{CD}$ bisects $\angle C$ and $\overline{AB}$. $\angle A \cong \angle B$, $\overline{CD} \cong \overline{BD}$
Find each of the following.

43. $m\angle ACD$
44. $m\angle CBD$
45. AD
46. AB

47. Find the coordinates of the midpoints D and E. How do the lengths of $\overline{DE}$ and $\overline{AB}$ compare? Draw a different triangle on a coordinate grid and find these midpoints and segment lengths. Do the segments compare in the same way?
48. Points A and B divide $\overline{CD}$ into the ratio 7:4:3. $CD = 56$ and A is between C and B. Draw a figure for the situation, find the length of each segment shown, and determine which point is the midpoint of $\overline{CD}$.

24 Chapter 1 Basic Ideas of Geometry

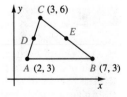

Critical Thinking

49. Write a formula for finding the midpoint of $\overline{AB}$ on the number line, where the coordinates of A and B are a and b.
(HINT: Draw a number line and try some specific segments.)

50. The figure shows the compass marks (red) and the lines (dotted red) that were made to construct the bisector of a segment and the bisector of an angle. Study the diagrams. Then draw and bisect a segment and an angle.

Bisect a segment

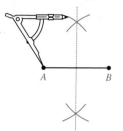

Bisect an angle

51. Collect the needed data, make a scale drawing of a baseball diamond, and use the words "midpoint" and "angle bisector" to describe the location of the pitcher's mound as accurately as possible.

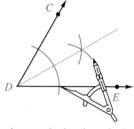

49. $\frac{a+b}{2}$ **50.** Answers may vary.   **51.** The pitcher's mound is on the angle bisector of the angle formed by third base, home plate (vertex), and first base. It is near the midpoint of the segment joining first base and third base.

Algebra Review Answers

1. 5   **2.** 10   **3.** $\sqrt{29}$
4. 5   **5.** $\sqrt{37}$ **6.** $\sqrt{34}$

Calculator Activity Answers

1. 8   **2.** 12.5   **3.** -0.5
4. 0   **5.** 5   **6.** 178
7. -22.5 **8.** 2.1

Algebra Review

Simplify.

1. $\sqrt{4^2 + 3^2}$

2. $\sqrt{6^2 + 8^2}$

3. $\sqrt{5^2 + (-2)^2}$

4. $\sqrt{(6-2)^2 + (4-1)^2}$

5. $\sqrt{(7-1)^2 + (2-3)^2}$

6. $\sqrt{(5-8)^2 + (7-12)^2}$

Calculator Investigation

A calculator can help you find the coordinate of the midpoint of a segment when you know the coordinates of its endpoints.

If A and B have coordinates a and b respectively, then the coordinate of the midpoint of $\overline{AB}$ is $\frac{a+b}{2}$.

Example

Find the coordinate of the midpoint of $\overline{AB}$ if $a = 6$ and $b = 24$.

Enter: 6 ⊞ 24 ⊟ ⊞ 2 ⊟   Display: 15   The coordinate of the midpoint of $\overline{AB}$ is 15.

Use a calculator to find the coordinate of the midpoint of $\overline{AB}$.

1. $a = 7, b = 9$ **2.** $a = 8, b = 17$ **3.** $a = 0, b = -1$ **4.** $a = -3, b = 3$
5. $a = -5, b = 15$ **6.** $a = 107, b = 249$ **7.** $a = -5, b = -40$ **8.** $a = 1.5, b = 2.7$

1-4 Congruent Segments and Angles   **25**

OBJECTIVE: *Identify triangles and classify them according to the number of congruent sides and types of angles. Apply the Distance Formula.*

1-5 Triangles

Since triangles are used so often in geometry and its applications, it is important to be able to define triangles and to classify the different types of triangles.

■ DEFINITION

A **triangle** is a figure formed by three segments joining three noncollinear points.

We can name triangle ABC by writing $\triangle ABC$, $\triangle BCA$, $\triangle ACB$, $\triangle CBA$, $\triangle CAB$, or $\triangle BAC$. In the figure, A, B, and C are the **vertices**; $\overline{AB}$, $\overline{BC}$, and $\overline{AC}$ are the **sides**; and $\angle A$, $\angle B$, and $\angle C$ are the **angles of the triangle.** Every triangle has *three* vertices, *three* sides, and *three* angles.

The words *opposite* and *included* are used to talk about relationships between sides and angles of a triangle. In $\triangle ABC$, for example,
$\overline{AB}$ is *opposite* $\angle C$ and $\angle C$ is *opposite* $\overline{AB}$;
$\angle C$ is *included* between side $\overline{BC}$ and side $\overline{AC}$;
$\overline{AB}$ is *included* between $\angle A$ and $\angle B$.

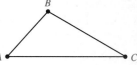

Triangles can be classified according to the types of angles they have, as shown in the figures below.

Acute triangle

All acute angles—
$\angle A$, $\angle B$, and $\angle C$ are all acute.

Right triangle

One right angle
$\angle G$ is a right angle.

Obtuse triangle

One obtuse angle
$\angle D$ is obtuse.

Equiangular triangle

All angles congruent
$\angle J \cong \angle K \cong \angle L$

In a right triangle, the side opposite the right angle is called the **hypotenuse.** The other two sides are called the **legs.**

Example 1

Name an equiangular triangle.

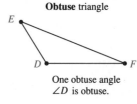

Solution

$\triangle PQS$

Try This

Name two right triangles.

Another way of classifying triangles is by the number of congruent sides they have as shown in the figures below.

Scalene triangle

No sides congruent

Isosceles triangle

At least 2 sides congruent
$\overline{EF} \cong \overline{FG}$

Equilateral triangle

All sides congruent
$\overline{HI} \cong \overline{IJ} \cong \overline{JH}$

Example 2

Name an isosceles triangle and give its congruent sides.

Solution

$\triangle STV$ is isosceles.
$\overline{ST} \cong \overline{SV}$

Try This

Name an equilateral triangle and give its congruent sides.

A coordinate grid is useful for exploring side length relationships in triangles and other figures.

In algebra, you learned that the length of $\overline{AB}$ on a coordinate grid—where A has coordinates (x_1, y_1) and B has coordinates (x_2, y_2)—can be found using the following.

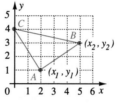

Distance Formula $\qquad AB = \sqrt{(x_2 - x_1)^2 + (y_2 - y_1)^2}$

This formula will be used to explore relationships and solve problems throughout the book and will be proved in Chapter 12. The following example illustrates its use.

Example 3

Find the length of $\overline{AB}$ in $\triangle ABC$ on the coordinate grid above.

Solution

$AB = \sqrt{(x_2 - x_1)^2 + (y_2 - y_1)^2}$ *Use the Distance Formula with*
$AB = \sqrt{(5 - 2)^2 + (3 - 1)^2}$ $A(2, 1)$ *and* $B(5, 3)$.
$AB = \sqrt{3^2 + 2^2}$ $x_2 = 5, x_1 = 2, y_2 = 3,$ *and*
$AB = \sqrt{9 + 4}$ $y_1 = 1$
$AB = \sqrt{13} \approx 3.6$

Try This

Find the length of $\overline{AC}$ in $\triangle ABC$ on the coordinate grid above and decide if $\triangle ABC$ is an isosceles triangle.

Point out that triangles are classified by their sides (scalene, isosceles, equilateral) and by their angles (acute, obtuse, right, equiangular); and that the hypotenuse and legs refer to sides of right triangles only.

The distance formula will be discussed in detail in Chapter 12.

Key Questions

1. Are triangles formed in every situation above?
2. Can a generalization or rule be made when it is not possible to form a triangle given the measures of its three sides?
3. Using a protractor, compare the angle measures of the triangles formed in d and e.

Key Terms

triangle	right triangle
vertex	scalene
hypotenuse	isosceles
legs	equilateral
acute triangle	equiangular
obtuse triangle	

Guided Practice

Chalkboard Examples

1. Name a right triangle. $\triangle BCD$

Answer to **Try This** $\triangle PRS$, $\triangle STQ$

2. Name two scalene triangles. $\triangle STU$, $\triangle SUV$

Answer to **Try This** $\triangle TUV$, $\overline{UV} \cong \overline{TV} \cong \overline{TU}$

3. Find the length of $\overline{CB}$ in $\triangle ABC$. $\sqrt{26}$

Answer to **Try This** $\sqrt{13}$; $\triangle ABC$ is isosceles since $\overline{AB} \cong \overline{AC}$.

Class Exercises

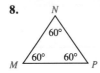

Short Answer

1. Name the vertices of △*KLM*.
2. Name the sides of △*KLM*.
3. Give five other names for △*KLM*.
4. Does △*KLM* appear to be scalene, isosceles, or equilateral?
5. Does △*KLM* appear to be acute, right, obtuse, or equiangular?
6. If ∠*L* is a right angle, name the hypotenuse and legs of △*KLM*.

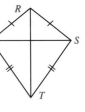

Sample Exercises

7. $\overline{US} \cong \overline{UT}$, $\overline{US} \cong \overline{TS}$ Other congruences are marked. Use the labeled points to name an isosceles, an equilateral, and a scalene triangle.

Classify these triangles as acute, obtuse, right, or equiangular.

8.   9. 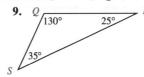   10. 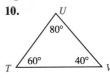   11.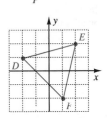

The lengths of the segments are given in the figure. Name each of the following.

12. an isosceles triangle that is not equilateral
13. an equilateral triangle
14. a scalene triangle

15. Use the Distance Formula to find the length of the shortest side of a triangle with vertex coordinates $(2, 6)$, $(6, 3)$, and $(-6, -5)$.

Discussion

16. Can a triangle be both equilateral and isosceles? Explain.
17. Is it possible to find three points with integer coordinates that can be graphed and connected to form an equilateral triangle? Test some examples using the Distance Formula. Then form a hypothesis.

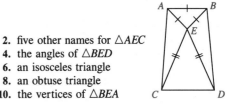

Equilateral ?

Exercises

A

Name each of the following.

1. four triangles
2. five other names for △*AEC*
3. the sides of △*BED*
4. the angles of △*BED*
5. an equilateral triangle
6. an isosceles triangle
7. a scalene triangle
8. an obtuse triangle
9. an acute triangle
10. the vertices of △*BEA*

28   *Chapter 1   Basic Ideas of Geometry*

Classify each triangle as equilateral, isosceles, or scalene.

11.
8
8   8

12.
10
12
7

13.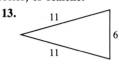
11
6
11

14.
6
4
4

Classify each triangle as acute, obtuse, right, or equiangular.

15.
51°
84°   45°

16.
60°
30°

17.
115°   30°
35°

18.
60°
60°
60°

Classify each triangle.

19. △ABC with AB = BC
20. △DEF with m∠E = 90
21. △JKL with JK = KL = LJ
22. △MNP with MN ≠ NP ≠ PM
23. △QRS with m∠Q = 145, m∠R = 15, and m∠S = 20

24. Find the length of a segment with endpoint coordinates (2, 3) and (8, 11).
25. A triangle has vertex coordinates (1, 1), (1, 5), and (5, 3). Find the length of each side and decide what type of triangle it is.
26. A typical type of rig for a sailboat consists of two sails—a jib and a mainsail. Classify each triangle as one or more of the following: acute, obtuse, right, isosceles, equiangular.

mainsail
jib

B

Determine whether each statement is always, sometimes, or never true.

27. A right triangle is an isosceles triangle.
28. A right triangle is an acute triangle.
29. An equilateral triangle is an isosceles triangle.
30. An isosceles triangle is an equilateral triangle.
31. A scalene triangle is an obtuse triangle.

Write and solve an equation to find each of the following.

32. Find RT.

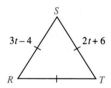
S
3t − 4   2t + 6
R   T

33. Find UW.

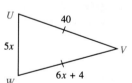
U   40
5x
W   6x + 4   V

34. Find GI.

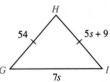
H
54   5s + 9
G   7s   I

35. Find m∠T and m∠Z.

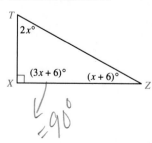
T
2x°
X   (3x + 6)°   (x + 6)°   Z

36. Find CE and DE.

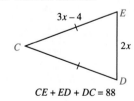
3x − 4   E
C   2x
D
CE + ED + DC = 88

37. Find m∠A.

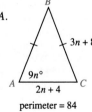
B
3n + 8
A   9n°   C
2n + 4
perimeter = 84

1-5 Triangles   **29**

---

7. △BED   **8.** △BED
9. △AEB   **10.** B, E, A
11. equilateral   **12.** scalene
13. isosceles   **14.** isosceles
15. acute   **16.** right
17. obtuse   **18.** equiangular
19. isosceles   **20.** right
21. equilateral   **22.** scalene
23. obtuse   **24.** 10   **25.** 4,
2√5, 2√5; isosceles
26. jib: right; mainsail: right
27. sometimes
28. never   **29.** always
30. sometimes
31. sometimes   **32.** 26
33. 30   **34.** 63
35. m∠T = 56, m∠Z = 34
36. CE = 32, DE = 24
37. m∠A = 72

38. 6 triangles, 4 triangles
39. 5, 6, 5; isosceles
40. $2\sqrt{5}$, $\sqrt{73}$, $\sqrt{37}$; scalene; no change
41–42. Constructions may vary.
43.

44. △OMN, △OJL, △OFI, △OAE, △MJK, △MFH, △MAD, △NKL, △NGI, △NBE, △JFG, △JAC, △KGH, △KBD, △LHI, △LCE, △FAB, △GBC, △HCD, △IDE, △HDI, △GCH, △FBG, △JGK, △KHL, △MKN, △JCL

Mixed Review Answers

1. 75   **2.** 24   **3.** 30
4. ∠RTQ, ∠1

Quiz Answers

1. 22   **2.** E B, D; A, B, C
3. 10   **4.** 15   **5.** 32
6. ∠EAC and ∠CAD
7. equilateral   **8.** right

---

c

38. The playground equipment pictured to the right is built by forming equilateral triangles with several pieces of metal. Assume each piece of metal is 2 ft long (e.g., $AB = 2$ ft). What is the greatest number of equilateral triangles in the structure that can be made with 24 ft of metal? the fewest number?

39. Graph the coordinates $(2, -3)$, $(5, 1)$, and $(8, -3)$ and connect them to form a triangle. Find the length of each side and decide what type of triangle it is.

40. Find the length of each side of △PQR having vertices with the coordinates $(4, 1)$, $(2, 5)$ and $(-4, 4)$. What type of triangle is it? Multiply each number in the coordinates by -1 and do the exercise again.

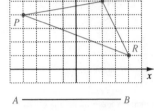

41. Choose a segment and construct an equilateral triangle that has sides congruent to the chosen segment.

42. Use a compass and straightedge to construct a triangle that has sides congruent to $\overline{AB}$, $\overline{CD}$, and $\overrightarrow{EF}$.

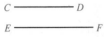

Critical Thinking

43. How could you glue six toothpicks together to form four triangles? (HINT: Regardless of the size of the toothpicks, you will need to use plenty of space!)

44. There are 27 different equilateral triangles in the figure to the right. How many of them can you name?

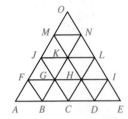

Mixed Review

Complete each statement.

1. $m\angle RTS = 45$, $m\angle QTR = 30$, $m\angle QTS =$ ___
2. If $m\angle PTR = 5x$, $m\angle PTQ = 2x$, and $m\angle QTR = 36$, then $m\angle PTQ =$ ___ .
3. $\overrightarrow{TQ}$ bisects $\angle PTR$. If $m\angle PTR = 62$ and $m\angle QTR = x + 1$, then $x =$ ___ .
4. Two other names for $\angle QTR$ are ___ and ___ .

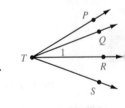

Quiz

1. Find the distance between the pair of points with coordinates -8 and 14.
2. Name two sets of three collinear points.
3. $AC = 25$, $AB = 2x + 2$, $BC = 6x - 9$ Find AB.
4. B is the midpoint of $\overline{ED}$. $EB = 2y + 1$, $BD = 3y - 6$ Find BD.
5. $m\angle DAC = 43$, $m\angle EAD = 75$ Find $m\angle EAC$.
6. $\overrightarrow{AC}$ bisects $\angle EAD$. Name a pair of congruent angles.
7. $\overline{AB} \cong \overline{BD} \cong \overline{AD}$ What type of triangle is △ABD?
8. $m\angle EBA = 90$ What type of triangle is △BAE?

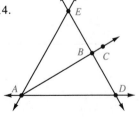

COMPARING APPROACHES IN GEOMETRY

Three Basic Transformations

Three basic transformations used in Euclidean Geometry are the **translation, reflection,** and **rotation.**

A translation slides a figure in one direction.

translation direction

For a reflection there is a line that acts like a mirror. A figure is reflected across this mirror line.

reflection line

A rotation turns a figure through some angle about a fixed center point.

rotation center

One of the important properties of these transformations is that they preserve segment lengths and angle measures as illustrated in the figures below.

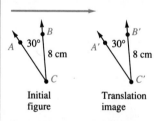

Initial figure | Translation image

An angle and its translation image have the same measure. A segment and its translation image have the same length.

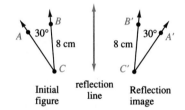

Initial figure | reflection line | Reflection image

An angle and its reflection image have the same measure. A segment and its reflection image have the same length.

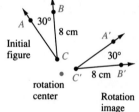

Initial figure | rotation center | Rotation image

An angle and its rotation image have the same measure. A segment and its rotation image have the same length.

Exercises

1. $\overline{CD}$ is the reflection image of $\overline{AB}$ in the y-axis. Use the distance formula to show that these segments are congruent.

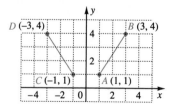

2. $\overline{CD}$ is the 90° rotation image of $\overline{AB}$ with rotation center (0, 0). Use the distance formula to show these segments congruent.

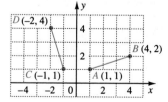

Point out that the three basic transformations are translation, reflection, and rotation. The exercises use the distance formula to illustrate that segment length is preserved under these transformations.

While the topic of transformations is covered completely in Chapter 13, it is introduced at this time because the basic concepts are used in some of the Explores throughout the text.

Exercise Answers

1. $AB = \sqrt{(4-1)^2 + (3-1)^2}$
$= \sqrt{9+4} = \sqrt{13}$
$CD = \sqrt{(4-1)^2 + (-3-(-1))^2}$
$= \sqrt{9+4} = \sqrt{13}$
$\overline{AB} \cong \overline{CD}$

2. $AB = \sqrt{(4-1)^2 + (2-1)^2} = \sqrt{9+1} = \sqrt{10}$
$CD = \sqrt{(-2-(-1))^2 + (4-1)^2}$
$= \sqrt{1+9} = \sqrt{10}$
$\overline{AB} \cong \overline{CD}$

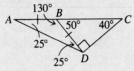
REASONING

OBJECTIVE: *Given a statement, change it to a conditional or biconditional and state its converse, inverse, or contrapositive.*

1-6 Conditional Statements

This advertisement uses an **if-then statement** to encourage you to draw a positive conclusion about the product. The *if* part is called the **hypothesis** and the *then* part is called the **conclusion.** This type of statement is also very important in geometry. Here are some other examples.

If you want economy, then drive a Gazelle.

hypothesis	conclusion
If you want economy,	*then* drive a Gazelle.
If $x = 5$,	*then* $x^2 = 25$.
If $\triangle ABC$ is equilateral,	*then* $\triangle ABC$ is isosceles.

You can use symbols to express an if-then statement by writing "if *p*, then *q*" or "*p* → *q*" where *p* represents the hypothesis and *q* represents the conclusion. "*p* → *q*" is read "*p* implies *q*."

An if-then statement can be called a **conditional statement,** or simply a conditional. Example 1 presents some skills you will need in order to understand and use conditionals.

Example 1

State the hypothesis and conclusion of this conditional.
If it rains before noon, then we will not play tennis.

Solution

Hypothesis: It rains before noon.
Conclusion: We will not play tennis.

Try This

Give a conditional with the following hypothesis and conclusion.
Hypothesis: All angles of $\triangle KLM$ have measure less than 90.
Conclusion: $\triangle KLM$ is acute.

Some statements do not contain *if* and *then* but can be written as an if-then statement. For example, each of these statements has the same meaning.

If a number is even, *then* it has a factor.	(*if* p, *then* q)
A number has a factor *if* it is even.	(q, *if* p)
A number is even *implies* it has a factor.	(p *implies* q)
A number is even *only if* it has a factor.	(p *only if* q)
All even numbers *are* numbers that have a factor.	(*all* p *are* q)

A conditional may be true, or it may be false. Suppose, for example, that your teacher stated this conditional.

$$p \qquad\qquad\qquad\qquad q$$

If you get an A on every geometry test, *then* you will get an A in the course.

The only time when you would be treated unfairly and the conditional would be false is if you received an A on every test (p is true) but did not get an A in the course (q is false). This **truth table** shows that a conditional is false only when an example can be found where the hypothesis is true, but the conclusion is false.

Truth Table

p	q	$p \rightarrow q$
T	T	T
T	F	F
F	T	T
F	F	T

Example 2

State as a conditional. Show that the conditional is false.
All right triangles are isosceles.

Solution

Conditional: If a triangle is a right triangle, then it is isosceles.

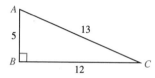

The hypothesis is true: $\triangle ABC$ is a right triangle.
The conclusion is false: $\triangle ABC$ is *not* isosceles.
Therefore the conditional is false.

Try This

State as a conditional. Show that the conditional is false.
Two lines form right angles if they intersect.

A single example, such as the one in Example 2, that shows a general conditional statement to be false is called a **counterexample.**

The **converse** of a conditional is formed by interchanging the hypothesis and the conclusion. For example,

Conditional ($p \rightarrow q$): If you live in Dallas, then you live in Texas.
Converse ($q \rightarrow p$): If you live in Texas, then you live in Dallas.

In this case, the conditional is true but the converse is false. On the other hand, the following conditional is true and so is its converse.

Conditional: If you are a native Texan, then you were born in Texas.
Converse: If you were born in Texas, then you are a native Texan.

Remember, *a true statement may or may not have a true converse.*

When a conditional and its converse are both true, we can combine the two statements into one statement, called a **biconditional,** by using the phrase *if and only if*. For example, you are a native Texan *if and only if* you were born in Texas. A definition should always be interpreted as a biconditional even though it may not be stated in the *if and only if* form.

Use the example below, along with the truth table, to help students understand the reasonableness of when a conditional is true or false. For example, Bobby makes this statement to his girlfriend. "If I earn $20 cutting grass, then I will take you to the movies." Written symbolically, "if p, then q."

Consider the four possibilities:
1. Bobby earns $20 and takes his girlfriend to the movies. (He keeps his promise, therefore his statement is true.)
2. Bobby earns $20 and does not take his girlfriend to the movies. (He breaks his promise, therefore his statement is false.)
3. Bobby does not earn $20 and does not take his girlfriend to the movies. (He does not break his promise, therefore his statement is true).
4. Bobby does not earn $20 and takes his girlfriend to the movies. (He still does not break his promise, therefore his statement is true).

	p	q	$p \rightarrow q$
1.	T	T	T
2.	T	F	F
3.	F	F	T
4.	F	T	T

Emphasize that a true conditional may or may not have a true converse.

Point out that all definitions are biconditional statements because definitions are reversible.

Key Terms

conditional   inverse
biconditional   contrapositive
converse

For initial discussion of conditional statements, use nonmathematical examples, such as "If you live in Houston, then you live in Texas."

Chalkboard Examples

1. State the hypothesis and conclusion of this conditional. If you are not in class by 8:00, then you will be considered absent. H: You are not in class by 8:00. C: You will be considered absent.

Answer to **Try This** If all angles of △KLM have measure less than 90, then △KLM is acute.

2. State as a conditional. Show that the conditional is false. All congruent angles are obtuse. If two angles are congruent, then they are obtuse.

∠A and ∠B are congruent, but they are not obtuse.

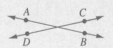

Answer to **Try This** If two lines intersect, then they form right angles. $\overline{AB}$ and $\overline{CD}$ intersect but do not form right angles.

3. State the converse of the given statement. If m∠A < 90, then ∠A is an acute angle. If ∠A is an acute angle, then m∠A < 90.

Answer to **Try This** If M is between A and B, then M is the midpoint of $\overline{AB}$. (not true)

4. State the inverse and contrapositive of the statement. If M is the midpoint of $\overline{PR}$, then $\overline{PM} \cong \overline{MR}$. I: If M is not the midpoint of $\overline{PR}$, then PM ≇ MR. C: If $\overline{PM} \not\cong \overline{MR}$, then M is not the midpoint of $\overline{PR}$.

Answer to **Try This**
I: If △EFG is not an obtuse triangle, then it does not contain an obtuse angle. C: If △EFG does not contain an obtuse angle, then it is not an obtuse triangle.

Example 3
State the converse of the given statement. If both the statement and the converse are true, state them as a biconditional.
If a triangle has at least two congruent sides, then it is isosceles.

Solution

Converse: If a triangle is isosceles, then it has at least two congruent sides.
Biconditional: A triangle is isosceles if and only if it has at least two congruent sides.

Try This
State the converse of the given statement. If both statements are true, state them as a biconditional.
If M is the midpoint of $\overline{AB}$, then M is between A and B.

If you begin with a conditional, such as "If you live in Dallas, then you live in Texas," you can form two other types of statements.

The **inverse** is formed by negating both the hypothesis and the conclusion.

Inverse (not $p \rightarrow$ not q): If you do not live in Dallas, then you do not live in Texas.

The **contrapositive** is formed by interchanging the hypothesis and the conclusion and negating both.

Contrapositive (not $q \rightarrow$ not p): If you do not live in Texas, then you do not live in Dallas.

Example 4
State the inverse and contrapositive of the statement.
If two segments have the same length, then they are congruent.

Solution

Inverse: If two segments do not have the same length, then they are not congruent.
Contrapositive: If two segments are not congruent, then they do not have the same length.

Try This
State the inverse and contrapositive of the given statement.
If △EFG is an obtuse triangle, then it contains an obtuse angle.

Class Exercises

Short Answer

Complete each statement.

1. The *if* part of a conditional is called the ___.
2. The *then* part of a conditional is called the ___.

3. When the hypothesis and the conclusion of a conditional are interchanged, the resulting statement is the ___ of the conditional.
4. If a statement and its converse are true, they can be combined to form a ___ .
5. When the hypothesis and conclusion of a conditional are negated, the resulting statement is the ___ of the conditional.
6. When the hypothesis and conclusion of a conditional are interchanged and negated, the resulting statement is the ___ of the conditional.
7. Is the converse of a true conditional always true?

Sample Exercises

Give the hypothesis and the conclusion of each statement.

8. If a triangle has all sides congruent, then the triangle must be equilateral.
9. If two distinct lines intersect, then their intersection is a point.
10. If a line and a plane intersect and the line does not lie in the plane, then their intersection is a point.
11. If a nonzero whole number has exactly two factors, then the number is prime.

State a conditional with the given hypothesis and conclusion.

12. Hypothesis: A line is the bisector of a segment.
    Conclusion: The line contains the midpoint of the segment.
13. Hypothesis: A triangle has no sides congruent.
    Conclusion: The triangle is scalene.

State as a conditional.

14. A line bisects a segment if it divides the segment into two congruent segments.
15. *m* ending in 0, 2, 4, 6, or 8 implies that *m* is an even number.
16. You will fail the course only if you get an F on the final exam.

Give a counterexample to show that the given conditional is false.

17. If three points are coplanar, then they are collinear.
18. If a triangle is isosceles, then it is equilateral.
19. If two angles are acute, then they are congruent.
20. State as a conditional. Then state the converse, inverse, and contrapositive of the conditional.
    All hard workers improve.
21. Give an example of a true conditional that has a true converse and state it as a biconditional.

Discussion

22. When asked how she decided if a conditional was true or false, Mary said, "I assume that the hypothesis is true and ask myself if the conclusion could possibly be false. If it can, I say that the conditional is false." Does Mary's method work? Explain, using an example.
23. Give a convincing argument that the contrapositive of a conditional is the same as the converse of the inverse of the conditional.

Class Exercise Answers

1. hypothesis 2. conclusion
3. converse 4. biconditional
5. inverse 6. contrapositive
7. no 8. H: A △ has all sides congruent. C: It is equilateral. 9. H: Two distinct lines intersect. C: Their intersection is a point. 10. H: A line and a plane intersect and the line does not lie in the plane. C: Their intersection is a point. 11. H: A nonzero whole number has exactly two factors. C: The number is prime. 12. If a line is the bisector of a segment, then the line contains the midpoint of the segment. 13. If a △ has no sides congruent, then the △ is scalene. 14. If a line divides a segment into two congruent segments, then it bisects the segment. 15. If *m* ends in 0, 2, 4, 6, or 8, then *m* is an even number. 16. If you failed the course, then you got an F on the final exam.
17. *A, B,* and *C* are coplanar but not collinear.
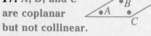
18. △*DEF* is isosceles but not equilateral.
19. ∠*G* and ∠*H* are acute but not congruent.
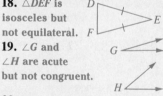
20. If you are a hard worker, then you will improve. Converse: If you improve, then you are a hard worker. Inverse: If you are not a hard worker, then you will not improve. Contrapositive: If you do not improve, then you are not a hard worker.
21. If *n* is divisible by 2, then *n* is even. *n* is divisible by 2 if and only if *n* is even.
22. The method works. For example, use "If Singh lives in Texas, then he lives in Dallas." Assuming "Singh lives in Texas" is true, he might not live in Dallas so the conditional is false.

Exercises

A

State the hypothesis and conclusion for each statement.

1. If you are funny, then you will make people laugh.
2. If point A is the midpoint of $\overline{EF}$, then A divides $\overline{EF}$ into two congruent segments.
3. If a point is in the interior of an angle, then it cannot be in its exterior.
4. If Michele's age is 15, then she is too young to vote.
5. If $\angle A \cong \angle B$, then $m \angle A = m \angle B$.
6. If A is between B and C, then A, B, and C are collinear.
7. If $\triangle JKL$ has three acute angles, then $\triangle JKL$ is acute.

Write a conditional with the given hypothesis and conclusion.

8. Hypothesis: A number is prime.
   Conclusion: The number has exactly two divisors.
9. Hypothesis: A man lives in Houston.
   Conclusion: He lives in Texas.
10. Hypothesis: The angles of a triangle are congruent to each other.
    Conclusion: The triangle is equiangular.
11. Hypothesis: Four points are all in one plane.
    Conclusion: The points are coplanar.
12. Hypothesis: B is between A and C.
    Conclusion: $AB + BC = AC$.
13. Hypothesis: R is between S and U, and T is between R and U.
    Conclusion: T is between S and U.

Write each statement as a conditional. Then determine whether it is true or false.

14. A number ends in five if it is even.
15. A line which bisects a segment contains the midpoint of the segment.
16. An angle is obtuse only if it has measure less than 90.
17. Collinear points are points that lie on the same line.
18. All left-handed people are male.
19. Go to law school and you will become a judge.
20. All acute angles are congruent.
21. Every equilateral triangle is also an isosceles triangle.

Write the converse of each statement.

22. If a person is swimming, then that person is wet.
23. If two angles have the same measure, then they are congruent.
24. If $ab = 0$, then $a = 0$ or $b = 0$.
25. If two angles each measure 30, then they are congruent.
26. If you are 21 years old or older, then you can legally vote.
27. If two lines have a common point, then they are intersecting lines.
28. If an angle is an acute angle, then its measure is less than 90.
29. If $\triangle ABC$ is equilateral, then $\triangle ABC$ is isosceles.

30. The statements in Exercises 22–29 are all true. For those that also have true converses, write the statement and its converse as a biconditional.
31. Write the inverse and contrapositive of the statements in Exercises 25–26.

36   *Chapter 1   Basic Ideas of Geometry*

B

Write two conditionals that are equivalent to the given biconditional.

32. An angle is a right angle if and only if its measure is 90.
33. Two angles are congruent if and only if they have the same measure.
34. M is the midpoint of $\overline{AB}$ if and only if M is between A and B and $\overline{AM} \cong \overline{MB}$.
35. $\overrightarrow{BD}$ is the bisector of $\angle ABC$ if and only if D is in the interior of the angle and $\angle ABD \cong \angle DBC$.
36. A triangle is a right triangle if and only if it has one right angle.

Give the hypothesis and conclusion of each statement.

37. Jim may vote if and only if he is at least 18 years old.
38. A, B, and C are collinear provided A, B, and C are all on one line.
39. A number is odd whenever it ends in five.
40. A person can be president if and only if the person is at least 35 years old.
41. Angles with the same measure are congruent.
42. All lines with a common point are intersecting lines.

Write a conditional for each figure. Is the converse of each statement true?

43. 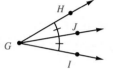 44.   45.

C

46. Using biconditionals, write complete definitions of the following types of triangles:
    scalene, isosceles, equilateral.
47. Using biconditionals, write complete definitions of the following types of triangles:
    acute, obtuse, right, equiangular.
48. Write the converse, inverse, and contrapositive of the following statement. Determine whether each is true or false.
    If a figure is a triangle, then it has three segments.
49. Use the conditional to show that the contrapositive of the inverse of a conditional is the same as the converse of the conditional.
    If a triangle is an equilateral triangle, then it is an isosceles triangle.

Critical Thinking

50. Write as many conditionals as you can that have the same meaning as the statements in this advertisement from the Nowork Company.

    Join the Nowork Company and make a fast buck. Work for Nowork and get promoted fast. We hire only smart people who are too dumb to know they are smart. Nowork assures you excellent training at no pay. You will like working for the Nowork Company. We hire any human. We fire any human.

46. A triangle is scalene if and only if none of its sides are congruent. A triangle is isosceles if and only if two of its sides are congruent. A triangle is equilateral if and only if all of its sides are congruent.

48. Converse: If a figure has three segments, then it is a triangle. (F) Inverse: If a figure is not a triangle, then it does not have three segments. (F) Contrapositive: If a figure does not have three segments, then it is not a triangle. (T)   **50.** If you join the Nowork Company, then you will make a fast buck. If you work for Nowork, then you will get promoted fast, etc.

52. If $\overline{AB} \cong \overline{BC}$, then $AB = BC$.
a. $AB = BC$ if $\overline{AB} \cong \overline{BC}$.
b. $\overline{AB} \cong \overline{BC}$ only if $AB = BC$.
c. $\overline{AB} \cong \overline{BC}$ is all that is needed to ensure $AB = BC$.
d. $AB = BC$ must be true in order for $\overline{AB} \cong \overline{BC}$ to be true.
e. $\overline{AB} \cong \overline{BC}$ implies $AB = BC$.
All of these statements are true.

Mixed Review Answers

1. right   **2.** isosceles
3. equiangular   **4.** acute

Connections Answers

1.

2.

3. 8

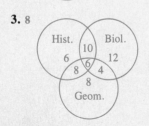

---

51. In this truth table, the symbol $\sim p$ is used for "not p." When p is true, $\sim p$ is false; when p is false, $\sim p$ is true. $\sim q$ has the same meaning. Use this idea and the Truth Table on page 33 to complete this table.

If two statements involving p and q have the same truth values for all truth values of p and all truth values of q, then the statements are **equivalent.** Are a conditional and its contrapositive equivalent? Make truth tables to answer this question for the converse and for the inverse.

| | | Conditional | | Contrapositive | |
p	q	$p \to q$	$\sim q$	$\sim p$	$\sim q \to \sim p$
T	T	T	F	F	T
T	F				
F	T				
F	F				

52. Write a true conditional (if a, then b), and then rewrite it in each of the following forms. Which of these statements do you think are true?
a. b if a **b.** a only if b **c.** a is all that is needed to ensure b
d. b must be true in order for a to be true   **e.** a implies b.

Mixed Review

Classify each triangle.

1. $\triangle ABC$ with $m\angle C = 90$ **2.** $\triangle KLM$ with $\overline{KL} \cong \overline{LM}$
3. $\triangle XYZ$ with $\angle X \cong \angle Y \cong \angle Z$ **4.** $\triangle DEF$ with $m\angle D = 50$, $m\angle E = 60$, $m\angle F = 70$

CONNECTIONS ◈

Reasoning and Venn Diagrams

Venn diagrams can be used to represent statements. For example, the statement "All lizards are reptiles" can be represented by the Venn diagram to the right. We can see that if an animal is a lizard, then it is also a reptile; but the converse is not necessarily true.

Venn diagrams are also useful in showing the relationship between groups of objects or people. The relationship between people who jog and people who swim is shown in the Venn diagram at the right. The green region represents people who both swim and jog.

Draw a Venn diagram to represent each statement.

1. All apples are fruits.
2. If a woman is a doctor, then she is a college graduate.

Use a Venn diagram to solve.

3. At Cortez High School 32 students take biology, 30 students take history, and 26 students take geometry. Ten students take both geometry and biology, 14 students take geometry and history, and 16 students take history and biology. Six students take all three subjects. How many students take geometry but not history or biology?

38   *Chapter 1   Basic Ideas of Geometry*

OBJECTIVE: *Use definitions, postulates, and other true statements to draw and support conclusions.*

1-7 Drawing and Supporting Conclusions

In Lesson 1-6, you analyzed both real-world and geometric conditional statements. In this section, you will see how true conditionals can be used to help you draw conclusions in geometry. This process is described here and analyzed below.

Drawing a Conclusion in Geometry

You know this conditional is true:

If at least two sides of a triangle are congruent, then the triangle is isosceles.

You are given: ΔABC with $\overline{AC} \cong \overline{AB}$

You conclude: ΔABC is isosceles.

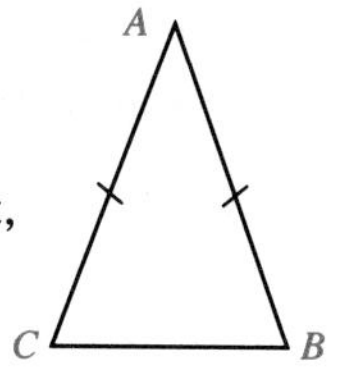

Notice the following about the situation above.

- The conditional is a true general statement. (a definition, a postulate, or a statement that has been proved to be true)
- The *given* information establishes the truth of the *hypothesis* of the conditional.
- The *specific conclusion* about ΔABC follows from the *conclusion* of the conditional.

The reasoning process described above is called **affirming the hypothesis.** It is a pattern of inference often used in geometric proofs and is logically represented as shown to the right.

Affirming the Hypothesis

$p \rightarrow q$ is true.
p is given.

Conclude that q is true.

Example 1

Use the conditional and the given information to draw a conclusion.

Conditional (true): If a point is the midpoint of a segment, then it divides the segment into two congruent segments.

Given: M is the midpoint of $\overline{CD}$.

Conclusion: ?

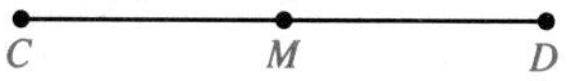

Solution

$\overline{CM} \cong \overline{MD}$

Try This

Does the following conditional support the conclusion?
If not, restate the conditional so that it will.

Conditional: If the measure of an angle is greater than 90, then it is obtuse.

Given: $\angle 1$ is obtuse.

Conclusion: $m\angle 1 > 90$

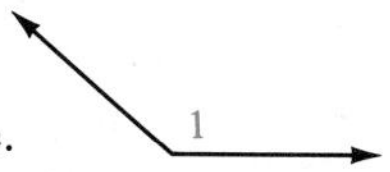

A conclusion drawn from given information can be supported by citing a definition, a postulate, or another conditional known to be true. A complete knowledge of the definitions, postulates, and true statements studied so far will help you do this. Also, paying careful attention to the key words and symbols in the given information often suggests the correct supporting statement.

First Five Minutes

(Quiz on previous lesson)

Statement A: If today is Monday, then tomorrow is Tuesday.

Statement B: All right angles measure 90.

1. What is the hypothesis and the conclusion of Statement A?
H: Today is Monday.
C: Tomorrow is Tuesday.

2. Rewrite Statement B in if-then form. Label as true or false. **If an angle is a right angle, then it measures 90. (T)**

3. Write the converse, inverse, and contrapositive of Statement A. Label each as true or false.
If tomorrow is Tuesday, then today is Monday. (T) If today is not Monday, then tomorrow is not Tuesday. (T) If tomorrow is not Tuesday, then today is not Monday. (T)

Lesson Opener

This section is about a very important pattern of reasoning often used in proofs—affirming the hypothesis. First establish that a conditional is true and that its hypothesis is true. Then conclude that its conclusion is true.

Written symbolically: Whenever $p \rightarrow q$ is true and p is true, it follows that q is true.

Materials

student notebooks

Teaching Notes

The exercises and examples in this section are important because they give students practice in setting up the "given" and "prove" of geometric proofs.

1-7 Drawing and Supporting Conclusions **39**

1. If it is raining on Thursday, will the game be postponed?
2. It is not raining on Friday night, will the game be postponed?
3. On Friday night it rained. Was the game postponed?

Guided Practice

Chalkboard Examples

1. Use the conditional and the given information to draw a conclusion.

Conditional (true): If a ray bisects an angle, then it divides the angle into two congruent angles.
Given: $\overrightarrow{BD}$ bisects $\angle ABC$.
Conclusion: ? $\angle ABD \cong \angle DBC$

Answer to Try This

No; if an angle is obtuse, then it is greater than 90°.

2. State a conditional that supports the given conclusion.
Conditional: ?
Given: M is the midpoint of $\overline{AC}$.
Conclusion: $\overline{AM} \cong \overline{MC}$

If a point is the midpoint of a segment, then it divides the segment into 2 congruent segments.

Answer to Try This

$\overline{SW} \cong \overline{WT}$; If a line bisects a segment, then it divides the segment into 2 congruent segments.

Class Exercise Answers

1. true   **2.** true   **3.** true
4. false   **5.** true   **6.** I, J, and K are collinear.   **7.** E, F, and G are all on one line.
8. $BC + CD = BD$ **9.** Planes P and Q intersect in exactly one line.   **10.** If a banana is yellow, then it is ripe. ($p \rightarrow q$ is true.) This banana is yellow. (p is true.) This banana is ripe. (q is true.)

Example 2

State a conditional that supports the given conclusion.
Given: $\overrightarrow{GH}$ bisects $\angle FGI$.
Conclusion: $\angle 1 \cong \angle 2$
Conditional: ?

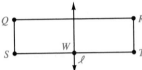

Solution

If a ray bisects an angle, then it divides the angle into two congruent angles.

Try This

Draw a conclusion from the given information. State a conditional to support the conclusion.
Given: Line ℓ bisects $\overline{ST}$ at W.
Conclusion: ?
Conditional: ?

Class Exercises

Short Answer

Determine whether each statement is true or false.

1. Conditionals are used in geometry to draw conclusions.
2. A false conditional cannot be used to support a conclusion.
3. A postulate can be used to support a conclusion.
4. A definition cannot be used to support a conclusion.
5. In order to draw a conclusion, the specific given information must meet the conditions of the hypothesis of a true conditional.

Sample Exercises

Use the given definition or postulate to draw a conclusion

6. Definition: If three points are all on one line, then the points are collinear.
   Given: Points I, J, and K are all on line ℓ.
   Conclusion: ?

7. Definition: If three points are collinear, then the points are all on one line.
   Given: E, F, and G are collinear.
   Conclusion: ?

8. Postulate: If point Q is between P and R, then $PQ + QR = PR$.
   Given: Point C is between B and D.
   Conclusion: ?

9. Postulate: If two planes intersect, then they intersect in exactly one line.
   Given: Planes P and Q intersect.
   Conclusion: ?

Discussion

10. Give an example of the reasoning described by the following.
    "If $p \rightarrow q$ is true and p is true, then q is true,"
    where p and q are replaced by real-world statements.

Exercises

A

Use the conditional and given information to draw a conclusion.

1. Conditional: If a triangle is equiangular, then all sides of the triangle are congruent.
   Given: $\triangle LMN$ is equiangular.

2. Conditional: If a ray bisects an angle, then it divides the angle into two congruent angles.
   Given: $\overrightarrow{JK}$ bisects $\angle TJR$.

3. Conditional: If a triangle contains a right angle, then it is a right triangle.
   Given: $\triangle GEF$, with right angle, $\angle E$

4. Conditional: If a and b are the coordinates of points A and B on the number line, then the distance between A and B is $|a - b|$.
   Given: The coordinate of point A is -7. The coordinate of point B is 9.5.

Change the conditional so that it will be true and will support the conclusion.

5. Conditional: (to be changed) If an angle measures 90, then it is a right angle.
   Given: $\angle 6$ is a right angle.
   Conclusion: $m\angle 6 = 90$

6. Conditional: (to be changed) If a point is the midpoint of a segment, then it divides the segment into two segments.
   Given: T is the midpoint of $\overline{PQ}$.
   Conclusion: $\overline{PT} \cong \overline{TQ}$

7. Conditional: (to be changed) If a triangle has at least two congruent sides, then it is equilateral.
   Given: $\triangle DEF$ with $\overline{DE} \cong \overline{DF} \cong \overline{EF}$
   Conclusion: $\triangle DEF$ is isosceles.

8. Conditional: (to be changed) If two angles have the same measure, then the angles are congruent.
   Given: $\angle A \cong \angle B$
   Conclusion: $m\angle A = m\angle B$

State a true conditional that supports the conclusion.

9. Given: $\angle QCN \cong \angle NCK$
   Conclusion: $\overrightarrow{CN}$ bisects $\angle QCK$.

10. Given: $\overrightarrow{CN}$ bisects $\angle QCK$.
    Conclusion: $\angle QCN \cong \angle NCK$

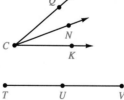

11. Given: $\overline{TU} \cong \overline{UV}$
    Conclusion: U is the midpoint of $\overline{TV}$.

12. Given: U is the midpoint of $\overline{TV}$.
    Conclusion: $\overline{TU} \cong \overline{UV}$

13. Explain why the conditional "If a triangle is equilateral, then all of its sides are congruent" does not support the conclusion that has been drawn from the given information below.
    Given: $\triangle MNP$ with $\overline{MN} \cong \overline{MP} \cong \overline{NP}$
    Conclusion: $\triangle MNP$ is equilateral.

14. Explain why the conditional "If M is between A and B, then A, B, and M are collinear" does not support the conclusion that has been drawn from the given information below.
    Given: M is between A and B.
    Conclusion: $AM = MB$

Assignment Guide
Minimum: 1–33 e/o, 38, AR
Regular: 1–37 e/o, 38, AR
Advanced: 1–21 e/o, 23–38, AR

Applications
Class Exercise 10
Exercise 38

Algebra
Algebra Review

Lesson Closure

Use the conditional and the given information to draw conclusions in each of the following.

1. If a triangle is equilateral, then all sides of the triangle are congruent.
   Given: $\triangle ABC$ is equilateral.
   $\overline{AB} \cong \overline{BC} \cong \overline{CA}$

2. If a triangle contains a right angle, then it is a right triangle.
   Given: $\triangle MNP$ with right $\angle N$
   $\triangle MNP$ is a right triangle.

3. If two segments have equal lengths, then they are congruent.
   Given: $AB = ST$
   $\overline{AB} \cong \overline{ST}$

4. The bisector of an angle divides the angle into two congruent angles.
   Given: $\overrightarrow{BD}$ bisects $\angle ABC$.
   $\angle ABD \cong \angle DBC$

5. The midpoint of a segment divides the segment into two congruent segments.
   Given: R is the midpoint of $\overline{XZ}$.
   $\overline{XR} \cong \overline{RZ}$

Teacher's Resource Materials

Practice Master 7

Draw a conclusion from the given information and state a true conditional to support it.

15. Conditional: ?
    Given: $\overrightarrow{EF}$ bisects $\angle GEH$.
    Conclusion: ?

16. Conditional: ?
    Given: $\angle GEF \cong \angle FEH$
    Conclusion: ?

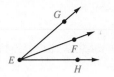
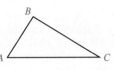

17. Conditional: ?
    Given: $\triangle ABC$ is scalene.
    Conclusion: ?

18. Conditional: ?
    Given: No sides of $\triangle ABC$ are congruent.
    Conclusion: ?

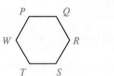

19. Conditional: ?
    Given: $m\angle PQR = m\angle STW$
    Conclusion: ?

20. Conditional: ?
    Given: $\angle PQR \cong \angle STW$
    Conclusion: ?

21. Conditional: ?
    Given: $m\angle 1 = 30$, $m\angle 2 = 60$
    Conclusion: ?

22. Conditional: ?
    Given: $\overrightarrow{LN}$ bisects $\angle KLM$
    Conclusion: ?

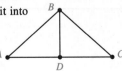

B

For each given, write two different conditionals that lead to two different conclusions.

23. Line ℓ bisects $\overline{GH}$ at point M.
24. $\triangle ABC$ with $\overline{AB} \cong \overline{BC} \cong \overline{AC}$
25. Point N is between points S and T.

Draw a conclusion from each figure. Name a definition that supports your conclusion.

26.

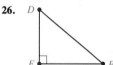

27.

28.

29.

Draw a conclusion from the true statement and the given information. You may need to rewrite the statement as a conditional.

30. True statement: The bisector of an angle divides it into two congruent angles.
    Given: $\overrightarrow{BD}$ bisects $\angle ABC$.

31. True statement: A midpoint divides a segment into two congruent segments.
Given: T is the midpoint of $\overline{GH}$.

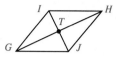

32. True statement: Congruent angles have the same measure.
Given: $\angle 3 \cong \angle PQR$
$\angle 2 \cong \angle PQR$

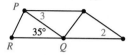

33. True statement: An average of 90% or more will earn an A.
Given: Jerome had an average of 93%.

C

Another useful pattern of reasoning, denying the conclusion, is described to the right—p and q represent the hypothesis and conclusion of a conditional. Use this pattern to draw conclusions from the given information.

34. If a triangle is isosceles, then it has at least two congruent sides. $\triangle JKL$ has no congruent sides.

35. If $\overrightarrow{AB}$ is the bisector of $\angle CAD$, then $\angle CAB \cong \angle BAD$. $m\angle CAB \neq m\angle BAD$.

A third important pattern of reasoning, the chain rule, is described to the right. Use it to draw a conclusion from the given information.

36. If it rains today, then we will not have a picnic. If we do not have a picnic, then we will not see our friends.

37. If a line is a bisector of a segment, then it divides the segment into two congruent segments. If a line divides a segment into two congruent segments, then it contains the midpoint of the segment.

Critical Thinking

38. Three people named Glynn, Harding, and MacFeely fill the positions of accountant, clerk, and cashier in a department store. If MacFeely is the cashier, Harding is the clerk. If MacFeely is the clerk, Harding is the accountant. If Harding is not the cashier, Glynn is the clerk. If Glynn is the accountant, MacFeely is the clerk. What is each person's job?

Algebra Review

State a property that asserts that each of the following is true.

1. $a + b = b + a$
2. $6(x + y) = 6x + 6y$
3. $(m + n) + 1 = m + (n + 1)$
4. If $c = d$ and $d = e$, then $c = e$.

Denying the Conclusion
Conditional: $p \rightarrow q$
Given: q is false.
Conclusion: p is false.

The Chain Rule
Conditional 1: $p \rightarrow q$
Conditional 2: $q \rightarrow r$
Conclusion: $p \rightarrow r$

20. Conditional: If two angles are congruent, then they have equal measures. Conclusion: $m\angle PQR = m\angle STW$
21. Conditional: If N is in the interior of $\angle KLM$, then $m\angle KLN + m\angle NLM = m\angle KLM$. Conclusion: $m\angle KLM = 90$.
22. Conditional: If a ray is an angle bisector, then it divides the angle into two congruent angles. Conclusion: $\angle KLN \cong \angle NLM$ **23.** (1) If a line bisects a segment, then it divides it into two congruent segments. (2) If a line bisects a segment, then it contains the segment's midpoint.   **24.** (1) If a triangle has at least two congruent sides, then it is isosceles. (2) If all three sides of a triangle are congruent, then it is equilateral.   **25.** (1) If N is between S and T, then $SN + NT = ST$ (2) If a point is between two other points, then the three points are collinear. **26.** $\triangle DEF$ is a right triangle. (definition of right triangle) **27.** $\triangle KML$ is isosceles. (definition of isosceles triangle) **28.** Q is the midpoint of $\overline{PR}$. (definition of midpoint) **29.** $\angle S \cong \angle T$ (definition of congruent angles) **30.** $\angle ABD \cong \angle DBC$ **31.** $\overline{GT} \cong \overline{TH}$ **32.** $m\angle 3 = 35$, $m\angle 2 = 35$ **33.** Jerome earned an A.   **34.** $\triangle JKL$ is not isosceles.   **35.** $\overrightarrow{AB}$ is not the bisector of $\angle CAD$.   **36.** If it rains today, then we will not see our friends.   **37.** If a line is a bisector of a segment, then it contains the midpoint of the segment.   **38.** MacFeely is the accountant; Harding is the cashier; Glynn is the clerk.

Algebra Review Answers

1. commutative   2. distributive
3. associative   4. transitive

Enrichment

Symbolic logic is a way of representing complicated statements by symbols. In this way, the statements can be manipulated and understood more easily. Point out that this is similar to the use of algebra in simplifying and solving word problems.

Ask students to create conditionals relating to their weekend plans. Have them represent these statments using the symbols discussed here.

Exercise Answers

1. Alice will not visit Hawaii.
2. Alice will buy a car and Alice will visit Hawaii.   **3.** Alice will not buy a car or Alice will not visit Hawaii.   **4.** Alice will not buy a car or Alice will visit Hawaii.   **5.** $\sim p$
6. $p \vee q$ **7.** $\sim p \wedge \sim q$
8. $p \vee \sim q$ **9.** $\sim(\sim p)$ is "This idea is not not good" which is the same as "This idea is good," so $\sim(\sim p)$ is equivalent to p.   **10.** $p \vee \sim p$ is "This idea is good or this idea is not good," a statement that is always true.   **11.** $p \wedge \sim p$ is "This idea is good and this idea is not good," a contradictory statement, so $p \wedge \sim p$ is always false.

Enrichment
Symbolic Logic

You have already seen that letters and symbols can be used to represent statements. For example, if p represents the statement "William lives in Houston" and q represents the statement "William lives in Texas," then $p \rightarrow q$ represents the conditional "If William lives in Houston, then William lives in Texas."

Other symbols are often used to modify or connect statements.
    The symbol $\sim$ is used to represent the word "not."
    The symbol $\wedge$ is used to represent the word "and."
    The symbol $\vee$ is used to represent the word "or."

Example

p	We will go to a movie.
q	We will play basketball.
$\sim p$	We will *not* go to a movie.
$p \wedge q$	We will go to a movie *and* we will play basketball.
$p \vee q$	We will go to a movie *or* we will play basketball.

These symbols can also be used to represent more complicated statements as in the following examples.

$\sim p \wedge \sim q$	We will *not* go to a movie *and* we will *not* play basketball.
$\sim(p \wedge q)$	We will *not* go to a movie *and* play basketball.

Notice the difference between these statements and how this difference is reflected in their symbolic equivalents.

Exercises

Suppose p represents the statement "Alice will buy a car" and q represents the statement "Alice will visit Hawaii."

Write each statement in words.

1. $\sim q$ 2. $p \wedge q$
3. $\sim p \vee \sim q$ 4. $\sim p \vee q$

Write each statement using symbols.

5. Alice will not buy a car.
6. Alice will buy a car or Alice will visit Hawaii.
7. Alice will not buy a car and Alice will not visit Hawaii.
8. Alice will buy a car or Alice will not visit Hawaii.

Let p represent the statement "This idea is good" to help answer each of the following.

9. Explain why $\sim(\sim p)$ is equivalent to p.
10. Explain why $p \vee \sim p$ always represents a true statement.
11. Explain why $p \wedge \sim p$ always represents a false statement.

1-8 Deductive Reasoning—Using Algebraic Properties

Charlie's dog was born the same time as Patty's dog. While talking with Sally, Patty learned that her dog was the same age as Sally's dog. What can you conclude from this information?

When you conclude that Charlie's dog is the same age as Sally's dog, you are using **deductive reasoning,** a process in which conclusions are drawn logically from given information. This conclusion is true because of the transitive property of equality reviewed in the table below.

© 1958 United Feature Syndicate, Inc.

The measures of segments and angles are real numbers, so the properties you used in algebra are also important in geometry.

Properties of Equality

For all real numbers a, b, c, and d the following are true.

Reflexive Property	$a = a$
Symmetric Property	If $a = b$, then $b = a$
Transitive Property	If $a = b$ and $b = c$, then $a = c$
Addition Property	If $a = b$ and $c = d$, then $a + c = b + d$
Subtraction Property	If $a = b$ and $c = d$, then $a - c = b - d$
Multiplication Property	If $a = b$ and $c = d$ then $ac = bd$
Division Property	If $a = b$ and $c \neq 0$, then $\frac{a}{c} = \frac{b}{c}$
Substitution Property	If $a = b$, then a and b may be substituted for each other in any equation or inequality.

Properties of Real Numbers

Commutative Property	$a + b = b + a$, $ab = ba$
Associative Property	$a + (b + c) = (a + b) + c$, $a(bc) = (ab)c$
Distributive Property	$a(b + c) = ab + ac$

1-8 Deductive Reasoning—Using Algebraic Properties **45**

First Five Minutes

(Quiz on previous lesson)

Draw a conclusion from the given information.

1. Given: $\triangle ABC$ with right $\angle B$
$\triangle ABC$ is a right triangle.
2. Given: All three sides of $\triangle MNP$ are congruent. $\triangle MNP$ is equilateral.
3. Given: S is the midpoint of $\overline{RT}$. $\overline{RS} \cong \overline{ST}$
4. Given: $\triangle JKL$ is an acute triangle. $\triangle JKL$ has an acute angle.

Lesson Opener

As an introduction to this lesson, ask students about situations in which they might have used deductive reasoning to arrive at a conclusion. For example, certain state curriculums mandate that students have three credits in mathematics before they can receive a regular high school diploma. In order to receive an advanced high school diploma, certain math courses are required (Algebra 1, Algebra 2, and Geometry). An example of a state with these requirements is Texas. Discuss reasons for selecting geometry as one math course. Point out that if students chose to take geometry in order to be eligible for an advanced high school diploma, then they used deductive reasoning to arrive at their decision.

Key Questions

1. Why did you select geometry this year?
2. What math course are you planning to take next year?

Materials

student notebooks

Point out that in algebra students also used deductive reasoning to solve equations.

For example,

$4(x + 7) = 52$

$4x + 28 = 52$		Distributive Property
$4x = 24$		Subtraction Property
$x = 6$		Division Property

Point out that these properties of real numbers that were used in algebra will also be used in geometry, since the measures of segments and angles are real numbers.

Emphasize that each statement in a proof must be justified by a property of real numbers, a definition, a postulate, or a previously proven theorem.

Guided Practice

Chalkboard Examples

1. Which property allows you to conclude that the following is true? $m\angle 1 + m\angle 2 = m\angle 2 + m\angle 1$
Commutative Property

Answer to Try This
Addition Property

2. Give a paragraph proof that if $3x + 1 = 16$, then $x = 5$.
Since $3x + 1 = 16$, $3x = 15$ (Subtraction Property) and so $x = 5$ (Division Property).

Answer to Try This
Since $3(x - 2) = 9$, $3x - 6 = 9$ (Distributive Property). Also, $3x = 15$ (Addition Property), and so $x = 5$ (Division Property).

Example 1

Which property allows you to conclude that the following is true?
If $m\angle J = m\angle K$ and $m\angle K = m\angle L$,
then $m\angle J = m\angle L$.

Solution
Transitive Property

Try This

Which property allows you to conclude that the following is true?
If $CD = EF$ and $GH = IK$,
then $CD + GH = EF + IK$.

In algebra, deductive reasoning and the above properties can be used to **prove** that the procedure used for solving an equation is correct. The following example illustrates the idea of a **paragraph proof.**

Example 2

Give a paragraph proof that the following is true.
If $4(x + 7) = 52$, then $x = 6$.

Proof Since $4(x + 7) = 52$, it follows from the Distributive Property that $4x + 28 = 52$. Also, using the Subtraction Property, $4x = 24$. Then, applying the Division Property, it can be concluded that $x = 6$.

Try This

Give a paragraph proof that the following is true.
If $3(x - 2) = 9$, then $x = 5$.

The following describes the deductive reasoning process used in the above proof. It should be distinguished from the **inductive reasoning** process in which a conjecture is made by looking at several specific examples. (See page 429 for an example of this type of reasoning.)

Deductive Reasoning

• Start with the *given* conditions (the hypothesis).
• Present a series of statements, with reasons, that lead logically to the desired conclusion.
  (The reasons can be definitions, accepted properties or postulates, or statements that have been proved.)
• Assert the result you wanted to *prove* (the conclusion).

When the deductive reasoning process is used correctly, a proof results. This proof provides a valid argument that a mathematical statement, called a **theorem,** is true. Consider the following geometry theorem.

◆ **THEOREM 1.1**
Congruence of segments and angles is reflexive, symmetric, and transitive.

The definitions of congruent segments and angles allow you to interchange congruence statements with statements about measures or real numbers. These ideas and the properties of equality and real numbers can be used to write a paragraph proof that the above theorem is true as illustrated in the following example.

Example 3

Write a paragraph proof that congruence of segments is symmetric, that is, if $\overline{AB} \cong \overline{CD}$, then $\overline{CD} \cong \overline{AB}$.

Proof Since $\overline{AB} \cong \overline{CD}$, $AB = CD$. But then, from the Symmetric Property of Equality, $CD = AB$. It follows, from the definition of congruent segments, that $\overline{CD} \cong \overline{AB}$.

Try This

Complete the following paragraph proof that congruence of angles is reflexive, that is, $\angle E \cong \angle E$.

Proof Since ___ is a real number, $m\angle E = m\angle E$ by the ___ Property of Equality. But then, $\angle E \cong \angle E$ by the definition of ___ .

You will be asked to give a paragraph proof for other parts of Theorem 1.1 in Exercises 32–34.

Theorem 1.2 will be useful in later proofs. It ties together the symmetric and transitive parts of Theorem 1.1.

◆ THEOREM 1.2

If two segments are congruent to the same segment, then they are congruent to each other.

Example 4

Write a paragraph proof that Theorem 1.2 is true. Indicate where you used Theorem 1.1.

Proof Suppose $\overline{AB} \cong \overline{EF}$ and $\overline{CD} \cong \overline{EF}$. From symmetry of congruence (Theorem 1.1), $\overline{EF} \cong \overline{CD}$. But then $\overline{AB} \cong \overline{EF}$ and $\overline{EF} \cong \overline{CD}$, so transitivity of congruence (Theorem 1.1) allows the conclusion that $\overline{AB} \cong \overline{CD}$.

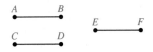

Try This

Give a paragraph proof for Theorem 1.3 below. Indicate where you used Theorem 1.1.

◆ THEOREM 1.3

If two angles are congruent to the same angle, then they are congruent to each other.

---

3. Write a paragraph proof that congruence of angles is symmetric; that is, if $\angle A \cong \angle B$, then $\angle B \cong \angle A$. Since $\angle A \cong \angle B$, $m\angle A = m\angle B$ (definition of congruent angles). So $m\angle B = m\angle A$ (Symmetric Property) and $\angle B \cong \angle A$ (definition of congruent angles).

Answer to **Try This**

$m\angle E = m\angle E$ (Reflexive Property) so $\angle E \cong \angle E$ (definition of congruent angles).

4. Write a paragraph proof that if $\overline{AB} \cong \overline{CD}$, $\overline{CD} \cong \overline{EF}$, and $\overline{EF} \cong \overline{GH}$, then $\overline{AB} \cong \overline{GH}$. Since $\overline{AB} \cong \overline{CD}$ and $\overline{CD} \cong \overline{EF}$, $\overline{AB} \cong \overline{EF}$ by transitivity of congruence (Theorem 1.1). But then $\overline{AB} \cong \overline{EF}$ and $\overline{EF} \cong \overline{GH}$, so $\overline{AB} \cong \overline{GH}$ by transitivity of congruence (Theorem 1.1).

Answer to **Try This**

Suppose $\angle A \cong \angle C$ and $\angle B \cong \angle C$. From symmetry of congruence (Theorem 1.1), $\angle C \cong \angle B$. But then $\angle A \cong \angle C$ and $\angle C \cong \angle B$, so transitivity of congruence (Theorem 1.1) allows the conclusion that $\angle A \cong \angle B$.

Class Exercise Answers

1. Reflexive Property
2. Symmetric Property
3. Transitive Property
4. Addition Property
5. symmetric **6.** symmetric
7. reflexive **8.** transitive
9. symmetric **10.** reflexive
11. Angle congruence is symmetric. **12.** Segment congruence is transitive. **13.** Angle congruence is reflexive.
14. Angle congruence is transitive. **15.** Segment congruence is symmetric. **16.** If $\angle A \cong \angle B$ and $\angle B \cong \angle C$, then $m\angle A = m\angle B$ and $m\angle B = m\angle C$ by the def. of congruence. Thus, $m\angle A = m\angle C$ by transitivity of real numbers and $\angle A \cong \angle C$ by the def. of congruence.
17. a. symmetric **b.** transitive

Assignment Guide

Minimum: 1–6, 7–31 e/o, 35, MR
Regular: 1–6, 7–34 e/o, 35, MR
Advanced: 10–17 e/o, 18–35, MR

Applications
Class Exercise 17
Algebra
Exercises 18–21

Lesson Closure

Ask students to state the property, definition, postulate, or theorem that makes each statement true.

1. If $AB = CD$, then $CD = AB$. Symmetric Property
2. $5 = 5$ Reflexive Property
3. If $\angle A \cong \angle B$ and $\angle B \cong \angle C$, then $\angle A \cong \angle C$. Theorem 1.1
4. If M is the midpoint of $\overline{WY}$, then $\overline{XM} \cong \overline{MY}$. definition of midpoint

Teacher's Resource Materials

Manipulatives 6 Practice 8
Quiz 2 Transparency 5

Class Exercises

Short Answer

Which property asserts that

1. a number is equal to itself?
2. the sides of an equality can be interchanged?
3. if a first number equals a second and the second number equals a third, then the first number equals the third number?
4. you can add the same number to each side of an equation and the equality is preserved?

Sample Exercises

Name the property of equality (reflexive, symmetric, or transitive) that allows you to conclude that each statement is true.

5. If $JK = LM$, then $LM = JK$.
6. If $m\angle R = m\angle S$, then $m\angle S = m\angle R$.
7. $MN = MN$
8. If $AB = CD$ and $CD = EF$, then $AB = EF$.
9. If $x = 3$, then $3 = x$.
10. $m\angle C = m\angle C$

Give the part of Theorem 1.1 that allows you to conclude that each statement is true.

11. If $\angle R \cong \angle S$, then $\angle S \cong \angle R$.
12. If $\overline{EF} \cong \overline{GH}$ and $\overline{GH} \cong \overline{CD}$, then $\overline{EF} \cong \overline{CD}$.
13. $\angle PQR \cong \angle PQR$
14. If $\angle GHI \cong \angle JKL$ and $\angle JKL \cong \angle PQR$, then $\angle GHI \cong \angle PQR$.
15. If $\overline{LM} \cong \overline{PQ}$, then $\overline{PQ} \cong \overline{LM}$.

Discussion

16. Plan and give a paragraph proof that congruence of angles is transitive.
17. Which property supports each of the following?
    a. If 12 in. = 1 ft, then 1 ft = 12 in.
    b. If Sue is Deborah's sister and Deborah is Jane's sister, then Sue is Jane's sister.
    Give some other real-world situations that illustrate the Reflexive, Symmetric, and Transitive Properties.

Exercises

A

Use the given property of equality to draw a conclusion.

1. Symmetric Property: If $a = b$, then $b = a$.
   Given: $PQ = RS$
2. Reflexive Property: If a is a real number, then $a = a$.
   Given: CD is a real number.

3. Transitive Property: If $a = b$ and $b = c$, then $a = c$.
   Given: $JK = LM$, $LM = PQ$
4. Symmetric Property: If $a = b$, then $b = a$.
   Given: $m\angle W = m\angle X$
5. Reflexive Property: If a is a real number, then $a = a$.
   Given: $m\angle T$ is a real number.
6. Transitive Property: If $a = b$ and $b = c$, then $a = c$.
   Given: $m\angle 1 = m\angle 2$, $m\angle 2 = m\angle 3$

Use the given property to draw a conclusion.

7. Addition Property: If $a = b$ and $c = d$, then $a + c = b + d$.
   Given: $AB = CD$, $EF = GH$
8. Subtraction Property: If $a = b$ and $c = d$, then $a - c = b - d$.
   Given: $m\angle A = m\angle B$, $m\angle R = m\angle S$
9. Multiplication Property: If $a = b$ and $c = d$, then $ac = bd$.
   Given: $PQ = RS$, $TU = VW$
10. Division Property: If $a = b$ and $c \neq 0$, then $\frac{a}{c} = \frac{b}{c}$.
    Given: $m\angle A = m\angle B$, $m\angle C = 30$
11. Substitution Property: If $a = b$, then a and b can replace each other in any equation or inequality.
    Given: $ST = XY + 60$, $XY = 90$

State a part of Theorem 1.1 as a reason for each statement.

12. $\overline{GH}$ is congruent to itself.
13. If $\overline{AB} \cong \overline{EF}$, then $\overline{EF} \cong \overline{AB}$.
14. If $\angle R \cong \angle S$ and $\angle S \cong \angle T$, then $\angle R \cong \angle T$.
15. If $\angle CDE \cong \angle FGH$, then $\angle FGH \cong \angle CDE$.
16. Any angle is congruent to itself.
17. If $\overline{GH} \cong \overline{CD}$ and $\overline{CD} \cong \overline{EF}$, then $\overline{GH} \cong \overline{EF}$.

B

Write a paragraph proof to prove that each conditional is true.

18. If $\frac{x}{4} - 7 = 16$, then $x = 92$.
19. If $15p + 4 = 64$, then $p = 4$.
20. If $5x - 4 = 24 + (-2x)$, then $x = 4$.
21. If $3(n + 1) = 99$, then $n = 32$.

Use the given property to complete each statement.

22. Symmetric Property: If $\angle DEF \cong \angle GHI$, then ___ .
23. Transitive Property: If $AB + CD = EF$ and $EF = GH$, then ___ .
24. Substitution Property: If $m\angle 1 - m\angle 2 = 90$ and $m\angle 2 = m\angle 4$, then ___ .
25. Reflexive Property: $m\angle RST = $ ___
26. Addition Property: If $MN = RS$ and $AB = CD$, then ___ .
27. Subtraction Property: If $m\angle 1 + 45 = m\angle 2 + 45$, then ___ .
28. Multiplication Property: If $\frac{1}{5}CD = 15$, then ___ .
29. Division Property: If $3m\angle JKL = 111$, then ___ .

30. $\angle APB \cong \angle DPE$, $\angle CPD \cong \angle DPE$, $\angle DPE \cong \angle BPF$
    Which other angles are congruent?
31. $\overline{AB} \cong \overline{CD}$, $\overline{EF} \cong \overline{CD}$, $\overline{AC} \cong \overline{DF}$, $\overline{DF} \cong \overline{CE}$
    Which other segments are congruent?

A   B   C   D   E   F

1-8 Deductive Reasoning—Using Algebraic Properties   **49**

c

32. Write a paragraph proof that congruence of segments is transitive.
33. Write a paragraph proof that congruence of segments is reflexive.
34. Write a paragraph proof that congruence of angles is symmetric.

Critical Thinking

35. A relation that is reflexive, symmetric, and transitive is called an **equivalence relation.** For example, all three of these properties hold for "is congruent to," and so it is an equivalence relation. Which of the following are equivalence relations? If a relation is not an equivalence relation, give a counterexample.

a. is younger than
b. is in the same class in school as
c. is the same type of angle as
d. is greater than (for segment lengths)

Mixed Review

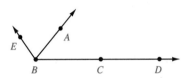

1. Name three collinear points.
2. $BD = 15$, $CD = 8$ Find BC.
3. Name the vertex of $\angle ABD$.
4. Name the point in the interior of $\angle EBD$.
5. $m\angle EBC = 125$, $m\angle ABD = 70$ Find $m\angle ABE$.
6. $m\angle EBA = 3x + 10$, $m\angle ABC = 7x - 10$,
    $m\angle EBC = 100$ Find $m\angle EBA$.
7. $\overrightarrow{BA}$ bisects $\angle EBC$. C is the midpoint of $\overline{BD}$.
    Name two congruent angles and two congruent segments.

Quiz

Use the statement "If an angle is a right angle, then it measures 90."

1. Write the hypothesis and conclusion of the statement.
2. Write the converse of the statement.
3. Write the inverse of the statement.
4. Write the contrapositive of the statement.
5. Write the statement as a biconditional.
6. Given that $\angle RST$ is a right angle, use the statement to draw a conclusion.

7. Which property allows you to conclude that the following is true?
    If $ST = UV$, then $UV = ST$.
8. Use the addition property (if $a = b$ and $c = d$, then $a + c = b + d$) to draw a conclusion.
    Given: $EF = FG$, $AB = BC$
9. State a part of Theorem 1.1 as a reason for the following statement.
    If $\angle B \cong \angle C$, then $\angle C \cong \angle B$.

CRITICAL THINKING

Common Errors in Everyday Reasoning

These situations will help you discover or review some common reasoning errors.

Situation 1

Jason saw an advertisement on television that stated, "If you want top power and control, then buy a Smasher tennis racket." He assumed that, "If I buy a Smasher, then I'll have top power and control."

1. If the statement in the advertisement is represented by $p \rightarrow q$, how would you represent Jason's assumption?
2. Do you think Jason's reasoning was logically correct? Explain why or why not.

Situation 2

Martina's teacher said, "If you don't get an A on this test, then you won't get an A in the course." Martina assumed that, "If I do get an A on this test, then I will get an A in the course."

1. If Martina's teacher's statement is represented by $p \rightarrow q$, how would you represent Martina's assumption?
2. Do you think Martina's reasoning was logically correct? Explain why or why not.

You learned earlier that when the statement is true, the converse and inverse are not necessarily true. In the situation above, Jason was making a very common error in reasoning called *assuming the converse*. Martina was making a common error in reasoning called *assuming the inverse*.

Try These Situations

Is there a reasoning error in each situation? If so, explain what error was made.

1. Isaac's little brother Ted knew that if a vehicle was a car, then it had four wheels. When given a toy wagon with four wheels, he concluded that it was a car.
2. Jose's coach said, "If you win the most tryout games, then you will make the tennis team." Jose did not make the team, so he concluded that he did not win the most games.
3. Tanya read that if a dog is show quality, then it has registration papers. She told her friend Marta that a dog that has no registration papers is not show quality.
4. Mr. Wilson read an advertisement that said, "If you take one ABC tablet each day, then you will keep your good health." He began to feel uneasy thinking, "If I don't take an ABC tablet each day, then I won't keep my good health."

If you take one ABC tablet each day, then you will keep your good health.

5. Cathy's mother told her, "If you don't keep your room clean, then you won't get new wallpaper next spring." Cathy kept her room clean and was angry when she did not get new wallpaper. She felt her mother had broken her promise.
6. Copy a television or magazine advertisement that you think wants the viewer to assume the converse or inverse. Explain your interpretation.

CHAPTER SUMMARY

Vocabulary

acute (1-3)
angle (1-3)
biconditional (1-6)
bisector (1-4)
collinear (1-1)
conclusion (1-6)
conditional (1-6)
congruent (1-4)
contrapositive (1-6)
converse (1-6)
coordinate(s) (1-2)
coplanar (1-1)
counterexample (1-6)
deductive reasoning (1-8)
degree (1-3)

distance (1-2)
equiangular (1-5)
equilateral (1-5)
exterior (1-3)
hypotenuse (1-5)
hypothesis (1-6)
interior (1-3)
intersection (1-1)
inverse (1-6)
isosceles (1-5)
leg (1-5)
line (1-1)
midpoint (1-4)
noncollinear (1-1)
noncoplanar (i-1)

obtuse (1-3)
plane (1-1)
point (1-1)
postulate (1-1)
proof (1-8)
protractor (1-3)
ray (1-3)
right (1-3)
scalene (1-5)
segment (1-2)
side (1-3)
space (1-1)
theorem (1-8)
triangle (1-5)
vertex (1-3)

Key Ideas

1. Three basic undefined terms in geometry are *point*, *line*, and *plane*. These are used to define other terms.

2. A postulate is a statement accepted as true without proof. We have studied the Ruler Postulate, the Segment and Angle Addition Postulates, the Protractor Postulate, the Midpoint Postulate, and the Angle Bisector Postulate.

3. Lines are denoted $\overleftrightarrow{AB}$, rays $\overrightarrow{AB}$, and segments $\overline{AB}$. The length of $\overline{AB}$ is denoted AB.

4. An angle consists of two rays with a common endpoint and is denoted ∠ABC, with the letter in the middle representing the vertex. Angles are classified as acute, right, or obtuse depending upon their measure.

5. Congruent segments are segments that have the same length. Congruent angles are angles that have the same measure.

6. The midpoint of a segment is the point that divides the segment into two congruent segments. The bisector of an angle is a ray in the interior of the angle that divides the angle into two congruent angles.

7. A triangle is a figure formed by three segments joining three noncollinear points and is denoted △ABC. Triangles are classified by the number of congruent sides they have or by the type of angles they have.

8. An if-then statement is called a conditional. The *if* part is the hypothesis, the *then* part is the conclusion. The converse is formed by interchanging the hypothesis and the conclusion.

9. A conclusion drawn from given information can be supported by citing a definition, a postulate, or a conditional known to be true.

10. Deductive reasoning is a process in which conclusions are drawn logically from given information. A theorem is a mathematical statement that can be proved to be true using deductive reasoning.

CHAPTER REVIEW

1-1

Determine whether each statement is true or false.

1. The intersection of $\overleftrightarrow{RT}$ and $\overleftrightarrow{UV}$ is point S.
2. Points R, S, and T are coplanar.
3. V is between R and T.

1-2

4. Find the distance betweeen the pair of points with coordinates -10 and 7.
5. B is betwen A and C. $AB = 3x - 4$, $BC = x - 5$, $AC = 19$
   Find AB.

1-3

Complete each statement.

6. The vertex of $\angle DCE$ is point ___ .
7. $m\angle DCA = 37$, $m\angle ACF = 20$, $m\angle DCF = $ ___

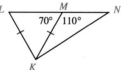

1-4

8. $\overrightarrow{CF}$ bisects $\angle ACB$. Name two congruent angles.
9. $\overrightarrow{BD}$ bisects $\overline{AE}$. $AC = 4x - 3$, $CE = 3x + 5$ Find x.

1-5

10. Name an isosceles triangle in the figure to the right.
11. Name an obtuse triangle in the figure to the right.
12. Find the distance between the points with coordinates $(1, -4)$ and $(9, -10)$.

1-6

13. State the hypothesis and conclusion.
    If a number is positive, then it is greater than zero.
14. Write a conditional using the following.
    Hypothesis: Mr. Wong lives in Ohio.
    Conclusion: He lives in the United States.
15. Write the converse.
    If a triangle is equilateral, then its sides are congruent.

1-7

16. Use the conditional "If two segments are congruent, then they have the same length" to draw a conclusion.
    Given: $\overline{EF} \cong \overline{GH}$
17. State a conditional that supports the conclusion:
    Given: $m\angle A = 90$ Conclusion: $\angle A$ is a right angle.

1-8

18. Use the transitive property (if $a = b$ and $b = c$, then $a = c$) to draw a conclusion.
    Given: $AB = BC$, $BC = CD$
19. Which property of equality allows you to conclude that if $RS = TU$, then $TU = RS$?

Teacher's Resource Materials

Chapter 1 Tests

Test Answers

1. A, B, C **2.** point D
3. $\overleftrightarrow{GH}$ **4.** 11   **5.** 6
6. J and K **7.** VW **8.** 4
9. M **10.** X **11.** 85
12. 30   **13.** $\overline{VX} \cong \overline{XY}$
14. 112   **15.** 45
16. scalene   **17.** two
18. obtuse   **19.** 10   **20.** 5
21. $\sqrt{65}$ **22.** H: It is raining. C: We will play chess.
23. If we play chess, then it is raining.   **24.** If we do not play chess, then it is not raining.   **25.** false   **26.** $\angle BCD$ is acute.   **27.** If a triangle is isosceles, then two of its sides are congruent.   **28.** false
29. $m\angle Z = m\angle A$
30. Theorem 1.1 (Congruence of segments is transitive.)

CHAPTER TEST

1. Name three collinear points.
2. Name the intersection of $\overleftrightarrow{CD}$ and $\overleftrightarrow{ED}$.
3. Name the intersection of the plane containing G, F, H and the plane containing B, C, H.
4. Find the distance between the points with coordinates 4 and -7.
5. Find JL.
6. The distance between which pair of points is 2?

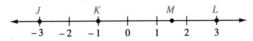

Complete each statement.

7. The Segment Addition Postulate states that if V is between U and W, then $UV + \underline{\quad} = UW$.
8. Q is between P and R. $PQ = t + 7$, $QR = 8t - 4$, $PR = 12$, $QR = \underline{\quad}$
9. If $MP = 5$, $NP = 17$, and $NM = 12$, then point $\underline{\quad}$ is between the other two.

10. The vertex of $\angle WXY$ is point $\underline{\quad}$.
11. $m\angle WXY = 40$, $m\angle YXZ = 45$, $m\angle WXZ = \underline{\quad}$
12. $m\angle WXZ = 74$, $m\angle WXY = 2x + 10$, $m\angle YXZ = x - 26$, $x = \underline{\quad}$
13. X is the midpoint of $\overline{VY}$. Name two congruent segments.
14. $\overrightarrow{XY}$ bisects $\angle WXZ$. $m\angle WXY = 56$ Find $m\angle WXZ$.
15. $\angle WXZ$ is a right angle. $\overrightarrow{XY}$ bisects $\angle WXZ$.   Find $m\angle YXZ$.

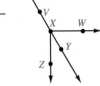

Complete each statement.

16. A triangle with no sides congruent is called $\underline{\quad}$.
17. An isosceles triangle has $\underline{\quad}$ congruent sides.
18. If $m\angle J = 30$, $m\angle K = 140$, and $m\angle L = 10$, then $\triangle JKL$ is a(n) $\underline{\quad}$ triangle.
19. The distance between the points with coordinates $(0, 0)$ and $(6, 8)$ is $\underline{\quad}$.
20. The distance between the points with coordinates $(2, 1)$ and $(5, 5)$ is $\underline{\quad}$.
21. The distance between the points with coordinates $(-2, -1)$ and $(5, -5)$ is $\underline{\quad}$.

Use the statement "If it is raining, then we will play chess."

22. Write the hypothesis and the conclusion of the statement.
23. Write the converse of the statement.
24. Write the contrapositive of the statement.

25. True or false? A postulate cannot be used to support a conclusion.
26. Use the conditional "If an angle is less than 90°, then it is acute" to draw a conclusion. Given: $m\angle BCD = 79$
27. State a conditional that supports the conclusion.
    Given: $\triangle MNP$ is isosceles. Conclusion: Two sides of $\triangle MNP$ are congruent.
28. True or false? Deductive reasoning is a process in which hypotheses are drawn logically from given information.
29. Use the symmetric property to draw a conclusion. Given: $m\angle A = m\angle Z$
30. Which property or theorem allows you to conclude that the following statement is true? If $\overline{AB} \cong \overline{CD}$ and $\overline{CD} \cong \overline{EF}$, then $\overline{AB} \cong \overline{EF}$.

PROBLEM SOLVING

Draw a Diagram

Problems can be fun to solve if you know different ways to tackle them. There are several techniques for solving mathematical problems. One of these is to Draw a Diagram.

Example

The manager of a shopping mall was asked to rope off a rectangular section of the parking lot for an automobile show. The area roped off was 200 ft by 300 ft. Posts were to be placed every 25 ft around the lot. How many posts were needed?

UNDERSTAND the problem.
Question: How many posts were needed?
Data: The area was 200 ft by 300 ft. Posts were placed every 25 ft around the lot.

Develop and carry out a PLAN.
Draw a diagram.

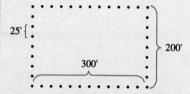

Find the ANSWER and CHECK.
From the diagram we see that 40 posts were needed.
The answer is reasonable.

Problems

Draw a diagram to help solve each problem.

1. How many spokes does a wheel have if there are 16 spaces between the spokes?

2. What is the greatest number of pieces into which a pie can be cut with four straight cuts? (The pieces may not be stacked.)

3. Four cars are parked in a row. The white car is 25 ft to the right of the blue car and 15 ft to the right of the grey car. The grey car is 35 ft to the left of the red car. What is the distance between the blue car and the red car?

4. A bug crawls up a pole 2 in. in 2 minutes, then slips down 1 in. in one minute, then crawls up 2 in. in 2 minutes, and so on. At this rate, how long will it take the bug to reach a height of 10 inches?

5. Roberto can hang wallpaper on a square wall with 12-ft sides in 40 minutes. Assuming the wallpaper is hung at the same rate, how long will it take him to cover a square section of wall with 6-ft sides?

6. Mapleton is midway between Elmville and Jefferson. Hoover City is midway between Elmville and Mapleton. Plymouth is midway between Elmville and Hoover City. If the distance between Elmville and Plymouth is 12 mi, what is the distance between Elmville and Jefferson?

Problem Solving

Draw a Diagram
Emphasize that drawing a picture or diagram to describe a problem can be helpful in understanding the problem. Use the example to demonstrate how drawing a picture helps sort out and visualize the information in the problem. Drawing a diagram can also be a useful intermediate step toward writing an equation to solve a problem.

Problem Answers

1. 16 spokes
2. 11 pieces
3. 45 ft
4. 26 min
5. 10 min
6. 96 mi

CHAPTER 2

Introduction to Proof

Chapter Overview

This chapter is designed to gradually introduce two-column proofs. The exercises begin by setting up proofs for students and having the students fill in the missing reasons. Many students will need time and constant reminders to set up the *Given, Prove,* diagram, and two-column format for the proof.

Objectives

2-1 ■ Complete two-column proofs.
2-2 ■ Understand and use linear pair, complementary, supplementary, and vertical angles.
2-3 ■ State and use the definition of perpendicular lines and state, prove, and use theorems about perpendicular lines.
2-4 ■ Draw and use appropriate diagrams for a proof.
2-5 ■ Analyze, plan, and write two-column proofs.
2-6 ■ Prove and apply theorems about segments and lines.
2-7 ■ Prove and apply theorems about angles.

TEACHING CHAPTER 2

Cooperative Learning Opportunities

The thinking behind the two-column proof comes naturally to some students but not at all to others. Pair checking is a form of cooperative learning that is easy to use and can be a profitable way to work on proof.

After some of the exercises on pages 59–61 have been done as homework for Lesson 2-1, assign students in pairs. Have them exchange papers. Each student then checks the other's work, without having his or her own paper to look at. This will force them to review each statement and reason. They may mark the other paper to indicate mistakes. Then have students, in pairs, go over the papers together discussing each exercise and agreeing on the correct answer. Explain that you are not going to grade the papers but want students to learn from the activity.

This activity also encourages students to do their homework because otherwise they cannot participate in the class activity.

Multicultural Note: *Lewis Carroll and Logic*

Lewis Carroll (1832–1898), as he is known to us, was the author of *Alice in Wonderland* and was also a well-known English mathematician. His real name was Charles Lutwidge Dodgson. He wrote a book on geometry and had a particular interest in logic. Some of his problem situations are amusing and can be used to test students ability to draw conclusions. Consider the following set of statements that make connections among six sets.

a. No kitten that loves fish is unteachable.
b. No kitten without a tail will play with a gorilla.
c. Kittens with whiskers always love fish.
d. No teachable kitten has green eyes.
e. No kittens have tails unless they also have whiskers.
Will a green-eyed cat play with a gorilla? This is most easily solved through the use of Venn diagrams.

Answer:

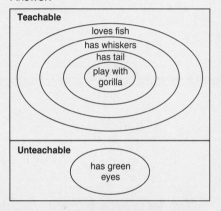

Alternative Assessment and Communication Ideas

The concepts of complementary, supplementary, and vertical angles, and perpendicular lines can be checked through an open-ended form of alternative assessment.

With books closed, ask students to write everything they know or can deduce about complementary and supplementary angles. Have them use diagrams and give reasons for their statements. Much of what they say will have already been covered but students will have an increased sense of ownership and a more thorough understanding based on their own work.

Investigations and Projects

Suggest that students find out how mathematics in general, and geometry in particular, is used in one of the following or other careers: surveyor, architect, carpenter, city planner, civil engineer.

Students might start with library work, looking through special reference works that a librarian will help them find. Trade journals will also give a good idea of the knowledge needed in different areas. Students can write to organizations that represent these professions asking for information about the skills and knowledge needed. Finally, encourage them to talk with people they know who work in jobs that require the use of mathematics. You may wish to have students prepare a poster of their findings that can be displayed on a bulletin board or presented to the class.

Lesson	PACING CHART (DAYS)			Opening Activity	Cooperative Activity	Seat or Group Work
	1-Year Minimum	1-Year Regular	1-Year Advanced			
2-1	2	2	2	Chapter Opener: **TE** p. 56; Lesson Opener: **TE** p. 57		
2-2	1	1	1	First Five Minutes 2-2: *FFM Transparency Masters* p. 4 or **TE** p. 63; Lesson Opener: **TE** p. 63	✂ Lab Worksheet 2-2A: *Laboratory Manual* p. 15; ✂ Lab Worksheet 2-2B: *Laboratory Manual* p. 16	Try This Exercises; Check for Understanding: **TE** p. 64
2-3	1	1	1	First Five Minutes 2-3: *FFM Transparency Masters* p. 5 or **TE** p. 69; Lesson Opener: **TE** p. 69	Explore: **SE** p. 69; ✂ Lab Worksheet 2-3A: *Laboratory Manual* p. 17; ✂ Lab Worksheet 2-3B: *Laboratory Manual* p. 18; ✂ Lab Worksheet 2-3C: *Laboratory Manual* p. 19	Try This Exercises
2-4	1	1	1	First Five Minutes 2-4: *FFM Transparency Masters* p. 6 or **TE** p. 75; Lesson Opener: **TE** p. 75	Enrichment: **SE** p. 79	Try This Exercises
2-5	2	2	2	First Five Minutes 2-5: *FFM Transparency Masters* p. 7 or **TE** p. 80; Lesson Opener: **TE** p. 80	Algebra Review: **SE** p. 623	Exercises 1–3: **SE** p. 83
2-6	2	2	2	First Five Minutes 2-6: *FFM Transparency Masters* p. 8 or **TE** p. 86; Lesson Opener: **TE** p. 87	Explore: **SE** p. 86	Try This Exercises
2-7	1	1	1	First Five Minutes 2-7: *FFM Transparency Masters* p. 9 or **TE** p. 92; Lesson Opener: **TE** p. 92	✂ Lab Worksheet 2-7: *Laboratory Manual* p. 20	Try This Exercises
Review	1	1	1			
Test	1	1	1			

FFM = First Five Minutes

Enrichment	Review/Assess	Reteach	Technology	Lesson
Historical Note: **SE** p. 62; ✄ Enrichment Using Manipulatives 2-1: *Enrichment* p. 7	Class Exercises: **SE** p. 58; Mixed Review: **SE** p. 62	Practice Worksheet 2-1: *Practice and Mixed Review* p. 9		**2-1**
✄ Enrichment Using Manipulatives 2-2: *Enrichment* p. 8; Calculator Worksheet 2-2: *Technology* p. CL2; BASIC 2-2: *Technology* p. B7	Class Exercises: **SE** p. 65; Algebra Review **SE** p. 68	Practice Worksheet 2-2: *Practice and Mixed Review* p. 11	Computer Activity: **SE** p. 68; Calculator Worksheet 2-2: *Technology* p. CL2; BASIC 2-2: *Technology* p. B7	**2-2**
✄ Enrichment Using Manipulatives 2-3: *Enrichment* p. 9	Class Exercises: **SE** p. 71; Mixed Review: **SE** p. 74; Quiz: **SE** p. 74; Quiz: *Assessment* p. 81	Practice Worksheet 2-3: *Practice and Mixed Review* p. 13		**2-3**
Enrichment: **SE** p. 79; Enrichment Using Manipulatives 2-4: *Enrichment* p. 10	Class Exercises: **SE** p. 76; Algebra Review: **SE** p. 79	Practice Worksheet 2-4: *Practice and Mixed Review* p. 15		**2-4**
Study Skills: **SE** p. 85; ✄ Enrichment Using Manipulatives 2-5: *Enrichment* p. 11	Class Exercises: **SE** p. 82; Mixed Review: **SE** p. 85; Algebra Review: **SE** p. 623	Practice Worksheet 2-5: *Practice and Mixed Review* p. 17		**2-5**
Math Contest Problem: **SE** p. 91; ✄ Enrichment Using Manipulatives 2-6: *Enrichment* p. 12	Class Exercises: **SE** p. 88; Algebra Review: **SE** p. 91	Practice Worksheet 2-6: *Practice and Mixed Review* p. 19		**2-6**
✄ Enrichment Using Manipulatives 2-7: *Enrichment* p. 13	Class Exercises: **SE** p. 95; Mixed Review: **SE** p. 98; Quiz: **SE** p. 98; Quiz: *Assessment* p. 82	Practice Worksheet 2-7: *Practice and Mixed Review* p. 20		**2-7**
Critical Thinking: **SE** p. 99;	Summary & Review: **SE** p. 100–101	Mixed Review: *Practice and Mixed Review* p. 103		**Review**
Preparing for College Entrance Exams: **SE** p. 103	Chapter 2 Test: **SE** p. 102; Chapter 2 Tests: *Assessment* p. 7–12; *MathTest*			**Test**

2

Introduction to Proof

The horizontal and vertical lines on this building are perpendicular. Give a convincing argument that they form congruent vertical angles.

PROOF: SEGMENTS, LINES, AND ANGLES

OBJECTIVE: *Complete two-column proofs.*

2-1 Two-Column Proofs

In Chapter 1, you learned that the proof of a theorem can be written in paragraph form. In this chapter, you will learn how to organize your reasoning to write a proof in two-column form.

In a **two-column proof,** such as the one shown below, statements that lead to the desired conclusion are listed in the left column and a reason for each statement is listed in the right column.

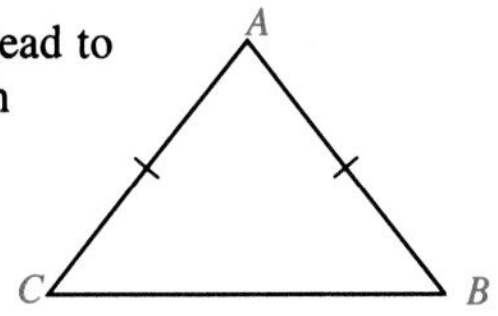

Given: $\triangle ABC$ with $\overline{AB} \cong \overline{AC}$

Prove: $\triangle ABC$ is isosceles.

Proof

Statements	Reasons
1. $\triangle ABC$ with $\overline{AB} \cong \overline{AC}$	1. Given
2. $\triangle ABC$ is isosceles.	2. Definition of isosceles triangle (If at least two sides of a triangle are congruent, then the triangle is isosceles.)

These reasons can be any of the following: given information, definitions, postulates (including algebraic properties), or previously proven theorems.

In the left column, Statement 1 is the given information. Statement 2 is the conclusion. In the right column, Reason 1, "Given," tells why Statement 1 is true. Reason 2 is a definition that, coupled with the given information, supports the conclusion. In this proof, an abbreviated statement of a definition is given in parentheses, but in the proofs that follow it is sufficient to state only the name of the definition. This example shows a two-column proof that has more than two steps.

Example

Complete the proof by supplying the missing reasons.

Given: B is the midpoint of $\overline{AC}$. C is the midpoint of $\overline{BD}$.

Prove: $\overline{AB} \cong \overline{CD}$

Proof

Statements	Reasons
1. B is the midpoint of $\overline{AC}$.	1. Given
2. C is the midpoint of $\overline{BD}$.	2. ___
3. $\overline{AB} \cong \overline{BC}$	3. Definition of midpoint
4. $\overline{BC} \cong \overline{CD}$	4. ___
5. $\overline{AB} \cong \overline{CD}$	5. Segment congruence is transitive. (Theorem 1.1)

Solution

2. Given

4. Definition of midpoint

An introduction to two-column proofs could involve a discussion of statements used everyday such as, "I know that's right. I can prove it." or "Can you prove what you are saying?" Discuss situations in which such statements are made and the types of evidence or proof used by a person making the statement.

In geometry, a two-column proof is used to organize and prove statements.

Materials

student notebooks

Teaching Notes

Point out that the *Given* is usually included in the first steps of a two-column proof and the last step is what is to be proved.

Emphasize that *every* statement must have a corresponding reason.

Since a reason in a proof can only be the *Given,* a definition, a postulate, or a previously proven theorem—look for "key words" in the *Given* and try to think of a definition, postulate, or theorem that uses those key words.

Chalkboard Example

Supply the reasons for this proof.

Given: *S* is the midpoint of $\overline{RT}$.
$\overline{ST} \cong \overline{UV}$
Prove: $\overline{RS} \cong \overline{UV}$

```
   R    S    T
   •────•────•
        U    V
        •────•
```

Proof 1. *S* is the midpoint of $\overline{RT}$. Given
2. $\overline{RS} \cong \overline{ST}$ Definition of midpoint
3. $\overline{ST} \cong \overline{UV}$ Given
4. $\overline{RS} \cong \overline{UV}$ Segment congruence is transitive.

Class Exercise Answers

1. Given, Diagram, Prove, Statements, Reasons   2. Given information, definitions, postulates, previously proven theorems   3. 1. b 2. b 3. c 4. c 5. a   4. 3 and 4   5. $p \rightarrow q$: If a first angle is congruent to a second angle and the second angle is congruent to a third angle, then the first angle is congruent to the third angle. (true) $p: \angle BAC \cong \angle CAD$, $\angle CAD \cong \angle DAE$ (true) $q: \angle BAC \cong \angle DAE$ 6. No, since these 20 people may not have gotten a cold anyway.

The summary below describes the parts of a two-column proof. The steps for constructing a two-column proof to prove a theorem will be given in Lesson 2-5.

> **Key Elements of a Two-Column Proof**
>
> 1. *Given:* a statement of the facts given to be true
> 2. *Diagram:* a figure that shows the given information
> 3. *Prove:* a statement of the conclusion to be established
> 4. *Statements:* numbered statements in the left column that must be shown to be true in order to prove the conclusion
> 5. *Reasons:* numbered reasons in the right column that support the statements in the left column—can be given information, definitions, postulates (including properties of algebra), or previously proven theorems

---

Class Exercises

Short Answer

1. What are five main parts of a two-column proof?
2. What four types of reasons can be used to support statements in a two-column proof?

Sample Exercises

3. Complete the proof by choosing a reason for each statement.

   Given: $\overrightarrow{AC}$ bisects $\angle BAD$. $\overrightarrow{AD}$ bisects $\angle CAE$.

   Prove: $\angle BAC \cong \angle DAE$

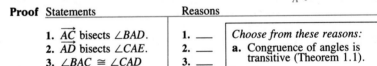

Proof Statements	Reasons	
1. $\overrightarrow{AC}$ bisects $\angle BAD$.	1. ___	*Choose from these reasons:*
2. $\overrightarrow{AD}$ bisects $\angle CAE$.	2. ___	**a.** Congruence of angles is transitive (Theorem 1.1).
3. $\angle BAC \cong \angle CAD$	3. ___	**b.** Given
4. $\angle CAD \cong \angle DAE$	4. ___	**c.** Definition of angle bisector
5. $\angle BAC \cong \angle DAE$	5. ___	

4. In the proof in Class Exercise 3, which two statements were used, together with Theorem 1.1, to establish the truth of Statement 5?

Discussion

5. Explain how the following reasoning process is used in the proof in Class Exercise 3.

   "Whenever $p \rightarrow q$ is true and *p* is true, then *q* is true." (See Ch. 1, p. 39.)

6. A research scientist claimed he had found a compound which would prevent the common cold. Suppose he gave this compound to 20 people for a period of two months. If none of these people had gotten a cold in these two months, would the scientist have proven that the compound is a preventive? Why or why not? Discuss the meaning of "proof."

Exercises

A

Complete each proof by choosing a reason for each statement.

1. Given: $\overrightarrow{RV}$ bisects $\angle SRT$.

$\angle 3 \cong \angle 1$

Prove: $\angle 3 \cong \angle 2$

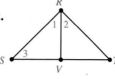

Proof	Statements	Reasons	
	1. $\overrightarrow{RV}$ bisects $\angle SRT$.	1. ___	*Choose from these reasons:*
	2. $\angle 3 \cong \angle 1$	2. ___	**a.** Definition of angle bisector
	3. $\angle 1 \cong \angle 2$	3. ___	**b.** Angle congruence is transitive.
	4. $\angle 3 \cong \angle 2$	4. ___	**c.** Given

2. Given: $BD = AD$

D is between A and C.

Prove: $BD + DC = AC$

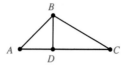

Proof	Statements	Reasons	
	1. $BD = AD$	1. ___	*Choose from these reasons:*
	2. D is between A and C.	2. ___	**a.** Substitution Property
	3. $AD + DC = AC$	3. ___	**b.** Given
	4. $BD + DC = AC$	4. ___	**c.** Segment Addition Postulate

Choose reasons from the following list for each proof.

a. Substitution Property
b. Angle Addition Postulate
c. Definition of midpoint
d. Congruence of segments is transitive (Theorem 1.1).
e. Definition of angle bisector

f. Two angles $\cong$ to the same angle are $\cong$. (Theorem 1.3)
g. Given
h. Segment Addition Postulate
i. Addition of real numbers

3. Given: $\overrightarrow{AH}$ is the bisector of $\angle GAI$.

Prove: $\angle GAH \cong \angle HAI$

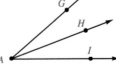

Proof	Statements	Reasons
	1. $\overrightarrow{AH}$ is the bisector of $\angle GAI$.	1. ___
	2. $\angle GAH \cong \angle HAI$	2. ___

4. Given: $\angle 1 \cong \angle 3$, $\angle 5 \cong \angle 3$

Prove: $\angle 1 \cong \angle 5$

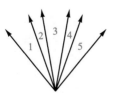

Proof	Statements	Reasons
	1. $\angle 1 \cong \angle 3$	1. ___
	2. $\angle 5 \cong \angle 3$	2. ___
	3. $\angle 1 \cong \angle 5$	3. ___

Assignment Guide
Minimum: 1–10, 16, MR
Regular: 1–14, 16, MR
Advanced: 1, 3, 5–16, MR

Applications
Class Exercise 6
Exercise 16

Lesson Closure

Review the five key elements of a two-column proof. Ask students to name the types of reasons that can be used in a two-column proof.

Teacher's Resource Materials

Manipulatives 7   Practice 9

Exercise Answers

1. 1. c, 2. c, 3. a, 4. b
2. 1. b, 2. b, 3. c, 4. a
3. 1. g, 2. e   **4.** 1. g, 2. g, 3. f

5. **Given:** N is in the interior of $\angle GAB$.

Prove: $m\angle GAN + m\angle NAB = m\angle GAB$

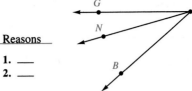

Proof | Statements | Reasons

1. N is in the interior of $\angle GAB$.   1. ___
2. $\angle GAN + m\angle NAB = m\angle GAB$ 2. ___

6. **Given:** B is between A and C.

$AB = 9$
$BC = 7$

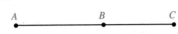

Prove: $16 = AC$

Proof | Statements | Reasons

1. B is between A and C.   1. ___
2. $AB = 9$, $BC = 7$ 2. ___
3. $AB + BC = AC$ 3. ___
4. $9 + 7 = AC$ 4. ___
5. $16 = AC$ 5. ___

7. **Given:** $\overline{NA} \cong \overline{AM}$

M is the midpoint of $\overline{AB}$.

Prove: $\overline{NA} \cong \overline{MB}$

Proof | Statements | Reasons

1. $\overline{NA} \cong \overline{AM}$ 1. ___
2. M is the midpoint of $\overline{AB}$.   2. ___
3. $\overline{AM} \cong \overline{MB}$ 3. ___
4. $\overline{NA} \cong \overline{MB}$ 4. ___

Complete each proof by supplying the missing reasons.

8. **Given:** $\overline{PQ} \cong \overline{RS}$
$\overline{QR} \cong \overline{RS}$

Prove: $\triangle PQR$ is isosceles.

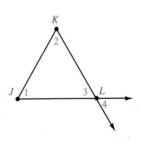

Proof | Statements | Reasons

1. $\overline{PQ} \cong \overline{RS}$ 1. ___
2. $\overline{QR} \cong \overline{RS}$ 2. ___
3. $\overline{PQ} \cong \overline{QR}$ 3. ___
4. $\triangle PQR$ is isosceles.   4. ___

9. **Given:** $\triangle JKL$ is equiangular.
$\angle 4 \cong \angle 3$

Prove: $\angle 4 \cong \angle 1$

Proof | Statements | Reasons

1. $\angle 4 \cong \angle 3$ 1. ___
2. $\triangle JKL$ is equiangular.   2. ___
3. $\angle 1 \cong \angle 3$ 3. ___
4. $\angle 4 \cong \angle 1$ 4. ___

10. **Given:** H is the midpoint of $\overline{GI}$. $\overline{JH} \cong \overline{HI}$
Prove: $\triangle GHJ$ is isosceles.

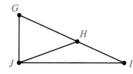

Proof

Statements	Reasons
1. $\overline{JH} \cong \overline{HI}$	1. ___
2. H is the midpoint of $\overline{GI}$.	2. ___
3. $\overline{GH} \cong \overline{HI}$	3. ___
4. $\overline{GH} \cong \overline{HJ}$	4. ___
5. $\triangle GHJ$ is isosceles.	5. ___

B

Complete each proof by supplying the missing statements or reasons.

11. **Given:** Q is between P and R.
Prove: $PQ = PR - QR$

Proof

Statements	Reasons
1. ___	1. ___
2. $PQ + QR = PR$	2. ___
3. $QR = QR$	3. Reflexive Property
4. $PQ + QR - QR = PR - QR$	4. ___
5. ___	5. Subtraction of real numbers

12. **Given:** $\triangle ABD$ is equilateral. $\overline{BD} \cong \overline{BC}$
Prove: $\triangle CBA$ is isosceles.

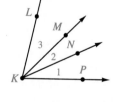

Proof

Statements	Reasons
1. $\triangle ABD$ is equilateral.	1. ___
2. ___	2. Given
3. $\overline{AB} \cong \overline{BD}$	3. ___
4. ___	4. Congruence of segments is transitive.
5. $\triangle CBA$ is isosceles.	5. ___

13. **Given:** $\overrightarrow{KM}$ is in the interior of $\angle LKN$ and $\angle LKP$.
$\overrightarrow{KN}$ is in the interior of $\angle PKM$.
Prove: $m \angle LKP = m \angle 1 + m \angle 2 + m \angle 3$

Proof

Statements	Reasons
1. $\overrightarrow{KM}$ is in the interior of $\angle LKN$ and $\angle LKP$. $\overrightarrow{KN}$ is in the interior of $\angle PKM$.	1. ___
2. $m \angle PKM = m \angle 1 + m \angle 2$	2. ___
3. $m \angle LKP = m \angle PKM + m \angle 3$	3. ___
4. ___	4. Substitution Property

C

14. Write a two-column proof.
Given: $\overline{TU}$ bisects $\overline{RS}$.
$\overline{UM} \cong \overline{MS}$
Prove: $\overline{RM} \cong \overline{UM}$

10. 1. Given 2. Given
3. Definition of midpoint
4. Theorem 1.2 5. Definition of
isosceles triangle   **11.** 1. Q
is between P and R. (Given)
2. Segment Addition Postulate
4. Subtraction Property
5. $PQ = PR - QR$
12. 1. Given 2. $\overline{BD} \cong \overline{BC}$ 3.
Definition of equilateral triangle
4. $\overline{AB} \cong \overline{BC}$ 5. Definition of
isosceles triangle
13. 1. Given 2. Angle Addition
Postulate 3. Angle Addition Postulate 4. $m \angle LKP = m \angle 1 +$
$m \angle 2 + m \angle 3$
14. 1. $\overline{TU}$ bisects $\overline{RS}$. (Given)
2. $\overline{RM} \cong \overline{MS}$ (Definition of bisector) 3. $\overline{UM} \cong \overline{MS}$ (Given)
4. $\overline{RM} \cong \overline{UM}$ (Theorem 1.2)

15. Conclusion: *GI* = *IJ* 1. *G, H, I,* and *J* are collinear. (Given) 2. *GH* + *HI* = *GI* (Segment Addition Postulate) 3. *GH* + *HI* = *IJ* (Given) 4. *GI* = *IJ* (Substitution)   **16.** 1. The starter grinds very slowly. (Given) 2. The battery voltage is low. (Theorem 2) 3. The battery needs recharging. (Theorem 3)

Mixed Review Answers

1. $\overline{DE} \cong \overline{EF}$ **2.** 5
3. 50   **4.** 18

15. Draw a conclusion from the given data. Then write a two-column proof to show that your conclusion follows from the given data.

Given: *G, H, I* and *J* are collinear.
$$GH + HI = IJ$$

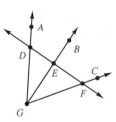

Critical Thinking

16. A car mechanic often uses "theorems" to "prove" things. Suppose it was given that (a) the car will not start and (b) the starter grinds very slowly. Choose reasons from the following "theorems" and write a two-column proof that the battery needs recharging.

Theorem 1: If the battery is dead, then the car will not start.

Theorem 2: If the starter grinds very slowly, then the battery voltage is low.

Theorem 3: If the battery voltage is low, then the battery needs recharging.

Mixed Review

1. $\vec{GB}$ bisects $\overline{DF}$. Name the congruent segments formed.
2. *GF* = 12, *GC* = 17, $\overline{FC} \cong \overline{EB}$
Find *EB*.
3. $m \angle AGC = 10x$, $m \angle AGB = 5x + 3$, $m \angle BGC = 22$
Find $m \angle AGC$.
4. $\vec{GB}$ bisects $\angle AGC$. $m \angle AGB = 2x$, $m \angle AGC = 3x + 9$
Find $m \angle BGC$.

Historical Note

The Beginning of Geometry

Geometry is derived from two Greek words—*ge*, meaning earth, and *metrein*, meaning to measure. Geometry was used by Egyptians as long ago as 3000 B.C., when annual flooding and channel changes of the Nile River required officials to establish new boundaries and to calculate the areas of lands to be taxed. Their calculations were based on observation and measurement.

The uncertainty of the rules that were arrived at by Egyptians through "trial and error" was a major concern of many Greek scholars. Around 300 B.C., Greek scholars began developing a geometry based upon logical deduction. The most famous among the Greek scholars was Euclid, a mathematician and teacher who combined the geometric knowledge of his time with a more logical system. His famous book, *The Elements*, presents geometry in an organized fashion. It is this logical pattern of thinking, commonly called Euclidean Geometry, that you will study in this book.

OBJECTIVE: *Understand and use linear pair, complementary, supplementary, and vertical angles.*

2-2 Complementary, Supplementary, and Vertical Angles

The ideas about angles you learned in Chapter 1 will be used in this section to help you see that pairs of angles are often related in special ways. You will see how some of these relationships can be proved using a two-column proof. Consider the following definitions.

■ DEFINITION

Complementary angles are two angles whose measures have a sum of 90.

Each angle is called the complement of the other. $\angle P$ and $\angle Q$ are complementary since $m\angle P + m\angle Q = 90$.

■ DEFINITION

Supplementary angles are two angles whose measures have a sum of 180.

Each angle is called the supplement of the other. $\angle E$ and $\angle F$ are supplementary since $m\angle E + m\angle F = 180$.

Example 1

$\angle ABD$ is complementary to $\angle DBC$. Find $m\angle DBC$ and $m\angle ABD$.

Solution

$x + 5x = 90$ *The sum of the measures of complementary angles is 90.*
$6x = 90$
$x = 15, m\angle DBC = 15$
$5x = 75, m\angle ABD = 75$

Try This

$\angle EFH$ is supplementary to $\angle HFG$. Find $m\angle HFG$ and $m\angle EFH$.

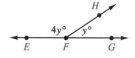

First Five Minutes

(Quiz on previous lesson) Supply the missing reasons in the proof.

Given: Y is between X and Z.
            $WX = YZ$
Prove: $XY + WX = XZ$

Statements

1. Y is between X and Z.
2. $XY + YZ = XZ$
3. $WX = YZ$
4. $XY + WX = XZ$

1. Given 2. Segment Addition Postulate 3. Given 4. Substitution

Lesson Opener

Introduce complementary angles and supplementary angles by discussing what it means when someone says that two people "complement" each other or when someone "supplements" his income by working part-time in the evenings.

Materials

student notebooks

Teaching Notes

Review the classification of angles according to their measures (acute, obtuse, right). Then, discuss ways that a pair of angles can be classified.

A pair of angles can be classified by the sum of their measures:

1. complementary angles
2. supplementary angles

A pair of angles can be classified by their relative positions:

1. adjacent angles
2. vertical angles

Point out that with complementary angles each angle is called the complement of the other. Likewise, with supplementary angles, each angle is called the supplement of the other.

If x is the measure of an angle, then $90 - x$ is the measure of its complement.

If x is the measure of an angle, then $180 - x$ is the measure of its supplement.

Point out that according to Webster's dictionary "adjacent" means adjoining or bordering. In geometry, "adjacent angles" are adjoining or bordering angles. This is another example of the similarities between everyday language and the language of geometry.

Check for Understanding
Ask students to identify which angles are/are not adjacent angles and why.

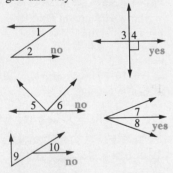

Stress that although linear pairs are adjacent, not all complementary and supplementary angles are adjacent.

Two angles that have the same vertex and a common side, but which have no common interior points, are called **adjacent angles.** Angles 1 and 2 are adjacent. They each have vertex B and common side $\overrightarrow{BD}$.

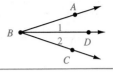

■ DEFINITION

A **linear pair** of angles is a pair of adjacent angles with the two noncommon sides on the same line.

Angles 3 and 4 form a linear pair. They are adjacent and their noncommon sides, $\overrightarrow{HK}$ and $\overrightarrow{HG}$, are on a line.

The following postulate describes an important property of a linear pair of angles.

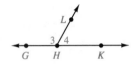

● POSTULATE 12   Linear Pair Postulate

Two angles that form a linear pair are supplementary.

Postulate 12 can be used to prove Theorem 2.1.

◆ THEOREM 2.1

The sum of the measures of the angles in a linear pair is 180.

Proof Since the two angles of a linear pair are supplementary (Postulate 12), it follows from the definition of supplementary angles that the sum of the measures of the two angles is 180.

Example 2
$\angle 1$ and $\angle 2$ form a linear pair. $m\angle 2$ is three times $m\angle 1$.
Find $m\angle 1$ and $m\angle 2$.

   Solution
   Let $x = m\angle 1$. Then $3x = m\angle 2$.
   So, $x + 3x = 180$ *The sum of the measures of the angles in a*
   $\qquad 4x = 180$ *linear pair is 180.*
   $\qquad x \doteq 45, 3x = 135$ $m\angle 1 = 45, m\angle 2 = 135$

Try This
$\angle 3$ and $\angle 4$ form a linear pair. $m\angle 4$ is 30 more than double $m\angle 3$.
Find $m\angle 3$ and $m\angle 4$.

Vertical angles are two nonadjacent angles formed by a pair of intersecting lines. $\angle 1$ and $\angle 3$ are vertical angles, as are $\angle 2$ and $\angle 4$.

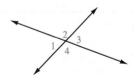

The following is a useful theorem about vertical angles.

◆ **THEOREM 2.2**　Vertical Angle Theorem

If two angles are vertical angles, then they are congruent.

Given: ∠1 and ∠3 are vertical angles.
Prove: ∠1 ≅ ∠3

Proof

Statements	Reasons
1. ∠1 and ∠3 are vertical angles.	1. Given
2. $m\angle 1 + m\angle 2 = 180$ $m\angle 3 + m\angle 2 = 180$	2. The sum of the measures of the angles in a linear pair is 180 (Theorem 2.1).
3. $m\angle 1 + m\angle 2 = m\angle 3 + m\angle 2$	3. Substitution Property of Equality
4. $m\angle 1 = m\angle 3$	4. Subtraction Property of Equality
5. ∠1 ≅ ∠3	5. Definition of congruent angles

Class Exercises

Short Answer

1. Name an angle that is supplementary to ∠QMS.
2. Name an angle that is complementary to ∠QMS.
3. Name a pair of adjacent angles with noncommon sides not on a line.
4. Name a pair of adjacent angles with noncommon sides on a line.
5. Which angle forms a linear pair with ∠QMS? with ∠PMR?
6. Name a pair of vertical angles.
7. Name an angle that is complementary but not adjacent to ∠TMQ.

Sample Exercises

Assume that $m\angle QMS = 40$ and give the measure of each angle.

8. $m\angle TMQ$　9. $m\angle RMP$　10. $m\angle PMS$　11. $m\angle RMQ$

12. If $m\angle RMP = 2x + 6$ and $m\angle QMS = 5x - 24$, find $m\angle RMP$ and $m\angle QMS$.

Give the measure of the complement and supplement of each angle.

13. $m\angle A = 40$　14. $m\angle B = 65$　15. $m\angle D = 87$
16. $m\angle M = x$　17. $m\angle Q = 20 - x$　18. $m\angle J = x^2$

19. Find the measure of an angle that is half the measure of its complement.

Discussion

Determine whether each statement is true or false. If true, give a convincing argument to support the statement. If false, give a counterexample.

20. The supplement of an acute angle is an obtuse angle.
21. The supplement of the complement of ∠A always measures 90 more than $m\angle A$.

Key Terms

complementary angles
supplementary angles
adjacent angles
linear pair
vertical angles

Guided Practice

Chalkboard Examples

1. ∠ABD is complementary to ∠DBC. Find the measures of the angles if one of the two angles is three more than twice the other. 29, 61

Answer to **Try This**
$m\angle EFH = 144$, $m\angle HFG = 36$

2. ∠1 and ∠2 form a linear pair. If $m\angle 1$ is 70 more than $m\angle 2$, find $m\angle 1$ and $m\angle 2$.
$m\angle 1 = 125$, $m\angle 2 = 55$

Answer to **Try This** $m\angle 3 = 50$, $m\angle 4 = 130$

Class Exercise Answers

1. ∠RMQ　**2.** ∠TMQ
3. ∠TMQ, ∠QMS　**4.** ∠RMQ, ∠QMS　**5.** ∠RMQ, ∠RMQ
6. ∠RMP, ∠QMS　**7.** ∠RMP
8. 50　**9.** 40　**10.** 140
11. 140　**12.** 26　**13.** 50, 140　**14.** 25, 115　**15.** 3, 93　**16.** $90 - x$, $180 - x$
17. $70 + x$, $160 + x$
18. $90 - x^2$, $180 - x^2$
19. 30　**20.** True, an acute angle measures less than 90. Its supp. measures 180 minus its measure. This is greater than 90; ie, obtuse.
21. True, let $m\angle A = x$. Its comp. measures $90 - x$. The supp. of the comp. measures $180 - (90 - x) = 90 + x$.

Assignment Guide
Minimum: 1–38 e/o, 42, AR
Regular: 1–26 e/o, 27–39, 42, AR
Advanced: 10–33 e/o, 34–41, 42, AR

Applications
Exercise 21

Algebra
Class Exercises 12, 16–18
Exercises 12–14, 19, 20, 28–37, 39, AR

Lesson Closure

A summary of the lesson could include a review of
- complementary angles
- supplementary angles
- adjacent angles
- linear pair
- vertical angles
- Theorem 2.2 (Vertical Angle Theorem)
- Linear Pair Postulate

Teacher's Resource Materials

Manipulatives 8 Practice 10
Calculator 2 BASIC 5
Software 3 Transparency 6

Exercise Answers

1. $\angle GCA$, $\angle ACD$ **2.** $\angle ACD$, $\angle ACE$ **3.** $\angle GCB$, $\angle ECD$ **4.** $\angle ACE$, $\angle ECD$ **5.** $\angle ACE$, $\angle GCB$ **6.** 50 **7.** 30 **8.** 90 **9.** 150 **10.** 130 **11.** 70 **12.** $m\angle BXD = m\angle GXE = 70$ **13.** $m\angle AXG = 60$, $m\angle GXF = 30$ **14.** $m\angle GXF = 79$, $m\angle GXC = 101$ **15.** 45 and 45 **16.** 1. Given 2. Addition Property 4. Definition of comp. angles **17.** 1. Given 2. Given 3. Theorem 2.2 4. Theorem 1.3 **18.** 1. Given 2. Given 3. Theorem 2.1 4. Substitution Property 5. Definition of supp. angles

Exercises

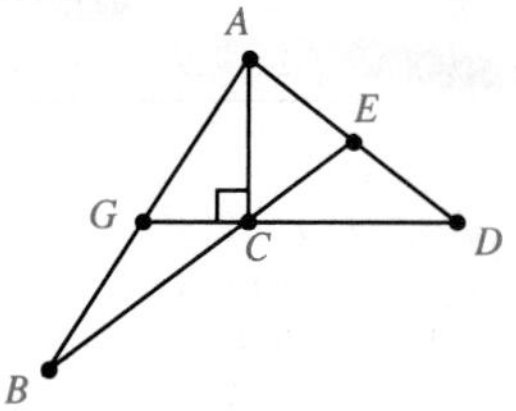

A

1. Name a pair of angles that are both congruent and supplementary.
2. Name a pair of angles that are not congruent.
3. Name a pair of vertical angles.
4. Name a pair of adjacent angles that do not form a linear pair.
5. Name a pair of nonadjacent complementary angles.

Assume that $m\angle GXF = 40$ and $m\angle FXE = 30$. Find each measure.

6. $m\angle AXG$ **7.** $m\angle CXB$ **8.** $m\angle AXC$
9. $m\angle BXF$ **10.** $m\angle AXD$ **11.** $m\angle BXD$

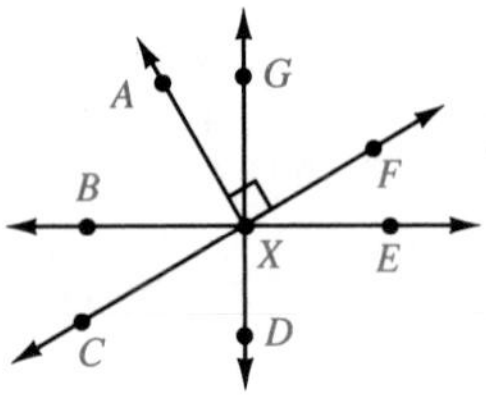

12. If $m\angle BXD = 4x - 50$ and $m\angle GXE = 2x + 10$, find $m\angle BXD$ and $m\angle GXE$.

13. If $m\angle AXG = 3x$ and $m\angle GXF = 2x - 10$, find $m\angle AXG$ and $m\angle GXF$.

14. If $m\angle GXF = 2x + 15$ and $m\angle GXC = 3x + 5$, find $m\angle GXF$ and $m\angle GXC$.

15. If two angles are congruent and complementary, what are their measures?

Complete each proof.

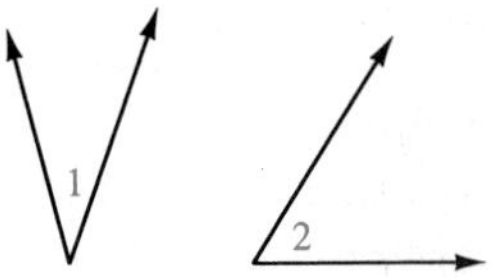

16. Given: $m\angle 1 = 35$, $m\angle 2 = 55$

Prove: $\angle 1$ and $\angle 2$ are complementary.

Proof

Statements	Reasons
1. $m\angle 1 = 35$, $m\angle 2 = 55$	1. __
2. $m\angle 1 + m\angle 2 = 35 + 55$	2. __
3. $m\angle 1 + m\angle 2 = 90$	3. Addition of real numbers
4. $\angle 1$ and $\angle 2$ are complementary.	4. __

17. Given: $\angle 1$ and $\angle 2$ are vertical angles. $\angle 3 \cong \angle 2$

Prove: $\angle 3 \cong \angle 1$

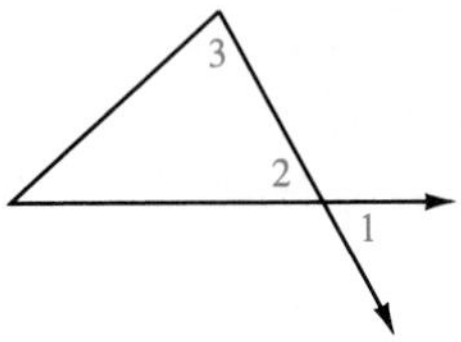

Proof

Statements	Reasons
1. $\angle 3 \cong \angle 2$	1. __
2. $\angle 1$ and $\angle 2$ are vertical angles.	2. __
3. $\angle 1 \cong \angle 2$	3. __
4. $\angle 3 \cong \angle 1$	4. __

18. Given: $\angle 1$ and $\angle 2$ form a linear pair. $m\angle 3 = m\angle 1$

Prove: $\angle 2$ and $\angle 3$ are supplementary.

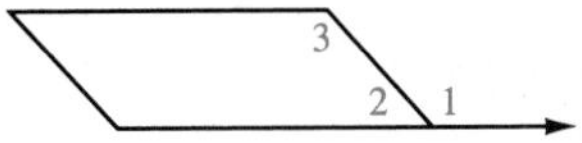

Proof

Statements	Reasons
1. $m\angle 3 = m\angle 1$	1. __
2. $\angle 1 + \angle 2$ form a linear pair.	2. __
3. $m\angle 1 + m\angle 2 = 180$	3. __
4. $m\angle 3 + m\angle 2 = 180$	4. __
5. $\angle 2$ and $\angle 3$ are supplementary.	5. __

66 Chapter 2 Introduction to Proof

19. The measure of one angle is twice the measure of its complement. Find the measures of the angles.
20. The measure of one angle is eight times the measure of its supplement. Find the measures of the angles.
21. In order to gain maximum distance, an Olympic ski jumper is interested in the measure of the angle formed by his or her body and skis. If $m\angle 1 = 155$, find $m\angle 2$.

B

Determine whether each statement is always, sometimes, or never true. Draw a figure to show your answer.

22. Two complementary angles are also adjacent angles.
23. Two angles in a linear pair are adjacent angles.
24. Vertical angles are adjacent angles.
25. An acute and an obtuse angle are complementary.
26. An angle and its supplement are congruent.

Find the measure of the complement and supplement of $\angle A$.

27. $m\angle A = 67.5$ 28. $m\angle A = 2y - 10$ 29. $m\angle A = 30 - 2x$

30. $m\angle AEC = 2x + 30$, $m\angle DEB = 3x + 10$.   Find $m\angle FED$ and $m\angle CEB$.
31. $m\angle AEC = 2x + 7$, $m\angle BEC = 5x - 2$.   Find $m\angle DEB$ and $m\angle FED$.
32. $m\angle AEC = 12x + 4$, $m\angle GEC = 6x + 14$.   Find $m\angle DEB$ and $m\angle FED$.
33. $m\angle AEC = 3x + 5$ and $m\angle DEF = 2x - 10$.   Find $m\angle DEF$ and $m\angle DEB$.

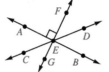

34. The difference in the measures of two supplementary angles is 38. Find the measures of the two angles.
35. The measure of the supplement of an angle is 30 more than twice the measure of the angle. Find the measures of the angles.
36. The difference in the measures of two complementary angles is 39. Find the measures of the two angles.
37. The ratio of the measure of an angle to its complement is $3:2$. Find the measure of the angles.
38. Complete the proof.

Given: $\angle 1$ and $\angle 2$ form a linear pair.
$\angle 1$ and $\angle 4$ are supplementary.

Prove: $m\angle 4 = m\angle 2$

Proof Statements

Statements	Reasons
1. $\angle 1$ and $\angle 2$ form a linear pair.	1. ___
2. ___	2. Given
3. $m\angle 1 + m\angle 2 = 180$	3. ___
4. ___	4. Definition of supplementary angles
5. $m\angle 1 + m\angle 4 = m\angle 1 + m\angle 2$	5. ___
6. $m\angle 4 = m\angle 2$	6. ___

19. 30, 60   20. 20, 160
21. 25
22. some-times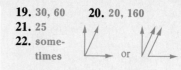
23. always
24. never
25. never
(sum of measures > 90)
26. sometimes

27. comp.: 22.5, supp.: 112.5
28. comp.: $100 - 2y$, supp.: $190 - 2y$
29. comp.: $60 + 2x$, supp.: $150 + 2x$
30. $m\angle FED = 20$, $m\angle CEB = 110$ 31. $m\angle DEB = 57$, $m\angle FED = 33$
32. $m\angle DEB = 52$, $m\angle FED = 38$
33. $m\angle DEF = 28$, $m\angle DEB = 62$
34. 71 and 109   35. 50 and 130   36. 25.5 and 64.5
37. 54, 36   38. 1. Given 2. $\angle 1$ and $\angle 4$ are supp. 3. Theorem 2.1 4. $m\angle 1 + m\angle 4 = 180$ 5. Substitution Property 6. Subtraction Property   39. 72
40. 90   41. 1. $\angle 1$ is supp. to $\angle 2$. $\angle 4$ is supp. to $\angle 3$. (Given) 2. $m\angle 1 + m\angle 2 = 180$, $m\angle 4 + m\angle 3 = 180$ (Definition of supp. angles) 3. $\angle 2 \cong \angle 3$ (Given) 4. $m\angle 2 = m\angle 3$ (Definition of congruent angles) 5. $m\angle 1 + m\angle 2 = m\angle 4 + m\angle 3$ (Substitution) 6. $m\angle 1 = m\angle 4$ (Subtraction Property) 7. $\angle 1 \cong \angle 4$ (Definition of congruent angles)
42. The difference is 90. Proof: supp. − comp. = $(180 - x) - (90 - x) = 180 - 90 - x + x = 90$
43. Let the measures of the angles be x. Then $x + x = 180$, so $x = 90$ and the angles are right angles.

C

39. The measure of ∠A is twice the measure of ∠B and the measure of ∠B is twice
the measure of ∠C. If ∠A and ∠C are supplementary, find the measure of ∠B.

40. ∠ABC and ∠CBD form a linear pair. If $\overrightarrow{BE}$ bisects ∠ABC and $\overrightarrow{BF}$
bisects ∠CBD, find the measure of ∠EBF.

41. Write a two-column proof.

> **Given:** ∠1 is supplementary to ∠2. ∠2 ≅ ∠3
> ∠4 is supplementary to ∠3.
>
> **Prove:** ∠1 ≅ ∠4

Critical Thinking

42. Part of a mathematician's work involves forming generalizations that describe useful relationships among mathematical ideas, such as the following.
For any acute angle, what is the difference between its supplement and
its complement? Form a generalization and use algebraic expressions to
prove that the generalization is true.

Write a convincing argument to support each statement.

43. If two congruent angles form a linear pair, then each is a right angle.
44. The supplement of an obtuse angle is an acute angle.
45. The measure of an angle added to twice the measure of its complement
equals the measure of its supplement.

Algebra Review

Solve for x.

1. 3(x − 20) = 5(28 − x)   **2.** 2(x + 1) + 3 = 3(x − 1)
3. 3x − 4(x + 2) = x − 8   **4.** −2(x − 4) = −1(x − 11)

Computer Activity

This program finds the supplement of an angle.

```
10  REM FIND THE SUPPLEMENT OF AN ANGLE
20  INPUT "ENTER THE ANGLE MEASURE IN WHOLE
       DEGREES ";M
30  PRINT "THE SUPPLEMENT OF "M" DEGREES IS
       "180-M" DEGREES."
40  END
```

1. Change the program to output the complement of an angle.
2. Change the program so that the user is reprompted for the angle measure
if the angle input is of measure less than 1 or of measure greater than 179.
3. Change the program so that the output will also state whether the input
angle is obtuse, right, or acute.

OBJECTIVE: *State and use the definition of perpendicular lines and state, prove, and use theorems about perpendicular lines.*

2-3 Perpendicular Lines

 **EXPLORE**

Draw a point P on a line q on a piece of wax paper. Figure out how to fold the wax paper so that the fold line r goes through P and forms right angles with line q. Notice that the reflection image of line q in line r is the line q again.

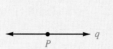

As you may have discovered in Exercise 43 on page 68, when the angles in a linear pair are congruent, they are right angles. This idea will be used to describe special pairs of intersecting lines that play an important role in geometry and its practical applications.

Consider the following definition.

■ **DEFINITION**

Perpendicular lines are two lines that intersect at right angles.

To indicate that l is perpendicular to m, you can write $l \perp m$.

This definition may be used in proofs as follows.

- When you know that $l \perp m$, the definition allows you to conclude that each angle ($\angle 1$, $\angle 2$, $\angle 3$, or $\angle 4$) is a right angle.
- When you know that any of these angles is a right angle, you may conclude that $l \perp m$.

Intersecting segments or rays on perpendicular lines are also considered perpendicular. In the figure, $\overline{PQ} \perp \overline{RS}$ and $\overrightarrow{PQ} \perp \overrightarrow{RS}$.

Example 1
$\overline{BC} \perp \overline{AD}$, $m\angle ABC = \frac{1}{2}x$, $m\angle ACB = 5x - 10$
Find $m\angle ABC$.

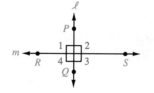

Solution
$5x - 10 = 90$ *Since $\overline{BC} \perp \overline{AD}$, $\angle ACB$ is a right angle*
$\quad\quad 5x = 100$ *and has measure 90.*
$\quad\quad\quad x = 20$
$m\angle ABC = \frac{1}{2}x = \frac{1}{2}(20) = 10$

Try This
Suppose $\overline{BC} \perp \overline{AD}$, $m\angle BDC = 3x$ and $m\angle ACB = 4x - 6$.   Find $m\angle BDC$.

First Five Minutes

(Quiz on previous lesson)

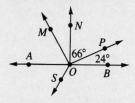

1. Name two angles adjacent to $\angle NOP$. ∠MON, ∠POB
2. Find $m\angle NOB$. Classify $\angle NOB$. 90, right
3. $\angle AOM$ and $\angle MOB$ are called ____ angles. $\angle NOP$ and $\angle POB$ are called ____ angles. supplementary, complementary
4. Are $\angle AOM$ and $\angle BOS$ vertical angles? If not, why? No, they are not formed by two intersecting lines.
5. Can a pair of vertical angles also be adjacent angles? No.

Lesson Opener

Introduce perpendicular lines by first reviewing how vertical angles are formed. Draw two intersecting lines (as shown below) on the board and then measure each angle with a protractor. Ask students to give other real-world situations that suggest intersecting lines.

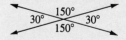

Mention examples such as weather vanes, crosspieces on a telephone pole, and graph paper. Ask students to find the measures of the four angles formed. Point out that these special pairs of intersecting lines, where four right angles are formed, play an important role in geometry and in its everyday applications.

Even though there are many lines perpendicular to a given line and many
lines through a given point, it is natural to feel that there could not be more
than one perpendicular to a line through a given point on the line. The
following is a convincing argument that this is true.

It would be impossible for both l and k to be perpendicular to m through
point P because this would produce a situation in which $m\angle QPR = 90$ and
$m\angle QPS = 90$. Since l and k are different lines, $m\angle 1$ is a positive number.
From the Angle Addition Postulate, $m\angle QPR + m\angle 1 = m\angle QPS$. But 90
plus a positive number cannot equal 90.

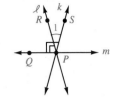

This leads to the following theorem.

◆ THEOREM 2.3

Through a given point on a line, there is exactly one line in the plane
perpendicular to the given line.

A **line perpendicular to a plane** at P is a line through P that is
perpendicular to *every* line in the plane that passes through P. For example,
in this figure, line l is perpendicular to plane M, so it is also perpendicular to
$\overrightarrow{AB}$ and $\overrightarrow{CD}$. The concept of a line being perpendicular to a plane is
sometimes used in proofs.

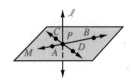

The following definition combines the ideas of perpendicular lines and the
bisector of a segment.

■ DEFINITION

A **perpendicular bisector** of a segment is a line, segment, ray, or plane
that is perpendicular to the segment and bisects it.

In the figure, $l \perp \overline{RS}$ at the midpoint M and so l is the perpendicular
bisector of $\overline{RS}$.

Example 2

$\overleftrightarrow{AB}$ is the perpendicular bisector of $\overline{XY}$.
Draw four conclusions from this information.

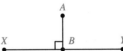

Solution
$\overleftrightarrow{AB} \perp \overline{XY}$
$\angle ABX$ and $\angle ABY$ are right angles.
B is the midpoint of $\overline{XY}$.
$\overline{XB} \cong \overline{BY}$

Try This
$\triangle PQR$ is a right triangle and $\overline{RS}$ bisects $\overline{PQ}$.
Draw three conclusions.

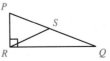

70   *Chapter 2   Introduction to Proof*

Class Exercises

Short Answer

1. When you know that two intersecting lines forming angles 1, 2, 3, and 4 are perpendicular, what can you conclude?
2. When you know that any one of the angles 1, 2, 3, or 4 formed by intersecting lines is a right angle, what can you conclude?
3. Describe two characteristics of a perpendicular bisector.

Give three real-world situations that illustrates each idea.

4. perpendicular lines   5. the perpendicular bisector of a segment

Sample Exercises

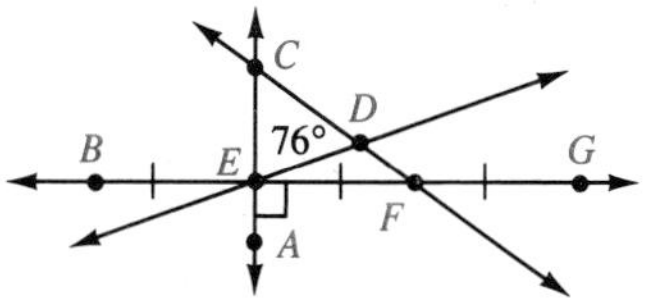

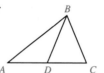

6. Which line is a perpendicular bisector?
7. Which line is a bisector but not perpendicular?
8. Name four right angles.
9. Find $m \angle DEF$.

10. If $\overline{MN} \perp \overline{ST}$ at X and X is the midpoint of $\overline{ST}$, state two conclusions.

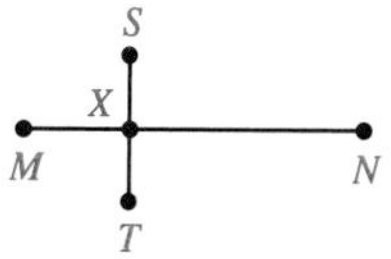

Discussion

Use the figure to determine whether each statement is always, sometimes, or never true. Redraw the figure to support your answer.

11. If $\overleftrightarrow{BD}$ is the perpendicular bisector of $\overline{AC}$, then $\overleftrightarrow{AC}$ is the perpendicular bisector of $\overline{BD}$.
12. If D is the midpoint of $\overline{AC}$, then $\overline{BD} \perp \overline{AC}$.
13. If $\overline{BD} \perp \overline{AC}$, then D is the midpoint of $\overline{AC}$.
14. Are the reflexive, symmetric, and transitive properties true for the relation "is perpendicular to"?

Exercises

A

Use these figures.

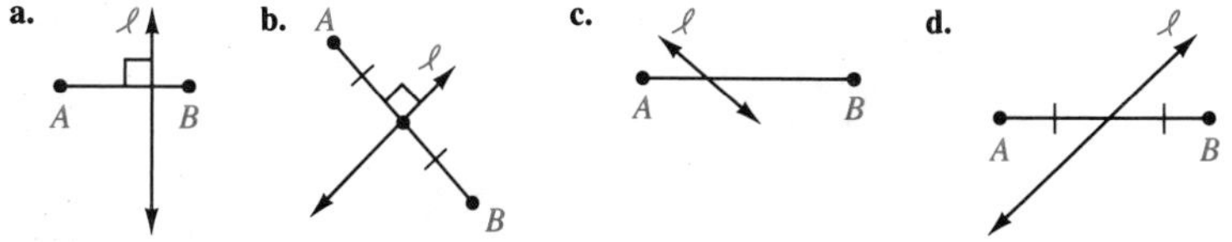

a.   b.    c.   d.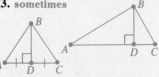

1. Which figure shows a perpendicular bisector?
2. Which figure shows a perpendicular but no bisector?
3. Which figure shows a bisector but no perpendicular?
4. Which figure shows no perpendicular and no bisector?

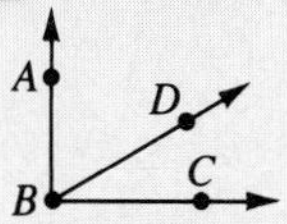

1. Suppose $\overrightarrow{BA} \perp \overrightarrow{BC}$ and $\angle ABD$ is five times as large as $\angle DBC$. Find $m \angle ABD$. 75

Answer to **Try This** 72

2. If line m is the perpendicular bisector of $\overline{EF}$, what can you conclude? $m \perp \overline{EF}$, m contains the midpoint of $\overline{EF}$.

Answer to **Try This** $\overline{PS} \cong \overline{SQ}$, $\overline{PR} \perp \overline{RQ}$, S is the midpoint to $\overline{PQ}$.

Class Exercise Answers

1. $m \angle 1 = m \angle 2 = m \angle 3 = m \angle 4 = 90$ **2.** The lines are $\perp$.
3. (1) intersects at rt. angles (2) bisects segment   **4.** edges of a desk, the corner of a book, window frame   **5.** the letter "T", crosspiece on a telephone pole, body and wings of an airplane   **6.** $\overrightarrow{CA}$ **7.** $\overleftrightarrow{DE}$
8. $\angle BEC$, $\angle CEF$, $\angle BEA$, $\angle FEA$
9. 14   **10.** $\overleftrightarrow{MN}$ is the $\perp$ bisector of $\overline{ST}$, $\overline{SX} \cong \overline{XT}$
11. never   **12.** sometimes

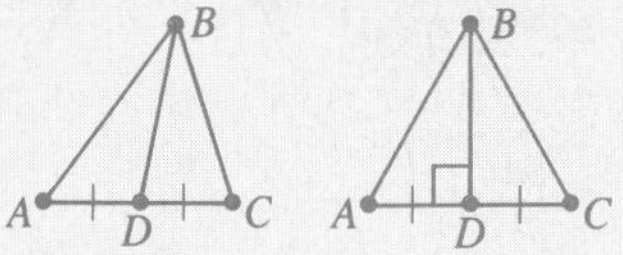

13. sometimes

14. reflexive: no, symmetric: yes, transitive: no

Assignment Guide

Minimum: 1–31 e/o, 34–37, MR
Regular: 5–33 e/o, 34–37, MR
Advanced: 5–31 e/o, 32–37, MR

Constructions
Exercises 20, 37

Coordinate Geometry
Exercise 31

Algebra
Exercises 12–14, 28–30

Lesson Closure

Ask students to determine whether each statement below is true or false.

1. If two intersecting lines form two congruent adjacent angles, then the lines are perpendicular. true

2. Intersecting segments are perpendicular to each other if the lines containing them are perpendicular. true

3. If a point is on a line in a given plane, then there is exactly one line in that plane perpendicular to the given line. false

Teacher's Resource Materials

Manipulatives 9
Practice Master 11   Quiz 3
Transparency 7

Exercise Answers

1. b   **2.** a   **3.** d
4. c   **5.** $m\angle 1 =$
$m\angle 2 = m\angle 3 = m\angle 4 =$
90   **6.** $\angle MBF$, $\angle FBN$, $\angle NBG$,
$\angle GBM$ **7.** $\angle TXS$, $\angle SXR$
8. $\overline{TR} \perp \overline{XS}$, $\overline{TS} \perp \overline{SR}$
9. 63,   **10.** 45   **11.** 60
12. 30   **13.** 36   **14.** 54

---

5. Line *l* is perpendicular to line *m* forming $\angle 1$, $\angle 2$, $\angle 3$, and $\angle 4$. What can you conclude about these angles?

6. $\overline{MN} \perp \overline{FG}$ at *B*   Name four right angles.

7. $\overline{SX} \perp \overline{TR}$ in $\triangle RST$ Name a pair of congruent adjacent angles.

8. $\angle TSR$ and $\angle TXS$ are right angles in $\triangle RST$.   Name two pairs of perpendicular lines.

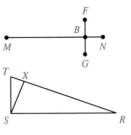

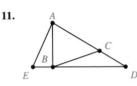

Find the measure of $\angle ABC$.

9.

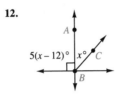

$\overrightarrow{AB} \perp \overrightarrow{BD}$
$m\angle 1 = 27$

10.

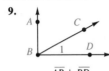

$\overrightarrow{BC}$ bisects $\angle ABE$.
$\overline{AB} \perp \overline{BE}$

11.

$\overline{AB} \perp \overline{BE}$
$m\angle ABC = 2m\angle CBD$

12.

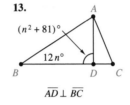

$5(x-12)°$ $x°$

13.

$(n^2 + 81)°$ $12n°$

$\overline{AD} \perp \overline{BC}$

14.

$2t°$ $\left(\dfrac{10t}{3}\right)°$

$\overline{CD} \perp \overline{AB}$

15. Complete the proof.

Given: $\angle 1$ is a right angle.
  Q is the midpoint of $\overline{PR}$.

Prove: $\overline{CD}$ is the $\perp$ bisector of $\overline{PR}$.

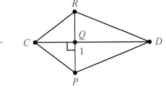

Proof Statements	Reasons
1. *Q* is the midpoint of $\overline{PR}$.	1. ___
2. $\angle 1$ is a right angle.	2. ___
3. $\overline{CD} \perp \overline{PR}$	3. ___
4. $\overline{CD}$ is the $\perp$ bisector of $\overline{PR}$.	4. ___

B

Complete each proof.

16. Given: $m\angle 2 = 90$
   $\angle 1$ and $\angle 2$ form a linear pair.

Prove: $m\angle 1 = 90$

Proof Statements	Reasons
1. $m\angle 2 = 90$	1. ___
2. ___	2. Given
3. $m\angle 1 + m\angle 2 = 180$	3. ___
4. $m\angle 1 + 90 = 180$	4. Substitution
5. ___	5. ___

17. Given: ∠1 is complementary to ∠2.

Prove: $\overline{PQ} \perp \overline{PR}$

Proof

Statements	Reasons
1. ∠1 is complementary to ∠2.	1. ___
2. $m\angle 1 + m\angle 2 = 90$	2. ___
3. $m\angle 1 + m\angle 2 = m\angle QPR$	3. ___
4. ___	4. Substitution
5. ∠QPR is a right angle.	5. ___
6. ___	6. ___

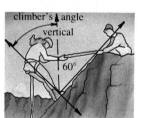

18. To avoid slipping, mountain climbers try to keep their legs perpendicular to the side of the ledge. If the ledge is 60° off the vertical, find the climber's angle.

19. Draw two intersecting lines that contain line segments that do not intersect.

20. Draw a segment and use a compass and straightedge to construct its perpendicular bisector.

21. Draw a figure in which $\overline{AB}$ is the perpendicular bisector of $\overline{CD}$, but $\overline{CD}$ is not the perpendicular bisector of $\overline{AB}$.

22. Draw a figure in which $\overline{ST}$ is the perpendicular bisector of $\overline{UV}$, $\overline{WX}$, and $\overline{YZ}$.

23. $\overline{BD}$ is the perpendicular bisector of $\overline{AC}$ at X.
$\overline{EF}$ is the perpendicular bisector of $\overline{XC}$ at Y.
What is the ratio $\frac{YC}{AC}$? $\frac{YC}{XC}$? $\frac{AX}{YC}$?

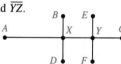

Determine whether each statement is always, sometimes, or never true.

24. If $\overline{AB}$ is the perpendicular bisector of $\overline{GH}$, then $\overline{GH}$ is the perpendicular bisector of $\overline{AB}$.

25. If $\overline{JK}$ is the perpendicular bisector of $\overline{LM}$, then $\overline{LM}$ contains the midpoint of $\overline{JK}$.

26. If $\overline{EF} \perp \overline{GH}$, then $\overline{GH} \perp \overline{EF}$.

27. Line l and line m are both perpendicular to line t at point P on t.

Write an algebraic expression for each of the following, given that $\overline{CD}$ is the perpendicular bisector of $\overline{AB}$.

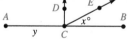

28. Express $m\angle DCE$ in terms of x.

29. Express $m\angle ACE$ in terms of x.

30. Express AB in terms of y.

31. Consider points $A(3, 0)$, $B(0, 2)$, $C(-1, 0)$, $D(0, -1)$ and $O(0, 0)$. Find $m\angle AOB$ and $m\angle COD$.

C

Write a two-column proof for each exercise.

32. Given: $\overline{AB} \perp \overline{BC}$, $\overline{BC} \perp \overline{CD}$

Prove: ∠ABC ≅ ∠BCD

33. Given: ∠1 is complementary to ∠2.

Prove: $\overline{JK} \perp \overline{KL}$

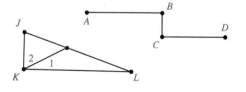

15. 1. Given 2. Given 3. Definition of perpendicular 4. Definition of perpendicular bisector

16. 1. Given 2. ∠1 and ∠2 form a linear pair. 3. Theorem 2.1 5. $m\angle 1 = 90$ (Subtraction Property)

17. 1. Given 2. Definition of complementary angles 3. Angle Addition Postulate 4. $m\angle QPR = 90$ 5. Definition of right angle 6. $\overline{PQ} \perp \overline{PR}$ (Definition of perpendicular)

18. 30

19.

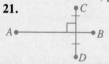

20. See Exercise 50, page 25.

21.

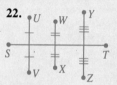

22.

23. $\frac{YC}{AC} = \frac{1}{4}$, $\frac{YC}{XC} = \frac{1}{2}$, $\frac{AX}{YC} = 2$

24. sometimes **25.** sometimes

26. always **27.** never

28. $90 - x$ **29.** $180 - x$

30. $2y$ **31.** 90, 90

32. 1. $\overline{AB} \perp \overline{BC}$ (Given)
2. $\overline{BC} \perp \overline{CD}$ (Given) 3. ∠ABC and ∠BCD are rt. angles. (Definition of perpendicular)
4. $m\angle ABC = m\angle BCD = 90$ (Definition of rt. angle)
5. $m\angle ABC = m\angle BCD$ (Substitution) 6. ∠ABC ≅ ∠BCD (Definition of congruent angles) **33.** 1. ∠1 is complementary to ∠2. (Given)
2. $m\angle 1 + m\angle 2 = 90$ (Definition of complementary)
3. $m\angle 1 + m\angle 2 = m\angle JKL$ (Angle Addition Postulate)
4. $m\angle JKL = 90$ (Substitution)
5. ∠JKL is a rt. angle. (Definition of rt. angle.)
6. $JK \perp KL$ (Definition of perpendicular)

34. false

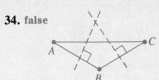

35. false

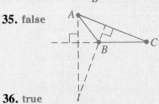

36. true

37. Put compass tip on P and make an arc that forms a segment on l. Construct the $\perp$ bisector to this segment.

Mixed Review Answers

1. H: A triangle is isosceles. C: It has two congruent sides.
2. If a triangle does not have two congruent sides, then it is not isosceles.   **3.** If a triangle has two congruent sides, then it is isosceles.
4. true   **5.** $m\angle B = m\angle D$

Quiz Answers

1. 90   **2.** $\angle CGD$ **3.** 75
4. $\angle BGC$ **5.** 1.c 2.b 3.c 4.a

Critical Thinking

Determine whether each statement is true or false. If false, give a counterexample.

34. Given any triangle ABC, the perpendicular bisector of $\overline{AB}$ intersects the perpendicular bisector of $\overline{BC}$ at a point inside the triangle.

35. Given any triangle ABC, the line through A perpendicular to $\overline{BC}$ and the line through B perpendicular to $\overline{AC}$ intersect at a point inside the triangle.

36. Given any equilateral triangle, the line which is a perpendicular bisector of a side contains a vertex.

37. Figure out how to use a compass and unmarked straightedge to construct a perpendicular to a line l through a point P not on l. (HINT: Start by putting the compass tip on the point and making an arc that forms a segment on the line.)

Mixed Review

Use the statement "If a triangle is isosceles, then it has two congruent sides."

1. Write the hypothesis and the conclusion of the statement.
2. Write the contrapositive of the statement.
3. Write the converse of the statement.
4. Determine whether the converse is true or false.

5. Use the transitive property to draw a conclusion.
Given: $m\angle B = m\angle C$, $m\angle C = m\angle D$

Quiz

$\overleftrightarrow{AD}$ **is perpendicular to** $\overleftrightarrow{BE}$**. Complete each statement.**

1. $m\angle EGA =$ ___
2. $\angle BGC$ is complementary to ___ .
3. If $m\angle FGD = 105$, then $m\angle AGF =$ ___ .
4. $\angle EGF \cong$ ___

Complete the proof by choosing a reason for each statement.

5. Given: $\overrightarrow{CA}$ bisects $\angle BCD$. $\angle 2 \cong \angle 3$

   Prove: $\angle 1 \cong \angle 3$

   Proof Statements   Reasons

   1. $\overrightarrow{CA}$ bisects $\angle BCD$.   1. ___ | Choose from these reasons:
   2. $\angle 1 \cong \angle 2$ 2. ___ | **a.** Angle congruence is transitive
   3. $\angle 2 \cong \angle 3$ 3. ___ | **b.** Definition of angle bisector
   4. $\angle 1 \cong \angle 3$ 4. ___ | **c.** Given

PLANNING AND WRITING PROOFS

OBJECTIVE: *Draw and use appropriate diagrams for a proof.*

2-4 Drawing and Using Diagrams

A diagram in a two-column proof often helps supply given information. The guidelines below help you decide what information you can and cannot assume as given from a diagram when writing a two-column proof.

Information That May Be Assumed To Be Given From a Diagram

1. Straightness of lines
2. Betweenness of points
3. Collinearity of points on a line, coplanarity of points
4. Intersection of lines
5. Relative locations (interior, exterior, opposite)
6. Adjacency, nonadjacency of angles
7. Existence of the figures shown

Information That May *Not* Be Assumed From a Diagram

1. Congruence of segments or angles
2. Measures of segments or angles
3. Relative sizes of segments and angles
4. Midpoint of a segment or bisector of an angle
5. Perpendicular lines or right angles
6. Nonintersecting lines
7. Special types of figures (isosceles triangle, square, etc.)

Example 1

Which of the following may be assumed from the figure to be given?

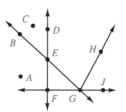

1. $\overleftrightarrow{BG}$ is a straight line.
2. $\overline{EF} \cong \overline{FG}$
3. Point E is between D and F.
4. $\angle DEB \cong \angle EFG$
5. $\angle EFG$ is a right angle.
6. $\angle BEF$ is obtuse.
7. C is in the interior of $\angle DEB$.
8. E is the midpoint of $\overline{DF}$.
9. $\angle EGH$ is adjacent to $\angle HGJ$.
10. $\overrightarrow{GH}$ is the bisector of $\angle EGJ$.
11. The figure formed by $\overline{EF}$, $\overline{FG}$, and $\overline{EG}$ is a triangle.

Solution

1, 3, 7, 9, 11

Try This

Give another statement that may be assumed from the diagram.

It is often necessary to draw a reasonably accurate diagram to represent given data when writing a proof. Such diagrams should contain all the information in the *Given* plus the type of assumed information in the chart above, but should not suggest any other additional information. For example, if the given information refers to a *triangle*, the diagram should not show what appears to be a *right triangle*.

Also, diagrams are sometimes marked to emphasize given data as shown in Example 2.

First Five Minutes

(Quiz on previous lesson)

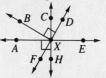

Complete each statement.
1. $m\angle BXD =$ _90_
2. If $m\angle EXD = 70$, then $m\angle DXC =$ _20_ .
3. $m\angle AXB + m\angle BXC =$ _90_
4. $m\angle AXH + m\angle HXE =$ _180_

Lesson Opener

Diagrams are as important in mathematics as blueprints are to a builder. Discuss other situations where diagrams are valuable.

Materials

student notebooks

Teaching Notes

Emphasize that drawing a diagram to represent given data before beginning a proof can be a tremendous help in understanding proofs. The diagram should contain all the information in the "Given" and be as accurate as possible.

Guided Practice

Chalkboard Examples

1. Can these statements be assumed from the diagram?
   a. G is between F and J. yes
   b. $\overline{BE} \cong \overline{EG}$ no
   c. G is the midpoint of $\overline{FJ}$. no
   d. $\overline{EF} \perp \overline{FG}$ no

Answer to **Try This** *A* is in the interior of $\angle BEF$.

2. Draw a diagram to show the given information. Mark it for emphasis. Given: $\triangle ACB$ with right angle C. $\overline{CD} \perp \overline{AB}$, $\overline{AC} \cong \overline{BC}$

Answer to **Try This**

Example 2

Draw a diagram to show the given information. Mark it for emphasis.
Given: $\triangle EFG$ with $\angle EFH \cong \angle FGH$, $\overline{EF} \cong \overline{EH}$, $\overline{FH} \cong \overline{HG}$
$\angle EFG$ is a right angle. $m\angle FEH = 60$

Solution

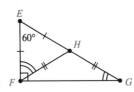

Note that the sides of $\triangle EFG$ are drawn to appear of different lengths since nothing was given to indicate otherwise.

Try This
Given: $\triangle ABC$ with $\overline{AB} \cong \overline{AC}$, $BC = 6$, $m\angle A = 35$
Draw and mark a diagram.

Class Exercises

Short Answer

State whether or not you can assume the information from the figure. Give a guideline from the charts on page 75 to justify your answer.

1. $\angle P$ and $\angle S$ are right angles.
2. V is inside the square.
3. $\overline{PQ} \cong \overline{RP}$
4. T is between P and R.
5. $\overline{PU}$ is shorter than $\overline{UQ}$.
6. P, Q, and R are noncollinear.
7. $\overrightarrow{PQ}$ and $\overleftrightarrow{RS}$ do not intersect.
8. $\overrightarrow{PQ}$ and $\overrightarrow{PR}$ intersect.
9. $\angle WRT$ and $\angle TRS$ are adjacent.
10. T is the midpoint of $\overline{PR}$.

Sample Exercises

11. Choose the best diagram for the given data. Justify your choice.
Given: $\triangle DEF$, with $\overrightarrow{EG}$ bisecting $\angle DEF$

a. 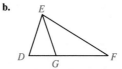   b. 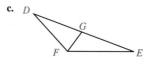   c.

Determine whether each of the following can be assumed from a diagram.

12. Two lines are perpendicular.
13. A ray is in the interior of an angle.
14. Two points are on opposite sides of a line.
15. One angle is smaller than another.

Discussion

16. Give as many statements as possible that a) can be assumed from this diagram and b) appear to be true but cannot be assumed.

Exercises

A

Indicate whether or not the information can be assumed from the diagram.

1. $\overrightarrow{NQ} \perp \overrightarrow{LQ}$
2. N, P, and Q are collinear.
3. M is the midpoint of $\overline{LN}$.
4. $\overline{NP} \cong \overline{PQ}$
5. $\angle MLP$ and $\angle PLQ$ are adjacent angles.
6. LP is greater than MN.
7. $\angle RMN$ and $\angle NMP$ form a linear pair.
8. The figure formed by $\overline{MN}$, $\overline{NP}$, and $\overline{PM}$ is a triangle.
9. $\angle NLQ \cong \angle QNL$
10. Point M is between L and N.
11. $\angle RML$ and $\angle NMP$ are vertical angles.
12. $\angle NQL$ is a right angle.
13. $\overrightarrow{LP}$ bisects $\angle MLQ$.
14. $\overleftrightarrow{RP}$ intersects $\overleftrightarrow{LM}$.
15. R and Q are on opposite sides of $\overleftrightarrow{LN}$.

16. Choose the best diagram for the given data. Justify your choice.
    Given: $\overline{RS}$ is the perpendicular bisector of $\overline{TU}$.

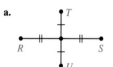

   a.   **b.**   **c.**

Draw a diagram to show the given information.

17. Given: $\overline{AB} \perp \overline{CD}$ intersecting at B, $\overrightarrow{BF}$ bisects $\angle ABD$.
18. Given: M is the midpoint of $\overline{RS}$. $\overleftrightarrow{JK}$ is the perpendicular bisector of $\overline{MS}$.
19. Given: $\triangle XYZ$ with $\angle Y \cong \angle Z$, T is between Y and Z.
    U is between T and Z.
20. Given: $\angle 1$ is supplementary and adjacent to $\angle 2$. $\angle 3$ is complementary and adjacent to $\angle 2$.
21. Given: $\angle 4$ and $\angle 5$ are vertical angles. $\angle 5$ is a right angle.

Draw a diagram and mark it to indicate the given information.

22. Given: $\triangle ABC$ with $\overline{AB} \cong \overline{AC}$, $m\angle A = 30$
23. Given: $\triangle SAT$ with $\angle A$ a right angle, $AT = 5$
24. Given: $\overline{FP}$ is the perpendicular bisector of $\overline{GY}$ and $\overline{GY}$ is the perpendicular bisector of $\overline{FP}$. $\overline{FY} \cong \overline{PG}$, $\overline{GF} \cong \overline{PY}$
25. Given: $\triangle JKL$ and $\triangle RST$, with $\overline{JK} \cong \overline{RS}$, $\overline{KL} \cong \overline{ST}$, and $\angle K \cong \angle S$

Draw a diagram and mark it as needed.

26. G, H, I are collinear. G, J, and K are collinear. H, J, and K are noncollinear.
27. $\triangle ABC$ is a right triangle. $\overrightarrow{BH}$ bisects the right angle. H, A, and C are collinear.

Exercise Answers

1. no	**2.** yes	**3.** no
4. no	**5.** yes	**6.** no
7. yes	**8.** yes	**9.** no
10. yes	**11.** yes	**12.** no
13. no	**14.** yes	**15.** yes

16. c (since $\overline{TU}$ may not bisect $\overline{RS}$)

17.

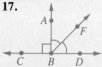

18.

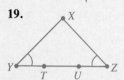

19.

20.   **21.**

22.   **23.**

24.

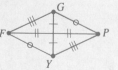

25.

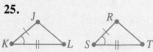

26.   **27.**

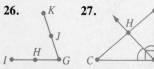

28.

29.

1. Given 2. Definition of perpendicular 3. $m\angle 1 = 90$, $m\angle 2 = 90$
4. $m\angle 1 = m\angle 2$

30.

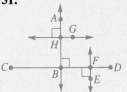

1. Given 2. $\overrightarrow{ST}$ bisects $\angle RSU$. 3. $\angle RST \cong \angle TSU$ 4. Definition of congruent angles 5. Substitution

31.

32.

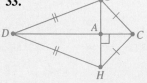

33.

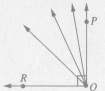

$\angle GAC$ is a right angle, $CG < HD$, etc.

34. 9, 18, 27, 36

---

28. A surveyor often gathers field data at a work site and does computations later in the office. Set up and label a diagram that would illustrate the following data.

• A, B, and C are three noncollinear locations.
• The distance from location A to B is 174 ft.
• The distance from location B to C is 153 ft.
• $m\angle B$ is 23 degrees.
• C is to the north of A and B.

B

Draw a diagram and complete each proof.

29. Given: $l \perp m$ forming a linear pair of angles, $\angle 1$ and $\angle 2$

Prove: $m\angle 1 = m\angle 2$

Proof Statements

1. $l \perp m$	**1.** ___
2. $\angle 1$ and $\angle 2$ are right angles.	**2.** ___
3. ___	**3.** Definition of right angles
4. ___	**4.** Substitution

30. Given: $m\angle JKL = m\angle RST$
$\overrightarrow{ST}$ bisects $\angle RSU$.

Prove: $m\angle JKL = m\angle TSU$

Proof Statements | Reasons

1. $m\angle JKL = m\angle RST$	**1.** ___
2. ___	**2.** Given
3. ___	**3.** Definition of angle bisector
4. $m\angle RST = m\angle TSU$	**4.** ___
5. $m\angle JKL = m\angle TSU$	**5.** ___

31. Draw and label a diagram for the given information.
Given: $\overleftrightarrow{AB}$ is the perpendicular bisector of $\overline{CD}$, intersecting at B.
$\overleftrightarrow{EF}$ is the perpendicular bisector of $\overline{BD}$, intersecting at F.
$\overleftrightarrow{GH}$ is the perpendicular bisector of $\overline{AB}$, intersecting at H.

32. Draw and label a right triangle with 30° and 60° angles, shortest side 1, next longest side approximately 1.7, and longest side 2.

C

33. Draw and label a diagram for the given information. Then write some other statements that are true about the figure.
Given: Point A is between C and D. A is also between G and H. $\overline{CH} \cong \overline{CG}$ and $\overline{HD} \cong \overline{GD}$, but $CH < HD$. $\angle HAC$ is a right angle.

34. Draw and label a diagram for the given information. Then find the measure of each angle.
Given: $\overrightarrow{QP} \perp \overrightarrow{QR}$ Three other rays with endpoint Q are in the interior of $\angle PQR$. These rays form nonoverlapping angles which have measures in the ratio $1:2:3:4$.

Critical Thinking

When you answer the question "What seems to be true about a situation?" you have formed a *hypothesis* about the situation. Consider Exercise 35.

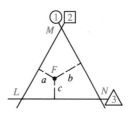

35. Highways 1, 2, and 3 intersect to enclose an equilateral triangle. Where should a factory be built inside this triangle so that the sum of the perpendicular distances from the factory to the highways (a + b + c) is the least? Form a hypothesis. How could you test your hypothesis?

36. A machinist is to make a metal plate like the one shown in this diagram. Interpret and analyze the diagram to find the missing dimensions indicated by A, B, C, D, and E.

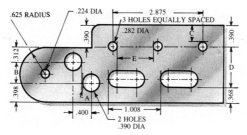

35. The sum of these distances is the same no matter what point is chosen. (The sum is equal to the altitude of the triangle.) To test this, pick any point, measure the distances, find the sum, and then try this with other points.

36. A = 0.01, B = 0.54, C = 0.249, D = 0.882, E = 1.1555

Algebra Review Answers

1. $(x + 2)(x + 1)$
2. $(y + 6)(y + 2)$
3. $(m - 3)(m - 2)$
4. $(x + 5)^2$
5. $(n - 7)(n + 3)$
6. $(m - 2)(m + 2)$
7. $(2y + 1)(y - 2)$
8. $(3s - 1)(s + 1)$
9. $(3x - 1)(2x + 3)$

Enrichment Answers

1. same   2. *A*   3. same

Algebra Review

Factor.

1. $x^2 + 3x + 2$
2. $y^2 + 8y + 12$
3. $m^2 - 5m + 6$
4. $x^2 + 10x + 25$
5. $n^2 - 4n - 21$
6. $m^2 - 4$
7. $2y^2 - 3y - 2$
8. $3s^2 + 2s - 1$
9. $6x^2 + 7x - 3$

Enrichment

Optical Illusions

The optical illusions below help show why you should rely more on logical reasoning and less on visual information. Answer the questions. Then check with a ruler.

1. Which is longer, $\overline{AB}$ or $\overline{CD}$?

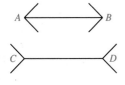

2. Will line k, when extended, meet point A, point B, or point C?

3. Which is longer, $\overline{AB}$ or $\overline{CD}$?

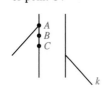

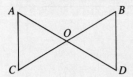

**Which of the following may
be assumed from the diagram?**

1. *C*, *O*, and *B* are collinear.
yes

2. $\overleftrightarrow{AD}$ is a straight line. yes

3. *O* is between *C* and *B*. yes

4. $\overline{AO} \cong \overline{OD}$ no

5. *O* is the midpoint of $\overline{AD}$. no

Lesson Opener

As an introduction to this and
the next two lessons, begin with
a review of two-column proofs.
In this lesson, students look
more closely at what it means to
prove a theorem.

Materials

student notebooks

Teaching Notes

Sample proofs appear throughout this text. Encourage students to read them carefully because they serve as excellent
examples.

Continue to stress the importance of drawing a diagram before beginning a proof. Another
problem-solving strategy, which
is illustrated in Example 2, is
working backward.

Point out that Theorem 2.5, the
Midpoint Theorem, uses the
definition of a midpoint to
prove additional properties of
midpoints not given in the
definition.

OBJECTIVE: *Analyze, plan, and write two-column proofs.*

2-5 Planning and Writing a Proof

In proofs so far, you have started with the *Given* statement and used
deductive reasoning to establish the truth of the *Prove* statement. In this
section you will look more carefully at what it means to prove a theorem. To
prove a theorem follow these five steps.

Proving a Theorem

Step 1: Write the theorem in IF-THEN form.
Step 2: Write the GIVEN from the hypothesis and the PROVE from the
conclusion.
Step 3: Draw and label a DIAGRAM to show the given information.
Step 4: Analyze the situation and devise a PLAN.
Step 5: Write STATEMENTS leading from the *Given* to the *Prove* and
give REASONS to support these statements.

In Step 2, keep in mind that the hypothesis is the *if* part of the if-then
statement and the conclusion is the *then* part. The guidelines described in
Lesson 2-4 may be helpful when drawing the diagram in Step 3. In Step 5,
recall that you must use given information, definitions, postulates (including
algebraic properties), or previously proven theorems as reasons for your
statements.

Example 1 illustrates how to use Steps 1, 2, and 3 to begin the proof of Theorem 2.4.

◆ **THEOREM 2.4**
All right angles are congruent.

Example 1
Rewrite Theorem 2.4 in if-then form, write the *Given* and *Prove,* and draw a
diagram showing the given information.

Solution
If two angles are right angles, then the angles are congruent.

Given: ∠1 is a right angle.
∠2 is a right angle.
Prove: ∠1 ≅ ∠2

The next example illustrates how Steps 4 and 5 are used to complete the
proof of Theorem 2.4. Notice that to analyze the situation, you first look at
what is to be proved and work backwards from there.

80 *Chapter 2 Introduction to Proof*

Example 2

Analyze the situation to devise a plan and prove Theorem 2.4.

Solution

Analysis I want to prove that $\angle 1 \cong \angle 2$. I can do this if I can show that they have the same measure. I can show they have the same measure since they are both right angles.

(This analysis shows how someone might work backwards to figure out how to prove Theorem 2.4. It is a mental process that is not usually written.)

Plan Since $\angle 1$ and $\angle 2$ are right angles, they each have measure 90. Since the measures of the angles are equal, they are congruent. (This proof shows how someone might carry out the plan to write the two-column proof.)

(This plan shows how someone might organize the proof of Theorem 2.4 after having analyzed the situation.)

Proof

Statements	Reasons
1. $\angle 1$ and $\angle 2$ are right angles.	1. Given
2. $m\angle 1 = 90$, $m\angle 2 = 90$	2. Definition of right angles
3. $m\angle 1 = m\angle 2$	3. Substitution Property
4. $\angle 1 \cong \angle 2$	4. Definition of congruent angles

◆ **THEOREM 2.5** Midpoint Theorem

The midpoint M of $\overline{AB}$ divides $\overline{AB}$ so that $AM = \frac{1}{2} AB$.

Example 3

Prove the Midpoint Theorem.

Solution

Theorem: If M is the midpoint of $\overline{AB}$, then $AM = \frac{1}{2} AB$.

Given: M is the midpoint of $\overline{AB}$.

Prove: $AM = \frac{1}{2} AB$.

Analysis I can prove $AM = \frac{1}{2} AB$ if I can show that $2AM = AB$ or $AM + AM = AB$. I can show that $AM + AM = AB$ if I can show that $AM + MB = AB$, since $AM = MB$. But I know that $AM + MB = AB$ because of the Segment Addition Postulate.

Plan $AM + MB = AB$ from the Segment Addition Postulate. Since $AM = MB$, it follows that $AM + AM = AB$, $2AM = AB$, and $AM = \frac{1}{2} AB$.

Proof

Statements	Reasons
1. M is the midpoint of $\overline{AB}$.	1. Given
2. $AM = MB$	2. Definition of midpoint
3. $AM + MB = AB$	3. Segment Addition Postulate
4. $AM + AM = AB$	4. Substitution Property
5. $2AM = AB$	5. Distributive Property
6. $AM = \frac{1}{2} AB$	6. Division Property of Equality

2-5 Planning and Writing a Proof **81**

Guided Practice

Chalkboard Example

Rewrite the following in if-then form, write the *Given* and *Prove*, and draw a diagram showing the given information.

Whenever M is the midpoint of $\overline{CD}$, $2\,MC = CD$. If M is the midpoint of $\overline{CD}$, then $2MC = CD$. Given: M is the midpoint of $\overline{CD}$. Prove: $2MC = CD$

Class Exercise Answers

1. d, e, b, a, c **2.** If two lines intersect, then they are contained in exactly one plane. **3.** If a figure is a segment, then it has exactly one midpoint. **4.** If two lines intersect, then they have exactly one point in common. **5.** Given: $\angle 1$ and $\angle 2$ form a linear pair. $\angle 1$ is a right angle. Prove: $\angle 2$ is a right angle. **6.** Given: $\overline{AB}$ Prove: $\overline{AB}$ has only one $\perp$ bisector. **7.** Given: $\overrightarrow{BD}$ is the bisector of $\angle ABC$. Prove: $m\angle ABD = \frac{1}{2} m\angle ABC$ **8.**

9. $\angle 2 \cong \angle 3$, $\angle 1 \cong \angle 2$ **10.** Convincing Argument: Kim was clocked at more than 3 mph over the speed limit and the radar was correctly operating.

You will be asked to prove Theorem 2.5 in Exercise 26.

◆ **THEOREM 2.6**   Angle Bisector Theorem
If $\overrightarrow{BD}$ is the bisector of ∠*ABC*, then $m \angle ABD = \frac{1}{2} m \angle ABC$.

Class Exercises

Short Answer

1. Arrange the steps for proving a theorem in the correct order.
   a. Analyze and plan.   **b.** Draw a diagram   **c.** Write the statements and reasons.
   d. Write the theorem in if-then form.   **e.** Write the *Given* and *Prove*.

State the theorem as a conditional.

2. Two intersecting lines are contained in exactly one plane.
3. A segment has exactly one midpoint.
4. Two intersecting lines have exactly one point in common.

Sample Exercises

State the *Given* and the *Prove* for each conditional.

5. If one angle of a linear pair is a right angle, then the other is also a right angle.
6. If a figure is a segment, then it has only one perpendicular bisector.
7. If $\overrightarrow{BD}$ is the bisector of ∠*ABC*, then $m\angle ABD = \frac{1}{2} m\angle ABC$.
8. Draw a diagram that shows the given information in this theorem. Every equilateral triangle is also an isosceles triangle.
9. Complete the following analysis of a proof.
   Given: ∠1 and ∠2 are vertical angles. ∠2 ≅ ∠3
   Prove: ∠1 ≅ ∠3
   I can prove ∠1 ≅ ∠3 if I can prove that ___ and ___ .

Discussion

10. The definition a local police force used for speeding is, "Being clocked by correctly operating radar as traveling at least 3 mph over a posted speed limit." If a police officer wanted to convince a judge that a person was speeding, what would he need to prove? Suppose you were given that (a) Kim was clocked at 40 mph in a posted 35 mph zone and (b) Officer Sharpeye had a receipt showing that her radar had recently passed the operating check.
    How would you write a convincing informal argument that Kim was speeding? How would you write a two-column proof?
11. How would you use the steps for proving a theorem to prove that the following statement is true? An angle divided by a ray into two complementary angles is a right angle.

Exercises

A

1. Write this theorem as a conditional. Two intersecting lines that form congruent adjacent angles are perpendicular.
2. Write the *Given* and *Prove* for this theorem. Two angles supplementary to the same angle are congruent.
3. Draw a diagram to show the given information for this theorem. If one angle of a linear pair is a right angle, then the other angle is also a right angle.

Rewrite the theorem as a conditional, write the *Given* and *Prove*, and draw a diagram showing the given information.

4. Two perpendicular lines form congruent adjacent angles.
5. Two angles are right angles if they are congruent and supplementary.
6. An equilateral triangle is also an equiangular triangle.
7. Vertical angles are congruent.
8. Every equilateral triangle is also an isosceles triangle.

Complete the first line in the analysis of each proof.

9. **Given:** $m\angle 1 = 30$, $m\angle 2 = 13$, $m\angle 3 = 17$
   Prove: $\overrightarrow{BD}$ bisects $\angle ABC$.

I can prove that $\overrightarrow{BD}$ bisects $\angle ABC$ if I can first prove that ___ .

10. **Given:** $\angle 1 \cong \angle 2$, $\angle 3 \cong \angle 4$
    Prove: $\angle 1 \cong \angle 4$

I can prove that $\angle 1 \cong \angle 4$ if I can first prove that ___ .

11. **Given:** $\angle 1$ is complementary to $\angle 2$.
    Prove: $\overline{JK} \perp \overline{KL}$

I can prove that $\overline{JK} \perp \overline{KL}$ if I can first prove that ___ .

12. **Given:** $\overline{RT} \perp \overline{SX}$, $\overline{WY} \perp \overline{SX}$
    Prove: $\angle 1 \cong \angle 3$
    I can prove that $\angle 1 \cong \angle 3$ if I can first prove that $\angle 1$ and $\angle 3$ are both ___ .

13. **Given:** $\overline{WX} \cong \overline{XY}$, $\angle SXW$ is a right angle.
    Prove: $\overline{SX}$ is the perpendicular bisector of $\overline{WY}$.
    I can prove that $\overline{SX}$ is the perpendicular bisector of $\overline{WY}$ if I can first prove that ___ .

Exercise Answers

1. If two intersecting lines form $\cong$ adj. $\angle$s, then they are $\perp$.

2. Given: $\angle 1$ is supp. to $\angle 2$. $\angle 3$ is supp. to $\angle 2$ Prove: $\angle 1 \cong \angle 3$

3.

4. If two lines are $\perp$, then they form $\cong$ adj. $\angle$s.

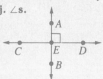

Given: $\overleftrightarrow{AB} \perp \overleftrightarrow{CD}$ Prove: $\angle AEC \cong \angle AED$

5. If two $\angle$s are $\cong$ and supp., then they are right $\angle$s.

Given: $\angle 1 \cong \angle 2$, $\angle 1$ and $\angle 2$ are supp. Prove: $\angle 1$ and $\angle 2$ are right $\angle$s.   **6.** If a $\triangle$ is equilat., then it is equiang.

Given: $\triangle ABC$ is equilat. Prove: $\triangle ABC$ is equiang.   **7.** If two $\angle$s are vertical $\angle$s, then they are $\cong$.

Given: $\angle 1$ and $\angle 2$ are vertical $\angle$s. Prove: $\angle 1 \cong \angle 2$ **8.** If a $\triangle$ is equilateral, then it is isos.

Given: $\triangle ABC$ is equilat. Prove: $\triangle ABC$ is isos.

9. $\angle ABD \cong \angle DBC$
10. $\angle 2 \cong \angle 3$ **11.** $m\angle JKL = 90$
12. right $\angle$s   **13.** $\overline{SX} \perp \overline{WY}$
14. 1. $m\angle DPW = 90$ (Given)
2. $\angle DPW$ is a right $\angle$. (Def. right $\angle$) 3. $\overleftrightarrow{DP} \perp \overleftrightarrow{WP}$ (Def. $\perp$)

15. 1. ∠1 ≅ ∠2, ∠3 ≅ ∠4
(Given) 2. ∠2 ≅ ∠3 (Th. 2.2)
3. ∠1 ≅ ∠3 (Th. 1.1)
4. ∠1 ≅ ∠4 (Th. 1.1)
16. 1. ∠1 is comp. to ∠2.
(Given) 2. $m\angle 1 + m\angle 2 = 90$
(Def. of comp.)
3. $m\angle 1 + m\angle 2 = m\angle JSX$
(Angle Addition Post.)
4. $m\angle JSX = 90$ (Subst.)
5. ∠JSX is a right ∠. (Def. right
∠) 6. $\overline{JS} \perp \overline{XS}$ (Def. ⊥)
17. 1. $\overline{RT} \perp \overline{PQ}$, $\overline{WY} \perp \overline{PQ}$
(Given) 2. ∠1 and ∠3 are right
∠s. (Def. right ∠) 3. ∠1 ≅ ∠3
(Th. 2.4)   **18.** 1. ∠ADE is a
right ∠. (Given) 2. $\overline{AD} \perp \overline{CE}$
(Def. ⊥) 3. $CD = DE$ (Given)
4. D is the midpoint of $\overline{CE}$. (Def.
midpoint) 5. $\overline{AD}$ is the ⊥ bisector of $\overline{CE}$. (Def. of ⊥ bisector)
19.

1. $\overline{LM} \perp \overline{ST}$ (Given) 2. ∠LMS is
a right ∠. (Def. ⊥)
3. $m\angle LMS = 90$ (Def. right ∠)
20.

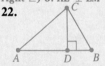

1. $GH = HJ$, H is between G and
J. (Given) 2. H is the midpoint
of $\overline{GJ}$. (Def. midpoint)
3. $GH = \frac{1}{2}GJ$ (Th. 2.5)
21.

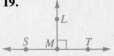

1. $m\angle KLM = 90$ (Given)
2. ∠KLM is a right ∠. (Def. a
right ∠) 3. $\overline{KL} \perp \overline{LM}$ (Def. ⊥)
22.

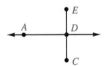

1. $\overline{CD} \perp \overline{AB}$ (Given) 2. ∠CDA is
a right ∠. (Def. ⊥)
3. $m\angle CDA = 90$ (Def. right ∠)
23.

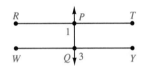

1. $\overline{AB} \perp \overline{BC}$, $\overline{DC} \perp \overline{BC}$ (Given) 2.
∠ABC is a right ∠. ∠DCB is a
right ∠. (Def. ⊥)

The statements provided for each proof are correct but in the wrong
order. Order them correctly and supply reasons as you write the proof.

14. Given: $m\angle DPW = 90$
   Prove: $\overrightarrow{DP} \perp \overleftrightarrow{WP}$

   a. ∠DPW is a right angle. **b.** $\overrightarrow{DP} \perp \overline{WP}$ **c.** $m\angle DPW = 90$

15. Given: ∠1 ≅ ∠2, ∠3 ≅ ∠4
   Prove: ∠1 ≅ ∠4

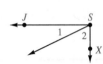

  a. ∠1 ≅ ∠3 **b.** ∠1 ≅ ∠2, ∠3, ≅ ∠4 **c.** ∠1 ≅ ∠4 **d.** ∠2 ≅ ∠3

16. Given: ∠1 is complementary to ∠2.
   Prove: $\overline{JS} \perp \overline{XS}$

  a. ∠JSX is a right angle. **b.** $m\angle 1 + m\angle 2 = 90$ **c.** $m\angle 1 + m\angle 2 = m\angle JSX$
  d. ∠1 is complementary to ∠2 **e.** $\overline{JS} \perp \overline{XS}$ **f.** $m\angle JSX = 90$

17. Given: $\overline{RT} \perp \overline{PQ}$, $\overline{WY} \perp \overline{PQ}$
   Prove: ∠1 ≅ ∠3

  a. $\overline{RT} \perp \overline{PQ}$, $\overline{WY} \perp \overline{PQ}$ **b.** ∠1 ≅ ∠3 **c.** ∠1 and ∠3 are right angles.

18. Given: $CD = DE$, ∠ADE is a right angle.
   Prove: $\overline{AD}$ is the perpendicular bisector of $\overline{CE}$.

  a. $CD = DE$ **b.** ∠ADE is a right angle. **c.** D is the midpoint of $\overline{CE}$.
  d. $\overline{AD} \perp \overline{CE}$ **e.** $\overline{AD}$ is the perpendicular bisector of $\overline{CE}$.

B

Draw a diagram for the given information and write a two-column proof.

19. Given: $\overline{LM} \perp \overline{SM}$
   Prove: $m\angle LMS = 90$

20. Given: $GH = HJ$, H is between G and J.
   Prove: $GH = \frac{1}{2}GJ$

21. Given: $m\angle KLM = 90$
   Prove: $\overline{KL} \perp \overline{LM}$

22. Given: D is between vertices A and B of
   △ABC. $\overline{CD} \perp \overline{AB}$
   Prove: $m\angle CDA = 90$

23. Given: $\overline{AB} \perp \overline{BC}$
   $\overline{DC} \perp \overline{BC}$
   Prove: ∠ABC ≅ ∠DCB

24. Given: M is the midpoint of $\overline{AB}$. N is
   the midpoint of $\overline{CD}$. $CD = AB$
   Prove: $AM = CN$

---

25. Write a two-column proof.

Given: O is the midpoint of $\overline{BC}$.
$\triangle AOB$ is isosceles with $\overline{OA} \cong \overline{OB}$.

Prove: $\triangle AOC$ is isosceles.

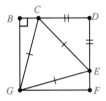

C

26. Prove Theorem 2.6.
27. Prove the following theorem. If B is between A and C on one line, E is between D and F on another line, $AC = DF$, $BC = EF$, then $AB = DE$.

Critical Thinking

28. New hypotheses which lead to theorems are sometimes formed by asking, "What if . . . ?" This exercise comes from the question, "What if you think about angles instead of segments in the theorem in Exercise 27?". Write and prove a theorem about angles that is similar to the theorem in Exercise 27.

Mixed Review

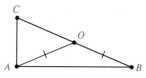

Complete each statement.

1. $\triangle GCE$ is a(n) ___ triangle.
2. ___ is an isosceles triangle.
3. ___ is a right triangle.

4. Find the distance between the pair of points with coordinates $(7, 10)$ and $(1, 2)$.
5. Find the distance between the pair of points with coordinates $(1, -2)$ and $(-2, -3)$.

2-5 Planning and Writing a Proof **85**

3. $\angle ABC \cong \angle DCB$ (Th. 2.4)
24.

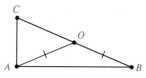

1. M is the midpoint of $\overline{AB}$. N is the midpoint of $\overline{CD}$. (Given)
2. $CD = AB$ (Given)
3. $AM = \frac{1}{2}AB$, $CN = \frac{1}{2}CD$ (Th. 2.5) **4.** $\frac{1}{2}CD = \frac{1}{2}AB$ (Multiplication Prop.) **5.** $AM = CN$ (Subst.)
25. **1.** O is the midpoint of $\overline{BC}$. $\triangle AOB$ is isos. with $\overline{OA} \cong \overline{OB}$ (Given) **2.** $\overline{CO} \cong \overline{OB}$ (Def. midpoint) **3.** $\overline{OA} \cong \overline{CO}$ (Th. 1.2) **4.** $\triangle AOC$ is isos. (Def. isos. $\triangle$)
26. **1.** $\overrightarrow{BD}$ bisects $\angle ABC$ (Given) **2.** $\angle ABD \cong \angle DBC$ (Def. bisector) **3.** $m\angle ABD = m\angle DBC$ (Def. $\cong \angle$s) **4.** $m\angle ABD + m\angle DBC = m\angle ABC$ ($\angle$ Addition Post.) **5.** $m\angle ABD + m\angle ABD = m\angle ABC$ (Subst.) **6.** $2m\angle ABD = m\angle ABC$ (Distributive Prop.) **7.** $m\angle ABC = \frac{1}{2}m\angle ABC$ (Division Prop.)   **27.** **1.** B is between A and C. E is between D and F. (Given) **2.** $AB + BC = AC$, $DE + EF = DF$ (Seg. Addition Post.) **3.** $AC = DF$, $BC = EF$ (Given) **4.** $AB + EF = DF$ (Subst.) **5.** $AB + EF = DE + EF$ (Subst.) **6.** $AB = DE$ (Subtraction Prop.)   **28.** Th.: If D is in the int. of $\angle ABC$ and H is in the int. of $\angle EFG$, and $m\angle ABC = m\angle EFG$ and $m\angle ABD = m\angle EFH$, then $m\angle DBC = m\angle HFG$. Proof: **1.** D is in the int. of $\angle ABC$. H is in the int. of $\angle EFG$. (Given) **2.** $m\angle ABD + m\angle DBC = m\angle ABC$, $m\angle EFH + m\angle HFG = m\angle EFG$ ($\angle$ Addition Post.) **3.** $m\angle ABC = m\angle EFG$, $m\angle ABD = m\angle EFH$ (Given) **4.** $m\angle EFH + m\angle DBC = m\angle EFG$ (Subst.) **5.** $m\angle EFH + m\angle DBC = m\angle EFH + m\angle HFG$ (Subst.) **6.** $m\angle DBC = m\angle HFG$ (Subtraction Prop.)

Mixed Review Answers

1. equilateral   **2.** $\triangle CDE$
3. $\triangle BCG$ **4.** 10   **5.** $\sqrt{10}$

(Quiz on previous lesson)

1. State in correct order the five steps for proving a theorem.
1. Write in *if-then* form. 2. Write the *Given* and *Prove*. 3. Draw a diagram. 4. Devise a plan.
5. Write statements and reasons.

2. Rewrite as a conditional. "Vertical angles are congruent."

If two angles are vertical angles, then they are congruent.

3. Write the *Given* and the *Prove* for the conditional "If two lines are perpendicular, then the lines form congruent adjacent angles." Draw a diagram to show the given information. **Given:** $\overleftrightarrow{AB} \perp \overleftrightarrow{CD}$ Prove: $\angle AXC \cong \angle AXD$

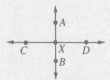

4. Arrange the statements for the proof in the correct order and supply reasons.

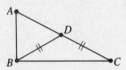

Given: D is the midpoint of $\overline{AC}$. $\overline{BD} \cong \overline{DC}$
Prove: $\triangle ABD$ is isosceles.

Statements: a. $\overline{AD} \cong \overline{DB}$ b. D is the midpoint of $\overline{AC}$.
c. $\overline{AD} \cong \overline{DC}$ d. $\triangle ABD$ is isosceles. e. $\overline{BD} \cong \overline{DC}$
1. $\overline{BD} \cong \overline{DC}$ (Given) 2. D is the midpoint of $\overline{AC}$. (Given)
3. $\overline{AD} \cong \overline{DC}$ (Definition of midpoint) 4. $\overline{BD} \cong \overline{AD}$ (Theorem 1.2) 5. $\triangle ABD$ is isosceles. (Definition of isosceles triangle)

OBJECTIVE: *Prove and apply theorems about segments and lines.*

2-6 Theorems: Segments and Lines

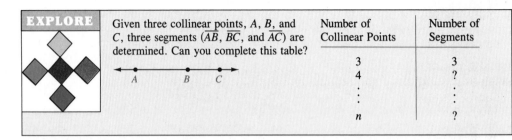

	Number of Collinear Points	Number of Segments
	3	3
	4	?
	.	.
	.	.
	.	.
	n	?

In Lessons 1-8 and 2-3 you learned some methods for proving that two segments are congruent and two lines perpendicular. Other useful methods are presented and summarized in this lesson.

In the Explore, you developed skill in visualizing segments that overlap other segments. In the figure below, $\overline{AC}$ and $\overline{BD}$ share the common segment $\overline{BC}$. If you know that $\overline{AB} \cong \overline{CD}$, you should be able to prove that $\overline{AC} \cong \overline{BD}$.

This is the conclusion of the Common Segment Theorem, stated and proved below.

◆ **THEOREM 2.7** Common Segment Theorem
1. If $\overline{AB} \cong \overline{CD}$, then $\overline{AC} \cong \overline{BD}$.
2. If $\overline{AC} \cong \overline{BD}$, then $\overline{AB} \cong \overline{CD}$.

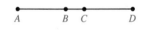

Part 1
Given: $\overline{AB} \cong \overline{CD}$
Prove: $\overline{AC} \cong \overline{BD}$

Proof Statements	Reasons
1. $\overline{AB} \cong \overline{CD}$	1. Given
2. $AB = CD$	2. Definition of congruent segments
3. $BC = BC$	3. Reflexive Property
4. $AB + BC = CD + BC$	4. Addition Property
5. $AC = BD$	5. Segment Addition Postulate
6. $\overline{AC} \cong \overline{BD}$	6. Definition of congruent segments

The proof of Part 2 of Theorem 2.7 is similar to that of Part 1 and will be called for in Exercise 29.

Example 1

$\overline{PR} \cong \overline{QS}$ What can you conclude? Why?

Solution

$\overline{PQ} \cong \overline{RS}$ *Common Segment Theorem*

Try This

$\overline{GH} \cong \overline{IJ}$ What can you conclude? Why?

The following list summarizes the ways you have studied to prove that two segments are congruent.

Methods of Proving Two Segments Congruent

1. Prove that their measures are equal using the Segment Addition Postulate or properties of equality.
2. Prove that each segment is congruent to a third segment.
3. Prove that they are the two parts of a bisected segment.
4. Prove that they are sides of a triangle given to be isosceles or equilateral.
5. Prove that they are formed by adding or subtracting a common segment.

One way to prove that two lines are perpendicular is to first prove that the lines meet to form a right angle. The following theorem provides another way.

◆ **THEOREM 2.8**

   If two lines form congruent adjacent angles, then they are perpendicular.

Given: $\angle 1 \cong \angle 2$
Prove: $\overline{BC} \perp \overline{AD}$
Analysis I can prove $\overline{BC} \perp \overline{AD}$ if I can prove that $\angle 1$ and $\angle 2$ are right angles. I can prove they are right angles if I can prove that the measure of each is 90. I can prove this if I can prove that they have the same measure and the sum of their measures is 180. They are a linear pair and are congruent, so I can do this.

Plan   Start at the end of the analysis and work backwards.

You will be asked to prove Theorem 2.8 in Exercise 36.

Example 2

$\angle 3 \cong \angle 4$ What can you conclude about $\triangle ABC$?

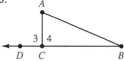

Solution

   $\angle 4$ is a right angle, so $\triangle ABC$ is a right triangle.   *Since $\angle 3$ and $\angle 4$ are congruent adjacent angles, $\overline{AC} \perp \overline{BC}$.*

Try This

If $\angle 3 \cong \angle 4$ and $\overline{DC} \cong \overline{BC}$, what can you conclude about $\overleftrightarrow{AC}$?

2-6   *Proving Theorems: Segments and Lines*   **87**

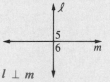

The following summarizes the ways you have studied to prove two lines perpendicular.

Methods of Proving Two Lines Perpendicular

1. Prove that the lines intersect to form a right angle.
2. Prove that the lines intersect to form congruent adjacent angles.

Theorem 2.9 will be proved in Lesson 5-6.

◆ THEOREM 2.9

Only one perpendicular can be drawn from a point to a line.

Class Exercises

Short Answer

Identify the common segment and tell whether you used addition or subtraction to arrive at the conclusion.

1. Given: $PR = QS$
Conclusion: $PQ = RS$

2. Given: $JK = LM$
Conclusion: $JL = KM$

3. $\overline{JL} \cong \overline{KM}$ in the figure in Class Exercise 2. What can you conclude?
4. Lines j and k intersect to form congruent adjacent angles. What can you conclude?

Sample Exercises

Find the length of each segment.

5. $\overline{PQ} \cong \overline{ST}$, $RT = 9$,
$RS = 5$ Find PQ.

6. $\overline{PR} \cong \overline{QS}$, $RS = 6$,
$QR = 4$ Find PR.

Use the Common Segment Theorem to draw a conclusion.

7. $\overline{JK} \cong \overline{LM}$ ·

8. $\overline{PQ} \cong \overline{RS}$

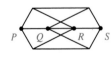

9. $\overline{WX} \cong \overline{YZ}$

Discussion

10. Complete the following in three different ways.
If I know that ___ , then I can conclude that $l \perp m$.

11. Give a convincing informal argument that when two adjacent angles are complementary their noncommon sides are perpendicular.

88   *Chapter 2   Introduction to Proof*

Exercises

A

Use the Common Segment Theorem to draw a conclusion.

1. $\overline{MN} \cong \overline{PQ}$

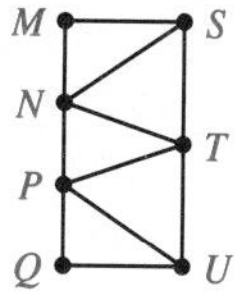

2. $\overline{KB} \cong \overline{PN}$

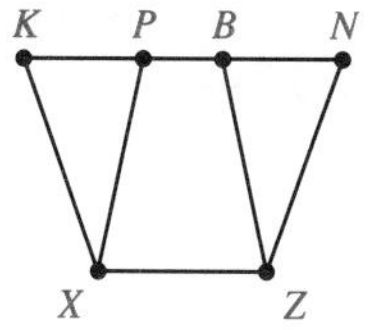

3. $\overline{IK} \cong \overline{EA}$

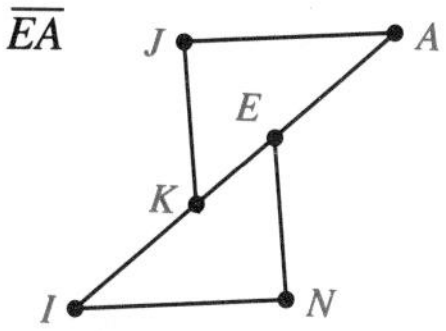

4. $\overline{EX} \cong \overline{WG}$

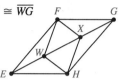

Find the length of each segment.

5.

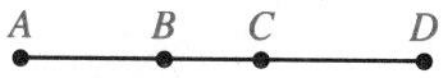

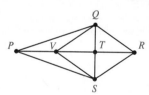

$\overline{AB} \cong \overline{CD}$, $BD = 12$, $BC = 4$ Find AB

6. E F G H

$\overline{EG} \cong \overline{FH}$, $GH = 6$, $FG = 24$ Find EG

7. 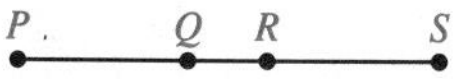 P. Q R S

$\overline{PQ} \cong \overline{RS}$, $QR = 8$, $RS = 2x$,
$QS = 4x - 2$ Find PR

8. W X Y Z

$\overline{WY} \cong \overline{XZ}$, $WY = 3x + 6$
$XY = 12$, $WX = x + 2$ Find YZ

Draw a conclusion stating that two segments are congruent.

9. $\triangle QRS$ is equilateral.
10. $\overline{PR}$ bisects $\overline{QS}$.
11. $\overline{QR} \cong \overline{QS}$, $\overline{RS} \cong \overline{QS}$
12. $\overline{PV} \cong \overline{RT}$

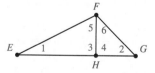

Draw a conclusion.

13. $\angle 3 \cong \angle 4$
14. $\angle 5$ and $\angle 6$ are complementary.

Determine whether each statement is true or false.

15. It is impossible for two different lines to be perpendicular to a given line.
16. If two lines are perpendicular, then they form congruent adjacent angles.
17. There is only one way to prove two segments congruent.
18. The Common Segment Theorem, as stated in this section, contains a
statement and its converse.

1. $\overline{MP} \cong \overline{NQ}$ **2.** $\overline{KP} \cong \overline{BN}$
3. $\overline{IE} \cong \overline{KA}$ **4.** $\overline{EW} \cong \overline{XG}$
5. 8 **6.** 30 **7.** 18 **8.** 6
9. $\overline{QR} \cong \overline{RS}$ **10.** $\overline{QT} \cong \overline{TS}$
11. $\overline{QR} \cong \overline{RS}$ **12.** $\overline{PT} \cong \overline{VR}$
13. $\overline{FH} \perp \overline{EG}$ **14.** $\overline{EF} \perp \overline{FG}$
15. false **16.** true
17. false **18.** true
19. 1. $\angle 1$ and $\angle 2$ are complementary. (Given)
2. $m \angle 1 + m \angle 2 = 90$ (Definition
of complementary angles)
3. $m \angle 1 + m \angle 2 = m \angle UTW$
(Angle Addition Postulate)
4. $m \angle UTW = 90$ (Substitution)
5. $\angle UTW$ is a right angle.
(Definition of right angle)
6. $\triangle UTW$ is a right triangle.
(Definition of right triangle)

20. 1. ∠3 ≅ ∠ABC, ∠4 ≅ ∠ABC
(Given) 2. ∠3 ≅ ∠4 (Theorem
1.3) 3. $\overline{BD}$ ⊥ $\overline{AC}$ (Theorem 2.8)
21. 1. $\overline{AB}$ ≅ $\overline{BD}$, $\overline{BC}$ ≅ $\overline{DE}$
(Given) 2. $\overline{BD}$ ≅ $\overline{CE}$ (Common
Segment Theorem) 3. $\overline{AB}$ ≅ $\overline{CE}$
(Theorem 1.1)   **22.** $\overline{DC}$ ≅ $\overline{CE}$
and $\overline{DE}$ ≅ $\overline{CE}$ **23.** $\overline{RS}$ ≅ $\overline{MN}$
and $\overline{TU}$ ≅ $\overline{MN}$ **24.** $\overline{GJ}$ ≅ $\overline{HI}$
25. Yes; AB = CD by the Com-
mon Segment Theorem.
26. 1. $\overline{AB}$ ≅ $\overline{CD}$, $\overline{BC}$ ≅ $\overline{DE}$
(Given) 2. $\overline{AC}$ ≅ $\overline{BD}$, $\overline{BD}$ ≅ $\overline{CE}$
(Common Segment Theorem)
3. $\overline{AC}$ ≅ $\overline{CE}$ (Theorem 1.1)
27. 1. $\overline{GI}$ ≅ $\overline{HJ}$, $\overline{IK}$ ≅ $\overline{JL}$ (Given)
2. $\overline{GH}$ ≅ $\overline{IJ}$, $\overline{IJ}$ ≅ $\overline{KL}$ (Common
Segment Theorem) 3. $\overline{GH}$ ≅ $\overline{KL}$
(Theorem 1.1)   **28.** 1. $\overline{PR}$ bi-
sects $\overline{ST}$ (Given) 2. $\overline{TU}$ ≅ $\overline{SU}$
(Definition of bisector)
3. $\overline{UY}$ ≅ $\overline{SU}$ (Given) 4. △UYX is
equilateral. (Given) 5. $\overline{UX}$ ≅ $\overline{UY}$
(Definition of equilateral trian-
gle) 6. $\overline{UX}$ ≅ $\overline{SU}$ (Theorem 1.1)
7. $\overline{TU}$ ≅ $\overline{UX}$ (Theorem 1.2)
29. $\overline{AC}$ ≅ $\overline{BD}$ (Given)
2. AC = BD (Definition of con-
gruent segments) 3. BC = BC
(Reflexive Property)
4. AC − BC = BD − BC (Subtraction Property) 5. AB = CD
(Segment Addition Postulate)
6. $\overline{AB}$ ≅ $\overline{CD}$ (Definition of congruent segments)   **30.** Yes;
both need to travel the same
distance (DE = FG, so DF = EG)
and travel at the same speed, so
d = rt and t = $\frac{d}{r}$ is the same for
both elevators.   **31.** always
32. sometimes   **33.** never
34. AC = $\sqrt{50}$, BD = $\sqrt{50}$, so
AC = BD, $\overline{AC}$ ≅ $\overline{BD}$ and
$\overline{AB}$ ≅ $\overline{CD}$ by the Common Segment Theorem. AB = $\sqrt{18}$
CD = $\sqrt{18}$, so AB = CD,
$\overline{AB}$ ≅ $\overline{CD}$

Write a two-column proof for each exercise.

19. Given: ∠1 and ∠2 are complementary.
Prove: △UTW is a right triangle.

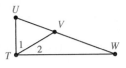

20. Given: ∠3 ≅ ∠ABC, ∠4 ≅ ∠ABC
Prove: $\overline{BD}$ ⊥ $\overline{AC}$

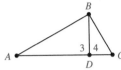

21. Given: $\overline{AB}$ ≅ $\overline{BD}$, $\overline{BC}$ ≅ $\overline{DE}$
Prove: $\overline{AB}$ ≅ $\overline{CE}$

Complete each statement. Refer to the chart on page 87 as needed.

22. If I knew that ___,
then I could conclude that $\overline{DC}$ ≅ $\overline{DE}$.

23. If I knew that ___,
then I could conclude that $\overline{RS}$ ≅ $\overline{TU}$.

24. If I knew that ___,
then I could conclude that $\overline{GH}$ ≅ $\overline{JI}$.

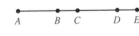

25. An architect was checking plans his assistant had made for a bowling
alley. The information that AC = BD was included, but he wondered if
the gutters were the same width. Does he have enough information to
tell? Explain.

B

Write a two-column proof for each exercise.

26. Given: $\overline{AB}$ ≅ $\overline{CD}$, $\overline{BC}$ ≅ $\overline{DE}$
Prove: $\overline{AC}$ ≅ $\overline{CE}$

27. Given: $\overline{GI}$ ≅ $\overline{HJ}$, $\overline{IK}$ ≅ $\overline{JL}$
Prove: $\overline{GH}$ ≅ $\overline{KL}$

28. Given: $\overline{PR}$ bisects $\overline{ST}$. $\overline{UY}$ ≅ $\overline{SU}$
△UYX is equilateral.
Prove: $\overline{TU}$ ≅ $\overline{UX}$

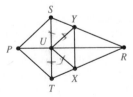

29. Write a two-column proof for Part 2 of Theorem 2.7.

30. Elevator A is just as far below the top floor as elevator B is above the ground floor. Elevator A is traveling down at the same rate elevator B is traveling up. If the elevators do not stop, will A reach the ground at the same time that B reaches the top? What theorem supports your answer? Explain.

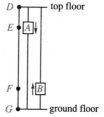

Determine whether each statement is always, sometimes, or never true.

31. If two lines form at least one right angle, then they are perpendicular.
32. If two segments overlap in a common segment, then the noncommon parts of the two segments are congruent.
33. Two lines can be drawn through a point perpendicular to a given line.

34. Use the Distance Formula to show that $\overline{AC} \cong \overline{BD}$. What other segments do you know to be congruent? Verify this using the Distance Formula.

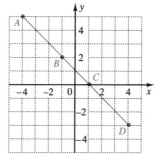

c

35. **Given:** $\angle 1$ and $\angle 3$ are complementary.
   Prove: $\overline{AD} \perp \overline{DB}$

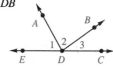

36. Complete a two-column proof for Theorem 2.8.

Critical Thinking

37. Given that $\overline{AB} \cong \overline{DE}$ and $\overline{AC} \cong \overline{DF}$, a geometry student concluded that $\overline{BC} \cong \overline{EF}$. She gave the Common Segment Theorem as a reason. Do you think she reasoned correctly? Give a convincing argument to support your position. If the reasoning is not correct, write a proof that $\overline{BC} \cong \overline{EF}$ using the correct reasoning.

Algebra Review

Solve each inequality.

1. $3x > 21$
2. $6 + 5y \geq 36$
3. $2x + 4 < 4$
4. $8y \leq 3y - 25$
5. $-2x < x + 9$
6. $x + 7 \geq 2 - x$

Math Contest Problem

At what exact times between 12 and 1 o'clock are the hands of a clock perpendicular to each other?

---

35. 1. $\angle 1$ and $\angle 3$ are complementary. (Given)
2. $m\angle 1 + m\angle 3 = 90$ (Definition of complementary angles)
3. $m\angle 2 + m\angle 3 = m\angle ADC$ (Angle Addition Postulate)
4. $m\angle 1 + m\angle ADC = 180$ (Theorem 2.1)
5. $m\angle 1 + m\angle 2 + m\angle 3 = 180$ (Substitution)
6. $m\angle 2 + 90 = 180$ (Substitution) 7. $m\angle 2 = 90$ (Subtraction Property) 8. $\angle 2$ is a right angle. (Definition of right angle)
9. $\overline{AD} \perp \overline{DB}$ (Definition of perpendicular)   **36.** 1. $\angle 1 \cong \angle 2$ (Given) 2. $m\angle 1 = m\angle 2$ (Definition of congruent angles)
3. $m\angle 1 + m\angle 2 = 180$ (Theorem 2.1) 4. $m\angle 1 + m\angle 1 = 180$ (Substitution) 5. $2m\angle 1 = 180$ (Distributive Property)
6. $m\angle 1 = 90$ (Division Property) 7. $\angle 1$ is a right angle. (Definition of right angle)
8. $\overline{BC} \perp \overline{AD}$ (Definition of perpendicular lines)
37. Incorrect Reasoning: There is no common segment in the figure. Proof: 1. $\overline{AB} \cong \overline{DE}$, $\overline{AC} \cong \overline{DF}$ (Given) 2. $AB = DE$, $AC = DF$ (Definition of congruent segments) 3. $AB + BC = AC$, $DE + EF = DF$ (Segment Addition Postulate) 4. $DE + BC = DF$ (Substitution) 5. $EF = DF - DE$, $BC = DF - DE$ (Subtraction Property) 6. $EF = BC$ (Substitution) 7. $\overline{EF} \cong \overline{BC}$ (Definition of congruent segments)

Algebra Review Answers

1. $x > 7$ 2. $y \geq 6$
3. $x < 0$ 4. $y \leq -5$
5. $x > -3$ 6. $x \geq -\frac{5}{2}$

Math Contest Problem Answer
$12:16\frac{4}{11}$ ($\approx 12:16:22$), $12:49\frac{1}{11}$ ($\approx 12:49:05$)

First Five Minutes

(Quiz on previous lesson)

1. State five methods of proving two segments congruent.
1. Prove their lengths are equal. 2. Prove each is congruent to a third segment. 3. Prove they are the parts of a bisected segment. 4. Prove they are sides of an isosceles or equilateral triangle. 5. Common Segment Theorem
2. State two methods of proving two lines perpendicular.
1. Prove they intersect at a right angle. 2. Prove they form congruent adjacent angles.

Lesson Opener

Review the definition of congruent angles. Then ask students to state ways of proving angles congruent that they have learned so far.

Another method is Theorem 2.10, the Common Angle Theorem, which is covered in this lesson. Point out that the Angle Addition Postulate and the Reflexive Property are both used to prove two angles are congruent by "adding" a common angle.

A brief discussion of the need for congruent angles, such as in the construction of a building (see photo), may emphasize the importance of congruent angles.

OBJECTIVE: *Prove and apply theorems about angles.*

2-7 Proving Theorems: Angles

In the building of houses and other structures, many boards need to be cut at congruent angles. To prove a theorem, you often need to show that two angles are congruent. Some useful methods for doing this are presented or reviewed in this lesson. One method, the Common Angle Theorem, is similar to the Common Segment Theorem and is stated and proved below.

Notice that the *common angle, $\angle BOC$,* is *added* in Part 1 and *subtracted* in Part 2.

◆ **THEOREM 2.10** Common Angle Theorem
  1. If $\angle AOB \cong \angle COD$, then $\angle AOC \cong \angle BOD$.
  2. If $\angle AOC \cong \angle BOD$, then $\angle AOB \cong \angle COD$.

Part 1

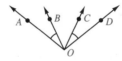

Given: $\angle AOB \cong \angle COD$
Prove: $\angle AOC \cong \angle BOD$

Proof Statements

Statements	Reasons
1. $\angle AOB \cong \angle COD$	**1.** Given
2. $m\angle AOB = m\angle COD$	**2.** Definition of congruent angles
3. $m\angle BOC = m\angle BOC$	**3.** Reflexive Property
4. $m\angle AOB + m\angle BOC = m\angle COD + m\angle BOC$	**4.** Addition property
5. $m\angle AOC = m\angle BOD$	**5.** Angle Addition Postulate
6. $\angle AOC \cong \angle BOD$	**6.** Definition of congruent angles

You will be asked to prove Part 2 in Exercise 30.

Example 1

$\angle VTU \cong \angle WTX$
What can you conclude about other angles?

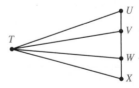

  Solution
    $\angle WTU \cong \angle VTX$

Try This

$\angle XTV \cong \angle UTW$
What can you conclude about other angles?

The following theorem is the converse of Theorem 2.8.

◆ THEOREM 2.11

If two lines are perpendicular, then they form congruent adjacent angles.

Given: $\overline{RS} \perp \overline{XY}$

Prove: $\angle RSX \cong \angle RSY$

Analysis I can prove $\angle RSX \cong \angle RSY$ if I can prove that each is a right angle.
I can prove that each is a right angle by the definition of perpendicular lines.

Plan Start at the end of the analysis and work backwards.

You will be asked to prove this theorem in Exercise 31.

Example 2

If $\overline{MN}$ is the perpendicular bisector of $\overline{PQ}$, what angles must be congruent?

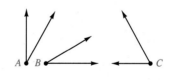

Solution

$\angle PNM \cong \angle QNM$

Try This

If $\overline{RT} \perp \overline{MQ}$, what angles must be congruent?

The following two theorems show how complementary and supplementary angles can sometimes be used to prove that two angles are congruent.

◆ THEOREM 2.12   Congruent Complements Theorem

Two angles that are complementary to the same angle (or to congruent angles) are congruent.

Given: $\angle A$ is complementary to $\angle C$. $\angle B$ is complementary to $\angle C$.

Prove: $\angle A \cong \angle B$

Plan Use the definition of complementary angles and algebraic properties to prove that $m\angle A + m\angle C = 90$, $m\angle B + m\angle C = 90$, and $\angle A \cong \angle B$.

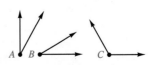

◆ THEOREM 2.13   Congruent Supplements Theorem

Two angles that are supplementary to the same angle (or to congruent angles) are congruent.

Given: $\angle A$ and $\angle C$ are supplementary. $\angle B$ and $\angle C$ are supplementary.

Prove: $\angle A \cong \angle B$

Plan The plan is similar to that of Theorem 2.12.

Materials

student notebooks
investigative software

Teaching Notes

Stress the importance of being able to apply Theorems 2.10, 2.11, 2.12, and 2.13. These are all ways of proving two angles are congruent.

Review the definition of complementary and supplementary angles before discussing Theorems 2.12 and 2.13

Emphasize the importance of learning the eight methods of proving two angles congruent and the three methods of proving an angle a right angle.

Chalkboard Examples

1.

$MRP \cong \angle NRQ$ What can you conclude about other angles?
$\angle MRN \cong \angle PRQ$

Answer to Try This
$\angle XTW \cong \angle UTV$

2.

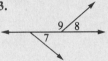

If $\overline{XY} \perp \overline{WZ}$, what angles must be congruent? $\angle WXY \cong \angle ZXY$

Answer to Try This
$\angle MRT \cong \angle QRT$

3.

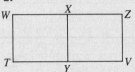

$\angle 7$ is supplementary to $\angle 9$. $\angle 8$ is supplementary to $\angle 9$. What can you conclude? $\angle 7 \cong \angle 8$

Answer to Try This $\angle 3 \cong \angle 5$

You will be asked to prove Theorems 2.12 and 2.13 in Exercises 32–33.

Example 3

Given: $\angle 2 \cong \angle 3$, $\angle 2$ is complementary to $\angle 3$.
$\angle 5$ is complementary to $\angle 3$.
What can you conclude?

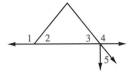

Solution

$\angle 2 \cong \angle 5$	*Since $\angle 2$ and $\angle 5$ are complementary to $\angle 3$, they are congruent. (Theorem 2.12)*
$\angle 1 \cong \angle 4$	*Since $\angle 1$ and $\angle 4$ are supplementary to congruent angles ($\angle 2$ and $\angle 3$), they are congruent. (Theorem 2.13)*

Try This

Suppose $\angle 5$ is supplementary to $\angle 4$. What can you conclude? Why?

The following chart summarizes the ways you can prove that two angles are congruent. It will provide a helpful reference when writing proofs.

Methods of Proving Two Angles Congruent

1. Prove that their measures are equal using the Angle Addition Postulate and the properties of equality.
2. Prove that each angle is congruent to a third angle.
3. Prove that they are formed by a bisected angle.
4. Prove that they are vertical angles.
5. Prove that they are right angles.
6. Prove that they are formed by perpendicular lines.
7. Prove that they are formed by adding or subtracting a common angle.
8. Prove that they are supplements or complements of the same or congruent angles.

You have learned some ways to prove that an angle is a right angle. The following theorem provides another method that you will find useful in later proofs.

◆ THEOREM 2.14

If one angle of a linear pair is a right angle, then the other angle is also a right angle.

Given: $\angle 1$ is a right angle. $\angle 1$ and $\angle 2$ form a linear pair.

Prove: $\angle 2$ is right angle.

Plan $\angle 1$ and $\angle 2$ form a linear pair, so $m\angle 1 + m\angle 2 = 180$. $m\angle 1 = 90$ so, by using algebra, $m\angle 2 = 90$ and $\angle 2$ is a right angle.

You will be asked to prove this theorem in Exercise 34. The following chart summarizes the methods you have now studied for proving that an angle is a right angle.

94   *Chapter 2   Introduction to Proof*

Methods of Proving an Angle a Right Angle

1. Prove that it has a measure of 90.
2. Prove that it is formed by perpendicular lines.
3. Prove that it forms a linear pair with a right angle.

Class Exercises

Short Answer

Identify the common angle and tell whether you used addition or subtraction to arrive at the conclusion.

1.

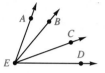

Given: $m \angle AEB = m \angle CED$
Conclusion: $m \angle AEC = m \angle BED$

2.

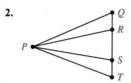

Given: $m \angle QPS = m \angle TPR$
Conclusion: $m \angle QPR = m \angle SPT$

3. $\angle 4$ and $\angle 2$ are both complementary to $\angle 5$. What can you conclude?
4. $\angle 1$ and $\angle 3$ are both supplementary to $\angle 6$. What can you conclude?
5. $\angle 7$ and $\angle 8$ form a linear pair. $\angle 7$ is a right angle. What can you conclude?

Sample Exercises

What conclusions can you draw? State a reason to support each conclusion.

6. Given: $\angle 1 \cong \angle 3$
7. Given: $\angle KON \cong \angle FOM$
8. Given: $\angle 3 \cong \angle 5$, $\angle 1 \cong \angle 5$
9. Given: $\overline{JE} \perp \overline{DH}$
10. Given: $\angle 4 \cong \angle 7$
11. Given: $\overline{OK}$ bisects $\angle DOM$.

Complete each statement.

12. If I knew that ___, then I could conclude that $\angle 3 \cong \angle 4$.
13. If I knew that ___, then I could conclude that $\angle WXV \cong \angle ZXY$.
14. If I knew that ___, then I could conclude that $\angle WXZ \cong \angle VXZ$.

15. Complete the following in three different ways. If I can prove that ___, then I can prove that $\angle A$ is a right angle.

Discussion

Determine whether each statement is always, sometimes, or never true. Give reasons for your decisions.

16. If two lines intersect, then they form congruent adjacent angles.
17. If one angle of a linear pair is acute, then the other angle is also acute.
18. Two angles that are each supplementary to $\angle A$ are congruent.

Exercises

A

Use the Common Angle Theorem to draw a conclusion.

1.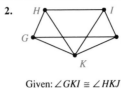

Given: $\angle STQ \cong \angle PTR$

2.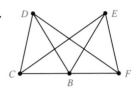

Given: $\angle GKI \cong \angle HKJ$

3.

Given: $\angle CBD \cong \angle FBE$

4. What angle is "subtracted" from $\angle GKI$ and $\angle HKJ$ in Exercise 2?

Draw a conclusion stating that two angles are congruent. State a postulate, definition, or theorem that supports your conclusion.

5. $\angle 7 \cong \angle 9$
6. $\angle 8$ is complementary to $\angle 9$.
  $\angle 5$ is complementary to $\angle 9$.
7. $\angle EBC$ is supplementary to $\angle 1$.
  $\angle 2$ is supplementary to $\angle 1$.
8. $\angle 7 \cong \angle 2$, $\angle 9 \cong \angle 2$
9. $\overline{BF} \perp \overline{EG}$
10. $\overrightarrow{BF}$ bisects $\angle EBG$.
11. $\angle EBG$ and $\angle BFG$ are right angles.

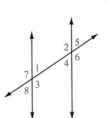

12. $\angle 3$ is supplementary to $\angle 4$.
  $\angle 2$ is supplementary to $\angle 4$.
  If $m\angle 3 = 125$, find $m\angle 2$. Why?
13. $\angle 5$ is supplementary to $\angle 6$.
  $\angle 4$ is supplementary to $\angle 6$.
  If $m\angle 5 = 55$, find $m\angle 4$.
  Give two theorems that support your answer.
14. Use the data from Exercises 12 and 13 to give the measures of angles 1–8.
15. $\angle 5$ and $\angle 8$ are both supplementary to $\angle 7$. If $m\angle 7 = 104$, find $m\angle 5$.

16. When installing a windowpane, a carpenter must make sure the pane forms a right angle with the window ledge. If she finds that $\angle 1$ is a right angle, must she also measure $\angle 2$? What theorem supports your decision?

Determine whether each statement is true or false.

17. Two angles that are complementary and adjacent are congruent.
18. When two lines intersect, at least two pairs of congruent angles are formed.
19. An angle congruent to its supplement has measure 90.
20. An angle that forms a linear pair with an acute angle is obtuse.

Write a two-column proof for each exercise.

21. Given: ∠LMQ ≅ ∠PMN
Prove: ∠LMP ≅ ∠QMN

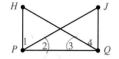

22. Given: ∠2 ≅ ∠3
Prove: ∠1 ≅ ∠4

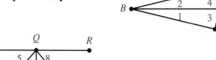

23. Given: ∠2 ≅ ∠3, $\overline{HP} \perp \overline{PQ}$, $\overline{JQ} \perp \overline{PQ}$
Prove: ∠1 ≅ ∠4

B

Write a two-column proof for each exercise.

24. Given: ∠1 is complementary to ∠4. ∠2 is complementary to ∠3. $\overrightarrow{BD}$ bisects ∠ABC.
Prove: ∠4 ≅ ∠3

25. Given: $\overrightarrow{QT}$ bisects ∠SQU. $\overline{TQ} \perp \overline{PR}$
Prove: ∠5 ≅ ∠8

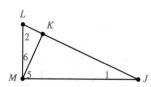

26. Given: ∠LMJ is a right angle.
∠5 is complementary to ∠1.
Prove: ∠1 ≅ ∠6

27. Given: ∠1 ≅ ∠2, ∠3 ≅ ∠4
Prove: ∠1 ≅ ∠3

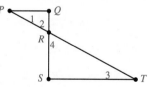

28. Given: ∠ABD is complementary to ∠BAD.
∠EBC is complementary to ∠BAD.
Prove: ∠ABE ≅ ∠CBD

29. Given: ∠BFE ≅ ∠ECA, ∠CFD ≅ ∠ECA
Prove: ∠BFD ≅ ∠CFE

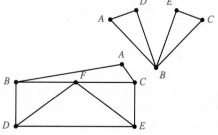

25. 1. $\overrightarrow{QT}$ bisects ∠SQU. (Given) 2. $\overline{TQ} \perp \overline{PR}$ (Given) 3. ∠6 ≅ ∠7 (Definition of ∠ bisector) 4. ∠PQT and ∠RQT are right angles. (Definition of ⊥) 5. m∠PQT = m∠RQT = = 90 (Definition of right ∠) 6. m∠5 + m∠6 = 90, m∠7 + m∠8 = 90 (Angle Addition Postulate) 7. ∠5 is complementary to ∠6. ∠8 is complementary to ∠7. (Definition of complementary ∠s) 8. ∠5 ≅ ∠8 (Congruent Complements Theorem)
26. 1. ∠LMJ is a right ∠. ∠5 is complementary to ∠1. (Given) 2. m∠LMJ = 90 (Definition of right ∠) 3. m∠5 + m∠6 = 90 (Angle Addition Postulate) 4. ∠6 is complementary to ∠5. (Definition of complementary ∠s) 5. ∠1 ≅ ∠6 (Congruent Complements Theorem)
27. 1. ∠1 ≅ ∠2, ∠3 ≅ ∠4 (Given) 2. ∠2 ≅ ∠4 (Vertical Angles Theorem) 3. ∠1 ≅ ∠4 (Theorem 1.1) 4. ∠1 ≅ ∠3 (Theorem 1.3)   **28.** 1. ∠ABD is complementary to ∠BAD. ∠EBC is complementary to ∠BAD. (Given) 2. ∠ABD ≅ ∠EBC (Congruent Complements Theorem) 3. ∠ABE ≅ ∠CBD (Common Angle Theorem)
29. 1. ∠BFE ≅ ∠ECA, ∠CFD ≅ ∠ECA (Given) 2. ∠BFE ≅ ∠CFD (Theorem 1.3) 3. ∠BFD ≅ ∠CFE (Common Angle Theorem)
30. 1. ∠AOC ≅ ∠BOD (Given) 2. m∠AOC = m∠BOD (Definition of congruent ∠s) 3. m∠BOC = m∠BOC (Reflexive Property) 4. m∠AOC − m∠BOC = m∠BOD − m∠BOC (Subtraction Property) 5. m∠AOB = m∠COD (Angle Addition Postulate) 6. ∠AOB ≅ ∠COD (Definition of congruent ∠s)
31. 1. $\overline{RS} \perp \overline{XY}$ (Given) 2. ∠RSX and ∠RSY are right ∠s. (Definition of ⊥ lines) 3. ∠RSX ≅ ∠RSY (Theorem 2.4)

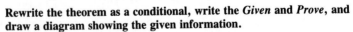
30. Prove Part 2 of the Common Angle Theorem (Theorem 2.10).

c

31. Prove Theorem 2.11.   **32.** Prove Theorem 2.12.
33. Prove Theorem 2.13.   **34.** Prove Theorem 2.14.

Critical Thinking

35. A student wrote the following formula to describe a relationship that is true for a certain set of angles. $A = S - 2C$, where A = measure of the angle, S = measure of the supplement of the angle, and C = measure of the complement of the angle. For what set of angles does the above formula hold?

Mixed Review

Complete each statement.

1. ∠MGL is complementary to ___ .
2. ∠PGN is supplementary to ___ .
3. ∠PGM and ___ are vertical angles.
4. If $m\angle KGL = 56$, then $m\angle MGL = $ ___ .
5. If $m\angle MGN = 3x + 6$ and $m\angle NGP = 4x$, then $m\angle NGP = $ ___ .
6. ∠MGN and ___ are a linear pair of angles.
7. $m\angle PGN + $ ___ $= 90$

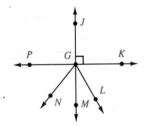

Quiz

Indicate whether the information can be assumed from the diagram.

1. Points B, D, and E are collinear.
2. $\angle ABC \cong \angle AED$

3. Use the Common Segment Theorem to draw a conclusion. Given: $\overline{BC} \cong \overline{DE}$
4. If $\angle BAD \cong \angle CAE$, $m\angle CAD = 35$, and $m\angle CAE = 85$, find $m\angle BAC$.
5. If $\angle ACD$ is supplementary to $\angle ADE$, then $\angle ADC \cong $ ___?___ .

Complete the first line in the analysis of the proof.

6. Given: $\overleftrightarrow{XY} \perp \overleftrightarrow{YZ}$
   $\overleftrightarrow{YZ} \perp \overleftrightarrow{ZW}$

   Prove: $\angle 1 \cong \angle 2$
   I can prove $\angle 1 \cong \angle 2$ if I can first prove that ___ .

Rewrite the theorem as a conditional, write the _Given_ and _Prove_, and draw a diagram showing the given information.

7. The legs of a right triangle are perpendicular.

CRITICAL THINKING

Recognizing and Analyzing Assumptions

A statement of opinion, a discussion, an argument, and a proof are all based on assumptions. Sometimes these assumptions are not stated. You must figure out that assumptions are being made and identify what they are. Consider the following examples.

Example 1

Jeff's teacher said, "Proving theorems in geometry helps you develop more general reasoning abilities."
State several assumptions that Jeff's teacher may be making.

Solution

a. It is important to develop general reasoning abilities.
b. There is a need to justify proving theorems in geometry.
c. The logic used in geometric proof relates to the logic used in everyday reasoning.
d. This statement will motivate students to work harder when proving theorems.

Example 2

Lauren saw a television advertisement showing a marathon runner drinking Sunnyside orange juice. She said, "I'm going to drink that juice before my next aerobics class."
State an assumption she may be making.

Solution

Lauren might be assuming that the juice increased the marathon runner's energy level.

Example 3

Ah-hode said, "An altitude from any vertex of a triangle divides it into two triangles, each with an area smaller than the original."
State an assumption that Ah-hode is making.

Solution

Ah-hode was making the assumption that the original triangle was an acute triangle.

Exercises

1. Accept this story as an accurate depiction of an event that actually happened.

   Little Jack Horner sat in a corner
   eating his Christmas pie.
   He put in his thumb, pulled out a plum
   and said, "What a good boy am I."

   Which of these assumptions have you accepted as true?

   a. Jack was eating a plum pie.
   b. Jack felt he was a good boy because he pulled out a plum.
   c. It was Christmas day.
   d. Jack was sitting in the corner because he was being punished.
   e. Jack was a child.
   f. Jack was small.

2. Now reread the story. Which of these assumptions are valid, based only on the information in the story?

State an assumption that each speaker is making.

3. "I can't wait until I'm 16 years old!"
4. "I've enjoyed all of this author's other books, so this new one should be good."
5. "Extend the sides of a quadrilateral until they intersect. Call the point of intersection A."
6. "Let line m intersect line n at a point between A and B."
7. "Since $\angle RSV$ is the result of bisecting $\angle RST$ its measure is less than 45."
8. "The product of two positive numbers is always greater than either of the factors."
9. "Since n is a prime number, I know that n is odd."
10. "When evaluated, $-x$ is negative."
11. "I can construct an isosceles triangle with sides congruent to $\overline{AB}$, $\overline{CD}$, and $\overline{EF}$."
12. "I can find the square root of x."
13. Describe a situation that you have recently observed where unstated assumptions were involved.

Exercise Answers
1. Answers may vary.
2. none   3. It is good to be 16 years old.   4. The author will write in the same style.
5. The quadrilateral has sides that will intersect when extended.   6. Lines m and n intersect.   7. $\angle RST$ is acute.
8. The numbers are greater than one.   9. n is not 2.
10. x is positive.   11. Two of these segments are congruent.
12. x is not negative.
13. Answers may vary.

CHAPTER SUMMARY

Vocabulary

adjacent angles (2-2)   perpendicular (2-3)   two-column proof (2-1)
complementary angles (2-2)   perpendicular bisector (2-3) vertical angles (2-2)
linear pair (2-2)   supplementary angles (2-2)

Key Ideas

1. In a two-column proof, the left column contains statements that lead to the desired conclusion. The right column gives reasons why the statements are true.
2. The reasons in a two-column proof can be any of the following: given information, definitions, postulates (including algebraic properties), or previously proven theorems.
3. Two angles are complementary if the sum of their measures is 90. Two angles are supplementary if the sum of their measures is 180.
4. Two angles that form a linear pair are supplementary. The sum of the measures of a linear pair of angles is 180.
5. Perpendicular lines are two lines that intersect to form right angles.
6. Through a given point on a line there is exactly one line in the plane perpendicular to the given line.
7. Only certain information may be assumed from a diagram. This is listed in the chart on page 75.
8. The five steps in proving a theorem are listed on page 80.
9. Methods of proving two segments congruent are listed on page 87. Methods of proving two lines perpendicular are listed on page 88. Methods of proving two angles congruent and methods of proving that an angle is a right angle are listed on pages 94 and 95.
10. Only one perpendicular can be drawn from a point to a line.

CHAPTER REVIEW

2-1

Complete the proof by choosing a reason for each statement.

1. **Given:** $\overline{DE} \cong \overline{BE}$
   E is the midpoint of $\overline{BC}$.

   Prove: $\overline{DE} \cong \overline{EC}$

   Proof

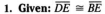

Statements	Reasons
1. $\overline{DE} \cong \overline{BE}$	1. ___
2. E is the midpoint of $\overline{BC}$.	2. ___
3. $\overline{BE} \cong \overline{EC}$	3. ___
4. $\overline{DE} \cong \overline{EC}$	4. ___

Choose from these reasons:
a. Definition of midpoint
b. Given
c. Congruence of segments is transitive.

2-2

2. If $m\angle AFB = 3x + 10$ and $m\angle BFC = 5x$, find $m\angle AFB$.
3. Name two angles supplementary to $\angle BFD$.
4. If $m\angle EFD = x$ and $m\angle AFB = 3x - 40$, find x.

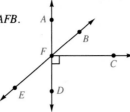

2-3

Suppose $\overline{CF}$ is the perpendicular bisector of $\overline{AD}$. Complete the following.

5. $m\angle CFD = $ ___
6. $\overline{AF} \cong$ ___

2-4

Which of the following may be assumed from the figure to be given information?

7. Point Q is between P and R.
8. Points M, Q, and T are collinear.
9. $\overrightarrow{LT}$ is a straight line.

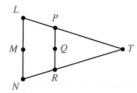

2-5

10. Rewrite the theorem as a conditional, write the *Given* and *Prove*, and draw a diagram showing the given information.

   All equilateral triangles are also isosceles triangles.

11. The statements provided for the proof are correct, but in the wrong order. Order them correctly and supply reasons as you write the proof.

   Given: $\angle 2 \cong \angle 3$
   Prove: $\angle 1 \cong \angle 4$

   a. $\angle 2 \cong \angle 3$ **b.** $\angle 3 \cong \angle 4$ **c.** $\angle 1 \cong \angle 4$
   d. $\angle 1 \cong \angle 2$ **e.** $\angle 1 \cong \angle 3$

2-6

12. Use the Common Segment Theorem to draw a conclusion.
   Given: $\overline{PQ} \cong \overline{RS}$
13. If $\overline{PQ} \cong \overline{RS}$, $PR = 8$, and $QR = 3$, find RS.

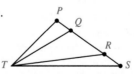

2-7

14. Use the Common Angle Theorem to draw a conclusion.
   Given: $\angle QTS \cong \angle PTR$
15. Write a two-column proof.

   Given: $\angle 3$ is supplementary to $\angle 1$. $m\angle 1 + m\angle 2 = 180$
   Prove: $\angle 2 \cong \angle 3$

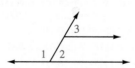

Chapter Review Answers

1. 1. b 2. b 3. a 4. c
2. 40   **3.** $\angle AFB$, $\angle EFD$
4. 20   **5.** 90   **6.** $\overline{FD}$
7. yes   **8.** no   **9.** yes
10. If a triangle is an equilateral triangle, then it is an isosceles triangle. Given: $\triangle IJK$ is equilateral. Prove: $\triangle IJK$ is isosceles.

11. 1. $\angle 1 \cong \angle 2$ (Vertical Angle Theorem) 2. $\angle 2 \cong \angle 3$ (Given)
3. $\angle 1 \cong \angle 3$ (Theorem 1.1)
4. $\angle 3 \cong \angle 4$ (Vertical Angle Theorem)   5. $\angle 1 \cong \angle 4$ (Theorem 1.1)   **12.** $\overline{PR} \cong \overline{QS}$
13. 5 **14.** $\angle PTQ \cong \angle RTS$
15. 1. $\angle 3$ is supplementary to $\angle 1$. (Given)
2. $m\angle 1 + m\angle 2 = 180$ (Given)
3. $\angle 2$ is supplementary to $\angle 1$. (Definition of supplementary angles) 4. $\angle 2 \cong \angle 3$ (Congruent Supplements Theorem)

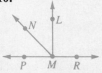
CHAPTER TEST

1. Complete the proof by choosing a reason for each statement.
Given: *U* is between *T* and *V*. *WU* = *TU*
Prove: *WU* + *UV* = *TV*

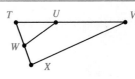

Proof Statements

1. *WU* = *TU*
2. *U* is between *T* and *V*.
3. *TU* + *UV* = *TV*
4. *WU* + *UV* = *TV*

Reasons

1. ___
2. ___
3. ___
4. ___

Choose from these reasons:
a. Given
b. Substitution Property
c. Segment Addition Postulate

2. Name a pair of complementary angles.
3. *m*∠*NRS* is eight times *m*∠*QRS*.   Find *m*∠*NRS*.
4. If *m*∠*NRP* = 50, find *m*∠*QRS*.
5. Name a pair of perpendicular segments.
6. If *m*∠*MRP* = 11*x* + 2 and *m*∠*MRQ* = 12*x*, find *m*∠*MRQ*.
7. If $\overline{RP}$ is the perpendicular bisector of $\overline{MS}$ and *MS* = 17, find *RS*.

Indicate which of the following may be assumed from the figure to be given information.

8. Points *M*, *R*, and *S* are collinear.   **9.** $\overline{RN} \cong \overline{RQ}$
10. Draw a diagram to show the given information.
$\overline{LM} \perp \overline{PR}$ intersecting at *M*, $\overline{MN}$ bisects ∠*PML*.
11. Complete the first line in the analysis of this proof.
Given: $\overline{TX} \cong \overline{XU}$, $\overline{XU} \cong \overline{XS}$
Prove: *X* is the midpoint of $\overline{TS}$.

I can prove *X* is the midpoint of $\overline{TS}$ if I can first prove that ___.
12. The statements provided for the proof in Problem 11 are correct, but in the wrong order. Order them correctly and supply reasons as you write the proof.
a. $\overline{TX} \cong \overline{XS}$ **b.** $\overline{XU} \cong \overline{XS}$ **c.** *X* is the midpoint of $\overline{TS}$.   **d.** $\overline{TX} \cong \overline{XU}$
13. $\overline{BC} \cong \overline{DE}$ Name another pair of congruent segments.
Give a reason to support your conclusion.
14. Write a two-column proof.
Given: $\overline{AB} \cong \overline{BD}$, $\overline{BC} \cong \overline{DE}$
Prove: $\overline{AB} \cong \overline{CE}$
15. ∠*BAD* = ∠*CAE*   Name another pair of congruent angles.
Give a reason to support your conclusion.
16. Draw a conclusion that two angles are congruent. State a postulate, definition, or theorem that supports your conclusion.
∠*BDA* is supplementary to ∠*ADE*. ∠*FAD* is supplementary to ∠*ADE*.
17. Write a two-column proof.
Given: ∠*DAF* ≅ ∠*CAE*, ∠*BAC* ≅ ∠*DAE*
Prove: ∠*DAF* ≅ ∠*BAD*

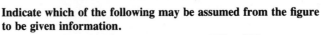

PREPARING FOR COLLEGE ENTRANCE EXAMS

Give the one correct answer for each question.

1. If $x - y = 7$, then $9 + y - x =$

    (A) 16   (B) 2   (C) -2
    (D) 0   (E) -16

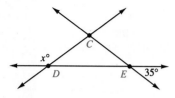

2. In the figure above, if $\angle CDE \cong \angle CED$, then $x =$

    (A) 35   (B) 155   (C) 55
    (D) 70   (E) 145

3. Which of the following is not evenly divisible by $3x^2$?

    (A) $9x^3$ (B) $12x^4y$ (C) $3x^3 + 6x$
    (D) $6(x^3 + x^2)$ (E) $3x(x + xy)$

4. Which of the following must be less than M if $M > 0$?

    (A) $2M$ (B) M^2 (C) $\frac{2M}{3}$
    (D) $\sqrt{M}$ (E) $\frac{1}{M}$

5. Which of the following is the graph of all x values such that $-x \geq -2$ and $x \geq -1$?

    (A) ⟷ $-1 \quad 0 \quad 1 \quad 2$

    (B) ⟷ $-1 \quad 0 \quad 1 \quad 2$

    (C) ⟷ $-1 \quad 0 \quad 1 \quad 2$

    (D) ⟷ $-1 \quad 0 \quad 1 \quad 2$

    (E) ⟷ $-1 \quad 0 \quad 1 \quad 2$

6. The fraction $\frac{18}{24}$ equals all of the following EXCEPT

    (A) $\frac{9}{12}$ (B) $\frac{36}{48}$ (C) $\frac{12}{16}$
    (D) $\frac{20}{30}$ (E) $\frac{15}{20}$

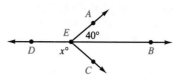

7. In the figure above, if $\overrightarrow{EB}$ bisects $\angle AEC$, then $x =$

    (A) 140   (B) 40   (C) 120
    (D) 80   (E) 50

8. R years ago, Juan was three times as old as Ellen was. If Ellen is now 31 years old, how old is Juan now in terms of R?

    (A) $31 + 3R$ (B) $93 + 4R$ (C) $3R - 93$
    (D) $93 - 2R$ (E) $31 - 3R$

9. If $y < 0$, which of the following must be true?

    (A) $-y < y$ (B) $-y > 0$ (C) $|y| < 0$
    (D) $y - y > 0$ (E) $y^2 < 0$

10. If N is an even number, which of the following must be true?

    I. $\frac{N}{2}$ is odd.

    II. $2N - 1$ is odd.

    III. $2N - 2$ is even.

    (A) II only   (B) III only   (C) I and II
    (D) I and III   (E) II and III

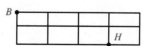

11. A bear located at point B wants to eat some honey located at point H. If the bear can only go down or to the right along the lines shown, how many different paths can he take from B to H?

    (A) 7   (B) 3   (C) 16
    (D) 24   (E) 10

12. If $pq = -2$ and $(p + q)^2 = 9$, then $p^2 + q^2 =$

    (A) 7   (B) 11   (C) 13
    (D) -7 (E) 5

CHAPTER 3

Parallel Lines and Planes

Chapter Overview

This chapter covers the idea of parallelism in the plane and in space. The theorems in this chapter include many important concepts used in standardized tests and present relationships used in similar triangles.

Objectives

3-1 ▪ Identify parallel planes, parallel lines, and skew lines.
Name angle pairs formed when a transversal intersects two lines.

3-2 ▪ State and apply theorems about angles when parallel lines are cut by a transversal.

3-3 ▪ State and apply theorems that can be used to prove lines parallel.

3-4 ▪ Apply the Angle Sum Theorem for Triangles and related corollaries.

3-5 ▪ Use the Exterior Angle Theorem to find the measure of an angle of a triangle.

3-6 ▪ Apply angle sum theorems for the interior and exterior angles of a polygon.

TEACHING CHAPTER 3

Cooperative Learning Opportunities

Many of the geometry lessons begin with an **Explore** activity and these are usually well suited to cooperative learning.

Group students in pairs to do the **Explore** activities that open Lessons 3-4 and 3-5. Both of these involve constructions and measurement. Assign one student to draw and measure and the other to record the results and, if called on, to present them to the class.

After students have done the **Explore** in Lesson 3-4 by tracing and using congruent triangles, suggest that they do it by drawing a triangle, cutting off two of the angles and placing them adjacent to the third angle, to form a straight angle.

For Lesson 3-5, suggest that they extend all of the sides of the triangle—to reinforce the concept of exterior angles.

Multicultural Note: *Omar Khayyam and Euclid's Fifth Postulate*

Omar Khayyam lived in Persia, now Iran, from about 1050 to 1122. Though known in Europe and America for his romantic poetry, he was an outstanding mathematician and astronomer.

Within geometry, Khayyam focused on Euclid's fifth postulate which states, in a revised form, that: through a point outside a line only one line can be drawn parallel to the given line. Khayyam, like many European mathematicians after him, tried to prove this as a theorem using Euclid's first four postulates. It is now known that Euclid's fifth postulate is independent of the first four postulates and cannot be proven from them. However, the attempts to prove Euclid's fifth postulate laid the foundation for other systems of geometry, known as Non-Euclidean geometry.

For more information, see page 95 of **Multiculturalism in Mathematics, Science, and Technology**.

Alternative Assessment and Communication Ideas

Efforts must be made not to lose students in the early chapters of geometry. Some have trouble with proof and can become discouraged. Group-graded quizzes can help give students support and confidence.

The B Exercises can form the basis of group quizzes. You might start, for example, with Exercises 32 through 34 on page 115. Assign students in groups of three. The following roles should be assigned randomly. One student reads the given conditions. A second student re-draws the figure large enough for the group to work on. The third student tries to find the answer. If the other two students agree, then the student charged with the drawing fills in the angle measure.

Students then rotate roles, answering the questions for the next exercise and figure.

Only one paper is submitted by the group and the grade for the paper is given to each member of the group. Other B Exercises throughout the chapter are suitable for this kind of quiz.

Investigations and Projects

We are surrounded by polygons and other geometric figures that are used to communicate in symbolic form. Road signs such as those for stop, yield, and one way are among the most obvious. But there are many more and some students will enjoy looking for them.

Ask students to look for and collect geometric emblems or logos and explain what they stand for. Some of these, like the stylized Olympic figures are intended to communicate without words. Others aid quick recognition from a moving car. Others help build brand loyalty.

Almost every company now has a logo that it wants recognized. Ask students to collect these, particularly those that are geometric in design. Have them also evaluate the appeal of different signs and logos. Students can display their results on the bulletin board.

Lesson	PACING CHART (DAYS)			Opening Activity	Cooperative Activity	Seat or Group Work
	1-Year Minimum	1-Year Regular	1-Year Advanced			
3-1	2	2	2	Chapter Opener: **TE** p. 104; Lesson Opener: **TE** p. 105	Computer Activity: **SE** p. 110	Try This Exercises
3-2	1	1	1	First Five Minutes 3-2: **FFM** **Transparency Masters** p. 9 or TE p. 111; Lesson Opener: **TE** p. 111	✂ Explore: **SE** p. 111; Lab Worksheet 3-2: **Laboratory Manual** p. 21	Try This Exercises
3-3	1	1	1	First Five Minutes 3-3: **FFM** **Transparency Masters** p. 10 or TE p. 117; Lesson Opener: **TE** p. 117	Explore: **SE** p. 117; ✂ Lab Worksheet 3-3: **Laboratory Manual** p. 22	Try This Exercises
3-4	2	2	2	First Five Minutes 3-4: **FFM** **Transparency Masters** p. 10 or TE p. 123; Lesson Opener: **TE** p. 123	✂ Explore: **SE** p. 117; ✂ Lab Worksheet 3-4A: **Laboratory Manual** p. 23; ✂ Lab Worksheet 3-4B: **Laboratory Manual** p. 25	Try This Exercises
3-5	2	2	2	First Five Minutes 3–5: **FFM** **Transparency Masters** p. 12 or TE p. 129; Lesson Opener: **TE** p. 129	✂ Explore: **SE** p. 129	Try This Exercises
3-6	1	1	1	First Five Minutes 3–6: **FFM** **Transparency Masters** p. 12 or TE p. 135; Lesson Opener: **TE** p. 135	✂ Lab Worksheet 3-6A: **Laboratory Manual** p. 27; Lab Worksheet 3-6B: **Laboratory Manual** p. 29; ✂ Lab Worksheet 3-6C: **Laboratory Manual** p. 30; ✂ Lab Worksheet 3-6D: **Laboratory Manual** p. 31	Try This Exercises
Review	1	1	1			
Test	1	1	1			
Cum. Review	1	1	1			

FFM = First Five Minutes

Enrichment	Review/Assess	Reteach	Technology	Lesson
✄ Enrichment Using Manipulatives 3-1: *Enrichment* p. 14	Class Exercises: **SE** p. 107; Mixed Review: **SE** p. 110	Practice Worksheet 3-1: *Practice and Mixed Review* p. 21	Computer Activity: **SE** p. 110	3-1
Connections: **SE** p. 116; ✄ Enrichment Using Manipulatives 3-2: *Enrichment* p. 15	Class Exercises: **SE** p. 113; Algebra Review: **SE** p. 115	Practice Worksheet 3-2: *Practice and Mixed Review* p. 22	Lab Worksheet 3-2: *Laboratory Manual* p. 21	3-2
Optional Explore: **TE** p. 117; Comparing Approaches in Geometry; **SE** p. 122; ✄ Enrichment Using Manipulatives 3-3: *Enrichment* p. 16	Class Exercises: **SE** p. 119; Quiz: **SE** p. 121; Mixed Review **SE** p. 121; Quiz: *Assessment* p. 83	Practice Worksheet 3-3: *Practice and Mixed Review* p. 23	Computer Exploration 1: **SE** p. 634	3-3
Enrichment: **SE** p. 128; ✄ Enrichment Using Manipulatives 3-4: *Enrichment* p. 17	Class Exercises: **SE** p. 125; Mixed Review: **SE** p. 127	Practice Worksheet 3-4: *Practice and Mixed Review* p. 24	Computer Exploration 2: **SE** p. 635	3-4
Historical Note: **SE** p. 134; ✄ Enrichment Using Manipulatives 3-5: *Enrichment* p. 18	Class Exercises: **SE** p. 131; Algebra Review: **SE** p. 134	Practice Worksheet 3-5: *Practice and Mixed Review* p. 25		3-5
✄ Enrichment Using Manipulatives 3-6: *Enrichment* p. 19; Calculator Worksheet 3-6: *Technology* p. CL3; BASIC 3-6: *Technology* p. B8	Class Exercises: **SE** p. 138; Quiz: **SE** p. 140; Mixed Review: **SE** p. 140; Quiz: *Assessment* p. 84	Practice Worksheet 3-6: *Practice and Mixed Review* p. 26	Calculator Worksheet 3-6: *Technology* p. CL3; BASIC 3-6: *Technology* p. B8	3-6
Critical Thinking: **SE** p. 141	Summary & Review: **SE** p. 142–143	Mixed Review: *Practice and Mixed Review* p. 104		Review
Problem Solving: **SE** p. 145	Chapter 3 Test: **SE** p. 144; Chapter 3 Tests: *Assessment*, p. 13–18; *MathTest*			Test
	Cumulative Review: **SE** p. 146–147			Cum. Review

3

Parallel Lines and Planes

Rows of corn form parallel lines. Describe other real-world examples of parallel lines.

PARALLELISM IN LINES AND PLANES

OBJECTIVE: *Identify parallel planes, parallel lines, and skew lines. Name angle pairs formed when a transversal intersects two lines.*

3-1 Parallel Planes, Lines, and Transversals

In Chapter 1 you learned that two figures that intersect have a set of points in common. Figures that do not intersect have no points in common.

■ **DEFINITION**

    Parallel planes are planes that do not intersect.

■ **DEFINITION**

    Parallel lines are coplanar and do not intersect.

Lines that are not coplanar and do not intersect are called **skew lines.**

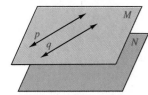 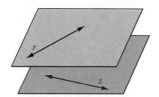

Planes *M* and *N* are parallel. (*M* ∥ *N*)
Lines *p* and *q* are parallel. (*p* ∥ *q*)

Lines *r* and *s* are skew.

Segments and rays are parallel if they are contained in parallel lines. Two parallel lines determine a unique plane and two intersecting lines determine a unique plane.

Example 1
Refer to the box on the right.
a. Name a pair of parallel planes.
b. Name a pair of parallel lines.

    Solution
    a. plane *ADHE* ∥ *BCGF*   **b.** $\overline{AB}$ ∥ $\overline{HG}$

Try This
Name a pair of skew lines.

Lesson Opener

Begin by reminding students that the first two chapters concerned points, lines, and planes and their subsets—segments, angles, and triangles. This chapter deals with relationships of lines in a plane and in space. Review coplanar lines and noncoplanar lines (intersecting, nonintersecting) asking students to give real-world examples of lines that intersect and those that do not.

Materials
student notebooks
compasses
straightedges

Teaching Notes

Emphasize that a transversal (prefix "trans" means "across") intersects two coplanar lines in two distinct points. Point out that four pairs of vertical angles are formed when two coplanar lines are intersected by a transversal and that pairs of adjacent supplementary angles are also formed. Stress the importance of recognizing alternate interior/exterior angles, sameside interior angles, and corresponding angles. These pairs of angles will appear later in more complicated diagrams.

Key Terms

alternate interior angles
alternate exterior angles
same-side interior angles
transversal
parallel lines
parallel planes

Key Questions

1. What are the possible relationships between two planes? between two lines in the same plane? either intersect or are parallel
2. If the intersection of two lines in the same plane is the empty set, the lines are __?__. parallel
3. What do you call lines that do not intersect and are in different planes? skew

Point out that coplanar lines either intersect or do not.

Guided Practice

Chalkboard Examples

1. Name other pairs of parallel planes, parallel lines, and skew lines in the figure.
Answers may vary.

Answer to **Try This**
Answers may vary.

2. Write using symbols.
f is parallel to *e*. $f \parallel e$
f is parallel to *d*. $f \parallel d$

Answer to **Try This** $\angle ADB$ and $\angle DBC$, $\angle DAC$ and $\angle ACB$

Common Errors

Emphasize that, although coplanar lines cut by a transversal do not have to be parallel, in the figure below, *t* is not a transversal.

NOTE: You may want to have students construct a line parallel to a given line. (See page 397, Construction 7.)

Emphasize that segments and rays are parallel if the lines that contain them are parallel.

◆ **THEOREM 3.1**

If two parallel planes are cut by a third plane, the lines of intersection are parallel.

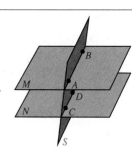

Given: Plane *M* is parallel to plane *N*; plane *S* intersects plane *M* in $\overline{AB}$; plane *S* intersects plane *N* in $\overline{CD}$.

Prove: $\overline{AB} \parallel \overline{CD}$

Proof

Statements	Reasons
1. $M \parallel N$; *S* and *M* intersects in $\overline{AB}$; *S* and *N* intersect in $\overline{CD}$.	1. Given
2. $\overline{AB}$ and $\overline{CD}$ do not intersect.	2. Def. of $\parallel$ planes
3. $\overline{AB}$ and $\overline{CD}$ are coplanar.	3. Both lines are in plane *S*.
4. $\overline{AB} \parallel \overline{CD}$	4. Def. of $\parallel$ lines

A line that intersects two coplanar lines in two different points is called a **transversal**. A transversal that intersects two coplanar lines forms eight angles. In the figure to the right, transversal *t* intersects lines *m* and *n*.

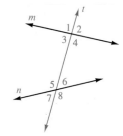

Angles 3, 4, 5, and 6 are interior angles.
Angles 1, 2, 7, and 8 are exterior angles.

The pairs of angles have special names.

Alternate interior angles are two nonadjacent interior angles on opposite sides of the transversal. There are two pairs of alternate interior angles: $\angle 3$ and $\angle 6$, $\angle 4$ and $\angle 5$.

Alternate exterior angles are two nonadjacent exterior angles on opposite sides of the transversal. There are two pairs of alternate exterior angles: $\angle 1$ and $\angle 8$, $\angle 2$ and $\angle 7$.

Same-side interior angles are two interior angles on the same side of the transversal. There are two pairs of same-side interior angles: $\angle 3$ and $\angle 5$, $\angle 4$ and $\angle 6$.

Corresponding angles are two nonadjacent angles on the same side of the transversal such that one is an exterior angle and the other is an interior angle. There are four pairs of corresponding angles: $\angle 1$ and $\angle 5$, $\angle 3$ and $\angle 7$, $\angle 2$ and $\angle 6$, $\angle 4$ and $\angle 8$.

Example 2

a. Name two lines in the figure that appear to be parallel.
b. Name two pairs of alternate interior angles for lines *AB* and *CD*.

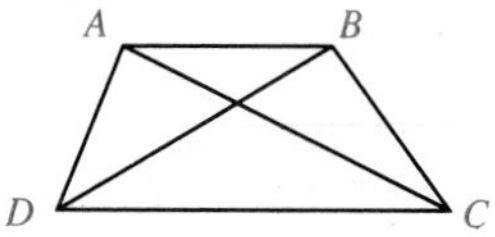

Solution

a. $\overline{AB}$, $\overline{CD}$
b. $\angle BAC$ and $\angle ACD$, $\angle ABD$ and $\angle BDC$

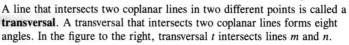

Try This

Name two pairs of alternate interior angles for lines *AD* and *BC*.

106 Chapter 3 Parallel Lines and Planes

Class Exercises

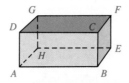

Short Answer

1. Name three pairs of parallel planes.
2. Name all the lines that are parallel to $\overline{EF}$.
3. How many lines are parallel to each line in the figure?
4. Name all the lines that are skew to $\overline{HE}$.
5. How many lines are skew to each line in the figure?

6. Name two pairs of streets that appear to be parallel.
7. Which streets are transversals for streets a and b?
8. Which streets are transversals for streets d and e?
9. Name the only street that is a transversal for streets a and d.

Sample Exercises

Identify each angle pair as alternate interior, alternate exterior, same-side interior, corresponding, or none of these.

10. $\angle 13$ and $\angle 5$ 11. $\angle 1$ and $\angle 3$
12. $\angle 7$ and $\angle 12$ 13. $\angle 3$ and $\angle 16$
14. $\angle 7$ and $\angle 10$ 15. $\angle 13$ and $\angle 4$

Discussion

16. Draw a diagram to illustrate the statement:
    If plane M is parallel to plane N, not every line in M is parallel to a given line AB in plane N.
17. Draw and label a pair of lines and a transversal. Label the figure so that $\angle 7$ and $\angle 8$ are corresponding angles. Must their supplements be corresponding angles? Give a convincing argument for your answer.

Exercises

A

Refer to the figure to name the plane that is parallel to the given plane.

1. plane $ABHG$
2. plane $CDJI$
3. plane $BCIH$

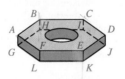

4. Is plane $ABHG$ parallel to plane $FEKL$? Explain.
5. Name four pairs of parallel planes.
6. Name three lines parallel to $\overline{CD}$.
7. Which lines in plane $AGLF$ are skew to $\overline{CD}$?
8. Name four lines that are skew to both $\overline{EK}$ and $\overline{BH}$.
9. Name two lines that are parallel to $\overline{AB}$ and skew to $\overline{BC}$.
10. Are any lines both parallel and skew to $\overline{FE}$?

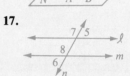

Exercise Answers

1. plane *EDJK*   **2.** plane *AFLG*
3. plane *FEKL*   **4.** No; they
intersect.   **5.** Answers may
vary. plane *ABCDEF*∥plane *GHIJKL*,
plane *ABHG*∥plane *EDJK*,
plane *BCIH*∥plane *FEKL*,
plane *CDJI*∥plane *AFLG*
6. $\overline{IJ}$, $\overline{AF}$, $\overline{GL}$ **7.** $\overline{AG}$, $\overline{FL}$
8. $\overline{AF}$, $\overline{GL}$, $\overline{CD}$ and $\overline{IJ}$
9. $\overline{GH}$, $\overline{JK}$ **10.** no
11. ∠3 and ∠7, ∠2 and ∠6
12. ∠1 and ∠5, ∠4 and ∠8
13. ∠2 and ∠3, ∠7 and ∠6
14. ∠1 and ∠3, ∠2 and ∠4,
∠8 and ∠6, ∠7 and ∠5
15. ∠8 and ∠6   **16.** ∠2 and ∠6
17. corresponding
18. same-side interior
19. alternate exterior
20. none of these
21. alternate interior
22. none of these
23. alternate exterior
24. corresponding
25. ∠1 and ∠6, ∠5 and ∠4
26. Answers may vary.
∠2 and ∠14, ∠3 and ∠15,
∠1 and ∠13, ∠4 and ∠16
27. ∠*DCA*   **28.** ∠*DAC*
29. always   **30.** always
31. sometimes   **32.** sometimes
33. sometimes   **34.** always
35. always   **36.** sometimes
37. never   **38.** The planes
containing $\overline{MN}$ and $\overline{AF}$ are parallel so $\overline{MN}$ and $\overline{AF}$ do not intersect. Since $\overline{MN}$ and $\overline{AF}$ lie in the
same plane, $\overline{MN}\parallel\overline{AF}$.

**Name the indicated angles determined by intersecting lines *q* and *r* cut
by transversal *p*.**

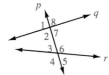

11. two pairs of alternate interior angles
12. two pairs of alternate exterior angles
13. two pairs of same-side interior angles
14. four pairs of corresponding angles
15. a pair of corresponding angles that includes ∠6
16. a pair of alternate interior angles that includes ∠6

**Identify each pair of angles as alternate interior, alternate exterior,
same-side interior, corresponding, or none of these.**

17. ∠1 and ∠13   **18.** ∠6 and ∠10
19. ∠12 and ∠14   **20.** ∠4 and ∠10
21. ∠11 and ∠13   **22.** ∠8 and ∠15
23. ∠1 and ∠15   **24.** ∠5 and ∠2

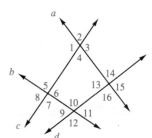

25. Name two pairs of alternate interior angles for lines *a* and *b* cut by
transversal *c*.
26. Name two pairs of corresponding angles for lines *c* and *d* cut by
transversal *a*.

27. For $\overline{AB}$ and $\overline{DC}$ cut by transversal $\overline{AC}$, name the angle that is the
alternate interior angle to ∠*BAC*.
28. For $\overline{BC}$ and $\overline{AD}$ cut by transversal $\overline{AC}$, name the angle that is the
alternate interior angle to ∠*BCA*.

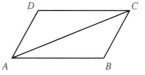

B

Determine whether each statement is always, sometimes, or never true.

29. If two lines in space are parallel to the same line, then they are parallel
to each other.
30. If a plane intersects one of two parallel planes, then it intersects the
other parallel plane.
31. If two planes are parallel to the same line, then they are parallel to each
other.
32. If a plane is parallel to one of two skew lines, then it intersects the other
skew line.
33. If two lines do not intersect, then they are parallel.
34. If a line and a plane do not intersect, then they are parallel.
35. If ∠1 and ∠2 are alternate interior angles, then the vertical angles
relative to them are alternate exterior angles.
36. If ∠3 and ∠4 are same-side interior angles, then their supplements are
also same-side interior angles.
37. If ∠7 and ∠8 are corresponding angles, then the vertical angles relative
to them are alternate interior angles.

38. In the box to the right, opposite sides are parallel. Suppose a
plane cuts the box at *A*, *F*, *N*, and *M*. Explain why $\overline{MN}\parallel\overline{AF}$.

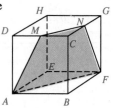

108   *Chapter 3   Parallel Lines and Planes*

Indicate which of the following are examples of intersecting, parallel, or skew lines.

39. railroad tracks
40. picture frames
41. bowling alleys
42. airplane flight paths
43. rows of corn
44. a picket fence
45. lines on a football field
46. a TV antenna

Name each of the following, if it exists, in the crystal.

47. one line that appears to be parallel to $\overline{BE}$
48. the line that appears to be parallel to $\overline{BC}$
49. a plane parallel to $ABCD$
50. a plane parallel to ABE
51. one line that appears to be skew to $\overline{AD}$

52. How many edges are skew to $\overline{AD}$?
53. How many segments are shown in the figure?
54. How many pairs of parallel segments do there appear to be?

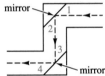

$ABCD$ is a square.

55. A carpenter builds a stairway by cutting triangles like $\triangle ABC$ and $\triangle CDE$ from a piece of lumber. $\angle DCE$ and $\angle FEG$ are corresponding angles relative to what pair of parallel lines and what transversal?

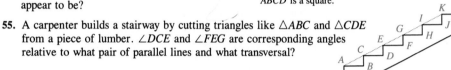

56. In a periscope a pair of mirrors are mounted parallel to each other, as shown. The path of light becomes a transversal. Name a pair of alternate interior angles.

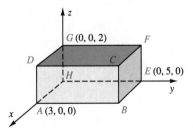

c

In the coordinate graph shown, $\overline{AG}$ and $\overline{HL}$ are parallel.

57. Find the coordinates of each labeled point on $\overline{AG}$ and on $\overline{HL}$.
58. For each pair of points on $\overline{HL}$ construct a triangle like the one shown and calculate the ratio $\frac{y}{x}$ where x and y are the lengths of the sides of the triangle. Do the same for $\overline{AG}$.
59. Write a generalization that is based on your results in Exercise 58

60. Just as any point in an x-y coordinate plane can be named by a pair of coordinates, any point in an x-y-z coordinate space can be named by a triple of coordinates. In the box shown, the x-y-z coordinates of three of the points have been given. Find the coordinates for each of the remaining corners of the box.
61. How many pairs of parallel segments exist in the box to the right?

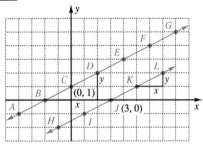

39. parallel lines   40. both parallel and intersecting lines
41. parallel lines   42. skew and parallel lines   43. parallel lines   44. parallel lines
45. parallel and intersecting lines   46. intersecting and parallel lines   47. $\overline{DF}$
48. $\overline{AD}$ 49. none
50. plane DFC 51. Answers may vary. $\overline{BE}$, $\overline{CE}$, $\overline{BF}$, $\overline{CF}$
52. 4   53. 12   54. 6
55. parallel lines $\overline{CD}$ and $\overline{EF}$ cut by transversal $\overline{AK}$
56. $\angle 2$ and $\angle 3$ 57. $A(-4, -1)$, $B(-2, 0)$, $D(2, 2)$, $E(4, 3)$; $F(6, 4)$, $G(8, 5)$, $H(-1, -2)$, $I(1, -1)$, $K(5, 1)$, $L(7, 2)$
58. $\frac{y}{x} = \frac{1}{2}$ in each case
59. Parallel lines in a coordinate plane have equal ratios of $\frac{y}{x}$.   60. $B(3, 5, 0)$, $C(3, 5, 2)$, $D(3, 0, 2)$, $F(0, 5, 2)$, $H(0, 0, 0)$
61. 18 (3 groups of 6 parallel lines)

62–65. Answers may vary.
66. always true
67. not always true
68. 0 points, 1 point, 3 points,
4 points, 5 points, 6 points

Mixed Review Answers

1. ∠PUQ and ∠TUS   **2.** ∠RUP
3. ∠PUQ and ∠QUR   **4.** ∠TUS
and ∠QUR   **5.** ∠TUR
6. ∠PUT or ∠QUS

**Computer Activity
Answers**

1. If two parallel lines are cut
by a transversal, corresponding
angles are congruent.
2. Alternate interior angles are
congruent; alternate exterior
angles are congruent.
3. If two parallel lines are cut
by a transversal, same-side interior angles are supplementary.

Draw each figure if possible.

62. Line $l \parallel m$, lines l and n are skew, lines m and n are skew.
63. Line $s \parallel t$, line $s \parallel w$, lines t and w are skew.
64. Line $a \perp b$, lines a and c are skew, lines b and c are skew.
65. Line $d \parallel$ plane P, plane $P \parallel$ plane Q, d is ∦ to Q.

Critical Thinking

**Some statements that are true about lines in a plane are not necessarily
true about lines in space. Determine whether each statement is always
true about lines in space.**

66. Two lines parallel to a third line are parallel to each other
67. If a line is perpendicular to one of two parallel lines, then it is
perpendicular to the other parallel line.

68. The number of points that are formed by intersections of a given number
of lines depends upon their positions relative to one another. Three lines
form 0, 1, 2, or 3 points of intersection. Investigate the number of points
of intersection that are possible for four coplanar lines.

0 points   1 point   2 points   3 points

Mixed Review

1. Name a pair of vertical angles.
2. Name an angle that forms a linear pair with ∠RUS.
3. Name a pair of adjacent, complementary angles.
4. Name a pair of complementary angles that are not adjacent.
5. Name an angle that is the supplement of ∠QUR.
6. Name an angle that is the supplement of ∠TUS.

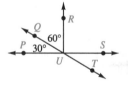

Computer Activity
Parallel Lines and Transversals

Use computer software to draw two parallel lines and a transversal.

1. Measure pairs of corresponding angles in the figure you have drawn.
   What do you notice? Do you think this is true for any pair of
   parallel lines and any transversal? State a generalization.
2. Measure other angles and find pairs that are congruent. State an
   appropriate generalization for each pair.
3. Measure pairs of same-side interior angles. Find the sum of the
   measures of each pair. What do you notice? State a generalization.

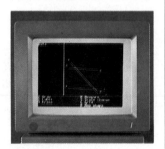

OBJECTIVE: *State and apply theorems about angles formed when parallel lines are cut by a transversal.*

3-2 Properties of Parallel Lines

 **EXPLORE**

Use a ruler to draw two parallel lines, one on each side of the ruler. Draw a transversal and number the angles as shown. Use tracing paper or a protractor to find pairs of congruent angles.

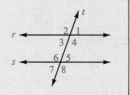

In the last lesson, special pairs of angles formed by two lines and a transversal were defined. You may have discovered while completing the Explore in this lesson, that when the two lines cut by a transversal are parallel, certain pairs of angles are congruent. This observation is the basis for the following postulate.

● **POSTULATE 13**

If two parallel lines are cut by a transversal, then corresponding angles are congruent.

Postulate 13 is used to prove the next theorem.

◆ **THEOREM 3.2**

If two parallel lines are cut by a transversal, then alternate interior angles are congruent.

Given: $a \parallel b$
Prove: $\angle 1 \cong \angle 2$

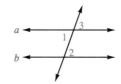

Proof Statements	Reasons
1. $a \parallel b$	1. Given
2. $\angle 2 \cong \angle 3$	2. If two parallel lines are cut by a transversal, then corresponding $\angle$s are $\cong$.
3. $\angle 3 \cong \angle 1$	3. Vertical $\angle$s are $\cong$.
4. $\angle 1 \cong \angle 2$	4. Congruence of $\angle$s is transitive.

(Quiz on previous lesson)

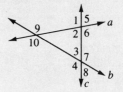

1. Which line is a transversal to *a* and *b*? c
2. Classify $\angle 5$ and $\angle 4$.
alternate exterior angles
3. Classify $\angle 6$ and $\angle 7$.
same-side interior angles
4. Classify $\angle 9$ and $\angle 10$.
vertical angles
5. Classify $\angle 6$ and $\angle 8$.
corresponding angles

Lesson Opener

The last lesson introduced special pairs of angles formed by two coplanar lines and a transversal. This lesson continues with development of these special pairs of angles. Deductive reasoning can be used to draw certain conclusions about properties of these pairs of angles when the lines cut by a transversal are parallel.

In the Explore, ask students to use either a geometry template that has lines or lined notebook paper to draw one pair of parallel lines and a second pair of lines that are not parallel. Have students draw a transversal for each pair of lines, then use a protractor to measure the following in each diagram: two pairs of corresponding angles, a pair of alternate interior angles, a pair of alternate exterior angles, and a pair of same-side interior angles. Have students examine the data and respond to the key questions.

This activity leads to
Postulate 13. Remind students
that a postulate is a statement
that is accepted as true without
proof.

Key Questions

1. Which angles are congruent?
corr. angles, alt. int. angles, alt.
ext. angles
2. What generalization/rule can
you make about the angles that
are congruent? If two ∥ lines are
cut by a transversal, then corr.
(alt. int., alt. ext.) angles are ≅.
3. What appears to be true
about the same-side interior angles? supplementary

Materials

student notebooks
protractors
geometry templates

Teaching Notes

Remind students to focus on the
meanings of the theorems in
this lesson rather than on memorizing the theorem numbers.
Once prove, they can be used
as reasons in proofs.

Emphasize the importance of
learning the four properties of
parallel lines; they are used in
many proofs throughout the text.

Guided Practice

Chalkboard Examples

1. If $p \parallel q$, $m \angle 2 = 38$ and
$m \angle 3 = 121$, find $m \angle 1$. 159

Answer to **Try This** 60

2. If $\overline{AB} \parallel \overline{CD}$, $m \angle D = x + 50$
and $m \angle DCE = 3x + 20$, find
$m \angle B$. 65

Answer to **Try This** 42.5

Example 1

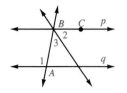

$p \parallel q$, $m \angle 1 = 100$, $m \angle 2 = 55$ Find $m \angle 3$.

Solution

$m \angle 1 = m \angle ABC$ *If two parallel lines are cut by a transversal,*
                              then alternate interior angles are congruent.
$m \angle 1 = m \angle 2 + m \angle 3$ *(Theorem 3.2)*
$100 = 55 + m \angle 3$ *Substitution*
$45 = m \angle 3$

Try This

$p \parallel q$, $m \angle 1 = 135$, $m \angle 3 = 75$ Find $m \angle 2$.

Two additional relationships you might have discovered in the Explore are
stated in Theorems 3.3 and 3.4, which you will be asked to prove in
Exercises 30–31.

◆ **THEOREM 3.3**

If two parallel lines are cut by a transversal, then alternate exterior
angles are congruent.

◆ **THEOREM 3.4**

If two parallel lines are cut by a transversal, then same-side interior
angles are supplementary.

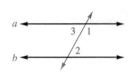

Example 2

$\overline{AB} \parallel \overline{CD}$ Find $m \angle B$.

Solution

$m \angle ABC = m \angle DCE$ *If two parallel lines are cut by a*
                                transversal, then corresponding angles
                                are congruent. (Postulate 13)
$4x - 40 = x + 20$ *Substitution*
$3x = 60$
$x = 20$ $m \angle B = 40$

Try This

$\overline{AD} \parallel \overline{BC}$, $m \angle D = 3x - 25$, $m \angle DCE = x + 20$ Find $m \angle D$.

Properties of Parallel Lines Cut by a Transversal

1. Corresponding angles are congruent.
2. Alternate interior angles are congruent.
3. Alternate exterior angles are congruent.
4. Same-side interior angles are supplementary.

112   *Chapter 3   Parallel Lines and Planes*

Class Exercises

Short Answer

$a \parallel b$ State the postulate or theorem that justifies each conclusion.

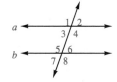

1. $\angle 1 \cong \angle 8$
2. $\angle 4 \cong \angle 5$
3. $m\angle 4 + m\angle 6 = 180$
4. $\angle 3 \cong \angle 7$
5. $\angle 2 \cong \angle 7$
6. $\angle 6 \cong \angle 3$

Sample Exercises

$a \parallel b$, $m\angle 1 = 65$

7. Find $m\angle 5$.
8. Find $m\angle 8$.
9. Find $m\angle 6$.
10. If $\overline{AB} \parallel \overline{CD}$, name a pair of congruent angles.
11. If $\overline{AD} \parallel \overline{BC}$, name two pairs of supplementary angles.

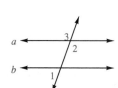

Discussion

12. If $a \parallel b$, give a convincing argument that $\angle 1$ and $\angle 3$ are supplementary.
13. If $a \parallel b$, give a convincing argument that $\angle 1$ and $\angle 2$ are supplementary.

Exercises

A

$p \parallel q$, $m\angle 3 = 65$

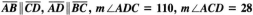

1. Find $m\angle 1$.
2. Find $m\angle 2$.
3. Find $m\angle 4$.
4. Find $m\angle 5$.
5. Find $m\angle 6$.
6. Find $m\angle 7$.

$\overline{AB} \parallel \overline{CD}$, $\overline{AD} \parallel \overline{BC}$, $m\angle ADC = 110$, $m\angle ACD = 28$

7. Find $m\angle 1$.
8. Find $m\angle 2$.
9. Find $m\angle 3$.
10. Find $m\angle 4$.
11. Find $m\angle 5$.
12. Find $m\angle 6$.
13. Find $m\angle 7$.
14. Find $m\angle 8$.
15. Find $m\angle 9$.

16. Name all the angles congruent to $\angle 1$.
17. Name all the angles congruent to $\angle 3$.
18. Name all the angles supplementary to $\angle 1$.
19. Name all the angles supplementary to $\angle 3$.

$l \parallel m$ Find x.

20. $m\angle 1 = 3x + 7$, $m\angle 5 = 5x - 3$
21. $m\angle 4 = 8x + 12$, $m\angle 6 = 2x + 54$
22. $m\angle 3 = 4x + 7$, $m\angle 6 = 2x + 23$
23. $m\angle 4 = x^2 + 5x$, $m\angle 8 = 9x + 12$
24. $m\angle 2 = x^2 - 6x$, $m\angle 5 = 7x + 220$

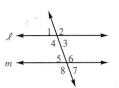

Class Exercise Answers

1. If two $\parallel$ lines are cut by a trans., alt. ext. $\angle$s are $\cong$.
2. If two $\parallel$ lines are cut by a trans., alt. int. $\angle$s are $\cong$.
3. If two $\parallel$ lines are cut by a trans., same-side int. $\angle$s are supplementary.
4. If two $\parallel$ lines are cut by a trans., corr. $\angle$s are $\cong$.
5. If two $\parallel$ lines are cut by a trans., alt. ext. $\angle$s are $\cong$.
6. If two $\parallel$ lines are cut by a trans., alt. int. $\angle$s are $\cong$.
7. 65
8. 65
9. 115
10. $\angle 1 \cong \angle 4$
11. $\angle ABC$ and $\angle BAD$, $\angle ADC$ and $\angle DCB$
12. By placing a tracing of $\angle 1$ next to $\angle 3$, I can show that $\angle 1$ and $\angle 3$ form a linear pair and so are supplementary.
13. By placing a tracing of $\angle 1$ next to $\angle 2$, I can show that $\angle 1$ and $\angle 2$ form a linear pair and so are supplementary.

Assignment Guide

Minimum: 1–29 e/o, 33, AR
Regular: 1–28, e/o, 30–34, AR
Advanced: 1–22 e/o, 23–34, AR

Applications
Exercise 29

Algebra
Exercises 20–24, 28, AR

Lesson Closure

Summarize the lesson by having students state the four properties of parallel lines.

Teacher's Resource Materials

Enrichment Using
    Manipulatives 15
Practice Master 17
Technology: Computer
    Software 4
Transparency 10

Exercise Answers

1. 115   2. 65   3. 115
4. 115   5. 65   6. 65
7. 110   8. 42   9. 28
10. 110   11. 70   12. 70
13. 70   14. 110   15. 42
16. ∠4, ∠8, ∠ADC   17. ∠ACD
18. ∠5, ∠6, ∠7, ∠DAB, ∠DCB
19. None have names.
20. x = 5   21. x = 7
22. x = 25   23. 6
24. no solution   25. x = 53,
y = 62   26. x = 32, y = 32
27. x = 30, y = 90
28. x = 43, y = 57
29. m∠CEF = 75, m∠CGH = 75
30. 1. Given   2. Vertical ∠s are
≅.   3. If ∥ lines are cut by a
trans., corr. ∠s are ≅.   4. Congruence of ∠s is transitive.
31. 1. a∥b (Given)   2. ∠2 ≅ ∠3
(If ∥ lines are cut by a trans., alt.
int. ∠s are ≅.)   3. m∠1 +
m∠3 = 180 (Def. of linear pair)
4. m∠1 + m∠2 = 180 (Substitution)   5. ∠1 and ∠2 are supplementary. (Def. of supplementary
angles)   32. 62   33. 28
34. 118   35. 56
36. 1. DE∥BC (Given)
2. m∠1 = m∠DEB
(Theorem 3.2)   3. m∠2 =
m∠DEA (If ∥ lines are cut by a
trans., corr. ∠s are ≅.)
4. m∠1 = m∠2 (Given)
5. m∠DEB = m∠DEA
(Subst.)   6. ED bisects ∠AEB.
(Def. of ∠ bisector)
37. 1. p∥q (Given)   2. ∠1 ≅ ∠6
(If ∥ lines are cut by a trans.,
alt. int. ∠s are ≅.)   3. s∥t
(Given) 4. ∠6 ≅ ∠7 (If ∥ lines
are cut by a trans., alt. int. ∠s
are ≅.)   5. ∠1 ≅ ∠7 (Congruence of ∠s is transitive.)
38. 1. p∥q (Given)   2. ∠2 ≅ ∠5
(If ∥ lines are cut by a trans.,
alt. int. ∠s are ≅.)   3. s∥t
(Given)   4. ∠5 ≅ ∠9 (If ∥ lines
are cut by a trans., corr. ∠s
are ≅.)   5. ∠2 = ∠9 (Congruence of ∠s is transitive.)

Find the values of x and y.

25. BE∥CD

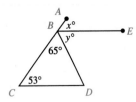

26. BC bisects ∠ABD.
m∠ABD = 64, BC∥DE

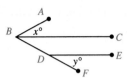

27. AB∥CD, AB ⊥ BC

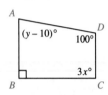

28. AB∥CD, AB ⊥ AD

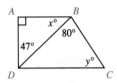

29. A developer is dividing a plot of land into lots so that the sides of each lot are parallel to the street AC. If m∠ACD = 105, find m∠CEF and m∠CGH.

30. Complete the proof of Theorem 3.3.
    Given: a∥b
    Prove: ∠1 ≅ ∠2

Proof	Statements	Reasons
	1. a∥b	1. ____
	2. ∠1 ≅ ∠3	2. ____
	3. ∠3 ≅ ∠2	3. ____
	4. ∠1 ≅ ∠2	4. ____

31. Write a two-column proof for Theorem 3.4.
    Given: a∥b
    Prove: ∠1 and ∠2 are supplementary.
    Plan   First show that ∠2 ≅ ∠3.
    Then use the fact that ∠1
    is the supplement of ∠3.

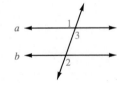

B

$\overline{AB} \parallel \overline{CD}$, $\overline{DG}$ bisects $\angle ADC$.
$\overline{AF}$ bisects $\angle DAB$. $m\angle ADC = 124$

32. Find $m\angle ADG$.
33. Find $m\angle DAF$.
34. Find $m\angle DGB$.

35. $\overline{AB} \parallel \overline{DC}$, $\overline{AD} \parallel \overline{BC}$
    Find $m\angle EAD$.

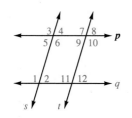

36. **Given:** $m\angle 1 = m\angle 2$, $\overline{DE} \parallel \overline{BC}$
    Prove: $\overline{ED}$ bisects $\angle AEB$.

37. **Given:** $p \parallel q$, $s \parallel t$
    Prove: $\angle 1 \cong \angle 7$
38. **Given:** $p \parallel q$, $s \parallel t$
    Prove: $\angle 2 \cong \angle 9$

C

39. **Given:** $\overline{CA}$ bisects $\angle DAB$. $\overline{AD} \parallel \overline{BE}$
    $\angle 1$ and $\angle 2$ are complementary.
    Prove: $\overline{BC}$ bisects $\angle ABE$.

40. **Given:** $\overline{BC}$ and $\overline{DE}$ are coplanar.
    plane $M \parallel$ plane N
    Prove: $\angle ABC \cong \angle ADE$, $\angle ACB \cong \angle AED$

41. Draw a diagram and prove the statement: If $\overline{BD}$ bisects $\angle ABC$ and $\overline{AM} \parallel \overline{BD}$ with point M on $\overrightarrow{CB}$, then $m\angle ABD = m\angle AMB$.

Critical Thinking

42. If a theorem is accepted as a postulate, then the statement earlier accepted as a postulate might be proven as a theorem. Suppose Theorem 3.2 is accepted as a postulate. Prove Postulate 13 as a theorem.
43. Assume Theorem 3.4 is a postulate. Prove Postulate 13 as a theorem.

Algebra Review

Solve each system of equations.

1. $x + y = 10$
   $y = x + 8$
2. $y = x - 6$
   $x + y = -2$
3. $x - y = 5$
   $x + 2y = 7$
4. $x + 2y = 10$
   $3x + 4y = 8$

---

39. 1. $\overline{AD} \parallel \overline{BE}$ (Given) 2. $\angle DAB$ and $\angle EBA$ are supplementary (If $\parallel$ lines are cut by a trans., same-side int. $\angle$s are $\cong$.) 3. $m\angle DAB + m\angle EBA = 180$ (Def. of supplementary) 4. $\overline{CA}$ bisects $\angle DAB$. (Given) 5. $m\angle 1 = \frac{1}{2}m\angle DAB$ (Def. of $\angle$ bisector) 6. $2m\angle 1 = m\angle DAB$ (Mult. Prop. of =) 7. $m\angle 2 + m\angle EBC = m\angle EBA$ ($\angle$ Add. Post.) 8. $2m\angle 1 + m\angle 2 + m\angle EBC = 180$ (Subst.) 9. $\angle 1$ and $\angle 2$ are complementary. (Given) 10. $m\angle 1 + m\angle 2 = 90$ (Def. of complementary) 11. $m\angle 1 + m\angle EBC = 90$ (Add. Prop. of =) 12. $m\angle EBC = m\angle 2$ (Subst.) 13. $\overline{BC}$ bisects $\angle ABE$. (Def. of $\angle$ bisector) **40.** 1. points B and C in plane M, points D and E in plane N, $\overline{BC} \parallel \overline{DE}$ (Given) 2. $\overline{BC}$ and $\overline{DE}$ are coplanar. (Def. of $\parallel$ lines) 3. $\angle ABC \cong \angle ADE$ and $\angle ACB \cong \angle AED$ (If $\parallel$ lines are cut by a trans., corr. $\angle$s are $\cong$.) **41.** 1. $\overline{AM} \parallel \overline{BD}$ (Given) 2. $\angle AMB \cong \angle CBD$ (If $\parallel$ lines are cut by a trans., corr. $\angle$s are $\cong$.) 3. $\overline{BD}$ bisects $\angle ABC$. (Given) 4. $\angle CBD \cong \angle ABD$ (Def. of $\angle$ bisector) 5. $\angle ABD \cong \angle AMB$ (Congruence of $\angle$s is transitive.) **42.** (Refer to figure on page 111.) Given: $a \parallel b$ Prove: $\angle 3 \cong \angle 2$ 1. $a \parallel b$ (Given) 2. $\angle 1 \cong \angle 2$ (If $\parallel$ lines are cut by a trans., alt. int. $\angle$s are $\cong$.) 3. $\angle 3 \cong \angle 1$ (Vert. $\angle$s are $\cong$.) 4. $\angle 3 \cong \angle 2$ (Congruence of $\angle$s is transitive.) **43.** (Refer to figure for Class Exercises 1–6.) Given: $a \parallel b$ Prove: $\angle 1 \cong \angle 5$ 1. $a \parallel b$ (Given) 2. $\angle 5$ and $\angle 3$ are supplementary. (If $\parallel$ lines are cut by a trans., same-side int. $\angle$s are supplementary.) 3. $\angle 1$ and $\angle 3$ are supplementary. (Linear Pair Post.) 4. $\angle 1 \cong \angle 5$ (Two $\angle$s supplementary to the same $\angle$ are $\cong$.)

CONNECTIONS ◇◇

Vectors

Representing quantities that have both direction and magnitude is often
done through the use of directed segments called vectors. The vector
AB (written $\overrightarrow{AB}$) is a vector whose direction is about 15 degrees above
horizontal and whose magnitude, or length, is $\sqrt{53}$.

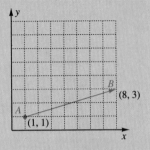

Vectors can also be represented by an ordered pair of numbers. The
vector $\overrightarrow{AB}$ can also be written as $(7, 2)$. The point A is the origin of the
vector and the point B is the terminal point of $\overrightarrow{AB}$. The ordered pair
notation for a vector results from subtracting the components of
the ordered pair representing the origin from the components of the
ordered pair representing the terminal point. In the case of $\overrightarrow{AB}$, the
origin is $A(1, 1)$ and the terminal point is $B(8, 3)$. Thus, $\overrightarrow{AB} =$
$(8 - 1, 3 - 1)$ or $(7, 2)$.

Two vectors (a, b) and (c, d), or the lines or line segments containing
them, are parallel if $\frac{a}{b} = \frac{c}{d}$. Two vectors (a, b) and (c, d), or the lines
or line segments containing them, are perpendicular if $\frac{a}{b} \cdot \frac{c}{d} = \frac{ac}{bd} = -1$.

Example

a. Test to see if the vectors $(1, 3)$
and $(17, 51)$ are parallel.

b. Test to see if the vectors $(1, 3)$
and $(-12, 4)$ are perpendicular.

Solution

a. They are parallel since $\frac{1}{3} = \frac{17}{51}$. **b.** They are perpendicular since $\frac{1}{3} \cdot \frac{-12}{4} = \frac{-12}{12} = -1$.

Try This

a. Test to see if the vectors $(1, 7)$
and $(13, 91)$ are parallel.

b. Test to see if the vectors $(4, 3)$
and $(-6, 8)$ are perpendicular.

Exercises

Find the ordered pairs representing the following vectors if $A(5, 3)$,
$B(4, 0)$, $C(1, 2)$, and $D(2, 5)$.

1. $\overrightarrow{AB}$ **2.** $\overrightarrow{AC}$ **3.** $\overrightarrow{CD}$ **4.** $\overrightarrow{DC}$

5. Is $\overrightarrow{CD}$ the same as $\overrightarrow{DC}$? Explain the relationship between these vectors.
6. Use the distance formula on page 27 to find the magnitude of vectors $\overrightarrow{CD}$ and $\overrightarrow{DC}$.
7. Two vectors having the same ordered pair representation, and therefore
the same magnitude, are called equal vectors. What can you say about
how equal vectors are related geometrically?
8. What can you say about two vectors that are contained in the same line
and are pointed in the same direction?

Indicate which pairs of vectors among the following are parallel and
which are perpendicular.

9. $(3, 4)$ **10.** $(2, -4)$ **11.** $(-8, 6)$ **12.** $(6, 8)$ **13.** $(6, -12)$

OBJECTIVE: *State and apply theorems that can be used to prove lines parallel.*

3-3 Proving Lines Parallel

EXPLORE

Draw line *m* and point *A* on the line and point *P* above the line. Then draw a transversal through *P* that intersects line *m* at *A*.

Locate and draw the translation image in the direction of vector $\overrightarrow{AP}$ of this figure using tracing paper. (Trace the figure and slide the tracing the distance and direction of $\overrightarrow{AP}$.) Since translations preserve angle measure $m\angle 1 = m\angle 2$. Do you think line *m* and its translation image are parallel?

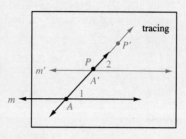

In the previous lesson, the hypothesis of each theorem stated that two lines were parallel and the conclusion concerned angle measures. In this lesson, the hypothesis of each theorem is a statement about angle measures and the conclusion states that two lines are parallel.

● **POSTULATE 14**

If two lines are cut by a transversal and a pair of corresponding angles are congruent, then the lines are parallel.

◆ **THEOREM 3.5**

If two lines are cut by a transversal and a pair of alternate interior angles are congruent, then the lines are parallel.

Given: $\angle 1 \cong \angle 2$
Prove: $a \| b$

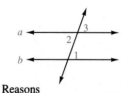

Proof

Statements	Reasons
1. $\angle 1 \cong \angle 2$	1. Given
2. $\angle 2 \cong \angle 3$	2. Vertical angles are $\cong$.
3. $\angle 1 \cong \angle 3$	3. Congruence of $\angle$s is transitive.
4. $a \| b$	4. If two lines are cut by a transversal and corr. $\angle$s are $\cong$, the lines are $\|$.

First Five Minutes

(Quiz on previous lesson)

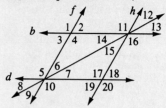

If $b \| d$, $f \| h$, $m\angle 5 = 120$ and $m\angle 14 = 25$, **find the measure of each angle.**

1. $m\angle 2$ 60
2. $m\angle 3$ 60
3. $m\angle 4$ 120
4. $m\angle 7$ 25
5. $m\angle 9$ 35
6. $m\angle 11$ 120
7. $m\angle 13$ 25
8. $m\angle 15$ 35
9. $m\angle 18$ 60
10. $m\angle 20$ 120

Lesson Opener

Begin by reviewing the four properties of parallel lines. In this lesson, the situation is reversed from that of the previous lesson. Ask the questions: If certain relationships between angles formed by a transversal and two lines exist, are the two lines parallel? Is the converse of Postulate 13 true? Help students recall from Chapter 1 that the converse of a conditional is formed by reversing the hypothesis and conclusion.

Optional Explore

Draw a transversal *t* through a point *P* and then construct congruent corresponding angles, $\angle 1$ and $\angle 2$. (See page 391, Construction 2.) This construction produces parallel lines. Therefore Postulate 14, the converse of Postulate 13, is true.

Materials

student notebooks
compasses
protractors

Guided Practice

Chalkboard Example

$m\angle 1 + m\angle 2 + m\angle 3 = 180$
Which lines are parallel? State the theorem or postulate that justifies your answer. $\overline{AB}\,\|\,\overline{DC}$, If two lines are cut by a trans. and a pair of same-side int. angles are supplementary, then the lines are parallel.

Answer to **Try This**
$m\angle 4 + m\angle 5 = 180$

2. $m\angle 1 = 4x + 17$, $m\angle 2 = 9x - 43$ Find the value of x for which $a\,\|\,b$. $4x + 17 = 9x - 43$, $5x = 60$, $x = 12$

Answer to **Try This** 11

Class Exercise Answers

1. $\overline{AB}\,\|\,\overline{DC}$ (If two lines are cut by a trans. and alt. int. $\angle$s are $\cong$, the lines are $\|$.)   **2.** $c\,\|\,d$ (If two lines are cut by a trans. and alt. ext. $\angle$s are $\cong$, the lines are $\|$.)   **3.** $\overline{QR}\,\|\,\overline{NP}$ (If two lines are cut by a trans. and corr. $\angle$s are $\cong$, the lines are $\|$.) **4.** $\overline{AD}\,\|\,\overline{BC}$ (If two lines are cut by a trans. and same-side int. $\angle$s are supplementary, the lines are $\|$.)   **5.** $\overline{AD}\,\|\,\overline{BC}$ (If two lines are cut by a trans. and corr. $\angle$s are $\cong$, the lines are $\|$.)
6. $x = 30$ **7.** $x = 68$
8. $x = 40$ **9.** $m\angle 3$ must double.   **10.** $m\angle 2$ must decrease by 30.

◆ **THEOREM 3.6**

If two lines are cut by a transversal and a pair of alternate exterior angles are congruent, then the lines are parallel.

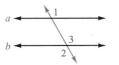

◆ **THEOREM 3.7**

If two lines are cut by a transversal and a pair of same-side interior angles are supplementary, then the lines are parallel

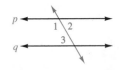

You will be asked to prove Theorems 3.6 and 3.7 in Exercises 20 and 25.

Example 1

Use the given information to determine which lines are parallel. State the theorem or postulate that justifies your answer.

a. $\angle 3 \cong \angle 5$ **b.** $m\angle 1 + m\angle 2 = m\angle 4$

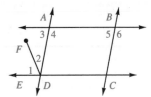

    Solution

    a. $\overline{AD}\,\|\,\overline{BC}$ *If two lines are cut by a transversal and a pair of corr. $\angle$s are $\cong$, then the lines are $\|$.*

    b. $\overline{AB}\,\|\,\overline{CD}$ *If two lines are cut by a transversal and a pair of alternate interior $\angle$s are $\cong$, then the lines are $\|$.*

Try This

Write a statement about a pair of same-side interior angles that makes $\overline{AD}\,\|\,\overline{BC}$.

Example 2

$m\angle 2 = 12x + 7$, $m\angle 3 = 8x - 7$ Find the value of x for which $a\,\|\,b$.

    Solution

$$(12x + 7) + (8x - 7) = 180$$
$$20x = 180$$
$$x = 9$$

If same-side interior angles are supplementary, then the lines are parallel.

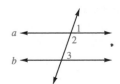

Try This

$m\angle 1 = 2x + 6$, $m\angle 3 = 3x - 5$ Find the value of x for which $a\,\|\,b$.

◆ **THEOREM 3.8**

In a plane, two coplanar lines perpendicular to the same line are parallel.

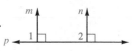

You will be asked to prove Theorems 3.8 and 3.9 in Exercises 30–31.

◆ **THEOREM 3.9**

Two lines parallel to a third line are parallel to each other.

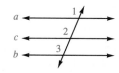

Ways to Prove Two Lines Parallel Using a Transversal

1. Show that a pair of corresponding angles are congruent.
2. Show that a pair of alternate interior angles are congruent.
3. Show that a pair of alternate exterior angles are congruent.
4. Show that a pair of same-side interior angles are supplementary.
5. Show that two coplanar lines are perpendicular to the same line.

Class Exercises

Short Answer

Congruent angles are marked. State which lines are parallel. Give the theorem or postulate that justifies your answer.

1.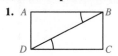

2.

3.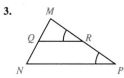

Sample Exercises

Use the given information to state which lines are parallel. Give the theorem or postulate that justifies your answer.

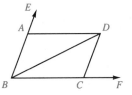

4. $m\angle BAD = 113$, $m\angle ABC = 67$, $m\angle BCD = 103$

5. $m\angle EAD = 57$, $m\angle ABC = 57$, $m\angle DCF = 67$

Find the value of x for which $a \parallel b$.

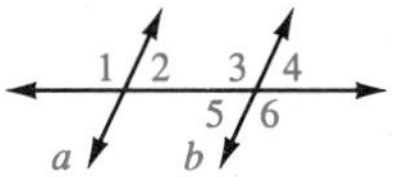

6. $m\angle 2 = 2x$, $m\angle 3 = 4x$

7. $m\angle 1 = 2x$, $m\angle 6 = 136$

8. $m\angle 1 = 3x$, $m\angle 5 = 60$

Discussion

9. If $\overline{AD} \parallel \overline{BC}$ and $m\angle 1$ is doubled, how must $m\angle 3$ change if $\overline{AD}$ is to remain parallel to $\overline{BC}$?

10. If $\overline{AB} \parallel \overline{DC}$ and $m\angle 1$ is increased by 30 degrees, how must $m\angle 2$ change if $\overline{AB}$ is to remain parallel to $\overline{DC}$?

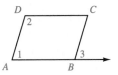

Assignment Guide
Minimum: 1–27 e/o, 30, MR
Regular: 1–27 e/o, 28–30, MR
Advanced: 1–17 e/o, 18–30, MR

Algebra
Class Exercises 6–8
Exercises 14–19, 21–24

Lesson Closure

Summarize the lesson by asking students to name the five ways of proving two lines parallel. (Illustrate on the chalkboard or overhead.)

Teacher's Resource Materials

Manipulatives 16
Practice 18   Quiz 5
Transparency 11

Exercise Answers

1. $a \parallel c$ (If two lines are cut by a trans. and corr. ∠s are ≅, the lines are ∥.)   **2.** $a \parallel b$ (If two lines are cut by a trans. and alt. int. ∠s are ≅, the lines are ∥.)
3. $b \parallel c$ (If two lines are cut by a trans. and same-side int. ∠s are supplementary, the lines are ∥.)

4. $a \| c$ (If two lines are cut by a trans. and alt. int. ∠s are ≅, the lines are ∥.) **5.** $b \| c$ (If two lines are cut by a trans. and corr. ∠s are ≅, the lines are ∥.)
6. $a \| b$ (If two lines are cut by a trans. and alt. ext. ∠s are ≅, the lines are ∥.) **7.** yes (If two lines are cut by a trans. and same-side int. ∠s are supplementary, the lines are ∥.)
8. yes ($m\angle 1 + m\angle 2 + m\angle 4 = 180$, so ∠4 and ∠7 are equal; ∠4 and ∠7 are alt. int. ∠s, so $a \| b$ by Theorem 3.5.)
9. ∠3 and ∠7, ∠1 and ∠8
10. yes   **11.** yes   **12.** no
13. no   **14.** $x = 19$
15. $x = 15$ **16.** $x = 60$
17. $x = 12$ **18.** $x = 3$
19. $x = 8$ **20** 1. Given
2. Vertical ∠s are ≅. 3. Congruence of ∠s is transitive. 4. If two lines are cut by a trans. and corr. ∠s are ≅, the lines are ∥.)
21. $x = 118, y = 0$
22. $x = 45, y = 15$
23. $x = 15, y = -12$
24. $x = 3, y = -20$
25. 1. ∠1 and ∠3 are supplementary. (Given) 2. ∠1 and ∠2 are supplementary. (Def. of linear pair) 3. ∠3 ≅ ∠2 (Substitution) 4. $p \| q$ (If two lines are cut by a trans. and alt. int. ∠s are ≅, the lines are ∥.)
26. $\overline{AD} \| \overline{CB}$ **27.** 65
28. $\overline{AD} \| \overline{BC}$ **29.** 1. $m \perp p$, $n \perp p$ (Given) 2. ∠1 and ∠2 are rt. ∠s (Def. of ⊥) 3. ∠1 ≅ ∠2 (Rt. ∠s are ≅.) 4. $m \| n$ (If two lines are cut by a trans. and corr. ∠s are ≅, the lines are ∥.)
30. 1. $a \| c$ (Given) 2. ∠1 ≅ ∠2 (If two ∥ lines are cut by a trans., then corr. ∠s are ≅.) 3. $b \| c$ (Given) 4. ∠2 ≅ ∠3 (If two ∥ lines are cut by a trans., then corr. ∠s are ≅.) 5. ∠1 ≅ ∠3 (Transitive Prop.) 6 $a \| b$ (If two lines are cut by a trans. and corr. ∠s are ≅, the lines are ∥.)

Exercises

A

Use the given information to state which lines are parallel. Give the theorem or postulate that justifies your answer.

1. ∠1 ≅ ∠9   **2.** ∠3 ≅ ∠6   **3.** $m\angle 8 + m\angle 10 = 180$
4. ∠4 ≅ ∠9   **5.** ∠8 ≅ ∠12   **6.** ∠1 ≅ ∠8

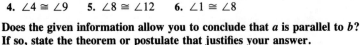

Does the given information allow you to conclude that a is parallel to b? If so, state the theorem or postulate that justifies your answer.

7. $m\angle 4 + m\angle 5 + m\angle 8 = 180$
8. $m\angle 1 + m\angle 2 + m\angle 7 = 180$

9. Name two pairs of corresponding angles that, if congruent, would allow you to conclude that a is parallel b.

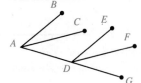

Use the given information to determine if $\overline{AC}$ is parallel to $\overline{DF}$.

10. $m\angle BAD = 42$, $m\angle BAC = 25$, $m\angle FDG = 17$
11. $m\angle BAD = 68$, $m\angle FDG = 34$, $\overline{AC}$ bisects ∠BAD.
12. $m\angle EDF = 28$, $m\angle EDA = 100$, $m\angle CAD = 54$
13. $m\angle BAC = 35$, $m\angle BAD = 61$, $m\angle ADE = 119$, $m\angle ADF = 144$

Find the value of x for which p is parallel to q.

14. $m\angle 1 = 3x + 13$, $m\angle 4 = 4x - 6$
15. $m\angle 3 = 4x + 2$, $m\angle 5 = 8x - 2$
16. $m\angle 2 = \frac{2}{3}x - 16$, $m\angle 5 = 24$
17. $m\angle 1 = 2x + 12$, $m\angle 6 = \frac{3}{4}x + 27$
18. $m\angle 2 = x^2 + 7x$, $m\angle 5 = 9x + 3$
19. $m\angle 3 = x^2 + 8x$, $m\angle 5 = 4x + 20$

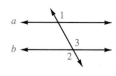

20. Complete the proof of Theorem 3.6.

Given: ∠1 ≅ ∠2
Prove: $a \| b$

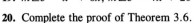

Proof

Statements	Reasons
1. ∠1 ≅ ∠2	1. ___
2. ∠2 ≅ ∠3	2. ___
3. ∠1 ≅ ∠3	3. ___
4. $a \| b$	4. ___

B

Determine the values of x and y for which $m \| n$.

21. $m\angle 1 = x + y$, $m\angle 4 = x - y$, $m\angle 8 = 118$
22. $m\angle 3 = 2x - y$, $m\angle 6 = x + 2y$, $m\angle 7 = 75$
23. $m\angle 1 = 6x - 3y$, $m\angle 4 = 2x - 8y$, $m\angle 5 = 126$
24. $m\angle 2 = 63$, $m\angle 3 = x - 3y$, $m\angle 6 = 7x - 2y + 2$
25. Write a two-column proof for Theorem 3.7.

Given: ∠1 and ∠3 are supplementary.
Prove: $p \| q$

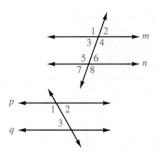

26. In figure *ABCD*, $\overline{AD} \perp \overline{BA}$ and $\overline{CB} \perp \overline{AB}$. Draw the figure and determine which lines, if any, are parallel.

27. In figure *ABCD*, $\overline{CD} \perp \overline{BC}$, $\overline{AB} \perp \overline{BC}$, and $m\angle DAB = 115$. Draw the figure and find the measure of $\angle ADC$.

28. In figure *ABCD*, $m\angle A = 115$, $m\angle ABD = 35$, $m\angle DBC = 30$, and $m\angle BDC = 30$. Draw the figure and determine which lines are parallel.

29. Write a proof for Theorem 3.8.
    Given: $m \perp p$
           $n \perp p$
    Prove: $m \| n$

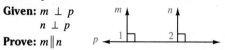

30. Write a proof for Theorem 3.9.
    Given: $a \| c$, $b \| c$
    Prove: $a \| b$

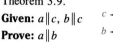

C

31. **Given:** $\angle BCD \cong \angle CDE$, $m\angle B + m\angle D = 180$
    Prove: $\overline{AB} \| \overline{DC}$

32. Draw two parallel lines, *a* and *b*, and a transversal *t*. Use a protractor to bisect a pair of alternate exterior angles. Write a statement about these bisectors. Prove the statement.

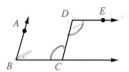

Critical Thinking

33. Consider the relation "is parallel to." Determine whether the reflexive, symmetric, and transitive properties hold for this relation for **a.** lines in a plane **b.** lines in space.

Mixed Review

Classify each triangle as acute, right, or obtuse.

1.
2.
3.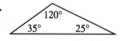
4.

Quiz

Determine whether each statement is true or false.

1. $\angle 1$ and $\angle 3$ are alternate interior angles.
2. $\angle 3$ and $\angle 2$ are corresponding angles.
3. If $t \| v$, then $m\angle 2 + m\angle 5 = 180$.
4. If $\angle 2 \cong \angle 4$, then $t \| v$.
5. If $t \| v$, $r \| s$, and $m\angle 4 = 24$, then $m\angle 3 = 24$.

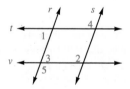

Use the given information to name the lines, if any, that are parallel.

6. $\angle 3 \cong \angle 7$ 7. $\angle 2 \cong \angle 6$
8. $\angle 2 \cong \angle 3$ 9. $\angle ACE \cong \angle BDC$
10. $m\angle ACD + m\angle BDC = 180$
11. $m\angle 2 = 3x + 10$, $m\angle 5 = x + 28$. Find the value of *x* for which $\overline{AB} \| \overline{CD}$.

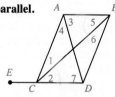

---

31. 1. $\angle BCD \cong \angle CDE$, $m\angle B + m\angle D = 180$ (Given) **2.** $m\angle B + m\angle C = 180$ (Substitution) **3.** $\overline{AB} \| \overline{CD}$ (If two lines are cut by a trans. and same-side int. $\angle$s are supplementary, the lines are $\|$.)

32.

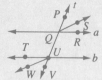

If two $\|$ lines are cut by a trans., then the bisectors of their alt. ext. $\angle$s are also $\|$. Given: $a \| b$, $\overrightarrow{QS}$ bisects $\angle PQR$. $\overrightarrow{UW}$ bisects $\angle TUV$. Prove: $\overrightarrow{QS} \| \overrightarrow{UW}$
1. $a \| b$ (Given) **2.** $\angle PQR \cong \angle TUV$ (If two $\|$ lines are cut by a trans. then alt. ext. $\angle$s are $\cong$.) **3.** $\overrightarrow{QS}$ bisects $\angle PQR$. $\overrightarrow{UW}$ bisects $\angle TUV$. (Given) **4.** $m\angle PQS = \frac{1}{2} m\angle PQR$, $m\angle WUV = \frac{1}{2} m\angle TUV$ (Def. of $\angle$ bisector) **5.** $\angle PQS \cong \angle WUV$ (Substitution) **6.** $\overrightarrow{QS} \| \overrightarrow{UW}$ (If two lines are cut by a trans. and alt. ext. $\angle$s are $\cong$, the lines are $\|$.)
33. a. reflexive: no, symmetric: yes, transitive: no.
b. reflexive: no, symmetric: yes, transitive: no

Mixed Review Answers

1. acute   **2.** acute
3. obtuse   **4.** right

Quiz Answers

1. true   **2.** false   **3.** false
4. true   **5.** false
6. $\overline{AB} \| \overline{ED}$ **7.** No lines are $\|$.
8. No lines are $\|$.   **9.** $\overline{AC} \| \overline{BD}$
10. $\overline{AC} \| \overline{BD}$ **11.** $x = 9$

$3x + 10 = x + 28$
$2x = 18$
$x = 9$

Exercise Answers
1. point C
2. line r
3. They are equal.
4. line p
5. line q
6. Theorem 3.6

COMPARING APPROACHES IN GEOMETRY

Synthetic and Transformation Geometry

Theorem 3.5

If two lines are cut by a transversal and a pair of alternate interior angles are congruent, then the lines are parallel.

Theorem 3.5 is proven on page 117 using what is called a synthetic approach, as are all other proofs based on the set of axioms that you are learning.

Transformation proofs are usually based on the properties that are preserved by the transformation being used. For example, on page 31, you learned that translations, reflections, and rotations preserve segment length and angle measure. A property of 180° rotations used below is that a line and its rotation image are parallel.

Compare the synthetic and transformation approaches to a proof of Theorem 3.5.

Synthetic Approach	**Transformation Approach**
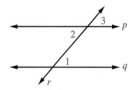	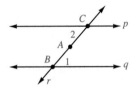

Plan for Proof

It is given that $\angle 1 \cong \angle 2$. By the vertical angles theorem you know that $\angle 2 \cong \angle 3$. Finally use the fact that congruence of angles is transitive to conclude that $\angle 1 \cong \angle 3$. Since corresponding angles are congruent, the lines must be parallel.

Plan for Proof

Consider the 180° rotation with center A—the midpoint of $\overline{BC}$. The rotation image of point B is C and of line r is again line r. Since $\angle 1 \cong \angle 2$, the rotation image of $\angle 1$ must be $\angle 2$. Therefore, the rotation image of p is q. It follows that $p \parallel q$.

Exercises

A is the midpoint of $\overline{BC}$ and the alternate exterior angles $\angle 3$ and $\angle 4$ are congruent. Consider the 180° rotation image centered at A.

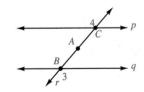

1. Find the rotation image of point B.
2. Find the rotation image of line r.
3. How does the rotation image of $\angle 3$ compare with $\angle 3$ in measure?
4. Find the rotation image of line q.
5. Since the 180° rotation image of line q is parallel to q itself, you can conclude that line p is parallel to __?__ .
6. The statements in Exercises 1–5 outline a transformation proof to what theorem?

122   *Chapter 3 Parallel Lines and Planes*

ANGLE SUM THEOREMS

OBJECTIVE: *Apply the Angle Sum Theorem for Triangles and related corollaries.*

3-4 Angles of a Triangle

 **EXPLORE** Draw any triangle. Use tracing paper to draw the 180° rotation image of the triangle centered at points A and B—the midpoints of two sides of the triangle. What can you conclude about $m\angle 1 + m\angle 2 + m\angle 3$?

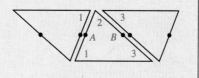

You may have discovered in the Explore that you need the following postulate to prove the theorem.

● POSTULATE 15

Given a line *l* and a point *P* not on *l*, there exists one and only one line through *P* parallel to *l*.

A line added to a figure is called an **auxiliary line**. An auxiliary line is added in the proof of the following theorem.

◆ THEOREM 3.10 Angle Sum Theorem for Triangles

The sum of the measures of the angles of a triangle is 180.

Given: △ABC
Prove: $m\angle 1 + m\angle 2 + m\angle 3 = 180$

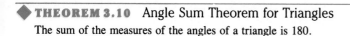

Proof

Statements	Reasons
1. Let *l* be the only line through $\overline{A}$ parallel to $\overline{BC}$.	1. Given a line *l* and a point *P* not on *l*, there exists one and only one line through *P* parallel to *l*. (Postulate 15)
2. $m\angle 4 = m\angle 2,\ m\angle 1 = m\angle 5$	2. If two ∥ lines are cut by a transversal, then the alternate interior ∠s are ≅.
3. $m\angle 5 + m\angle 4 + m\angle 3 = 180$	3. Linear Pair Postulate
4. $m\angle 1 + m\angle 2 + m\angle 3 = 180$	4. Substitution

3-4 Angles of a Triangle **123**

First Five Minutes

(Quiz on previous lesson)

Draw a conclusion by stating which lines are parallel, if any. Then state the definition, postulate, or theorem that justifies your answer.

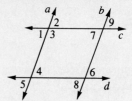

1. Given: $\angle 1 \cong \angle 7$
Conclusion: ? $a \| b$ **(If two lines are cut by a trans. and corr. ∠s are ≅, the lines are ∥.)**
2. Given: $\angle 4 \cong \angle 8$
Conclusion: ? $a \| b$ **(If two lines are cut by a trans. and alt. int. ∠s are ≅, the lines are ∥.)**
3. Given: $\angle 3$ and $\angle 4$ are supplementary. Conclusion: ? $c \| d$ **(If two lines are cut by a trans. and same-side ∠s are supp., the lines are ∥.)**
4. Given: $\angle 5 \cong \angle 6$
Conclusion: ? $a \| b$ **(If two lines are cut by a trans. and alt. ext. ∠s are ≅, the lines are ∥.)**
5. Given: $\angle 7 \cong \angle 9$
Conclusion: ? none

Lesson Opener

Theorem 3.10 may be familiar to some students. It is sometimes introduced in algebra to solve word problems. Some students may have already concluded, on the basis of intuition or through experimentation, that the sum of the measures of the three angles of any triangle is 180.

Have students draw several triangles and measure the angles to the nearest degree. Then ask students what the sum of the measures of the three angles is.

Materials

student notebooks
protractors
straightedges

Teaching Notes

The proof of Theorem 3.10 uses an auxiliary line. Remind students that auxiliary lines should be drawn *only* when they are useful and necessary. Point out how drawing the parallel through one vertex in effect arranges the three angles of the triangle at the vertex in the same way as in the Explore.

Guided Practice

Chalkboard Examples

1. Find $m\angle A$, $m\angle B$, and $m\angle C$ if $\triangle ABC$ is equiangular. $m\angle A = m\angle B = m\angle C = 60$

Answer to **Try This** 40

2. If the measures of the three angles of $\triangle ABC$ are in the ratio 4:5:6, is the measure of its largest angle less than or greater than the measure of the largest angle of a triangle whose angles are in the ratio 1:2:3? **less than**

Answer to **Try This** acute

REMINDER: Since a corollary is derived from another theorem, Corollaries 3.10a and 3.10b can be used as reasons in proofs.

Example 1

Find the measure of each angle.
a. $\angle A$ **b.** $\angle B$

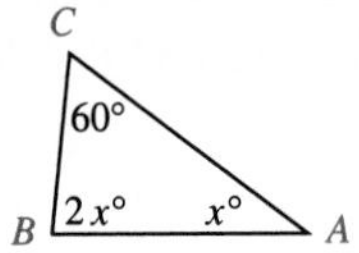

Solution

a. $x + 2x + 60 = 180$ *The sum of the measures of the angles of a triangle is 180.*
$3x = 120$
$x = 40$
$m\angle A = 40$

b. $m\angle B = 2x$
$m\angle B = 2(40)$
$m\angle B = 80$

Try This

In $\triangle ABC$, $\angle B \cong \angle C$ and $m\angle CAB = 100$. Find $m\angle B$.

Example 2

The measures of the angles of $\triangle ABC$ are in the ratio 1 : 2 : 3. Classify the triangle as acute, right, or obtuse.

Solution

Let $x = m\angle A$
$2x = m\angle B$
$3x = m\angle C$
$x + 2x + 3x = 180$ *The sum of the measures of the angles of a triangle is 180.*
$6x = 180$
$x = 30$
$m\angle A = 30$, $m\angle B = 60$, $m\angle C = 90$
Therefore $\triangle ABC$ is a right triangle.

Try This

The measures of the angles of $\triangle PQR$ are in the ratio of 2 : 3 : 4. Classify the triangle as acute, right, or obtuse.

A statement that is a direct consequence of a particular theorem is called a **corollary** of the theorem. Below are two corollaries of Theorem 3.10. They are corollaries because they are easily derived from the Angle Sum Theorem for Triangles.

▶ **COROLLARY 3.10a**

The angles of an equiangular triangle each have a measure of 60.

▶ **COROLLARY 3.10b**

The acute angles of a right triangle are complementary.

You will be asked to prove these corollaries in Exercises 24 and 25.

124 Chapter 3 Parallel Lines and Planes

Class Exercises

Short Answer

Find the value of x.

1.

2.

3.

4. Two angles of a triangle have measures of 50 and 100. Find the measure of the third angle.
5. Two angles of a triangle have measures of 25 and 55. Classify the triangle as acute, right, or obtuse.
6. Two angles of a right triangle are congruent. Find the measures of the angles.

Sample Exercises

Find the value of x. Congruent angles are marked.

7.

8.
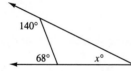

9.
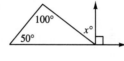

10. $\triangle ABC$ has $\angle B \cong \angle C$. If $m\angle A$ is increased by 20 and $\angle B$ remains congruent to $\angle C$, by how much are $m\angle B$ and $m\angle C$ decreased?
11. $\triangle ABC$ has $\angle B \cong \angle C$. If $m\angle B$ is increased by 15 and $\angle C$ is altered to remain congruent to $\angle B$, what is the effect on $m\angle A$?

Draw the indicated triangle, or write *not possible*.

12. acute equiangular triangle   13. obtuse equiangular triangle

Discussion

14. What is the greatest number of right angles a triangle can have?
15. What is the greatest number of acute angles a triangle can have?

Exercises

A

Draw the indicated triangle, or write *not possible*.

1. right triangle with two congruent angles
2. right equiangular triangle
3. obtuse right triangle
4. acute scalene triangle
5. acute triangle with two congruent angles
6. obtuse equiangular triangle
7. right scalene triangle
8. scalene isosceles triangle

7. 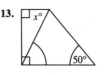 **8.** not possible

9. 70 **10.** 60 **11.** 55
12. 35 **13.** 50 **14.** 26
15. 50 **16.** 100 **17.** 104
18. 48, 60, 72; acute
19. 20, 60, 100; obtuse
20. 36, 54 **21.** 80, 80, 20
22. 116 **23.** Given: △ABC is
equiangular. Prove: $m\angle A =$
$m\angle B = m\angle C = 60$. 1. △ABC is
equiangular. (Given) 2. $m\angle A =$
$m\angle B = m\angle C$ (Def. of equiangular) 3. $m\angle A + m\angle B + m\angle C =$
180 (Sum of measures of ∠s of
△ = 180) 4. $3(m\angle A) = 180$
(Subst.) 5. $m\angle A = 60$ (Mult.
Prop. of =) 6. $m\angle A = m\angle B =$
$m\angle C = 60$ (Subst.)
24. Given: △ABC, ∠A is a rt. ∠.
Prove: ∠B and ∠C are comp.
1. ∠A is a rt. ∠. (Given)
2. $m\angle A = 90$ (Def. of rt. ∠)
3. $m\angle A + m\angle B + m\angle C = 180$
(Sum of measures of ∠s of △ =
180) 4. $90 + m\angle B + m\angle C =$
180 (Subst.) 5. $m\angle B + m\angle C =$
90 (Add. Prop. of =) 6. ∠B and
∠C are comp. (Def. of comp. ∠s)
25. 18, 18, 144
26. 55, 40, 85
27. 31, 31, 118
28. 18, 72, 90
29. 130 **30.** 80 **31.** 40
32. 110 **33.** 54 **34.** 46
35. Extend $\overline{BA}$ to form a △CBF.
1. $\overline{AB} \parallel \overline{DE}$ (Given) 2. ∠D ≅
∠BFC (If ∥ lines are cut by a
trans., corr. ∠s are ≅.)
3. $m\angle B + m\angle C + m\angle BFC =$
180 (The sum of the measures
of the ∠s of a △ is 180.)
4. $m\angle B + m\angle C + m\angle D =$
180 (Subst.)

Find the value of x. Congruent angles are marked.

9.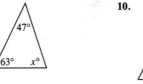

10.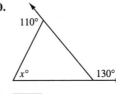

11.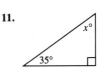

12.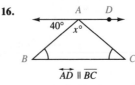

13.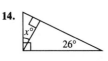

14.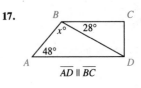

15.
$\overline{BC} \parallel \overline{DE}$

16.
$\overrightarrow{AD} \parallel \overline{BC}$

17.
$\overline{AD} \parallel \overline{BC}$

18. The ratio of the measures of the angles of a triangle is 4 : 5 : 6. Find the measures of the angles and classify the triangle as acute, right, or obtuse.
19. The ratio of the measures of the angles of a triangle is 1 : 3 : 5. Find the measures of the angles and classify the triangle as acute, right, or obtuse.
20. The ratio of the measures of the acute angles of a right triangle is 2 : 3. Find the measures of the two acute angles.
21. The measure of each of two angles of a triangle is four times that of the third angle. Find the measures of the angles.
22. The rafters of a roof form an angle of 32° at the base. What angle do the rafters form at the ridge?
23. Write a two-column proof for Corollary 3.10a.
   Given: △ABC is equiangular.
   Prove: $m\angle A = m\angle B = m\angle C = 60$
24. Write a two-column proof for Corollary 3.10b.
   Given: △ABC, ∠A is a right angle.
   Prove: ∠B and ∠C are complementary.

B

25. The measures of the angles of a triangle are x, x, and $\frac{4}{3}x$. If the largest angle is doubled and the triangle remains isosceles, how would you represent the measures of the angles in the new triangle?
26. The measures of the angles of a triangle are represented by $2x + 15$, $x + 20$, and $3x + 25$. Find the measures of the angles.
27. The measures of the angles of a triangle are x, x, and $3x$. If the measure of the largest angle is increased by ten and the triangle remains isosceles, how would you represent the measures of the angles in the new triangle?
28. In a right triangle, the measure of one acute angle is four times the measure of the other. Find the measures of the angles of △MNO.

Find the value of *x*. Congruent angles are marked.

29.

30.

31.

32.

33.

34.

35. **Given:** $\overline{AB} \parallel \overline{DE}$
    Prove: $m \angle B + m \angle C + m \angle D = 180$

36. **Given:** $\overline{DE} \perp \overline{AE}, \overline{BD} \perp \overline{AB}$
    Prove: $m \angle CAB = m \angle CDE$

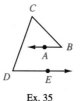

Ex. 35

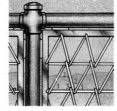

Ex. 36

37. The pattern of triangles shown, a chain-link fence, illustrates the Angle Sum Theorem for Triangles. Use the figure to demonstrate the Angle Sum Theorem for Triangles.

C

38. **Given:** $\overline{AD}$ bisects $\angle CAB$.
    $\overline{BD}$ bisects $\angle CBA$.
    $m \angle CAB = m \angle CBA$
    Prove: $\angle ADB \cong \angle CBE$

39. $\overline{AD}$ bisects $\angle CAB$.
    $\overline{BD}$ bisects $\angle EBC$. $m \angle D = 40$
    Find $m \angle C$.

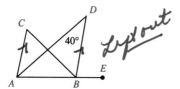

Critical Thinking

40. Accept as a postulate that the acute angles of a right triangle are complementary. Use this to prove that the sum of the measures of the angles of triangles is 180. (HINT: Draw a perpendicular from *A* to $\overline{BC}$.)

Mixed Review

1. The measure of the supplement of an angle is three times the measure of the angle. Find the measure of the angle and its supplement.
2. The measure of the complement of an angle is five times the measure of the angle. Find the measure of the angle and its complement.

3-4 Angles of a Triangle **127**

---

36. 1. $\overline{DE} \perp \overline{AE}, \overline{BD} \perp \overline{AB}$ (Given) 2. $m \angle DEC = 90$, $m \angle DBA = 90$ (Def. of $\perp$ lines) 3. $\triangle CDE$ and $\triangle ABC$ are rt. $\triangle$s (Def. of rt. $\triangle$) 4. $\angle CAB$ is comp. to $\angle ACB$. $\angle CDE$ is comp. to $\angle DCE$. (Acute $\angle$s of a rt. $\triangle$ are comp.) 5. $\angle ACB \cong \angle DCE$ (Vert. $\angle$s). 6. $\angle CAB \cong \angle CDE$ (Congruent Comp. Theorem) 7. $m \angle CAB = m \angle CDE$ (Def. of $\cong \angle$s)

37. $\angle$s labeled 1 are $\cong$ (corr. $\angle$s); $\angle$s labeled 2 are $\cong$ (alt. int. $\angle$s); $m \angle 1 + m \angle 2 + m \angle 3 = 180$ 38. 1. $\overline{AD}$ bisects $\angle CAB$. $\overline{BD}$ bisects $\angle CBA$. $m \angle CAB = m \angle CBA$ (Given) 2. $m \angle DAB = \frac{1}{2} m \angle CAB$, $m \angle DBA = \frac{1}{2} m \angle CBA$, $m \angle CBD = \frac{1}{2} m \angle CBA$ (Def. of $\angle$ bisector) 3. $m \angle DAB = \frac{1}{2} m \angle CBA$ (Subst.) 4. $m \angle DBA = m \angle CBD = m \angle DAB$ (Subst.) 5. $m \angle DAB + m \angle DBA + m \angle ADB = 180$ (The sum of the measures of the $\angle$s of a $\triangle$ is 180.) 6. $m \angle CBA + m \angle CBE = 180$ (Linear Pair Post.) 7. $m \angle CBD + m \angle DBA + m \angle CBE = 180$ ($\angle$ Add. Post. Subst.) 8. $m \angle ADB = m \angle CBE$ (Subst.) 9. $\angle ADB \cong \angle CBE$ (Def. of $\cong \angle$s)   39. 80

40. 1. Construct $\overline{AD} \perp \overline{BC}$. (Construction) 2. $\angle ADB, \angle ADC$ are rt. $\angle$s. (Def. of $\perp$ lines) 3. $\triangle ADB, \angle ADC$ are rt. $\triangle$s. (Def. of rt. $\triangle$) 4. $m \angle DBA + m \angle BAD = 90$, $m \angle DAC + m \angle ACD = 90$ (acute $\angle$s of a rt. $\triangle$ are comp.) 5. $m \angle DBA + m \angle BAD + m \angle DAC + m \angle ACD = 180$ (Add. Prop.) 6. $m \angle BAD + m \angle DAC = m \angle BAC$ ($\angle$ Add. Prop.) 7. $m \angle DBA + m \angle BAC + m \angle ACD = 180$ (Subst.)

Mixed Review Answers

1. 45, 135   **2.** 15, 75

Enrichment

Exercise Answers
"No-Parallel" Geometry:
1. >180   **2.** Have points *A*
and *C* as far apart as possible,
directly opposite one another.

"Many-Parallels" Geometry:
1. infinitely many   **2.** <180

Enrichment

Non-Euclidean Geometry

In this book you are studying Euclidean geometry, in which it is assumed that through a given point *P* not on a given line *l* there is exactly one line through *P* that is parallel to line *l*. But there are other geometries that differ from Euclidean geometry in their assumptions about the number of lines that contain *P* and are parallel to line *l*. Two such assumptions are (1) there are no lines through *P* parallel to line *l*, and (2) there are more than one line through *P* parallel to line *l*. (See the Historical Note on page 134.)

The "No-Parallel" Geometry

In this geometry, sometimes called "spherical" geometry, points are points on a sphere and lines are "great circles." A great circle on a sphere is a circle whose center is also the center of the sphere. Consider the equator as line *l* and New York as point *P*. Are there lines (great circles) through *P* that do not intersect the equator? Why or why not?

Exercises

Use a string and a globe to answer these questions.

   1. Use string to identify three lines (great circles) that intersect to form a spherical triangle *ABC*. Estimate the measure of each angle of △*ABC*. Does the sum of the measures of △*ABC* appear to be equal to, less than, or greater than 180?
   2. Consider the equator as one line and two other lines that pass through the north and south poles to form a triangle. How can *BA* and *BC* be placed to maximize the sum of the measures of the angles of △*ABC*?

The "Many-Parallels" Geometry

In this geometry, points consist of only those points that are in the interior of a given circle. Lines consist of arcs of circles that form "right angles" with the given circle. Thus *CD* is a line but *AB* is not a line, since *AB* is not the arc of a circle. Line *CD* is parallel to line *EF* since they do not intersect. Point *Q* is a point in this geometry, but point *X* is not a point, since it is not in the interior of the circle.

Exercises

   1. How many lines (arcs of circles) can be drawn through *P* that are parallel to line (arc) *XY*?

   2. Draw a "triangle" consisting of three arcs. Estimate the measure of each of the three angles indicated. Estimate the sum of the measures of the angles of the triangle. Does the sum of the measures appear to be equal to, less than, or greater than 180?

128   *Chapter 3   Parallel Lines and Planes*

OBJECTIVE: *Use the Exterior Angle Theorem to find the measure of an angle of a triangle.*

3-5 Theorems Related to the Angle Sum Theorem for Triangles

 **EXPLORE**   Draw triangles with one side extended, as shown. Use a protractor to measure $\angle 1$, $\angle 2$, and $\angle 3$. Compare $m\angle 1$ with $m\angle 2 + m\angle 3$. What do you discover?

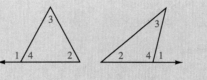

If you extend one side of a triangle, an exterior angle is formed. An **exterior angle** of a triangle forms a linear pair with the adjacent interior angle of the triangle. The two angles of the triangle that are not adjacent to the exterior angle are called the **remote interior angles** of that exterior angle.

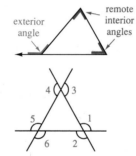

Every triangle has six exterior angles that form three pairs of vertical angles. Each angle in such a pair of vertical angles has the same remote interior angles. For example, $\angle 3$ and $\angle 4$ have the same remote interior angles.

The following theorem is a consequence of the Angle Sum Theorem for Triangles and states a relationship between an exterior angle of a triangle and its remote interior angles.

◆ **THEOREM 3.11**   The Exterior Angle Theorem
The measure of an exterior angle of a triangle is equal to the sum of the measures of its two remote interior angles.

Given: $\triangle ABC$ with exterior $\angle 1$
Prove: $m\angle 1 = m\angle A + m\angle B$

Proof

Statements	Reasons
1. $\triangle ABC$ with exterior $\angle 1$	1. Given
2. $\angle 1$ and $\angle 4$ form a linear pair.	2. Definition of linear pair
3. $m\angle 1 + m\angle 4 = 180$	3. Two angles that form a linear pair are supplementary.
4. $m\angle 1 = 180 - m\angle 4$	4. Addition Property of Equations
5. $m\angle A + m\angle B + m\angle 4 = 180$	5. Angle Sum Theorem for Triangles
6. $m\angle A + m\angle B = 180 - m\angle 4$	6. Addition Property of Equations
7. $m\angle A + m\angle B = m\angle 1$	7. Substitution Property

3-5 Theorems Related to the Angle Sum Theorem for Triangles   **129**

First Five Minutes

(Quiz on previous lesson)

Find the numerical measures of the three angles described in each triangle.

1. A triangle with angle measures x, $x + 10$, and $x - 10$.
60, 70, 50
2. A triangle with angle measures x, $2x - 5$, and $2x - 15$.
40, 75, 65
3. A triangle with angle measures in the ratio 2:5:5.
30, 75, 75

Lesson Opener

Introduce the lesson by drawing several triangles and extending one side of each as shown in the Explore. Label the angles. Explain that $\angle 3$ and $\angle 2$ are sometimes called interior angles to distinguish them from the exterior angles of a triangle, of which $\angle 1$ is an example. Notice that $\angle 4$ forms a linear pair with $\angle 1$. Recall from Chapter 2 that two angles that form a linear pair are supplementary; that is, the sum of the meaures of a linear pair of angles is 180.

Using a protractor, measure $\angle 1$, $\angle 2$, and $\angle 3$ and record the results inside the angles.

Key Questions

1. Is it necessary to measure $\angle 4$? why not?
No; $m\angle 4 = 180 - m\angle 1$.
2. What is $m\angle 1 + m\angle 2 + m\angle 3$? Justify your answer.
$m\angle 1 = 180 - m\angle 4$ and $m\angle 3 + m\angle 2 = 180 - m\angle 4$, so
$m\angle 1 + m\angle 2 + m\angle 3 = 2(180 - m\angle 4)$.

3. Which is larger, $m\angle 1$ or $m\angle 2$? *m∠1* Which is larger, $m\angle 1$ or $m\angle 3$? *m∠1*
4. How does $m\angle 1$ compare with $m\angle 2 + m\angle 3$?
m∠1 = m∠2 + m∠3

Materials

student notebooks
protractors
straightedges

Teaching Notes

Point out that there are six possible exterior angles of a triangle—two exterior angles at each vertex which are vertical angles.

Emphasize that the proofs of Theorems 3.11 and 3.12 are based on the Angle Sum Theorem for Triangles. These are important theorems that will be used in future proofs.

Key Terms

exterior angle
interior angle
remote interior angles

Guided Practice

Chalkboard Examples

1. Find $m\angle 1$ if $m\angle 4 = 105$ and $m\angle 2 = 35$. *70*

Answer to **Try This** *45*

2. Find the value of x if the measure of the exterior angle is $4x - 10$ and the measure of the remote interior angles are 50 and $2x + 10$. *x = 35*

Answer to **Try This** *100*

Example 1

$m\angle 5 = 130$, $m\angle 3 = 38$ Find $m\angle 1$.

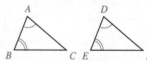

Solution

$m\angle 5 = m\angle 1 + m\angle 3$ *Exterior Angle Theorem*
$130 = m\angle 1 + 38$
$m\angle 1 = 130 - 38$
$m\angle 1 = 92$

Try This

$m\angle 6 = 87$, $m\angle 2 = 42$ Find $m\angle 3$.

Example 2

$m\angle B$ is twice $m\angle A$.   Find $m\angle ABC$.

Solution

$x + 2x = 120$ $m\angle A + m\angle B = m\angle ACD$ by the Exterior Angle Theorem
$3x = 120$
$x = 40$
$2x = 80$ $m\angle ABC = 80$

Try This

$m\angle B$ is five times $m\angle A$.   Find $m\angle B$.

◆ **THEOREM 3.12**

If two angles of one triangle are congruent to two angles of another triangle, then the third angles are congruent.

You will be asked to prove this theorem in Exercise 16.

Example 3

Identify which angles of $\triangle ABC$ are congruent to angles of $\triangle CDE$. State reasons why the angles are congruent.

Solution

$\angle ABC \cong \angle CDE$ *All right angles are congruent.*
$\angle ACB \cong \angle ECD$ *Vertical angles are congruent.*
$\angle BAC \cong \angle CED$ *If two angles of one triangle are congruent to two angles of another triangle, then the third angles are congruent.*

Try This

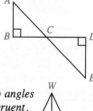

$\overline{WY}$ bisects $\angle XWZ$. Identify which angles of $\triangle WYX$ are congruent to angles of $\triangle WYZ$. State reasons why the angles are congruent.

130   *Chapter 3 Parallel Lines and Planes*

Class Exercises

Short Answer

Name the remote interior angles related to ∠4.

1.

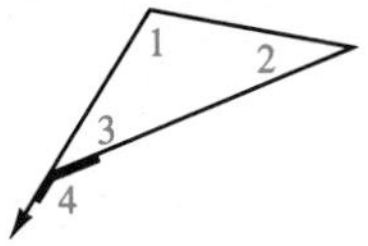

2.
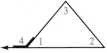

3.
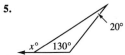

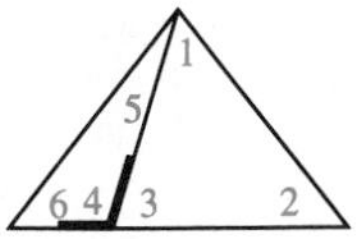

Find the value of x.

4.

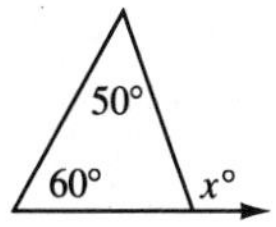

5.

6.

Sample Exercises

Find the value of x.

7.

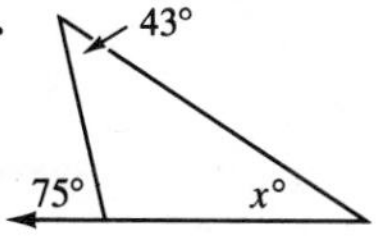

8.
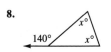

9.
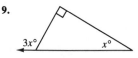

10.
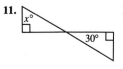

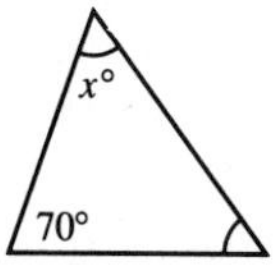

11.

12.
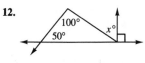

13. Complete the proof.

Given: $\overline{AD} \parallel \overline{BC}$, $\overline{AB} \parallel \overline{CD}$

Prove: $\angle B \cong \angle D$

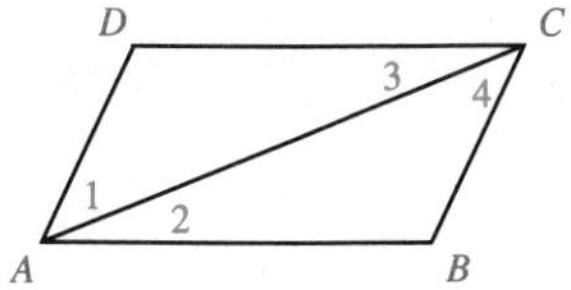

Proof

Statements	Reasons
1. $\overline{AD} \parallel \overline{BC}$	1. Given
2. $\overline{AB} \parallel \overline{CD}$	2. Given
3. $\angle 2 \cong \angle 3$	3. _____
4. $\angle 1 \cong \angle 4$	4. _____
5. $\angle B \cong \angle D$	5. _____

Discussion

14. If two angles of one triangle are congruent to two angles of another triangle, is it possible for the third angles not to be congruent? Give a convincing argument to support your answer.

15. If two sides of one triangle are congruent to two sides of another triangle, is it possible for the third sides not to be congruent? Give a convincing argument to support your answer.

3.
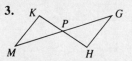

If $\overline{GH} \parallel \overline{KM}$, identify which angles of both triangles are congruent and state reasons why the angles are congruent.

∠*M* ≅ ∠*G* and ∠*K* ≅ ∠*H* (If two ∥ lines are cut by a trans., alt. int. ∠s are ≅.) ∠*KPM* ≅ ∠*GPH* (Vert. ∠s are ≅.)

Answer to **Try This**

∠*WYZ* ≅ ∠*WYX*

All right angles are congruent.

∠*XWY* ≅ ∠*ZWY*

An angle bisector forms two congruent angles.

∠*WXY* ≅ ∠*WZY*

If two angles of one triangle are congruent to two angles of another triangle, then the third angles are congruent.

Class Exercise Answers

1. ∠1 and ∠2 **2.** ∠2 and ∠3
3. ∠1 and ∠2 **4.** 110
5. 150 **6.** 65 **7.** 32
8. 70 **9.** 45 **10.** 55
11. 60 **12.** 60
13. 3. If two ∥ lines are cut by a trans., alt. int. ∠s are ≅. 4. If two ∥ lines are cut by a trans., alt. int. ∠s are ≅. 5. If two ∠s of one △ are ≅ to two ∠s of another △, the third ∠s are ≅.
14. no; the sum of the ∠s of a △ = 180, so the third ∠s are determined. **15.** yes; consider an equil. △ with sides of length 1 and a △ with sides of length 1, 1, 1.5.

Exercises

A

Find the measure of the indicated angle.

1. If $m\angle 4 = 75$ and $m\angle 2 = 40$, find $m\angle 5$.
2. If $m\angle 1 = 125$ and $m\angle 3 = 90$, find $m\angle 5$.
3. If $m\angle 5 = 40$ and $m\angle 1 = 115$, find $m\angle 4$.
4. If $m\angle 6 = 150$ and $m\angle 2 = m\angle 3$, find $m\angle 2$.
5. If $m\angle 4 = 80$ and $m\angle 2 = m\angle 5$, find $m\angle 2$.
6. If $m\angle 2 = m\angle 5$ and $m\angle 4 = 80$, find $m\angle 6$.
7. If $m\angle 1 = 100$ and $m\angle 4 = 90$, find $m\angle 6$.
8. If $m\angle 4 = 100$ and $m\angle 2$ is three times $m\angle 5$, find $m\angle 2$.
9. If $m\angle 5 = 30$ and $m\angle 4$ is twice $m\angle 2$, find $m\angle 4$.

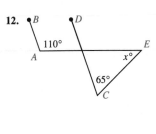

$\overline{AB} \parallel \overline{CD}$.   **Find $m\angle CEA$.**

10.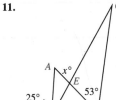

11.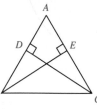

12.

13. Complete the proof.

   Given: $\angle ADC$ and $\angle AEB$ are right angles.

   Prove: $\angle ABE \cong \angle ACD$

Proof Statements	Reasons
1. $\angle ADC$ is a right angle.	1. Given
2. $\angle AEB$ is a right angle.	2. Given
3. $\angle ADC \cong \angle AEB$	3. _____
4. $\angle A \cong \angle A$	4. _____
5. $\angle ABE \cong \angle ACD$	5. _____

14. **Given:** $\angle 1 \cong \angle 2$

   Prove: $\angle 3 \cong \angle 4$

15. **Given:** $\overline{AB} \perp \overline{BD}$, $\overline{CD} \perp \overline{BD}$

   $\angle 1 \cong \angle 2$

   Prove: $\angle A \cong \angle C$

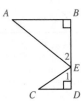

16. Write a two-column proof for Theorem 3.12.

    Given: $\angle A \cong \angle D$, $\angle B \cong \angle E$

    Prove: $\angle C \cong \angle F$

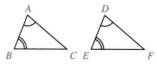

B

Find the value of x.

17.

18.

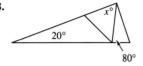
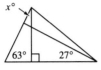

19.

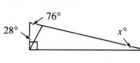

20.

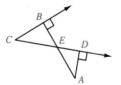

21.

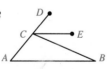

22.

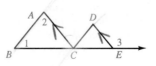

23. If the measures of the exterior angles of the acute angles of a right triangle are $2x + 15$ and $3x + 5$, find the measures of the acute angles.

24. If the ratio of the measures of the angles of a triangle is $1:2:3$, find the ratio of the measures of the exterior angles of the triangle.

25. The design for a drafting table is shown. If the line of the slant of the table top is extended to the floor a 15° angle is formed. If $\triangle ABC$ is equiangular, what are the four angles of the table leg $ADEF$?

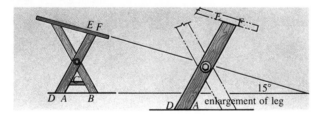

26. Given: $\overline{AB} \perp \overline{BC}$, $\overline{AD} \perp \overline{CD}$

    Prove: $\angle A \cong \angle C$

27. Given: $\overleftrightarrow{CE}$ bisects $\angle BCD$. $\angle A \cong \angle B$

    Prove: $\overline{CE} \parallel \overline{AB}$

28. Given: $\overline{AC} \parallel \overline{DE}$

    Prove: $m\angle 3 = m\angle 1 + m\angle 2$

3-5 Theorems Related to the Angle Sum Theorem for Triangles   **133**

16. Given: $\triangle ABC$ and $\triangle DEF$, $\angle A \cong \angle D$, $\angle B \cong \angle E$ Prove: $\angle C \cong \angle F$ 1. $\angle A \cong \angle D$, $\angle B \cong \angle E$ (Given) 2. $m\angle A + m\angle B + m\angle C = 180$, $m\angle D + m\angle E + m\angle F = 180$ (Triangle Angle Sum Theorem) 3. $m\angle C = 180 - (m\angle A + m\angle B)$, $m\angle F = 180 - (m\angle C + m\angle D)$ (Add. prop. of =) 4. $m\angle A + m\angle B = m\angle C + m\angle D$ (Subst.) 5. $m\angle C = m\angle F$ (Subst.)

17. 20   **18.** 60   **19.** 52

20. 53   **21.** 27   **22.** 14

23. 65 and 25   **24.** 3:4:5

25. $m\angle FAD = 120$, $m\angle DEF = 105$, $m\angle ADE = 60$, $m\angle AFE = 75$

26. 1. $\overline{AB} \perp \overline{BC}$, $\overline{AD} \perp \overline{CD}$ (Given) 2. $\angle CBE$ and $\angle ADE$ are rt. $\angle$s (Def. of $\perp$ lines) 3. $m\angle CBE = m\angle ADE = 90$ (Def. rt. $\angle$) 4. $\angle CEB \cong \angle AED$ (Vert. $\angle$s are $\cong$.) 5. $\angle A \cong \angle C$ (If two $\angle$s of one $\triangle$ are $\cong$ to two $\angle$s of another $\triangle$, the third $\angle$s are $\cong$.)

27. 1. $\overleftrightarrow{CE}$ bisects $\angle BCD$. (Given) 2. $\angle DCE \cong \angle ECB$ (Def. of $\angle$ bisector) 3. $m\angle DCE = m\angle ECB$ (Def. of $\cong \angle$s) 4. $m\angle DCE + m\angle ECB = m\angle DCB$ ($\angle$ Add. Post.) 5. $2m\angle DCE = m\angle DCB$ (Subst.) 6. $m\angle DCB = m\angle A + m\angle B$ (Ext. $\angle$ Theorem) 7. $2(m\angle DCE) = m\angle A + m\angle B$ (Subst.) 8. $\angle A \cong \angle B$ (Given) 9. $m\angle A = m\angle B$ (Def. of $\cong \angle$s) 10. $2(m\angle DCE) = 2(m\angle A)$ (Subst.) 11. $m\angle DCE = m\angle A$ (Mult. prop. of =) 12. $m\angle DCE \cong \angle A$ (Def. of $\cong \angle$s) 13. $\overline{CE} \parallel \overline{AB}$ (If two lines are cut by a trans. and corr. $\angle$s are $\cong$, the lines are $\parallel$.)

28. 1. $\overline{AC} \parallel \overline{DE}$ (Given) 2. $\angle 3 \cong \angle ACE$ (If two $\parallel$ lines are cut by a trans., corr. $\angle$s are $\cong$.) 3. $m\angle 3 = m\angle ACE$ (Def. of $\cong \angle$s) 4. $m\angle ACE = m\angle 1 + m\angle 2$ (Ext. $\angle$ Theorem) 5. $m\angle 3 = m\angle 1 + m\angle 2$ (Subst.)

29. 1. Label E on line $\overleftrightarrow{AB}$ so that A is between E and B. Draw auxiliary $\overline{AC}$. (Two points determine a line.)
2. $m\angle EAC = m\angle B + m\angle BCA$ (Ext. $\angle$ Theorem)
3. $m\angle EAC = m\angle 1 + m\angle DAC$ ($\angle$ Add. Post.) 4. $m\angle 1 + m\angle DAC = m\angle B + m\angle BCA$ (Subst.) 5. $m\angle 2 = m\angle DAC + m\angle DCA$ (Ext. $\angle$ Theorem)
6. $m\angle 1 + m\angle DAC + m\angle 2 = m\angle B + m\angle BCA + m\angle 2$ (Add. Prop. of =) 7. $m\angle 1 + m\angle DAC + m\angle 2 = m\angle B + m\angle BCA + m\angle DAC + m\angle DCA$ (Subst.) 8. $m\angle 1 + m\angle 2 = m\angle B + m\angle BCA + m\angle DCA$ (Add. Prop. of =) 9. $m\angle BCA + m\angle DCA = m\angle C$ (Angle Add.)
10. $m\angle 1 + m\angle 2 + = m\angle B + m\angle C$ (Subst.)

30. Let R be the vertex of $\angle 3$. Extend $\overrightarrow{QR}$ to intersect line a at S.
1. $a\parallel b$ (Given)
2. $m\angle 3 = m\angle 1 + m\angle PSR$ (Ext. $\angle$ Theorem)
3. $\angle 2 \cong PSR$ (If two $\parallel$ lines are cut by a trans., alt. int. $\angle$s are $\cong$.) 4. $m\angle 2 = m\angle PSR$ (Def. of $\cong$) 5. $m\angle 3 = m\angle 1 + m\angle 2$ (Subst.)   **31.** 1. Draw auxiliary $\overrightarrow{DB}$; label E so that B is between E and D. (Two points determine a line.) 2. $m\angle ABE = m\angle 2 + m\angle ADB$ (Ext. $\angle$ Theorem) 3. $m\angle EBC = m\angle BDC + m\angle 4$ (Ext. $\angle$ Theorem)
4. $m\angle 1 = m\angle ABE + m\angle EBC$ ($\angle$ Add. Post.) 5. $m\angle 3 = m\angle ADB + m\angle BDC$ ($\angle$ Add. Post.) 6. $m\angle ABE + m\angle EBC = m\angle 2 + m\angle 3 + m\angle 4$ (Subst.)
7. $m\angle 1 = m\angle 2 + m\angle 3 + m\angle 4$ (Subst.)   **32.** In all cases, $m\angle 1 = 120$ and $m\angle 2 = 60$. See Selected Answers.

Algebra Review Answers

1. 9 and 17
2. 14 girls, 23 boys

C

29. Given: $\overline{AB}, \overline{BC}, \overline{CD}, \overline{AD}$ as shown
   Prove: $m\angle 1 + m\angle 2 = m\angle C + m\angle B$

31. Given: figure $ABCD$
   Prove: $m\angle 1 = m\angle 2 + m\angle 3 + m\angle 4$

Critical Thinking

32. $\overline{AE}\parallel\overline{BF}$, $\overline{BD}$ and $\overline{BE}$ trisect $\angle ABF$. $\overline{AC}$ and $\overline{AF}$ trisect $\angle BAE$. Find $m\angle 1$ and $m\angle 2$ if
   a. $m\angle ABF = 45$
   b. $m\angle ABF = 60$
   c. $m\angle ABF = 75$
   What seems to be true about $\angle 1$ and $\angle 2$? Prove your conjecture.

30. Given: $a\parallel b$
   Prove: $m\angle 3 = m\angle 1 + m\angle 2$

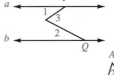

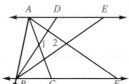

Algebra Review

Translate to a system of equations and solve.

1. Find two integers whose sum is 26 and whose difference is 8.
2. There are 37 students in geometry class. There are 9 more boys than girls. How many girls and boys are in class?

Historical Note

The Parallel Postulate

One of the most famous postulates in Euclidean geometry is Euclid's fifth postulate, known as the parallel postulate. It appears on page 123 of this book in this revised form:

Given a line l and a point P not on l, there exists one and only one line through P parallel to l.

For hundreds of years mathematicians tried without success to prove the postulate as a theorem, that is, to deduce it from Euclid's other four postulates. It was not until the last century that three mathematicians, Bolyai, Lobachevsky, and Gauss, working independently, discovered that Euclid's parallel postulate could not be proven from his other postulates. Their discovery paved the way for the development of other kinds of geometry, called non-Euclidean geometries.

OBJECTIVE: *Apply angle sum theorems for the interior and exterior angles of a polygon.*

3-6 Angles of a Polygon

Some of the terms you have been using with triangles apply to other polygons as well. A polygon is a union of segments that meet only at endpoints such that

(1) at most two segments meet at one point
(2) each segment meets exactly two other segments.

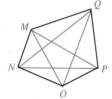

Points M, N, O, P, and Q are vertices of polygon $MNOPQ$.
$\overline{MN}$, $\overline{NO}$, $\overline{OP}$, $\overline{PQ}$, and $\overline{QM}$ are sides of the polygon.
$\overline{MO}$, $\overline{MP}$, $\overline{NP}$, $\overline{NQ}$, and $\overline{OQ}$ are diagonals of polygon $MNOPQ$.

A polygon divides a plane into three parts: the interior of the polygon, the exterior of the polygon, and the polygon itself. A polygon is convex if all the diagonals of the polygon are in the interior of the polygon.

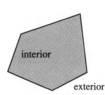

Convex polygons   Nonconvex polygons

A polygon is named by the number of sides it has.

Number of sides	Polygon
4	quadrilateral
5	pentagon
6	hexagon
7	heptagon
8	octagon
9	nonagon
10	decagon
.	.
.	.
.	.
n	n-gon

3-6 Angles of a Polygon **135**

First Five Minutes

(Quiz on previous lesson)
Complete the table.

$m\angle 1$	$m\angle 2$	$m\angle 3$	$m\angle 4$
1. 115	——	70	——
2. ——	——	45	40
3. 120	——	80	——
4. 120	——	x	x
5. ——	40	$2x - 5$	$3x$

1. 65, 45 **2.** 85, 95
3. 60, 40 **4.** 60 **5.** 140

Lesson Opener

To introduce the study of polygons, have students name examples of the many polygons they see around them every day. Street signs are good physical models.

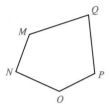

YIELD SCHOOL STOP

Materials

student notebooks

The word *polygon* means *many angles*. Emphasize that in naming polygons, vertices are stated in consecutive order. For example, polygon *NOPQM* and polygon *PONMQ* are correct names for the same polygon.

Some geometry books use the term "concave" instead of "nonconvex."

NOTE: Unless otherwise specified, the term polygon will mean a convex polygon.

The sum of the measures of the interior angles of a convex polygon can be determined by drawing diagonals from only one vertex.

Sides	4	5	6	7
Triangles	2	3	4	5
Angle sum	2(180) = 360	3(180) = 540	4(180) = 720	5(180) = 900

Observe that in each case the number of triangles formed is two less than the number of sides. This suggests the following theorem.

◆ THEOREM 3.13

The sum of the measures of the angles of a convex polygon of n sides is $(n - 2)\,180$.

Example 1

Find the sum of the measures of the angles of a nonagon.

Solution

$(n - 2)\,180$ *Theorem 3·13; a nonagon has nine sides.*
$(9 - 2)\,180 = 1260$ $n = 9$

Try This

The sum of the measures of the angles of a polygon is 1620. How many sides does the polygon have?

A polygon is *equilateral* if all of its sides are congruent, *equiangular* if all of its angles are congruent. If it is both equilateral and equiangular, it is a *regular polygon*.

 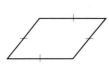

   Equiangular polygon   Equilateral polygon   Regular polygon

If the sum of the angle measures of a regular polygon is divided by the number of its sides, the resulting quotient is the measure of each angle.

▶ COROLLARY 3.13a

The measure of each angle of a regular polygon of n sides is $\dfrac{(n - 2)180}{n}$.

Example 2

Find the measure of each angle of a regular decagon.

Solution

$$m\angle A = \frac{(n-2)180}{n}$$ *Let $m\angle A$ be the measure of one angle of a regular decagon.*

$$m\angle A = \frac{(10-2)180}{10}$$ $n = 10$

$$m\angle A = 144$$

Try This

Each angle of a regular polygon has a measure of 140. How many sides does the polygon have?

A property of the exterior angles of a polygon can be developed by the following method.

At each vertex of pentagon *ABCDE* there is a linear pair of angles.

Use the Linear Pair Postulate.

$$m\angle 1 + m\angle 2 = 180$$
$$m\angle 3 + m\angle 4 = 180$$
$$m\angle 5 + m\angle 6 = 180$$
$$m\angle 7 + m\angle 8 = 180$$
$$m\angle 9 + m\angle 10 = 180$$

Add the left members and the right members of the above equations to obtain

(exterior sum) + (interior sum) = 5(180)
(exterior ∠ sum) + (5 − 2)180 = 5(180)
(exterior ∠ sum) = 5(180) − 3(180)
(exterior ∠ sum) = 2(180)
(exterior ∠ sum) = 360

If five sides is replaced by *n* sides, the sum will still be 360.

◆ **THEOREM 3.14**

The sum of the measures of the exterior angles of a convex polygon is 360.

Example 3

The measure of an exterior angle of a regular polygon is 24. How many sides does the polygon have?

Solution

$24x = 360$ *Let x = the number of sides.*
$x = 15$

Try This

The sum of the measures of four exterior angles of a pentagon is 300. What is the measure of the fifth exterior angle?

Class Exercise Answers

1. nonconvex   **2.** convex
3. nonconvex   **4.** octagon,
not regular   **5.** pentagon, not
regular   **6.** hexagon, regular
7. 12, 30
8. 120, 135, 144, 168
9. 60, 45, 36, 30, 18
10. increases, no limit
11. decreases with 0 as a limiting value

Assignment Guide

Minimum: 1–35 e/o, 41, MR
Regular: 1–35 e/o, 36–42, MR
Advanced: 1–42 e/o, MR

Applications
Exercises 25–28

Algebra
Exercises 31–34

Lesson Closure

Make a chart on the chalkboard
to help students form an
overview of the lesson. Across
the top, list the following: Number of Sides, Number of Diagonals, Number of Triangles, Sum
of Interior Angles, Each Interior
Angle of a Reg. Polygon, Sum
of Exterior Angles, Each Exterior Angle of a Reg. Polygon.

Under each category, record the
appropriate formula. Then have
students help fill in each category for the following polygons:
triangle, quadrilateral, pentagon, hexagon, heptagon, octagon.

Teacher's Resource Materials

Enrichment Using
  Manipulatives 19
Practice Master 21
Quiz 6
Technology: Calculator 3
Technology: BASIC 6
Transparency 13

Class Exercises

Short Answer

Indicate which of the polygons are convex.

1.   **2.**   **3.**

Name each polygon and indicate if it is a regular polygon.

4.   **5.**   **6.**

Sample Exercises

Complete the table below for regular polygons.

	Number of sides	6	8	10		20	
7.	Number of sides	6	8	10		20	
8.	Measure of each interior ∠				150	162	
9.	Measure of each exterior ∠						12

Discussion

10. As the number of sides of a convex polygon increases, what happens to
the sum of the measures of its interior angles? What is the greatest
possible sum of the measures of the interior angles of a polygon?

11. As the number of sides of a regular polygon increases, what happens to
the measure of each exterior angle? What is the least possible measure of
an exterior angle of a polygon?

Exercises

A

The number of sides of a convex polygon is given. Find the sum of the
measures of the interior angles of each polygon.

1. 8   **2.** 12   **3.** 14   **4.** 16   **5.** p

The sum of the measures of the interior angles of a convex polygon is
given. Find the number of sides of each polygon.

6. 7020   **7.** 1980   **8.** 6120   **9.** 1800   **10.** 3420

The number of sides of a regular polygon is given. Find the measure of
each interior angle of each polygon.

11. 7   **12.** 9   **13.** 11   **14.** 15   **15.** 17

Find the measure of each exterior angle of the regular polygon.

16. pentagon   17. heptagon   18. decagon   19. 18-gon   20. 20-gon

21. Home plate on a baseball field has three right angles and two congruent angles shown as $\angle 1$ and $\angle 2$ in the figure. Find $m\angle 1$ and $m\angle 2$.

22. The sum of the measures of seven angles of an octagon is 1000. Find the measure of the eighth angle.

23. How many sides does a regular polygon have if each exterior angle has a measure of 15?

24. How many sides does a regular polygon have if each interior angle has a measure of 108?

B

25. Draw a diagram to show that a floor can be tiled with equilateral triangles. Give a convincing argument that the sum of the measures of the angles sharing a common vertex is 360.

26. The tiling pattern to the right consists of regular hexagons. Find $m\angle 1$, $m\angle 2$, and $m\angle 3$ and verify that their sum is 360.

27. The tiling pattern to the right consists of regular octagons and a square. Find $m\angle 1$, $m\angle 2$, and $m\angle 3$ and verify that their sum is 360.

28. Explain why three regular pentagons cannot form a tiling pattern.

29. Explain why two regular pentagons and a regular 10-gon will fit around a point.

30. Explain why an equiangular triangle, a regular 7-gon, and a regular 42-gon will fit around a point.

31. Find the number of sides of a polygon if the sum of the measures of its interior angles is twice the sum of the measures of its exterior angles.

32. Find the number of sides of a polygon if the sum of the measures of its interior angles is four times the sum of the measures of its exterior angles.

33. The measure of each interior angle of a regular polygon is eight times that of an exterior angle. How many sides does the polygon have?

34. In quadrilateral $ABCD$ the measures of $\angle A$, $\angle B$, $\angle C$, and $\angle D$ are in the ratio of 1 : 2 : 3 : 4, respectively. Find the measures of the four angles and determine which segments are parallel.

35. $ABCDEFGH$ is a regular octagon. If sides $\overline{AB}$ and $\overline{GH}$ are extended to meet at X, find $m\angle BXG$.

C

The numbered angles in each figure are congruent. Find the sum of the numbered angles.

36. 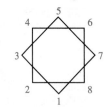   **37.**    **38.**

39. Write a generalization about the sums you found in Exercises 36–38.

Critical Thinking

40. Complete the table below by drawing each polygon and its diagonals.

Number of sides	3	4	5	6	7	8	9
Number of diagonals	0	2	5				

41. Predict how many diagonals a decagon has.
Write a formula expressing the relationship between the number of sides
(*n*) and the number of diagonals (*d*). Use it to check Exercise 40.

Mixed Review

1. The midpoint of $\overline{SV}$ is *T*. Name the congruent segments formed.
2. Line *l* bisects $\overline{MN}$ at *P*. Name the congruent segments formed.
3. $\overrightarrow{BC}$ is the bisector of $\angle ABD$. Name the congruent angles formed.

Quiz

Determine whether each statement is true or false.

1. An obtuse triangle may have a right angle.
2. The acute angles of a right triangle are complementary.
3. A triangle may have an obtuse exterior angle.
4. In any triangle, the remote interior angles are acute.
5. If two angles of one triangle are congruent to two angles of another
   triangle, then the third pair of angles are congruent.
6. The sum of the measures of the angles of a nonagon is 1440.

a ∥ *b* **Find the measure of each angle.**

7. $m \angle QRS$ **8.** $m \angle PQT$ **9.** $m \angle PQR$

10. In an octagon, the sum of the measures of the interior angles is
    __?__ and the sum of the measures of the exterior angles is __?__ .

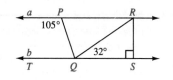

CRITICAL THINKING

Introducing the Process

Critical Thinking has been described as a thinking process used to decide what to believe or do. Consider the following situation.

Inspector Glueso arrived at the scene of a murder at Motley Motel early in the morning. The first thing he found was a broken pocket watch clutched in the victim's hand. Other evidence led Glueso to determine that the murder was committed at the time shown on the watch and that the murderer was one of three people at the motel: Mae East, Mr. Clean, or Joe Monitor. The hotel operator verified that Mae East, an actress, had been talking on the telephone from 12:32 AM to 12:47 AM. Joe Monitor, the motel manager, had been seen using his computer from about 12:20 AM until he shut it off sometime after 12:30 AM. The computer log showed that it was shut off at 12:34 AM. Mr. Clean, the night custodian, had punched out at 12:31 AM and had left promptly. The only fact that Glueso could remember about the watch was that the hour and minute hands were in a straight line when he picked it up. Who should Glueso arrest as the prime suspect?

The major points below outline the steps in Critical Thinking. Answer each question as you work, with Glueso, to solve his problem.

1. **Understand the Situation**
   a. What is the situation about?
   b. What conclusion, decision, or solution is required?
   c. Are there any questions you could ask to clarify the situation?

2. **Deal with the Data/Evidence/Assumptions**
   a. Make a list of the most important data/evidence. Is more needed?
   b. Which evidence is opinion, not fact? Which is not relevant?
   c. What assumptions are made? Can other assumptions be made?

3. **Go Beyond the Data/Evidence/Assumptions**—Read the notes Glueso made in his notebook to the right. How could you use this and the evidence to solve the mystery?
   (HINT: Since the hour hand travels through 5-minute spaces while the minute hand travels through 60-minute spaces, the distance the hour hand had traveled was equal to $\frac{1}{12}$ the distance the minute hand had traveled.)

4. **State and Support Your Conclusion**—State your solution to the mystery in writing. Write a paragraph supporting your conclusion.

5. **Apply the Conclusion/Decision/Solution**—The solution of a similar mystery depended upon the fact that a crime occurred the first time after midnight that the hands of a clock were both at the same place. At what time (to the nearest second) did this crime take place?

1. a. a murder that took place at the time indicated on a broken pocket watch b. Who should Glueso arrest as the prime suspect? c. What was the time shown on the broken pocket watch? Which of the three suspects might have been unaccounted for at the time shown on the watch?
2. a. Mae East was accounted for from 12:32 AM to 12:47 AM. Joe Monitor was accounted for from 12:20 AM to 12:30 AM. Mr. Clean left at 12:31 AM. The hour and minute hands on the broken watch were in a straight line. c. The murder took place at the first time after midnight that the hour and minute hands form a straight line. Whoever was unaccounted for at the time shown on the pocket watch should be a prime suspect.
3.
$$12d = d + 30$$
$$11d = 30$$
$$d = \frac{30}{11} = 2\frac{8}{11}$$
$$d + 30 = 2\frac{8}{11} + 30 = 32\frac{8}{11}$$
Therefore 12:32$\frac{8}{11}$ (or about 12:33 AM) was the time on the watch and the time of the murder. **4.** Since Mae East and Joe Monitor were both accounted for at 12:33, the prime suspect should be Mr. Clean who was unaccounted for after 12:31.
5. 1:05:27 AM

CHAPTER SUMMARY

Vocabulary

alternate interior angles (3-1)   diagonal of a polygon (3-6)   remote interior angles (3-5)
alternate exterior angles (3-1)   exterior angle of a triangle (3-5)   same-side interior angles (3-1)
auxiliary line (3-4)   parallel lines (3-1)   skew lines (3-1)
convex polygon (3-6)   parallel planes (3-1)   transversal (3-1)
corresponding angles (3-1)   regular polygon (3-6)

Key Ideas

1. Two coplanar lines that do not intersect are called parallel lines.
2. When two parallel lines are cut by a transversal,
   a. corresponding angles are congruent.
   b. alternate interior angles are congruent.
   c. alternate exterior angles are congruent.
   d. same-side interior angles are supplementary.
3. The following are ways to prove two lines parallel.
   a. Show that corresponding angles are congruent.
   b. Show that alternate interior angles are congruent.
   c. Show that alternate exterior angles are congruent.
   d. Show that same-side interior angles are supplementary.
4. The sum of the measures of the angles of a triangle is 180. The measure of an exterior angle of a triangle is equal to the sum of the measures of its remote interior angles.
5. The sum of the measure of the angles of a convex polygon with n sides is $(n - 2)\,180$. The sum of the exterior angles is 360.

CHAPTER REVIEW

3-1

1. Name two pairs of alternate interior angles.
2. Name two pairs of same-side interior angles.
3. Name two pairs of alternate exterior angles.
4. Name four pairs of corresponding angles.

3-2

$\overleftrightarrow{DE} \parallel \overleftrightarrow{FG}$ **State the postulate or theorem that justifies each conclusion.**

5. $\angle EAC \cong \angle ACB$ **6.** $m\angle EAC + m\angle ACG = 180$
7. $\angle DAH \cong \angle FBH$ **8.** $\angle HAE \cong \angle JBF$
9. $\overline{DE} \parallel \overline{FG}$, $m\angle DAB = 5x - 22$, $m\angle ABC = 2x + 5$. Find $m\angle DAH$.

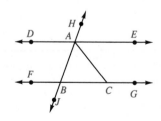

3-3

Use the given information to state which segments are parallel. Identify the postulate or theorem that justifies your answer.

10. $\angle 1 \cong \angle 2$ **11.** $m\angle SRU + m\angle RUT = 180$
12. $\angle SRU \cong \angle TUV$ **13.** $\overline{ST} \perp \overline{TU}, \overline{RU} \perp \overline{TU}$

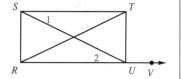

Find the value of x for which $a \parallel b$.

14. $m\angle 2 = 5x + 12, m\angle 4 = 2x + 18$
15. $m\angle 2 = 4x + 6, m\angle 5 = 14$
16. $m\angle 1 = \frac{3}{4}x + 42, m\angle 6 = x + 2$

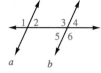

17. Given: $\overline{AB} \parallel \overline{CD}, \angle 1 \cong \angle 2$
   Prove: $\overline{AD} \parallel \overline{BC}$

3-4

Find the measure of $\angle B$.

18.

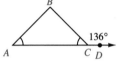

19.

$(3x + 30)°$

$6x°$

20. $\overline{BD}$ bisects $\angle ADC$.
   $\angle A \cong \angle DBA$
   $\overline{BC} \perp \overline{BD}, m\angle A = 50$
   Find $m\angle C$.

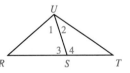

$50°$

3-5

21. Name an exterior angle of $\triangle RUS$.
22. If $m\angle R = 35$ and $m\angle 1 = 20$, find $m\angle 4$.
23. If $m\angle 3 = 5x + 10, m\angle 2 = 50$, and $m\angle T = 3x + 10$, find $m\angle T$.
24. $\angle 3$ is an exterior angle for $\triangle \underline{\ ?\ }$ and its remote interior angles are $\angle \underline{\ ?\ }$ and $\angle \underline{\ ?\ }$.

3-6

25. Find the sum of the measures of the angles of a decagon.
26. Find the number of sides of a convex polygon if the sum of the measures of its interior angles is 4140.
27. Find the measure of an interior angle of a regular hexagon.
28. Find the measure of an exterior angle of a regular octagon.

10. $\overline{ST} \parallel \overline{RU}$ (If alt. int. $\angle$s are $\cong$, the lines are $\parallel$.)
11. $\overline{SR} \parallel \overline{TU}$ (If same-side int. $\angle$s are supplementary, the lines are $\parallel$.)
12. $\overline{SR} \parallel \overline{TU}$ (If corr. $\angle$s are $\cong$, the lines are parallel.)
13. $\overline{ST} \parallel \overline{RU}$ (If, in a plane, two lines are $\perp$ to the same line, the lines are $\parallel$.) **14.** $x = 2$
15. $x = 2$ **16.** $x = 160$
17. 1. $\overline{AB} \parallel \overline{CD}, \angle 1 \cong \angle 2$ (Given)
2. $\angle 1 \cong \angle ABC$ (Theorem 3.2)
3. $\angle 2 \cong \angle ABC$ (Substitution)
4. $\overline{AD} \parallel \overline{BC}$ (Postulate 14)
18. 92 **19.** 50 **20.** 10
21. $\angle UST$ **22.** 55 **23.** 85
24. $SUT, \angle 2, \angle T$ **25.** 1440
26. 25 **27.** 120 **28.** 45

CHAPTER TEST

Determine whether each statement is true or false.

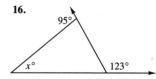

1. $\overline{AB}$ and $\overline{HG}$ are parallel.
2. $\overline{AB}$ and $\overline{CD}$ are skew.
3. Plane $ABEF$ and plane $BCFG$ are parallel.
4. If two parallel lines are cut by a transversal, then corresponding angles are congruent.
5. If two parallel lines are cut by a transversal, then same-side interior angles are congruent.
6. If two coplanar lines are perpendicular to the same line, then they are perpendicular to each other.
7. In a triangle, the measure of an exterior angle is equal to the sum of the measures of its remote interior angles.
8. The sum of the angles of a heptagon is 900°.

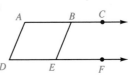

Identify each pair of angles as alternate interior, alternate exterior, same-side interior, corresponding, or none of these.

9. $\angle 4$ and $\angle 8$
10. $\angle 3$ and $\angle 6$
11. $\angle 1$ and $\angle 7$

Use the given information to determine which segments are parallel.

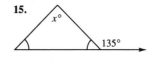

12. $\angle D \cong \angle BEF$
13. $m\angle ABE + m\angle BAD = 180$

Find the value of x. Congruent angles are marked.

14.
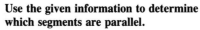

15.
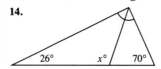

16.
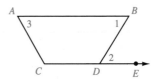

17. If $m\angle 4 = 85$ and $m\angle 2 = 38$, find $m\angle 5$.
18. If $m\angle 1 = 118$ and $m\angle 3 = 95$, find $m\angle 5$.
19. Find the measure of each interior angle of an 18-sided regular polygon.
20. Find the number of sides of a convex polygon if the measures of its interior angles have a sum of 5940.

21. **Given:** $\overline{AB} \| \overline{CE}$, $\angle 2 \cong \angle 3$
    Prove: $\angle 1 \cong \angle 3$

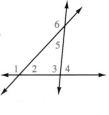

Problem Solving

Make a Table,
Look for a Pattern

Problem Answers
1. 1296 (Sum of cubes:
$1^3 + \ldots + 8^3$)   **2.** 6
3. $T^5 = 15$, $T^6 = 21$ $T^{10} = 55$
4. $P^5 = 35$, $P^6 = 51$, $P^{10} = 145$

PROBLEM SOLVING

Make a Table, Look for a Pattern

Two strategies useful in solving problems involving numerical relationships are Make a Table and Look for a Pattern. By organizing data in a table you will often be able to recognize patterns more easily.

Example

How many squares are on an 8 × 8 checkerboard?

Solution

Size of Square	Number of squares
1 × 1	64
2 × 2	49
3 × 3	36
4 × 4	25
5 × 5	?
6 × 6	?
7 × 7	?
8 × 8	?

Make a table and record the number of 1 × 1, 2 × 2, 3 × 3, and 4 × 4 squares. Look for a pattern. The number of 1 × 1 squares is 8^2 squares. The number of 2 × 2 squares is 7^2. Note that the pattern appears to be decreasing perfect squares. Complete the table by filling in 16, 9, 4, and 1.

64 + 49 + 36 + 25 + 16 + 9 + 4 + 1 = 204   *Add the numbers in the*
There are 204 squares   *completed right-hand column.*

Problem-Solving Strategies
Draw a Diagram
Make a Table
Look for a Pattern

The problem-solving strategies that have been introduced up to this point in the book are presented in the chart.

Problems

1. How many cubes are in an 8 × 8 × 8 cube? (HINT: Make a table similar to the one above. In one column list the cube sizes—1 × 1 × 1, 2 × 2 × 2, 3 × 3 × 3, etc. In the second column give the number of cubes for each size.)

2. A yo-yo on a 36-in. string is thrown so that the string is fully extended. On each jerk it comes up 12 in. then falls back 7 in. How many jerks of the string are made by the time the yo-yo returns to the thrower's hand?

3. A triangular number (T) is one that can be represented geometrically. T_1, T_2, T_3, and T_4.

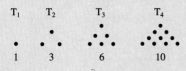

Find T_5 and T_6. Predict what the tenth triangular number (T_{10}) is.

4. A pentagonal number (P) is another number that can be represented geometrically.

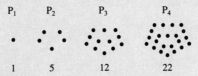

Find P_5 and P_6. Predict what the tenth pentagonal number (P_{10}) will be.

Cumulative Review Objectives

Item	Objective
1, 2, 3	1-1
4, 17	1-2
5, 18	1-3
6, 7, 20	1-4
8, 9	1-5
10, 11	1-6
12, 13, 14	2-2
15,16	2-3
19	2-5
21	2-7
22	3-1
23,24	3-3
25,26	3-6

CUMULATIVE REVIEW

Chapters 1–3

1. Name two pairs of intersecting lines in the figure below. $j \parallel k$

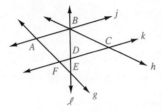

a. j and k, l, and g
b. l and g, l and k
c. $\overline{AF}$ and $\overline{BC}$, $\overline{AB}$ and $\overline{FC}$
d. h and k, j and k

2. Which of these sets of points is collinear?

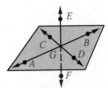

a. C, G, B **b.** E, G, D
c. A, G, B **d.** C, G, F

3. Which type of statement is accepted as true without proof?

a. theorem   **b.** postulate
c. definition   **d.** corollary

4. X is between W and Y. If $WY = 12$ and $WX = 5$, find XY.

a. 7   **b.** -7 **c.** 17   **d.** none of these

5. Which of the following is not another name for $\angle RST$?

a. $\angle 1$ **b.** $\angle TSR$ **c.** $\angle S$ **d.** $\angle SRT$

6. M is the midpoint of $\overline{AB}$ and $\overline{CD}$. Which conclusion is correct?

a. $CM = MD$ **b.** $AM = CM$
c. $CM = CD$ **d.** $BM = MD$

7. If $\overrightarrow{CS}$ bisects $\angle GCM$, which angles must be congruent?

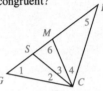

a. $\angle 1$ and $\angle 2$ **b.** $\angle 5$ and $\angle 6$
c. $\angle 2$ and $\angle 3$ **d.** $\angle 2$, $\angle 3$, and $\angle 4$

8. A triangle with three congruent sides is

a. isosceles   **b.** equilateral
c. scalene   **d.** obtuse

9. It is not possible for a triangle to be isosceles and also

a. right   **b.** obtuse   **c.** scalene   **d.** acute

10. What is the hypothesis of the statement "all right angles are congruent"?

a. two angles are right angles
b. two angles are congruent
c. two right angles are congruent
d. congruent angles are right angles

11. To show that a generalization is false, you can give a(n)

a. inverse   **b.** counterexample
c. hypothesis   **d.** reason

12. If $\angle 1$ and $\angle 2$ are complementary, then

a. $\angle 1 \cong \angle 2$ **b.** $m\angle 1 + m\angle 2 = 180$
c. $\angle 1$ and $\angle 2$ are adjacent
d. $m\angle 1 + m\angle 2 = 90$

13. $\angle AOC$ and $\angle COB$ are

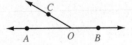

a. complementary   **b.** vertical angles
c. a linear pair   **d.** congruent

14. The measure of an angle is 50 less than its supplement. Find the measure of the smaller angle.

　a. 50　**b.** 65　**c.** 20　**d.** 115

15. If r and t are coplanar, $r \perp t$, and $s \perp t$, then which of the following is true?

　a. $r \parallel s$　　**b.** $t \parallel s$
　c. $r \perp s$　　**d.** none of these

16. $\overline{AB}$ is the perpendicular bisector of $\overline{CD}$ at point E. Which one of these is not true?

　a. $\overline{AE} \cong \overline{EB}$
　b. $\overline{AB} \perp \overline{CD}$
　c. $\overline{CE} \cong \overline{ED}$
　d. A, E, and B are collinear

17. In RST, $RX = XT$. Which of the following is not correct?

　a. R, X, and T are collinear.
　b. X is the midpoint of $\overline{RT}$.
　c. $RX = \frac{1}{2}RT$
　d. $m \angle RSX = m \angle TSX$

18. If $\angle MON \cong NOR$, $m \angle MON = 15$, and $m \angle NOS = 35$, then $m \angle ROS =$ _____ .

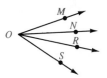

　a. 45　**b.** 20　**c.** 15　**d.** 30

19. $\overline{LM}$ and $\overline{NO}$ intersect at T.
$m \angle LTN = 3x + 10$
$m \angle OTM = 5x - 60$
Find $m \angle LTO$.

　a. 65　**b.** 35　**c.** 70　**d.** 115

20. $\overline{ST}$ bisects $\angle RSU$. $m \angle RST = 34$
Find $m \angle RSU$.

　a. 34　**b.** 56　**c.** 146　**d.** 68

21. Which one of the statements is false?

　a. If two angles are vertical, then they are congruent.
　b. If two angles are supplements of congruent angles, then they are supplementary.
　c. If two angles are complements of the same angle, then they are congruent.
　d. If two angles are supplements of the same angle, then they are congruent.

22. Which line is skew with $\overleftrightarrow{BC}$?

　a. $\overleftrightarrow{AD}$　**b.** $\overleftrightarrow{EF}$　**c.** $\overleftrightarrow{FG}$　**d.** $\overleftrightarrow{AB}$

23. Which of the following would prove $r \parallel s$?

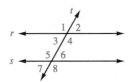

　a. $\angle 2 \cong \angle 8$
　b. $\angle 3 \cong \angle 5$
　c. $m \angle 4 + m \angle 6 = 180$
　d. $\angle 1 \cong \angle 4$

24. In Exercise 23, $r \parallel s$, $m \angle 3 = 5x + 32$, and $m \angle 5 = 4x + 40$. Find $m \angle 5$.

　a. 12　**b.** 92　**c.** 72　**d.** 88

25. Find the sum of the interior angles of a polygon with 12 sides.

　a. 1440　**b.** 1980　**c.** 1800　**d.** 3420

26. If the sum of the measures of four exterior angles of a pentagon is 270, what is the measure of the fifth exterior angle?

　a. 70　**b.** 90　**c.** 45　**d.** 30

Cumulative Review Answers

(Chapters 1–3)

1. b	**2.** c	**3.** b	**4.** a
5. d	**6.** a	**7.** c	**8.** b
9. c	**10.** a	**11.** b	
12. d	**13.** c	**14.** b	
15. d	**16.** a	**17.** d	
18. b	**19.** a	**20.** d	
21. b	**22.** b	**23.** c	
24. d	**25.** c	**26.** b	

Congruent Triangles

Chapter Overview

This chapter introduces the postulates that may be used to show two triangles congruent. Proving the congruence of triangles will be important throughout the book. The last lesson of the chapter deals with special segments associated with triangles.

Objectives

4-1   ■ Given two congruent triangles, identify congruent parts.

4-2   ■ State and apply the SSS, ASA, and SAS Postulates.

4-3   ■ Use definitions and the SSS, SAS, and ASA congruence postulates to prove triangles congruent.

4-4   ■ Deduce that segments and angles are congruent by first proving that triangles are congruent.

4-5   ■ Prove triangles congruent using overlapping triangles.

4-6   ■ Prove and apply the theorems about isosceles triangles.

4-7   ■ Use the AAS Congruence Postulate in proofs. Use the HL and HA Congruence Postulates in proofs.

4-8   ■ Apply theorems about medians, altitudes, and angle and side bisectors of triangles.

TEACHING CHAPTER 4

Cooperative Learning Opportunities

The **Sample Exercises** that are included in the **Class Exercises**, particularly those in Lessons 4-4, 4-5, and 4-6, are well suited for group work.

In Lesson 4-4, have students work in pairs with one student working the even exercises and the other working the odd. Students should redraw each figure, and then mark it to reflect the given relationships. Upon completion, students should exchange papers, discuss, and agree on each conclusion.

In assigning the Sample Exercises for Lesson 4-5, page 174, have student pairs discuss the reason for each congruence. When reviewing these as a class, ask students to give these reasons.

Similarly, for Exercises 12 through 15 on page 179 have students prepare reasons and identify the appropriate triangles to support their conclusions.

Multicultural Note: *The Amish*

The Amish people have communities located in various parts of the United States. They live a life of religious simplicity and do without most of the modern conveniences that we take for granted. They place great value on the traditions and symbols that unite their people.

The Amish make quilts rich in geometric patterns using congruent squares, rectangles, parallelograms, triangles, and diamond shapes. This figure shows many small parallelograms forming one point of a star.

For more about Amish quilts, see Granick, Eve Wheatcroft, *The Amish Quilt*. Intercourse, PA: Good Books, 1989.

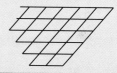

Alternative Assessment and Communication Ideas

The **Discussion** exercises found at the conclusion of the **Class Exercises** can be used as the basis for a formal class recitation used as a form of individualized assessment. Although you need not give actual grades, your notes may serve as the basis for a brief discussion of student progress, after class.

For Lesson 4-2, allow students a few minutes to prepare their, "convincing argument," before you call on some one. You can keep your notes according to a check-list and use it as the basis for your follow-up discussion. This list might contain the following items.

(1) Understands the question
(2) Calls on relevant information
(3) Applies the information correctly
(4) Carries through successfully

Keep your notes for future reference.

Investigations and Projects

Students may think that congruence has little application to the world in which they live. You can point out that while congruence is useful in doing geometric proof, it is also an indispensable part of our modern world.

How and where is congruence so important? The answer is in the mass production of clothes, shoes and other articles in sizes that would fit many people.

As a project, have students individually or in small groups, gather information about standardization in different areas: clothing, cars, computers. Ask them whether congruence of parts, in the geometric sense, is found in automobile parts, for example.

What is the importance of interchangeable parts? What is meant by tolerance in manufacturing? What are some of the advantages and disadvantages of standardization? Students may collect pictures, cartoons, and other items that would lead to a bulletin board display.

Lesson	PACING CHART (DAYS)			Opening Activity	Cooperative Activity	Seat or Group Work
	1-Year Minimum	1-Year Regular	1-Year Advanced			
4-1	2	2	2	Chapter Opener: **TE** p. 148; Lesson Opener: **TE** p. 149	✂ Lab Worksheet 4-1A: *Laboratory Manual* p. 33; ✂ Lab Worksheet 4-1B: *Laboratory Manual* p. 34	Try This Exercises
4-2	1	1	1	First Five Minutes 4-2: *FFM Transparency Masters* p. 13 or **TE** p. 153; Lesson Opener: **TE** p. 153	Explore: **SE** p. 153; ✂ Lab Worksheet 4-2: *Laboratory Manual* p. 35	Try This Exercises
4-3	1	1	1	First Five Minutes 4-3: *FFM Transparency Masters* p. 13 or **TE** p. 159; Lesson Opener: **TE** p. 159	Computer Activity: **SE** p. 165	Exercise 1: **SE** p. 162
4-4	2	2	2	First Five Minutes 4-4: *FFM Transparency Masters* p. 14 or **TE** p. 166; Lesson Opener: **TE** p. 166		Exercises 1-4: **SE** p. 169
4-5	1	1	1	First Five Minutes 4-5: *FFM Transparency Masters* p. 14 or **TE** p. 172; Lesson Opener: **TE** p. 172	Computer Exploration 3: **SE** p. 636	Try This Exercises
4-6	1	1	1	First Five Minutes 4-6: *FFM Transparency Masters* p. 15 or **TE** p. 177; Lesson Opener: **TE** p. 177	Explore: **SE** p. 177; ✂ Lab Worksheet 4-6A: *Laboratory Manual* p. 36; ✂ Lab Worksheet 4-6B: *Laboratory Manual* p. 37	Try This Exercise
4-7	1	1	1	First Five Minutes 4-7: *FFM Transparency Masters* p. 15 or **TE** p. 184; Lesson Opener: **TE** p. 184	Explore: **SE** p. 184 ✂ Lab Worksheet 4-7: *Laboratory Manual* p. 40	Exercises 1-6: **SE** p. 186
4-8	1	1	1	First Five Minutes 4-8: *FFM Transparency Masters* p. 16 or **TE** p. 189; Lesson Opener: **TE** p. 189	Algebra Review: **SE** p. 624	Try This Exercises
Review	1	1	1			
Test	1	1	1			

FFM = First Five Minutes

Enrichment	Review/Assess	Reteach	Technology	Lesson
Study Skills: **SE** p. 152; ✂ Enrichment Using Manipulatives 4-1: *Enrichment* p. 20	Class Exercises: **SE** p. 150; Mixed Review: **SE** p. 152	Practice Worksheet 4-1: *Practice and Mixed Review* p. 27		4-1
✂ Enrichment Using Manipulatives 4-2: *Enrichment* p. 21	Class Exercises: **SE** p. 155; Mixed Review: **SE** p. 158; Quiz: **SE** p. 158	Practice Worksheet 4-2: *Practice and Mixed Review* p. 28		4-2
✂ Enrichment Using Manipulatives 4-3: *Enrichment* p. 22; BASIC 4-3: *Technology* p. B9	Class Exercises: **SE** p. 160; Mixed Review: **SE** p. 164	Practice Worksheet 4-3: *Practice and Mixed Review* p. 29	Computer Activity: **SE** p. 165; BASIC 4-3: *Technology* p. B9	4-3
Enrichment: **SE** p. 171;	Class Exercises: **SE** p. 168; Algebra Review: **SE** p. 171	Practice Worksheet 4-4: *Practice and Mixed Review* p. 30		4-4
✂ Enrichment Using Manipulatives 4-5: *Enrichment* p. 23	Class Exercises: **SE** p. 174; Algebra Review: **SE** p. 176; Quiz: *Assessment* p. 85	Practice Worksheet 4-5: *Practice and Mixed Review* p. 31	Computer Exploration 3: **SE** p. 636	4-5
Biographical Note: **SE** p. 183; ✂ *Enrichment* Using Manipulatives 4-6: *Enrichment* p. 24; ✂ Lab Worksheet 4-6C: *Laboratory Manual* p. 39	Class Exercises: **SE** p. 179; Mixed Review: **SE** p. 183	Practice Worksheet 4-6: *Practice and Mixed Review* p. 32	Computer Exploration 3: **SE** p. 636; Calculator Worksheet 4-6: *Technology* p. CL4;	4-6
Connections: **SE** p. 188; ✂ Enrichment Using Manipulatives 4-7: *Enrichment* p. 25	Class Exercises: **SE** p. 186; Algebra Review: **SE** p. 188	Practice Worksheet 4-7: *Practice and Mixed Review* p.33		4-7
Comparing Approaches in Geometry: **SE** p. 194; ✂ Enrichment Using Manipulatives 4-8: *Enrichment* p. 26	Class Exercises: **SE** p. 191; Algebra Review: **SE** p. 193; Quiz: **SE** p. 193; Quiz: *Assessment* p. 86	Practice Worksheet 4-8: *Practice and Mixed Review* p.34		4-8
Critical Thinking: **SE** p. 195	Summary & Review: **SE** p. 196–197	Mixed Review: *Practice and Mixed Review* p. 105		Review
Discrete Math: **SE** p. 199	Chapter 4 Test: **SE** p. 198; Chapter 4 Tests: *Assessment* p. 19–24; *MathTest*			Test

4

Congruent Triangles

Give a convincing argument that the equilateral triangles of this structure are congruent.

TRIANGLES AND CONGRUENCE

OBJECTIVE: *Given two congruent triangles, identify congruent parts.*

4-1 Congruent Triangles

You learned in Chapter 1 that congruent segments have the same length and that congruent angles have the same measure. Use these ideas to define congruent triangles. Two figures are called congruent if they have the same size and shape.

If you were to trace triangle *ABC* shown below and position the tracing over triangle *DEF*, you would see that triangles *ABC* and *DEF* are identical in size and shape.

Individual parts must be made identical in size and shape so that they fit any one of the items on the assembly line.

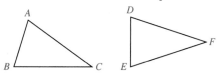

When the tracing of triangle *ABC* matches up with triangle *DEF*, the vertices of the two triangles match up as follows:

$$A \leftrightarrow D \qquad B \leftrightarrow E \qquad C \leftrightarrow F$$

You can also see a **correspondence** between the angles and the sides of the two triangles.

Corresponding angles: $\angle A \leftrightarrow \angle D, \angle B \leftrightarrow \angle E, \angle C \leftrightarrow \angle F$
Corresponding sides: $\overline{AB} \leftrightarrow \overline{DE}, \overline{BC} \leftrightarrow \overline{EF}, \overline{AC} \leftrightarrow \overline{DF}$

◼ DEFINITION

Two triangles are congruent if and only if there is a correspondence between the vertices such that each pair of corresponding sides and each pair of corresponding angles are congruent.

You write $\triangle ABC \cong \triangle DEF$.

In a diagram congruent sides can be indicated with "hatch" marks and congruent angles by "arc" marks as shown in this figure. When using the notation $\triangle ABC \cong \triangle DEF$, list corresponding vertices in the same order. In this pair of congruent triangles, the corresponding vertices are *A* and *D*, *B* and *E*, and *C* and *F*. These six statements are correct as written.

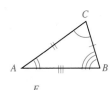

$\triangle ABC \cong \triangle DEF$	$\triangle ACB \cong \triangle DFE$	$\triangle BCA \cong \triangle EFD$
$\triangle BAC \cong \triangle EDF$	$\triangle CAB \cong \triangle FDE$	$\triangle CBA \cong \triangle FED$

However, it would not be correct to write $\triangle ABC \cong \triangle EDF$ since vertices *A* and *E*, and *B* and *D* are not corresponding vertices.

4-1 Congruent Triangles **149**

Lesson Opener

In this lesson the concept of congruency is applied to the study of triangles. For two triangles to be congruent, they must have the same size and shape. The definition of congruent triangles says that two triangles are congruent if all pairs of corresponding parts are congruent.

Have students trace $\triangle ABC$ on a sheet of paper and then move the tracing to coincide with $\triangle DEF$. Ask them if the triangles are identical in size and shape. Whenever you can "fit" one triangle onto the other so that all matching parts are congruent, you can say that the triangles are congruent.

Materials

student notebooks
compasses
straightedges
investigative software

Teaching Notes

Emphasize the importance of listing corresponding vertices in the same order when naming congruent triangles. This helps identify the corresponding parts of the triangles easily and correctly.

Stress that hatch marks for segments and arcs for angles are used to indicate congruent sides and congruent angles.

Draw congruent triangles using investigative software.

Key Terms

congruent
correspondence

Guided Practice

Chalkboard Examples

1. $\triangle RST \cong \triangle XYZ$
Complete each statement.
$\overline{RS} \cong$ $\overline{XY}$, $\overline{ST} \cong$ $\overline{YZ}$,
$\overline{RT} \cong$ $\overline{XZ}$, $\angle X \cong$ $\angle R$,
$\angle Y \cong$ $\angle S$, $\angle Z \cong$ $\angle T$,
$\triangle STR \cong$ $\triangle YZX$,
$\triangle XZY \cong$ $\triangle RTS$

Answer to **Try This** $\overline{VU}$, $\angle W$

2. $\triangle EFG \cong \triangle LMN$
Complete each statement.

$EG =$ 15, $NM =$ 12,
$ML =$ 7, $m\angle M =$ 97,
$m\angle G =$ 31, $m\angle E =$ 52

Answer to **Try This** 73, 14

Class Exercise Answers

1. $\angle X \cong \angle U$, $\angle Y \cong \angle V$, $\angle Z \cong \angle W$ **2.** $\overline{XY} \cong \overline{UV}$, $\overline{XZ} \cong \overline{UW}$, $\overline{YZ} \cong \overline{VW}$ **3.** true
4. false **5.** false **6.** true
7. $\triangle YZX \cong \triangle VWU$
8. $\overline{XZ} \cong \overline{UV}$ **9.** $\overline{CE}$
10. $\overline{BD}$ **11.** $\angle CBE$
12. $\overline{BA}$ **13.** $\triangle BEC$
14. $\triangle ADB$ **15.** $\angle H$
16. $\overline{AT}$ **17.** $m\angle T$ **18.** $\overline{HT}$
19. $\angle O$ **20.** $\overline{MO}$
21. Answers may vary.

Assignment Guide

Minimum: 1–43 e/o, 51, MR
Regular: 1–50 e/o, 51, MR
Advanced: 13–43 e/o, 44–51 MR

Applications
Exercise 39

Example 1

$\triangle UVW \cong \triangle XYZ$ **Complete each statement.**

a. $\overline{VW} \cong$ __ **b.** $\angle V \cong$ __

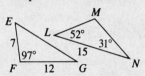

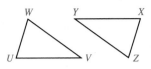

Solution

a. $\overline{VW} \cong \overline{YZ}$ **b.** $\angle V \cong \angle Y$

Try This

Complete each statement.

a. $\overline{YX} \cong$ __ **b.** $\angle Z \cong$ __

Example 2

$\triangle ABC \cong \triangle DEC$ **Complete each statement.**

a. $m\angle D =$ __ **b.** $CD =$ __

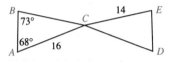

Solution

a. $m\angle D = 68$ **b.** $CD = 16$

Try This

a. $m\angle E =$ __ **b.** $BC =$ __

Class Exercises

Short Answer

$\triangle XYZ \cong \triangle UVW$

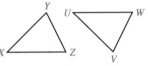

1. Name the three pairs of corresponding angles.
2. Name the three pairs of corresponding sides.

Determine whether each statement is true or false for the above figure.

3. $\triangle YZX \cong \triangle VWU$ 4. $\triangle XZY \cong \triangle UVW$ 5. $\overline{XY} \cong \overline{VY}$ 6. $\angle Y \cong \angle V$

7. Which statement is correct?
$\triangle YZX \cong \triangle UVW$, $\triangle YZX \cong \triangle VWU$, $\triangle ZXY \cong \triangle WVU$
8. Which statement is not correct? $\overline{XZ} \cong \overline{UW}$, $\angle Y \cong \angle V$, $\overline{XZ} \cong \overline{UV}$

Sample Exercises

$\triangle ABD \cong \triangle CBE$ **Complete each statement.**

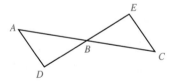

9. $\overline{AD} \cong$ __ 10. $\overline{BE} \cong$ __ 11. $\angle ABD \cong$ __
12. $\overline{BC} \cong$ __ 13. $\triangle BDA \cong$ __ 14. $\triangle CEB \cong$ __

$\triangle MOP \cong \triangle HAT$ **Complete each statement.**

15. $\angle M \cong$ __ 16. $\overline{OP} \cong$ __ 17. $m\angle P =$ __
18. $\overline{MP} \cong$ __ 19. $\angle A \cong$ __ 20. $\overline{HA} \cong$ __

Discussion

21. Given that the two triangles to the right are congruent, explain how the figure could be labeled and what notation should be used to show that these triangles are congruent.

150 *Chapter 4 Congruent Triangles*

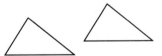

Exercises

A

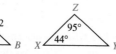

$\triangle ABC \cong \triangle DEF$ Complete each statement.

1. $\overline{AB} \cong$ __   2. $\overline{EF} \cong$ __
3. $\angle B \cong$ __   4. $\angle D \cong$ __
5. $\angle F \cong$ __   6. $\overline{AC} \cong$ __
7. $\triangle FED \cong$ __   8. $\triangle BCA \cong$ __

$\triangle ABC \cong \triangle XYZ$ Complete each statement.

9. $AB =$ __   10. $m\angle A =$ __
11. $m\angle C =$ __   12. $YZ =$ __

The two triangles shown are congruent. Name three pairs of angles and three pairs of sides that appear to be congruent for each pair of triangles.

13.   14.   15.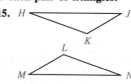

$\triangle ABF \cong \triangle CDE$, $EF = 11$, $FC = 6$ Complete each statement.

16. $AB =$ __   17. $AF =$ __
18. $m\angle AFB =$ __   19. $m\angle CDE =$ __
20. $m\angle CFB =$ __   21. $m\angle FAB =$ __

$\triangle JIP \cong \triangle MAT$ Complete each statement.

22. $\angle J \cong$ __   23. $\angle P \cong$ __   24. $\angle I \cong$ __
25. $\overline{IP} \cong$ __   26. $\overline{JP} \cong$ __   27. $\overline{JI} \cong$ __

28. Draw $\triangle ABC$. Use a compass and a straightedge to construct a $\triangle XYZ$, such that $\triangle XYZ \cong \triangle ABC$. Use hatch marks and arc marks to label all congruent parts of these figures.

B

$\triangle ABC \cong \triangle CED$ Complete each statement.

29. $m\angle ABC =$ __   30. $m\angle ECD =$ __
31. $m\angle ABD =$ __   32. $m\angle ACE =$ __

$\triangle FKH \cong \triangle FKG$ Complete each statement.

33. $m\angle KFL =$ __   34. $m\angle FKH =$ __   35. $m\angle HKJ =$ __
36. $m\angle FHK =$ __   37. $m\angle FLK =$ __   38. $m\angle FJK =$ __

39. This quilt pattern is made by sewing together triangular shapes. How many different (non-congruent) shapes are used? (Consider the shapes of the pieces only, not the fabric design in the shapes.)

40. Explain why these two triangles , though congruent, must be treated as different if you are cutting out the pieces for this quilt.

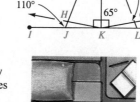

Ex. 29–32

Ex. 33–38

Lesson Closure

Review the definition of congruent triangles.

Remind students to note the order of vertices in the naming of triangles to help determine corresponding parts of the triangles.

Teacher's Resource Materials

Enrichment Using Manipulatives 20
Practice Master 22

Exercise Answers

1. $\overline{DE}$ 2. $\overline{BC}$ 3. $\angle E$
4. $\angle A$ 5. $\angle C$ 6. $\overline{DF}$
7. $\triangle CBA$ 8. $\triangle EFD$ 9. 17
10. 44   11. 95   12. 12
13. $\angle A \cong \angle F$, $\angle B \cong \angle E$, $\angle C \cong \angle D$, $\overline{AB} \cong \overline{FE}$, $\overline{AC} \cong \overline{FD}$, $\overline{BC} \cong \overline{ED}$
14. $\angle R \cong \angle T$, $\angle RUS \cong \angle TUS$, $\angle USR \cong \angle UST$, $\overline{RU} \cong \overline{TU}$, $\overline{RS} \cong \overline{TS}$, $\overline{US} \cong \overline{US}$
15. $\angle K \cong \angle L$, $\angle J \cong \angle M$, $\angle H \cong \angle N$, $\overline{KJ} \cong \overline{LM}$, $\overline{JH} \cong \overline{MN}$, $\overline{KH} \cong \overline{LN}$ 16. 16   17. 17
18. 85   19. 68   20. 95
21. 27   22. $\angle M$ 23. $\angle T$
24. $\angle A$ 25. $\overline{AT}$ 26. $\overline{MT}$
27. $\overline{MA}$ 28. Answers may vary.   29. 50   30. 40
31. 130   32. 50   33. 20
34. 65   35. 25   36. 95
37. 70   38. 70   39. 3

40. If you treat them the same, when you flip one over, you will expose the back of the fabric.
41. yes   **42.** yes
43. no   **44.** If $\triangle ABC \cong \triangle DEF$ and $\triangle ABC$ is isosceles with legs $\overline{AB}$ and $\overline{AC}$, then $\overline{DE} \cong \overline{AB}$, $\overline{AB} \cong \overline{AC}$, and $\overline{AC} \cong \overline{DF}$ so by the transitivity of congruence, $\overline{DE} \cong \overline{DF}$. This means $\triangle DEF$ is isosceles.   **45.** $\overline{AB}$, $\overline{AC}$, and $\overline{AD}$ or $\overline{BE}$, $\overline{CE}$, and $\overline{DE}$
46. $\angle B$, $\angle C$, $\angle D$; or $\angle AEB$, $\angle AEC$, $\angle AED$; or $\angle BAE$, $\angle CAE$, $\angle DAE$ **47.** $\angle L$
48. $\angle D$ **49.** $\overline{JK}$
50. $\overline{FE}$ **51. a.** 4 **b.** 2 The triangles are congruent if either $\triangle ABC \cong \triangle XYZ$ or $\triangle ABC \cong \triangle YXZ$.

Mixed Review Answers

1. 16   **2.** 81   **3.** 97
4. $\triangle EAB$, $\triangle EBC$, $\triangle EAC$, $\triangle EBD$, $\triangle EAD$, $\triangle ECD$ **5.** obtuse

Study Skills Answers

1. congruent   **2.** The vertices of the triangles must be written to show the correct correspondence.   **3.** $\triangle ABC \cong \triangle FDE$

Plot each point on a rectangular coordinate system. Choose the unit of length large enough that the resulting triangles are easy to measure. Measure the lengths and angles of these triangles. Is $\triangle ABC$ congruent to $\triangle DEF$?

41. $A(-4, 1)$, $B(-4, 3)$, $C(-1, 3)$, $D(1, 1)$, $E(1, 3)$, $F(4, 3)$
42. $A(-1, -2)$, $B(-3, 1)$, $C(-2, 5)$, $D(1, -2)$, $E(3, 1)$, $F(2, 5)$
43. $A(-3, 1)$, $B(-1, -1)$, $C(-4, 4)$, $D(1, 2)$, $E(1, 4)$, $F(3, 3)$

c

44. Explain why, if one of two congruent triangles is isosceles, then the other triangle is also isosceles.

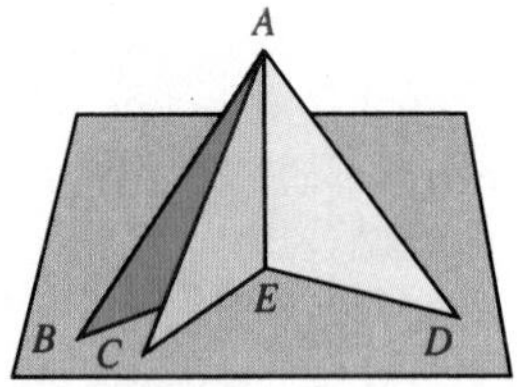

The three shaded triangles are congruent.

45. List a collection of three sides that are congruent to one another.
46. List a collection of three angles that are congruent to one another.

These figures are congruent, and the congruence symbol in the statement $ABCDEF \cong JKLMNO$ is interpreted just as it is for triangles. Complete each statement.

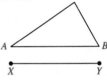

47. $\angle C \cong$ ___   **48.** $\angle M \cong$ ___
49. $\overline{AB} \cong$ ___   **50.** $\overline{ON} \cong$ ___

Critical Thinking

51. In the figure at the right, $XY = AB$. For how many different points Z is it true that

a. triangles ABC and XYZ are congruent?
b. $\triangle ABC \cong \triangle XYZ$?

Explain why the answers to these two questions are different.

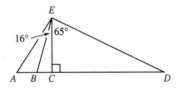

Mixed Review

$\overrightarrow{EB}$ **bisects** $\angle AEC$.   **Complete each statement.**

1. $m\angle AEB =$ ___   **2.** $m\angle BED =$ ___
3. $m\angle AED =$ ___

4. Name six triangles.
5. What type of triangle is $\triangle AED$?

Study Skills

1. Find a word in this lesson that means "same size and shape."
2. Suppose $\triangle ABC \cong \triangle DEF$. Explain why it is wrong to write $\triangle ABC \cong \triangle FED$.
3. Suppose triangle ABC is congruent to triangle DEF with angles A and F congruent, angles B and D congruent, and angles C and E congruent. Describe the congruence between these triangles using the appropriate symbols.

OBJECTIVE: *State and apply the SSS, ASA, and SAS Postulates.*

4-2 Congruence Postulates

EXPLORE

Cut a 4-in., a 5-in., and a 6-in. strip of paper and arrange them to form a triangle. Repeat this experiment. How do the two triangles compare in size and shape? State any generalizations that you discover.

4 in. [＿＿＿＿＿]
5 in. [＿＿＿＿＿＿]
6 in. [＿＿＿＿＿＿＿]

You learned in the last section that when two triangles are congruent, there are three pairs of congruent sides and three pairs of congruent angles. In the Explore above, you may have discovered that you do not need to show all six of these congruence relationships true to conclude that two triangles are congruent as state in the following postulate.

● **POSTULATE 16   SSS Postulate**

If each of the three sides of one triangle are congruent respectively to corresponding sides of another triangle, then the two triangles are congruent.

In △*ABC*, ∠*B* is *opposite* $\overline{AC}$ and $\overline{AB}$ is *opposite* ∠*C*. ∠*C* is *included* between $\overline{AC}$ and $\overline{BC}$, and $\overline{BC}$ is *included* between ∠*C* and ∠*B*.

Suppose that a segment and two angles are given as shown here.

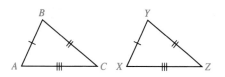

If an angle congruent to angle 1 is constructed at point *A* and an angle congruent to angle 2 is constructed at point *B*, then the sides of these angles can be extended to intersect at a point *C*, forming one and only one triangle.

This reasoning can be used as a convincing argument to describe how you might reach the conclusion given in Postulate 17.

4-2 Congruence Postulates   **153**

First Five Minutes

(Quiz on previous lesson)
△*HJP* ≅ △*FLR*

1. Name three pairs of corresponding angles. ∠*H* ↔ ∠*F*, ∠*J* ↔ ∠*L*, ∠*P* ↔ ∠*R*
2. Name three pairs of corresponding sides. $\overline{HJ}$ ↔ $\overline{FL}$, $\overline{JP}$ ↔ $\overline{LR}$, $\overline{HP}$ ↔ $\overline{FR}$
3. Name three pairs of corresponding vertices. *H* ↔ *F*, *J* ↔ *L*, *P* ↔ *R*
4. T/F △*JPH* ≅ △*RLF*
5. T/F △*FRL* ≅ △*HPJ*

Lesson Opener

Introduce this lesson by discussing the definition of congruent triangles. Then have students work in groups to cut out 4″, 5″, and 6″ strips of paper and arrange them to form a triangle. Repeat the experiment on the computer using investigative software.

Key Questions

1. How many different-shaped triangles were formed? 1
2. How do the triangles compare in size and shape? same

Materials

student notebooks
strips of paper
compasses
straightedges
investigative software

Teaching Notes

Encourage students to copy in their notebooks the triangles on pages 153–154 that illustrate the SSS Postulate, ASA Postulate, and the SAS Postulate. Make sure that they mark their diagrams to indicate the pairs of congruent parts. This will help them in determining which method to use to prove that two triangles are congruent.

Continue to emphasize the importance of naming and writing the vertices in order.

Guided Practice

Chalkboard Examples

1. $\overline{AB} \cong \overline{FE}$, $\overline{BC} \cong \overline{ED}$, $\overline{AC} \cong \overline{FD}$ Which postulate would you use to show that $\triangle ABC \cong \triangle FED$? **SSS**

Answer to **Try This** **ASA Postulate**

2. $\overline{EB} \cong \overline{BD}$, $\overline{AB} \cong \overline{CD}$ Name the pair of corresponding angles needed to prove $\triangle EAB \cong \triangle BCD$ by the SAS Postulate. **∠ABE, ∠CDB**

Answer to **Try This** **SAS Postulate**

3. Name an additional pair of congruent sides or angles that will justify that $\triangle ABC \cong \triangle DEF$ by the SSS Postulate. $\overline{AB} \cong \overline{CD}$, $\overline{BD} \cong \overline{DB}$

Answer to **Try This** **SSS Postulate**

● **POSTULATE 17** ASA Postulate

If two angles and the included side of one triangle are congruent to two angles and the included side of another triangle, then the two triangles are congruent.

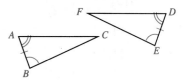

Example 1

Write a congruence between these triangles and state the postulate by which the triangles are congruent.

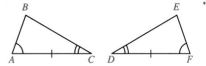

Solution

$\triangle ABC \cong \triangle FED$ ASA Postulate

Try This

$\angle V \cong \angle Y$, $\angle W \cong \angle Z$, $\overline{VW} \cong \overline{YZ}$
Which postulate would you use to show that $\triangle UVW \cong \triangle XYZ$?

● **POSTULATE 18** SAS Postulate

If two sides and the included angle of one triangle are congruent to two sides and the included angle of another triangle, then the two triangles are congruent.

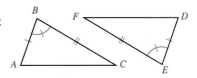

Example 2

Apply the SAS Postulate to show that a pair of triangles are congruent.

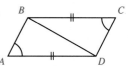

Solution

$\triangle BAE \cong \triangle DCB$ SAS Postulate

Try This

$\angle V \cong \angle Y$, $\overline{UV} \cong \overline{XY}$, $\overline{VW} \cong \overline{YZ}$
Which postulate would you use to show that $\triangle UVW \cong \triangle XYZ$?

Example 3

Name the additional congruent sides or angles needed to show these triangles are congruent by the given postulate.

a. SAS   **b.** ASA

Solution

a. $\overline{AB} \cong \overline{CD}$ **b.** $\angle ADB \cong \angle CBD$

Try This

$\overline{UV} \cong \overline{XY}$, $\overline{VW} \cong \overline{YZ}$, $\overline{UW} \cong \overline{XZ}$
Which postulate would you use to show $\triangle UVW \cong \triangle XYZ$?

154   *Chapter 4   Congruent Triangles*

Class Exercises

Short Answer

State the angle or side opposite the given side or angle.

1. $\overline{AD}$ 2. $\angle A$ 3. $\overline{AC}$ 4. $\angle BDC$

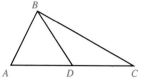

For each pair of sides or angles state the included angle or side.

5. $\overline{AB}, \overline{AD}$ 6. $\angle A, \angle C$ 7. $\angle ABD, \angle ADB$ 8. $\overline{AD}, \overline{BD}$

Sample Exercises

Write a congruence between each pair of triangles and state the postulate applied.

9.   10. 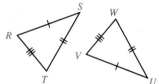   11.

Discussion

12. Give a convincing argument to describe how you might reach the conclusion in Postulate 17.
13. Give a convincing argument to describe how you might reach the conclusion in Postulate 18.
14. Give a convincing argument in favor of or against an AAA method of proving two triangles congruent: If three angles of one triangle are congruent to three angles of another triangle, the triangles are congruent.

Exercises

A

Write a congruence between each pair of triangles and state the postulate applied. If you cannot apply a postulate, write *no conclusion can be made*.

1. 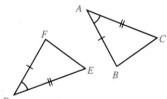   2. 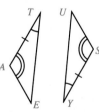   3.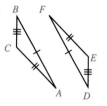

4. 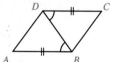   5. 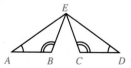   6.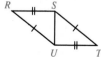

Exercise Answers

1. $\triangle ABC \cong \triangle DFE$, SAS
2. $\triangle AET \cong \triangle SUY$, ASA
3. $\triangle ABC \cong \triangle FDE$, SSS
4. $\triangle ABD \cong \triangle CDB$, SAS
5. No conclusion can be made.
6. $\triangle RSU \cong \triangle TUS$, SSS
7. $\overline{AC} \cong \overline{EF}$
8. $\angle FGE \cong \angle HGI$
9. $\overline{WX} \cong \overline{YZ}$ **10.** $\angle 2$
11. $\angle 2$ **12.** $\overline{DE}$
13. $\angle BCD$, $\overline{CD}$, or $\angle 1$, $\overline{BD}$
14. $\triangle WXZ$, $\triangle YXZ$ **15.** SAS
Postulate **16.** $\overline{WZ} \cong \overline{ZY}$ by
CPCTC **17.** $\triangle DCE$
18. ASA **19.** $\overline{BE} \cong \overline{EC}$ by
CPCTC **20.** $\triangle BAC$, $\triangle CDB$,
$\triangle DCA$ **21.** Place through the
midpoints of $\overline{AD}$ and $\overline{BC}$.
$\overline{AF} \cong \overline{FD}$, $\overline{BF} \cong \overline{FC}$,
$\angle AFB \cong \angle CFD$ (vert. $\angle$s);
$\triangle AFB \cong \triangle DFC$ by SAS,
$\overline{AB} \cong \overline{DC}$ by CPCTC.

Name the additional congruent sides or angles needed to show that the pair of triangles are congruent by the given postulate.

7.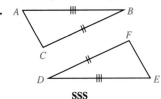
SSS

8.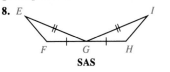
SAS

9.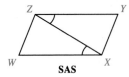
SAS

Complete each statement. Give the angle or side that allows you to show that each triangle is congruent to another triangle by the given postulate.

10. SAS for $\triangle ABC$: $\overline{AC}$, ___ , $\overline{BC}$
11. ASA for $\triangle BCE$: $\angle 1$, $\overline{BC}$, ___
12. SSS for $\triangle CDE$: ___ , $\overline{EC}$, $\overline{CD}$
13. SAS for $\triangle BCD$: $\overline{BC}$, ___ , ___

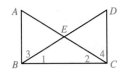

B

Tent pole $\overline{ZX}$ is placed perpendicular to the ground in such a way that X is the midpoint of the opening $\overline{WY}$ at the front of the tent.

14. Name a pair of congruent triangles.
15. What congruence postulate justifies your choice in Exercise 14?
16. Explain why $\triangle WYZ$ is an isosceles triangle.

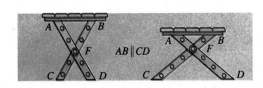

17. Name a triangle that is congruent to $\triangle ABE$.
18. Name a congruence postulate that can be used to show that the triangles in Exercise 17 are congruent.
19. Explain how you can conclude $\triangle BCE$ is an isosceles triangle.

$\overline{AB} \cong \overline{CD}$

20. Name three triangles that are congruent to $\triangle ABD$.

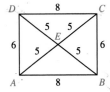

21. The legs of a table are hinged at points A and B. A bolt is placed at F in one of several predrilled holes. The height of the table is determined by the placement of the bolt F. Where should the bolt F be placed if the base CD is equal in length to the top AB? Explain your answer.

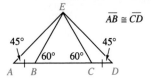
$AB \parallel CD$

156 *Chapter 4 Congruent Triangles*

22. $\angle A \cong \angle D$, $m\angle A = 3x + 15$, $m\angle D = x + 75$
$AB = 2x + 15$, $DE = 3x - 15$, $AC = x + 4$, $DF = 2x - 26$
Prove that $\triangle ABC$ and $\triangle DEF$ are congruent.

23. $\angle A \cong \angle D$, $m\angle A = 9x - 48$, $m\angle D = 6x - 15$
$AB = x + 5$, $DE = 2x - 6$, $AC = x - 1$, $DF = 3x - 23$
Prove that $\triangle ABC$ and $\triangle DEF$ are congruent.

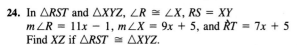

24. In $\triangle RST$ and $\triangle XYZ$, $\angle R \cong \angle X$, $RS = XY$
$m\angle R = 11x - 1$, $m\angle X = 9x + 5$, and $RT = 7x + 5$
Find XZ if $\triangle RST \cong \triangle XYZ$.

25. $\triangle KLM \cong \triangle NOP$, $m\angle K = 3x + 7$, $m\angle N = 2x + 24$, $m\angle L = 5x - 42$,
$m\angle O = 4x - 25$ Find the measure of $\angle P$.

26. $\triangle CDE \cong \triangle FGH$, $m\angle D = x^2 - 39$, $m\angle G = x + 17$, $m\angle E = 19 - x$,
$m\angle H = 27 - 2x$, $GH = 39 - 3x$ Find DE.

27. Name the coordinates of point F so that $\triangle ABC \cong \triangle DEF$.
28. Calculate the lengths of the sides and use the SSS Congruence
Postulate to verify the congruence stated in Exercise 27.

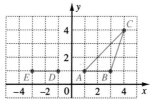

29. Name the coordinates of point R so that $\triangle MNO \cong \triangle PQR$.
30. Calculate the lengths of the sides and use the SSS Congruence
Postulate to verify the congruence stated in Exercise 29.

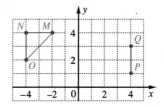

31. $\overline{AB} \cong \overline{BC} \cong \overline{CD} \cong \overline{DE}$, $\overline{AF} \cong \overline{EF}$, $\angle A \cong \angle E$
List all the pairs of triangles that you think could be shown to
be congruent in the figure to the right.
32. For each pair of triangles listed in Exercise 31 explain why you
think your choice is correct.
33. Which postulate can be used to show that $\triangle ACE \cong \triangle DBF$?
Explain your reasoning.
34. Given that $\overline{AE}$ bisects $\angle BAD$, $AD = AB = 21$, find x.
Explain how you found the answer.

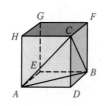

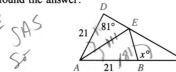

Critical Thinking
35. *ADBEHCFG* is a cube. Write a paragraph that would convince someone
that $\triangle ADC$, $\triangle BDC$, and $\triangle ADB$ are all congruent to one another.

---

22. $3x + 15 = x + 75$, $2x = 60$,
$x = 30$. $AB = 75$, $DE = 75$,
$AC = 34$, $DF = 34$, $\overline{AB} \cong \overline{DE}$
and $\overline{AC} \cong \overline{DF}$. By SAS,
$\triangle ABC \cong \triangle DEF$.
23. $9x - 48 = 6x - 15$, $3x = 33$,
$x = 11$, $AB = 16$, $DE = 16$,
$AC = 10$, $DF = 10$, $\overline{AB} \cong \overline{DE}$,
$\overline{AC} \cong \overline{DF}$. By SAS,
$\triangle ABC \cong \triangle DEF$.   **24.** 26
25. 79   **26.** 15
27. $(-4, 4)$ or $(-4, -2)$
28. $AB = 2$, $AC = 3\sqrt{2}$,
$BC = \sqrt{10}$, $DE = 2$, $DF = 3\sqrt{2}$
$EF = \sqrt{10}$, $\overline{AB} \cong \overline{DE}$, $\overline{AC} \cong \overline{DF}$,
$\overline{BC} \cong \overline{EF}$. By SSS,
$\triangle ABC \cong \triangle DEF$.   **29.** $(2, 3)$
or $(6,3)$ **30.** With R $(2, 3)$,
$MN = NO = RQ = QP = 2$,
$OM = RP = 2\sqrt{2}$, so by SSS,
$\triangle MNO \cong \triangle PQR$.
31. $\triangle FAB \cong \triangle FED$,
$\triangle FAC \cong \triangle FEC$, $\triangle FAD \cong \triangle FEB$,
$\triangle FBC \cong \triangle FDC$
32. $\triangle FAB \cong \triangle FED$ by SAS,
$\triangle FAC \cong \triangle FEC$ by SAS or SSS,
$\triangle FAD \cong \triangle FEB$ by SAS,
$\triangle FBC \cong \triangle FDC$ by SAS and
CPCTC   **33.** ASA,
$m\angle A = 61 = m\angle D$,
$AC = 14 + BC = BD$,
$m\angle ECA = 29 = m\angle FBD$
34. $x = 99$ $\overline{AD} \cong \overline{AB}$,
$\angle DAE \cong \angle BAE$, $\overline{AE} \cong \overline{AE}$,
$\triangle DAE \cong \triangle BAE$ by SAS,
$m\angle EBA = m\angle EDA = 81$,
$m\angle EBC = 180 - 81 = 99$
35. $AD = DC = DB$, $m\angle ADC =$
$m\angle ADB = m\angle CDB = 90$
By SAS $\triangle ADC \cong \triangle BDC$,
$\triangle ADC \cong \triangle ADB$, $\triangle BDC \cong \triangle ADB$

36.–37. Answers may vary.
38. $\triangle RST \cong \triangle XYZ$, ASA Post.

Mixed Review Answers

1. 45 **2.** 60 **3.** 45
4. 90 **5.** 60 **6.** 60
7. $\triangle GFH \cong \triangle JKL$, SAS
8. $\triangle RAS \cong \triangle LON$, ASA
9. $\triangle XYW \cong \triangle DEC$, SSS
10. 4

Quiz Answers

1. $\overline{HF}$ **2.** 30 **3.** 6
4. $\angle D$ **5.** 3 **6.** $\triangle FIH$
7. $\triangle JKL \cong \triangle JML$, ASA
8. $\triangle RQS \cong \triangle WXY$, SAS
9. $\triangle ABC \cong \triangle CDA$, SSS
10. $\angle A \cong Y$ **11.** $\angle B \cong \angle X$
12. $\overline{AC} \cong \overline{YZ}$

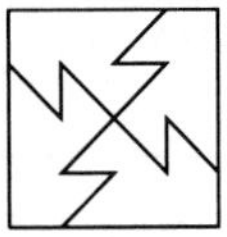

36. The figure to the right shows a square divided into four congruent eight-sided polygons. Draw a second way of doing this.

37. Draw a third way of dividing a square into four congruent eight-sided polygons.

38. Draw a triangle. Label it *RST*. Using a compass and straightedge, construct $\overline{XY} \cong \overline{RS}$, $\angle X \cong \angle R$, and $\angle Y \cong \angle S$. Extend the exterior sides of angles *X* and *Y* so that they meet in a point *Z*. State a congruence between the triangles. What postulate supports your statement?

Mixed Review

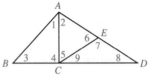

$\triangle ACE$ is equilateral. $\angle ACB$ is a right angle. $\angle 1 \cong \angle 3$
Complete each statement.

1. $m\angle 1 =$ ___ **2.** $m\angle 2 =$ ___ **3.** $m\angle 3 =$ ___
4. $m\angle 4 =$ ___ **5.** $m\angle 5 =$ ___ **6.** $m\angle 6 =$ ___

Write a congruence between each pair of triangles and state the postulate applied.

7.

8.

9.

10. $\triangle ABC \cong \triangle LMN$, $m\angle B = x^2$, $m\angle L = 9x$, $BC = x - 2$, $MN = 16 - x$, $AB = 2x - 14$ How long is $\overline{LM}$?

Quiz

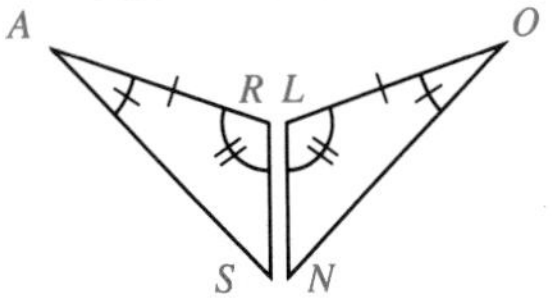

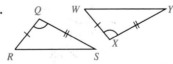

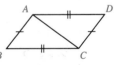

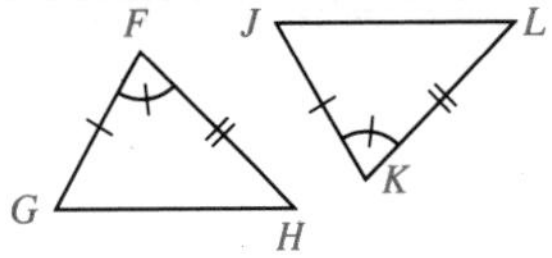

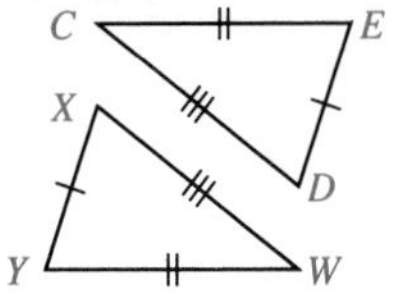

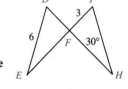

$\triangle DEF \cong \triangle IHF$ **Complete each statement.**

1. $\overline{EF} \cong$ ___ **2.** $m\angle E =$ ___ **3.** $IH =$ ___
4. $\angle I \cong$ ___ **5.** $DF =$ ___ **6.** $\triangle FDE \cong$ ___

Write a congruence between each pair of triangles and state the postulate applied.

7.

8.

9.

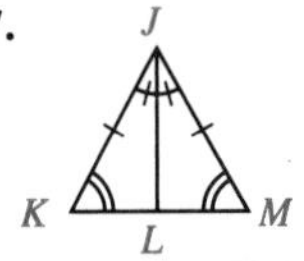

State the additional sides or angles that are needed to prove $\triangle ABC \cong \triangle YXZ$ by the indicated postulate.

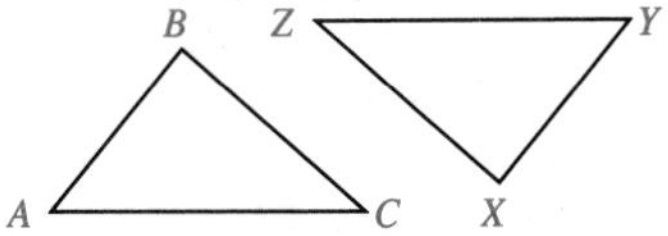

10. SAS: $\overline{AB} \cong \overline{YX}$, $\overline{AC} \cong \overline{YZ}$
11. ASA: $\angle C \cong \angle Z$, $\overline{BC} \cong \overline{XZ}$
12. SSS: $\overline{AB} \cong \overline{YX}$, $\overline{BC} \cong \overline{XZ}$

158 *Chapter 4 Congruent Triangles*

PROVING TRIANGLES CONGRUENT

OBJECTIVE: *Use definitions and the SSS, SAS, and ASA congruence postulates to prove triangles congruent.*

4-3 Proofs: Using Congruence Postulates

In this lesson you will use the SSS, SAS, and ASA congruence postulates to write proofs in the two-column format you learned to use in Chapter 2. The hypothesis and the conclusion of the SAS Postulate are highlighted.

If	two sides and the included angle of one triangle are congruent to two sides and the included angle of another triangle,	then	the two triangles are congruent.
	hypothesis		*conclusion*

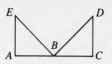

Many professionals must reason carefully and logically. Geometry proofs provide practice in logical thinking.

When you use a congruence postulate in a two-column proof, you must include statements to show that the hypothesis is true. The final statement is the conclusion.

Example 1

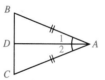

Given: $\overline{AB} \cong \overline{AC}$
$\qquad \angle 1 \cong \angle 2$

Prove: $\triangle ABD \cong \triangle ACD$

Proof

Statements	Reasons
1. $\overline{AB} \cong \overline{AC}$	1. Given
2. $\angle 1 \cong \angle 2$	2. Given
3. $\overline{AD} \cong \overline{AD}$	3. Reflexive Property
4. $\triangle ABD \cong \triangle ACD$	4. SAS Postulate

In the above proof statements 1, 2, and 3 show that the hypothesis of the SAS Postulate is satisfied. Statement 4 is drawn from the conclusion of the SAS Postulate. Other congruence postulates are used similarly in proofs.

A statement and its reasons often refer to a previously learned definition. Use the sentences listed below as reasons in your proof when you are using the definitions listed. Note the third reason in Example 2.

An angle *bisector* forms two congruent angles.
A segment *bisector* forms two congruent segments.
A segment *midpoint* forms two congruent segments.
Perpendicular segments form right angles.

4-3 Proofs: Using Congruence Postulates **159**

First Five Minutes

(Quiz on previous lesson)

$\angle A \cong \angle C, \angle E \cong \angle D,$
$\overline{AE} \cong \overline{DC}$ Write a congruence between each triangle and state the postulate applied.
$\triangle ABE \cong \triangle CBD$, ASA

Lesson Opener

The goal of this lesson is to use the SSS, SAS, and ASA Postulates to write proofs in a two-column format.

Materials

student notebooks

Teaching Notes

Review the real-number properties in Chapter 1 before discussing the examples.

The reflexive property is useful when a common side of two triangles is involved.

Guided Practice

Chalkboard Examples

1. Given: $\angle ADB \cong \angle ADC,$
$\angle 1 \cong \angle 2$
Prove: $\triangle ABD \cong \triangle ACD$
1. $\angle ADB \cong \angle ADC$ (Given)
2. $\overline{AD} \cong \overline{AD}$ (Reflex.)
3. $\angle 1 \cong \angle 2$ (Given)
4. $\triangle ABD \cong \triangle ACD$ (ASA)

2. Given: $\overline{AB} \cong \overline{AC}$,
$\overline{BD} \cong \overline{CD}$
Prove: $\triangle ABD \cong \triangle ACD$
1. $\overline{AB} \cong \overline{AC}$ (Given) 2. $\overline{BD} \cong \overline{CD}$
(Given) 3. $\overline{AD} \cong \overline{AD}$ (Reflex.)
4. $\triangle ABD \cong \triangle ACD$ (SSS)

3. Given: $\overline{DB}$ bisects $\angle ADC$.
$\overline{DA} \cong \overline{DC}$
Prove: $\triangle ADB \cong \triangle CDB$
1. $DA \cong \overline{DC}$ (Given) 2. $\overline{DB}$ bisects $\angle ADC$. (Given) 3.
$\angle ADB \cong \angle CDB$ (Def. of $\angle$ bisector)
4. $\overline{DB} \cong \overline{DB}$ (Reflex.)
5. $\triangle ADB \cong \triangle CDB$ (SAS)

Class Exercise Answers

1. H: Three sides of one triangle are congruent respectively
to three sides of another triangle. C: The triangles are congruent.   **2.** H: Two sides and the
included angle of one triangle
are congruent respectively to
two sides and the included angle of another triangle. C: The
triangles are congruent.
3. H: Two angles and the included side of one triangle are
congruent respectively to two
angles and the included side of
another triangle. C: The triangles are congruent.   **4.** H:
Corresponding pairs of angles
and sides of two triangles are
congruent. C: The two triangles
are congruent.

Example 2

Given: $\overline{AD}$ bisects $\angle BAC$.
$\overline{AB} \cong \overline{AC}$
Prove: $\triangle ABD \cong \triangle ACD$

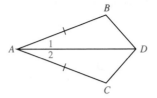

Proof Statements	Reasons
1. $\overline{AB} \cong \overline{AC}$	1. Given
2. $\overline{AD}$ bisects $\angle BAC$.	2. Given
3. $\angle 1 \cong \angle 2$	3. An angle bisector forms two congruent angles.
4. $\overline{AD} \cong \overline{AD}$	4. Reflexive Property
5. $\triangle ABD \cong \triangle ACD$	5. SAS Postulate

The proof in Example 3 uses the definition of a line perpendicular to a plane
introduced in Chapter 1.

Example 3

Given: $\overline{AB} \perp N$
B in plane N
$\overline{AB} \cong \overline{CB}$
Prove: $\triangle ABD \cong \triangle CBD$

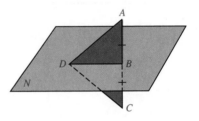

Proof Statements	Reasons
1. $\overline{AB} \perp N$, B in N	1. Given
2. $\overline{AB} \cong \overline{CB}$	2. Given
3. $\overline{AB} \perp \overline{BD}$	3. If a line is $\perp$ to plane N at B then it is $\perp$ to each line in N through B.
4. $\angle ABD$ and $\angle CBD$ are rt. $\angle$s.	4. $\perp$ lines form rt. $\angle$s.
5. $\angle ABD \cong \angle CBD$	5. All rt. $\angle$s are $\cong$.
6. $\overline{BD} \cong \overline{BD}$	6. Reflexive Property
7. $\triangle ABD \cong \triangle CBD$	7. SAS Postulate

Class Exercises

Short Answer

State the hypothesis and conclusion of each postulate.
 1. SSS Congruence Postulate   2. SAS Congruence Postulate   3. ASA Congruence Postulate

 4. State the hypothesis and conclusion of this statement.
   Two triangles are congruent if corresponding pairs of angles and sides are congruent.

A conclusion can be drawn from the information given in each of Exercises 5–9. State your conclusion and the postulate or definition on which it is based.

5. $\overline{DF} \cong \overline{AC}$, $\overline{DE} \cong \overline{AB}$, $\angle D \cong \angle A$
6. $\overline{EF} \cong \overline{BC}$, $\angle F \cong \angle C$, $\angle B \cong \angle E$

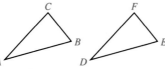

7. $\overline{MN}$ bisects $\angle KML$ and $\angle KNM \cong \angle MNL$.
8. N is the midpoint of $\overline{KL}$. $\overline{KM} \cong \overline{LM}$
9. $\overline{MN}$ bisects $\angle KML$. $\overline{KM} \cong \overline{LM}$

Sample Exercises

Complete each proof.

10. **Given:** $\overline{AE} \cong \overline{DE}$, $\angle A \cong \angle D$
   $\angle AEB \cong \angle DEC$

   Prove: $\triangle AEB \cong \triangle DEC$

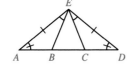

Statements	Reasons
1. $\angle AEB \cong \angle DEC$	1. ___
2. $\overline{AE} \cong \overline{DE}$	2. ___
3. $\angle A \cong \angle D$	3. ___
4. $\triangle AEB \cong \triangle DEC$	4. ___

11. **Given:** $\overline{AB} \cong \overline{AD}$
   C is the midpoint of $\overline{BD}$.

   Prove: $\triangle ABC \cong \triangle ADC$

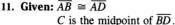

Statements	Reasons
1. $\overline{AB} \cong \overline{AD}$	1. ___
2. C is the midpoint of $\overline{BD}$.	2. ___
3. $\overline{BC} \cong \overline{DC}$	3. ___
4. ___	4. Reflexive Property
5. $\triangle ABC \cong \triangle ADC$	5. ___

12. **Given:** $\overline{RT} \cong \overline{VT}$, $\overline{ST} \cong \overline{UT}$

   Prove: $\triangle RST \cong \triangle VUT$

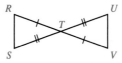

Statements	Reasons
1. $\overline{RT} \cong \overline{VT}$	1. ___
2. $\angle RTS \cong \angle VTU$	2. ___
3. $\overline{ST} \cong \overline{UT}$	3. ___
4. ___	4. ___

Discussion

13. Suppose that $\overline{AC}$ is the perpendicular bisector of $\overline{BD}$. Give a convincing argument that $\triangle ABC \cong \triangle ADC$.

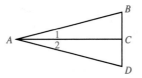

5. $\triangle ABC \cong \triangle DEF$ by SAS
6. $\triangle ABC \cong \triangle DEF$ by ASA
7. $\angle KMN \cong \angle LMN$ by definition of an angle bisector
8. $\triangle MNK \cong \triangle MNL$ by SSS
9. $\triangle MNK \cong \triangle MNL$ by SAS
10. 1. Given 2. Given 3. Given 4. ASA Post. **11.** 1. Given 2. Given 3. Def. of segment midpoint 4. $\overline{AC} \cong \overline{AC}$ 5. SSS Post. **12.** 1. Given 2. Vert. $\angle$s are $\cong$. 3. Given 4. $\triangle RTS \cong \triangle VTU$, SAS Post.
13. $\overline{AC} \perp \overline{BD}$, so $\angle ACB$ and $\angle ACD$ are rt. $\angle$s and $\cong$. $\overline{AC}$ bisects $\overline{BD}$, so $\overline{BC} \cong \overline{DC}$. $\overline{AC} \cong \overline{AC}$ by the Reflex. Prop. $\triangle ABC \cong \triangle ADC$ by the SAS Post.

Assignment Guide
Minimum: 1–26 e/o, 29, MR
Regular: 1–28 e/o, 29, MR
Advanced: 5–26 e/o, 27–31, MR

Lesson Closure
Review the three methods (SSS, SAS, ASA) of proving triangles congruent.
Applications
Exercise 22
Algebra
Exercises 23–25

Teacher's Resource Materials
Enrichment Using Manipulatives 22
Practice Master 24
Technology: BASIC 7

Exercise Answers

1. 1. Given 2. Given 3. Given
4. ASA Post.   **2.** 1. Given
2. Given 3. $\overline{AB} \cong \overline{AE}$ 4. SSS
Post.   **3.** 1. Given 2. Def. of
angle bisector 3. Reflex. Prop.
4. Given 5. $\triangle RTQ \cong \triangle RTS$
4. 1. Given 2. Def. of segment
bisector 3. Vert. $\angle$s are $\cong$.
4. $\overline{AC} \cong \overline{EC}$, (Given) 5. SAS
Post. **5.** 1. $\overline{DE} \cong \overline{DF}$ (Given)
2. $\overline{DH}$ bisects $\overline{EF}$. (Given)
3. $\overline{EH} \cong \overline{FH}$ (Def. of segment bisector) 4. $\overline{DH} \cong \overline{DH}$, (Reflex.
Prop.) 5. $\triangle DHE \cong \triangle DHF$ (SSS
Post.) **6.** 1. $\overline{DE} \cong \overline{DF}$ (Given)
2. $\overline{DH}$ bisects $\angle EDF$. (Given)
3. $\angle EDH \cong \angle FDH$ (Def. of angle bisector) 4. $\overline{DH} \cong \overline{DH}$
(Reflex. Prop.) 5. $\triangle DHE \cong$
$\triangle DHF$ (SAS Post.)
7. 1. $\overline{AB} \cong \overline{CD}$ (Given)
2. $\angle 1 \cong \angle 4$ (Given)
3. $\overline{AC} \cong \overline{CA}$ (Reflex. Prop.)
4. $\triangle ABC \cong \triangle CDA$ (SAS
Post.)   **8.** 1. $\angle 2 \cong \angle 3$,
$\angle 1 \cong \angle 4$ (Given) 2. $\overline{AC} \cong \overline{CA}$
(Reflex. Prop.)
3. $\triangle ABC \cong \triangle CDA$ (ASA Post.)

Exercises

A

Complete each proof.

1. Given: $\angle D \cong \angle X$, $\angle F \cong \angle Z$, $\overline{DF} \cong \overline{XZ}$

Prove: $\triangle DEF \cong \triangle XYZ$

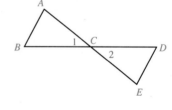

Statements	Reasons
1. $\angle D \cong \angle X$	1. —
2. $\overline{DF} \cong \overline{XZ}$	2. —
3. $\angle F \cong \angle Z$	3. —
4. $\triangle DEF \cong \triangle XYZ$	4. —

2. Given: $\overline{AC} \cong \overline{AD}$, $\overline{BC} \cong \overline{DE}$, $\overline{AB} \cong \overline{AE}$

Prove: $\triangle ABC \cong \triangle AED$

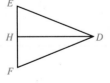

Statements	Reasons
1. $\overline{AC} \cong \overline{AD}$	1. —
2. $\overline{BC} \cong \overline{DE}$	2. —
3. —	3. Given
4. $\triangle ABC \cong \triangle AED$	4. —

3. Given: $\overline{RT}$ bisects $\angle QRS$. $\angle 1 \cong \angle 2$

Prove: $\triangle RTQ \cong \triangle RTS$

Statements	Reasons
1. $\overline{RT}$ bisects $\angle QRS$.	1. —
2. $\angle QRT \cong \angle SRT$	2. —
3. $\overline{RT} \cong \overline{RT}$	3. —
4. $\angle 1 \cong \angle 2$	4. —
5. —	5. ASA

4. Given: $\overline{AE}$ bisects $\overline{BD}$. $\overline{AC} \cong \overline{EC}$

Prove: $\triangle ABC \cong \triangle EDC$

Statements	Reasons
1. $\overline{AE}$ bisects $\overline{BD}$.	1. —
2. $\overline{BC} \cong \overline{DC}$	2. —
3. $\angle 1 \cong \angle 2$	3. —
4. —	4. —
5. $\triangle ABC \cong \triangle EDC$	5. —

Write a two-column proof for each exercise.

5. Given: $\overline{DE} \cong \overline{DF}$, $\overline{DH}$ bisects $\overline{EF}$.

  Prove: $\triangle DHE \cong \triangle DHF$

6. Given: $\overline{DE} \cong \overline{DF}$, $\overline{DH}$ bisects $\angle EDF$.

  Prove: $\triangle DHE \cong \triangle DHF$

7. Given: $\overline{AB} \cong \overline{CD}$, $\angle 1 \cong \angle 4$

  Prove: $\triangle ABC \cong \triangle CDA$

8. Given: $\angle 2 \cong \angle 3$, $\angle 1 \cong \angle 4$

  Prove: $\triangle ABC \cong \triangle CDA$

9. Given: $\overline{HI} \cong \overline{KI}$, $\angle 1 \cong \angle 2$
$\overline{JI} \cong \overline{IL}$

Prove: $\triangle HIJ \cong \triangle KIL$

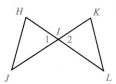

10. Given: $\overline{AB} \cong \overline{CD}$, $\angle 1 \cong \angle 2$
$\overline{AC}$ bisects $\overline{BD}$.

Prove: $\triangle ABE \cong \triangle CDE$

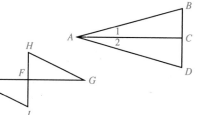

Write a conclusion that follows from the given information. State the congruence postulate and/or definition on which your conclusion is based.

11. $\overline{AB} \cong \overline{AD}$, $\overline{BC} \cong \overline{DC}$
12. $\overline{AB} \cong \overline{AD}$, $\angle 1 \cong \angle 2$
13. $\overline{AC}$ is perpendicular to $\overline{BD}$. $\overline{BC} \cong \overline{DC}$
14. $\overline{AC}$ is perpendicular to $\overline{BD}$. $\angle 1 \cong \angle 2$
15. F is the midpoint of $\overline{EG}$ and $\overline{HI}$.
16. $\overline{EG}$ and $\overline{HI}$ bisect each other.

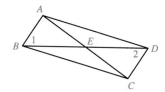

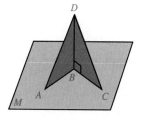

Write a two-column proof for each exercise.

17. Given: $\overline{BD} \perp$ to plane M
$\overline{AB} \cong \overline{BC}$

Prove: $\triangle ABD \cong \triangle CBD$

18. Given: $\overline{AB} \perp$ plane M, $\overline{DE} \perp$ plane M
C bisects $\overline{BD}$.

Prove: $\triangle ACB \cong \triangle ECD$

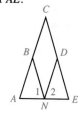

B

Write a two-column proof for each exercise.

19. Given: $\overline{AI}$ bisects $\angle BAC$.
$\overline{AB} \cong \overline{AC}$

Prove: $\triangle ABI \cong \triangle ACI$

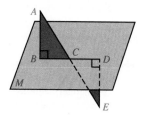

20. Given: $\angle 1 \cong \angle 2$, $\angle A \cong \angle E$
N is the midpoint of $\overline{AE}$.

Prove: $\triangle ABN \cong \triangle EDN$

4-3 Proofs: Using Congruence Postulates **163**

9. 1. $\overline{HI} \cong \overline{KI}$ (Given)
2. $\angle 1 \cong \angle 2$ (Given) 3. $\overline{JI} \cong \overline{IL}$
(Given) 4. $\triangle HIJ \cong \triangle KIL$ (SAS
Post.)   10. 1. $\overline{AC}$ bisects $\overline{BD}$.
(Given) 2. $\overline{BE} \cong \overline{DE}$ (Def. of
segment bisector) 3. $\angle 1 \cong \angle 2$
(Given) 4. $\overline{AB} \cong \overline{CD}$ (Given)
5. $\triangle ABE \cong \triangle CDE$ (SAS Post.)
11. $\triangle ABC \cong \triangle ADC$ by SSS
12. $\triangle ABC \cong \triangle ADC$ by SAS
13. $\triangle ABC \cong \triangle ADC$ by SAS
14. $\triangle ABC \cong \triangle ADC$ by ASA
15. $\triangle EFI \cong \triangle GFH$ by SAS
16. $\triangle EFI \cong \triangle GFH$ by SAS
17. 1. $\overline{BD} \perp$ plane M (Given)
2. $\overline{BD} \perp \overline{AB}$, $\overline{BD} \perp \overline{CB}$ (If a line
is $\perp$ to a plane at B, it is $\perp$ to
all lines in the plane that contain B) 3. $\angle ABD$, $\angle CDB$ are rt.
$\angle$s ($\perp$ segments form rt. $\angle$s.)
4. $\angle ABD \cong \angle CBD$ (All rt. $\angle$s
are $\cong$.) 5. $\overline{AB} \cong \overline{BC}$ (Given)
6. $\overline{BD} \cong \overline{BD}$ (Reflex. Prop.)
7. $\triangle ABD \cong \triangle CBD$ (SAS Post.)
18. 1. $\overline{AB} \perp$ plane M,
$\overline{DE} \perp$ plane M (Given) 2. $\overline{AB}$
$\perp \overline{BD}$, $\overline{DE} \perp \overline{BD}$ (If a line
is $\perp$ to a plane at P, it is $\perp$ to
all lines through P in the
plane.) 3. $\angle ABD$, $\angle EDB$ rt. $\angle$s
($\perp$ segments form rt. $\angle$s)
4. $\angle ABD \cong \angle EDB$ (All rt. $\angle$s
are $\cong$.) 5. C bisects $\overline{BD}$. (Given)
6. $\overline{BC} \cong \overline{DC}$ (Def. of segment bisector) 7. $\angle BCA \cong \angle DCE$ (Vert.
$\angle$ Theorem) 8. $\triangle ACB \cong \triangle ECD$
(ASA Post.)   19. 1. $\overline{AI}$ bisects
$\angle BAC$ (Given) 2. $\angle BAI \cong \angle CAI$
(Def. of angle bisector) 3. $\overline{AB} \cong$
$\overline{AC}$ (Given) 4. $\overline{AI} \cong \overline{AI}$ (Reflex.
Prop.) 5. $\triangle ABI \cong \triangle ACI$ (SAS)
20. 1. $\angle 1 \cong \angle 2$, $\angle A \cong \angle E$
(Given) 2. N is the midpoint of
$\overline{AE}$. (Given) 3. $\overline{AN} \cong \overline{EN}$
(A segment midpoint forms
two $\cong$ segments.)
4. $\triangle ABN \cong \triangle EDN$ (ASA)

21. Supporting struts are often added to a structure to form triangles so that the structure will become rigid. Explain how the congruence postulates relate to the fact that triangles form rigid figures.

A nonrigid figure collapses.   Triangles form rigid figures.

22. Give a convincing argument that quadrilaterals do not satisfy an SSSS congruence postulate.

23. D is the midpoint of $\overline{BC}$. $AB = 9x + 3$, $BD = 9x - 2$, $AC = 15x - 3$, $CD = 4x + 3$ Show that $\triangle ABD \cong \triangle ACD$.

24. $\overline{AD}$ bisects $\angle BAC$. $m\angle BAD = 31 - x$, $m\angle CAD = 15 + 3x$, $AB = 3x + 4$, $AC = 7x - 12$ Show that $\triangle BDA \cong \triangle CDA$.

25. $m\angle AOD = 2x + 9$, $m\angle BOC = 3x + 5$, $AO = x^2 - 2$, $OB = 3x + 2$, $OC = 2x^2 - 17$, $DO = 5x - 5$ Show that $\overline{AB}$ and $\overline{CD}$ bisect each other.

C

26. Given: In figure $ABCD$, O bisects $\overline{AC}$ and $\overline{BD}$.
Prove: $\overline{AB} \| \overline{CD}$, $\overline{BC} \| \overline{AD}$

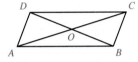

Critical Thinking

Decide whether each statement is always, sometimes, or never true. Draw a figure to explain your answer. Give a convincing argument when the statement is always true.

27. A ray that bisects one angle of a triangle divides the triangle into two congruent triangles.

28. The segment from a vertex of a triangle to the midpoint of the opposite side divides the triangle into a pair of congruent triangles.

29. If two sides of a triangle are congruent, the segment from the common vertex to the midpoint of the third side bisects the angle of the vertex.

Mixed Review

Complete each statement.

  1. Two lines in different planes that do not intersect are ___ .
  2. Four lines intersect in, at most, ___ points.
  3. Adjacent angles have no ___ points in common.
  4. Two lines that form congruent adjacent angles are ___ .
  5. If two sides of a triangle lie in a plane, the third side ___ .
  6. A triangle divides a plane into three sets of points, those on the exterior, those on the interior, and ___ .

Computer Activity

Suppose you have two boxes and each box contains eight dowel rods with lengths 8 cm, 9 cm, 10 cm, 11 cm, 12 cm, 13 cm, 14 cm, and 15 cm. Suppose you reach into one box with your right hand and select three rods at random, and then you reach into the other box with your left hand and select three rods at random.

What are the chances that the triangle made with the right-hand rods will be congruent to the triangle made with the left-hand rods? Are your chances very good?

The program provided here simulates this experiment. When you run the program, it asks how many times you want to simulate the experiment. Then it records the number of times the two randomly selected triangles are congruent. It also records the experimental probability of selecting a pair of congruent triangles.

```
10 INPUT "HOW MANY EXPERIMENTS DO YOU WANT TO RUN ";N
15 FOR COUNT = 1 TO N
20 INDEX = 0
25 FOR TRIANGLE 1 TO 2
30 GOSUB 1000
35 A(INDEX + 1) = NUMBER
40 GOSUB 1000
45 A(INDEX + 2) = NUMBER
50 IF A(INDEX + 1) = A(INDEX + 2) THEN GOTO 40
55 IF A(INDEX + 1) > A(INDEX + 2), THEN SWITCH = A(INDEX + 1):
    A(INDEX + 1) = A(INDEX + 2): A(INDEX + 2) = SWITCH
60 GOSUB 1000
65 A(INDEX + 3) = NUMBER
70 IF A(INDEX + 3) = A(INDEX + 2) OR A(INDEX + 3) = A(INDEX + 1)
    THEN GOTO 60
75 IF A(INDEX + 1) > A(INDEX + 3), THEN SWITCH = A(INDEX + 1):
    A(INDEX + 1) = A(INDEX + 3): A(INDEX + 3) = SWITCH
80 IF A(INDEX + 2) > A(INDEX + 3), THEN SWITCH = A(INDEX + 2);
    A(INDEX + 2) = A(INDEX + 3): A(INDEX + 3) = SWITCH
85 INDEX = 3
90 NEXT TRIANGLE
95 IF A(1) = A(4) AND A(2) = A(5) AND A(3) = A(6) THEN PAIRS = PAIRS + 1
100 NEXT COUNT
110 PRINT "THE NUMBER OF CONGRUENT PAIRS IS "; PAIRS
115 PRINT "THE EXPERIMENTAL PROBABILITY IS "; PAIRS/N
120 END
1000 NUMBER = INT(8*RND(1)) + 8: RETURN
```

Exercises

1. Run the program to simulate the experiment 100 times.
2. Run the program to simulate the experiment 500 times.
3. Which result do you think is closer to the actual probability? Why?

Write a two-column proof.
Given: $\angle M \cong \angle R$, O is the midpoint of $\overline{MR}$.
Prove: $\triangle MON \cong \triangle ROP$
1. $\angle M \cong \angle R$ (Given) 2. O is the midpt. of $\overline{MR}$ (Given)
3. $\overline{MO} \cong \overline{RO}$ (Def. midpt.)
4. $\angle POR \cong \angle NOM$ (Vert. $\angle$s $\cong$)
5. $\triangle MON \cong \triangle ROP$ (ASA)

Lesson Opener

The goal of this lesson is to prove two segments or angles congruent once they are shown to be corresponding parts of congruent triangles.

Key Questions

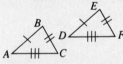

$\triangle ABC \cong \triangle DEF$ by SSS
Is $\angle A \cong \angle D$? yes
$\angle B \cong \angle E$? yes
$\angle C \cong \angle F$? yes
Why? Corr. parts of $\cong \triangle$s are $\cong$.

Materials

student notebooks

OBJECTIVE: *Deduce that segments and angles are congruent by first proving that triangles are congruent.*

4-4 Proving Segments and Angles Congruent

In this lesson you will prove two triangles are congruent in order to conclude that a pair of angles or sides are congruent. In this first example you will learn how a surveyor can use congruent triangles to find a distance that he or she is unable to measure directly.

Example 1

Application A surveyor is unable to measure the distances from docks A and B to point P on an island. Explain how to find distances AP and BP.

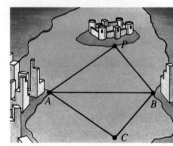

Solution

1. Measure $\angle BAP$ and $\angle ABP$.
2. Locate point C so that $m\angle BAP = m\angle BAC$ and $m\angle ABP = m\angle ABC$.
3. Use the ASA postulate to conclude that $\triangle ABP \cong \triangle ABC$.
4. Since corresponding sides of congruent triangles are the same length, we can conclude that $AP = AC$ and $BP = BC$. Measure $\overline{AC}$ and $\overline{BC}$.

Step 4 in Example 1 uses the fact that corresponding sides of congruent triangles are congruent. It is also true that corresponding angles of congruent triangles are congruent.

> Corresponding parts of congruent triangles are congruent.
> Abbreviation: Corr. parts of $\cong$s are $\cong$.

Example 2

Complete the proof.
Given: $\overline{AB} \cong \overline{AD}$, $\angle 1 \cong \angle 2$
Prove: $\overline{BE} \cong \overline{DE}$

Plan To prove that $\overline{BE} \cong \overline{DE}$, find a pair of congruent triangles that contain these segments. $\triangle ABE$ and $\triangle ADE$ include $\overline{BE}$ and $\overline{DE}$. Angles 1 and 2 are included angles that lead to the use of the SAS postulate.

Proof

Statements	Reasons
1. $\overline{AB} \cong \overline{AD}$	1. Given
2. $\angle 1 \cong \angle 2$	2. Given
3. $\overline{AE} \cong \overline{AE}$	3. Reflexive Property
4. $\triangle ABE \cong \triangle ADE$	4. SAS Postulates
5. $\overline{AB} \cong \overline{CD}$	5. ___

Solution

Corr. parts of $\cong \triangle$s are $\cong$.

166 *Chapter 4 Congruent Triangles*

A summary of the general procedure that can be used to prove two segments or two angles congruent by using congruent triangles is described as follows.

Proving Two Segments or Two Angles Congruent

1. Identify two triangles that contain the two segments or two angles as corresponding parts.
2. Prove that the two triangles are congruent.
3. State that the two segments or angles are congruent by using "Corr. parts of ≅ △s are ≅."

Example 3

Write a plan for proof and a two-column proof.

Given: $\overline{AC}$ and $\overline{BD}$ bisect each other.

Prove: $\angle 3 \cong \angle 4$

Solution

Plan To prove that $\angle 3 \cong \angle 4$, first prove that $\triangle ADC \cong \triangle CBA$ or that $\triangle AOD \cong \triangle COB$. Since $\angle 1$ and $\angle 2$ are vertical angles, they are congruent. I can use this fact together with the given information to prove $\triangle AOD \cong \triangle COB$ by SAS.

Proof

Statements	Reasons
1. $\overline{AC}$ and $\overline{BD}$ bisect each other.	1. Given
2. $\overline{AO} \cong \overline{CO}, \overline{BO} \cong \overline{DO}$	2. A segment bisector forms two ≅ segments.
3. $\angle 1 \cong \angle 2$	3. Vertical angles are ≅.
4. $\triangle AOD \cong \triangle COB$	4. SAS Postulates
5. $\angle 3 \cong \angle 4$	5. Corr. parts of ≅ △s are ≅.

Example 4

Write a plan for proof and a two-column proof. Use an auxiliary line.

Given: $\overline{AB} \cong \overline{CB}$, and $\overline{AD} \cong \overline{CD}$

Proof: $\angle A \cong \angle C$

Solution

Plan I can prove $\angle A \cong \angle C$ if these two angles are corresponding parts of a pair of congruent triangles. If I draw the auxiliary segment $\overline{BD}$, I can use the SSS congruence postulate to prove that $\triangle ABD \cong \triangle CBD$.

Proof

Statements	Reasons
1. Draw $\overline{BD}$.	1. For any two points, there is exactly one line containing them.
2. $\overline{BD} \cong \overline{BD}$	2. Reflexive Property
3. $\overline{AB} \cong \overline{CB}$	3. Given
4. $\overline{AD} \cong \overline{CD}$	4. Given
5. $\triangle ABD \cong \triangle CBD$	5. SSS Postulate
6. $\angle A \cong \angle C$	6. Corr. parts of ≅ △s are ≅.

4-4 *Proving Segments and Angles Congruent*   **167**

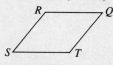

1. and 3. $\triangle ADE \cong \triangle CBF$, $\triangle ADC \cong \triangle CBA$

2. and 4. $\triangle AFB \cong \triangle CED$, $\triangle ACD \cong \triangle CAB$ **5.** $\angle 1 \cong \angle 2$, $\overline{AB} \cong \overline{CD}$, $\angle 3 \cong \angle 4$, $\triangle BFA \cong \triangle DEC$ by ASA $\overline{BF}$ and $\overline{DE}$ are corr. parts of $\triangle BFA$ and $\triangle DEC$.   **6.** $\overline{DA} \cong \overline{BC}$, $\angle 6 \cong \angle 5$, $\overline{AE} \cong \overline{CF}$, $\triangle DEA \cong \triangle BFC$ by SAS $\angle DEA$ and $\angle BFC$ are corr. parts of $\triangle DEA$ and $\triangle BFC$.

7. 1. Given 2. Reflex. 3. $\angle 3 \cong \angle 4$, Given 4. ASA 5. CPCTC

8. 1. Given 2. $\overline{NO} \cong \overline{PO}$ 3. Reflex. 4. SSS Post. 5. CPCTC 6. Def. of bisector

9. 1. $\overline{AB} \cong \overline{CD}$, $\angle 1 \cong \angle 2$ (Given) 2. $\overline{AC} \cong \overline{CA}$ (Reflex.) 3. $\triangle ABC \cong \triangle CDA$ (SAS) 4. $\angle 5 \cong \angle 6$ (CPCTC)

10. 1. $\angle 1 \cong \angle 2$ (Given) 2. $\overline{AC} \cong \overline{CA}$ (Reflex.) 3. $\angle 5 \cong \angle 6$ (Given) 4. $\triangle ABC \cong \triangle CDA$ (ASA) 5. $\angle B \cong \angle D$ (CPCTC)

11. Draw $\overline{BD}$. $\overline{BD} \cong \overline{DB}$ (Reflex.) $\triangle DAB \cong \triangle BCD$ (SSS) $\angle A \cong \angle C$ (CPCTC). Or draw $\overline{AC}$. $\triangle CDA \cong \triangle BAC$ (SSS) $\angle DAC \cong \angle BCA$, $\angle BAC \cong \angle DCA$ (CPCTC). $\angle A \cong \angle C$ ($\angle$ add.)

Assignment Guide
Minimum: 1–25 e/o, 31, AR
Regular: 1–29 e/o, 31, AR
Advanced: 7–25 e/o, 26–31, AR

Applications
Exercises 13–14

Coordinate Geometry
Exercises 22–25

Algebra
Exercises 16–17, AR

Lesson Closure

Review the general procedure for proving two segments and two angles congruent.

Class Exercises

Short Answer

Select a pair of triangles that you might try to prove congruent if you wanted to conclude each of the following.

1. $\overline{AD} \cong \overline{CB}$ **2.** $\angle 1 \cong \angle 2$

3. Select a second pair of triangles that you could use for Exercise 1.

4. Select a second pair of triangles that you could use for Exercise 2.

Sample Exercises

Give a plan for each proof.

5. Given: $\overline{AB} \cong \overline{CD}$, $\angle 1 \cong \angle 2$, $\angle 3 \cong \angle 4$
   Prove: $\overline{BF} \cong \overline{DE}$

6. Given: $\angle 5 \cong \angle 6$, $\overline{BC} \cong \overline{DA}$, $\overline{CF} \cong \overline{AE}$
   Prove: $\angle DEA \cong \angle BFC$

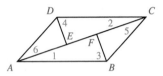

Complete each proof.

7. Given: $\angle 1 \cong \angle 2$, $\angle 3 \cong \angle 4$
   Prove: $\angle A \cong \angle C$

Statements	Reasons
1. $\angle 1 \cong \angle 2$	1. ___
2. $\overline{DB} \cong \overline{DB}$	2. ___
3. ___	3. ___
4. $\triangle ADB \cong \triangle CBD$	4. ___
5. $\angle A \cong \angle C$	5. ___

8. Given: $\overline{MN} \cong \overline{MP}$, $\overline{NO} \cong \overline{PO}$
   Prove: $\overline{MO}$ bisects $\angle PMN$.

Statements	Reasons
1. $\overline{MN} \cong \overline{MP}$	1. ___
2. ___	2. Given
3. $\overline{MO} \cong \overline{MO}$	3. ___
4. $\triangle PMO \cong \triangle NMO$	4. ___
5. $\angle 1 \cong \angle 2$	5. ___
6. $\overline{MO}$ bisects $\angle PMN$.	6. ___

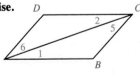

Write a two-column proof for each exercise.

9. Given: $\overline{AB} \cong \overline{CD}$, $\angle 1 \cong \angle 2$
   Prove: $\angle 5 \cong \angle 6$

10. Given: $\angle 1 \cong \angle 2$, $\angle 5 \cong \angle 6$
   Prove: $\angle B \cong \angle D$

Discussion

11. Suppose that $\overline{AB} \cong \overline{CD}$ and $\overline{BC} \cong \overline{DA}$. Explain how you would use an auxiliary line to prove that $\angle A \cong \angle C$. How many ways can this be done?

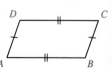

Exercises

A

Suppose that $\triangle ABC \cong \triangle XYZ$. **Complete each statement.**

1. $XY = 14$ cm, ___ $= 14$ cm
2. $m\angle B = 63$, then ___ $= 63$
3. $m\angle Z = 131$, ___ $= 131$
4. $AC = 21$ cm, ___ $= 21$ cm

Ex. 5–6

5. **Given:** $\overline{BD}$ bisects $\angle ABC$.
   $\overline{AB} \cong \overline{CB}$
   Prove: $\overline{AD} \cong \overline{CD}$

Statements	Reasons
1. $\overline{AB} \cong \overline{CB}$	1. ___
2. $\overline{BD}$ bisects $\angle ABC$.	2. ___
3. $\angle 1 \cong \angle 2$	3. ___
4. ___	4. Reflexive Property
5. $\triangle ABD \cong \triangle CBD$	5. ___
6. $\overline{AD} \cong \overline{CD}$	6. ___

6. **Given:** $\overline{AC} \perp \overline{BD}$
   $\overline{BD}$ bisects $\overline{AC}$.
   Prove: $\angle ABD \cong \angle CBD$

Statements	Reasons
1. $\overline{AC} \perp \overline{BD}$	1. ___
2. ___	2. $\perp$ lines form $\cong$ adjacent angles.
3. $\overline{BD}$ bisects $\overline{AC}$.	3. ___
4. $\overline{AE} \cong \overline{CE}$	4. ___
5. ___	5. Reflexive Property
6. $\triangle ABE \cong \triangle CBE$	6. ___
7. $\angle ABD \cong \angle CBD$	7. ___

Write a two-column proof for each exercise.

7. **Given:** $\overline{AC}$ and $\overline{BD}$ bisect each other.
   Prove: $\overline{AD} \cong \overline{CB}$

8. **Given:** O bisects $\overline{AC}$. $\angle 3 \cong \angle 4$
   Prove: $\overline{AC}$ and $\overline{BD}$ bisect each other.

9. **Given:** D bisects $\overline{CE}$. $\angle 1 \cong \angle 2$, $\angle C \cong \angle E$
   Prove: $\overline{BD} \cong \overline{FD}$

10. **Given:** N is the midpoint of $\overline{AB}$. $\overline{AD} \cong \overline{BC}$, $\angle 1 \cong \angle 2$
    Prove: $\overline{CN} \cong \overline{DN}$

11. **Given:** O is the midpoint of $\overline{AB}$ and $\overline{CD}$.
    Prove: $\overline{AD} \parallel \overline{BC}$

12. **Given:** $\overline{AD} \parallel \overline{BC}$, $\overline{AD} \cong \overline{BC}$
    Prove: O is the midpoint of $\overline{AB}$ and $\overline{CD}$.

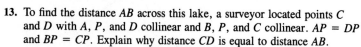

13. To find the distance AB across this lake, a surveyor located points C and D with A, P, and D collinear and B, P, and C collinear. $AP = DP$ and $BP = CP$. Explain why distance CD is equal to distance AB.

14. An engineer designing a bridge to be built across a deep canyon needs to find the distance AB across the canyon. He locates points P and C so that $AP = CP$. Next he uses a transit to measure $\angle PAB$. He then locates point D so that $m\angle PAB = m\angle PCD$. How can the engineer find the distance AB?

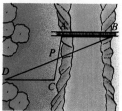

Teacher's Resource Materials

Practice Master 25

Exercise Answers

See Selected Answers for odd-numbered exercises.

2. $m\angle Y$ 4. XZ

6. 1. Given 2. $\angle AEB \cong \angle CEB$
3. Given 4. A segment bisector forms two $\cong$ segments.
5. $\overline{BE} \cong \overline{BE}$ 6. SAS 7. CPCTC

8. 1. O bisects $\overline{AC}$. (Given)
2. $\overline{AO} \cong \overline{CO}$ (A segment bisector forms two $\cong$ segments.)
3. $\angle 3 \cong \angle 4$ (Given) 4. $\angle 1 \cong \angle 2$ (Vert. $\angle$ Theorem) 5. $\triangle AOD \cong \triangle COB$ (ASA) 6. $\overline{DO} \cong \overline{BO}$ (CPCTC) 7. $\overline{AC}$ bisects $\overline{BD}$. $\overline{BD}$ bisects $\overline{AC}$. (Def. of bisector)

10. 1. N is the midpoint of $\overline{AB}$. (Given) 2. $\overline{AN} \cong \overline{BN}$ (A midpoint forms two $\cong$ segments.)
3. $\angle 1 \cong \angle 2$, $\angle AD \cong \angle BC$ (Given) 4. $\triangle ADN \cong \triangle BCN$ (SAS) 5. $\overline{DN} \cong \overline{CN}$ (CPCTC)

12. 1. $\overline{AD} \parallel \overline{BC}$ (Given)
2. $\angle A \cong \angle B$, $\angle D \cong \angle C$ (If $\parallel$ lines are cut by a trans., alt. int. $\angle$s are $\cong$.) 3. $\overline{AD} \cong \overline{BC}$ (Given) 4. $\triangle ADO \cong \triangle BCO$ (ASA) 5. $\overline{AO} \cong \overline{BO}$, $\overline{DO} \cong \overline{CO}$ (CPCTC) 6. O is the midpoint of $\overline{AB}$ and $\overline{CD}$. (Def. of midpoint)

14. $\triangle ABP \cong \triangle CDP$ by ASA, so $\overline{AB} \cong \overline{CD}$ by CPCTC and $AB = CD$ by def. of $\cong$ segments.

16. 87

18. Given:
$m\angle BGC = 65$, $m\angle DGC = 65$,
$\overline{BG} \cong \overline{DG}$ **Prove:** C is the midpoint of $\overline{BD}$. 1. $m\angle BGC = 65$,
$m\angle DGC = 65$ (Given)
2. $m\angle BGC = m\angle DGC$ (Substitution) 3. $\angle BGC \cong \angle DGC$ (Def.
of $\cong \angle$s) 4. $\overline{BG} \cong \overline{DG}$ (Given)
5. $\overline{GC} \cong \overline{GC}$ (Reflex.)
6. $\triangle BGC \cong \triangle DGC$ (SAS)
7. $\overline{BC} \cong \overline{DC}$ (CPCTC) 8. C is the
midpoint of $\overline{BD}$. (Def. of mid-
point)   **20. Given:** $\angle B \cong \angle E$,
$\angle ACD \cong \angle ADC$, $\overline{BC} \cong \overline{ED}$
1. $\angle B \cong \angle E$, $\angle ACD \cong \angle ADC$
(Given) 2. $\angle ABC \cong \angle AED$,
$\angle ACB \cong \angle ADE$ ($\cong$ Supplements
Theorem) 3. $\overline{BC} \cong \overline{ED}$ (Given)
4. $\triangle ABC \cong \triangle AED$ (ASA)
5. $\overline{AB} \cong \overline{AE}$ (CPCTC)
22. $AB =$
$\sqrt{(1-4)^2 + (2-1)^2} =$
$\sqrt{9+1} = \sqrt{10}$

$DE =$
$\sqrt{(-1+4)^2 + (2-1)^2} =$
$\sqrt{9+1} = \sqrt{10}$
24. $BC =$
$\sqrt{(2-1)^2 + (4-2)^2} =$
$\sqrt{1+4} = \sqrt{5}$

$EF =$
$\sqrt{(-2+1)^2 + (4-2)^2} =$
$\sqrt{1+4} = \sqrt{5}$
26. Construction: Extend $\overline{ED}$, intersecting $\overline{AC}$ at point G.
1. $\overline{AB} \| \overline{ED}$ (Given) 2. $\angle BAC \cong$
$\angle EGC$ (If two lines are cut by a
transversal, corr. $\angle$s are $\cong$.)
3. $\overline{AC} \| \overline{DF}$ (Given) 4. $\angle EGC \cong$
$\angle EDF$ (If two lines are cut by a
transversal, corr. $\angle$s are $\cong$.)
5. $\angle BAC \cong \angle EDF$ (Trans. prop.
of $\cong$.) 6. $\overline{AC} \cong \overline{DF}$, $\overline{AB} \cong \overline{DE}$
(Given) 7. $\triangle ABC \cong \triangle DEF$ (SAS)
8. $\angle B \cong \angle E$ (CPCTC)

15. Write a two-column proof.
Add auxiliary lines as needed.
Given: $\overline{AB} \cong \overline{DC}$, $\angle A \cong \angle D$
Prove: $\angle B \cong \angle C$

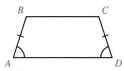

B

16. $\angle ADE \cong \angle ACB$, $m\angle ACB = 3x + 15$,
$m\angle ADC = 2x + 35$
Find $m\angle ADC$.
17. $\angle XWZ \cong \angle WXZ$, $m\angle XWZ = 3x + 40$,
$m\angle ZXY = 2x + 10$
Find $m\angle ZXY$.

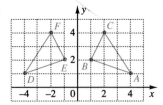

Ex. 17

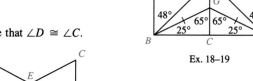

Ex. 16

**List sufficient given information (taken from each figure) and then
write a two-column proof.**
18. Prove that C is the midpoint of $\overline{BD}$.
19. Prove that $\overline{BF} \cong \overline{DF}$.
20. Prove that $\overline{AB} \cong \overline{AE}$.   **21.** Prove that $\angle D \cong \angle C$.

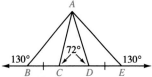

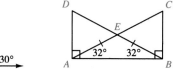

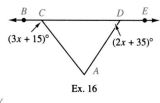

Ex. 18–19

Use the distance formula to calculate each length.
22. AB, DE
23. AC, DF
24. BC, EF
25. Use Exercises 22–24 to show that $\angle A \cong \angle D$.

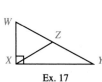

C

26. Given: $\overline{AC} \| \overline{DF}$, $\overline{AB} \| \overline{DE}$, $\overline{AC} \cong \overline{DF}$, $\overline{AB} \cong \overline{DE}$
Prove: $\angle B \cong \angle E$
(HINT: Draw auxiliary lines.)

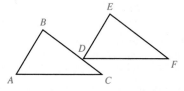

**In Exercises 27–30 you may need to prove one pair of triangles
congruent in order to gain information needed to show a second pair of
triangles congruent. Write a two-column proof for each exercise.**
27. Given: In figure ABCDEFGH, all sides are congruent to each other.
$\overline{AF} \perp \overline{AB}$, $\overline{BG} \perp \overline{GF}$, $\angle 1 \cong \angle 2$
Prove: $\triangle AHI \cong \triangle GHI$

28. Given: $\angle 1 \cong \angle 2, \angle 3 \cong \angle 4,$
$\angle 5 \cong \angle 6, \angle 7 \cong \angle 8$

Prove: $\angle A \cong \angle C$

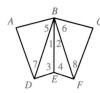

29. Prove that if $\overline{AD} \cong \overline{AB}$ and $\overline{CD} \cong \overline{CB}$, then $\angle D \cong \angle B$.

30. Prove that if $\overline{AB} \cong \overline{DE}, \overline{AF} \cong \overline{CD},$ $\overline{EF} \cong \overline{BC}$, and $\angle F \cong \angle C$, then $\overline{AB} \parallel \overline{ED}$.

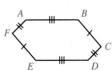

Critical Thinking

31. In the cube, all faces are squares and all edges are equal in length. Suppose that points B, C, and E are midpoints of edges. Write a convincing argument that $\triangle ABC$ is congruent to $\triangle DCE$.

Algebra Review

1. In $\triangle DEF$, $m \angle E$ is six more than $m \angle D$. The measure of $\angle F$ is ten less than twice $m \angle D$. Find the measure of each angle.
2. isosceles $\triangle LOR$ with vertex L, $LO = x^2 + 5$, $LR = 4x + 2$ Find LO and LR.
3. $\triangle CAW$ has $m \angle C = x^2 + 10x + 2$, $m \angle A = x^2 - 9$, and $m \angle W = 8x + 7$. Find the measure of each angle.

Enrichment

Factorials

If three dowel rods are selected from a box of eight rods of different lengths, how many different ways can this selection be completed? (See the Computer Activity on page 165.) If n is a positive whole number, n factorial ($n!$) is defined as $n! = n(n-1)(n-2) \ldots 3 \cdot 2 \cdot 1$.

Example

How many ways are there to select
a. three things from nine different things?
b. r things from n different things, where $r < n$?

Solution

a. $\frac{9!}{3!6!} = 84$ **b.** $\frac{n!}{r!(n-r)!}$

Part b of this example gives a general formula to count the number of ways to select r things from n different things.

Select seven points on a circle and use the general formula.

1. How many different segments can be drawn between pairs of these points?
2. How many different triangles can be drawn with vertices selected among these points?
3. How many different segments and triangles can be drawn with vertices selected from among nine points distributed around a circle?

4-4 Proving Segments and Angles Congruent **171**

28. 1. $\angle 1 \cong \angle 2, \angle 3 \cong \angle 4$ (Given) 2. $\overline{BE} \cong \overline{BE}$ (Reflex.)
3. $\triangle BED \cong \triangle BEF$ (ASA)
4. $\overline{BD} \cong \overline{BF}$ (CPCTC)
5. $\angle 5 \cong \angle 6, \angle 7 \cong \angle 8$ (Given)
6. $\triangle ABD \cong \triangle CBF$ (ASA)
7. $\angle A \cong \angle C$ (CPCTC)
30. Draw $\overline{AE}, \overline{BD}$, and $\overline{BE}$.
1. $\overline{AF} \cong \overline{DC}, \angle F \cong \angle C, \overline{EF} \cong \overline{BC}$ (Given) 2. $\triangle AFE \cong \triangle DCB$ (SAS)
2. $\triangle AFE \cong \triangle DCB$ (SAS)
3. $\overline{AE} \cong \overline{DB}$ (CPCTC) 4. $\overline{AB} \cong \overline{DE}$ (Given) 5. $\overline{EB} \cong \overline{BE}$ (Reflex.)
6. $\triangle ABE \cong \triangle DEB$ (SSS)
7. $\angle ABE \cong \angle DEB$ (CPCTC)
8. $\overline{AB} \parallel \overline{ED}$ (If two lines are cut by a transversal and alt. int. $\angle$s are $\cong$, the lines are $\parallel$.)

Algebra Review Answers

1. 46, 52, 82   **2.** 6 or 14
3. 98, 27, 55

Enrichment Answers

1. $\frac{7!}{2! \cdot 5!} = \frac{7 \cdot 6 \cdot 5 \cdot 4 \cdot 3 \cdot 2 \cdot 1}{2 \cdot 1 \cdot 5 \cdot 4 \cdot 3 \cdot 2 \cdot 1} = \frac{7 \cdot 6}{2} = 21$ different segments
2. $\frac{7!}{3! \cdot 4!} = \frac{7 \cdot 6 \cdot 5 \cdot 4 \cdot 3 \cdot 2 \cdot 1}{3 \cdot 2 \cdot 1 \cdot 4 \cdot 3 \cdot 2 \cdot 1} = \frac{7 \cdot 6 \cdot 5}{3 \cdot 2} = 35$ different triangles
3. $\frac{9!}{2! \cdot 7!} = \frac{9 \cdot 8}{2} = 36$ different segments, $\frac{9!}{3! \cdot 6!} = \frac{9 \cdot 8 \cdot 7}{3 \cdot 2} = 84$ different triangles

First Five Minutes

(Quiz on previous lesson)

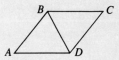

Given: $\angle ABD \cong \angle CDB$
$\angle ADB \cong \angle CBD$
Prove: $\angle A \cong \angle C$
1. $\angle ABD \cong \angle CDB$ (Given)
2. $\overline{BD} \cong \overline{DB}$ (Reflex.)
3. $\angle ADB \cong \angle CBD$ (Given)
4. $\triangle ABD \cong \triangle CDB$ (ASA)
5. $\angle A \cong \angle C$ (CPCTC)

Lesson Opener

Quilt patterns are good illustrations of overlapping triangles. Discuss other examples of overlapping triangles from everyday life.

Point out that in proofs it may sometimes be necessary to prove overlapping triangles congruent. Example 1 illustrates this procedure.

Materials

student notebooks

Teaching Notes

Encourage students to redraw triangles that overlap, which may help them visualize the congruence. If some students still have difficulty visualizing the congruence of overlapping triangles, outline the triangles on the chalkboard with colored chalk both before and after they have been separated.

OBJECTIVE: *Prove triangles congruent using overlapping triangles.*

4-5 Proofs: Overlapping Triangles

In the last lesson, you learned that to prove two segments or two angles congruent, it is often necessary to first prove that a pair of triangles are congruent. Sometimes it is difficult to visualize the triangles that you should prove congruent because they overlap.

So it is helpful to separate the triangles mentally, or to redraw the two triangles and then separate them—to help analyze the proof. The first example focuses on formulating a plan for a proof involving overlapping triangles.

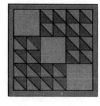

Example 1

Write a plan for the proof.
Given: $\angle 1 \cong \angle 6$, $\angle 3 \cong \angle 4$
$\overline{AE} \cong \overline{CD}$
Prove: $\angle ABE \cong \angle CBD$

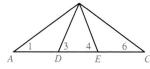

Solution

Plan I can prove that the overlapping angles $\angle ABE$ and $\angle CBD$ are congruent if I can show that they are corresponding angles in a pair of congruent triangles. Since the angles are overlapping, I can use the ASA Postulate to prove that the overlapping triangles $\triangle ABE$ and $\triangle CBD$ are congruent.

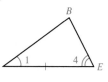

Sometimes the angles or segments that you want to prove congruent are not overlapping so there is no clue that you should be looking for overlapping triangles.

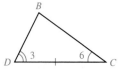

Try This

Write a plan for the proof.
Given: $\angle 1 \cong \angle 6$, $\overline{AE} \cong \overline{CD}$, $\overline{AB} \cong \overline{CB}$
Prove: $\angle 3 \cong \angle 4$

Example 2

Complete the proof.
Given: $\angle 1 \cong \angle 2$, $\overline{AC} \cong \overline{DF}$
$\angle 3 \cong \angle 4$
Prove: $\overline{EF} \cong \overline{BC}$

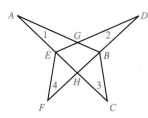

Plan To prove that $\overline{EF} \cong \overline{BC}$, I need to choose a pair of triangles that contain $\overline{EF}$ and $\overline{BC}$ as corresponding sides. I cannot prove $\triangle EFH \cong \triangle BCH$. I can prove overlapping triangles $\triangle EFD \cong \triangle BCA$ by using the ASA postulate.

Solution

Proof

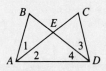

Statements	Reasons
1. $\angle 1 \cong \angle 2$	1. Given
2. $\overline{AC} \cong \overline{DF}$	2. Given
3. $\angle 3 \cong \angle 4$	3. Given
4. $\triangle ABC \cong \triangle DEF$	4. ASA Postulate
5. $\overline{EF} \cong \overline{BC}$	5. Corr. parts of $\cong \triangle$s are $\cong$.

Example 3

Complete the proof.

Given: $\angle 1 \cong \angle 6,\ \angle 3 \cong \angle 4,\ \overline{AD} \cong \overline{CE}$

Prove: $\angle ABE \cong \angle CBD$

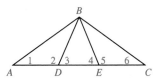

Plan To prove that $\angle ABE \cong \angle CBD$, I need to prove that a pair of congruent triangles contain these corresponding angles. I can prove (overlapping triangles) $\triangle AEB \cong \triangle CDB$ by ASA if I can show that $\overline{AE} \cong \overline{CD}$. I can do that by using the Common Segment Theorem and the fact that $\overline{AD} \cong \overline{DF}$.

Solution

Proof

Statements	Reasons
1. $\angle 1 \cong \angle 6$	1. Given
2. $\overline{AD} \cong \overline{CE}$	2. Given
3. $\overline{AE} \cong \overline{CD}$	3. Common Segment Theorem
4. $\angle 4 \cong \angle 3$	4. Given
5. $\triangle AEB \cong \triangle CDB$	5. ASA Postulate
6. $\angle ABE \cong \angle CBD$	6. Corr. parts. of $\cong \triangle$s are $\cong$.

Try This

Complete the proof.

Given: $\overline{AB} \cong \overline{CB},\ \angle 1 \cong \angle 6,\ \overline{AE} \cong \overline{CD}$

Prove: $\angle 2 \cong \angle 5$

Plan First show that $\triangle AEB \cong \triangle CDB$ by SAS. Then $\angle 3 \cong \angle 4$ by corresponding parts of congruent triangles and $\angle 2 \cong \angle 5$ by the Congruent Supplements Theorem.

Proof

Statements	Reasons
1. $\overline{AB} \cong \overline{CB},\ \angle 1 \cong \angle 6,\ \overline{AE} \cong \overline{CD}$	1. ___
2. ___	2. ___
3. $\angle 3 \cong \angle 4$	3. ___
4. ___	4. ___

Chalkboard Examples

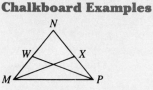

1. Given: $\overline{NM} \cong \overline{NP}$, $\overline{NX} \cong \overline{NW}$ **Prove:** $\overline{MX} \cong \overline{PW}$
1. $\overline{NM} \cong \overline{NP}$ (Given) 2. $\angle N \cong \angle N$ (Reflex.) 3. $\overline{NX} \cong \overline{NW}$ (Given) 4. $\triangle NXM \cong \triangle NWP$ (SAS) 5. $\overline{MX} \cong \overline{PW}$ (CPCTC)

Answer to Try This I can prove overlapping $\triangle BAE \cong \triangle BCD$ by SAS. Then $\angle 3 \cong \angle 4$ by CPCTC.

2. Given: $\angle 2 \cong \angle 4$, $\angle CDA \cong \angle BAD$
Prove: $\angle B \cong \angle C$
1. $\angle 2 \cong \angle 4$ (Given) 2. $\overline{AD} \cong \overline{AD}$ (Reflex.) 3. $\angle CDA \cong \angle BAD$ (Given) 4. $\triangle CAD \cong \triangle BDA$ (ASA) 5. $\angle B \cong \angle C$ (CPCTC)
3. Given: $\angle ABD \cong \angle CBE$, $\overline{AB} \cong \overline{CB}$, $\angle A \cong \angle C$ **Prove:** $\overline{AE} \cong \overline{CD}$
2. $\overline{AB} \cong \overline{CB}$ (Given)
3. $\angle ABD \cong \angle CBE$ (Given)
4. $\angle ABE \cong \angle CBD$ (Common Angle Theorem) 5. $\triangle ABE \cong \triangle CBD$ (ASA) 6. $\overline{AE} \cong \overline{CD}$ (CPCTC)

Answer to Try This
1. Given 2. $\triangle AEB \cong \triangle CDB$, SAS 3. CPCTC 4. $\angle 2 \cong \angle 5$, (Congruent Supplements Theorem)

Class Exercises

Short Answer

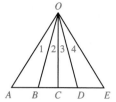

1. Name two different triangles that overlap △AOC.
2. Name two different triangles that overlap △BOD.
3. Name two different triangles that overlap △BOE.
4. Name two different triangles that overlap △AOD.

Sample Exercises

Use the Common Segment Theorem or the Common Angle Theorem to complete each statement.

5. If $\overline{AB}$ ≅ $\overline{DE}$, then $\overline{AD}$ ≅ ___ .
6. If $\overline{AB}$ ≅ $\overline{CD}$, then $\overline{AC}$ ≅ ___ .
7. If ∠1 ≅ ∠3, then ∠AOC ≅ ___ .
8. If ∠2 ≅ ∠4, then ∠EOC ≅ ___ .
9. If $\overline{AC}$ ≅ $\overline{BD}$, then $\overline{AB}$ ≅ ___ .
10. If $\overline{AD}$ ≅ $\overline{BE}$, then $\overline{AB}$ ≅ ___ .

11. Write a two-column proof for Example 1 on page 172.

Discussion

12. Suppose that in the above figure $\overline{AO}$ ≅ $\overline{EO}$, ∠1 ≅ ∠4, and $\overline{OB}$ ≅ $\overline{OD}$.
   Use this information to give a convincing argument that a pair of nonoverlapping triangles are congruent and a pair of overlapping triangles are congruent.

Exercises

A

Name a pair of overlapping triangles that appear to be congruent.

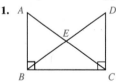

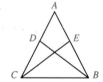

4. Name a second pair of overlapping triangles in Exercise 2.
5. Name a second pair of overlapping triangles in Exercise 3.

Use the Common Segment Theorem and the Common Angle Theorem to complete each statement.

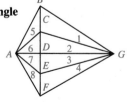

6. If ∠1 ≅ ∠4, then ∠BGE ≅ ___ .
7. If $\overline{BE}$ ≅ $\overline{FC}$, then $\overline{FE}$ ≅ ___ .
8. If ∠BAE ≅ ∠FAC, then ∠FAE ≅ ___ .
9. If ∠5 ≅ ∠8, then ∠BAE ≅ ___ .

Redraw each figure, separating the overlapping triangles that you plan to use in the proof. Write a two-column proof.

10. Given: $\overline{BC} \cong \overline{ED}$, $\angle ADC \cong \angle ACD$
    Prove: $\overline{BD} \cong \overline{CE}$

11. Given: $\angle ADC \cong \angle ACD$, $\angle 1 \cong \angle 2$
    Prove: $\overline{BC} \cong \overline{ED}$

12. Given: $\overline{BC} \cong \overline{ED}$, $\overline{BD} \cong \overline{EC}$
    Prove: $\angle 3 \cong \angle 4$

13. Given: $\angle 1 \cong \angle 2$, $\overline{PQ} \cong \overline{RQ}$
    Prove: $\overline{QT} \cong \overline{QV}$

14. Given: $\overline{PT} \cong \overline{RV}$, $\overline{TR} \cong \overline{VP}$
    Prove: $\angle 3 \cong \angle 4$

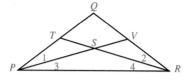

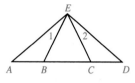

B

15. $AB = CD$, $AC = 3x + 5$, $BD = 4x - 3$, $BC = x + 2$
    Find AB and CD.

16. $\angle 1 \cong \angle 2$, $m\angle AEC = 14x - 3$, $m\angle DEB = 17x - 15$,
    $AE = 4x + 7$, $DE = 3x + 11$, $BE = 3x + 7$, $CE = 5x - 1$
    Show that $\triangle AEC \cong \triangle DEB$.

17. $\angle AEC \cong \angle DEB$, $\triangle AEB \cong \triangle DEC$, $m\angle 1 = 5x - 3$,
    $m\angle 2 = 3x + 5$, $AC = 3x - 1$
    Find DB.

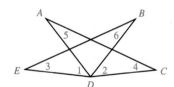

Write a two-column proof for each exercise.

18. Given: $\overline{RS} \cong \overline{UV}$
    $\overline{ST} \cong \overline{VW}$
    $\angle S \cong \angle V$
    Prove: $\overline{RW} \cong \overline{UT}$

19. Given: $\overline{ST} \cong \overline{VW}$
    $\angle S \cong \angle V$
    $\angle STR \cong \angle VWU$
    Prove: $\overline{RS} \| \overline{UV}$

20. Given: $\angle 1 \cong \angle 2$
    $\angle 3 \cong \angle 4$
    $\overline{ED} \cong \overline{CD}$
    Prove: $\overline{EB} \cong \overline{CA}$

21. Given: $\angle 1 \cong \angle 2$
    $\overline{AD} \cong \overline{BD}$
    $\overline{ED} \cong \overline{CD}$
    Prove: $\angle 5 \cong \angle 6$

22. Given: $\overline{AB} \cong \overline{DC}$
    $\angle A \cong \angle D$
    $\overline{AE} \cong \overline{DF}$
    Prove: $\overline{EC} \cong \overline{FB}$

23. Given: $\overline{AE} \cong \overline{DF}$
    $\angle E \cong \angle F$
    $\overline{EC} \cong \overline{FB}$
    Prove: $\overline{AB} \cong \overline{CD}$

24. Show that $\angle F \cong \angle G$.

10. 1. $\overline{BC} \cong \overline{ED}$ (Given)
2. $\angle ACD \cong \angle ADC$ (Given)
3. $\overline{CD} \cong \overline{DC}$ (Reflex.)
4. $\triangle BCD \cong \triangle EDC$ (SAS)
5. $\overline{BD} \cong \overline{CE}$ (CPCTC)

12. 1. $\overline{BC} \cong \overline{ED}$ (Given)
2. $\overline{BD} \cong \overline{EC}$ (Given)
3. $\overline{CD} \cong \overline{DC}$ (Reflex.)
4. $\triangle BCD \cong \triangle EDC$ (SSS)
5. $\angle CBD \cong \angle DEC$ (CPCTC)
6. $\angle 3 \cong \angle 4$ (If two $\angle$s are supplementary to $\cong \angle$s, they are $\cong$.)   **14.** 1. $\overline{PT} \cong \overline{RV}$ (Given) 2. $\overline{TR} \cong \overline{VP}$ (Given)
3. $\overline{PR} \cong \overline{RP}$ (Reflex.)
4. $\triangle PTR \cong \triangle RVP$ (SSS)
5. $\angle 3 \cong \angle 4$ (CPCTC)

16. By Common Angle Theorem $\angle AEC \cong \angle DEB$, so $14x - 3 = 17x - 15$. $12 = 3x$, so $x = 4$. $AE = 23$, $DE = 23$, $BE = 19$, $CE = 19$. By SAS, $\triangle AEC \cong \triangle DEB$.   **18.** 1. $\overline{RS} \cong \overline{UV}$, $\overline{ST} \cong \overline{VW}$, $\angle S \cong \angle V$ (Given)
2. $\triangle RST \cong \triangle UVW$ (SAS)
3. $\overline{RT} \cong \overline{UW}$ (CPCTC)
4. $\overline{RW} \cong \overline{UT}$ (Common Segment Theorem)   **20.** 1. $\angle 1 \cong \angle 2$ (Given) 2. $\angle EDB \cong \angle CDA$ (Common Angle Theorem)
3. $\overline{ED} \cong \overline{CD}$ (Given) 4. $\angle 3 \cong \angle 4$ (Given) 5. $\triangle EDB \cong \triangle CDA$ (ASA) 6. $\overline{EB} \cong \overline{CA}$ (CPCTC)

22. 1. $\overline{AB} \cong \overline{DC}$ (Given)
2. $\overline{AC} \cong \overline{DB}$ (Common Segment Theorem) 3. $\angle A \cong \angle D$ (Given)
4. $\overline{AE} \cong \overline{DF}$ (Given)
5. $\triangle ACE \cong \triangle DBF$ (SAS)
6. $\overline{EC} \cong \overline{FB}$ (CPCTC)

24. $EF = \sqrt{(3 - 2)^2 + (1 - 4)^2} = \sqrt{10}$, $DG = \sqrt{(4 - 1)^2 + (3 - 2)^2} = \sqrt{10}$, $EG = \sqrt{(4 - 2)^2 + (3 - 4)^2} = \sqrt{5}$, $DF = \sqrt{(3 - 1)^2 + (1 - 2)^2} = \sqrt{5}$ so $\overline{EF} \cong \overline{DG}$, $\overline{EG} \cong \overline{DF}$. By the Reflex. Prop. $\overline{ED} \cong \overline{ED}$. So $\triangle EFD \cong \triangle DGE$ by SSS. $\angle F \cong \angle G$ by CPCTC.

26. 1. $\overline{RS} \cong \overline{RU}$, $\angle 1 \cong \angle 2$
(Given) 2. $\overline{RT} \cong \overline{RT}$ (Reflex.)
3. $\triangle RST \cong \triangle RUT$ (SAS)
4. $\overline{ST} \cong \overline{UT}$, $\angle STR \cong \angle UTR$
(CPCTC) 5. $\overline{TX} \cong \overline{TX}$ (Reflex.)
6. $\triangle STX \cong \triangle UTX$ (SAS)
7. $\angle 3 \cong \angle 4$ (CPCTC)

**Algebra Review
Answers**

1. 4   **2.** 20   **3.** 108 or 84

Quiz Answers

1. 1. $\overline{JC}$ bisects $\angle EJA$. (Given)
2. $\angle EJC \cong \angle IJA$ (Def. of an
$\angle$ bisector) 3. $\overline{JE} \cong \overline{JI}$, $\angle E \cong$
$\angle JIA$ (Given) 4. $\triangle EJC \cong \triangle IJA$
(ASA) 5. $\overline{EC} \cong \overline{IA}$ (CPCTC)
2. 1. $\overline{JE} \cong \overline{JI}$, $\overline{JC} \cong \overline{JA}$, $\overline{EC} \cong \overline{IA}$
(Given) 2. $\triangle EJC \cong \triangle IJA$ (SSS)
3. $\angle EJC \cong \angle IJA$ (CPCTC) 4. $\overline{JC}$
bisects $\angle EJA$. (Def. of $\angle$ bisector)   **3.** 1. $\overline{BH} \cong \overline{BE}$,
$\overline{BK} \cong \overline{BD}$ (Given) 2. $\angle B \cong \angle B$
(Reflex.) 3. $\triangle BDH \cong \triangle BKE$
(SAS) 4. $\angle BDH \cong \angle BKE$
(CPCTC)   **4.** 1. $\overline{BD} \cong \overline{BK}$,
$\angle BDH \cong \angle BKE$ (Given)
2. $\overline{DH} \cong \overline{KE}$ (Given)
3. $\triangle BDH \cong \triangle BKE$ (SAS)
4. $\angle E \cong \angle H$ (CPCTC)

C

Write a two-column proof for each exercise.

25. Given: $\overline{BC} \cong \overline{ED}$
$\qquad \angle ADC \cong \angle ACD$
Prove: $\overline{AB} \cong \overline{AE}$

26. Given: $\overline{RS} \cong \overline{RU}$, $\angle 1 \cong \angle 2$
Prove: $\angle 3 \cong \angle 4$

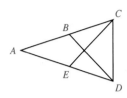

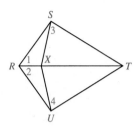

Critical Thinking

27. How many triangles in the figure to the right are congruent to triangle A? triangle B? triangle C?

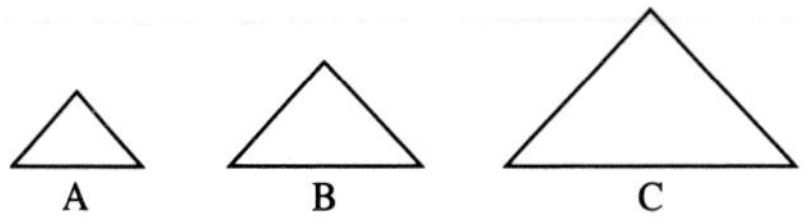

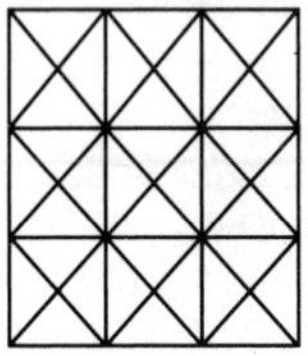

Algebra Review

1. $\triangle KAW$ is equiangular. $m \angle K = x^2 + 10x + 4$, $m \angle A = x^2 - x + 48$
$m \angle W = 2x^2 + 5x + 8$ Find x.

2. $\triangle JOR$, $\overline{JO} \cong \overline{JR}$, $JO = 2x + 1$, $JR = 4x - 15$, $OR = 3x - 4$
Find OR.

3. $\triangle PSN$, $m \angle P = 3x^2 - 4x - 11$, $m \angle S = x^2 - 2x + 1$
$m \angle N = 2x^2 - 6x - 20$ Find $m \angle P$.

Quiz

Write a two-column proof for each exercise.

1. **Given:** $\overline{JC}$ bisects $\angle EJA$.
$\overline{JE} \cong \overline{JI}$, $\angle E \cong \angle JIA$
Prove: $\overline{EC} \cong \overline{IA}$

2. **Given:** $\overline{JE} \cong \overline{JI}$, $\overline{JC} \cong \overline{JA}$
$\overline{EC} \cong \overline{IA}$
Prove: $\overline{JC}$ bisects $\angle EJA$.

3. **Given:** $\overline{BH} \cong \overline{BE}$, $\overline{BK} \cong \overline{BD}$
Prove: $\angle BDH \cong \angle BKE$

4. **Given:** $\overline{BK} \cong \overline{KE} \cong \overline{BD} \cong \overline{DH}$
$\angle BDH \cong \angle BKE$
Prove: $\angle E \cong \angle H$

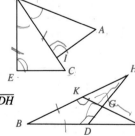

THEOREMS ABOUT TRIANGLES

OBJECTIVE: *Prove and apply the theorems about isosceles triangles.*

4-6 Isosceles Triangles

 **EXPLORE** Use square dot paper or graph paper to draw a large triangle with two sides equal in length. Fold the dot paper with the fold line through the vertex A and perpendicular to the side opposite A. (This fold line is the reflection line for a reflection transformation.) What do you discover about the angles of this triangle? Repeat for a variety of triangle shapes and state any generalizations that you discover.

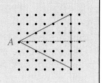

You have learned that an isosceles triangle has a pair of congruent sides. The congruent sides are called **legs** and the third side is called the **base**. The angles opposite the legs are called **base angles** and the third angle is called the **vertex angle**.

The following theorem describes a relationship between the legs and the base angles of an isosceles triangle. Note the use of the five steps in proving a theorem as discussed in Chapter 2.

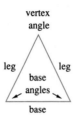

◆ **THEOREM 4.1** Isosceles Triangle Theorem

If two sides of a triangle are congruent then the angles opposite those sides are congruent.

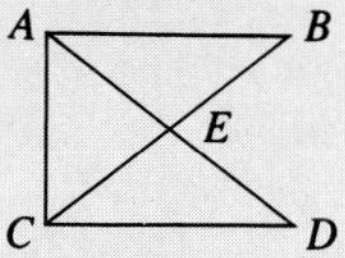

Given: $\overline{AB} \cong \overline{AC}$

Prove: $\angle 1 \cong \angle 2$

Plan Let D be the midpoint of $\overline{BC}$ and draw the auxiliary line $\overline{AD}$. Then prove that $\triangle ABD \cong \triangle ACD$ using the SSS Postulate and conclude that $\angle 1 \cong \angle 2$.

Proof Statements

1. $\overline{AB} \cong \overline{AC}$
2. D is the midpoint of $\overline{BC}$.
3. $\overline{BD} \cong \overline{CD}$
4. $\overline{AD} \cong \overline{AD}$
5. $\triangle ABD \cong \triangle ACD$
6. $\angle 1 \cong \angle 2$

Reasons

1. Given
2. A segment has exactly one midpoint.
3. A midpoint forms two $\cong$ segments.
4. Reflexive Property
5. SSS Postulate
6. Corr. parts of $\cong \triangle$s are $\cong$.

4-6 Isosceles Triangles **177**

Teaching Notes

Teaching Notes

Point out the use of an auxiliary line in the proof of Theorem 4.1. The auxiliary line $\overline{AD}$ was necessary because it formed two triangles. Point D is the midpoint of $\overline{BC}$. Therefore $\overline{BD} \cong \overline{DC}$ (Every segment has exactly one midpoint).

Restatement of Theorem 4.1: Base angles of an isosceles triangle are congruent.

Restatement of Theorem 4.2: Sides opposite congruent angles of a triangle are congruent.

Point out that Theorem 4.2 is the converse of Theorem 4.1 and that both are true.

Guided Practice

Chalkboard Example

$\triangle ABC$ is isosceles,
$m\angle 1 = 3x$, $m\angle 2 = x$
Find $m\angle 3$. 45

Answer to **Try This**
BA = BD = 14 by Theorem 4.2.
BD = DC = 14, so $\angle DBC \cong$
$\angle DCB$ by Theorem 4.1.

Sometimes a theorem can be stated concisely in a form that is not if-then form. Theorem 4.1 could have been stated as follows.
The base angles of an isosceles triangle are congruent.

Remember that a theorem that follows directly from another theorem is called a corollary. Below are several corollaries of Theorem 3.1. You will be asked to prove these corollaries in Exercises 30–31.

▶ **COROLLARY 4.1a**

If a triangle is equilateral then it is equiangular.

▶ **COROLLARY 4.1b**

The segment from the vertex of an isosceles triangle to the midpoint of the base bisects the vertex angle.

Recall that the converse of a conditional statement "if p, then q" is the statement "if q, then p." The next theorem is the converse of Theorem 4.1.

◆ **THEOREM 4.2**

If two angles of a triangle are congruent, then the sides opposite them are congruent.

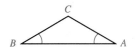

You will be asked to prove Theorem 4.2 in Exercise 37.

▶ **COROLLARY 4.2a**

If a triangle is equiangular, then the triangle is equilateral.

Example

Find BD and $m\angle ABC$.

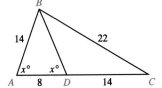

Solution

$BD = 14$ *Since $\angle BAD \cong \angle BDA$, then*
           AB = BD by Theorem 4.2.

$m\angle ABC = x$ *Since $AC = 8 + 14 = 22$ and*
           BC = 22, then $\angle A \cong \angle ABC$
           by Theorem 4.1.

Try This

Explain why $\angle DBC \cong \angle DCB$.

178   *Chapter 4   Congruent Triangles*

Class Exercises

Short Answer

1. Name the legs of △ABD.
2. Name the base angles of △ABC.
3. Name the base angles of △ABD.
4. Name the legs of △ABC.
5. Name the vertex angle of △ABC.
6. Name the vertex angle of △ABD.

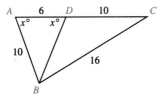

Sample Exercises

Complete each statement based on the theorems in this lesson.

7. The base angles of an isosceles triangle are ___ .
8. If two angles of a triangle are congruent, then ___ .
9. If all three sides of a triangle are congruent then ___ .
10. If all three angles of a triangle are congruent then ___ .
11. The legs of an isosceles triangle are ___ .

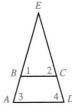

12. If $\overline{AE} \cong \overline{DE}$, then ___ ≅ ___ .
13. If $\angle 2 \cong \angle 3$, then ___ ≅ ___ .
14. If $\overline{BE} \cong \overline{CE}$, then ___ ≅ ___ .
15. If $\angle 1 \cong \angle 4$, then ___ ≅ ___ .

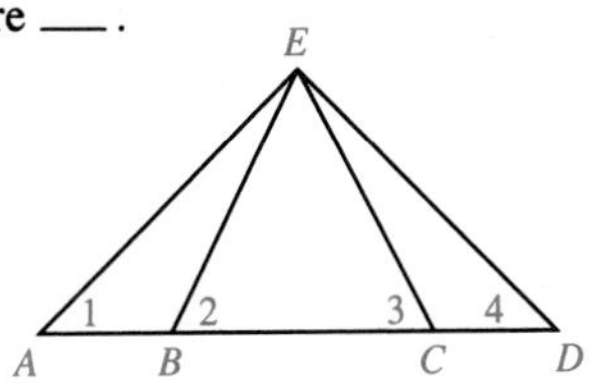

Discussion

16. In the figure to the right $\angle 1 \cong \angle 2$ and $\angle 3 \cong \angle 4$. Give a convincing argument that $AB = CD$.

Exercises

A

Complete each of the following statements. State the theorem that you used.

1. If $\angle 1 \cong \angle 2$, then ___ ≅ ___ .
2. If $\angle ABC \cong \angle ACB$, then ___ ≅ ___ .
3. If $\overline{DB} \cong \overline{DC}$, then ___ ≅ ___ .
4. If $m\angle 1 + m\angle 3 = m\angle 2 + m\angle 4$, then ___ ≅ ___ .
5. If $\overline{AB} \cong \overline{AC}$, then ___ ≅ ___ .

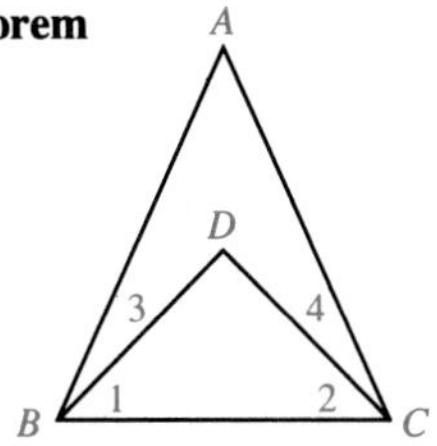

Use the theorems in this lesson to complete each statement.

6. $m\angle ABC =$ ___
7. $CE =$ ___

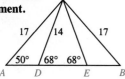

Class Exercise Answers

1. $\overline{BA}$, $\overline{BD}$ 2. $\angle A$, $\angle CBA$
3. $\angle A$, $\angle BDA$ 4. $\overline{CA}$, $\overline{CB}$
5. $\angle C$ 6. $\angle ABD$
7. congruent   8. The sides opp. them are ≅.   9. The triangle is equilateral.
10. The triangle is equiangular.
11. congruent   12. $\angle 1 \cong \angle 4$
13. $\overline{BE} \cong \overline{CE}$ 14. $\angle 2 \cong \angle 3$
15. $\overline{AE} \cong \overline{DE}$ 16. $\overline{BE} \cong \overline{CE}$, $\overline{AE} \cong \overline{DE}$. $AE - BE = DE - CE$ by the Additive Prop. of =, so $AB = CD$.

Assignment Guide

Minimum: 1–33 e/o, 39, MR
Regular: 1–35 e/o, 39, MR
Advanced: 13–33 e/o, 34–41, MR

Applications

Exercises 20, 29, 33

Coordinate Geometry

Exercise 32

Algebra

Exercises 21–24

Lesson Closure

Complete and justify each statement.

1. Base ∠s of an isos. △ are ≅. Theorem 4.1
2. An equilateral △ is also equiangular. Corollary 4.1a
3. The segment from the vertex of an isos. △ to the midpoint of the base bisects the vertex ∠. Corollary 4.1b

Teacher's Resource Materials

Enrichment Using Manipulatives 24
Practice Master 27
Technology: Calculator 4

Computer Software

See Computer Exploration 3, page 636.

1. $\overline{BD} \cong \overline{CD}$ (Theorem 4.2)
2. $\overline{AB} \cong \overline{AC}$ (Theorem 4.2)
3. $\angle 1 \cong \angle 2$ (Theorem 4.1)
4. $\overline{AB} \cong \overline{AC}$ (Theorem 4.2)
5. $\angle ABC \cong \angle ACB$
(Theorem 4.1)
6. 50　　7. 14　　8. 14
9. 14　　10. 31　　11. 59
12. 118　　13. 3　　14. 5
15. 9　　16. 9　　17. 9
18. 1. Given 2. Base $\angle$s of an isos. $\triangle$ are $\cong$. 3. Given
5. ASA　　19. 1. Given 2. Base
$\angle$s of an isos. $\triangle$ are $\cong$.
3. Given 4. ASA 5. CPCTC
7. Sides opp. $\cong \angle$s are $\cong$.
8. Def. of isos. $\triangle$
20. $m\angle EAD = m\angle AED$. By the Exterior Angle Theorem
$m\angle BDE = m\angle EAD + m\angle AED$.
So $m\angle BDE = 2m\angle EAD$.
21. $AB = BC = 30$
22. $DE = EF = 75$, $DF = 60$
23. $m\angle X = m\angle Z = 72$,
$m\angle Y = 36$
24. $AB = CB = 65$, $AC = 15$

Use the theorems in this lesson to complete each statement.

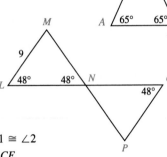

8. $BC =$ ___
9. $AB =$ ___
10. $m\angle ACD =$ ___
11. $m\angle ADB =$ ___
12. $m\angle ABC =$ ___

Use $\triangle ABF$ and $\triangle CED$ in the figure.

13. $CF =$ ___
14. $FE =$ ___

N is the midpoint of $\overline{LO}$ in the figure.

15. Find MN.
16. Find PN.
17. Find PO.

Complete each proof.

18. **Given:** $\overline{AC} \cong \overline{AD}$, $\angle 1 \cong \angle 2$

Prove: $\triangle ADB \cong \triangle ACE$

Statements	Reasons
1. $\overline{AC} \cong \overline{AD}$	1. ___
2. $\angle 5 \cong \angle 6$	2. ___
3. $\angle 1 \cong \angle 2$	3. ___
4. $\angle BAD \cong \angle EAC$	4. Common Angle Theorem
5. $\triangle ADB \cong \triangle ACE$	5. ___

19. Use the figure in Exercise 18.

Given: $\overline{AB} \cong \overline{AE}$, $\angle 1 \cong \angle 2$

Prove: $\triangle ACD$ is isosceles.

Statements	Reasons
1. $\overline{AB} \cong \overline{AE}$	1. ___
2. $\angle 3 \cong \angle 8$	2. ___
3. $\angle 1 \cong \angle 2$	3. ___
4. $\triangle ABC \cong \triangle AED$	4. ___
5. $\angle 4 \cong \angle 7$	5. ___
6. $\angle 5 \cong \angle 6$	6. Supplements of $\cong \angle$s are $\cong$.
7. $\overline{AD} \cong \overline{AC}$	7. ___
8. $\triangle ACD$ is isosceles.	8. ___

20. The device to the right can be used to determine one half of any angle. Point E is allowed to move along the slot so that $AD = DE$. Explain why the measure of $\angle EAD$ is always one half the measure of $\angle BDE$.

B

21. $\triangle ABC$ is isosceles with $AB = BC$. If $AB = 4x$ and $BC = 6x - 15$, find AB and BC.
22. $\triangle DEF$ is isosceles with base $\overline{DF}$. If $DE = 4x + 15$, $EF = 2x + 45$, and $DF = 3x + 15$, find the lengths of the sides of the triangle.
23. In $\triangle XYZ$, $XY = YZ$. If $m\angle X = 4x + 60$, $m\angle Y = 2x + 30$, and $m\angle Z = 14x + 30$, find $m\angle X$, $m\angle Y$, and $m\angle Z$.
24. In $\triangle ABC$, $\angle A \cong \angle C$. If $AB = 4x + 25$, $BC = 2x + 45$, and $AC = 3x - 15$, find the lengths of the three sides.

Write a two-column proof for each exercise.

25. **Given:** $\triangle ADC$ is isosceles with vertex A.
     $\overline{BC} \cong \overline{ED}$

    Prove: $\triangle ABE$ is isosceles.

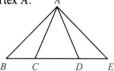

26. **Given:** $\triangle ABC$ is isosceles with vertex angle A.
     $\angle 1 \cong \angle 2$

    Prove: $\triangle BCD$ is isosceles.

27. **Given:** $\overline{AB} \cong \overline{AC}$
     $\overline{BE}$ bisects $\angle ABC$.
     $\overline{CD}$ bisects $\angle ACB$.

    Prove: $\overline{AD} \cong \overline{AE}$

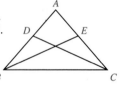

28. **Given:** $\angle ABC \cong \angle ADC$, $\angle 1 \cong \angle 2$
    Prove: $\overline{AB} \cong \overline{AD}$ and $\overline{BC} \cong \overline{DC}$

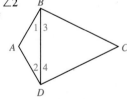

29. If a ship is moving in the direction $\overrightarrow{AD}$, its distance from a point on shore can be determined in the following way. At point A, $m\angle DAC$ can be determined. At some point B along $\overrightarrow{AD}$, $m\angle DBC$ is twice $m\angle DAC$. The distance AB, which can be determined by the ship's log, is the same as the distance BC. Explain why $m\angle DBC = 2m\angle DAC$ means that $AB = BC$.

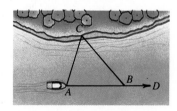

25. 1. $\triangle ADC$ is isos. with vertex A (Given) 2. $\overline{AC} \cong \overline{AD}$ (Def. of isos. $\triangle$) 3. $\angle ACD \cong \angle ADC$ (Base $\angle$s) 4. $\overline{BC} \cong \overline{ED}$ (Given) 5. $\overline{BD} \cong \overline{EC}$ (Common Segment Theorem) 6. $\triangle AEC \cong \triangle ABD$ (SAS) 7. $\overline{AE} \cong \overline{AB}$ (CPCTC) 8. $\triangle ABE$ is isos. (Def. of isos. $\triangle$) **26.** 1. $\triangle ABC$ is isos. with vertex A (Given) 2. $\angle ACB \cong \angle ABC$ (Base $\angle$s) 3. $\angle 1 \cong \angle 2$ (Given) 4. $\angle DCB \cong \angle DBC$ (Angle Add. Prop.) 5. $\overline{CD} \cong \overline{BD}$ (Sides opp. $\cong \angle$s are $\cong$.) 6. $\triangle BCD$ is isos. (Def. of isos. $\triangle$) **27.** 1. $\overline{AB} \cong \overline{AC}$ (Given) 2. $\angle ABC \cong \angle ACB$ (Base $\angle$s) 3. $\overline{BE}$ bisects $\angle ABC$. $\overline{CD}$ bisects $\angle ACB$. (Given) 4. $m\angle ABE = \frac{1}{2}m\angle ABC$, $m\angle ACD = \frac{1}{2}m\angle ACB$ ($\angle$ Bisector Theorem) 5. $\angle ABE \cong \angle ACD$ (Subst.) 6. $\angle ABE \cong \angle ACD$ (Def. of $\cong \angle$s) 7. $\angle A \cong \angle A$ (Reflex.) 8. $\triangle ABE \cong \triangle ACD$ (ASA) 9. $\overline{AD} \cong \overline{AE}$ (CPCTC) **28.** 1. $\angle 1 \cong \angle 2$ (Given) 2. $\overline{AB} \cong \overline{AD}$ (Sides opp. $\cong \angle$s are $\cong$.) 3. $\angle ABC \cong \angle ADC$ (Given) 4. $\angle 3 \cong \angle 4$ (Additive Prop.) 5. $\overline{BC} \cong \overline{DC}$ (Sides opp. $\cong \angle$s are $\cong$.) **29.** $m\angle ABC = m\angle BAC + m\angle BCA$ by the Exterior Angle Theorem. If $m\angle DBC = 2m\angle DAC$, then $m\angle DAC = m\angle BCA$, so $AB = BC$ by Theorem 4.2.

30. Prove Corollary 4.1a.
31. Prove Corollary 4.1b.
32. Use the distance formula and conclude that $m\angle ABC = m\angle ACB$.

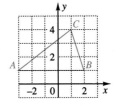

33. Two converging timbers are to be cut along a line as shown so that $m\angle CDB = m\angle ABD$. Two carpenter's squares are positioned so that $BE = DE$. (A carpenter's square has a right-angle corner.)
Prove that $\angle CDB \cong \angle ABD$.

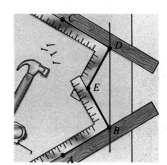

c

34. Suppose that △*ABC* is an isosceles triangle with vertex angle *A* and that *D* is a point on side $\overline{BC}$. Prove that $\overline{AD}$ bisects ∠*A* if *D* is the midpoint of $\overline{BC}$.

35. **Given:** $\overline{AD} \cong \overline{FC}$, $\overline{AB} \cong \overline{FE}$
∠*A* ≅ ∠*F*
Prove: △*CDG* is isosceles.

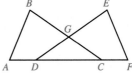

36. ∠*ABD* ≅ ∠*ADB*, $\overline{BF}$ and $\overline{DE}$ bisect ∠*ABD* and ∠*ADB* respectively. Prove that ∠1 ≅ ∠8.

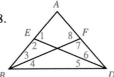

37. Given that, in △*ABC*, ∠*B* ≅ ∠*C*. Prove that △*ABC* ≅ △*ACB*. Explain why you have just proven Theorem 4.2.

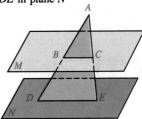

38. **Given:** $M \parallel N$, $\overline{BC}$ in plane *M*, $\overline{DE}$ in plane *N*
$m\angle ABC = m\angle ACB$
Prove: △*ADE* is isosceles.

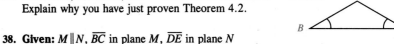

182 *Chapter 4 Congruent Triangles*

Critical Thinking

39. Suppose that $\overline{EB} \cong \overline{EC}$ and $\angle 1 \cong \angle 2$. Consider the following argument. Since $\overline{EB} \cong \overline{EC}$, $\triangle EBC$ is an isosceles triangle with the base angles at B and C congruent. This means that $\angle 3 \cong \angle 4$ since they are supplements of congruent angles and $\triangle ABE \cong \triangle DCE$. Therefore, $\overline{AE} \cong \overline{DE}$ since they are corresponding segments in congruent triangles. Consequently $\triangle AED$ is an isosceles triangle. Is this a convincing argument? Why or why not?

40. For pyramid $ABCD$, $m\angle ABC \cong \angle ACB \cong \angle ACD \cong \angle ADC$. What can you deduce about $\triangle ABD$?

41. Under what conditions is $\triangle ABD$ an equilateral triangle?

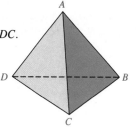

Mixed Review

1. The ratio of the measures of the angles of a triangle is $13:15:17$. Find the measures of the angles and classify the triangle as acute, right, or obtuse.

2. The ratio of the measures of the acute angles of a right triangle is $7:8$. Find the measures of the two acute angles.

3. $BC = CD$, $BD = AB - 1$, $AD = 9$ Find AB.

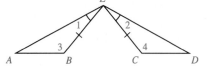
4-6 Isosceles Triangles **183**

---

36. 1. $\angle ABD \cong \angle ADB$ (Given)
2. $\overline{AB} \cong \overline{AD}$ (Sides opp. $\angle$s are =.) 3. $\overline{BF}$ bisects $\angle ABD$. $\overline{DE}$ bisects $\angle ADB$. (Given)
4. $m\angle ADE = \frac{1}{2}m\angle ADB$, $m\angle ABF = \frac{1}{2}m\angle ABD$ ($\angle$ Bisector Theorem) 5. $\angle ABF \cong \angle ADE$ (Transitive Prop.) 6. $\angle A \cong \angle A$ (Reflex.) 7. $\triangle ABF \cong \triangle ADE$ (ASA) 8. $\angle 1 \cong \angle 8$ (CPCTC)
37. 1. $\angle B \cong \angle C$ (Given)
2. $\overline{BC} \cong \overline{CB}$ (Reflex.)
3. $\triangle ABC \cong \triangle ACB$ (ASA: $\angle B \cong \angle C$, $\overline{BC} \cong \overline{CB}$, $\angle C \cong \angle B$)
4. $\overline{AB} \cong \overline{AC}$ (CPCTC)
38. 1. $M \| N$ (Given) 2. $\overline{BC} \| \overline{DE}$ (If two $\|$ planes are cut by a third plane, the lines of intersection are $\|$.)
3. $\angle ABC \cong \angle ADE$, $\angle ACB \cong \angle AED$ (If two $\|$ lines are cut by a transversal, corr. $\angle$s are $\cong$.)
4. $m\angle ABC = m\angle ACB$ (Given)
5. $\angle ADE \cong \angle AED$ (Trans. Prop.) 6. $\overline{AD} \cong \overline{AE}$ (Sides opp. $\cong \angle$s are $\cong$.)
7. $\triangle ADE$ is isos. (Def. of isos.)
39. No; it assumes that A, B, C, D are collinear and that $\angle 3$ and $\angle 4$ are exterior angles of $\triangle EBC$.   **40.** $\triangle ABD$ is isos. with vertex A, since Theorem 4.2 and $m\angle ABC = m\angle ACB$ imply $\overline{AB} \cong \overline{AC}$. Theorem 4.2 and $m\angle ACD = m\angle ADC$ imply $\overline{AC} \cong \overline{AD}$. By the Trans. Prop., $\overline{AB} \cong \overline{AD}$. But although $\triangle ABC \cong \triangle ACD$, you *cannot* conclude that $\triangle ABD \cong \triangle ABC$. $m\angle ABD = m\angle ADB$, but they may not equal the measures of the other base angles.
41. Answers may vary: e.g., if $m\angle DCB = m\angle DBC$ and $m\angle DAC = m\angle DCA$.

Mixed Review Answers

1. 52, 60, 68; acute   **2.** 42, 48
3. 5

Given: isosceles $\triangle ABC$, $\angle ABC$ is the vertex angle. D is the midpoint of $\overline{AC}$.

Prove: $\triangle ABD \cong \triangle CBD$

1. Isos. $\triangle ABC$ with vertex $\angle ABC$ (Given) 2. $\overline{BA} \cong \overline{BC}$ (Def. isos. $\triangle$) 3. D is the midpt. of $\overline{AC}$. (Given) 4. $\overline{BD}$ bisects $\overline{AC}$. (Def. seg. bis.) 5. $\angle ABD \cong \angle CBD$ (Seg. from vertex of isos. $\triangle$ to midpt. of base bisects vertex $\angle$.) 6. $\overline{BD} \cong \overline{BD}$ (Reflex.) 7. $\triangle ABD \cong \triangle CBD$ (SAS)

Lesson Opener

The Explore illustrates a fourth method of proving triangles congruent (AAS). Trace the following triangles. Then slide/turn/flip the triangles on top of each other to see if they match. Student answers to the questions below should reveal that only triangles 1 and 2 are congruent to each other.

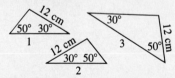

Key Questions

1. Is $\triangle 1 \cong \triangle 2$? yes
2. Is $\triangle 2 \cong \triangle 3$? Explain. No; sides do not correspond.

Materials

student notebooks
protractors
straightedges

OBJECTIVE: *Use the AAS Congruence Postulate in proofs. Use the HL and HA Congruence Postulates in proofs.*

4-7 AAS Congruence and Right Triangle Congruence

 **EXPLORE** Given angles A and B and a segment with length b. Use a protractor and ruler to draw a triangle DEF with $\angle D$ congruent to the given $\angle A$, $\angle E$ congruent to the given $\angle B$, and whose side opposite $\angle E$ has length b.

You have studied the SSS, SAS, and ASA methods of proving triangles congruent. The above Explore suggests the AAS method.

◆ **THEOREM 4.3** AAS Congruence

If two angles and a side opposite one of them in one triangle are congruent to the corresponding parts of another triangle, then the two triangles are congruent.

You will be asked to prove the AAS Theorem in Exercise 27. It is used to complete the proof of this example.

Example 1

Given: $\angle 1 \cong \angle 2$, $\angle C \cong \angle D$

Prove: $\overline{AD} \cong \overline{BC}$

Solution

Statements	Reasons
1. $\angle 1 \cong \angle 2$, $\angle C \cong \angle D$	1. Given
2. $\overline{AB} \cong \overline{AB}$	2. Reflexive
3. $\triangle ABC \cong \triangle BAD$	3. AAS Congruence Theorem
4. $\overline{AD} \cong \overline{BC}$	4. Corr. parts of $\cong \triangle$s are $\cong$.

In addition to the SSS, SAS, ASA, and AAS methods for proving triangles congruent, there are two methods that apply to right triangles only. The HA Congruence Theorem is a consequence of the AAS Congruence Theorem and will be proven in Exercise 28.

Recall that in a right triangle, the side opposite the right angle is called the *hypotenuse* and the other two sides are called *legs*.

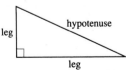

◆ THEOREM 4.4   HA Congruence

If the hypotenuse and one acute angle of a right triangle are congruent to the hypotenuse and one acute angle of another right triangle, then the triangles are congruent.

◆ THEOREM 4.5   HL Congruence

If the hypotenuse and a leg of one right triangle are congruent to the corresponding parts of a second right triangle, then the triangles are congruent.

Given: $\angle Y$ and $\angle RST$ are right $\angle$s in $\triangle XYZ$ and $\triangle RST$.
$\overline{XZ} \cong \overline{RT}$, $\overline{XY} \cong \overline{RS}$
Prove: $\triangle XYZ \cong \triangle RST$

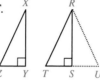

Plan   I will construct $\triangle RUS$, with U selected on $\overline{TS}$ so that $\overline{SU} \cong \overline{YZ}$. If I can show $\triangle XYZ \cong \triangle RSU$, then I can conclude that $\overline{ZX} \cong \overline{UR}$ and that $\triangle TRU$ is isosceles. Consequently $\angle T \cong \angle U$ by Theorem 4.1 and $\angle U \cong \angle Z$ by corr. parts of $\cong \triangle$s are $\cong$. Therefore $\angle T \cong \angle Z$ and I can conclude that $\triangle XYZ \cong \triangle RST$ by HA Congruence.

Example 2

Complete the proof.
Given: $\angle C$ and $\angle F$ are right angles in $\triangle ACB$ and $\triangle DFE$.
$\overline{AE} \cong \overline{DB}$, $\overline{AC} \cong \overline{DF}$
Prove: $\overline{EF} \cong \overline{BC}$

Proof

Statements	Reasons
1. $\angle C$ and $\angle F$ are rt. $\angle$s.	1. Given
2. $\triangle DEF$ and $\triangle ABC$ are rt. $\triangle$s.	2. ——
3. $\overline{AE} \cong \overline{DB}$, $\overline{AC} \cong \overline{DF}$	3. ——
4. $\overline{ED} \cong \overline{BA}$	4. ——
5. $\triangle DEF \cong \triangle ABC$	5. ——
6. $\overline{EF} \cong \overline{BC}$	6. Corr. parts of $\cong \triangle$s are $\cong$.

Solution

2. Definition of a right triangle
3. Given
4. Common Segment Theorem
5. HL Theorem

Six ways to prove triangles congruent have been presented in this chapter. Four ways apply to all triangles and two ways apply to right triangles only.

Summary of Ways To Prove Triangles Congruent

All triangles	SSS	SAS	ASA	AAS
Right triangles	HL	HA		

Point out that the AAS Congruence Postulate only applies when two angles and a side of one triangle are congruent to the corresponding parts of another triangle.

Emphasize the importance of identifying the hypotenuse and the legs in a right triangle.

The HA and HL ways of proving triangles congruent are only used for right triangles. Therefore, the proof must state that the triangle is a right triangle.

Guided Practice

Chalkboard Examples

1. Given: $\overline{EA} \cong \overline{EB}$,
$\angle C \cong \angle D$
Prove: $\overline{AD} \cong \overline{BC}$ 1. $\angle C \cong \angle D$ (Given) 2. $\overline{EA} \cong \overline{EB}$ (Given) 3. $\angle 1 \cong \angle 2$ (Base $\angle$s) 4. $\overline{AB} \cong \overline{BA}$ (Reflex.) 5. $\triangle ABC \cong \triangle BAD$ (AAS) 6. $\overline{AD} \cong \overline{BC}$ (CPCTC)

2. Given: $\angle C$ and $\angle F$ are rt. $\angle$s. $\angle E \cong \angle B$, $\overline{AE} \cong \overline{DB}$
Prove: $\overline{AC} \cong \overline{DF}$ 1. $\angle C$ and $\angle F$ are rt. $\angle$s. (Given) 2. $\triangle ABC$ and $\triangle DEF$ are rt. $\triangle$s. (Def. rt. $\triangle$) 3. $\angle E \cong \angle B$, $\overline{AE} \cong \overline{DB}$ (Given) 4. $\overline{AB} \cong \overline{DE}$ (Common Segment Theorem) 5. $\triangle ABC \cong \triangle DEF$ (HA) 6. $\overline{AC} \cong \overline{DF}$ (CPCTC)

Class Exercise Answers

1. ASA or HA   2. HL
3. none of these   4. AAS
5. HA   6. SSS
7. $\angle D \cong \angle ECB$ or $\angle ACD \cong \angle E$ 8. $\overline{DA} \cong \overline{CB}$ or $\overline{AC} \cong \overline{BE}$ 9. $\overline{DA} \cong \overline{CB}$ and $\overline{AC} \cong \overline{EB}$ 10. $\angle D \cong \angle ECB$ or $\angle ACD \cong \angle E$ 11. $\angle D \cong \angle ECB$ and $\angle ACD \cong \angle E$
12. $\overline{DA} \cong \overline{CB}$ and $\angle D \cong \angle ECB$, or $\overline{AC} \cong \overline{EB}$ and $\angle ACD \cong \angle E$

Class Exercises

Short Answer

Indicate whether the given pair of triangles is congruent by SSS, SAS, ASA, AAS, HA, HL, or none of these.

1.

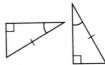

2.

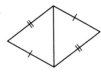

3.

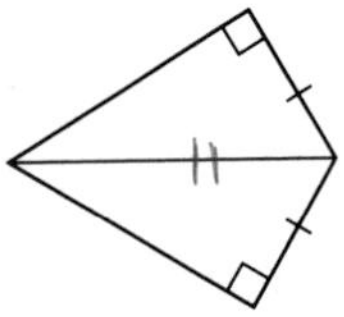

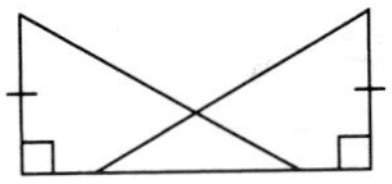

4.

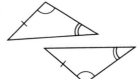

5.

6.

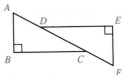

Sample Exercises

$\overline{CD} \cong \overline{CE}$ **State the additional information you need to prove $\triangle ACD \cong \triangle BEC$ by the given method.**

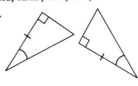

7. HA 8. HL 9. SSS
10. AAS 11. ASA 12. SAS

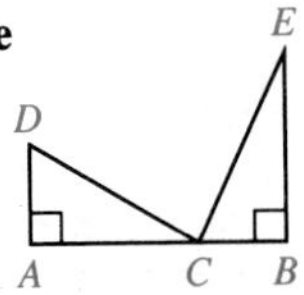

Discussion

13. Formulate a theorem that you would call the LL Congruence Theorem for right triangles. Do you think it is true? Why?
14. Formulate a theorem that you would call the LA Congruence Theorem for right triangles. Do you think it is true? Why?

Exercises

A

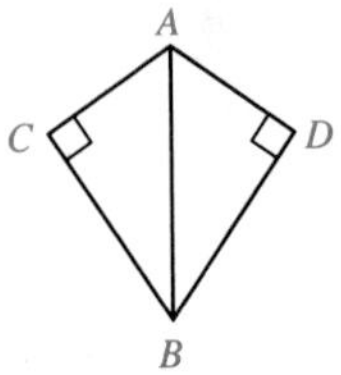

State the additional information you need to prove $\triangle ABC \cong \triangle ABD$ by the given method.

1. HA 2. HL 3. AAS
4. SAS 5. ASA 6. SSS

State the additional information you need for the given method to prove that $\triangle ABC \cong \triangle FED$ if $\overline{AD} \cong \overline{CF}$.

7. HA 8. ASA 9. HL

13. If the legs of a rt. △ are ≅ respectively to the legs of another rt. △, the △s are ≅. Yes, by SAS. **14.** If one leg and acute ∠ of a rt. △ are ≅ to a leg and acute ∠ of another rt. △, the △s are ≅. Not true: the leg and angle would have to be adjacent or opposite in both triangles.

Assignment Guide

Minimum: 1–29 e/o, 34, AR
Regular: 1–32 e/o, 34, AR
Advanced: 10–29 e/o, 30–34, AR

Applications
Exercises 17, 25–26

Algebra
Exercises 22, 23, AR

Lesson Closure

Summarize the six ways of proving triangles congruent.

Teacher's Resource Materials

Enrichment Using Manipulatives 25
Practice Master 28

Computer Software

See Computer Exploration 3, page 636.

Exercise Answers

See Selected Answers for odd-numbered exercises.

2. $\overline{AC} \cong \overline{AD}$ or $\overline{CB} \cong \overline{DB}$
4. $\angle CAB \cong \angle DAB$, $\overline{AC} \cong \overline{AD}$; or $\angle ABC \cong \angle ABD$, $\overline{CB} \cong \overline{DB}$; or $\overline{AC} \cong \overline{AD}$, $\overline{BC} \cong \overline{BD}$
6. $\overline{AC} \cong \overline{AD}$ and $\overline{CB} \cong \overline{DB}$
8. $\angle A \cong \angle F$, $\angle BCA \cong \angle EDF$
10. 1. Given 2. Def. rt. △ Given 4. Def. midpt. 5. Given HL 7. CPCTC **12.** 1. $\angle B$, $\angle D$ rt. ∠s (Given) 2. $\triangle ABC$, $\triangle CDA$ rt. △s (Def. rt. △) 3. $\angle 1 \cong \angle 2$ (Given) 4. $\overline{AC} \cong \overline{AC}$ (Reflex.) 5. $\triangle ABC \cong \triangle CDA$ (HA)

10. Complete the proof.

Given: B is the midpoint of $\overline{AC}$.
      $\angle E$ and $\angle D$ are right $\angle$s. $\overline{EB} \cong \overline{DB}$

Prove: $\angle A \cong \angle C$

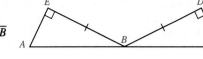

Statements	Reasons
1. $\angle E$, $\angle D$ are rt. $\angle$s.	1. ___
2. $\triangle ABE$ and $\triangle CBD$ are rt. $\triangle$s.	2. ___
3. B is the midpoint of $\overline{AC}$.	3. ___
4. $\overline{AB} \cong \overline{CB}$	4. ___
5. $\overline{EB} \cong \overline{DB}$	5. ___
6. $\triangle ABE \cong \triangle CBD$	6. ___
7. $\angle A \cong \angle C$	7. ___

Write a two-column proof for each exercise.

11. Given: $\angle B$ and $\angle D$ are rt. $\angle$s.
     $\overline{AB} \cong \overline{CD}$

Prove: $\triangle ABC \cong \triangle CDA$

12. Given: $\angle B$ and $\angle D$ are rt. $\angle$s.
     $\angle 1 \cong \angle 2$

Prove: $\triangle ABC \cong \triangle CDA$

Use each given to prove the right triangles $\triangle AOD$ and $\triangle BOC$ congruent.

13. O is the midpoint of $\overline{AB}$.
    $\angle A$ and $\angle B$ are rt. $\angle$s. $\overline{OD} \cong \overline{OC}$

14. $\angle A$ and $\angle B$ are rt. $\angle$s. $\overline{OC} \cong \overline{OD}$, $\angle D \cong \angle C$

15. O is the midpoint of $\overline{AB}$.
    $\angle A$ and $\angle B$ are rt. $\angle$s. $\angle AOD \cong \angle BOC$

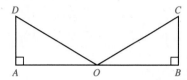

B

16. A basketball backboard is mounted on a wall with a metal bracket $ABCD$ so that $\angle B$ and $\angle D$ are right angles and $AB = CD$. Show that the two corners A and B of the backboard are equidistant from the wall

$\overline{DE} \perp \overline{AC}, \overline{BF} \perp \overline{AC}, \overline{AB} \cong \overline{CD}, \overline{DE} \cong \overline{BF}$

17. Prove that $\angle 1 \cong \angle 2$.
18. Prove that $\overline{AD} \cong \overline{CB}$.
19. Prove that $\overline{AE} \cong \overline{CF}$.

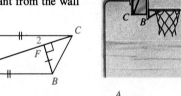

20. Given: $\overline{CD} \perp \overline{AB}, \overline{BE} \perp \overline{AC}, \triangle ABC$ is isosceles.

Prove: $\triangle BFC$ is isosceles.

21. Given: $\overline{CD} \perp \overline{AB}, \overline{BE} \perp \overline{AC}, \overline{BE} \cong \overline{CD}$

Prove: $\triangle ABC$ is isosceles.

22. $\overline{CD} \perp \overline{AB}, \overline{BE} \perp \overline{AC}, \overline{CD} \cong \overline{BE}, BD = 5x - 7, CE = 2x + 14$, $DF = 2x + 5, EF = 3x - 2$ Prove that $AEFD$ has two pairs of congruent sides.

23. $\overline{CD} \perp \overline{AB}, \overline{BE} \perp \overline{AC}, \overline{AC} \cong \overline{AB}, AD = 4x - 5, AE = 2x + 7$
    $m\angle A = 3x + 8$ Find $m\angle A$.

24. A milling cutter with seven teeth is made by cutting seven right triangles out of a seven-sided regular polygon. If $\overline{AB}$ is cut the same length for each tooth, why are the sharp points of the cutter all the same size angle?

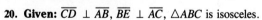

4-7 AAS Congruence and Right Triangle Congruence   **187**

26. 1. $\angle A \cong \angle D$, $\angle C \cong \angle F$
(Given) 2. $\angle B \cong \angle E$ (Theorem
3.12) 3. $\overline{AB} \cong \overline{DE}$ (Given)
4. $\triangle ABC \cong \triangle DEF$ (ASA)
28. Given: isos. $\triangle ABC$, D midpt.
of $\overline{AB}$, E midpt. of $\overline{AC}$, $DF \perp \overline{BC}$,
$\overline{EG} \perp \overline{BC}$ Prove: $\overline{DF} \cong \overline{EG}$
1. isos. $\triangle ABC$ (Given)
2. $\overline{AB} \cong \overline{AC}$ (Def. isos. $\triangle$)
3. D midpt. of $\overline{AB}$, E midpt. of
$\overline{AC}$ (Given) 4. $BD = \frac{1}{2}AB$,
$CE = \frac{1}{2}AC$ (Midpt. Theorem)
5. $\frac{1}{2}AB = \frac{1}{2}AC$ (Mult. Prop.)
6. $BD = CE$ (Trans. Prop.)
7. $\overline{BD} \cong \overline{CE}$ (Def. $\cong$) 8. $\angle B \cong$
$\angle C$ (Base $\angle$s) 9. $\overline{DF} \perp \overline{BC}$,
$\overline{EG} \perp \overline{BC}$ (Given) 10. $\angle DFB$,
$\angle EGC$ rt. $\angle$s ($\perp$ seg. form rt.
$\angle$s.) 11. $\triangle DFB$, $\triangle EGC$ rt. $\triangle$s
(Def. rt. $\triangle$) 12. $\triangle DFB \cong \triangle EGC$
(HA) 13. $\overline{DF} \cong \overline{EG}$ (CPCTC)
30. 1. A, B, C in plane M,
$\overline{AC} \cong \overline{BC}$, $\overline{CD} \perp$ plane M (Given)
2. $\overline{CD} \perp \overline{AC}$, $\overline{CD} \perp \overline{BC}$ (Line $\perp$ at
a point in a plane is $\perp$ to all
lines through that point.)
3. $\angle DCA$, $\angle DCB$ rt. $\angle$s. ($\perp$ lines
form rt. $\angle$s.) 4. $\angle DCA \cong \angle DCB$
(Rt. $\angle$s are $\cong$.) 5. $\overline{CD} \cong \overline{CD}$
(Reflex.) 6. $\triangle DCA \cong \triangle DCB$
(SAS) 7. $\overline{AD} \cong \overline{BD}$ (CPCTC)
8. $\triangle ABD$ isos. (Def. isos. $\triangle$)

Algebra Review Answers

1. $y^3 - 2y^2 + 3y$
2. $1 - ab^2 - a^3b$
3. $y - 5$ 4. $-2pq + 3p - 4q$
5. $y - 4$ 6. $4x^2 - 6x + 9$

Connections Answers

1. $\sqrt{10}, 2\sqrt{2}, \sqrt{2}$
2.

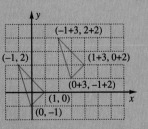

3. side lengths of both trian-
gles: $2\sqrt{10}, \sqrt{13}, \sqrt{17}$, $\cong$ by
SSS   4. The transformation
preserves congruence.

---

25. An antenna tower is perpendicular to a flat roof. Three wires are used to steady the tower, all attached to the same point D on the tower. If the three wires are all the same length, prove that their anchors A, B, and C are all the same distance from the base P.

26. Prove Theorem 4.3.

Given: $\angle A \cong \angle D$, $\angle C \cong \angle F$, $\overline{AB} \cong \overline{DE}$

Prove: $\triangle ABC \cong \triangle DEF$

27. Prove Theorem 4.4.

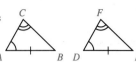

C

28. Prove that segments from the midpoints of the legs of an isosceles triangle perpendicular to the base are congruent.

29. Prove that segments from the midpoint of the base of an isosceles triangle perpendicular to the legs are congruent.

30. Points A, B, and C are in plane M, $\overline{CD} \perp$ plane M, and $\overline{AC} \cong \overline{BC}$. Prove that $\triangle ABD$ is an isosceles triangle.

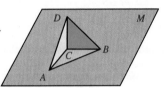

Critical Thinking

31. Write a statement that you would call the SSA Congruence Property. Construct two noncongruent triangles, both named $\triangle ABC$ in which $m\angle A = 45$, $AB = 20$, and $BC = 15$. Do you think that the SSA Property should become a postulate? Why or why not?

Algebra Review

Divide.

1. $(9y^4 - 18y^3 + 27y^2) \div 9y$
2. $(a^2b - a^3b^3 - a^5b^2) \div a^2b$
3. $(y^2 - 25) \div (y + 5$
4. $(6p^2q^2 - 9p^2q + 12pq^2) \div -3pq$
5. $(y^2 - 8y + 16) \div (y - 4)$
6. $(8x^3 + 27) \div (2x +$

CONNECTIONS ◇◇

Geometry and Transformations

Congruence as discussed in this chapter is related to concepts studied in algebra. Consider the transformation that associates each point (x, y) in the coordinate plane with the point $(x + 3, y + 2)$. This transformation moves the red triangle to the blue triangle.

1. Calculate the lengths of the sides of the red and blue triangles to show that they are congruent.
2. On graph paper, draw the triangle whose vertices are $(-1, 3)$, $(1, -3)$, and $(2, 1)$. Then draw the position that it moves to after the above transformation is performed.
3. Show that the two triangles in Exercise 2 are congruent.
4. State a generalization about this transformation.

OBJECTIVE: *Apply theorems about medians, altitudes, and angle and side bisectors of triangles.*

4-8 Medians, Altitudes, and Perpendicular Bisectors

A **median** of a triangle is a segment from a vertex to the midpoint of the opposite side.

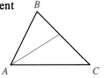 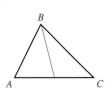 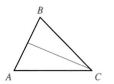

The three medians of △*ABC*

An **altitude** of a triangle is a segment from a vertex perpendicular to the line containing the opposite side.

 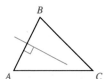 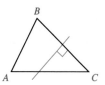

The three altitudes of △*ABC*

A perpendicular bisector of a side of a triangle is a line through the midpoint and perpendicular to the side.

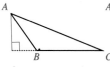 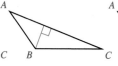

The three perpendicular bisectors of the sides of △*ABC*

Several theorems relate to perpendicular bisectors.

◆ **THEOREM 4.6**

In an isosceles triangle, the altitude to the base bisects the base and bisects the vertex angle.

Given: An isosceles triangle △*ABC* with legs $\overline{AB}$ and $\overline{AC}$ and $\overline{AD}$ altitude from *A*.

Prove: $\overline{BD} \cong \overline{CD}$, $\angle 1 \cong \angle 2$

Plan Both △*ABD* and △*ACD* are right triangles. Since $\overline{AB} \cong \overline{AC}$ and $\overline{AD}$ is a leg of each, we can use the HL Theorem to conclude that △*ABD* ≅ △*ACD*. Consequently $\overline{BD} \cong \overline{CD}$ and $\angle 1 \cong \angle 2$ by corr. parts of ≅ △s are ≅.

A point *P* is said to be **equidistant** from two points *A* and *B* if *PA* = *PB*. The next two theorems describe the relationship between a point on a perpendicular bisector and a point equidistant from two points.

(Quiz on previous lesson)

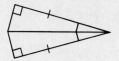

State the postulates that prove the triangles congruent. HA, HL, ASA, SAS

Lesson Opener

Two segments commonly used with triangles are introduced in this lesson: median and altitude.

The construction of medians and altitudes is covered in Chapter 9 and could be used as an introduction to this lesson.

Materials

student notebooks
compasses
straightedges
investigative software

Teaching Notes

Since several important and difficult concepts are in this section, allow 2–3 days to cover the material.

The median goes to the middle of the opposite side. The altitude is perpendicular to the line that contains the opposite side.

The material on paper folding located in *Enrichment Using Manipulatives* may help students visualize properties of the median and perpendicular bisector.

Challenge
Given: △*ABC* with medians $\overline{NC}$ and $\overline{MB}$, $\overline{NC} \cong \overline{MB}$
Prove: △*ABC* is isosceles.

Construct line ℓ through A ∥ to $\overline{BC}$. On one side mark off points U and V so that $\overline{AU} \cong \overline{UV} \cong \overline{BC}$. Extend $\overline{BC}$ on the same side, marking X and Y so that $\overline{BC} \cong \overline{CX} \cong \overline{XY}$. Draw $\overline{BU}$, $\overline{CU}$, $\overline{UX}$, $\overline{XV}$, $\overline{UY}$, and $\overline{VY}$. Label the ∩ of $\overline{AC}$ and $\overline{BU}$ point D. Label the ∩ of $\overline{UY}$ and $\overline{XV}$ point E. Show $\triangle ABC \cong \triangle CUA \cong$ $\triangle UCX \cong \triangle XVU \cong \triangle VXY$. Then show D is the midpt. of $\overline{AC}$ (so D is point M) and E is the midpt. of $\overline{VX}$. D is the midpt. of $\overline{BU}$ and E is the midpt. of UY. Show $\overline{EY} \cong \overline{CN}$ which, by hypothesis, is $\cong \overline{BD}$. Deduce $\overline{BU} \cong \overline{YU}$. Thus $\angle DBC \cong \angle EYX$ $(\cong \angle NCB)$. Using SAS show $\triangle DBC \cong \triangle EYX$, so $NB \cong DC$ and $\overline{AB} \cong \overline{AC}$.

Key Terms

median of a triangle
altitude of a triangle
perpendicular bisector
equidistant

◆ THEOREM 4.7

If a point is equidistant from the endpoints of a segment, then it is on the perpendicular bisector of the segment.

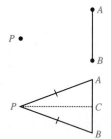

Given: $\overline{AB}$ and point P with $\overline{PA} \cong \overline{PB}$

Prove: P is on the perpendicular bisector of $\overline{AB}$.

Plan Draw auxiliary lines $\overline{PA}$, $\overline{PB}$, and median $\overline{PC}$ and use the SSS Postulate to prove that $\triangle PAC \cong \triangle PBC$. Then $\angle ACP \cong \angle BCP$ since corr. parts of $\cong \triangle$s are $\cong$. Since these two angles form a linear pair, prove they must both be right angles and $\overline{PC}$ is the perpendicular bisector of $\overline{AB}$.

◆ THEOREM 4.8

If a point is on the perpendicular bisector of a segment, then it is equidistant from the endpoints of the segment.

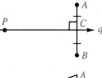

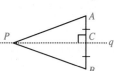

Given: q is the perpendicular bisector of $\overline{AB}$ and P is on q.

Prove: $\overline{PA} \cong \overline{PB}$

Plan Draw $\overline{PA}$ and $\overline{PB}$ and use the SAS Postulate to show that $\triangle PCA \cong \triangle PCB$. Then use the fact that corr. parts of $\cong \triangle$s are $\cong$ to conclude that $\overline{PA} \cong \overline{PB}$.

Example 1

Complete the statement in as many ways as possible.
$\overline{EC}$ is ___ in $\triangle AED$.

Solution

1. an altitude
2. a median *$\overline{EC}$ is the altitude to the base of an isosceles triangle. Consequently, it bisects the base by Theorem 4.6 and C is the midpoint of $\overline{AD}$.*
3. a perpendicular bisector

Try This

Complete each statement.

a. $\overline{EB}$ is ___ in $\triangle AEC$. **b.** $\overline{EC}$ is ___ in $\triangle ABE$.

The distance from a point P to a line r is the distance PQ where Q is the point on r such that $\overline{PQ} \perp r$. For example, the distance from P to line r is d.

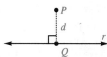

◆ THEOREM 4.9

If a point is equidistant from the sides of an angle,
then it is on the angle bisector.

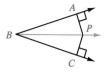

◆ THEOREM 4.10

If a point is on an angle bisector, then it is equidistant
from the sides of the angle.

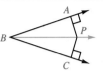

Example 2

What can you deduce from the information given in each part?

a. $AB = AD$ **b.** $\angle ABC$ and $\angle ADC$ are right angles and $BC = DC$.

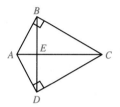

Solution

   a. A is on the perpendicular bisector of $\overline{BD}$.
   b. C is on the angle bisector of $\angle BAD$.

Try This

What can you deduce if you know that $BE = DE$?

Class Exercises

Short Answer

Determine whether the following statements are true or false.

1. If G is the midpoint of $\overline{ED}$, then $\overline{CG}$ is a median of $\triangle EBD$.
2. If $\overline{CF} \perp \overline{ED}$, then $\overline{CF}$ is an altitude of both $\triangle ECD$ and $\triangle ECG$.
3. If $\overline{EB} \perp$ to $\overline{BD}$, then $\overline{EB}$ is an altitude of $\triangle ECD$.
4. If $\overline{CF} \perp$ to $\overline{ED}$, then $\overline{CF}$ is a perpendicular bisector of $\triangle ECD$.
5. If $\overline{CG}$ is a median of $\triangle ECD$, then G is the midpoint of $\overline{ED}$.
6. Each leg of a right triangle is also an altitude of the triangle.

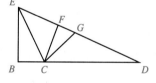

Sample Exercises

Complete each statement in as many ways as possible. Give reasons for your answer.

7. $\overline{FD}$ is ___ of $\triangle FCE$.   8. $\overline{FC}$ is ___ of $\triangle AFE$.
9. $\overline{FC}$ is ___ of $\triangle BFE$.   10. $\overline{FC}$ is an altitude of ___ triangles?
11. Trace $\triangle BFE$ and draw all three altitudes of the triangle.
12. Trace $\triangle BFE$ and draw all three medians of the triangle.

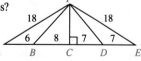

Discussion

13. Consider an equilateral triangle. Suppose a segment from a vertex is a
    median, an altitude, or a perpendicular bisector of the opposite side.
    Give a convincing argument that the segment is also the other two.

16. an ∠ bis. (not a median)

16. an ∠ bis. (not a median)
18. 8   **20.** *P* is equidistant
from $\overline{AB}$ and $\overline{CB}$. By Th. 4.9,
P is on the bis. of ∠*B*.
22. Since $\overline{CD}$ is a median, *D* is
the midpt. of $\overline{AB}$. *AD* = *BD*, so
$2x + 3 = 3x - 2$, *x* = 5, so
AD = *BD* = 13, and *AB* = 26. $\overline{BE}$
is a median so *AE* = *CE*.
AE = 4*x* − 7 = 13 = *CE*.
AC = 26. Thus *AB* = *AC*.
24. $CD = \sqrt{1^2 + 2^2} = \sqrt{5}$
$BD = \sqrt{1^2 + 2^2} = \sqrt{5}$
So *CD* = *BD*, hence $\overline{AD}$ is a
median.   **26.** From Ex. 25, *A*
is equidistant from *C* and *B*, so
A is on the ⊥ bis. of $\overline{BC}$, by Th.
4.7. From Ex. 24, *D* is equidis-
tant from *C* and *B*, so it too is
on the ⊥ bis. of *C* and *B*. As two
points determine a line, $\overline{AD}$ is
a ⊥ bis.   **28. a.** The water
intakes should be built where
the shoreline intersects
the ⊥ bis. of the line seg. connecting the plants.   **b.** The
transformer station should be
built where the bis. of the line
seg. connecting the plants intersects the ⊥ bis. of the line seg.
connecting the plants to the
city.   **30.** Given: isos. △*ABC*
with legs $\overline{AB}$ and $\overline{AC}$, alt. $\overline{AD}$
Prove: $\overline{BD} \cong \overline{CD}$, ∠1 ≅ ∠2
1. $\overline{AD}$ is an alt. (Given)
2. ∠*ADB*, ∠*ADC* rt. ∠s (Def.
alt.) 3. △*ABD*, △*ACD* rt. △s
(Def. rt. △) 4. isos. △*ABC* with
legs $\overline{AB}$ and $\overline{AC}$ (Given)
5. $\overline{AB} \cong \overline{AC}$ (Def. isos. △)
6. $\overline{AD} \cong \overline{AD}$ (Reflex.)
7. △*ABD* ≅ △*ACD* (HL)
8. $\overline{BD} \cong \overline{CD}$, ∠1 ≅ ∠2 (CPCTC)
32. Given: P is equidistant from
$\overline{AB}$ and $\overline{CB}$, ∠*PAB* and ∠*PCB* are
rt. ∠s. Prove: $\overline{BP}$ is the ∠bis.
1. ∠*PAB*, ∠*PCB* rt. ∠s (Given)
2. △*PAB*, △*PCB* rt. △s (Def. rt.
△) 3. P is equidistant from $\overline{AB}$
and $\overline{CB}$. (Given) 4. $\overline{PA} \cong \overline{PC}$
(Def. equidistant) 5. $\overline{PB} \cong \overline{PB}$
(Reflex.) 6. △*PAB* ≅ △*PCB* (HL)
7. ∠*PBA* ≅ ∠*PBC* (CPCTC)
8. $\overline{BP}$ is the ∠bis. (Def of
∠bis.)

Exercises

A

Complete each statement in as many ways as possible.
Give reasons for your answer.

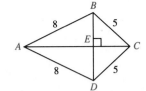

1. $\overline{BE}$ is ___ of △*ABC*.
2. $\overline{AC}$ is ___ of $\overline{BD}$.
3. $\overline{AE}$ is ___ of △*ABD*.
4. $\overline{AC}$ is ___ of ∠*BAD*.

What can you deduce from the information given in each problem?

5. *CD* = *ED*   **6.** *GB* = *GF*
7. ∠1 ≅ ∠2   **8.** *AC* = *AE*

Complete each statement.

9. $\overline{BG}$ is an altitude of △ ___.   **10.** $\overline{AF}$ is an altitude of △ ___.

Suppose that △*ACE* is isosceles and segments are perpendicular as shown.

11. Why do you know that $\overline{AD}$ is a median?
12. Why do you know that *BG* = *GF*?

Lines *q* and *r* are perpendicular bisectors of the sides of △*ABC*.

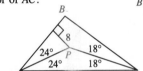

13. If PC = 9, then PB = ___ .
14. If PC = 9, then PA = ___ .
15. Explain why *P* is on the perpendicular bisector of $\overline{AC}$.

Complete each statement.

16. $\overline{AP}$ is ___ in △*ABC*.
17. $\overline{CP}$ is ___ in △*ABC*.
18. The distance from *P* to $\overline{AB}$ is ___ .
19. The distance from *P* to $\overline{BC}$ is ___ .

20. Give a convincing argument that *P* is on the angle bisector of ∠*B*.
21. Point *P* is equidistant from the sides of ∠*ABC*. Explain why
line *BP* is the angle bisector.

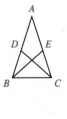

B

22. Suppose that $\overline{BE}$ and $\overline{CD}$ are medians. If *AD* = 2*x* + 3, *BD* = 3*x* − 2,
AE = 4*x* − 7, explain why *AB* = *AC*.
23. Suppose that $\overline{BE}$ is an altitude. If *m*∠*AEB* = 4*x* + 10, *AD* = 2*x* + 5,
BD = 3*x* − 15, is *CD* a median?
24. Show that $\overline{AD}$ is a median of △*ABC*.
25. Show that $\overline{AD}$ is an altitude of △*ABC*.
    (HINT: Show that △*ABC* is isosceles.)
26. Show that $\overline{AD}$ is a perpendicular bisector of $\overline{BC}$.
27. Show that the distance from *D* to $\overline{AB}$ is equal to
the distance from *D* to $\overline{AC}$.

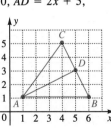

28. Two electrical power plants are using the same large lake as a cooling tank. Copy the diagram and show the following.
a. Show where, along the lake shoreline, the water intake should be built if they are to be equidistant from both plants.
b. Show where the transformer station should be built if it is to be equidistant from both power plants and the city.

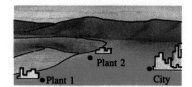

29. Lines *p* and *q* represent two major airline routes. A radio transmitter station must be built equidistant from these two routes. The Federal Aviation Administration wants to build it near the city, but a city ordinance does not allow it inside the city limits. Copy the diagram and draw all possible locations for the transmitter station.

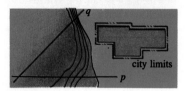

C

Write a two-column proof for each exercise. Draw and label a figure as shown in the statement of the theorem.

30. Theorem 4.6   **31.** Theorem 4.8   **32.** Theorem 4.9   **33.** Theorem 4.10

34. Prove that the altitudes from the base angles of an isosceles triangle are congruent.

35. Prove that an altitude to the base of an isosceles triangle is also a median of the triangle and a perpendicular bisector.

Critical Thinking

Inductive reasoning often culminates with a statement, or a conjecture, which the researcher thinks is true. Analyze the following conjectures. If you think they are true, prove them. If not, find a counterexample.

36. Conjecture: If a median of a triangle is also an altitude, then the triangle is isosceles.

37. Conjecture: If an altitude of a triangle bisects the angle it is drawn from, then the triangle is an acute triangle.

38. Conjecture: If two altitudes of an acute triangle are congruent, then the triangle is isosceles.

Algebra Review

Factor.

1. $49y^4 - 81$ **2.** $x^2 - 14x + 49$ **3.** $9y^2 - 64$
4. $a^2b^2 + 7ab + 12$ **5.** $72 - x - x^2$ **6.** $2y^2 - 3y - 2$

Quiz

$\overline{RQ} \cong \overline{RS}$, $\overline{TQ} \cong \overline{TS}$ Complete each statement.

1. $m\angle RQS = 6x + 10$, $m\angle RSQ = 9x - 17$, $m\angle QRS = \underline{\hphantom{00}}$
2. If $QS = RQ$, $m\angle RSQ = \underline{\hphantom{00}}$.
3. If $\angle QVT \cong \angle SVT$, $\triangle QVT \cong \triangle SVT$ by $\underline{\hphantom{00}}$.
4. If $\triangle RVQ$ and $\triangle RVS$ are right triangles, $\triangle RVQ \cong \triangle RVS$ by $\underline{\hphantom{00}}$.
5. If $QV = SV$, $\overline{VT}$ is a(n) $\underline{\hphantom{00}}$ or $\underline{\hphantom{00}}$ to $\overline{QS}$ and $\underline{\hphantom{00}}$ $\angle QTS$.
6. Point W is $\underline{\hphantom{00}}$ from $\overline{TQ}$ and $\overline{TS}$.

34. Given: isos. $\triangle ABC$ with legs $\overline{AB}$ and $\overline{AC}$, alt. $\overline{CD}$ and $\overline{BE}$ Prove: $\overline{BE} \cong \overline{CD}$ 1. alt. $\overline{CD}$ and $\overline{BE}$ (Given) 2. $\angle ADC$, $\angle AEB$ rt. $\angle$s (Def. alt.) 3. $\triangle ADC$, $\triangle AEB$ rt. $\triangle$s (Def. rt. $\triangle$) 4. isos. $\triangle ABC$ with legs $\overline{AB}$, $\overline{AC}$ (Given) 5. $\overline{AB} \cong \overline{AC}$ (Def. isos. $\triangle$) 6. $\angle A \cong \angle A$ (Reflex.) 7. $\triangle ADC \cong \triangle AEB$ (HA) 8. $\overline{CD} \cong \overline{BE}$ (CPCTC)

36. True; $\overline{AD}$ is a median and alt. to $\triangle ABC$. Prove that $\triangle ABC$ is isosceles. 1. $\overline{AD}$ is a median to $\triangle ABC$ (Given) 2. D is the midpt. of $\overline{BC}$ (Def. median) 3. $\overline{BD} \cong \overline{CD}$ (Midpt. forms two $\cong$ seg.) 4. $\overline{AD}$ is an alt. to $\triangle ABC$ (Given) 5. $\angle ADB$, $\angle ADC$ rt. $\angle$s (Def. of alt.) 6. $\angle ADB \cong \angle ADC$ (All rt. $\angle$s are $\cong$.) 7. $\overline{AD} \cong \overline{AD}$ (Reflex. Prop.) 8. $\triangle ADB \cong \triangle ADC$ (SAS) 9. $\overline{AB} \cong \overline{AC}$ (CPCTC) 10. $\triangle ABC$ is isos. (Def. isos.)

38. True; $\overline{CD}$ and $\overline{BE}$ are alt. of $\triangle ABC$ and $\overline{CD} \cong \overline{BE}$. Prove that $\triangle ABC$ is isos. 1. $\overline{CD} \cong \overline{BE}$ (Given) 2. $\angle CDA$, $\angle BEA$ rt. $\angle$s (Def. alt.) 3. $\angle CDA \cong \angle BEA$ (All rt. $\angle$s are $\cong$.) 4. $\angle A \cong \angle A$ (Reflex.) 5. $\triangle ADC \cong \triangle AEB$ (AAS) 6. $\overline{AC} \cong \overline{AB}$ (CPCTC) 7. $\triangle ABC$ isos. (Def. isos. $\triangle$)

Algebra Review Answers

1. $(7y^2 - 9)(7y^2 + 9)$
2. $(x - 7)^2$
3. $(3y - 8)(3y + 8)$
4. $(ab + 3)(ab + 4)$
5. $-1(x + 9)(x - 8)$
6. $(2y + 1)(y - 2)$

Quiz Answers

1. 52   **2.** 60   **3.** HL
4. HL   **5.** altitude, median, bisects   **6.** equidistant

Comparing Approaches in Geometry

Synthetic and Coordinate Geometry

Exercise Answers

1.

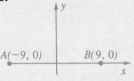

A(−9, 0)   B(9, 0)

2. $AC = \sqrt{(0 - (-9))^2 + (8 - 0)^2}$
$= \sqrt{145}$
$BC = \sqrt{(0 - 9)^2 + (8 - 0)^2}$
$= \sqrt{145}$

3. $(0, b)$ **4.** $A\left(-\frac{\ell}{2}, 0\right),$
$B\left(\frac{\ell}{2}, 0\right)$ **5.** Theorem 4.8

COMPARING APPROACHES IN GEOMETRY

Introduction to Synthetic and Coordinate Geometry

Theorem 4.8 states that each point on the perpendicular bisector of a segment is equidistant from the two endpoints. The approach taken on page 190 for this theorem is called a **synthetic approach.** A second approach is called a **coordinate approach** since it relies on a coordinate system. Here are the two approaches for a segment $\overline{AB}$ of length 14.

Synthetic Approach	**Coordinate Approach**
	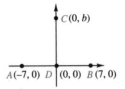

Plan Let C be a point on the $\perp$ bisector of $\overline{AB}$. Then use the SAS Congruence Postulate to prove that $\triangle ACD \cong \triangle BCD$ and conclude that $AC = BC$.

Plan Draw a coordinate system so that the y-axis is the perpendicular bisector of $\overline{AB}$ and point $C(0, b)$ is a general point on this bisector. Use the distance formula to find AC and BC.

In completing the plan for the coordinate proof you obtain the following.

$AC = \sqrt{(-7 - 0)^2 + (0 - b)^2}$
$\quad = \sqrt{49 + b^2}$
$BC = \sqrt{(7 - 0)^2 + (0 - b)^2}$
$\quad = \sqrt{49 + b^2}$

Notice that both approaches yield the same result, namely, that $AC = BC$. The exercises below provide more opportunities to use these two approaches.

Exercises

1. Suppose $\overline{AB}$ has length 18. Draw a coordinate system so that $\overline{AB}$ is on the x-axis and the y-axis is the perpendicular bisector of $\overline{AB}$. Find the coordinates of the points A and B.
2. If $C(0, 8)$ is a point on the perpendicular bisector of $\overline{AB}$, use the distance formula to show that $AC = BC$.
3. If C is a general point on the perpendicular bisector of $\overline{AB}$, how can the coordinates of point C be named?
4. If you want to let AB represent a general segment bisected by the y-axis rather than one of length 18, how can the coordinates of point A and B be named?
5. Using the coordinates for A, B, and C from Exercises 3–4, find lengths AC and BC. What theorem does this prove?

194   *Chapter 4   Congruent Triangles*

CRITICAL THINKING

Deciding on the Truth of a Statement

In the process of dealing with data or evidence in critical thinking, you have to decide if a statement is true. Every statement, no matter how simple or complicated, is either true or false. Statements can be represented by letters of the alphabet.

For example, if statement p "You passed geometry" is true, then the statement $\sim p$ (read "not p") "You did not pass geometry" is false, and vice versa. This is summarized in the truth table to the right.

p	$\sim p$
T	F
F	T

Consider the "p or q" statement below.

p	You will pass this geometry course.
q	You will be a sophomore again next year.
p or q	You will pass this geometry course or you will be a sophomore again next year.

p	q	p or q
T	T	T
T	F	T
F	T	T
F	F	F

The statement is false only when you fail geometry and so you are not a sophomore next year. In the first row p or q is true. You have passed geometry but you could still be a sophomore next year because you failed English!

Check the "p and q" statement below. Do you think the truth table to the right is correct for the "p and q" statement below?

p	We will review geometry.
q	The geometry test will be easy.
p and q	We will review geometry and the geometry test will be easy.

p	q	p and q
T	T	T
T	F	F
F	T	F
F	F	F

Exercises

1. Joe said "It is false that I don't like geometry." Does this mean that Joe doesn't like geometry? Explain. Use symbols to show the statement.
2. Kwan said, "Teenagers like movies or records." If this is true and Kwan likes both movies and records, could Kwan be a teenager? Explain.
3. Bill's mother said, "You can't go out of town and you must be in by 12 o'clock." Bill thought he must not go out of town or he must be in by 12 o'clock. Was he correct? Explain.
4. The salesman said, "You can drive this car home today for nothing down and just $349 a month." Will Corliss be able to drive the car home without having to pay anything on it today?
5. The truth table for "or" statements was defined in a way useful to geometry, but it could be defined in another way. Give a true "or" statement in which both parts cannot be true at the same time.

Critical Thinking

Deciding on the Truth of a Statement

Exercise Answers

1. Let p = "Joe likes geometry." Then if $\sim p$ is false, $\sim\sim p$ is true, so Joe *does* like geometry.
2. Kwan could be a teenager. If Kwan liked neither movies nor records, then she could *not* be a teenager.   **3.** Bill is wrong. His mother made an "and" statement, which is true only if both statements "You can't go out of town" and "You must be in by 12 o'clock" are true.
4. Yes, unless the first month's payment is due on that day.
5. Answers may vary. At 2 o'clock I will go shopping or go to the movies.

CHAPTER SUMMARY

Vocabulary

altitude (4-8)	correspondence (4-1)	legs (4-6)
base (4-6)	equidistant (4-8)	median (4-8)
base angles (4-6)	hypotenuse (4-7)	opposite angle (4-2)
corollary (4-6)	included angle (4-2)	vertex angle (4-6)

Key Ideas

1. Prove two triangles congruent using SSS, ASA, SAS, or AAS.
2. Prove two right triangles congruent using HL or HA.
3. Show two angles or two segments congruent by proving that they are corresponding parts of congruent triangles.
4. If two sides of a triangle are congruent, then the *angles* opposite them are congruent.
5. If two angles of a triangle are congruent, then the *sides* opposite them are congruent.
6. Every triangle has three medians, three altitudes, and three perpendicular bisectors.
7. In an isosceles triangle, the altitude to the base bisects the base and bisects the vertex angle.
8. If a point is equidistant from the endpoints of a segment, then it is on the perpendicular bisector of the segment.
9. If a point is equidistant from the sides of an angle, then it is on the angle bisector.

CHAPTER REVIEW

4-1

△*ABC* ≅ △*RST*   **Complete each statement.**

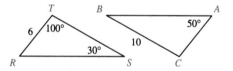

1. ∠*B* ≅ ___   **2.** $\overline{AB}$ ≅ ___
3. ∠*SRT* ≅ ___   **4.** *TS* = ___
5. *AC* = ___   **6.** △*BCA* = ___

4-2

Write a congruence between each pair of triangles and state the postulate applied. If you cannot apply a postulate, write *no conclusion can be made*.

7. 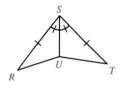   **8.** 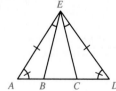   **9.**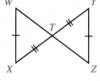

4-3

Write a conclusion that follows from the given information. State the congruence postulate or definition on which your conclusion is based.

10. $\overline{AB} \cong \overline{BC}$, $\overline{DA} \cong \overline{DC}$ **11.** $\overline{DB}$ bisects $\angle ADC$, $\overline{DA} \cong \overline{DC}$

12. Write a two-column proof.

   Given: E is the midpoint of $\overline{DC}$. $\angle 1 \cong \angle 2$

   Prove: $\triangle DEB \cong \triangle CEB$

4-4

Write a two-column proof.

13. Given: G bisects $\overline{DF}$. $\angle 1 \cong \angle 2$

   Prove: $\angle 3 \cong \angle 4$

14. Given: $\angle 1$ is a right angle. $\angle 3 \cong \angle 4$

   Prove: $\overline{DE} \cong \overline{EF}$

4-5

Use the Common Segment Theorem and Common Angle Theorem to complete each statement.

15. If $\overline{QW} \cong \overline{ST}$, then $\overline{QS} \cong$ ___ .

16. If $\angle QAS \cong \angle TAW$, then $\angle QAW \cong$ ___ .

17. Write a two-column proof.

   Given: $\angle QAS \cong \angle TAW$, $\overline{QA} \cong \overline{TA}$, $\overline{AW} \cong \overline{AS}$

   Prove: $\angle 1 \cong \angle 2$

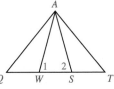

4-6

Write a conclusion that follows from the given information. State the theorem on which your conclusion is based.

18. $\angle 4 \cong \angle 7$ **19.** $\overline{HJ} \cong \overline{JG}$

20. $\triangle HEG$ is isosceles with vertex H. F is the midpoint of $\overline{EG}$.

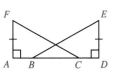

4-7

State the additional information you need for each method to prove $\triangle AFC \cong \triangle DEB$.

21. HA   **22.** AAS   **23.** HL

24. Write a two-column proof.

   Given: $\angle 1 \cong \angle 2$, $\overline{AB} \cong \overline{BC}$

   Prove: $\triangle AEC \cong \triangle CDA$

4-8

Indicate whether the following statements are true or false.

25. If $\overline{BC} \cong \overline{CD}$ and $\overline{CE} \perp \overline{BD}$, then $\angle 1 \cong \angle 2$.

26. If $\overline{BA} \cong \overline{AD}$, then $\overline{AC}$ is the perpendicular bisector of $\overline{BD}$.

27. If $\overline{AE}$ is an altitude for $\triangle DAB$, then $\overline{BE} \cong \overline{ED}$.

28. In $\triangle ABD$, if $\overline{AB} \cong \overline{AD}$ and $\overline{AE}$ is the median to $\overline{BD}$, then $\angle 3 \cong \angle 4$.

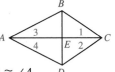

10. $\triangle DAB \cong \triangle DCB$, SSS

11. $\triangle DAB \cong \triangle DCB$, SAS

12. 1. E is midpt. of $\overline{DC}$ (Given)
2. $\overline{ED} \cong \overline{EC}$ (Def. midpt.)
3. $\angle 1 \cong \angle 2$ (Given) 4. $\overline{BE} \cong \overline{BE}$ (Reflex.) 5. $\triangle DEB \cong \triangle CEB$ (SAS)   **13.** 1. G bisects $\overline{DF}$ (Given) 2. $\overline{GD} \cong \overline{GF}$ (Def. bisector) 3. $\angle 1 \cong \angle 2$ (Given)
4. $\overline{EG} \cong \overline{EG}$ (Reflex.)
5. $\triangle EDG \cong \triangle EFG$ (SAS)
6. $\angle 3 \cong \angle 4$ (CPCTC)

14. 1. $\angle 1$ is a rt. $\angle$. (Given)
2. $m\angle 1 = 90$ (Def. rt. $\angle$)
3. $m\angle 1 + m\angle 2 = 180$ (Def. linear pair) 4. $m\angle 2 = 90$ (Subtraction)
5. $m\angle 1 = m\angle 2$ (Transitive)
$\angle 1 \cong \angle 2$ (Def. $\cong \angle$s)
7. $\overline{EG} \cong \overline{EG}$ (Reflex.)
8. $\angle 3 \cong \angle 4$ (Given)
9. $\triangle EDG \cong \triangle EFG$ (ASA)
10. $\overline{DE} \cong \overline{EF}$ (CPCTC)

15. $\overline{WT}$ **16.** $\angle TAS$

17. 1. $\overline{QA} \cong \overline{TA}$ (Given)
2. $\angle QAS \cong \angle TAW$ (Given)
3. $\overline{AW} \cong \overline{AS}$ (Given)
4. $\triangle QAS \cong \triangle TAW$ (SAS)
5. $\angle 1 \cong \angle 2$ (CPCTC)

18. $\overline{JE} \cong \overline{JG}$; Th. 4.2

19. $\angle 2 \cong \angle 8$; Th. 4.1

20. $\angle 1 \cong \angle 2$ (CPCTC)

21. $\overline{FC} \cong \overline{EB}$, $\angle F \cong \angle E$ or $\angle FCA \cong \angle EBD$

22. $\angle FCA \cong \angle EBD$

23. $\overline{FC} \cong \overline{EB}$ **24.** 1. $\angle 1 \cong \angle 2$ (Given) 2. $\overline{AB} \cong \overline{BC}$ (Given)
3. $\angle BAC \cong \angle BCA$ (Base $\angle$s of an isos. $\triangle$ are $\cong$.) 4. $\overline{AC} \cong \overline{AC}$ (Reflex.) 5. $\triangle AEC \cong \triangle CDA$ (AAS)   **25.** true   **26.** false

27. false   **28.** true

Teacher's Resource Materials

Chapter 4 Tests

Test Answers

1. $\overline{CD}$ **2.** ∠DCF **3.** △EBA
4. △HGI ≅ △JLK, SAS
5. △MNO ≅ △MSO, SSS
6. △WTY ≅ △TWX, ASA
7. △ACB ≅ △ECD, SAS
8. △ACB ≅ △ECD, ASA
9. true   **10.** false
11. false   **12.** true
13. false   **14.** false
15. $\overline{DB}$ **16.** ∠DEB
17. 9   **18.** 30
19. $\overline{AC} \cong \overline{CD}$
20. ∠A ≅ ∠D
21. 1. $\overline{AD} \cong \overline{CD}$ (Given)
2. ∠1 ≅ ∠3 (Base ∠s of isos.
△s are ≅.) 3. ∠5 ≅ ∠6 (Given)
4. $\overline{DB} \cong \overline{DB}$ (Reflex.)
5. △DAB ≅ △DCB (AAS)
22. 1. B is midpt. of $\overline{AC}$. (Given)
2. $\overline{AB} \cong \overline{CB}$ (Def. midpt.)
3. $\overline{DB} \perp \overline{AC}$ (Given) 4. ∠2 ≅
∠4(⊥ lines form ≅ adj. ∠s.)
5. $\overline{DB} \cong \overline{DB}$ (Reflex.)
6. △DAB ≅ △DCB (SAS)
7. ∠5 ≅ ∠6 (CPCTC)

CHAPTER TEST

△ABE ≅ △CDF   Complete each statement.
1. $\overline{AB} \cong$ ___   **2.** ∠BAE ___   **3.** ___ ≅ △FDC

Write a congruence between each triangle and state the postulate applied.

4. 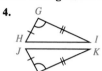 **5.** 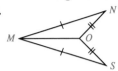 **6.**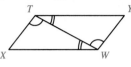

Write a conclusion that follows from the given information. State the congruence postulate on which your conclusion is based.
7. $\overline{AC} \cong \overline{CE}$, $\overline{BC} \cong \overline{CD}$
8. ∠1 ≅ ∠2, $\overline{AC} \cong \overline{CE}$

Determine whether each statement is true or false.
9. If △ABD ≅ △CBD, then $\overline{AD} \cong \overline{CD}$.
10. If $\overline{AB} \cong \overline{BC}$, then ∠5 ≅ ∠6.
11. If △DEA ≅ △DEC, then ∠1 ≅ ∠6.
12. If $\overline{BD} \perp \overline{AC}$ and AB = BC, then AD = CD.
13. If ∠5 ≅ ∠6 and $\overline{AB} \cong \overline{BC}$, then △DAC is isosceles.
14. If $\overline{DB}$ bisects ∠CDA, then EA = EC.

Use the Common Segment Theorem or the Common Angle Theorem to complete each statement.
15. If $\overline{AB} \cong \overline{CD}$, then AC = ___ .
16. If ∠AEB ≅ ∠DEC, then ∠AEC ≅ ___ .

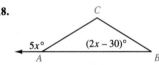

$\overline{AC} \cong \overline{BC}$ Solve for x.

17.   **18.**

State the additional information you need to prove △ABC ≅ △DBC by the given method.
19. HL   **20.** AAS

Write a two-column proof.
21. Given: $\overline{AD} \cong \overline{CD}$
        ∠5 ≅ ∠6
   Prove: △DAB ≅ △DCB

22. Given: B is the midpoint of $\overline{AC}$.
        $\overline{DB} \perp \overline{AC}$
   Prove: ∠5 ≅ ∠6

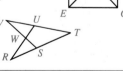

23. Given: ∠TUR ≅ ∠TSV
        $\overline{UW} \cong \overline{SW}$
   Prove: △UVW ≅ △SRW

24. Given: △UVW ≅ △SRW
   Prove: △TVS ≅ △TRU

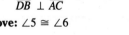

DISCRETE MATH

Graphs

There are several ways of representing data in problems. Mathematicians commonly use *graphs*. A graph is a set of points or *vertices* which are connected by lines or *edges*. In the graph representing airline routes, the vertices *C*, *B*, *A*, *D*, *L* represent Chicago, Boston, Atlanta, Dallas, Los Angeles. The edges tell whether the airline has nonstop flights connecting the cities.

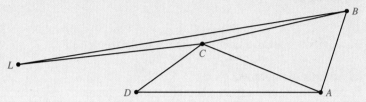

Example 1

Is there a route from Boston to Dallas?

Solution

Yes; fly from Boston to Atlanta and then from Atlanta to Dallas.

Due to their sizes and harbor regulations, some ships cannot visit certain cities. Suppose that the Delta can enter the ports of Charleston, Los Angeles, and Miami. The Voyager can enter Los Angeles and Portland. The Tidewater can enter Long Beach and Seattle. The Odyssey can visit Portland and Long Beach. The edges of the graph show which ships can visit which ports.

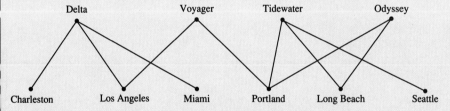

Example 2

Can cargo be moved by these ships from Charleston to Portland?

Solution

Yes; the cargo can be moved from Charleston to Los Angeles by the Delta and then shipped to Portland by the Voyager.

Exercises

1. Use the airline graph to find all the possible routes from Boston to Dallas which do not visit any city more than once.
2. Use the cargo graph to determine whether cargo can be moved by these ships from Seattle to Miami.

Discrete Math

Graphs

Discrete math is a term covering many topics related to finite sets. It includes the study of graphs, matrices, and probability and their applications.

Point out that the word *graph*, as it is used here, has a somewhat different meaning from the one students may be used to. Rather than representing an equation (e.g., the graph of a straight line), *graph* refers here to a set of points, called vertices, and the lines, called edges, that connect them.

Exercise Answers

1. *B - A - D*
   B - C - D
   B - L - C - D
   B - L - C - A - D
   B - C - A - D
   B - A - C - D
2. yes (Seattle to Long Beach by the Tidewater, Long Beach to Portland by the Odyssey, Portland to Los Angeles by the Voyager, Los Angeles to Miami by the Delta)

CHAPTER 5

Using Congruent Triangles and Parallel Lines

Chapter Overview

The first five lessons of this chapter discuss properties of quadrilaterals. Lesson 5-6 introduces the idea of indirect proof and gives students practice in this important type of reasoning. The final two lessons of the chapter cover inequalities associated with triangles.

Objectives

5-1 ■ Apply the definitions of a parallelogram and theorems about properties of parallelograms.

5-2 ■ Prove some quadrilaterals are parallelograms.

5-3 ■ Apply definitions and theorems about rectangles, rhombuses, and squares.

5-4 ■ Apply definitions and theorems about trapezoids.

5-5 ■ Apply theorems about segments that join midpoints of sides of triangles and quadrilaterals.

5-6 ■ Use the indirect method of proof.

5-7 ■ Apply the Exterior Inequality Theorem and theorems involving inequalities in one triangle.

5-8 ■ Apply the SAS and SSS Inequality Theorems involving triangles.

TEACHING CHAPTER 5

Cooperative Learning Opportunities

In Chapter 5, theorems in which the proof is left as an exercise can be the basis for cooperative learning groups. Have students work in groups of three and assign them the following roles: (1) talker, who reads the theorem, points out what is needed and, in general, facilitates the group; (2) note-taker, who prepares the outline and then the two-column proof; (3) presenter, who pays attention and prepares to present the proof orally to the class.

Most of these proofs depend on the use of congruent triangles. You might prepare students by telling them to consider how to look at the given figures with congruent triangles in mind.

You might assign the proof of **Theorems 5.6 and 5.7** without referring to the exercises. The groups will have to list what is given and what is to be proved. **Theorems 5.12 and 5.13** (page 215) as well as **Theorems 5.15 and 5.16** (page 221) are also good candidates for this activity. Have some groups present their proofs to the class.

Multicultural Note: *Thales and the Origins of Proof*

Deductive proof in mathematics appears fully developed in the work of Euclid. But Euclid had predecessors and Thales is usually named as the father of abstract mathematics.

Thales lived from about 624 until 548 B.C. (300 years before Euclid) in Miletus, a city in present-day Turkey. He is credited with outstanding achievements but it is difficult to separate fact from legend. It is said that he predicted an eclipse in 585 B.C. but this is doubtful. More reliable is the claim that he calculated the height of the pyramids by comparing their shadows with the shadow of a stick.

Thales has been hailed as the first true mathematician—as the originator of the deductive organization of geometry. The Theorem of Thales proves that an angle inscribed in a semi-circle is a right angle. Thales is also said to have proved:

- A circle is bisected by a diameter.
- The base angles of an isosceles triangle are equal.
- Vertical angles are equal.

Alternative Assessment and Communication Ideas

The **Critical Thinking** exercises at the end of each exercise set can be used as alternative assessment, either in the form of a quiz or homework. Have students write complete sentences stating all of the reasons for their answers. This activity helps reinforce logical connections.

A second kind of alternative assessment is to ask for definitions of new figures. Remind students that a good definition places an object in a class and then distinguishes it from everything else in the class.

Have students define trefoil based on the figure. Ask them to construct and define a quatrefoil.

Ans: A triangle bounded by 3 congruent arcs of a circle whose centers are the vertices of the triangle.

Investigations and Projects

Some teachers find it very helpful to use collapsible models of parallelograms and other figures of this type to introduce Lesson 5-3. If you do not have such models, you might ask students to construct one or another as a project. You might ask for a parallelogram, rhombus, and trapezoid.

The figures should be made of wood, sanded and possibly painted different colors for your convenience in use. Opposite sides must be exactly the required lengths. Holes should be drilled and the pieces held together with screws and wing-nuts.

This kind of project might appeal to some students who have a more practical interest in geometry. The constructions will teach some basic concepts and, if well done, will be useful to you for years to come.

Lesson	PACING CHART (DAYS)			Opening Activity	Cooperative Activity	Seat or Group Work
	1-Year Minimum	1-Year Regular	1-Year Advanced			
5-1	1	1	1	Chapter Opener: **TE** p. 200; Lesson Opener: **TE** p. 201	Explore: **SE** p. 201; ✂ Lab Worksheet 5-1: *Laboratory Manual* p. 41	Try This Exercises
5-2	2	2	2	First Five Minutes 5-2: *FFM Transparency Masters* p. 16 or **TE** p. 207; Lesson Opener: **TE** p. 207	Computer Activity: **SE** p. 212; ✂ Lab Worksheet 5-2: *Laboratory Manual* p.42	Try This Exercises
5-3	2	2	2	First Five Minutes 5-3: *FFM Transparency Masters* p. 17 or **TE** p. 213; Lesson Opener: **TE** p. 213	Explore: **SE** p. 213; ✂ Lab Worksheet 5-3A: *Laboratory Manual* p. 43; ✂ Lab Worksheet 5-3B: *Laboratory Manual* p. 44	Try This Exercise: Math Contest Problem: **SE** p. 218
5-4	2	2	2	First Five Minutes 5-4: *FFM Transparency Masters* p. 17 or **TE** p. 220; Lesson Opener: **TE** p. 220	Explore: **SE** p. 220; ✂ Lab Worksheet 5-4A: *Laboratory Manual* p. 45; ✂ Lab Worksheet 5-4B: *Laboratory Manual* p. 46	Try This Exercises
5-5	1	1	1	First Five Minutes 5-5: *FFM Transparency Masters* p. 18 or **TE** p. 224; Lesson Opener: **TE** p. 224	Explore: **SE** p. 224; ✂ Lab Worksheet 5-5A: *Laboratory Manual* p. 49; ✂ Lab Worksheet 5-5B: *Laboratory Manual* p. 50	Try This Exercises
5-6	1	1	1	First Five Minutes 5-6: *FFM Transparency Masters* p. 18 or **TE** p. 230; Lesson Opener: **TE** p. 230	Algebra Review: **SE** p. 625	Try This Exercises
5-7	1	1	1	First Five Minutes 5-7: *FFM Transparency Masters* p. 19 or **TE** p. 236; Lesson Opener: **TE** p. 236	✂ Lab Worksheet 5-7A: *Laboratory Manual* p. 54; ✂ Lab Worksheet 5-7B: *Laboratory Manual* p. 55	Try This Exercises
5-8	1	1	1	First Five Minutes 5-8: *FFM Transparency Masters* p. 19 or **TE** p. 243; Lesson Opener: **TE** p. 243	Explore: **SE** p. 243; ✂ Lab Worksheet 5-8: *Laboratory Manual* p. 58	Try This Exercise
Review	1	1	1			
Test	1	1	1			

FFM = First Five Minutes

Enrichment	Review/Assess	Reteach	Technology	Lesson
Study Skills: **SE** p. 206; ✂ Enrichment Using Manipulatives 5-1: *Enrichment* p. 27	Class Exercises: **SE** p. 203; Mixed Review: **SE** p. 206	Practice Worksheet 5-1: *Practice and Mixed Review* p.35	Computer Exploration 4: **SE** p. 637	5-1
Computer Activity: **SE** p. 212; ✂ Enrichment Using Manipulatives 5-2: *Enrichment* p. 28	Class Exercises: **SE** p. 209; Algebra Review: **SE** p. 212	Practice Worksheet 5-2: *Practice and Mixed Review* p.36	Computer Activity: **SE** p. 212; Computer Exploration 5: **SE** p. 638; BASIC 5-2; *Technology* p. B11	5-2
Math Contest Problem: **SE** p. 218; Comparing Approaches in Geometry: **SE** p. 219; ✂ Enrichment Using Manipulatives 5-3: *Enrichment* p. 29	Class Exercises: **SE** p. 216; Algebra Review: **SE** p. 218	Practice Worksheet 5-3: *Practice and Mixed Review* p. 37	Computer Exploration 5: **SE** p. 638; Computer Exploration 6: **SE** p. 639	5-3
✂ Enrichment Using Manipulatives 5-4: *Enrichment* p. 30; ✂ Lab Worksheet 5-4C: *Laboratory Manual* p. 47	Class Exercises: **SE** p. 221; Mixed Review: **SE** p. 223; Quiz: **SE** p. 223; Quiz: *Assessment* p. 87	Practice Worksheet 5-4: *Practice and Mixed Review* p. 38	Computer Exploration 7: **SE** p. 640	5-4
Enrichment: **SE** p. 229; ✂ Enrichment Using Manipulatives 5-5: *Enrichment* p. 31; ✂ Lab Worksheet 5-5C: *Laboratory Manual* p. 51; ✂ Lab Worksheet 5-5D: *Laboratory Manual* p. 53	Class Exercises: **SE** p. 226; Algebra Review: **SE** p. 228	Practice Worksheet 5-5: *Practice and Mixed Review* p. 39	Computer Exploration 8: **SE** p. 641; Computer Exploration 9: **SE** p. 642; Computer Exploration 10: **SE** p. 643; Calculator Worksheet 5-5: *Technology* p. CL5	5-5
Careers: **SE** p 235; ✂ Enrichment Using Manipulatives 5-6: *Enrichment* p. 32	Class Exercises: **SE** p. 232; Mixed Review: **SE** p. 235	Practice Worksheet 5-6: *Practice and Mixed Review* p.40		5-6
Connections: **SE** p. 242; ✂ Enrichment Using Manipulatives 5-7: *Enrichment* p. 33; ✂ Lab Worksheet 5-7C: *Laboratory Manual* p. 56; ✂ Lab Worksheet 5-7D: *Laboratory Manual* p. 57	Class Exercises: **SE** p. 238; Algebra Review: **SE** p. 241; Quiz: **SE** p. 223	Practice Worksheet 5-7: *Practice and Mixed Review* p. 41	Computer Exploration 11: **SE** p. 644; BASIC 5-7: *Technology* p. B12	5-7
Discrete Math: **SE** p. 248;	Class Exercises: **SE** p. 244; Algebra Review: **SE** p. 247; Quiz: **SE** p. 47; Quiz: *Assessment* p. 88	Practice Worksheet 5-8: *Practice and Mixed Review* p.42		5-8
Critical Thinking: **SE** p. 249	Summary & Review: **SE** p. 250–251	Mixed Review: *Practice and Mixed Review* p. 106		Review
Problem Solving: **SE** p. 253	Chapter 5 Test: **SE** p. 252; Chapter 5 Tests: *Assessment* p. 25–30; *MathTest*			Test

5

Using Congruent Triangles and Parallel Lines

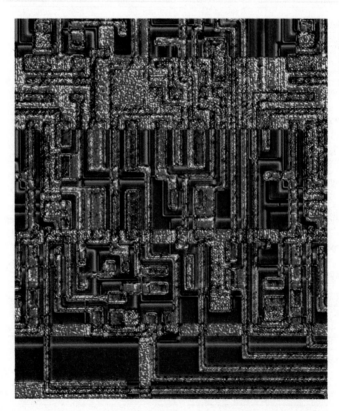

Circuits in a computer chip form a parallelogram. If one angle of the parallelogram is five times as large as another, find the measures of the angles of the parallelogram.

QUADRILATERALS

OBJECTIVE: *Apply the definition of a parallelogram and theorems about properties of parallelograms.*

5-1 Properties of Parallelograms

 **EXPLORE** Use ruled paper and a ruler to draw four different quadrilaterals in which both pairs of opposite sides are parallel. Use a ruler and protractor to measure the sides and angles of each quadrilateral. Make generalizations about properties you find to be true for all four quadrilaterals.

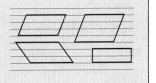

In Chapter 3 you learned that a quadrilateral is a polygon with four sides. In this chapter you will apply theorems you have learned about parallel lines and congruent triangles in your study of special quadrilaterals.

■ DEFINITION

A **parallelogram** ($\square$) is a quadrilateral with two pairs of parallel sides.

In $\square ABCD$, $\overline{AB}$ and $\overline{CD}$ are opposite sides and so are $\overline{AD}$ and $\overline{BC}$. Sides $\overline{AB}$ and $\overline{BC}$ are adjacent sides. $\angle A$ and $\angle C$ are opposite angles and so are $\angle B$ and $\angle D$. $\angle A$ and $\angle B$ are consecutive angles since they have a common side.

$\overline{AD} \parallel \overline{BC}$
$\overline{AB} \parallel \overline{CD}$

The theorems and corollaries that follow state properties about parallelograms that you may have discovered while completing the Explore.

◆ THEOREM 5.1

Opposite sides of a parallelogram are congruent.

Given: $ABCD$ is a parallelogram.
Prove: $\overline{AB} \cong \overline{CD}$, $\overline{AD} \cong \overline{BC}$

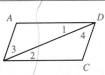

Proof Draw $\overline{BD}$. $\angle 1$ and $\angle 2$ are congruent alternate interior angles as are $\angle 3$ and $\angle 4$, since $\overline{AD} \parallel \overline{BC}$ and $\overline{AB} \parallel \overline{CD}$. Since $\overline{BD} \cong \overline{BD}$, $\triangle ABD \cong \triangle CDB$ by the ASA Postulate. So, $\overline{AB} \cong \overline{CD}$ and $\overline{AD} \cong \overline{BC}$ because corresponding parts of congruent triangles are congruent.

Lesson Opener

Review Lesson 3-6 by drawing a quadrilateral and asking students to name it, find the sum of the interior angle measures, and find the measure of each interior and exterior angle if it is a regular four-sided polygon. Ask for examples of quadrilaterals in the classroom.

Materials

student notebooks
protractors
compasses
straightedges
geoboards
investigative software

Key Terms

parallelogram
consecutive angles
consecutive sides

Alternate Explore

Provide examples of the following quadrilaterals for students to explore by measuring sides and angles with a protractor and ruler. **a.** parallelogram **b.** rectangle **c.** rhombus **d.** square **e.** trapezoid. Have students list the properties they discover for each. Suggest drawing diagonals for each quadrilateral.

Key Questions

1. How many of the figures can you identify by name? Answers may vary.
2. Name some properties all the figures have in common. Answers may vary. four sides, four vertices

▶ **COROLLARY 5.1a**

Two parallel lines are equidistant at all points.

You will be asked to prove Corollary 5.1a in Exercise 28.

Example 1

Find the lengths of $\overline{AB}$ and $\overline{DC}$ in $\square ABCD$.

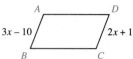

Solution

$3x - 10 = 2x + 1$ *Opposite sides of a $\square$ have equal measure.*
$x = 11$
$2(11) + 1 = 23$ *Replace x with 11 in 2x + 1.*
$AB = DC = 23$

Try This

Find the lengths of $\overline{AD}$ and $\overline{BC}$ if $AD = 2y + 22$ and $BC = 4y - 10$.

◆ **THEOREM 5.2**

Opposite angles of a parallelogram are congruent.

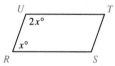

The following corollary can be proved using Theorem 5.2.

▶ **COROLLARY 5.2a**

Consecutive angles of a parallelogram are supplementary.

Convincing arguments to support Theorem 5.2 and Corollary 5.2a are asked for in Discussion Exercises 16–17.

Example 2

Find the measures of the four angles of $\square RSTU$ if the measure of $\angle U$ is twice the measure of $\angle R$.

Solution

$x + 2x = 180$ *Consecutive angles of a $\square$ are supplementary.*
$3x = 180$
$x = 60$
$m\angle R = m\angle T = 60$ $m\angle U = m\angle S = 120$

Try This

Find the measures of the four angles of $\square RSTU$ if the measure of $\angle S$ is ten less than four times the measure of $\angle T$.

◆ **THEOREM 5.3**

The diagonals of a parallelogram bisect each other.

Given: $MNOP$ is a parallelogram.
Prove: $\overline{MO}$ and $\overline{PN}$ bisect each other.

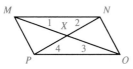

Plan Prove $\angle 1 \cong \angle 3$ and $\angle 2 \cong \angle 4$, since $\overline{MN} \| \overline{PO}$. Prove $\triangle MNX \cong \triangle OPX$ by ASA.
Then $\overline{MX} \cong \overline{XO}$ and $\overline{NX} \cong \overline{PX}$ by corresponding parts of congruent triangles.

Summary of Properties of Parallelograms

1. Opposite sides are parallel.
2. Opposite sides are congruent.
3. Opposite angles are congruent.
4. Consecutive angles are supplementary.
5. The diagonals bisect each other.

Class Exercises

Short Answer

ABCD is a parallelogram.

1. Name two pairs of congruent sides.
2. Name two pairs of congruent angles.
3. Name pairs of congruent segments that are not sides.
4. Name two pairs of supplementary angles.
5. If $m \angle CDB = 30$, find $m \angle ABD$.
6. If $m \angle ADC = 100$, find $m \angle ABC$ and $m \angle BAD$.

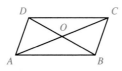

Sample Exercises

State the definition or theorem that justifies each conclusion.

7. $\overline{AB} \cong \overline{CD}$ 8. $AO = OC$
9. $\overline{AD} \| \overline{BC}$ 10. $\angle DAB$ and $\angle ADC$ are supplementary.

ABCD is a parallelogram. Complete each statement.

11. If $AB = 3x$, $CD = x + 10$, $AB =$ ___
12. If $AD = 3x + 15$, $BC = 21$, $AD =$ ___
13. If $AD = \frac{x}{2}$, $BC = 2x - 12$, $BC =$ ___
14. If $m \angle BAD = 100$, $m \angle DCE =$ ___
15. If $m \angle ADC = 135$, $m \angle ABD = 80$, $m \angle DBC =$ ___

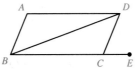

Discussion

16. Explain how Theorem 5.1 can be used to prove Theorem 5.2.
17. Explain how Theorem 5.2 can be used to prove Corollary 5.2a.

5-1 Properties of Parallelograms **203**

2. Find the measures of the four angles of $\square RSTU$ if $m \angle R = 3x$, $m \angle U = 2x + 10$, and $m \angle T = 102$.
$m \angle R = m \angle T = 102$,
$m \angle S = m \angle U = 78$

Answer to **Try This**
$m \angle T = m \angle R = 38$,
$m \angle S = m \angle U = 142$

Class Exercise Answers

1. $\overline{AD} \cong \overline{BC}$, $\overline{DC} \cong \overline{AB}$
2. $\angle DAB \cong \angle DCB$, $\angle ADC \cong \angle ABC$
3. $\overline{AO} \cong \overline{OC}$, $\overline{DO} \cong \overline{OB}$
4. $m \angle DAB + m \angle ABC = 180$, $m \angle DAB + m \angle ADC = 180$, $m \angle DCB + m \angle ABC = 180$, $m \angle BCD + m \angle CDA = 180$
5. 30   6. 100, 80
7. Opposite sides of a $\square$ are $\cong$.
8. The diagonals of a $\square$ bisect each other.   9. A $\square$ is a quadrilateral with two pairs of parallel sides.   10. The consecutive angles of a $\square$ are supplementary.   11. 15
12. 21   13. 4   14. 80
15. 55   16. Given $\square$ RSTU. Draw a diagonal $\overline{US}$. Show that $\triangle URS \cong \triangle STU$ by SSS, using Theorem 5.1 to establish that $\overline{UT} \cong \overline{RS}$ and $\overline{UR} \cong \overline{TS}$. Use corr. parts of $\cong \triangle s$ are $\cong$ to show that opposite $\angle s$ of $\square RSTU$ are $\cong$.
17. Given $\square$ RSTU. $\angle S$ and $\angle T$ are supplementary and $\angle V$ and $\angle R$ are supplementary because if parallel lines are cut by a transversal same-side int. $\angle s$ are supplementary. By Theorem 5.2, $\angle R \cong \angle T$ and $\angle V \cong \angle S$.

Assignment Guide

Minimum: 1–38 e/o, 42, MR
Regular: 1–38 e/o, 39–43, MR
Advanced: 1, 7, 12, 20, 23–43, MR

Applications
Exercise 25

Algebra
Class Exercises 11–13
Exercises 18–23, 26, 27

Lesson Closure

Ask students to state the five properties of a parallelogram and identify each as a theorem, a definition, or a corollary.

Teacher's Resource Materials

Enrichment Using
   Manipulatives 27
Practice Master 30

Computer Software

See Computer Exploration 4, page 637.

Exercise Answers

See Selected Answers for odd-numbered exercises.

2. The diagonals of a ▱ bisect each other.   **4.** Opposite sides of a ▱ are ≅.

6. 115   **8.** 36   **10.** 30

12. $2(m\angle BCD) = 120$

14. 132   **16.** 37

18. 16   **20.** ±4   **22.** ±4

24. 8,8   **26.** $AB = 17$

28. 1. $\overline{AB} \perp q$, $\overline{CD} \perp q$ (Given) 2. $\overline{AB} \parallel \overline{CD}$ (Two lines ⊥ to the same line are ∥ to each other.) 3. $p \parallel q$ (Given) 4. ABCD is a ▱. (Def. of ▱) 5. $\overline{AB} \cong \overline{CD}$ (Opposite sides of a ▱ are ≅.)

Exercises

A

ABCD is a parallelogram. State the theorem that justifies each conclusion.

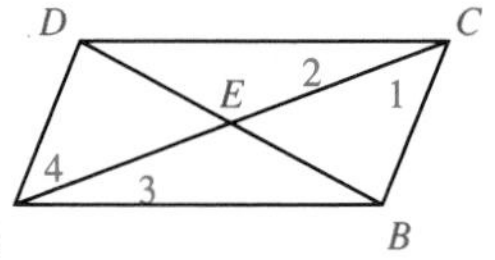

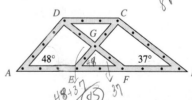

1. $\angle DAB \cong \angle DCB$ 2. $\overline{BE} \cong \overline{ED}$
3. $\overline{AD} \cong \overline{BC}$ 4. $\overline{DC} \cong \overline{AB}$

Complete each statement.

5. If $AD = 20$, $BC = $ ___.   6. If $m\angle ADC = 115$, $m\angle ABC$ ___.
7. If $DB = 22$, $DE = $ ___.   8. If $AE = 18$, $AC = $ ___.
9. If $m\angle DAB = 75$, $m\angle ADC = $ ___.
10. If $m\angle 2 = 30$, $m\angle 3 = $ ___.
11. If $BD = 10$ and $AE = 8$, $AC = $ ___.
12. If $m\angle ABC = 2(m\angle BCD)$, $m\angle ADC = $ ___.
13. If $m\angle ADC = 130$, $m\angle 1 = 35$, $m\angle 2 = $ ___.

Find the measure of each angle in ▱ MNST.

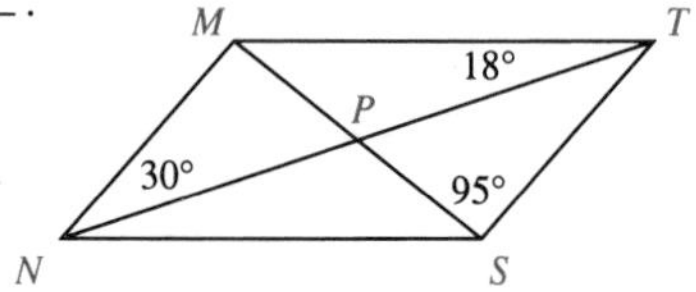

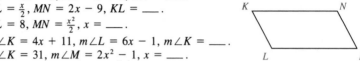

14. $m\angle TMN$ 15. $m\angle TSN$
16. $m\angle MSN$ 17. $m\angle SPN$

Complete each statement about ▱ KLMN.

18. If $KN = 3x - 5$, $LM = x + 9$, $KN = $ ___.
19. If $KL = \frac{x}{2}$, $MN = 2x - 9$, $KL = $ ___.
20. If $KL = 8$, $MN = \frac{x^2}{2}$, $x = $ ___.
21. If $m\angle K = 4x + 11$, $m\angle L = 6x - 1$, $m\angle K = $ ___.
22. If $m\angle K = 31$, $m\angle M = 2x^2 - 1$, $x = $ ___.
23. If $m\angle L = x - 40$, $m\angle N = \frac{3x}{4}$, $m\angle L = $ ___.

B

24. If $\overleftrightarrow{AC} \parallel \overleftrightarrow{XY}$ and the altitude, $\overline{BD}$, of $\triangle BXY$ is 8, what are the lengths of the altitudes of $\triangle AXY$ and $\triangle CXY$ from vertices A and C respectively?

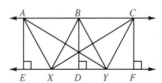

25. Part of the structural support system for a bridge is shown. $\overline{AB} \parallel \overline{CD}$, $\overline{DF} \parallel \overline{CB}$, and $\overline{AD} \parallel \overline{EC}$. Find $m\angle CGF$.

26. Given: ▱ ABCD with $AB = x + 5$ and $CD = 2x - 7$ Find the length of $\overline{AB}$.

27. Given: ▱ ABCD with $AB = 2x$, $CD = 3y + 4$, $BC = x + 7$, and $AD = 2y$ Find the lengths of the sides of the parallelogram.

28. Use the figure to the right to prove Corollary 5.1a.
   Given: $p \parallel q$, $\overline{AB} \perp q$, $\overline{CD} \perp q$
   Prove: $\overline{AB} \cong \overline{CD}$

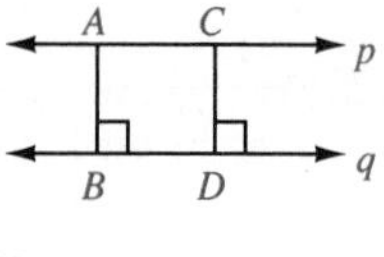

204   Chapter 5   Using Congruent Triangles and Parallel Lines

29. Given: ▱ABCD, ▱AECF
Prove: △CDF ≅ △ABE

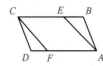

30. Given: ▱ABCD, $\overline{FG}$ bisects $\overline{DB}$.
Prove: $\overline{DB}$ bisects $\overline{FG}$.

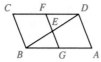

31. Given: ▱ABCD, A, F, E, and C are collinear. AF = CE
Prove: $\overline{DE} \| \overline{BF}$

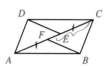

32. Given: ▱ABCD, AE = CF
Prove: CE = AF

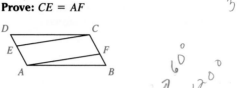

Assume the figure to the right is a regular 12-gon that has been divided into parallelograms and that $m\angle ALK = 150$. **Use the definition of a regular polygon and the theorems from this section for each exercise.**

33. Find $m\angle BPX$. 34. Find $m\angle 1$.
35. Find $m\angle 2$. 36. Find $m\angle 3$.
37. Find $m\angle 4$. 38. Find $m\angle 5$.

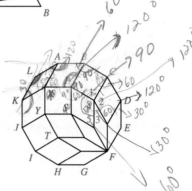

C

39. Given: ▱ABCD, $\overline{DE} \cong \overline{FB}$
Prove: X bisects $\overline{EF}$.

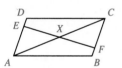

40. Given: EFGD is a ▱. $\overline{ED} \perp \overline{BE}$, $\overline{BF} \cong \overline{CD}$
Prove: △ABC is isosceles.

41. **Prove:** If from any point on the base of an isosceles triangle lines are drawn parallel to the congruent sides of the triangle, a parallelogram is formed whose perimeter is equal to the sum of the lengths of the congruent sides.

Critical Thinking

42. Use a ruler to draw several parallelograms. Use a protractor to bisect a pair of consecutive angles in each parallelogram. What generalization can you make about the angle bisectors? Write a paragraph proof to justify your generalization.

43. Write a statement similar to Corollary 5.1a but involving three dimensions. Give a convincing argument that your statement is true.

30. 1. ABCD is a ▱. (Given)
2. $\overline{CD} \| \overline{BA}$ (Def. of ▱)
3. ∠CDB ≅ ∠ABD (If two ∥ lines are cut by a transversal, alt. int. ∠s are ≅.) 4. $\overline{FG}$ bisects $\overline{DB}$. (Given) 5. $\overline{BE} \cong \overline{DE}$ (Def. of segment bisector) 6. ∠FED ≅ ∠GEB (Vertical ∠ Theorem)
7. △BEG ≅ △DEF (ASA)
8. $\overline{FE} \cong \overline{GE}$ (Corr. parts of ≅ △s are ≅.) 9. $\overline{DB}$ bisects $\overline{FG}$. (Def. of segment bisector)
32. 1. ABCD is a ▱. (Given)
2. ∠D ≅ ∠B (Opposite ∠s of a ▱ are ≅.) 3. $\overline{DC} \cong \overline{BA}$, $\overline{AD} \cong \overline{CB}$ (Opposite sides of a ▱ are ≅.) 4. AE = CF (Given)
5. AD = CB (Def. of ≅ segments) 6. AD = AE + ED, CB = CF + FB (Segment Add. Post.)
7. AE + ED = CF + FB (Subst.)
8. ED = FB (Add. Prop. of =)
9. $\overline{ED} \cong \overline{FB}$ (Def. of ≅ segments) 10. △DEC ≅ △BFA (SAS) 11. $\overline{CE} \cong \overline{AF}$ (Corr. parts of ≅ △s are ≅.) 12. CE = AF (Def of ≅ segments)
34. 90   **36.** 30   **38.** 60
40. 1. EFGD is a ▱. (Given)
2. $\overline{FG} \cong \overline{ED}$ (Opposite sides of a ▱ are ≅.) 3. $\overline{FG} \| \overline{ED}$ (Def. of a ▱) 4. ∠FGE ≅ ∠DEC (If two ∥ lines are cut by a transversal, alt. int. ∠s are ≅.) 5. $\overline{ED} \perp \overline{BE}$ (Given) 6. ∠DEC is a rt. ∠ (Def. of ⊥ lines) 7. ∠FGE is a rt. ∠ (Def. of ≅ ∠s) 8. ∠FGB is a rt. ∠. (If one ∠ of a linear pair is a rt. ∠, the other is also a rt. ∠.)
9. $\overline{BF} \cong \overline{CD}$ (Given)
10. △FBG ≅ △CDE (HL)
11. ∠ABC ≅ ∠ECD (Corr. parts of ≅ △s are ≅.) 12. ∠ECD ≅ ∠ACB (Vertical ∠ Theorem)
13. ∠ABC ≅ ∠ACB (Transitive Prop.) 14. $\overline{AC} \cong \overline{AB}$ (If two ∠s of a △ are ≅, the sides opposite them are ≅.) 15. △ABC is isosceles. (Def. of isosceles △)

42. The angle of bisectors of a
▱ are ⊥. Since *ABCD* is a ▱,
consecutive ∠s *DAB* and *ABC*
are supplementary, and so have
a sum of 180. $\overline{AE}$ bisects ∠*DAB*,
so $m\angle BAE = \frac{1}{2}m\angle DAB$ and $\overline{BE}$
bisects ∠*ABC*, so $m\angle ABE = \frac{1}{2}m\angle ABC$, by def. of ∠ bisector.
Since $m\angle DAB + m\angle ABC = 180$,
$\frac{1}{2}m\angle DAB + \frac{1}{2}m\angle ABC = \frac{1}{2}(180)$
or 90. By substitution,
$m\angle BAE + m\angle ABE = 90$. Therefore, $m\angle AEB$ must be 90, since
the sum of the measures of the
∠s of a △ = 180, and it follows
that ∠*AEB* is a rt. ∠ by def. of
rt. ∠.

Mixed Review Answers

1. △*BDA* ≅ △*BDC* (SAS)
2. △*BDA* ≅ △*BDC* (SSS)
3. △*BDA* ≅ △*BDC* (HL)
4. △*BDA* ≅ △*BDC* (AAS)
5. *p* ∥ *q* (If alt. int. ∠s are ≅,
the lines are ∥.)   **6.** *l* ∥ *m*
(If alt. ext. ∠s are ≅, the lines
are ∥.)   **7.** *p* ∥ *q* (If corr.
∠s are ≅, the lines are ∥.)
8. *l* ∥ *m* (If corr. ∠s are ≅, the
lines are ∥.)   **9.** *p* ∥ *q* (If alt.
ext. ∠s are ≅, the lines are ∥.)
10. *p* ∥ *q* (If corr. ∠s are ≅, the
lines are ∥.)   **11.** *p* ∥ *q* (If
same-side int. ∠s are supp., the
lines are ∥.)   **12.** *l* ∥ *m* (If
same-side int. ∠s are supp., the
lines are ∥.)

Mixed Review

**Use the given information to state which triangles are congruent. Give
the postulate or theorem that justifies your answer.**

1. $\overline{BD} \perp \overline{AC}$, $\overline{AD} \cong \overline{DC}$
2. $\overline{AB} \cong \overline{BC}$, $\overline{BD}$ bisects $\overline{AC}$.
3. $\overline{AB} \cong \overline{BC}$, $\overline{BD} \perp \overline{AC}$
4. ∠*A* ≅ ∠*C*, ∠*ABD* ≅ ∠*CBD*

**Use the given information to state which lines are parallel. Give the
postulate or theorem that justifies your answer.**

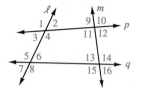

5. ∠4 ≅ ∠5   **6.** ∠3 ≅ ∠10
7. ∠2 ≅ ∠6   **8.** ∠7 ≅ ∠15
9. ∠1 ≅ ∠8   **10.** ∠10 ≅ ∠14
11. $m\angle 4 + m\angle 6 = 180$ **12.** $m\angle 8 + m\angle 15 = 180$

Study Skills

Working Backward to Check a Proof

While checking a proof you have just completed, it is helpful to start at the
conclusion and work backward, as demonstrated with Questions 1–4 with the
proof below.

Given: ∠1 ≅ ∠2
Prove: *a* ∥ *b*

	Proof Statements	Reasons
Question 4	**1.** ∠1 ≅ ∠2	1. Given
Question 3	**2.** ∠2 ≅ ∠3	2. Vertical ∠s are ≅.
Question 2	**3.** ∠1 ≅ ∠3	3. Congruence of ∠s is transitive.
Question 1	**4.** *a* ∥ *b*	4. If two lines are cut by a transversal and corr. ∠s are ≅, the lines are ∥.

Question 1: How can I prove the lines parallel? (Postulate 14, Theorem 3.5,
Theorem 3.6, or Theorem 3.7)
Question 2: Which method did I use? (Postulate 14)
Question 3: How do I know that ∠1 ≅ ∠3? (Statements 1–2 and
Theorem 1.1)
Question 4: Why is each of those statements true? (Statement 1 is given;
statement 2 is justified by the Vertical Angle Theorem.)

In addition to being a good method for checking a proof, working backward
is also a helpful problem-solving strategy if you are having difficulty
completing a proof.

OBJECTIVE: *Prove some quadrilaterals are parallelograms.*

5-2 Proving Quadrilaterals Are Parallelograms

The theorems in the last section can be given in conditional form as in the following general statement.
If ABCD is a parallelogram, then ABCD has . . . (a given property).
This lesson deals with the converses of those theorems, stating ways of proving that some quadrilaterals are parallelograms, as in the following conditional form.
If . . . (a given property) is true, then ABCD is a parallelogram.

One way to prove that a quadrilateral is a parallelogram is to show that both pairs of opposite sides are parallel and then use the definition of a parallelogram. The following theorems state other ways.

Why will the car of this amusement park ride always be parallel to the top frame?

◆ **THEOREM 5.4**

If both pairs of opposite sides of a quadrilateral are congruent, then the quadrilateral is a parallelogram.

Given: $\overline{AB} \cong \overline{CD}$, $\overline{AD} \cong \overline{BC}$
Prove: ABCD is a parallelogram.

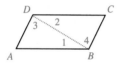

Proof Draw $\overline{BD}$ so △ABD ≅ △CDB by the SSS Postulate. ∠1 ≅ ∠2 and ∠3 ≅ ∠4 by corresponding parts of congruent triangles are congruent. Then $\overline{AB} \| \overline{CD}$ and $\overline{AD} \| \overline{BC}$ since the alternate interior angles are congruent. Hence, ABCD is a parallelogram by definition.

◆ **THEOREM 5.5**

If one pair of opposite sides of a quadrilateral are both parallel and congruent, then it is a parallelogram.

Given: $EF = GH$, $\overline{EF} \| \overline{GH}$
Prove: EFGH is a parallelogram.

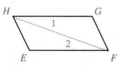

Proof Draw $\overline{HF}$. Since $\overline{EF} \| \overline{GH}$, ∠1 ≅ ∠2. Since $\overline{HF} \cong \overline{HF}$, △HGF ≅ △FEH by the SAS Postulate. $\overline{HE} \cong \overline{FG}$ by corresponding parts of congruent triangles are congruent. Therefore, EFGH is a parallelogram since both pairs of opposite sides are congruent.

First Five Minutes

(Quiz on previous lesson)

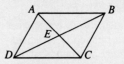

ABCD is a parallelogram.

1. If $AB = 12$, $DC = \underline{?}$. 12
2. If $m \angle D = 120$, $\underline{?} = 120$.
m ∠ B
3. If $AE = 7$ and $DE = 3.5$, $AC = \underline{?}$. 14
4. If $AB = 5x$ and $DC = 3x + 12$, find the value of x. 6
5. If $AE = x + 3$ and $AC = 22$, find the value of x. 8
6. If $m \angle C = 6x - 20$ and $m \angle A = 2x + 80$, find the value of x. 25
7. If $AB = 2x$, $CD = 3y + 4$, $BC = x + 7$, and $AD = 2y$, find the lengths of the sides of $\square ABCD$. $AB = CD = 58$, $BC = AD = 36$

Lesson Opener

This lesson presents ways to prove certain quadrilaterals are parallelograms. Point out that this is the opposite of Lesson 5-1, in which certain properties were derived on the basis of the definition of a parallelogram.

The following two theorems give methods of proving that a quadrilateral is a parallelogram by using the angles of the quadrilateral.

◆ **THEOREM 5.6**

If both pairs of opposite angles of a quadrilateral are congruent, then the quadrilateral is a parallelogram.

◆ **THEOREM 5.7**

If the consecutive angles of a quadrilateral are supplementary, then the quadrilateral is a parallelogram.

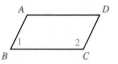

You will be asked to prove Theorems 5.6 and 5.7 in Exercises 33–34.

Example

For what values of x and y will $ABCD$ be a parallelogram?

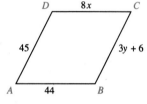

Solution

$$8x = 44$$
$$x = 5\tfrac{1}{2}$$
If opposite sides of a quadrilateral are congruent,
then the quadrilateral is a parallelogram.
$$3y + 6 = 45$$
$$3y = 39$$
$$y = 13$$

Try This

If $m\angle A = 80$, $m\angle B = 6y + 4$, $m\angle C = 5x$, and $m\angle D = 100$, for what values of x and y will $ABCD$ be a parallelogram?

The following method of proving that a quadrilateral is a parallelogram involves the diagonals of a quadrilateral.

◆ **THEOREM 5.8**

If the diagonals of a quadrilateral bisect each other, then the quadrilateral is a parallelogram.

Given: $\overline{VS}$ and $\overline{RT}$ bisect each other.
Prove: $RSTV$ is a parallelogram.

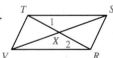

Plan Prove $\triangle TXS = \triangle RXV$ by the SAS postulate. Conclude $\overline{TS} \cong \overline{RV}$ and $\angle 1 \cong \angle 2$ since they are corresponding parts of congruent triangles. Since $\angle 1 \cong \angle 2$, prove $\overline{TS} \parallel \overline{VR}$. Use Theorem 5.5 to conclude $TSRV$ is a parallelogram.

208 *Chapter 5   Using Congruent Triangles and Parallel Lines*

The methods of proving that a quadrilateral is a parallelogram are summarized below.

Methods of Proving a Quadrilateral a Parallelogram

1. Prove that both pairs of opposite sides are parallel.
2. Prove that both pairs of opposite sides are congruent.
3. Prove that one pair of opposite sides is both congruent and parallel.
4. Prove that both pairs of opposite angles are congruent.
5. Prove that the consecutive angles are supplementary.
6. Prove that the diagonals bisect each other.

Class Exercises

Short Answer

State whether or not the figure is a parallelogram. If it is, state a theorem or definition that justifies your conclusion.

1.

2.

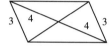

3.

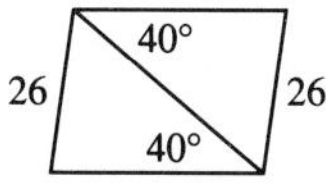

4. Of the six ways to prove that a quadrilateral is a parallelogram summarized in the lesson, which one is not a theorem? What is it?

Sample Exercises

Find the value of x for which each quadrilateral is a parallelogram.

5.

6.

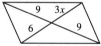

7.

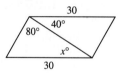

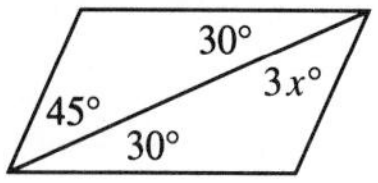

Draw a rectangular coordinate system, plot each point, and find the lengths of AB, BC, CD, and AD. Use Theorem 5.4 to decide whether $ABCD$ is a parallelogram.

8. $A(0, 0)$, $B(0, 3)$, $C(5, 3)$, $D(5, 0)$
9. $A(0, 0)$, $B(3, 4)$, $C(9, 4)$, $D(6, 0)$
10. $A(0, 0)$, $B(-4, 0)$, $C(-7, 4)$, $D(-3, 4)$
11. $A(3, -2)$, $B(8, -2)$, $C(8, -4)$, $D(3, -4)$

Discussion

Draw a figure, if needed, to support your argument.

12. Is it possible for a quadrilateral to have two congruent opposite sides and two parallel sides but not be a parallelogram? Explain.
13. Is it possible for a polygon to have two sides that are both congruent and parallel but not be a parallelogram? Explain.

Class Exercise Answers

1. Yes; if opposite ∠s of a quadrilateral are ≅, it is a ▱.
2. not enough information
3. not enough information
4. Prove that both pairs of opposite sides are ∥. (Definition)
5. 15 6. 2 7. 40
8. yes 9. yes 10. yes
11. yes 12. yes; consider an isos. trapezoid 13. yes; consider a reg. hexagon

Assignment Guide

Minimum: 1–34 e/o, 39, AR
Regular: 1–38 e/o, 39–40, AR
Advanced: 2, 5, 10, 15, 21, 22–40, AR

Applications
Exercises 22–25

Coordinate Geometry
Class Exercises 8–11
Exercises 15–20, 29, 30

Algebra
Class Exercises 5, 6
Exercises 9, 12–14, 26–28, AR

Lesson Closure

Ask students to state the six ways of proving a quadrilateral is a parallelogram and identify each as a definition, a theorem, or a corollary.

Teacher's Resource Materials

Enrichment Using Manipulatives 28
Practice Master 31
Technology: BASIC 8
Transparency 16

Computer Software

See Computer Exploration 5, page 638.

Exercises

A

State whether or not you can conclude that the figure is a parallelogram, based on the given information. If it is, state the theorem or definition that justifies your conclusion.

1. $RU = ST$, $RS = TU$
2. $\overline{RS} \parallel \overline{TU}$, $\overline{RU} \parallel \overline{ST}$
3. $\overline{RU} \parallel \overline{ST}$, $\overline{RS} \cong \overline{TU}$
4. $\overline{RS} \parallel \overline{TU}$, $\overline{RS} \cong \overline{TU}$
5. $RX = \frac{1}{2}RT$, $XU = \frac{1}{2}SU$
6. $RX = XU$, $SX = XT$
7. $RU = UT = TS = SR$
8. $m\angle SRU = m\angle UTS$, $m\angle RST = m\angle RUT$

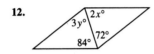

Determine the values of x and y so that the figure is a parallelogram.

9.

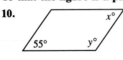

10.

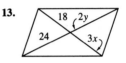

11.

12.

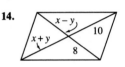

13.

14.

Draw a rectangular coordinate system, plot each point, and find the lengths of $\overline{AB}$, $\overline{BC}$, $\overline{CD}$, and $\overline{DA}$. Use Theorem 5.4 to decide whether $ABCD$ is a parallelogram.

15. $A(0, 0)$, $B(5, 0)$, $C(5, 4)$, $D(0, 4)$
16. $A(0, 0)$, $B(5, 0)$, $C(7, 2)$, $D(2, -2)$
17. $A(0, 0)$, $B(-4, 0)$, $C(-6, 3)$, $D(-1, 3)$
18. $A(0, 7)$, $B(3, 7)$, $C(5, 1)$, $D(2, 1)$
19. $A(1, 0)$, $B(0, 1)$, $C(-2, 0)$, $D(0, 2)$
20. $A(0, 1)$, $B(1, 0)$, $C(4, 3)$, $D(3, 4)$

21. **Given:** $\triangle ABC \cong \triangle CDA$
    Prove: $ABCD$ is a ▱.

B

22. The ironing board shown on the right is supported by legs that are equal in length. The legs also bisect each other at the point where they cross. Explain why the ironing board will always be parallel to the floor, regardless of the height to which it happens to be adjusted.

23. Consider the children's swing set shown to to right. The hangers $\overline{AD}$ and $\overline{BC}$ are the same length and the distances between the hangers, $\overline{AB}$ and $\overline{DC}$, are equal. Explain why the seat $\overline{DC}$ will always be parallel to the bar $\overline{AB}$ at the top of the swing.

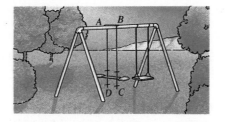

24. A carpenter wants to construct parallel lines on a board. This can be done by using a carpenter square twice. Each time the tool is placed at the same angles with the board and equal units are marked off. Explain why this method assures that $\overline{AB}$ will be parallel to $\overline{CD}$.

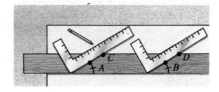

25. A parking lot is to be marked for slant parking. A string is stretched from A to B with marks made every 9 ft at $X_1, X_2, \ldots, X_6$. A second string is stretched parallel to $\overline{AB}$ from C to D, with marks located every 9 ft at $Y_1, Y_2, \ldots, Y_6$. Explain why all the painted lines will be parallel.

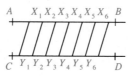

Draw a quadrilateral $ABCD$ and determine the values of x and y for which $ABCD$ is a parallelogram.

26. $AB = 2x + 4$, $CD = 4x - 20$, $AD = 2y$, $BC = y + 5$
27. $m\angle A = 2x - 60$, $m\angle D = x - 5$, $AB = 4y + 6$, $CD = 6y - 10$
28. $AB = 6x + 30$, $BC = 2x - 5$, $CD = 2y - 10$, $AD = y - 35$

Determine the coordinates of D for which $ABCD$ is a parallelogram.

29. $A(0, 0)$, $B(1, 4)$, $C(6, 5)$, $D(x, y)$
30. $A(0, 2)$, $B(2, 0)$, $C(-2, -4)$, $D(x, y)$

31. **Given:** $ABCD$ is a $\square$.
    $BCEF$ is a $\square$.
    Prove: $ADEF$ is a $\square$.

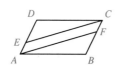

32. **Given:** $ABCD$ is a $\square$.
    E is the midpoint of $\overline{AD}$.
    F is the midpoint of $\overline{BC}$.
    Prove: AFCE is a $\square$.

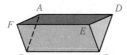

33. Prove Theorem 5.6.
    Given: $\angle A \cong \angle C$
    $\angle B \cong \angle D$
    Prove: $ABCD$ is a $\square$.

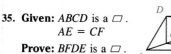

34. Prove Theorem 5.7.
    Given: $\angle 1$ and $\angle 2$ are supplementary.
    $\angle 2$ and $\angle 3$ are supplementary.
    Prove: $ABCD$ is a $\square$.

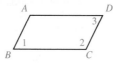

35. **Given:** $ABCD$ is a $\square$.
    $AE = CF$
    Prove: $BFDE$ is a $\square$.

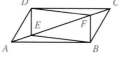

32. 1. $ABCD$ is a $\square$, E is the midpoint of $\overline{AD}$, F is the midpoint of $\overline{BC}$. (Given) 2. $\overline{AD} \parallel \overline{BC}$ (Def. of $\square$) 3. $\overline{AD} \cong \overline{BC}$ (Opp. sides of a $\square$ are $\cong$.) 4. $AD = BC$ (Def. $\cong$ segments) 5. $AE = \frac{1}{2}AD$, $FC = \frac{1}{2}BC$ (Midpoint Theorem) 6. $2AE = AD$, $2FC = BC$ (Mult.) 7. $2AE = 2FC$ (Subst.) 8. $AE = FC$ (Division) 9. $\overline{AE} \cong \overline{FC}$ (Def. $\cong$ segments) 10. $AFCE$ is a $\square$. (If one pair of opp. sides of a quadrilateral are both $\parallel$ and $\cong$, it is a $\square$.)

34. 1. $ABCD$ is a quadrilateral, $\angle 1$ and $\angle 2$ are supplementary, $\angle 2$ and $\angle 3$ are supplementary. (Given) 2. $\overline{AB} \parallel \overline{CD}$, $\overline{AD} \parallel \overline{BC}$ (If two lines are cut by a transversal and same-side int. $\angle$s are supplementary, the lines are $\parallel$.) 3. $ABCD$ is a $\square$. (Def. of $\square$)

36. 16

38.

1. $\overline{AM}$ is a median of $\triangle ABC$. (Given) 2. M is a midpoint of $\overline{CB}$. (Def. of median) 3. $\overline{CM} \cong \overline{MB}$ (Def. of midpoint of a segment) 4. $\overline{AM} \cong \overline{MD}$ (Given) 5. $ABCD$ is a ▱. (If diagonals of a quadrilateral bisect each other, it is a ▱.)

40. theorem

Algebra Review Answers

1. $(x - 9)(x + 5)$
2. $(y + 7)(y - 6)$
3. $(a + 5)(a - 3)$
4. $(a - 5b)(a - 2b)$
5. $(x + 8y)(x - 3y)$
6. $(b + 15)(b - 6)$
7. $|x|$ **8.** $2|y|$ **9.** 5
10. $3|a|$

Computer Activity Answers

1. a. If a ▱ has 4 rt. ∠s, its diagonals are ≅. **b.** no generalization **c.** If a ▱ has 4 rt. ∠s, its diagonals are ≅ and bisect each other. **2. a.** no generalization **b.** If a ▱ has 4 ≅ sides, its diagonals are ⊥. **c.** If a ▱ has 4 ≅ sides, its diagonals are ⊥. **3. a.** If a ▱ has 4 rt. ∠s, the 4 seg. formed by the diag. are ≅. **b.** If a ▱ has 4 ≅ sides, its diag. bis. each other. **c.** If a ▱ has 4 rt. ∠s, the 4 seg. formed by the diag. are ≅.

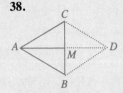

36. Polygon $ABCDE$ shown to the right is an equilateral pentagon. The perimeter of $ABCDE$ is 20. If $\overline{BD} \parallel \overline{AE}$ and $\overline{CE} \parallel \overline{BA}$, find the perimeter of $ABFE$.

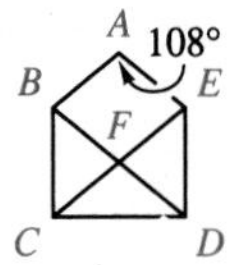

37. If $ABCDEF$ is a regular hexagon, prove that $BCEF$ is parallelogram.

38. Draw $\triangle ABC$ with median $\overline{AM}$. Extend $\overline{AM}$ so that $\overline{AM} \cong \overline{MD}$. Prove that $ABDC$ is a parallelogram.

Critical Thinking

39. Suppose a parallelogram is defined in the following way:
A parallelogram is a quadrilateral with opposite sides congruent.
Use this definition to prove the following statement:
If a quadrilateral has both pairs of opposite sides parallel, then it is a parallelogram.

40. If the definition of a parallelogram that is given in Exercise 39 is accepted, would the statement you proved using that definition in the same exercise be classified as a definition, postulate, or theorem?

Algebra Review

Factor.

1. $x^2 - 4x - 45$ 2. $y^2 + y - 42$ 3. $a^2 + 2a - 15$
4. $a^2 - 7ab + 10b^2$ 5. $x^2 + 5xy - 24y^2$ 6. $b^2 + 9b - 90$

Simplify.

7. $\sqrt{x^2}$ 8. $\sqrt{4y^2}$ 9. $\sqrt{(-5)^2}$ 10. $\sqrt{(-3a)^2}$

Computer Activity

Properties of Special Parallelograms

Use computer software to construct special parallelograms like the ones shown below.

a.

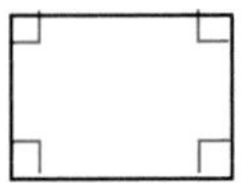

All right angles

b.

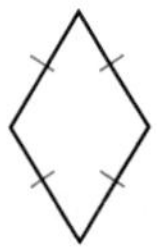

All sides congruent

c.

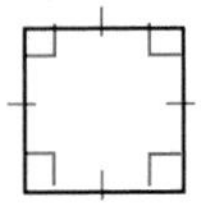

All right angles
All sides congruent

1. Measure the diagonals in each figure. What do you notice? State a generalization about your observation in each figure.
2. Measure the angles formed by the diagonals in each figure. What do you notice? State a generalization about your observation in each figure.
3. Measure the four segments formed by the diagonals in each figure. What do you notice? State a generalization about your observations.

212 *Chapter 5 Using Congruent Triangles and Parallel Lines*

OBJECTIVE: *Apply definitions and theorems about rectangles, rhombuses, and squares.*

5-3 Rectangles, Rhombuses, and Squares

 **EXPLORE** Take the linkage that forms a parallelogram (Position 1) and place it in the position of a rectangle (Position 2). What additional properties seem to be true about the rectangle?

Position 1   Position 2

In the last two lessons, you learned about the quadrilateral called a parallelogram. Three special parallelograms, *rectangles*, *rhombuses*, and *squares*, are defined below. They are classified by the special relationships of their angles and sides.

◼ **DEFINITION**

A **rectangle** is a quadrilateral with four right angles.

◼ **DEFINITION**

A **rhombus** is a quadrilateral with four congruent sides.

◼ **DEFINITION**

A **square** is a quadrilateral with four right angles and four congruent sides.

Based on the definitions of rectangle, rhombus, and square, the following statements are true.

    Every rectangle is a parallelogram.
    Every rhombus is a parallelogram.
    Every square is a parallelogram, a rectangle, and a rhombus.

This means that all of the properties of parallelograms—such as opposite sides that are congruent, opposite angles that are congruent, consecutive angles that are supplementary, and diagonals that bisect each other—are also properties of rectangles, rhombuses, and squares.

5-3 Rectangles, Rhombuses, and Squares   **213**

Teaching Notes

Emphasize that since a rectangle is a parallelogram, it has all the properties of a parallelogram. In addition, the diagonals of a rectangle are congruent and all angles are right angles.

Emphasize that since a rhombus (plural, rhombuses or rhombi) is a parallelogram, it has all the properties of a parallelogram, as well as all sides congruent. In addition, the diagonals of a rhombus not only bisect each other, they also bisect opposite angles of the rhombus and intersect to form four right angles.

The following diagram, called "the quadrilateral tree," shows the relationships among special types of quadrilaterals. This tree can help illustrate how each figure has the properties of quadrilaterals above it—along with properties of its own.

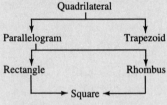

NOTE: The trapezoid will be discussed in Lesson 5-4.

Restated Definitions of Rectangle, Rhombus, and Square

A *rectangle* is an equiangular parallelogram. A *rhombus* is an equilateral parallelogram. A *square* is a regular parallelogram.

◆ **THEOREM 5.9**

The diagonals of a rectangle are congruent.

Given: *ABCD* is a rectangle.
Prove: $\overline{AC} \cong \overline{BD}$

Proof

Statements	Reasons
1. *ABCD* is a rectangle.	1. Given
2. $\overline{AD} \cong \overline{BC}$	2. Opposite sides of a ▱ are ≅.
3. $\overline{AB} \cong \overline{AB}$	3. Congruence of segments is reflexive.
4. ∠*DAB* and ∠*CBA* are rt. ∠s.	4. Definition of a rectangle
5. ∠*DAB* ≅ ∠*CBA*	5. All right angles are congruent.
6. △*DAB* ≅ △*CBA*	6. SAS Congruence Postulate
7. $\overline{AC} \cong \overline{BD}$	7. Corres. parts of ≅ △s are ≅.

◆ **THEOREM 5.10**

The diagonals of a rhombus are perpendicular.

Given: *ABCD* is a rhombus.
Prove: $\overline{AC} \perp \overline{BD}$

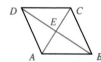

Plan Use the definition of a rhombus and the fact that the diagonals of a parallelogram bisect each other to show that △*AED* ≅ △*CED*. Conclude that $\overline{AC} \perp \overline{BD}$ since ∠*AED* and ∠*CED* are supplementary and congruent.

◆ **THEOREM 5.11**

Each diagonal of a rhombus bisects a pair of opposite angles.

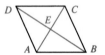

You will be asked to prove Theorem 5.11 in Exercise 43.

Example 1

If *ABCD* is a rhombus and *m*∠*BDC* = 35, find *m*∠*ACD*.

Solution

m∠*ACD* = 90 − 35 = 55   *The acute angles of a right triangle are complementary.*

Try This

If *ABCD* is a rhombus and *m*∠*CAD* = 68, find *m*∠*CBD*.

214   *Chapter 5   Using Congruent Triangles and Parallel Lines*

A summary of the properties of rectangles, rhombuses, and squares is given below.

Properties of Rectangles

A rectangle has all properties of a parallelogram as well as having all angles, right angles and congruent diagonals.

Properties of Rhombuses

A rhombus has all properties of a parallelogram as well as having all sides congruent, perpendicular diagonals, and diagonals that bisect opposite angles.

Properties of Squares

A square has all properties of a parallelogram, a rectangle, and a rhombus.

While it is the case that every rectangle, rhombus, and square is a parallelogram, it is not the case that every parallelogram is a rectangle, rhombus, or square. The following two theorems state conditions for which a parallelogram is either a rectangle or a rhombus.

 THEOREM 5.12

If a parallelogram has a right angle, then it is a rectangle.

 THEOREM 5.13

If a parallelogram has two adjacent sides congruent, then it is a rhombus.

You will be asked to prove Theorems 5.12 and 5.13 in Exercises 44–45. From Theorems 5.12 and 5.13, it follows that a parallelogram with a right angle and two adjacent sides congruent is a square.

Example 2

$ABCD$ is a parallelogram. If $AD = 2x + 10$ and $CD = 4x - 20$, for what value of x will $ABCD$ be a rhombus?

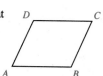

Solution

$4x - 20 = 2x + 10$ *If a parallelogram has two adjacent sides*
$2x = 30$ *congruent, then it is a rhombus.*
$x = 15$

Try This

 If $AB = 5 - 2x$ and $BC = 3x + 80$, for what value of x will $ABCD$ be a rhombus?

Guided Practice

Chalkboard Examples

1. If $ABCD$ is a rhombus and $m\angle BAD = 120$, find $m\angle CDB$. 30
Answer to **Try This** 22
2. If the perimeter of rhombus $ABCD$ is 72, find AD and CD.
$AD = CD = 18$

Answer to **Try This** −15

Class Exercise Answers

1. false   **2.** false
3. true   **4.** false   **5.** false
6. $\overline{AB} \cong \overline{CD}, \overline{AD} \cong \overline{BC}, \overline{AC} \cong \overline{BD}$,
$\overline{BE} \cong \overline{ED}, \overline{AE} \cong \overline{EC}$
7. $\overline{AB} \cong \overline{BC} \cong \overline{CD} \cong \overline{DA}$,
$\overline{BE} \cong \overline{ED}, \overline{AE} \cong \overline{EC}$ **8.** $\angle AEB$,
$\angle AED, \angle DEC, \angle CEB$
9. $\angle CAD, \angle ADB, \angle BDC, \angle ACD$,
$\angle ACB, \angle CBD, \angle ABD$
10. 90   **11.** 12   **12.** 70
13. All sides $\cong$, diagonals $\perp$ and
bisect opp. $\angle$s.   **14.** All
sides $\cong$, diagonals $\perp$ and bisect
op. $\angle$s. **15.** All angles right angles, $\cong$ diagonals.

Assignment Guide

Minimum: 1–38 e/o, 46–50, AR
Regular: 1–45 e/o, 46–50, AR
Advanced: 1, 5, 10, 19, 21, 22–50, AR

Applications
Exercises 35, 36

Coordinate Geometry
Exercises 29–34

Algebra
Exercises 12, 27, 28, AR

Class Exercises

Short Answer

Determine whether each statement is true or false.

1. The diagonals of a rectangle are perpendicular.
2. The diagonals of a rectangle bisect the opposite angles.
3. If $ABCD$ is a square, then $ABCD$ is a rhombus.
4. If $ABCD$ is a parallelogram, then $ABCD$ is a rhombus.
5. If $ABCD$ is a rectangle, then $ABCD$ is a rhombus.

Sample Exercises

6. If $ABCD$ is a rectangle, name all pairs of congruent segments.
7. If $ABCD$ is a rhombus, name all pairs of congruent segments.
8. If $ABCD$ is a rhombus, name all the angles that are right angles.
9. If $ABCD$ is a square, name all the angles that are congruent to $\angle CAB$.
10. If $ABCD$ is a square, what is $m\angle AED$?
11. If $ABCD$ is a rectangle and $BE = 6$, what is length AC?
12. If $ABCD$ is a rhombus and $m\angle BAC = 35$, what is $m\angle BCD$?

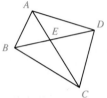

Discussion

Name two properties that are true for each of the following.

13. all squares but not all rectangles
14. all rhombuses but not all parallelograms
15. all rectangles but not all parallelograms

Exercises

A

1. State three properties that are true about the diagonals of a square.
2. $ABCD$ is a parallelogram. If $m\angle A = 90$, must $ABCD$ be a rectangle, a rhombus, or a square?
3. $ABCD$ is a parallelogram. If $\overline{AB} \cong \overline{BC}$, must $ABCD$ be a rectangle, a rhombus, or a square?
4. $ABCD$ is a parallelogram. If $m\angle A = 90$ and $\overline{AB} \cong \overline{BC}$, must $ABCD$ be a rectangle, a rhombus, or a square?

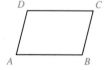

Assume that $GWAD$ is a rectangle. Find the indicated measure.

5. $GX = 6$ Find XW.
6. $XA = 9$ Find DW.
7. $m\angle GXD = 40$ Find $m\angle GDX$.
8. $m\angle WAG = 65$ Find $m\angle GXW$.

Assume that $GWAD$ is a rhombus. Find the indicated measure.

9. $m\angle GDX = 47$ Find $m\angle XGD$.
10. $m\angle GWA = 86$ Find $m\angle GWD$.

Assume that $GWAD$ is a square. Find the indicated measure.

11. Find $m\angle XDA$.
12. $GX = 3x + 6$, $XW = 4x - 10$ Find GA.

Determine whether each statement is true or false.

13. Every rectangle is a parallelogram.
14. Every rhombus is a rectangle.
15. Every parallelogram is a rectangle.
16. Every property of a parallelogram is also a property of a square.
17. Every property of a square is also a property of a rectangle.
18. The diagonals of a square bisect each other.

19. A picture frame is constructed of four pieces of wood that are glued together so that $AB = BC = CD = DA$. The ends of each piece of wood are cut at a 45° angle. Explain why the completed frame will form a square.

20. **Given:** $ABCD$ is a $\square$. $m\angle 3 = m\angle 4$
    Prove: $ABCD$ is a rhombus.
21. **Given:** $ABCD$ is a $\square$. $m\angle 3 + m\angle 4 = 90$
    Prove: $ABCD$ is a rectangle.

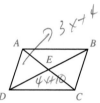

B

Draw a parallelogram for the given conditions or write *not possible*.

22. all angles congruent
23. diagonals that bisect each other
24. no right angles, diagonals congruent
25. congruent and perpendicular diagonals
26. all sides congruent with diagonals that are not perpendicular

27. $ABCD$ is a parallelogram. $AB = 2x + 4$, $DC = 3x - 11$, $AD = x + 19$ Show that $ABCD$ is a rhombus.
28. $ABCD$ is a rhombus. $m\angle DEC = 4x + 10$, $m\angle DAB = 3x + 4$ Find $m\angle ABC$.

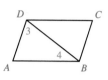

ABCD is a rectangle with the given coordinates. Find the lengths of the diagonals and verify that they are congruent.

29. $A(2, 5)$, $B(2, 1)$, $C(7, 1)$, $D(7, 5)$ 30. $A(-2, 3)$, $B(-4, 3)$, $C(-4, -2)$, $D(-2, -2)$

Determine the coordinates of D for which ABCD is a rectangle.

31. $A(-2, 5)$, $B(1, 5)$, $C(1, -2)$, $D(x, y)$ 32. $A(-3, -2)$, $B(4, -2)$, $C(4, -3)$, $D(x, y)$

Determine the coordinates of D for which ABCD is a square.

33. $A(3, -1)$, $B(-1, 3)$, $C(-5, -1)$, $D(x, y)$ 34. $A(3, 0)$, $B(1, 2)$, $C(3, 4)$, $D(x, y)$

35. A contractor is measuring for the foundation of a building that is to be 85 ft by 40 ft. Stakes and string are placed as shown. The outside corners of the building will be at the points where the strings cross. To make sure that $WXYZ$ is a rectangle, the contractor constructs $WX = ZY$ and $WZ = XY$. Prove that if $WY = ZX$, $WXYZ$ will be a rectangle.
36. If $WY = 93$ ft and $XZ = 94$ ft, is $WXYZ$ a rectangle? If not, which way should stakes E and F be moved to make $WXYZ$ a rectangle?

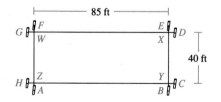

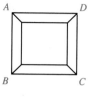

37. Given: $WXYZ$ is a rhombus.
R is the midpoint of $\overline{WV}$.
T is the midpoint of $\overline{VY}$.
S is any point on $\overline{ZV}$.
Prove: $\triangle SRT$ is isosceles.

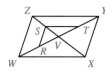

38. Given: $ABCD$ is a rectangle.
$ACBE$ is a parallelogram.
Prove: $\triangle DBE$ is isosceles.

C

39. Given: $ABCD$ is a square.
$FB = CB$
$\overline{EF} \perp \overline{BD}$
Prove: $DF = FE = EC$

What quadrilateral is determined by a cross section of the cube containing the given vertices? Write a paragraph proof to justify your choice.

40. vertices A, B, G, and H **41.** vertices A, C, G, and E

42. Draw and label a rectangle $ABCD$ and equilateral triangles ABX and BCY entirely outside the rectangle. Prove that $\triangle XDY$ is isosceles.

43. Prove Theorem 5.11   **44.** Prove Theorem 5.12   **45.** Prove Theorem 5.13

Critical Thinking

Answer the questions in Exercises 46–50 for each figure (a–f).

46. Must the figure be a quadrilateral?
47. Must the figure be a parallelogram?
48. Must the figure be a rectangle?
49. Must the figure be a rhombus?
50. Must the figure be a square?

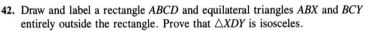

a b c

d e f

Algebra Review

Solve.

1. $x^2 - 9 = 6$ **2.** $25a^2 = 16$ **3.** $y^2 = \frac{4}{9}$

Math Contest Problem

The figure shown is a cube. $\overline{BC}$ and $\overline{BH}$ are diagonals of faces of the cube. Find the measure of $\angle CBH$.

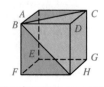

COMPARING APPROACHES IN GEOMETRY

Synthetic and Coordinate Geometry

In the last lesson, we proved that the diagonals of a rectangle are congruent. The approach that was used, a synthetic approach, does not rely on algebra. Recall from its introduction on page 194 that a coordinate approach relies on a coordinate system. Compare the two approaches for a 5 by 7 rectangle.

Synthetic Approach

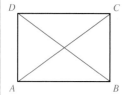

Coordinate Approach

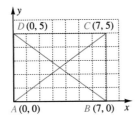

Plan Prove $\triangle ABC \cong \triangle DCB$ and use corresponding parts of congruent triangles are congruent to conclude that $AC = BD$.

Plan Name the coordinates of the vertices and use the distance formula to conclude that $AC = BD$.

In the coordinate approach use the distance formula to find AC and BD. Observe that these lengths are equal.

$$AC = \sqrt{(7 - 0)^2 + (5 - 0)^2} = \sqrt{49 + 25}$$
$$BD = \sqrt{(0 - 7)^2 + (5 - 0)^2} = \sqrt{49 + 25}$$

Exercises

When using a coordinate proof it is important to name the figure correctly after it has been positioned on a coordinate system.

1. Suppose that a coordinate system is selected as shown for a 4 by 9 rectangle. What are the x and y coordinates of vertex C?

2. Suppose that a coordinate system is placed on an 8 by 11 rectangle in the same manner as is shown for the 4 by 9 rectangle in the figure to the right. What are the coordinates of all four vertices A, B, C, and D?

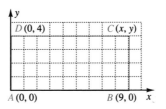

3. A general rectangle is represented by using variable coordinates rather than numerical coordinates. For example, suppose that a coordinate system is placed on a rectangle that is a units long and b units wide as is shown in the figure. What are the coordinates of all four vertices A, B, C, and D in terms of a and b?

4. Use the distance formula to find the distances AC and BD in the figure for Exercise 3. What theorem does your work prove?

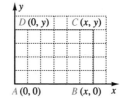

Comparing Approaches in Geometry

Synthetic and Coordinate Geometry
Many topics in geometry may be studied using either a synthetic approach or a coordinate approach. In some instances, one of these approaches may be better suited to a problem. Encourage students to consider both approaches before working a problem.

Exercise Answers
1. $(9, 4)$ 2. $A(0, 0)$, $B(11, 0)$, $C(11, 8)$, $D(0, 8)$
3. $A(0, 0)$, $B(b, 0)$, $C(b, a)$, $D(0, a)$ 4. $AC = \sqrt{b^2 + a^2}$, $BD = \sqrt{b^2 + a^2}$ The diagonals of a rectangle are congruent.

First Five Minutes

(Quiz on previous lesson)

Which quadrilateral(s) have the following properties?

1. All ∠s are rt. ∠s. rect.,
square

2. All sides are ≅. rhombus,
square

3. Opp. sides are ∥ and opp. ∠s
are ≅. all ▱s

4. Diagonals bisect each other.
all ▱s

5. Diagonals are ⊥ to each
other. rhombus, square

Lesson Opener

Ask students for examples of
trapezoids in the real world.

Materials

student notebooks
straightedges
protractors
investigative software

Teaching Notes

Show what happens to an
isosceles triangle when you slice
off the top to form an isosceles
trapezoid. Compare the
definition of a median of a triangle to that of a median of a
trapezoid.

Key Terms

trapezoid
isosceles trapezoid
median of a trapezoid

OBJECTIVE: *Apply definitions and theorems about trapezoids.*

5-4 Trapezoids

 **EXPLORE** Take several styrofoam cubes and cut three cross sections.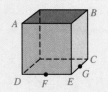
  a. a cross section containing vertices *A*, *B*, *C*, and *D*
  b. a cross section containing vertices *A* and *B* and
       midpoints *F* and *G*
  c. a cross section containing vertices *A*, *B*, and *E*
  Sketch the figure formed by each of the three cross sections.

Another classification of quadrilateral is the trapezoid.

■ DEFINITION

A **trapezoid** is a quadrilateral with exactly one pair of parallel sides.

The parallel sides of a trapezoid are called **bases.** The nonparallel sides are
called **legs.** The pairs of angles formed by a base and the legs are called
base angles. In trapezoid *ABCD*, ∠*ADC* and ∠*BCD* are base angles and
∠*DAB* and ∠*CBA* are base angles. An **isosceles trapezoid** is a trapezoid
with congruent nonparallel sides.

◆ THEOREM 5.14

Each pair of base angles of an isosceles trapezoid are congruent.

Given: Isosceles trapezoid *ABCD*, $\overline{AB} \cong \overline{DC}$
Prove: ∠*B* ≅ ∠*C*, ∠*BAD* ≅ ∠*CDA*

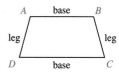

Plan Draw $\overline{AE}$ and $\overline{DF}$ perpendicular to $\overline{BC}$. Prove △*ABE* ≅ △*DCF* by the
Hypotenuse-Leg Theorem. It follows that ∠*B* ≅ ∠*C*. Prove that
∠*BAD* ≅ ∠*CDA* since supplements of congruent angles are congruent.

Example 1

Given isosceles trapezoid *EFGH* with *m*∠*EFG* = 55, find *m*∠*FGH*.

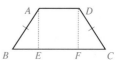

  Solution
    m∠*FGH* = 55   *Base angles of an isosceles trapezoid have the same measure.*

Try This
If *m*∠*E* is twice *m*∠*F*, find the measures of the four angles of trapezoid *EFGH*.

◆ THEOREM 5.15

The diagonals of an isosceles trapezoid are congruent.

The **median of a trapezoid** is the segment joining the midpoints of the legs. $\overline{PQ}$ is the median of trapezoid $WXYZ$. The median and the bases of a trapezoid are related in a special way.

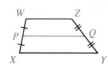

◆ THEOREM 5.16

The median of a trapezoid is parallel to the bases and has a length equal to half the sum of the lengths of the bases. That is, $PQ = \frac{1}{2}(XY + WZ)$.

You will be asked to prove Theorems 5.15 and 5.16 in Exercises 20 and 23.

Example 2

$ABCD$ is a trapezoid. $AB = 13$, $CD = 20$
Find the length EF of the median.

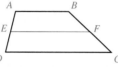

Solution

$EF = \frac{1}{2}(AB + CD)$ *Theorem 5.17*
$EF = \frac{1}{2}(13 + 20)$
$EF = 16.5$

Try This

Find the length of $\overline{CD}$ if $AB = 15$ and $EF = 21$.

Class Exercises

Short Answer

$ABCD$ is an isosceles trapezoid with median $\overline{XY}$.

1. Name the bases of trapezoid $ABCD$.
2. Name the legs of trapezoid $ABCD$.
3. Name two pairs of congruent angles.
4. Name two pairs of congruent segments.

Sample Exercises

Use isosceles trapezoid $ABCD$ with median $\overline{XY}$ to complete each statement.

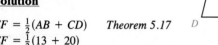

5. $AX = 4$, $CD = $ ___
6. $m\angle ABC = 110$, $m\angle BAD = $ ___
7. $m\angle BAD = 65$, $m\angle CDA = $ ___
8. $AD = 22$, $BC = 10$, $XY = $ ___
9. $BC = 20$, $XY = 32$, $AD = $ ___
10. $m\angle DCB = 105$, $m\angle DAB = $ ___

Discussion

Draw a trapezoid satisfying the following conditions. If not possible, explain.

11. two right angles
12. three right angles
13. three congruent sides
14. four congruent sides
15. congruent legs
16. congruent bases

Guided Practice

Chalkboard Examples

1. Find $m\angle F$, $m\angle G$, and $m\angle H$ in terms of x, if $m\angle E = 4.5x$ in isos. trap. $EFGH$. $m\angle H = 4.5x$, $m\angle F = m\angle G = 180 - 4.5x$

Answer to **Try This**
$m\angle F = m\angle G = 60$,
$m\angle E = m\angle H = 120$

2. Find the length of the median $\overline{EF}$ in terms of x and y, if $AB = 5x + 7y$ and $DC = 9x - 3y$. $7x + 2y$

Answer to **Try This** 27

Class Exercise Answers

1. $\overline{AD}$ and $\overline{BC}$ 2. $\overline{AB}$ and $\overline{DC}$
3. $\angle DAB \cong \angle ADC$, $\angle B \cong \angle C$
4. $\overline{AB} \cong \overline{DC}$, $\overline{AX} \cong \overline{XB}$, $\overline{DY} \cong \overline{YC}$
5. 8   6. 70   7. 65
8. 16   9. 44   10. 75
11.

12. not possible, rectangle
13.   14. not possible, rhombus
15.   16. not possible, parallelogram

Assignment Guide

Minimum: 1–24 e/o, 29, MR
Regular: 1–28 e/o, 29, MR
Advanced: 8–12, 14–29, MR

Applications

Exercise 12

Coordinate Geometry

Exercises 21, 22

Algebra

Exercises 5, 6, 13, 16

Exercises

A

ABCD is a trapezoid with median $\overline{EF}$.

1. $AB = 24$, $CD = 43$ Find EF.
2. $AB = 2\frac{1}{2}$, $CD = 4\frac{1}{2}$ Find EF.
3. $AB = 9.7$, $CD = 24.6$ Find EF.
4. $CD = 32$, $EF = 23$ Find AB.
5. $AB = x + 1$, $EF = 5x$, $CD = 35$ Find AB.
6. $AB = x + 11$, $EF = x - 20$, $CD = 9$ Find EF.

Indicate whether each statement is always, sometimes, or never true.

7. If the diagonals of a trapezoid are congruent, then the trapezoid is isosceles.
8. If a quadrilateral has more than two right angles, then it is not a trapezoid.
9. The opposite angles of an isosceles trapezoid are supplementary.
10. The diagonals of an isosceles trapezoid bisect each other.
11. If the consecutive angles of a quadrilateral are supplementary, it is a trapezoid.
12. A dam is constructed with a trapezoidal cross section that measures 38 ft across the top and 10 ft across the base. What is the average width of the dam?

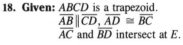

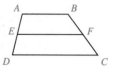

B

13. The length of one base of a trapezoid is four times the length of the other base. If the length of the median is 40, find the length of each base.
14. If the length of the shorter base of a trapezoid is doubled but the length of the median is not changed, how does the length of the longer base change?
15. If one base of a trapezoid is increased 12 cm and the other base remains the same length, by how much is the length of the median increased?
16. Suppose the lengths of the bases of a trapezoid are represented by x and y. If the length of the median is doubled, write an expression that represents the length of the median of the larger trapezoid.

17. Given: $ABCD$ is a trapezoid.
   $\overline{AB} \parallel \overline{CD}$
   $\overline{AP}$ bisects $\angle A$.

   Prove: $\triangle APD$ is isosceles.

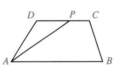

18. Given: $ABCD$ is a trapezoid.
   $\overline{AB} \parallel \overline{CD}$, $\overline{AD} \cong \overline{BC}$
   $\overline{AC}$ and $\overline{BD}$ intersect at E.

   Prove: $\triangle CDE$ is isosceles.

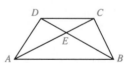

19. Given: $\triangle ABC$ is isosceles with base $\overline{BC}$.
   $\angle AED \cong \angle B$

   Prove: $BEDC$ is an isosceles trapezoid.

20. Prove Theorem 5.15
   Given: $RSTV$ is a trapezoid with $\overline{RV} \cong \overline{ST}$.
   Prove: $\overline{RT} \cong \overline{VS}$

Graph the given coordinates and determine if *ABCD* is an isosceles trapezoid.

21. *A*(3, 3), *B*(5, 3), *C*(8, 1), *D*(1, 1)   **22.** *A*(−4, 1), *B*(−4, 6), *C*(2, 4), *D*(2, 3)

C

23. Prove Theorem 5.16.

> **Given:** In trapezoid *ABCD*, *M* is a midpoint of leg $\overline{AB}$.
>   *N* is a midpoint of leg $\overline{DC}$.
> **Prove: a.** $\overline{MN} \| \overline{AD}$, $\overline{MN} \| \overline{BC}$ **b.** $MN = \frac{1}{2}(AD + BC)$
> (HINT: Draw a line through *N* parallel to $\overline{AB}$.
> Prove that *AMNF* is a parallelogram.)

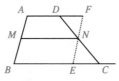

24. Prove Theorem 5.14 by constructing a line through *D* parallel to $\overline{AB}$.
   (NOTE: This is an alternate method of proving Theorem 5.15.)

> **Given:** *ABCD* is an isosceles trapezoid with $\overline{AB} \cong \overline{CD}$.
> **Prove:** $\angle B \cong \angle C$

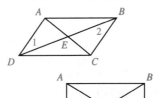

25. Prove that if the base angles of a trapezoid are congruent, then the trapezoid is isosceles.

26. Prove that if *ABCDEF* is a regular hexagon, then *ABEF* is an isosceles trapezoid.

Critical Thinking

27. *P* is a point above the plane *M* determined by the equilateral triangle *ABC*. If a plane parallel to *M* cuts the segments $\overline{PA}$, $\overline{PB}$, and $\overline{PC}$, how many trapezoids are formed? Where must *P* be located in order for the trapezoids to be isosceles?

Mixed Review

1. Find the sum of the measures of the angles of a regular hexagon.
2. Find the measure of each angle of a regular hexagon.
3. Find the measure of an exterior angle of a regular hexagon.

Quiz

ABCD is a parallelogram.

1. If *AD* = 6, find *BC*.   **2.** If *m*∠1 = 32, find *m*∠2.
3. If *m*∠*ABC* = 4*x* − 6 and *m*∠*BCD* = 2*x* + 54, find *m*∠*CDA*.

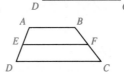

Determine whether each statement is true or false.

4. If $\overline{AB} \| \overline{CD}$ and $\overline{AD} \cong \overline{BC}$, then *ABCD* is a parallelogram.
5. If *ABCD* is a square, then $\overline{AC} \cong \overline{BD}$.
6. If *ABCD* is a rhombus and *m*∠*ABC* = 90, then *ABCD* is also a square.

ABCD is an isosceles trapezoid with median $\overline{EF}$.

7. If *AB* = 6 and *DC* = 18, find *EF*.
8. If *AB* = 2*x*, *EF* = 3*x* + 2, and *DC* = 24, find *EF*.

24. 1. Draw $\overline{DE} \| \overline{AB}$. (Post. 15) 2. *ABCD* is isos. trap. (Given) 3. $\overline{AD} \| \overline{BC}$ (Def. trap.) 4. *ABED* is a □. (Def. □) 5. *m*∠*B* + *m*∠*BED* = 180 (Consecutive ∠s of a □ are supp.) 6. *m*∠*BED* + *m*∠*DEC* = 180 (Linear Pair Post.) 7. *m*∠*B* = *m*∠*DEC* (Subst.) 8. ∠*B* ≅ ∠*DEC* (Def. ≅ ∠s) 9. $\overline{AB} \cong \overline{DC}$ (Given) 10. $\overline{AB} \cong \overline{DE}$ (Opposite ∠s of a □ are ≅.) 11. $\overline{DC} \cong \overline{DE}$ (Trans. Prop) 12. ∠*DEC* ≅ ∠*C* (If 2 sides △ ≅, the ∠s opp. them are ≅.) 13. ∠*B* ≅ ∠*C* (Trans. Prop.)   **26.** 1. *ABCDEF* is a reg. hexagon. (Given). 2. $\overline{AB} \cong \overline{EF}$ (Def. reg. hexagon) 3. *m*∠*A* = *m*∠*F* = 120 (Measure of each ∠ of a reg. *n*-gon is $\frac{(n-2)180}{n}$) 4. $\overline{AB}$ and $\overline{EF}$ are not ∥. (Same-side int. ∠s are not supp.) 5. Extend $\overline{AB}$ and $\overline{EF}$ to intersect at *G*. ($\overline{AB} \nparallel \overline{EF}$) 6. *m*∠*GAF* = *m*∠*GFA* = 60 (Linear Pair Post.) 7. *m*∠*AGF* = 60 (Sum of measures of ∠s of a △ = 180) 8. $\overline{AG} \cong \overline{GF}$ (Sides opp. ≅ ∠s in a △ are ≅.) 9. $\overline{BG} \cong \overline{GE}$ (Seg. Add. Post.) 10. △*GBE* is isos. (Def. isos. △) 11. ∠*GBE* ≅ ∠*GEB* (Base ∠s of an isos. △ are ≅.) 12. *m*∠*GBE* = *m*∠*GEB* (Def. ≅ ∠s) 13. *m*∠*GBE* + *m*∠*GEB* + *m*∠*AGF* = 180 (Sum of measures of ∠s of a △ = 180) 14. 2*m*∠*GBE* + 60 = 180, *m*∠*GBE* = 60 = *m*∠*GEB* (Subst.) 15. ∠*GAF* ≅ ∠*GBE* (Def. ≅ ∠s) 16. $\overline{AF} \| \overline{BE}$ (If 2 lines are cut by a trans. and corr. ∠s are ≅, then the lines are ∥.) 17. *ABEF* is an isos. trap. (Def. isos. trap.)

Mixed Review Answers

1. 720   **2.** 120   **3.** 60

Quiz Answers

1. 6   **2.** 32   **3.** 82
4. false   **5.** true
6. true   **7.** 12   **8.** 17

Which of these quadrilaterals—a. square, b. rectangle, c. rhombus, d. parallelogram, e. trapezoid, f. isosceles trapezoid—have the following properties?

1. both pairs of opposite sides ∥ a, b, c, d

2. diagonals ⊥ a, c

3. all angles ≅ a, b

4. consecutive angles supplementary a, b, c, d

5. exactly one pair of opposite sides ∥ e, f

6. all sides congruent a, c

7. opposite angles ≅ a, b, c, d

8. has a right angle a, b, some e

9. diagonals ≅ a, b, f

10. diagonals bisecting each other a, b, c, d

Lesson Opener

Start with an application involving surveying. A surveying team needs to find the distance across a large pond. The team chooses any point. From that point they measure to each side of the pond. They locate the two points that are halfway between the edge of the pond and their chosen point. The distance between these two midpoints will be one half the distance across the pond.

After comparing measurements, students should reach the conclusion that the segment that joins the midpoints of two sides of a triangle is half the length of the third side.

Materials

student notebooks
investigative software

TRIANGLES AND INEQUALITIES

OBJECTIVE: *Apply theorems about segments that join midpoints of sides of triangles and quadrilaterals.*

5-5 The Midsegment Theorem

EXPLORE Draw right triangles ABC_1, ABC_2, ABC_3 with $BC_1 = 1$ in., $BC_2 = 2$ in., and $BC_3 = 3$ in. Let D, E_1, E_2, and E_3 be the midpoints of their respective segments. Compare the lengths of $\overline{DE_1}$, $\overline{DE_2}$, and $\overline{DE_3}$ with the lengths of $\overline{BC_1}$, $\overline{BC_2}$, and BC_3. State a conclusion about your findings.

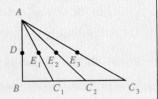

Consider the trapezoids *NEAT* and medians $\overline{XY}$ below. Note that in each figure the base $\overline{NT}$ gets smaller until finally the base is the point N (or T).

By Theorem 5.16, $\overline{XY} \parallel \overline{EA}$ and $XY = \frac{1}{2}(EA + NT)$. However, in the last case $\overline{NT}$ has length zero so $XY = \frac{1}{2}EA$. This suggests the next theorem. You will be asked to prove Theorem 5.17 in Exercise 31.

◆ **THEOREM 5.17** Midsegment Theorem

The segment that joins the midpoints of two sides of a triangle is parallel to the third side and has a length equal to half the length of the third side.

Example 1

D and E are midpoints of the sides of $\triangle ABC$. If $DE = x + 5$ and $AB = 4x - 16$, find the length of $\overline{AB}$.

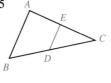

Solution

$$\frac{1}{2}(AB) = DE \quad \textit{Midsegment Theorem}$$
$$\frac{1}{2}(4x - 16) = x + 5$$
$$2x - 8 = x + 5$$
$$x = 13$$
$$AB = 4(13) - 16 = 36$$

Try This

If D and E are midpoints and $AB + DE = 36$, find the lengths of $\overline{AB}$ and $\overline{DE}$.

Example 2

P, Q, and R are midpoints of the sides of $\triangle MNO$. Find the perimeter of $\triangle PQR$ if $MN = 12$, $NO = 16$, and $OM = 14$.

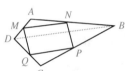

Solution

$PQ = \frac{1}{2}(ON) = \frac{1}{2}(16) = 8$ *Midsegment Theorem*

$QR = \frac{1}{2}(OM) = \frac{1}{2}(14) = 7$

$RP = \frac{1}{2}(MN) = \frac{1}{2}(12) = 6$

Perimeter $\triangle PQR = PQ + QR + RP$
$= 8 + 7 + 6$
$= 21$ The perimeter of $\triangle PQR$ is 21.

Try This

P, Q, and R are midpoints of the sides of $\triangle MNO$. If $MP = 3$, $QN = 5$ and $NR = 7$, find the perimeter of $\triangle PQR$.

The following theorem can be proved by using the Midsegment Theorem.

◆ THEOREM 5.18

The quadrilateral formed by joining the midpoints of the consecutive sides of another quadrilateral is a parallelogram.

Given: M, N, P, and Q are midpoints of the sides of quadrilateral $ABCD$.

Prove: $MNPQ$ is a parallelogram.

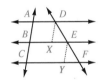

Plan   Draw $\overline{BD}$, forming triangles ABD and CBD. Prove that $MN = \frac{1}{2}BD$ and $\overline{MN} \parallel \overline{BD}$ by the Midsegment Theorem. Prove that $QP = \frac{1}{2}BD$ and $\overline{QP} \parallel \overline{BD}$ by the Midsegment Theorem. Conclude that $MN = QP$ and $\overline{MN} \parallel \overline{QP}$, and hence $MNPQ$ is a parallelogram.

◆ THEOREM 5.19

If three or more parallel lines cut off congruent segments on one transversal, then they will cut off congruent segments on every transversal.

You will be asked to prove Theorem 5.19 in Exercise 35.

▶ COROLLARY 5.19a

A line that contains the midpoint of one side of a triangle and is parallel to another side bisects the third side.

Teaching Notes

Review the definition of median of a trapezoid and Theorem 5.16. Note in the four diagrams from left to right that the base $\overline{NT}$ gets smaller and smaller until it becomes a point N (or T). Therefore, if $XY = \frac{1}{2}(EA + NT)$, in the fourth diagram $XY = \frac{1}{2}(EA + 0)$ or simply, $XY = \frac{1}{2}EA$.

Emphasize the difference between Theorem 5.16 and Theorem 5.17. Theorem 5.16 involves a segment (median) joining the midpoints of the legs of a trapezoid, whereas Theorem 5.17 involves a segment joining the midpoints of two sides of a triangle.

Guided Practice

Chalkboard Examples

1. If D and E are midpoints, $DE = 3x + 2$, and $AB = 7x - 1$, find the lengths of $\overline{DE}$ and $\overline{AB}$. **17, 34**

Answer to **Try This** 24, 12

2. If P, Q, and R are midpoints of the sides of $\triangle MNO$, find the perimeter of $\triangle PQR$ if $MN = 24$, $ON = 36$, and $OM = 42$. **51**

Answer to **Try This** 15

Class Exercises

Short Answer

D and *E* are midpoints of the sides of $\triangle ABC$. Complete each statement.

1. If $AB = 8$, then $DE =$ ___.   **2.** If $AC = 9$, then $AD =$ ___.
3. If $BE = 5$, then $BC =$ ___.   **4.** If $AB = 15$, then $DE =$ ___.

Sample Exercises

Find the value of *x* or state *cannot determine*.

5.   **6.**   **7.**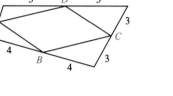

Determine whether Theorem 5.18 allows you to conclude that ABCD is a $\square$.

8. 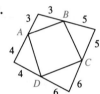   **9.**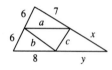

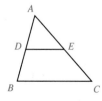

Discussion

10. Determine values for *x* and *y* so that only one of the segments *a*, *b*, and *c* can be determined. Explain your choices.

Exercises

A

D and *E* are midpoints of the sides of $\triangle ABC$. Complete each statement.

1. $DE = 10$, $BC =$ ___   **2.** $BC = 12$, $DE =$ ___   **3.** $DE = 8$, $BC =$ ___
4. $DE = 2x$, $BC = x + 10$, $DE =$ ___
5. $DE = x - 4$, $BC = x + 12$, $BC =$ ___
6. $DE = x + 2$, $BC = \frac{1}{2}x + 19$, $DE =$ ___

Find the value of *x*.

7.   **8.** 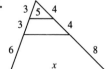   **9.**

Determine whether Theorem 5.18 allows you to conclude that *ABCD* is a parallelogram.

10.

11.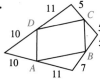

12.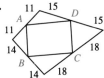

D, *E*, and *F* are midpoints of the sides of △*ABC*. Find the perimeter of △*DEF*.

13. $AB = 20$, $BC = 36$, $AC = 24$
14. $AB = 15$, $BC = 25$, $AC = 17$
15. $AD = 3$, $BF = 6$, $EC = 4$

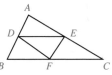

Exactly one of the values *a*, *b*, or *c* can be determined. Find it.

16.

17.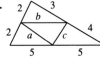

18.

19. If the dowel is cut where the diagram indicates, will it be divided into five equal lengths? Why or why not?

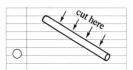

B

Determine the coordinates of the midpoint *X* of side $\overline{AB}$ and the midpoint *Y* of side $\overline{AC}$ of △*ABC*. Find *XY* and *BC* and verify that $XY = \frac{1}{2}BC$.

20. $A(0, 0)$, $B(8, 0)$, $C(0, 4)$ **21.** $A(0, 5)$, $B(0, 1)$, $C(-8, 5)$
22. $A(-2, -1)$, $B(2, -1)$, $C(-2, -7)$

23. Explain how the distance across the pond (*XY*) can be found by using △*ZXY* where *Z* is any point other than *X* or *Y*.
(HINT: Consider the midpoints of $\overline{XZ}$ and $\overline{ZY}$.)

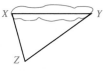

M and *N* are midpoints of sides $\overline{AC}$ and $\overline{BC}$.

24. If $MN = x^2 + x - 8$ and $AB = x^2 + x + 14$, find *MN* and *AB*.
25. If $AM = x + 5$, $MC = 2y + 6$, $MN = 2x - 5$, and $AB = y + 8$, find *MN* and *AB*.

D is the midpoint of $\overline{AB}$ and $\overline{DE} \parallel \overline{BC}$.

26. Find *AC* if $AE = 2x^2 - 4x$ and $EC = 2x + 20$.
27. Find *EC* if $AE = 3x + 4$ and $AC = x + 20$.

22. $X = (0, -1)$, $Y = (-2, -4)$, $XY = \sqrt{13}$, $BC = \sqrt{52} = 2\sqrt{13}$, $\sqrt{13} = \frac{1}{2}(2\sqrt{13})$ **24.** 22,
44   **26.** 60 or 32   **28.** 1. *F* is the midpoint of *AC*. *D* is the midpoint of *BC*. *E* is the midpoint of *AB*. (Given) 2. $\overline{DE} \parallel \overline{FA}$ (Midsegment Theorem) 3. $\overline{FD} \parallel \overline{AE}$ (Midsegment Theorem) 4. *AEDF* is a ▱. (Def. of ▱)
30. Draw auxiliary lines $\overline{AE}$ and $\overline{BD}$. 1. $\overline{AB} \parallel \overline{DE}$ (Given) 2. $\overline{AB} \cong \overline{DE}$ (Given) 3. *ABDE* is a ▱. (If a quadrilateral has one pair of sides both $\parallel$ and $\cong$, it is a ▱.) 4. $\overline{AE} \parallel \overline{BD}$ (Def. ▱) 5. $\overline{AE} \cong \overline{BD}$ (Opp. sides of a ▱ are $\cong$.) 6. $AE = BD$ (Def. $\cong$ segments) 7. *W*, *X*, *Y*, *Z* are midpoints. (Given) 8. $\overline{WZ} \parallel \overline{AE}$, $\overline{XY} \parallel \overline{BD}$ (Midsegment Theorem) 9. $\overline{WZ} \parallel \overline{XY}$ (If 2 lines are $\parallel$ to a third line, they are $\parallel$ to each other.) 10. $\frac{1}{2}AE = \frac{1}{2}BD$ (Mult. Prop. of =) 11. $WZ = \frac{1}{2}AE$, $XY = \frac{1}{2}BD$ (Midsegment Theorem) 12. $WZ = XY$ (Subst.) 13. $WZ \cong XY$ (Def. $\cong$ segments) 14. *WXYZ* is a ▱. (If one pair of opp. sides of a quadrilateral are both $\parallel$ and $\cong$, it is a ▱.)
32. 20   **34.** 1. Draw auxiliary line $\overline{AC}$. (Two points determine a line.) 2. *M* is midpoint of $\overline{AB}$, *N* is midpoint of $\overline{BC}$. (Given) 3. $\overline{MN} \parallel \overline{AC}$ (Midsegment Theorem) 4. *ABCDE* is a reg. pentagon. (Given) 5. $m\angle E = m\angle D = m\angle B = m\angle A = m\angle C = 108$ (Measure of int. $\angle$s of a polygon $= (n - 2)180$.) 6. $m\angle B + m\angle BAC + m\angle ACB = 180$ (Triangle Angle Sum Theorem) 7. $108 + m\angle BAC + m\angle ACB = 180$ (Subst.) 8. $m\angle BAC + m\angle ACB = 72$ (Add. Prop.) 9. $\overline{AB} \cong \overline{BC}$ (Def. reg. polygon)

10. $\angle BAC \cong \angle ACB$ (If 2 sides of a $\triangle$ are $\cong$, the angles opp. them are $\cong$.) **11.** $m\angle BAC = m\angle ACB$ (Def. $\cong$ segments) **12.** $2m\angle BAC = 72$ (Subst.) **13.** $m\angle BAC = 36$ (Mult. Prop. of =) **14.** $m\angle EAM = m\angle BAC + m\angle CAE$ (Angle Add. Post.) **15.** $108 - 36 = 72 = m\angle CAE$ (Subst.) **16.** $m\angle CAE + m\angle AED = 72 + 108 = 180$ (Subst.) **17.** $\angle CAE$ and $\angle AED$ are supp. (Def. supp. $\angle$s) **18.** $\overline{ED} \parallel \overline{AC}$ (If two lines are cut by a transversal and same-side int. $\angle$s are supp., the lines are $\parallel$.) **19.** $\overline{MN} \parallel \overline{ED}$ (If two lines are $\parallel$ to a third line, they are $\parallel$ to each other.) **36.** If the midpoints of the consecutive sides of an isosceles trapezoid are connected, a rhombus is formed. 1. *ABCD* is an isosceles trapezoid with midpoints *E*, *F*, *G*, and *H*. (Given) 2. $\overline{AC} \cong \overline{BD}$ (Diagonals of an isosceles trapezoid are $\cong$.) 3. $GH = \frac{1}{2}BD$, $EF = \frac{1}{2}BD$, $EH = \frac{1}{2}AC$, $FG = \frac{1}{2}AC$ (Midsegment Theorem) 4. $EH = \frac{1}{2}BD$, $FG = \frac{1}{2}BD$ (Subst.) 5. $GH = EF = EH = FG$ (Trans. Prop.) 6. $\overline{GH} \cong \overline{EF} \cong \overline{EH} \cong \overline{FG}$ (Def. $\cong$ segments) 7. *EFGH* is a rhombus. (Def. rhombus)

Algebra Review Answers

1. $x > 2$　　**2.** $y < -6$
3. $a > 2$　　**4.** $b > -6$
5. $x > 12$　　**6.** $a < 9$

28. **Given:** *F* is the midpoint of $\overline{AC}$.
　　D is the midpoint of $\overline{BC}$.
　　E is the midpoint of $\overline{AB}$.
　Prove: *AEDF* is a parallelogram.

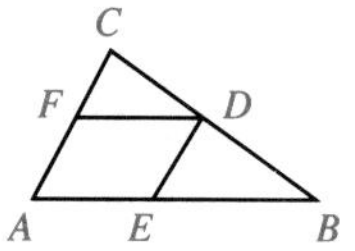

29. **Given:** $\overline{AB} \cong \overline{AC}$
　　E is the midpoint of $\overline{AB}$.
　　D is the midpoint of $\overline{CB}$.
　Prove: $\triangle BDE$ is isosceles.

30. **Given:** *ABCDEF* is a hexagon.
　　$\overline{AB} \parallel \overline{DE}$, $\overline{AB} \cong \overline{DE}$
　　W, *X*, *Y*, and *Z* are midpoints.
　Prove: *WXYZ* is a parallelogram.
　(HINT: Draw $\overline{AE}$ and $\overline{BD}$.)

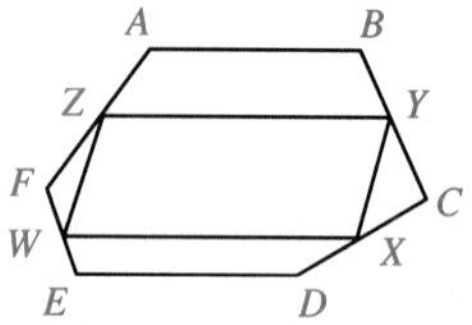

31. Prove Theorem 5.17.
　Given: *D* and *E* are midpoints.
　Prove: a. $\overline{DE} \parallel \overline{BC}$　　**b.** $DE = \frac{1}{2}BC$
　(HINT: Extend $\overline{DE}$ until $\overline{DE} \cong \overline{EF}$ as shown in the figure to the right.
　Prove *ADCF* is a parallelogram. Then prove *DBCF* is a parallelogram.)

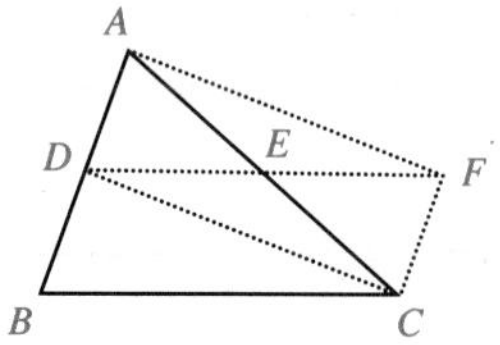

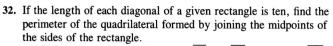

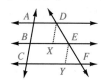

C

32. If the length of each diagonal of a given rectangle is ten, find the perimeter of the quadrilateral formed by joining the midpoints of the sides of the rectangle.

33. *ABCD* is a trapezoid with diagonals $\overline{AC}$ and $\overline{BD}$ and median $\overline{MN}$. Find *FG* if $MN = 27$, $AB = 7x$ and $CD = 4x^2 - x$.

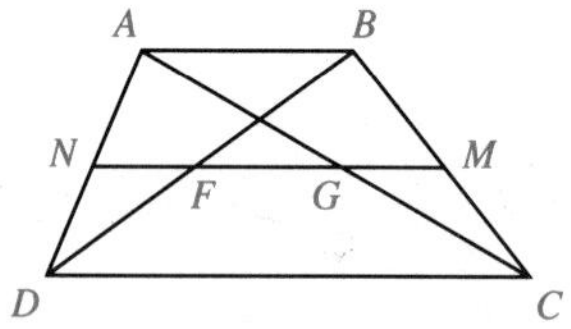

34. Given a regular pentagon *ABCDE* in which *M* is the midpoint of side $\overline{AB}$ and *N* is the midpoint of side $\overline{BC}$, prove $\overline{MN} \parallel \overline{ED}$.

35. Prove Theorem 5.19.
　Given: $\overleftrightarrow{AD} \parallel \overleftrightarrow{BE} \parallel \overleftrightarrow{CF}, \overline{AB} \cong \overline{BC}$
　Prove: $\overline{DE} \cong \overline{EF}$
　(HINT: Draw $\overline{DX}$ and $\overline{EY}$ parallel to $\overline{AC}$.)

Critical Thinking

36. Draw several isosceles trapezoids and connect the midpoints of the sides. In each case, what kind of quadrilateral is formed? Write a theorem that describes your discovery. Then write a paragraph proof.

37. A student studied the figure to the right and concluded that *ABCD* is not a parallelogram, giving Theorem 5.19 as the reason for this conclusion. Do you agree? Why or why not?

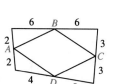

Algebra Review

Solve.

1. $x + 7 > 9$　　　**2.** $y + 12 < 6$　　　**3.** $2a + 3 - a > 5$
4. $b - 10 > -16$　**5.** $6x > 72$　　　　**6.** $9a < 81$

Enrichment

Tessellations

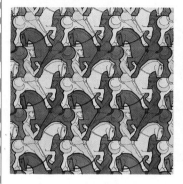

Regular hexagon

M. C. Escher, a Dutch graphic artist, created more than 150 drawings using tessellations. A **tessellation** is an arrangement of polygonal shapes that cover a plane such that no polygons overlap and there are no gaps. A question of interest to mathematicians is, "Which shapes or combinations of shapes tessellate the plane?" It is easy to show that a square tessellates the plane by using tracing paper to repeatedly trace the square until the entire sheet of paper is covered. As shown to the right, a plane can also be tessellated by a regular hexagon.

Exercises

Determine which of the polygons shown tessellate the plane.

1.

Parallelogram

2.

Trapezoid

3.

Kite

4.
NO
Any quadrilateral

5.

Equilateral triangle

6.
NO
Nonconvex quadrilateral

7.
NO
Regular pentagon

8.
NO
Regular octagon

9. Cut out several copies each of an equilateral triangle, a square, a regular hexagon, and a regular octagon so that each side of each polygon has the same length. Find several combinations of two or more of these polygons that will tessellate the plane.

In △ACE, B, D, and F are midpoints of $\overline{AC}$, $\overline{CE}$, and $\overline{AE}$, respectively.

1. If DF = 12, find the length of AC. 24
2. If AC = x, find the length of DF. $\frac{x}{2}$
3. If AC = 8, CE = 10, and AE = 14, find the perimeter of BFD. 16
4. If BF = x − 4 and CE = x + 12, find the lengths of $\overline{BF}$ and $\overline{CE}$. 16, 32

Lesson Opener

To introduce indirect proof, make a statement such as, "Jay received an after-school detention for being late to his geometry class today." A school rule states that the penalty for three tardies to class in a single semester is a detention. Thus, one would assume that Jay had been tardy at least three times.

Using indirect reasoning:
1. Assume that Jay has not been tardy for two of his classes this semester before today.
2. Reason that since a detention is assigned to a student who has been tardy to class three times, this contradicts the fact that Jay received after-school detention.
3. Therefore, the assumption that Jay has not been tardy for two of his classes this semester before today is false. Conclude that Jay was assigned detention for being late to class the third time this semester.

Materials

student notebooks

Key Terms

indirect proof
negation
contradiction

OBJECTIVE: *Use the indirect method of proof.*

5-6 Indirect Proof

In some cases it is easier to use indirect reasoning rather than to use direct reasoning as you have been doing in the proofs you have written so far. Indirect reasoning involves assuming the opposite of what you want to conclude. You then reason logically until you reach a **contradiction** involving two conflicting statements.

Indirect reasoning is illustrated by what might happen in this cartoon—if B.C. cooperates! Suppose B.C. eats the berry but does not die. The following illustrates the use of indirect reasoning to conclude that the berry is not poison.

> Suppose the berry is poison.
> If B.C. eats it, he will die.
> B.C. ate it but didn't die.
> Therefore, the berry is not poison!

In an **indirect proof** you use indirect reasoning to establish a statement or theorem. An important part of an indirect proof is assuming the negation of a statement. The **negation** of a statement is the opposite of the original statement. In an indirect proof you first assume the negation of what you want to prove. Then you reason logically until you have shown that the assumption leads to a contradiction involving two conflicting statements.

B.C. by permission of Johnny Hart and Field Enterprises, Inc.

Example 1
State the negation of each statement.
a. $m\angle 1 = m\angle 2$
b. $\overline{AB} \not\perp \overline{CD}$ (NOTE: $\not\perp$ means "is not perpendicular to.")

> **Solution**
> **a.** $m\angle 1 \neq m\angle 2$ **b.** $\overline{AB} \perp \overline{CD}$

Try This
State the negation of "$\overline{AB}$ intersects $\overline{CD}$."

Another part of an indirect proof is reaching a contradiction. The following pairs of statements each form a contradiction since they cannot both be true.
$\overline{XY}$ is longer than $\overline{MN}$. $\overline{MN}$ is longer than $\overline{XY}$.
$\angle A$ and $\angle B$ are right angles. $\angle A$ and $\angle B$ are not congruent angles.

Example 2

Determine which pairs of statements form a contradiction.

a. $\overline{AB} \| \overline{CD}$
$\overline{AB}$ and $\overline{CD}$ are perpendicular.
b. In $\triangle ABC$, $m \angle A = m \angle B$.
$\triangle ABC$ is scalene.
c. $ABCD$ is a rhombus.
$ABCD$ is a square.

Solution

Statements in **a** and **b** form a contradiction.

Try This

Which two of the following three statements form a contradiction?

a. $\triangle ABC$ is isosceles.   b. $\triangle ABC$ is equilateral.   c. ABC is a right triangle.

The steps for indirect proof are summarized below.

Steps for Using Indirect Proof

Step 1 Assume the negation of the *Prove* statement.
Step 2 Reason logically to show that the assumption leads to the contradiction of a known fact (theorem, definition, postulate, given information, etc.).
Step 3 Conclude that the assumption is false and that the *Prove* statement is true.

An indirect proof can be written in paragraph form, as in Examples 3 and 4.

Example 3

Given: $\angle 1$ and $\angle 2$ are not congruent.

Prove: $\angle 1$ and $\angle 2$ are not vertical angles.

Proof Assume that $\angle 1$ and $\angle 2$ are vertical angles. Then $\angle 1 \cong \angle 2$ by the Vertical Angle Theorem. This statement contradicts the given information which says that $\angle 1 \not\cong \angle 2$. Therefore, this assumption must be false. It follows that $\angle 1$ and $\angle 2$ are not vertical angles.

Example 4 presents an indirect proof for the statement: The base angles of an isosceles triangle must be acute.

Example 4

Given: $AB = AC$

Prove: $m \angle B < 90$

Proof Assume $m \angle B \geq 90$. Since $AB = AC$ then $m \angle B = m \angle C$ by the Isosceles Triangle Theorem. Therefore, $m \angle C \geq 90$. By addition, $m \angle B + m \angle C \geq 180$. This contradicts the fact that the sum of the measures of the angles of a triangle is 180. The assumption that $m \angle B = 90$ must be false. Therefore, $m \angle B < 90$.

3. Given: ∠1 and ∠3 are not supplementary.
Prove: ∠1 and ∠3 are not a linear pair.

Proof: Assume ∠1 and ∠3 are a linear pair. Then ∠1 and ∠3 are supp. by def. linear pair. This contradicts the fact that ∠1 and ∠3 are not supp. The assumption must be false. It follows that ∠1 and ∠3 are not a linear pair.

4. Given: $\overline{AB} \not\cong \overline{BC}$
Prove: ∠B ≇ ∠C

Proof: Assume ∠B ≅ ∠C. Then $\overline{AB} \cong \overline{BC}$ since if 2 ∠s of a △ are ≅, the sides opp. are ≅. This contradicts the fact that $\overline{AB} \cong \overline{BC}$. The assumption must be false. Therefore, ∠B ≇ ∠C.

Class Exercises
Answers

1. The sun is not shining.
2. It will rain.   **3.** m not ⊥ n
4. Adj. sides are ‖.
5. $\overline{AB} \not\cong \overline{CD}$ **6.** ∠A is acute.
7. △ABC is not an isos. △.
8. △ABC ≇ △DEF   **9.** a, c
10. b, c   **11.** b, c   **12.** a, b
13. a, c   **14.** b, c
15. Assume $AB = AC$. Since $AB = AC$, $m∠B = m∠C$ by Isos. △ Th. This contradicts the fact that $m∠B \neq m∠C$. The assumption must be false.
16. Assume △ABC equiang. By Cor. 4.2a, $AB = AC$. This contradicts the fact $AB > AC$. The assumption must be false.

Class Exercises

Short Answer
State the negation of each statement.

1. The sun is shining.
2. It will not rain.
3. $m \perp n$
4. The adjacent sides are not parallel.
5. $\overline{AB} \cong \overline{CD}$
6. ∠A is not acute.
7. △ABC is an isosceles triangle.
8. △ABC is congruent to △DEF.

Sample Exercises
Identify which two of the three statements, a, b, and c, form a contradiction.

9. **a.** △ABC is equilateral.
   b. △ABC is acute.
   c. △ABC is scalene.
10. **a.** ∠A ≅ ∠B
    b. ∠A and ∠B are supplementary.
    c. ∠A and ∠B are complementary.
11. **a.** ∠A and ∠B are adjacent angles.
    b. ∠A and ∠B form a linear pair of angles.
    c. ∠A and ∠B are acute angles.
12. **a.** ∠A and ∠B are supplementary.
    b. ∠A and ∠B are both acute angles.
    c. ∠A and ∠B are vertical angles.
13. **a.** Lines p and q are not parallel.
    b. Lines p and q have no points in common.
    c. Lines p and q lie in the same plane and have no points in common.
14. **a.** ∠A and ∠B are not right angles.
    b. ∠A and ∠B are congruent angles.
    c. $m∠A \neq m∠B$

Discussion
Discuss how an indirect proof could be used to prove the following.

15. **Given:** $m∠B \neq m∠C$
    Prove: $AB \neq AC$
    (HINT: Begin by assuming the negation $AB = AC$.)

16. **Given:** $AB > AC$
    Prove: △ABC is not equiangular.

Exercises

A

Write the negation you would use to begin an indirect proof.

1. Prove: ∠A is supplementary to ∠B.
2. Prove: ∠A is not a right angle.
3. Prove: ∠A and ∠B are not vertical angles.
4. Prove: There is at most one line through P that is parallel to m.
5. Prove: ABC is not an equilateral triangle.

Indicate whether each pair of statements would enable you to arrive at a contradiction in an indirect proof.

6. Lines p and q are parallel.
Lines p and q do not intersect.

7. $\angle A \cong \angle B$
$m\angle A > m\angle B$

8. $m \perp n$
$m \not\perp n$

9. $\angle A$ and $\angle B$ form a linear pair.
$m\angle A < 90$, $m\angle B < 90$

10. $\angle A$ and $\angle B$ are congruent.
$\angle A$ and $\angle B$ are supplementary.

11. $\angle A$ and $\angle B$ are obtuse angles.
$\angle A$ and $\angle B$ are supplementary.

12. Arrange statements **a–f** in the correct order to write the indirect proof in paragraph form.

Given: $\overline{AB} \perp \ell$

Prove: Any other line $\overline{AC}$ is not perpendicular to ℓ.

a. $m\angle ABC = 90$
b. Contradiction of Angle Sum Theorem for Triangles; therefore, $\overline{AC} \not\perp \ell$.
c. $\overline{AB} \perp \ell$ **d.** $m\angle ABC + m\angle ACB = 180$
e. Assume $\overline{AC} \perp \ell$.   **f.** $m\angle ACB = 90$

13. Complete the following indirect proof.

Given: In $\triangle ABC$, $AC \neq AB$, D is the midpoint of $\overline{BC}$.

Prove: $\overline{AD} \not\perp \overline{BC}$

Proof Assume $\overline{AD} \perp \overline{BC}$. Then $\angle ADC \cong \angle ADB$. Since D is the midpoint of $\overline{BC}$, then $\overline{CD} \cong \overline{BD}$. By the Reflexive Property, $\overline{AD} \cong \overline{AD}$. Therefore, $\triangle ADC \cong \triangle ADB$.
(HINT: Obtain a statement that contradicts a statement in the given information.)

Write an indirect proof in paragraph form.

14. Given: $\angle 4 \not\cong \angle 6$
Prove: $a \not\parallel b$

15. Given: $a \not\parallel b$
Prove: $\angle 3 \not\cong \angle 5$

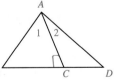

16. Given: $\angle 1 \not\cong \angle 8$
Prove: $\angle 4 \not\cong \angle 5$

17. Given: $\overline{AB} \cong \overline{AD}$, $\angle 1 \not\cong \angle 2$
Prove: $\overline{BC} \not\cong \overline{CD}$

B

18. Given: $\overline{AB} \cong \overline{AD}$, $\overline{BC} \not\cong \overline{CD}$
Prove: $\angle 1 \not\cong \angle 2$

19. Given: $\triangle ABD$ is scalene. $\overline{AC}$ is a median.
Prove: $\overline{AC} \not\perp \overline{BD}$

20. Given: $\overline{AC}$ bisects $\angle BAD$. $\overline{AC} \not\perp \overline{BD}$
Prove: $AB \neq AD$

5-6 *Indirect Proof*   **233**

Assignment Guide
Minimum: 1–24 e/o, 28, MR
Regular: 1–27 e/o, 28, MR
Advanced: 11–14, 18–28, MR

Applications
Exercises 28

Lesson Closure

Ask students to define indirect proof and give the major steps for its use.

Teacher's Resource Materials

Enrichment Using Manipulatives 32
Practice Master 35

Exercise Answers

See Selected Answers for odd-numbered exercises.
2. $\angle A$ is a right angle.
4. There is more than one line through P that is parallel to m.
6. no   **8.** yes   **10.** no
12. e, f, c, a, d, b
14. Assume $a \parallel b$. Then $\angle 4 \cong \angle 6$, since if $\parallel$ lines are cut by a transversal, corr. $\angle$s are $\cong$. This contradicts the fact that $\angle 4 \not\cong \angle 6$. The assumption must be false, and $a \not\parallel b$.
16. Assume $\angle 4 \cong \angle 5$. Since $\angle 1 \cong \angle 4$ and $\angle 5 \cong \angle 8$ (vert. $\angle$s), $\angle 1 \cong \angle 8$ by transitivity. This contradicts the fact that $\angle 1 \not\cong \angle 8$. The assumption that $\angle 4 \cong \angle 5$ must be false. Therefore, $\angle 4 \not\cong \angle 5$.

18. Assume ∠1 ≅ ∠2. Since $\overline{AB} ≅ \overline{AD}$ and $\overline{AC} ≅ \overline{AC}$, by the Reflexive Prop., △ABC = △ADC by the SAS Post. Then $\overline{BC} ≅ \overline{CD}$ because corr. parts of ≅ △s are ≅. This contradicts the fact that $BC ≠ CD$. The assumption that ∠1 ≅ ∠2 must be false. Therefore, ∠1 ≇ ∠2.

20. Assume $AB = AD$. Since $\overline{AC}$ bisects ∠BAD, then ∠BAC ≅ ∠CAD. $\overline{AC} ≅ \overline{AC}$ by the Reflexive Prop. Conclude that △BAC ≅ △CAD by SAS Post. Then ∠ACB ≅ ∠ACD by corr. parts of ≅ △s are ≅, and ∠ACB and ∠ACD must be right ∠s because they are a linear pair. This contradicts the fact that $\overline{AC} ⊥ \overline{BD}$. The assumption that $AB = AD$ must be false. Therefore, $AB ≠ AD$.

22. Assume $BC = DE$. Then $\overline{BD} ≅ \overline{CE}$ by Common Segment Theorem. Since $\overline{AB} ≅ \overline{AE}$, ∠$B$ ≅ ∠E by the Isos. Triangle Theorem. Conclude △ABD ≅ △AEC by SAS Post. Then $\overline{AC} ≅ \overline{AD}$ by corr. parts of ≅ △s are ≅. This contradicts the fact that $AC ≠ AD$. The assumption that $BC = DE$ must be false. Therefore, $BC ≠ DE$.

24. Assume △BCD is equilateral. Then $BC = CD = BD$. Since △ABC is equilateral, $BC = AB = AC$. Since △DAC is equilateral, $DA = AC = CD$. By the Transitive Prop., $AB = BD = AD$, so △ABD is equilateral. This contradicts the fact that △ABD is not equilateral. The assumption that △BCD is equilateral must be false. Therefore, △BCD is not equilateral.

26. Assume $\overline{AB}$ and $\overline{CD}$ intersect. Then $\overline{AB}$ and $\overline{CD}$ would form a triangle with base $\overline{BD}$ and base angles B and D.

21. Given: $\overline{MN} ⊥ \overline{NP}$
$\overline{QP} ⊥ \overline{NP}$
∠M ≇ ∠Q
Prove: $\overline{MN} ≇ \overline{QP}$

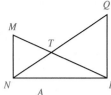

22. Given: $AB = AE$
$AC ≠ AD$
Prove: $BC ≠ DE$

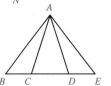

23. Given: $\overline{AC} ⊥ M$
∠B ≇ ∠D
Prove: ∠BAC ≇ ∠DAC

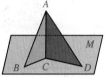

24. Given: △ABC is equilateral.
△DAC is equilateral.
△ABD is not equilateral.
Prove: △BCD is not equilateral.

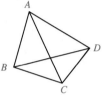

C

25. Write an indirect proof in paragraph form to prove the following statement. If a line is perpendicular to one side of an angle, it is not perpendicular to the other side of the angle.

26. Write an indirect proof in paragraph form to prove the following statement. Two lines perpendicular to the same plane do not intersect.

27. Write an indirect proof in paragraph form to prove the following statement. If point D is not in the same plane as △ABC, then $\overline{BD}$ and $\overline{AC}$ are skew lines.

Critical Thinking

28. A store owner claimed that an expensive radio had been stolen from her store. She was convinced that either Anna, Brenda, Carlos, or Dee had stolen the radio. Each person made a statement but only one of the four statements was true.
Anna said, "I didn't take it."
Brenda said, "Anna is lying."
Carlos said, "Brenda is lying."
Dee said, "Brenda took it."
Who told the truth? Who took the radio? Use indirect reasoning and write a paragraph proof to justify your choice.

Mixed Review

Find the measure of the indicated angle.

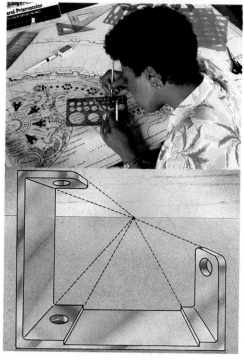

1. If $m\angle 4 = 50$ and $m\angle 5 = 75$, find $m\angle 1$.
2. If $m\angle 6 = 135$ and $m\angle 2 = m\angle 5$, find $m\angle 2$.
3. If $m\angle 3 = 120$ and $m\angle 4$ is twice $m\angle 5$, find $m\angle 4$.
4. If $m\angle 1$ is 160 and $m\angle 5$ is three times $m\angle 4$, find $m\angle 5$.

Determine whether each statement is always, sometimes, or never true. Draw a figure to illustrate your answer.

5. Two adjacent angles form a linear pair.
6. Adjacent angles are congruent.
7. Vertical angles are complementary.
8. An angle and its complement are congruent.
9. Vertical angles are congruent.
10. Two acute angles are supplementary.

Career

Technical Illustrator

The professional artist who prepares drawings that show how machines, tools, and equipment operate is a technical illustrator. Working from blueprints, designs, mockups, and photoprints, he or she may draw an object from different points of view to show its function, its relationship to other equipment, or the assembly sequence of its parts.

One skill technical illustrators develop is drawing in perspective. Using congruent triangles, the artist produces a two-dimensional representation in which parallel lines appear to converge at some distant point. He or she may also draw from schematic, orthographic, or oblique-angle views. Color or shading with ink, crayon, airbrush, or overlays helps emphasize details or eliminate unwanted backgrounds.

The artist may include instructions, comments, or cartoons to help describe how the object works. A technical illustrator uses drafting or optical equipment, photo-offset techniques, and projections transparencies. His or her work appears in reference or technical manuals, brochures, and safety manuals and on posters. Related professions include engineering and production illustration.

$\angle B$ and $\angle D$ are right angles since $\overline{AB} \perp$ plane M and $\overline{CD} \perp$ plane M. Therefore, $m\angle B + m\angle D = 180$. But since the sum of the measures of the angles of a triangle is 180, $\angle B$ and $\angle D$ cannot be two angles of a triangle. This contradicts the fact that $\overline{AB}$ and $\overline{CD}$ intersect. Therefore, $\overline{AB}$ and $\overline{CD}$ do not intersect. **28.** Assume Brenda's statement is false. Then Anna's statement is true. Then Carlos's and Dee's statements must be false, since only one of the four statements is true. But if Carlos's statement that Brenda is lying is false, it contradicts the assumption that Brenda's statement is false. The assumption that Brenda's statement is false must be false. Therefore, Brenda's statement is true. Anna is lying—she took the radio.

Mixed Review Answers

1. 125   2. 67.5   3. 80
4. 120
5. sometimes true

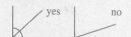

6. sometimes true

7. sometimes true

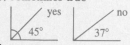

8. sometimes true

9. always true

10. never true

Write an indirect proof.

Given: $\angle 1 \cong \angle 5$
Prove: $m \parallel n$
Proof: Assume $m \nparallel n$. Then
$\angle 1 \ncong \angle 5$. This contradicts the
fact that $\angle 1 \cong \angle 5$. Therefore,
$m \parallel n$.

Lesson Opener

Begin with a review of the algebraic inequalities from Algebra 1. First, state the properties using variables. Then, substitute numerical values for the variables.

1. If $a > b$ and $b > c$, then $a > c$.
2. If $x + 2 > 5$, then $x > 3$.
3. If $x + 2 < 8$, then $x < 6$.
4. If $x > y$ and $z > 0$, then $xz > yz$.
5. If $x > y$ and $w > z$, then $x + w > y + z$.
6. If $x = y + z$ and $y > 0$, then $x > y$. (See 2. above)
7. If $x = y + z$ and $y > 0$, then $x > z$. (See 3. above).
8. Either $x > y$, $x < y$, or $x = y$.

Materials

student notebooks
protractors
rulers
investigative software

Key Terms

equality
inequality

OBJECTIVE: *Apply the Exterior Angle Inequality Theorem and theorems involving inequalities in one triangle.*

5-7 Inequalities in One Triangle

Many theorems concern equality of measures. This lesson deals with inequalities. The first theorem is related to the Exterior Angle Theorem.

◆ **THEOREM 5.20** Exterior Angle Inequality Theorem

The measure of an exterior angle of a triangle is greater than the measure of either remote interior angle.

Given: $\angle 1$ is an exterior angle of $\triangle ABC$.
Prove: $m \angle 1 > m \angle 2$, $m \angle 1 > m \angle 3$

Plan By the Exterior Angle Theorem for Triangles, $m \angle 1 = m \angle 2 + m \angle 3$. It follows that $m \angle 1 > m \angle 2$ and $m \angle 1 > m \angle 3$.

◆ **THEOREM 5.21**

If one side of a triangle is longer than a second side, then the measure of the angle opposite the longer side is greater than the measure of the angle opposite the shorter side.

Given: $BC > AB$
Prove: $m \angle A > m \angle C$

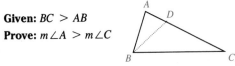

Proof Use the Ruler Postulate to select D on $\overline{AC}$ so $AB = BD$. Then $m \angle A = m \angle BDA$, since if two sides of a triangle are congruent, the angles opposite them are congruent. Therefore $m \angle ADB > m \angle C$ by the Exterior Angle Inequality Theorem. It follows that $m \angle A > m \angle C$ by substitution.

Example 1
Name the largest angle of $\triangle ABC$.
   Solution
   $\angle B$ Theorem 5.21

Try This
Name the smallest angle of $\triangle ABC$.

◆ **THEOREM 5.22**

If one angle of a triangle is larger than another angle, then the side
opposite the larger angle is longer than the side opposite the smaller angle.

Given: $m\angle A > m\angle C$
Prove: $BC > AB$

Proof Assume $BC = AB$. It follows that $m\angle A = m\angle C$. This contradicts the
given information. Assume $AB > BC$. By Theorem 5.22, $m\angle C > m\angle A$.
This contradicts the given information. Therefore, $BC > AB$.

▶ **COROLLARY 5.22a**

The perpendicular segment from a point to a line is the shortest segment
from the point to the line.

You will be asked to prove Corollary 5.22a in Exercise 33.

Example 2

Name the longest side of quadrilateral ABCD.

Solution
$\overline{AB}$ (or $\overline{AD}$)   *Theorem 5.22*

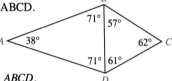

Try This

Name the shortest side of quadrilateral *ABCD*.

You will be asked to prove Theorem 5.23 in Exercise 41.

◆ **THEOREM 5.23** Triangle Inequality Theorem

The sum of the lengths of any two sides of a triangle is greater than the
length of the third side.

Example 3

Which numbers could represent the lengths of the sides of a triangle?
a. 3, 4, 6   **b.** 10, 11, 21   **c.** 2, 6, 9   **d.** 34, 35, 36

Solution
a and **d**   *Triangle Inequality Theorem*

Try This

Two sides of a triangle measure 5 and 13. Which could be the measure of the
third side?
a. 16   **b.** 8   **c.** 9   **d.** 19

Optional Explore

To introduce Theorem 5.21,
copy the three triangles below.

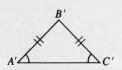

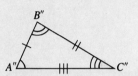

Have students measure the sides
and angles using a protractor
and ruler. Point out that since
$BC = BA$, then $m\angle C = m\angle A$;
since $B'C' = B'A'$, then
$m\angle C'' = m\angle A'$; since
$B''C'' > B''A''$, then $m\angle C'' <
m\angle A''$ or $m\angle A'' > m\angle C''$.

Guided Practice

Chalkboard Examples

1. In $\triangle ABC$, $AB = 2x - 1$,
$BC = 2x + 1$, and $AC = 2x$.
Name the largest angle and the
smallest angle. $\angle A$ largest, $\angle C$
smallest

Answer to **Try This** $\angle C$

2. In $\triangle ABD$, $m\angle A = x$,
$m\angle B = x + 2$, and $m\angle D =
60$. Name the longest side and
the shortest side. $\overline{AD}$ longest,
$\overline{BD}$ shortest

Answer to **Try This** *CD*

3. Two sides of a △ have lengths 15 and 20. The length of the third side must be a number between what two numbers? 5 and 35

Answer to **Try This** *a* and *c*

Class Exercise Answers

1. ∠*C* largest, ∠*B* smallest **2.** ∠*E* largest, ∠*D* smallest **3.** ∠*M* largest, ∠*PNM* and ∠*NPM* smallest **4.** $\overline{AC}$ longest, $\overline{AB}$ shortest **5.** $\overline{EF}$ longest, $\overline{DE}$ shortest **6.** $\overline{MN}$ and $\overline{NP}$ longest, $\overline{MQ}$ shortest **7.** ∠3 **8.** ∠4 **9.** not possible to determine **10.** ∠4 **11.** 7, 8, 9, 10, 11, 12, 13, 14, 15, 16, 17 **12.** >4 and <18 **13.** $\overline{BC}$, $\overline{AC}$, $\overline{AB}$ **14.** ∠*E*, ∠*D*, ∠*F*
15. Hypotenuse; because in a rt. △ the other two angles are acute, and therefore have a measure that is <90.
16. No; only when the measure of a base angle is >60.

Assignment Guide

Minimum: 1–40 e/o, 45, AR
Regular: 1–42 e/o, 45, AR
Advanced: 17–21, 25–45, AR

Applications
Exercises 25, 32, 35

Coordinate Geometry
Exercises 35–39

Algebra
Exercises 27, AR

Lesson Closure

Ask students to state and illustrate the theorems involving inequalities in a triangle.

Class Exercises

Short Answer

Name the largest angle and the smallest angle for each figure.

1.

2.

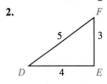

3.

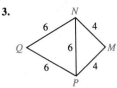

Name the longest side and the shortest side for each figure.

4.

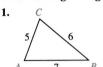

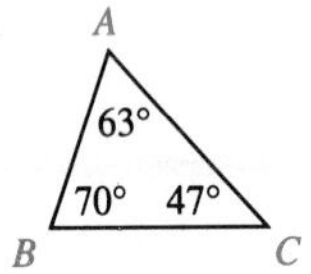

5.

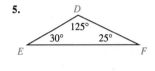

6.

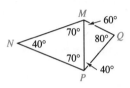

Sample Exercises

Decide which angle is the larger based on the Exterior Angle Inequality Theorem or state that it is not possible to determine which angle is larger.

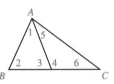

7. ∠3 and ∠6 **8.** ∠4 and ∠1 **9.** ∠3 and ∠1 **10.** ∠2 and ∠4

11. If the lengths of two sides of a triangle are 6 and 12, what are the possible whole numbers for the length of the third side?
12. If two sides of a parallelogram have lengths 7 and 11, then the lengths of the diagonals must be greater than __?__ and less than __?__.
13. In △*ABC*, $m\angle A = 30$, $m\angle B = 50$, and $m\angle C = 100$. List the sides of the triangle from the shortest to the longest.
14. In △*DEF*, $DE = 5$, $EF = 6$, and $DF = 8$. List the angles of the triangle from the largest to the smallest.

Discussion

15. Which side of a right triangle must be the longest side? Explain.
16. Is the base of an isosceles triangle always the shortest side? Explain.

Exercises

A

List the sides of each figure from the shortest to the longest.

1.

2.

3.

238 *Chapter 5 Using Congruent Triangles and Parallel Lines*

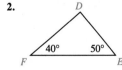

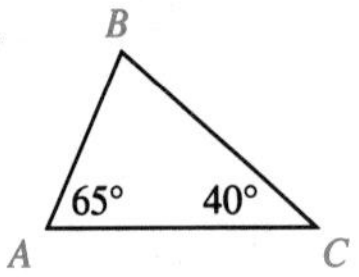

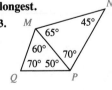

List the sides of △*ABC* from the shortest to the longest.

4. $m\angle A = 46$, $m\angle B = 30$ 5. $m\angle C = 101$, $m\angle B = 70$
6. $m\angle A = 59$, $m\angle C = 61$ 7. $m\angle B = 48$, $m\angle A = 47$

List the angles of △*ABC* from the smallest to the largest.

8. $AB = 17$, $BC = 21$, $AC = 18$ 9. $AB = 15$, $AC = 16$, $BC = 17$

10. List the sides of quadrilateral *ABCD* from the shortest to the longest.

11. List all the segments in the figure from the shortest to the longest.

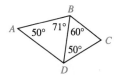

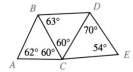

Which numbers could represent the lengths of the sides of a triangle?

12. 10, 20, 30   13. 10, 8, 6   14. 5, 14, 7
15. 4, 9, 15   16. 6, 6, 11   17. 1, 3, 5

18. If the sum of the lengths of two sides of a triangle is 15, what is the largest possible integral value for the third side?
19. If the base of an isosceles triangle is 10, what is the shortest possible integral value for each of the equal sides?
20. If the perimeter of a triangle is 8 and the lengths of the sides are integers, what is the length of the shortest side?

Use the Exterior Angle Inequality Theorem to determine which angle is larger or state *not possible*.

21. $\angle 1$ and $\angle 6$ 22. $\angle 1$ and $\angle 2$
23. $\angle 2$ and $\angle 4$ 24. $\angle 5$ and $\angle 2$

25. The three main work centers in the kitchen are the refrigerator, the sink, and the stove. You could picture them as the points of a triangle. It is recommended that the three sides of the kitchen triangle add up to more than 12 ft and less than 22 ft, with the shortest side of the triangle between the sink and the stove. Decide whether each kitchen triangle in the chart below is possible. Then state whether it follows the recommendation.

	a	b	c	d	e
stove/sink	5 ft	10 ft	6 ft	3 ft	3 ft
stove/refrigerator	4 ft	11 ft	8 ft	7 ft	8 ft
refrigerator/sink	8 ft	8 ft	7 ft	4 ft	4 ft

B

26. If the lengths of two sides of a triangle are 6 and p, where p is a whole number, give the possible whole numbers for the length of the third side.

Teacher's Resource Materials

Enrichment Using
  Manipulatives 33
Practice Master 36
Technology: BASIC 9

Computer Software

See Computer Exploration 11, page 644.

Exercise Answers

See Selected Answers for odd-numbered exercises.
2. $\overline{DE}$, $\overline{DF}$, $\overline{FE}$ 4. $\overline{AC}$, $\overline{BC}$, $\overline{AB}$
6. $\overline{BC}$, $\overline{AC}$, $\overline{AB}$ 8. $\angle C$, $\angle B$, $\angle A$
10. $\overline{BC}$, $\overline{DC}$, $\overline{AB}$, $\overline{AD}$
12. no   14. no   16. yes
18. 14   20. 2   22. not possible   24. $m\angle 2 > m\angle 5$
26. whole numbers greater than $|6 - p|$ and less than $6 + p$

28. 1. $AB = BC$ (Given)
2. $\overline{AB} \cong \overline{BC}$ (Def. $\cong$ segments)
3. $\angle A \cong \angle C$ (Isosceles $\triangle$ Theorem) 4. $m\angle 1 > m\angle A$ (Ext. $\angle$ Inequality Th.) 5. $m\angle 1 > m\angle C$ (Subst.)   **30.** 1. $AB + BC >$ AC, $CD + DA > AC$ (Triangle Inequality Th.) 2. $AB + BC +$ $CD + DA > AC + AC$ (Addition Prop. of $\neq$.) 3. $AB + BC + CD +$ $DA > 2AC$ (Addition)   **32.** at the point of intersection of the diagonals of $ABCD$ **34.** Part a: 1. Line l and pt. P not on l (Given) 2. Let Q be any pt. on l. (A line contains an infinite number of points). 3. Draw $m \perp l$ through Q (Through a given pt. on a line there is exactly one line in the plane $\perp$ to the given line.) 4. If P is not on m, draw n through P so $n \parallel m$. (Parallel Post.) 5. $n \perp l$ (If a line is $\perp$ to one of two $\parallel$ lines, it is $\perp$ to the other.) Part b: Either there is only one line through P $\perp$ to l or there is more than one line through $P \perp$ to l. Suppose there are two or more lines through $P \perp l$. Let s and t be two lines through $P \perp l$. Then $s \parallel t$ since both are $\perp$ to l. But this contradicts the fact that P is in both s and t. Therefore, the assumption is false. Conclude that there is only one line through $P \perp l$.   **36.** $(4, 1\frac{1}{3})$, $4 + 2\sqrt{10}$ mi or ≈ 10.3 mi
38. $\angle A$ **40.** Assume $\overline{YM}$ is an altitude to $\overline{XZ}$. By definition of altitude, $\overline{YM} \perp \overline{XZ}$. $\angle YMX \cong \angle YMZ$ by definition of $\perp$ lines. Since $\overline{YM}$ is the median to $\overline{XZ}$, M is the midpoint of $\overline{XZ}$ by definition of median. Then $\overline{XM} \cong \overline{MZ}$ by definition of midpoint. $\overline{YM} \cong$ $\overline{YM}$ by the Reflexive Prop. Hence, $\triangle YMZ \cong \triangle YMX$ by SAS Post.

27. If the longer side of a parallelogram has a length x, where x is a whole number, and the longer diagonal has a length of 10, give the possible whole numbers for the length of the shorter side of the parallelogram.

28. Given: $AB = BC$
Prove: $m\angle 1 > m\angle C$

29. Given: E is in the interior of $\angle BAC$:
Prove: $m\angle 1 > m\angle 2$
(HINT: Compare $m\angle 1$ and $m\angle 2$ with $m\angle EDC$.)

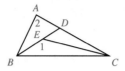

30. Given: quadrilateral $ABCD$
Prove: $AB + BC + CD + DA > 2(AC)$

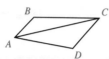

31. Given: quadrilateral $ABCD$
Prove: $AB + BC + CD > AD$

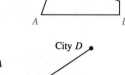

32. A railroad company is to build an engine house to service four cities located at the vertices $ABCD$ of a quadrilateral as shown here. Where should the engine house H be located so that the length, and hence the construction costs, of the roadbed $AH + BH + CH + DH$ is as small as possible?

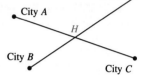

33. Use the figure to the right to prove Corollary 5.22a.
Given: Line ℓ with P not on ℓ, $\overline{PQ} \perp \ell$
Prove: $\overline{PQ}$ is the shortest segment from P to ℓ.

34. Use the figure to the right to prove Theorem 2.9.
Only one perpendicular can be drawn from a point not on a line to a line.
Given: Line ℓ and point P not on ℓ
Prove: a. There is one line through P perpendicular to ℓ.
     b. There is only one line through P perpendicular to ℓ.

35. Cities are located at A, B, C, and D as shown in the figure to the right. Railroad tracks are to be laid from H to each of the cities. What is the total length of track needed?
(HINT: The length of an altitude of an equilateral triangle is $\frac{\sqrt{3}}{2}$ times the length of a side.) Where should H be located so that the total length of the tracks is the least possible?

36. Suppose cities are located at points A, B, C, and D as shown on the coordinate grid. Where is a point H located if $AH + BH + CH + DH$ is a minimum? What is the value of this minimum? (Use the distance formula and a calculator.)

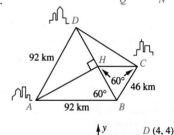

Determine the largest angle of $\triangle ABC$ for the given coordinates of A, B, and C.

37. $A(0, 0)$, $B(5, 0)$, $C(1, 5)$ **38.** $A(-1, 2)$, $B(-2, -1)$, $C(2, 0)$
39. $A(2, -5)$, $B(4, -1)$, $C(7, -4)$

240   *Chapter 5   Using Congruent Triangles and Parallel Lines*

40. Use the figure to the right to prove the statement. The median $\overline{YM}$ from vertex Y of scalene $\triangle XYZ$ is longer than the altitude $\overline{YN}$ from vertex Y.

Given: $\triangle XYZ$ is scalene. $\overline{YN}$ is an altitude. $\overline{YM}$ is a median.

Prove: $YM > YN$

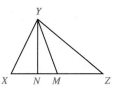

C

41. Use the figure to the right to prove Theorem 5.23.

Given: $\triangle ABC$

Prove: a. $AB + BC > AC$
b. $BC + AC > AB$
c. $AB + AC > BC$

(HINT: Assume one of the sides is the longest. Two of the statements are then easily established. To prove the third statement, drop a perpendicular from the appropriate vertex to the opposite side.)

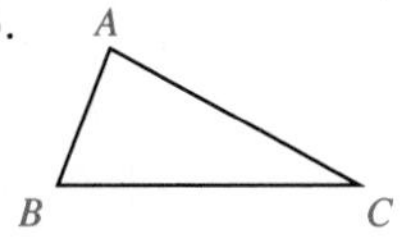

42. Given: P is in the interior of $\triangle ABC$.

Prove: $PB + PC < AB + AC$

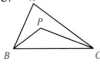

43. Prove that the sum of the lengths of the three altitudes of $\triangle ABC$ is less than the sum of the lengths of the sides of the triangle.

44. Prove that the sum of the lengths of the medians of $\triangle ABC$ is greater than half the perimeter.

Critical Thinking

45. Suppose a triangle is made of 12 chain linkages. List the lengths of the sides of possible triangles. Assume each link is one unit.

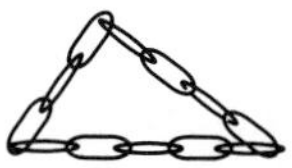

Algebra Review

Find all values of x.

1. $|x| = 7$
2. $|-x| = -7$
3. $|-x| = 7$
4. $x = |7|$
5. $2|x| = 7$
6. $x = |-7|$
7. $|x| + 1 = 7$
8. $|x| + |-1| = 7$
9. $x - |-1| = 7$
10. $-2|x| = -14$
11. $|2x + 1| = 14$
12. $|x - 1| - 1 = 7$

Translate to an equation and solve.

13. The product of two consecutive integers is 132. Find the integers

14. The product of two consecutive even integers is 168. Find the integers.

15. The square of a number is six more than the number. Find the number.

16. Twice the square of a number is 10 more than the number. Find the number.

17. Twice the square of a number plus one is 73. Find the number.

18. The square of a number minus twice the number is 48. Find the number.

Then $\overline{YX} \cong \overline{YZ}$ by corr. parts of $\cong \triangle$s are $\cong$. This contradicts the fact that $\overline{YX} \neq \overline{YZ}$ by definition of scalene $\triangle$. Therefore, $\overline{YM}$ is not an altitude to $\overline{XZ}$. Since $\overline{YN}$ is an altitude, $\overline{YN} \perp \overline{XZ}$. Conclude that $YM > YN$ since the $\perp$ segment from a point to a line is the shortest segment from the point to the line. **42.** Extend $\overline{BP}$ to intersect $\overline{AC}$ at point E. 1. $AB + AE > BE$, $CE + EP > PC$ (Sum of lengths of two sides of a $\triangle$ is greater than the length of the third side.) 2. $AB + AE + CE + PE > BE + PC$ (Add. Prop. of $\neq$) 3. $AE + CE = AC$, $BE - PE = BP$ (Seg. Add. Post.) 4. $AB + AC + PE > BE + PC$ (Subtr.) 5. $AB + AC > BE - PE + PC$ (Subtr. Prop. of $\neq$) 6. $PB + PC < AB + AC$ (Subst.) **44.** Given: $\triangle ABC$, $\overline{BE}$, $\overline{DC}$, and $\overline{AF}$ are medians. Prove: $AF + BE + DC > \frac{1}{2}(AB + BC + AC)$ 1. $AX + DX > AD$, $BX + XF > BF$, $CX + XE > CE$ (Sum of lengths of two sides of a $\triangle$ is greater than the length of the third side.) 2. $AX + DX + BX + XF + CX + XE > AD + BF + CE$ (Add. Prop. of $\neq$) 3. $AF = AX + XF$, $BE = BX + XE$, $DC = DX + XC$ (Seg. Add. Post.) 4. $AF + BE + DC > AD + BF + CE$ (Subst.) 5. $AD = \frac{1}{2}AB$, $BF = \frac{1}{2}BC$, $CE = \frac{1}{2}AC$ (Def. median of $\triangle$) 6. $AF + BE + DC > \frac{1}{2}AB + \frac{1}{2}BC + \frac{1}{2}AC$ (Subst.) 7. $AF + BE + DC > \frac{1}{2}(AB + BC + AC)$ (Distr. Prop.)

Algebra Review Answers

1. $-7, 7$ **2.** no value
3. $-7, 7$ **4.** 7 **5.** $-\frac{7}{2}, \frac{7}{2}$
6. 7 **7.** $-6, 6$ **8.** $-6, 6$
9. 8 **10.** $-7, 7$
11. $-7\frac{1}{2}, 6\frac{1}{2}$ **12.** $-7, 9$
13. $11, 12; -11, -12$ **14.** $12, 14; -12, -14$ **15.** $3, -2$
16. $-2, \frac{5}{2}$ **17.** ± 6
18. $8, -6$

Connections Answers

1. a and $b \geq 0$ or a and $b \leq 0$ 2. If vectors (a, b) and (c, d) form sides of a triangle of lengths $\sqrt{a^2 + b^2}$ and $\sqrt{c^2 + d^2}$ and the third side is formed by their sum $(a + c, b + d)$, a vector of length $\sqrt{(a + c)^2 + (b + d)^2}$, then $\sqrt{a^2 + b^2} + \sqrt{c^2 + d^2} > \sqrt{(a + c)^2 + (b + d)^2}$ because of the Triangle Inequality Theorem.   3. if $a = b$ 4. if $a = b$ and $a, b \geq 0$ 5. For all non-negative values of a and b, when $a \neq b$ the segment $\sqrt{ab}$ must be on one side or the other of the segment $\frac{a + b}{2}$, and so must have a lesser value.

CONNECTIONS ◇◇

Geometric and Algebraic Inequalities

The Triangle Inequality Theorem, one of the most famous in geometry, has an important counterpart with the same name in algebra. There the theorem states that for any two real numbers a and b, $|a| + |b| > |a + b|$. The triangle inequality takes many other forms. With vectors, which were introduced in the Connections on page 116, the vector sum of two vectors (a, b) and (c, d) can be defined as the vector $(a + c, b + d)$. Then, as shown by the graph of these three vectors, we can see that the triangle inequality could be written as

$$\sqrt{a^2 + b^2} + \sqrt{c^2 + d^2} > \sqrt{(a + c)^2 + (b + d)^2}$$

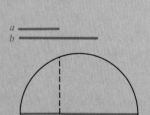

Many other famous inequalities that occur in geometry have algebraic counterparts. Two of the most famous are the arithmetic mean and the geometric mean of numbers. Two numbers a and b have an arithmetic mean $\frac{(a + b)}{2}$ and a geometric mean $\sqrt{ab}$. A famous result provides an inequality relating these two means.

$$\frac{(a + b)}{2} > \sqrt{ab} \text{ for all nonnegative real numbers } a \text{ and } b$$

The arithmetic mean of two numbers is simply their common average. The geometric mean of two nonnegative real numbers a and b can be illustrated by the following process. Find a segment having lengths a and b. Put these segments end to end and draw a semicircle having the two segments as diameter. Construct a segment perpendicular to the two segments at their common endpoint and extend it until it intersects the circle. The length of this segment is the geometric mean of a and b, which is $\sqrt{ab}$.

You will study more about the geometric mean in Chapter 7.

Exercises

1. For what real numbers a and b is it the case that $|a| + |b| = |a + b|$?
2. Use the fact that the length of the vector (x, y) is $\sqrt{x^2 + y^2}$ and the geometric Triangle Inequality Theorem presented in this section to argue that $\sqrt{a^2 + b^2} + \sqrt{c^2 + d^2} > \sqrt{(a + c)^2 + (b + d)^2}$ for the vectors (a, b), (c, d), and their sum, $(a + c, b + d)$.
3. Under what conditions will the arithmetic mean, $\frac{(a + b)}{2}$, of two numbers a and b be equal to the numbers themselves?
4. Under what conditions will the inequality involving the arithmetic mean and geometric mean of two numbers a and b assume the equality $\frac{(a + b)}{2} = \sqrt{ab}$?
5. Give a convincing argument that, for all nonnegative values of a and b, other than those cited in the answer to Exercise 4, $\frac{(a + b)}{2} > \sqrt{ab}$.

OBJECTIVE: *Apply the SAS and SSS Inequality Theorems involving triangles.*

5-8 Inequalities in Two Triangles

 **EXPLORE**

Use straws or other suitable objects to make three triangles with the following lengths (in inches): **a.** 3, 4, 2 **b.** 3, 4, 5 **c.** 3, 4, 6. In which triangle is the angle included between the sides of length 3 and 4 the smallest? the largest?

Write a generalization about your findings.

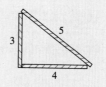

The theorems in this lesson involve two triangles in which two sides of one triangle are congruent to two sides of another triangle.

◆ **THEOREM 5.24** SAS Inequality Theorem

If two sides of one triangle are congruent to two sides of a second triangle and the included angle of the first triangle is larger than the included angle of the second triangle, then the third side of the first triangle is longer than the third side of the second triangle.

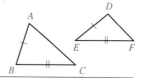

The above theorem says that if $AB = DE$ and $BC = EF$, then the relationship between the lengths of $\overline{AC}$ and $\overline{DF}$ depends on the measures of $\angle B$ and $\angle E$.

You will be asked to prove Theorem 5.24 in Exercise 26.

◆ **THEOREM 5.25** SSS Inequality Theorem

If two sides of one triangle are congruent to two sides of a second triangle, and the third side of the first triangle is longer than the third side of the second triangle, then the angle opposite the third side of the first triangle is larger than the angle opposite the third side of the second triangle.

Given: $AB = DE$, $BC = EF$, $AC > DF$

Prove: $m\angle B > m\angle E$

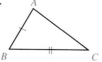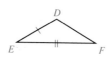

Plan Use an indirect proof. Assume $m\angle B \ngtr m\angle E$

Case 1: Let $m\angle B = m\angle E$. Show $\triangle ABC \cong \triangle DEF$ by SAS and obtain the contradiction that $AC = DF$.

Case 2: Let $m\angle B < m\angle E$. Obtain the contradiction that $AC < DF$ by the SAS Triangle Inequality Theorem. Conclude that $m\angle B > m\angle E$.

First Five Minutes

(Quiz on previous lesson)

Can a triangle with sides of the following lengths be constructed? If not, explain why.

1. 6,8,10 yes
2. 3,4,5 yes
3. 11,9,4 yes
4. 2,4,6 No; sum of two sides must be greater than third side. $2 + 4 = 6$
5. 2.5,4.1,5 yes

Lesson Opener

Begin by discussing the Explore and the effect on the length of $\overline{AC}$ as $\angle B$ increases. If students are having difficulty seeing the effect on the measures of the included angles, have them copy $\triangle ABC$, measure $\angle B$, then draw another triangle in which $AB = BC$ but $\angle B$ is larger.

Other physical models, such as pencils or toothpicks, can also be used to illustrate the SAS and SSS Inequality Theorems.

Have students consider a top view of a door opening and the distance between the edge of the door and the door frame.

Materials

student notebooks
rulers
protractors
pencils/toothpicks
investigative software

Teaching Notes

Emphasize the difference between the theorems in this lesson and the SSS and SAS Congruence Postulates. Point out that the SAS and SSS Inequality Theorems are sometimes referred to as the "hinge theorems." Ask why these theorems are called hinge theorems.

Guided Practice

Chalkboard Example

State the conclusion you can draw if $AD = BC$ and $m\angle 2 > m\angle 4$. $DC > AB$

Answer to **Try This**

$m\angle 1 > m\angle 3$

Class Exercise Answers

1. $>$ 2. $>$ 3. $=$
4. $>$ 5. $>$ 6. $<$
7. $>$ 8. $<$ 9. never
10. always   11. $\angle CGE$ is a rt. $\angle$ formed by $\perp$ lines. $\angle EGF$ is a 45° $\angle$ formed by the diagonal bisecting rt. $\angle FGH$. Therefore, $m\angle CGE > m\angle EGF$. Since $CG = FG$ and $EG = EG$, by the SAS Inequality Theorem, $EC > FE$.

Assignment Guide

Minimum: 1–23 e/o, 29, AR
Regular: 1–28 e/o, 29, AR
Advanced: 4, 10–12, 14–29, AR

Coordinate Geometry

Exercises 17, 18

Algebra

Exercise 14, AR

Example 1

What conclusions can be drawn from the given information?

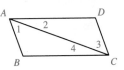

a. $AB = CD$, $m\angle 1 > m\angle 3$
b. $AB = CD$, $m\angle 1 = m\angle 3$
c. $AD = BC$, $AB > CD$

Solution

a. $BC > AD$ **b.** $\triangle ABC \cong \triangle CDA$ **c.** $m\angle 4 > m\angle 2$

Try This

What conclusions can be drawn if $AB = CD$ and $BC > AD$?

Class Exercises

Short Answer

Given $\triangle ABC$ and $\triangle DEF$, $AB = DE$ and $BC = EF$, complete each statement by using $>$, $<$, or $=$.

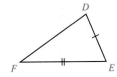

1. If $m\angle B > m\angle E$, then AC ___ DF.
2. If $DF < AC$, then $m\angle B$ ___ $m\angle E$.
3. If $AC = DF$, then $m\angle E$ ___ $m\angle B$.
4. If $m\angle E > m\angle B$, then DF ___ AC.
5. If $AC < DF$, then $m\angle E$ ___ $m\angle B$.

Sample Exercises

Complete each statement by using $>$, $<$, or $=$.

6.

$m\angle 1$ ___ $m\angle 2$

7.
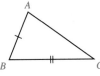

CD ___ BD

8.

$m\angle 1$ ___ $m\angle 2$

Determine whether the statement is always, sometimes, or never true.

9. If $PN = RT$, $MN = RS$, and $m\angle N < m\angle R$, then $PM > ST$.
10. If $PM = ST$, $MN = RS$ and $PN > RT$, then $m\angle M > m\angle S$.

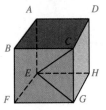

Discussion

11. Consider the cube to the right. Each edge of the cube has a length of one unit. Consider $\triangle EGC$ and $\triangle EGF$ and use the SAS Inequality Theorem to explain why $EC > FE$.

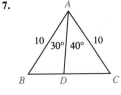

Exercises

A

What conclusion can be drawn from the given information?

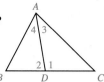

1. $BD = DC$, $m\angle 1 > m\angle 2$
2. $AB = AC$, $m\angle 3 > m\angle 4$
3. $\overline{AD}$ is a median. $AB > AC$
4. $\triangle ABC$ is isosceles with base $\overline{BC}$. $CD > BD$

Determine whether each statement is always, sometimes, or never true.

5. If $AB = DE$, $BC = FD$, and $m\angle B > m\angle D$, then $FE > AC$.
6. If $AB = DE$, $AC = FE$ and $BC < FD$, then $m\angle A < m\angle E$.
7. If $m\angle B < m\angle D$, $m\angle C < m\angle F$, then $m\angle A > m\angle E$.
8. If $BC = FD$, $m\angle C > m\angle F$ then $m\angle A > m\angle E$.
9. If $AB = DE$, $BC = FD$, $AC > FE$, then $m\angle D > m\angle B$.
10. If $BC = FD$, $AC = FE$, and $m\angle C < m\angle F$, then $DE > AB$.

11. **Given:** $AB = CD$, $m\angle ABC > m\angle BCD$
    Prove: $AC > BD$

12. **Given:** $AB = CD$, $m\angle 1 > m\angle 2$
    Prove: $ABCD$ is not a $\square$.
    (HINT: Use an indirect proof.)

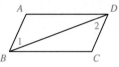

13. **Given:** $\overline{AC}$ is a median. $m\angle 1 > m\angle 2$
    Prove: $AB > AD$

B

14. In $\triangle MNP$, $\overline{MX}$ is a median, $m\angle MXN = 4x + 6$ and $m\angle MXP = 7x - 2$.
    Which side is longer, $\overline{MN}$ or $\overline{MP}$? Which angle is larger, $\angle N$ or $\angle P$?
15. Quadrilateral $ABCD$ has $AB = AC = AD$, $m\angle DCA = 50$, and $m\angle ACB = 55$.
    Which side is longer, $\overline{CD}$ or $\overline{BC}$? Which angle is larger, $\angle B$ or $\angle D$?
16. P is a point above the plane determined by equilateral $\triangle ABC$. If $PC > PB$, which
    angle is larger, $\angle PAC$ or $\angle PAB$?

**Determine whether $m\angle A < m\angle D$, $m\angle A = m\angle D$, or $m\angle A > m\angle D$,
given the following coordinates for triangles ABC and DEF.**

17. $A(1, 1)$, $B(2, 3)$, $C(4, 0)$,
    $D(1, -2)$, $E(2, 0)$, $F(-2, -3)$
18. $A(-2, 3)$, $B(-3, 0)$, $C(1, 2)$,
    $D(3, 0)$, $E(2, 3)$, $F(0, 1)$

Lesson Closure

Ask students to restate the SAS and SSS Inequality Theorems.

Teacher's Resource Materials

Practice Master 37
Quiz 10

Exercise Answers

See Selected Answers for odd-numbered exercises.
2. $DC > BD$ **4.** $m\angle 3 > m\angle 4$ **6.** always
8. sometimes   **10.** always
12. Assume $ABCD$ is a $\square$.
Then $\overline{AD} \cong \overline{BC}$. It is given that
$AB = CD$ and $m\angle 1 > m\angle 2$.
$BD = BD$ by the Reflexive
Prop. Conclude that $AD > BC$
by SAS Inequality Th. This
contradicts the assumption that
$ABCD$ is a $\square$. The assumption
must be false. Therefore, $ABCD$
is not a $\square$.   **14.** $MN < MP$,
$m\angle N > m\angle P$
16. $m\angle PAC > m\angle PAB$
18. $m\angle A > m\angle D$

20. 1. $AB = AD$ (Given)
2. $AC = AC$ (Reflexive Prop.)
3. $BC > DC$ (Given) 4. $m\angle 2 > m\angle 1$ (SSS Inequality Th.)

22. 1. $\overline{CD} \perp$ bisector of $\overline{AB}$ (Given) 2. $\overline{AD} \cong \overline{DB}$ (Def. $\perp$ bisector) 3. $\overline{CD} \cong \overline{CD}$ (Reflexive Prop.) 4. $\triangle CDA \cong \triangle CDB$ (SAS Congruence Post.) 5. $\angle A \cong \angle DBC$ (Corr. parts of $\cong \triangle$s are $\cong$.) 6. $m\angle A = m\angle DBC$ (Def. $\cong \triangle$s) 7. $m\angle DBE = m\angle DBC + m\angle CBE$ (Angle Add. Post.) 8. $m\angle DBE > m\angle DBC$ (Algebra) 9. $m\angle DBE < m\angle A$ (Subst.) 10. $AE > BE$ (If one side of a $\triangle$ then the measure of the $\angle$ opposite the longer side is greater than the measure of the $\angle$ opposite the shorter side.)

24. 1. $AC > AB$ (Given)
2. $m\angle ABC > m\angle ACB$ (If one side of a $\triangle$ is longer than a second side, the measure of the $\angle$ opposite the longer side is greater than the measure of the $\angle$ opposite the shorter side.)
3. $\overline{DC}$ and $\overline{EC}$ trisect $\angle ACB$, $\overline{DB}$ and $\overline{EB}$ trisect $\angle ABC$. (Given)
4. $m\angle EBC = \frac{1}{3}m\angle ABC$, $m\angle ECB = \frac{1}{3}m\angle ACB$ (Def. trisector) 5. $\frac{1}{3}m\angle ABC > \frac{1}{3}m\angle ACB$ (Mult. Prop. of =) 6. $m\angle EBC > m\angle ECB$ (Subst.) 7. $EC > BE$ (If one $\angle$ of a $\triangle$ is larger than another $\angle$, the side opposite the larger $\angle$ is longer than the side opposite the smaller $\angle$.)

26. 1. $m\angle 1 = m\angle 2$ (Given)
2. $\overline{BE} \cong \overline{EC}$ (If two $\angle$s of a $\triangle$ are $\cong$, the sides opposite them are $\cong$.) 3. $\overline{AE} \cong \overline{AE}$ (Reflexive Prop.) 4. $AB > AC$ (Given) 5. $m\angle AEB > m\angle AEC$ (SSS Inequality Th.) 6. $m\angle AEB + m\angle 3 = 180$, $m\angle AEC + m\angle 4 = 180$ (Linear Pair)

19. Given: D is the midpoint of $\overline{AB}$.
   $AE = BF$
   $AC < BC$
   Prove: $DF < DE$

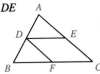

21. Given: $RU > RT$
   $VU = ST$
   Prove: $SU > TV$

23. Given: N, P, Q are in plane T.
   $m\angle MNQ > m\angle MNP$
   $NP = NQ$
   Prove: $m\angle MPQ > m\angle MQP$

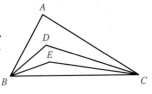

C

24. Given: $AC > AB$
   $\overline{DC}$ and $\overline{EC}$ trisect $\angle ACB$.
   $\overline{DB}$ and $\overline{EB}$ trisect $\angle ABC$.
   Prove: $EC > BE$

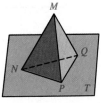

25. Given: $m\angle 1 = m\angle 2$
   $m\angle 3 > m\angle 4$
   Prove: $AC > AB$

26. Given: $m\angle 1 = m\angle 2$
   $AB > AC$
   Prove: $m\angle 3 < m\angle 4$

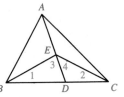

27. Given: $\overline{AC} \perp$ plane N
   $AD > AB$
   Prove: $CD > BC$
   (HINT: Select point E on $\overleftrightarrow{CD}$ so that $BC = CE$.)

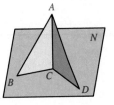

20. Given: $AB = AD$
   $BC > DC$
   Prove: $m\angle 2 > m\angle 1$

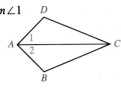

22. Given: $\overline{CD} \perp$ bisector of $\overline{AB}$
   E is on $\overleftrightarrow{AC}$.
   Prove: $AE > BE$

28. Complete the following proof for Theorem 5.24. Draw $\overline{BP}$ so that $\angle PBC \cong \angle E$. Select M so that $BM = DE$. There are two possibilities. Either M is on $\overline{AC}$ or M is not on $\overline{AC}$. Regardless, $\triangle BMC \cong \triangle EDF$ and $MC = DF$.
Case 1: M is on $\overline{AC}$. Explain why $AC > DF$.
Case 2: M is not on $\overline{AC}$. Let $\overline{BN}$ bisect $\angle ABM$. Draw $\overline{NM}$ and $\overline{MC}$. $AB = BM = DE$. Use the fact that $\triangle ABN \cong \triangle MBN$ and that $AN = NM$ to explain why $AC > DF$.

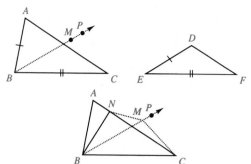

Critical Thinking

29. $\overrightarrow{PA}$ is perpendicular to the plane determined by the equilateral triangle ABC. Which segment is the longest: $\overline{AB}$, $\overline{BC}$, $\overline{CA}$, $\overline{PA}$, $\overline{PB}$, or $\overline{PC}$? Write a paragraph proof to justify your choice.

Algebra Review

Solve for x.

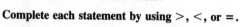

1. $\frac{x}{3} = \frac{4}{2}$ **2.** $\frac{12}{16} = \frac{6}{x}$ **3.** $\frac{16}{x} = \frac{x}{4}$

Quiz

E, F, and G are the midpoints of sides $\overline{AC}$, $\overline{AB}$, and $\overline{CB}$ respectively.

1. If $AC = 24$, find FG.
2. If $EG = 2x + 12$ and $AF = 16$, find EG.
3. If $EG = 7$, $FG = 8$, and $CB = 12$, find the perimeter of $\triangle ABC$.

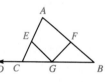

Refer to the figure to the right.
4. In $\triangle LMO$, name the smallest angle.
5. In $\triangle MNO$, name the shortest side.
6. Which is shorter, $\overline{LO}$ or $\overline{MN}$?
7. Using the Triangle Inequality Theorem, $m\angle NMO > m\underline{\ ?\ }$ and $m\underline{\ ?\ }$.

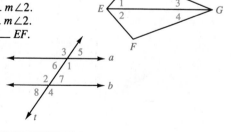

Complete each statement by using $>$, $<$, or $=$.
8. If $DE = EF$ and $DG < FG$, then $m\angle 1 \underline{\ \ } m\angle 2$.
9. If $DG = GF$ and $EF = DE$, then $m\angle 1 \underline{\ \ } m\angle 2$.
10. If $m\angle 3 > m\angle 4$ and $DG = FG$, then $DE \underline{\ \ } EF$.

11. Write an indirect proof for the following.
Given: $\angle 1 \not\cong \angle 2$
Prove: $\angle 3 \not\cong \angle 4$

7. $m\angle AEB + m\angle 3 = m\angle AEC + m\angle 4$ (Trans. Prop.)
8. $m\angle 3 < m\angle 4$ (Algebra)
28. Case 1: $AC > MC$ by Segment Add. Post. and Algebra. $AC > DF$ by Subst. (since $MC = DF$). Case 2: Since $\triangle ABN \cong \triangle MBN$ by SAS Post., $\overline{AN} \cong \overline{NM}$. $MN + NC > MC$ because the sum of the lengths of any two sides of a $\triangle$ is greater than the length of the third side. By Subst. Prop., $AN + NC > MC$, or $AC > MC$. Then $AC > DF$ by Subst. Prop.

Algebra Review Answers

1. 6   **2.** 8   **3.** ±8

Quiz Answers

1. 12   **2.** 16   **3.** 42
4. $\angle MOL$ **5.** $\overline{NO}$
6. $\overline{MN}$ **7.** $\angle L$, $\angle MOL$
8. <   **9.** =   **10.** >
11. Assume $\angle 3 \cong \angle 4$. Then $a \parallel b$ since if two lines are cut by a transversal and alt. ext. $\angle$s are $\cong$, the lines are $\parallel$. Then $\angle 1 \cong \angle 2$ since they are alt. int. $\angle$s. This contradicts the fact that $\angle 1 \not\cong \angle 2$. The assumption must be false. Therefore, $\angle 3 \not\cong \angle 4$.

You may want to begin with a review of graphs. (See Discrete Math, page 199.) Point out that a graph is a good model for a set of towns connected by cables.

Ask students to name other real-world situations in which finding shortest connections would be useful.

Exercise Answers
1. 21   2. 12.5   3. 12

DISCRETE MATH

Finding Shortest Connections

Mathematics is used in planning telephone or other services to find the optimal way of hooking towns, offices, etc. together using the minimal amount of cable or wire. Consider the map for several towns to be served by a cable television network. The problem is to find the minimum amount of cable to connect all of the towns.

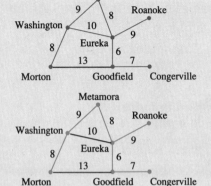

The path shown in red illustrates one method of connecting the towns but it uses more than the minimum; as it connects Washington into the network of towns twice, once through Eureka and once through Metamora. Since the link through Eureka is not needed to connect any other town, it can be deleted. This reduces the amount of cable required by 10 mi.

To find the minimum amount for a task such as shown to the right, you start by identifying one of the towns as the beginning point. This choice has no bearing on the minimal amount, as each town must eventually be connected into the network. Start at this town, say Eureka, and look for the closest town. This is Goodfield, so you would connect the two with a cable. Now look for the next closest town to either town connected and add it to the network, in this case, Congerville. Next look for the town not yet connected that is closest to Eureka, Goodfield, or Congerville. This is Metamora. Include it and then continue asking for the next closest town. In this example, you can see that there is a tie between Washington and Roanoke, so either can be chosen at this point. Suppose you choose Washington. You would next add Morton and then Roanoke. What would have happened if you had chosen Roanoke instead of Washington? All of the towns are now connected and the amount of cable needed to complete the cable network is the sum of the lengths shown in blue, 6 + 7 + 8 + 9 + 8 + 9, or 47 mi of cable.

A collection of edges that touch all of the points in a graph, but which allow only one way of traveling from point to point without repeating other points is called a tree. The process of finding this shortest connecting set of links is known as finding a minimal spanning tree. Sometimes more than one minimal spanning tree exists, but the minimal distances for each tree will be the same.

Exercises

Find the minimal spanning tree and the total length for each of the following.

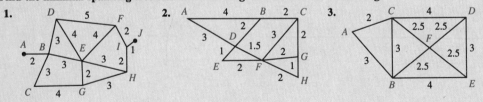

CRITICAL THINKING

Analyzing and Evaluating Evidence

Sometimes it is possible to jump to a conclusion on the basis of evidence that is unreliable or incomplete. Some evidence is **possibly true,** other evidence is **probably true,** and still other evidence is **accepted as true.** Consider the following examples.

Example 1

a. By observation only, decide if line k, when extended, will meet point A, B, C, or none of these points.

b. Read the following silently and then aloud.

A BIRD IN THE
THE HAND IS WORTH
TWO IN THE BUSH

What do you notice? What kind of evidence are you using in these examples?

Solution

a. point A
b. The word *the* is repeated.
In both cases, observational evidence was used. These examples show that we do not always see what we think we see. Observational evidence should be treated with caution and classified as possibly or probably true.

Example 2

As Jerry came around a corner, he saw his steady girlfriend Rhonda walking into a theater with another boy. Jerry concluded that Rhonda was dating someone else and was very angry. What kind of evidence was Jerry using in his decision?

Solution

Jerry based his conclusion on circumstantial evidence. The truth was that Rhonda was meeting her aunt at the theater and was only walking through the door next to a boy from school. Circumstantial evidence should be considered as possibly true.

Example 3

Mr. Higami was clocked traveling 48 mph in a 35 mph zone by a policeman's radar gun. Two reputable witnesses, who had checked the radar gun before and after Mr. Higami's ticket was issued, testified that the gun was working properly. Another policeman who was riding in the car with the officer verified the officer's story. What kind of evidence do you have in this case?

Solution

The evidence here is of the type that is accepted to be true. In a case such as this, many different facts corroborate the fact in contention. Even in such cases where the evidence is considered true beyond any reasonable doubt, there is always a small possibility that it could be false.

Exercises

1. After Karen began dating Javier, her report card showed she was getting a lower grade in each of her classes. Her mother checked Karen's study time and found that she spent an average of only four hours a week on homework. Karen seemed to be trying to get better grades and did not want to talk about her lower grades. Decide if each of the following statements of evidence is possibly true, probably true, or accepted as true.
   a. Karen was getting better grades before she started dating Javier.
   b. Karen is spending less time on homework since she started dating Javier.
   c. Karen feels guilty or embarrassed about her lower grades.
2. Plan and rehearse a brief incident that a group of three or four students could act out in class. After a group presents an incident, write a careful "eyewitness report" of exactly what happened. How does your report compare to that of a classmate?
3. Describe a situation in which you drew an incorrect conclusion based on circumstantial evidence.

Recognizing Common Errors in Thought

Exercise Answers
1. **a.** accepted as true
   b. possibly true
   c. probably true
2. Answers may vary.
3. Answers may vary.

CHAPTER SUMMARY

Vocabulary

bases of a trapezoid (5-4)
contradiction (5-6)
indirect proof (5-6)
isosceles trapezoid (5-4)

median of a trapezoid (5-4)
midsegment of a triangle (5-5)
negation (5-6)
parallelogram (5-1)

rhombus (5-3)
rectangle (5-3)
square (5-3)
trapezoid (5-4)

Key Ideas

1. A parallelogram has the following properties.
   a. Opposite sides are parallel.   **b.** Opposite sides are congruent.
   c. Opposite angles are congruent.   **d.** Consecutive angles are supplementary.
   e. Diagonals bisect each other.
2. Rectangles, rhombuses, and squares are special types of parallelograms.
3. A quadrilateral is a parallelogram if any one of the following is true.
   a. Both pairs of opposite sides are parallel.
   b. Both pairs of opposite sides are congruent.
   c. One pair of sides are parallel and congruent.
   d. Both pairs of opposite angles are congruent.
   e. Consecutive angles are supplementary.
   f. Diagonals bisect each other.
4. The median of a trapezoid is parallel to the bases and its length is half the sum of the lengths of the bases.
5. A segment that joins the midpoints of two sides of a triangle is parallel to the third side and its length is half the length of the third side.
6. In an indirect proof, you assume the negation of the *prove* statement and reason logically to reach a contradiction. Then conclude that the assumption is false and the *prove* statement is true.
7. In a triangle, the measure of an exterior angle is greater than the measure of either of the remote interior angles.
8. In a triangle, the longer side is opposite the largest angle. The converse is also true.
9. The sum of any two sides of a triangle is greater than the third side.
10. The SAS and SSS Inequality Theorems are two methods for comparing angles and sides of two triangles.

CHAPTER REVIEW

5-1

Use parallelogram *STAR* to complete each statement.

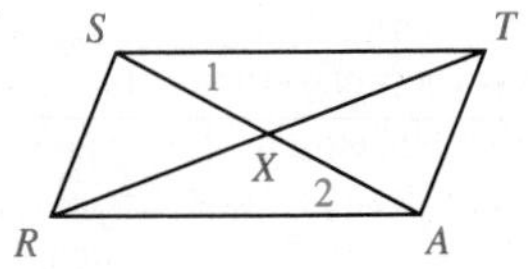

1. If $m\angle 1 = 32$, then $m\angle 2 =$ ___ .
2. If $m\angle TSR = 125$, then $m\angle SRA =$ ___ and $m\angle TAR =$ ___ .
3. If $ST = 8$, then ___ $= 8$.
4. If $RT = 16$, then $XT =$ ___ .
5. If $SR = 5x + 10$ and $TA = 2x + 43$, then $TA =$ ___ .

5-2

Determine if the quadrilateral is a parallelogram. If so, state the theorem or definition that justifies the conclusion. If not, write *no conclusion*.

6.   7.   8.   9.

5-3

Classify each statement as always, sometimes, or never true.

10. Opposite sides of a rhombus are parallel.
11. All angles of a rhombus are right angles.
12. Diagonals of a square bisect the opposite angles.
13. All sides of a parallelogram are congruent.

5-4

MATH is a trapezoid and $\overline{XY}$ is a median. Complete each statement.

14. $\overline{MA}$ and $\overline{HT}$ are called the ___ of the trapezoid.
15. If $m\angle H = 35$, then $m\angle MXY = $ ___ .
16. If $AY = 5$, then $AT = $ ___ .
17. If $MA = 10$ and $HT = 24$, then $XY = $ ___ .

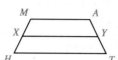

5-5

Indicate whether each statement is true or false.

18. If $\overline{SV} \| \overline{TU}$, then $SV = \frac{1}{2}TU$.
19. If $\overline{RW} \| \overline{SX} \| \overline{TU}$ and $RS = ST$, then $WX = XU$.
20. A parallelogram results if the midpoints of the consecutive sides of quadrilateral $RWUT$ are joined.
21. If S is the midpoint of $\overline{RT}$, then $\overline{SV}$ bisects $\overline{RU}$.

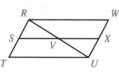

5-6

22. Write the negation of the following statement. $\angle ABC$ is an obtuse angle.
23. The statement "$\angle A \cong \angle B$ and $\angle A \not\cong \angle B$" is called a __?__ .

5-7

24. In $\triangle RST$, $m\angle R = 35$ and $m\angle S = 40$. List the sides of the triangle from shortest to longest.
25. In $\triangle WXY$, if $WX > WY > XY$, name the largest angle in the triangle.
26. A triangle has two sides of lengths 3 and 7. The length of the third side must be greater than __?__ and less than __?__ .

5-8

Complete each statement and state the theorem that supports your conclusion.

27. If $ED = DG$ and $m\angle 1 = m\angle 2$, then ___ = ___ .
28. If $EF = FG$ and ___ < ___ , then $m\angle 3 < m\angle 4$.
29. If $EF = GD$ and $m\angle 3 > m\angle 2$, then ___ > ___ .

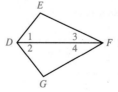

Chapter Review Answers

1. 32   2. 55, 125   3. *RA*
4. 8   5. 65   6. Yes, if both pairs of opposite $\angle$s are $\cong$, then the quadrilateral is a $\square$.
7. Yes, if diagonals bisect each other, then the quadrilateral is a $\square$.   8. Yes, 2 $\triangle$s are $\cong$ by SAS Post., so opp. sides are $\cong$ and the quadrilateral is a $\square$.
9. Yes, if both pairs of opposite sides are $\|$, then the quadrilateral is a $\square$.   10. always
11. sometimes   12. always
13. sometimes   14. bases
15. 35   16. 10   17. 17
18. false   19. true   20. true
21. false   22. $\angle ABC$ is not an obtuse angle.   23. contradiction   24. *ST, RT, RS*
25. $\angle Y$ 26. 4, 10
27. $EF = FG$; SAS Post.
28. $DE < DG$; Th. 5.25
29. $DE > FG$; Th. 5.24

Test Objectives

Item	Objective
6, 7, 10	5-1
5, 8, 9	5-2
1, 2, 3	5-3
4, 11, 12	5-4
13, 14, 18	5-5
21, 22, 24	5-6
15, 16, 17	5-7
19, 20, 23	5-8

Teacher's Resource Materials

Chapter 5 Tests

Test Answers

1. *d, f*   **2.** *c, d, e, f*   **3.** *e, f*
4. *b*   **5.** *c, d, e, f*   **6.** *c, d, e, f*
7. If opp. sides of a quadrilateral are ≅, the quadrilateral is a ▱. **8.** If one pair of sides are both ∥ and ≅, then the quadrilateral is a ▱.
9. If diagonals bisect each other, then the quadrilateral is a ▱.
10. Def. of ▱   **11.** 10
12. 5   **13.** =   **14.** 17 cm
15. true   **16.** false
17. true   **18.** false
19. true   **20.** false
21. false   **22.** Assume △*ABC* is an isosceles △.
23. 1. *ABCD* is a ▱. (Given)
2. *m*∠*B* = *m*∠*D* (Opp. ∠s of a ▱ are ≅.) 3. *m*∠1 > *m*∠*B* (Given) 4. *m*∠1 > *m*∠*D* (Subst.)
5. *AD* > *AE* (If one ∠ of a △ is larger than another, then the side opp. the larger ∠ is longer than the side opp. the smaller ∠.) 6. *AD* = *BC* (Opp. sides of a ▱ are ≅.) 7. *BC* > *AE* (Subst.)
24. Assume *RSTU* is isosceles. Then $\overline{RT} \cong \overline{US}$, since diagonals of an isosceles trapezoid are ≅. This contradicts the fact that $\overline{RT} \not\cong \overline{US}$. The assumption must be false. Therefore, *RSTU* is not isosceles.

CHAPTER TEST

List the letters of all the figures that have each of the following properties.

1. Diagonals are congruent.
2. Both pairs of opposite sides are congruent.
3. Diagonals are perpendicular.
4. Exactly one pair of opposite sides are parallel.
5. Diagonals bisect each other.
6. Opposite sides are parallel.

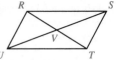

    a. quadrilateral
    b. trapezoid
    c. parallelogram
    d. rectangle
    e. rhombus
    f. square

Use the given information to write the theorem or definition that supports the conclusion that *RSTU* is a parallelogram.

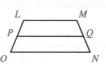

7. *RS* = *UT* and *RU* = *ST*   8. $\overline{RU} \parallel \overline{ST}$ and *RU* = *ST*
9. *RV* = *VT* and *UV* = *VS*   10. $\overline{RS} \parallel \overline{UT}$ and $\overline{RU} \parallel \overline{ST}$

Refer to trapezoid *LMNO* and median $\overline{PQ}$.

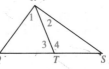

11. If *LM* = 7 and *ON* = 13, find *PQ*.
12. If *PQ* = 2*x* − 6, *LM* = 5*x* − 25, and *ON* = 7, find *LM*.
13. If $\overline{LM} \parallel \overline{PQ}$ and *LP* = *PO*, then *MQ* __?__ *QN*.

14. Find the perimeter of the triangle that is formed by joining the midpoints of the sides of a triangle with sides of lengths 8 cm, 12 cm, and 14 cm.

Classify each statement as true or false.

15. A triangle can have sides of lengths 7 in., 13 in., and 15 in.
16. In △*ABC*, if *AB* > *AC*, then *m*∠*B* > *m*∠*C*.
17. In △*RST*, if *m*∠*R* < *m*∠*S*, then *ST* < *RT*.
18. If a line is parallel to one side of a triangle, then it contains the midpoints of the other two sides.
19. If *RQ* = *TS* and *m*∠1 > *m*∠4, then *QT* > *RS*.
20. If *RQ* = *TS* and *QT* > *RS*, then *m*∠1 < *m*∠4.
21. The negation of *QR* = *RT* is $\overline{QR} \parallel \overline{RT}$.

22. Write the negation you would use to begin an indirect proof.
    Prove: △*ABC* is not an isosceles triangle.

23. Write a two-column proof.   24. Write an indirect proof.

  Given: ▱ *ABCD*   **Given:** trapezoid *RSTU*
        m∠1 > *m*∠*B* $\overline{RT} \not\cong \overline{US}$

  Prove: *BC* > *AE*   **Prove:** *RSTU* is not isosceles.

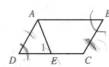

PROBLEM SOLVING

Work Backward

The strategy Work Backward is sometimes helpful in solving problems. Ask yourself, "What information do I need in order to reach the conclusion I want?" Consider statements **a–f** in the following example.

Example

Suppose you have one pail that holds 4 L of water and another that holds 9 L. There are no markings on either pail to indicate how many liters it contains. How can you measure out exactly 6 L of water using these two pails?

Solution

   a. I want to end with 6 L. I can do this if I can pour 3 L from the 9 L pail.
   b. I can pour 3 L from the 9 L pail if there is space for only 3 L in the 4 L pail.
   c. There would be space for only 3 L in the 4 L pail if I could first put 1 L in it.
   d. I can put 1 L in the 4 L pail if I can use the 9 L to measure 1 L.
   e. I can measure 1 L in the 9 L pail if I can pour out 8 L.
   f. I can pour 8 L from the 9 L pail by filling the 4 L pail twice.
Now work backward and use statements **a–f** to write a solution to the problem.

Problem-Solving Strategies	
Draw a Diagram	Find a Pattern
Make a Table	Work Backward

The problem-solving strategies that have been introduced up to this point in the book are presented in the chart.

Problems

Solve each problem by using one of the strategies presented so far.

1. How can you measure out exactly 4 L if you have only an unmarked 5 L pail and an unmarked 7 L pail?
2. A goat owner wanted to make a rectangular pen with as much grazing area as possible. He had only 72 m of fence and wanted the length and width of his pen to be whole numbers. What should the dimensions of his pen be?
3. Suppose there are eight balls that look alike. All are the same weight except one, which is heavier than all the rest. How could you use a balance scale only twice to find the heavier ball? (HINT: Start with the second use of the balance scale. Figure out how you could decide which of two (or three) balls is heavier in only one balancing and work backward.)
4. What is the minimum number of pieces of pizza than can be obtained if a circular pizza is cut eight times with straight cuts.
5. A rhombus-shaped flower bed is to be built in the center of a circular patio. The plans show the rhombus inside a dotted rectangle. $EF = 4$ m and $FG = 6$ m. The builder thinks it will be difficult to calculate the length of the side of the flower bed. Her assistant thinks it will be very easy to find the length with almost no calculation at all. What do you think? Find the length.

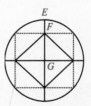

Problem Answers
1. Pour 5 L out of the 7-L pail. Pour the remaining 2 L into the 5-L pail. Fill the 7-L pail and then fill the remainder of the 5-L pail. 4 L are left in the 7-L pail.   **2.** 18 m by 18 m
3. Divide the balls into two groups of two balls and one group of three balls. Test the two pairs of two balls. If these balance, the heavier ball is in the group of three. If these do not balance, the heavier ball is in the heavier pair. If the heavier ball is in the group of three, choose any two balls and see if they balance. If so, the remaining ball is the heavy one. If not, the balance will determine the heavier ball. If the heavy ball is in a group of two, use the balance to find out which it is.
4. 9   **5.** 10 m

Similarity

Chapter Overview

This chapter covers the concept of similarity. Because they are so important in the study of similar figures, the first two lessons of the chapter give students practice in manipulating ratios and proportions. This is followed by three lessons on similar figures with emphasis on similarity postulates for triangles. The final lesson of the chapter deals with proportions related to parallel lines cut by a transversal and proportions related to angle bisectors of a triangle.

Objectives

6-1   ■ Express a ratio in simplest form. Write a proportion and solve for an unknown part.

6-2   ■ Given a proportion, express it in equivalent forms.

6-3   ■ Deduce information about the measures of sides and angles of two similar figures.

6-4   ■ Use the AA Similarity Postulate to draw conclusions about triangles.

6-5   ■ Use the SAS and SSS Similarity Theorems to draw conclusions about triangles.

6-6   ■ Solve proportions related to parallel lines cut by transversals. Solve proportions related to a triangle and an internal angle bisector.

TEACHING CHAPTER 6

Cooperative Learning Opportunities

Study groups are becoming increasingly popular. Students should be made aware of the benefits of studying together and be taught that a cooperative review or problem solving session is not the same as copying homework.

Chapter 6 lends itself to study groups. First, the concept and use of propor-tion, which some students have trouble grasping, will be of great importance in future mathematics and science courses. Second, the chapter contains substantial review of algebra which some students will need explained. Third, the similarity theorems review congruence and other basic concepts while they also look forward to right triangles and the ideas of trigonometry.

A study group does not have to be highly structured. Simply encourage groups of 3, 4, or 5 students to get together whenever they can to review a lesson or to prepare for a test. If time permits, allow some class time for study groups to meet.

Multicultural Note: *Eratosthenes*

Eratosthenes, a mathematician, was born in Cyrene, in present day Libya, and taught in Alexandria. He died in about 194 B.C.

Eratosthenes is best known for his indirect measurement of the circumference of the earth. Eratosthenes knew that on June 21, the summer solstice, the sun cast no shadow at Syene but did cast a shadow at Aléxandria, a city 500 miles away. Considering the sun's rays to be parallel lines, Eratosthenes calculated $m\angle 1$ to be 7.2°. The equality of corresponding angles 2 and 3 shows that the circumference of the earth must be 50 times the distance between Syene and Alexandria.

For more information, see page 69 of **Multiculturalism in Mathematics, Science, and Technology**.

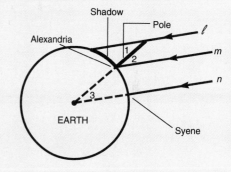

Alternative Assessment and Communication Ideas

Every day you learn more and more about the strengths and weaknesses of individual students as they answer class questions, volunteer information, complete assignments, and perform on quizzes and tests. The following step-by-step analysis can help you understand how an individual student attacks a problem and where difficulties might reside. Have a student respond to the following.

(1) Read the problem.
(2) What are you asked to do or find?
(3) What information will you use?
(4) What is your plan?

These steps allow you to identify in sequence the possible sources of the student's mistakes.

(1) Identifies errors in reading.
(2) Covers comprehension.
(3) Checks ability to find relevant data.
(4) Reviews ability to call on appropriate knowledge and skills.

Investigations and Projects

Initiate a project on similarity by discussing some of the real-world examples of similarity that are mentioned in the chapter.

Then have students begin to collect examples of similarity and write a paragraph about the use and importance of proportion in each case and what life would be like without this instance of similarity. Some examples are given below.

Maps. A map, like a scale drawing, shows relative distances, direction, and relationships. Proportion is very important for judging distances and time.

Photos. A photograph is a two dimensional representation that is similar to the object.

Toys. Many children's toys are representations of objects in the adult world.

Scientific models. Models represent scientific objects: molecules, dinosaurs, the solar system.

Encourage students to display their results on the bulletin board.

Lesson	PACING CHART (DAYS)			Opening Activity	Cooperative Activity	Seat or Group Work
	1-Year Minimum	1-Year Regular	1-Year Advanced			
6-1	1	1	1	Chapter Opener: **TE** p. 254; Lesson Opener: **TE** p. 255	Lab Worksheet 6-1A: *Laboratory Manual* p. 59; ✂ Lab Worksheet 6-1B: *Laboratory Manual* p. 60	Try This Exercises
6-2	2	2	2	First Five Minutes 6-2: *FFM Transparency Masters* p. 20 or **TE** p. 259; Lesson Opener: **TE** p. 259	Explore: **SE** p. 259; Calculator Worksheet 6-2: *Technology* p. CL6	Try This Exercises
6-3	2	2	2	First Five Minutes 6-3: *FFM Transparency Masters* p. 20 or **TE** p. 264; Lesson Opener: **TE** p. 264	✂ Lab Worksheet 6-3A: *Laboratory Manual* p. 61; ✂ Lab Worksheet 6-3B: *Laboratory Manual* p. 62	Try This Exercise
6-4	1	1	1	First Five Minutes 6-4: *FFM Transparency Masters* p. 21 or **TE** p. 269; Lesson Opener: **TE** p. 269	Explore: **SE** p. 269; ✂ Lab Worksheet 6-4: *Laboratory Manual* p. 63	Try This Exercises
6-5	2	2	2	First Five Minutes 6-5: *FFM Transparency Masters* p. 22 or **TE** p. 275; Lesson Opener: **TE** p. 275	✂ Lab Worksheet 6-5: *Laboratory Manual* p. 64	Try This Exercises
6-6	1	1	1	First Five Minutes 6-6: *FFM Transparency Masters* p. 23 or **TE** p. 281; Lesson Opener: **TE** p. 281	Explore: **SE** p. 281; ✂ Lab Worksheet 6-6: *Laboratory Manual* p. 65	Try This Exercises
Review	1	1	1			
Test	1	1	1			
Cum. Review	1	1	1			

FFM = First Five Minutes

Enrichment	Review/Assess	Reteach	Technology	Lesson
✂ Enrichment Using Manipulatives 6-1: *Enrichment* p. 34	Class Exercises: **SE** p. 257; Mixed Review: **SE** p. 258	Practice Worksheet 6-1: *Practice and Mixed Review* p. 43	Calculator Investigation: **SE** p. 258	**6-1**
Enrichment: **SE** p. 263; ✂ Enrichment Using Manipulatives 6-2: *Enrichment* p. 35	Class Exercises: **SE** p. 260; Mixed Review: **SE** p. 262	Practice Worksheet 6-2: *Practice and Mixed Review* p. 44	Calculator Worksheet 6-2: *Technology* p. CL6	**6-2**
✂ Enrichment Using Manipulatives 6-3: *Enrichment* p. 36	Class Exercises: **SE** p. 265; Algebra Review: **SE** p. 268; Quiz: **SE** p.268; Quiz: *Assessment* p. 89	Practice Worksheet 6-3: *Practice and Mixed Review* p. 45		**6-3**
Connections: **SE** p. 274; ✂ Enrichment Using Manipulatives 6-4: *Enrichment* p. 37	Class Exercises: **SE** p. 271; Mixed Review: **SE** p. 274	Practice Worksheet 6-4: *Practice and Mixed Review* p. 46		**6-4**
✂ Enrichment Using Manipulatives 6-5: *Enrichment* p. 38; BASIC 6-5: *Technology* p. B13	Class Exercises: **SE** p. 277; Algebra Review: **SE** p. 280	Practice Worksheet 6-5: *Practice and Mixed Review* p. 47	Computer Activity: **SE** p.280; BASIC 6-5: *Technology* p. B13	**6-5**
✂ Enrichment Using Manipulatives 6-6: *Enrichment* p. 39	Class Exercises: **SE** p. 284; Mixed Review: **SE** p. 286; Quiz: **SE** p. 286; Quiz: *Assessment* p. 90	Practice Worksheet 6-6: *Practice and Mixed Review* p. 48	Computer Exploration 12: **SE** p. 645; Computer Exploration 13: **SE** p. 646; Computer Exploration 14: **SE** p. 647; Calculator Worksheet 6-6: *Technology* p. CL7	**6-6**
Critical Thinking: **SE** p. 287	Summary & Review: **SE** p. 288–289	Mixed Review: *Practice and Mixed Review* p. 107		**Review**
Preparing for College Entrance Exams: **SE** p. 291	Chapter 6 Test: **SE** p. 290; Chapter 6 Tests: *Assessment* p. 31–36; *MathTest*			**Test**
	Cumulative Review: **SE** p. 292–293; Mid-Year Test: *Assessment* p. 105–110			**Cum. Review**

6

Similarity

A dollhouse is built using a scale factor of $\frac{1}{24}$. Find the dimensions of the dollhouse kitchen if the actual kitchen measures 8 ft by 10 ft.

RATIO, PROPORTION, AND SIMILARITY

OBJECTIVE: *Express a ratio in simplest form. Write a proportion and solve for an unknown part.*

6-1 Ratio and Proportion

For any two numbers, x and y, the **ratio** of x to y is the quotient obtained by dividing x by y. For example, the ratio of the length to the width of the poster on the left is 42 to 24. The ratio is represented in any of the following ways.

$$42:24 \qquad 42 \text{ to } 24 \qquad \frac{42}{24} \qquad 42 \div 24$$

Note that the ratio 42 to 24 is not the same as the ratio 24 to 42. A ratio that is expressed in lowest terms is said to be in *simplest* form. For example, the ratio 6 to 8 or $\frac{6}{8}$ in simplest form is 3 to 4 or $\frac{3}{4}$.

42

24

18

72

These posters are much alike but differ in their ratio of width to length.

Example 1

Give each ratio in simplest form.

a. AB to BD **b.** $m\angle A$ to $m\angle C$ **c.** BD to CD

  Solution

    a. $\frac{AB}{BD} = \frac{6}{9} = \frac{2}{3}$ **b.** $\frac{m\angle A}{m\angle C} = \frac{62}{39}$ **c.** $\frac{BD}{CD} = \frac{9}{10}$

Try This

Give each ratio in simplest form.

a. AB to CD **b.** CD to BD

Example 2

$x = 5, y = 15, z = 12$

Give each ratio in simplest form.

a. $\frac{x}{y}$ **b.** y to z **c.** $x + y : z$

  Solution

    a. $\frac{x}{y}$ is $\frac{5}{15}$ or $\frac{1}{3}$.   **b.** y to z is 15 to 12 or 5 to 4.

    c. $x + y : z$ is $20 : 12$ or $5 : 3$.

Try This

Give the ratio $\frac{y}{x + z}$ in simplest form.

A **proportion** is an equation stating that two ratios are equal. Two ways of expressing the same proportion are $\frac{3}{4} = \frac{12}{16}$ or $3 : 4 = 12 : 16$.

In the proportions to the right, a is the first term, b is the second term, c is the third term, and d is the fourth term. The blue first and fourth terms are called the **extremes,** and the red second and third terms are called the **means** of the proportion. This proportion is read: a is to b as c is to d. The next theorem describes a relationship between the means and extremes.

$$\frac{a}{b} = \frac{c}{d}$$

$$a : b = c : d$$

The relationships among ratio, proportion, and similarity are topics students have studied previously but a review may still be helpful.

To begin, discuss some everyday examples of ratios.

1. Some recipes require a 3 to 1 ratio of certain ingredients.
2. Some school districts require a 22 to 1 student/teacher ratio.
3. Which is the better buy: 3 batteries for $5 or 1 for $2?

Ask students to give other examples of ratios.

Materials

student notebooks
rulers
calculators
investigative software

Teaching Notes

To illustrate the importance of using a proportion in solving problems, ask students to find the actual dimensions of their bedrooms. Then, have them make a scale drawing of their room using a scale of 1 in. = 2 ft. (Extension: Include in the model furniture with dimensions.) As students make their scale drawings, point out that 1 in. on their drawing is equal to an actual length of 2 ft, that is, the ratio of 1 in. to 2 ft. Tell students that whenever two ratios are equal, a true proportion exists. Thus, the ratio of the actual length and width of their bedroom should be proportional to the length and width of their scale drawing. Stress the following difference between ratio and proportion.

A ratio compares two numbers by division, e.g., $\frac{3}{4}$. A proportion is an equation containing two equal ratios, e.g., $\frac{3}{4} = \frac{9}{12}$.

Discuss the use of a ratio as it relates to a fraction, e.g., Mark saved $\frac{2}{9}$ of his paycheck.

Show that Theorem 6-1 can be used (1) to determine whether two ratios are equal and (2) to determine if two or more proportions are equivalent forms.

Emphasize that when the $\div$ format of a ratio $(\frac{x}{y})$ is used, assume that y is *not* equal to zero (0) unless otherwise stated. Division by zero is undefined. NOTE: In previous math courses some students may have used "cross multiply" instead of "product of means = product of extremes." Point out that some mathematicans view "cross multiply" as slang and *not* a good mathematical expression.

Key Terms

ratio
proportion
means/extremes

Guided Practice

Chalkboard Examples

1. Find the ratio of the measure of the largest angle of $\triangle ABC$ to that of the smallest angle. $\frac{79}{39}$

Answer to **Try This a.** $\frac{3}{5}$ **b.** $\frac{10}{9}$

2. What is the ratio of $\frac{z + x}{z - x}$ in simplest form? $\frac{17}{7}$

Answer to **Try This** $\frac{15}{17}$

3. Do the ratios form a proportion? $\frac{x + 5}{4x + 20} = \frac{1}{4}$ yes

Answer to **Try This**
a. yes   **b.** no   **c.** yes

4. Find the value of x.
a. $\frac{12}{x} = \frac{4}{3}$ 9   **b.** $\frac{x + 2}{x + 3} = \frac{4}{5}$ 2

Answer to **Try This**
a. 5   **b.** 3

◆ **THEOREM 6.1**   Means—Extremes Products Theorem

In a proportion, the product of the means equals the product of the extremes.

Given: $\frac{a}{b} = \frac{c}{d}$
Prove: $ad = bc$
Proof

Statements	Reasons
1. $\frac{a}{b} = \frac{c}{d}$	1. Given
2. $\frac{a}{b} \cdot bd = \frac{c}{d} \cdot bd$	2. Multiplication Property of Equality
3. $ad = bc$	3. Property of Real Numbers

The converse of Theorem 6.1 is also true.

Example 3
Determine whether each pair of ratios can be written as a proportion.
a. $\frac{6}{15}, \frac{9}{22}$ **b.** $\frac{6}{8}, \frac{9}{12}$

Solution

a. $\frac{6}{15} \stackrel{?}{=} \frac{9}{22}$

$6 \cdot 22 \stackrel{?}{=} 15 \cdot 9$ *Check the product of the means and the extremes.*

$132 \neq 135$ *Since the product of the means and the extremes are not equal, these ratios do not form a proportion.*

$\frac{6}{15} \neq \frac{9}{22}$ *Note how the contrapositive of Theorem 6.1 is used.*

b. $\frac{6}{8} \stackrel{?}{=} \frac{9}{12}$

$6 \cdot 12 \stackrel{?}{=} 8 \cdot 9$

$72 = 72$ *Since the product of the means and the extremes are*

$\frac{6}{8} = \frac{9}{12}$ *equal, these ratios form a proportion.*

Try This
Determine whether each pair of ratios form a proportion.
a. $\frac{3}{5}, \frac{27}{45}$ **b.** $\frac{4}{7}, \frac{9}{17}$ **c.** $\frac{3x}{2y}, \frac{6x}{4y}$

Example 4
Find x in the proportion $6 : x = 5 : 15$.

Solution

$\frac{6}{x} = \frac{5}{15}$

$5x = 6 \cdot 15$ *The product of the means equals the product of the extremes.*

$(\frac{1}{5})5x = (\frac{1}{5}) \cdot 6 \cdot 15$

$x = 18$

Try This
Find x in each proportion.
a. $4 : 20 = x : 25$ **b.** $x : 9 = 6 : 18$

256   *Chapter 6   Similarity*

Class Exercises

Short Answer

Give each ratio in simplest form.

1. $\frac{4}{20}$ 2. $2x$ to $3x$ 3. $35x : 7x^2$ 4. $\frac{3xy}{6y}$

State the means and the extremes in each proportion.

5. $5 : 8 = 10 : 16$ 6. $\frac{7}{12} = \frac{35}{60}$ 7. $8 : 2 = 100 : x$ 8. $\frac{17}{48} = \frac{96}{x}$

Determine whether each pair of ratios form a proportion.

9. $\frac{2}{5}, \frac{4}{10}$ 10. $\frac{3}{9}, \frac{4}{12}$ 11. $\frac{2}{7}, \frac{3}{14}$ 12. $\frac{1}{2}, \frac{3}{8}$

Sample Exercises

Find the value of x in each proportion.

13. $1 : 2 = x : 4$ 14. $3 : 5 = 6 : x$ 15. $x : 3 = 3 : 9$ 16. $3 : 4 = 6 : x$

Discussion

17. $ad = bc$ How many different proportions can you obtain using a, b, c, and d?

Exercises

A

Give each ratio in simplest form.

1. $\frac{UT}{TW}$ 2. $\frac{VW}{TW}$ 3. $\frac{m\angle UTV}{m\angle VTW}$ 4. $\frac{m\angle VTW}{m\angle W}$
5. TV to TW 6. UT to VW

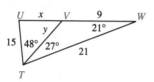

$x = 6, y = 10, z = 15$ **Give each ratio in simplest terms.**

7. $\frac{x}{y}$ 8. $(x + y) : z$ 9. $(z - y) : x$ 10. $(y - x) : z - x$

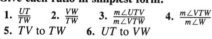

Determine whether each pair of ratios form a proportion.

11. $\frac{5}{8}, \frac{15}{24}$ 12. $\frac{4}{9}, \frac{12}{27}$ 13. $\frac{3x}{5}, \frac{6x}{10}$ 14. $\frac{xy}{3}, \frac{14}{6xy}$

Find the value of x in each proportion.

15. $x : 15 = 20 : 25$ 16. $\frac{x}{7} = \frac{12}{25}$ 17. $5 : x = 8 : 15$ 18. $\frac{3}{7} = \frac{5}{x}$

B

Write two proportions for each equation.

19. $3 \cdot 4 = 6 \cdot 2$ 20. $6 \cdot 4 = 8 \cdot 3$ 21. $3 \cdot 12 = 9 \cdot 4$
22. $9 \cdot x = 15 \cdot 8$ 23. If $2y = 3z$, find the ratio z to y.
24. If $x + 3 = 2y$, find the ratio $x + 3 : y$.

Give the measure of each angle.

25. Two supplementary angles are in a ratio of 2 to 1.
26. The acute angles of a right triangle are in a ratio of 5 to 4.
27. Two numbers are in a ratio of $2 : 3$. What is the ratio of their squares?

28. A 56-cm segment is divided in a ratio of 3 to 5. What is the length of each segment?

---

29. $\frac{5}{2}$ **30.** 5 **31.** $\frac{AD}{DB} =$
$\frac{\sqrt{5}}{2\sqrt{5}} = \frac{AE}{EC} = \frac{\sqrt{2}}{2\sqrt{2}} = \frac{1}{2}$
32. $\frac{AC}{AE} = \frac{3\sqrt{2}}{\sqrt{2}} = 3 \frac{AB}{AD} = \frac{\sqrt{45}}{\sqrt{5}} =$
$\frac{3\sqrt{5}}{\sqrt{5}} = 3$ **33.** Answers may
vary. $\frac{AD}{AB} = \frac{DE}{BC} = \frac{\sqrt{5}}{3\sqrt{5}} = \frac{1}{3}, \frac{AB}{AC} =$
$\frac{AD}{AE} = \frac{\sqrt{5}}{\sqrt{2}} = \frac{\sqrt{10}}{2}$ **34.** $\frac{DF}{AD} =$
$\frac{1 + x}{1} \frac{AD}{FH} = \frac{1}{x}, \frac{DF}{AD} = \frac{AD}{FH} = \frac{1 + x}{1} =$
$\frac{1}{x}$ **35.** $\frac{1 + x}{1} = \frac{1}{x}, x^2 + x = 1,$
$x^2 + x - 1 = 0, x = 1 - x^2$
$x = (1 - x)(1 + x), \frac{x}{1 - x} = \frac{1 + x}{1},$
$\frac{1 + x}{1} = \frac{x}{1 - x} = \frac{DF}{AD} = \frac{FH}{HC}$
36. Use the quadratic equation.
$x = \frac{-b \pm \sqrt{b^2 - 4ac}}{2a} =$
$\frac{-1 + \sqrt{1^2 - 4(1)(-1)}}{2(1)} =$
$\frac{-1 + \sqrt{1 + 4}}{2} = \frac{-1 + \sqrt{5}}{2}$
37. You cannot draw a diagonal
from a vertex to itself or to its
two adjacent vertices. So the
number of diagonals $= n - 3$.
If $\frac{n - 3}{360} = \frac{2}{7}, 7n - 21 = 720,$
$7n = 741, n = \frac{741}{7}$, not a whole
number. The proposition is contradictory since the polygon
must have a whole number for
the number of sides.
38. The number of diagonals
from all vertices is $n(n - 3)$.
Since each diagonal has been
counted twice, the total number
of unique diagonals is $\frac{n(n - 3)}{2}$.
If $n - 3$ to $\frac{n(n - 3)}{2}$ equals 3 to 5,
then $\frac{2}{n} = \frac{3}{5}$ and $n = \frac{10}{3}$. However,
n must be a whole number, so
the original proportion is not
possible.

Mixed Review Answers

1. 56   **2.** 56   **3.** 68
4. 68   **5.** 56   **6.** 56

**Calculator
Investigation Answers**

3. $DF = 1.618$ Substitute this
into both sides of the equation.
4. 144, 233, 377   **5.** Ratios approach 1.618.

The gear ratio of a bicycle can be defined in two ways.

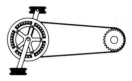

$$\text{gear ratio} = \frac{\text{number of pedal gear teeth}}{\text{number of sprocket gear teeth}} = \frac{\text{number of sprocket revolutions}}{\text{number of pedal revolutions}}$$

29. If a bicycle has 60 teeth on the pedal gear and 24 teeth on the
sprocket gear, find its gear ratio in simplest form?

30. If the pedal on the bicycle in Exercise 29 makes two revolutions,
how many revolutions does the sprocket gear make?

pedal   sprocket
gear   gear

31. Calculate the lengths of the segments to verify that $\frac{AD}{DB} = \frac{AE}{EC}$ is a
proportion.

32. Calculate the lengths of the segments to verify that $\frac{AC}{AE} = \frac{AB}{AD}$ is a
proportion.

33. Write and verify two other proportions from this figure.

C

In rectangle *ACFH*, *ABED* is a square and *EFHG* is a square.
Suppose that *DF*:*AD* = *AD*:*FH*.

34. Show that $\frac{1 + x}{1} = \frac{1}{x}$.   **35.** Show that $\frac{DF}{AD} = \frac{FH}{HC}$.

36. Show that $x = \frac{-1 + \sqrt{5}}{2}$.

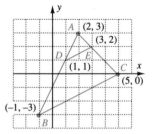

Critical Thinking

37. Suppose a polygon has n sides. Give a convincing argument that the
number of diagonals from one vertex is $n - 3$. Give a convincing
argument that the ratio $n - 3$ to 360 can never be 2 to 7.

38. Suppose a polygon has n sides. Give a convincing argument that the total
number of diagonals is $\frac{n(n - 3)}{2}$. Give a convincing argument that the ratio
of the number of diagonals from one vertex to the total number of
diagonals can never be 3 to 5.

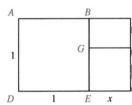

Mixed Review

$\overline{AB} \parallel \overline{CE}, BC = BD, \overline{AC} \parallel \overline{BD}$ Find the measure of each angle.

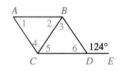

1. $m\angle 1 =$ ___   **2.** $m\angle 2 =$ ___   **3.** $m\angle 3 =$ ___
4. $m\angle 4 =$ ___   **5.** $m\angle 5 =$ ___   **6.** $m\angle 6 =$ ___

Calculator Investigation

1. Use a calculator to calculate the ratio $\frac{DF}{AD}$ in Exercises 34–36 and verify
that it is 1.618.

2. Calculate the ratio $\frac{DF}{FH}$ and verify that it is 2.618.

3. Show that DF is a solution of the equation $x^2 = x + 1$.

4. The sequence 1, 1, 2, 3, 5, 8, 13, 21, 34, 55, 89 is called the Fibonacci
sequence. Discover the pattern and write the next three terms of the sequence.

5. Calculate the sequence of ratios of successive terms $\frac{2}{1}, \frac{3}{2}, \frac{5}{3}, \frac{8}{5}, \ldots$ of the
Fibonacci sequence. How does this sequence relate to the ratio $\frac{DF}{AD}$ in Exercises 34–36?

OBJECTIVE: *Given a proportion, express it in equivalent forms.*

6-2 Properties of Proportions

 EXPLORE Form a proportion by substituting the numbers 4, 6, 10, and 15 in these boxes.

☐ : ☐ = ☐ : ☐

Find other proportions by rearranging these numbers. State any generalizations you discover.

In geometry, proportions are used to compare lengths of segments. Often an unknown length can be found by solving a proportion. Solving proportions sometimes requires you to first rewrite a proportion into an equivalent form.

To obtain equivalent forms of a proportion you can use the properties summarized in the following theorem. You will be asked to prove this theorem in Exercises 43–47.

◆ **THEOREM 6.2** Properties of Proportions

If $\frac{a}{b} = \frac{c}{d}$, and a, b, c, and $d \neq 0$, then each of the following is true.

a. $\frac{a}{c} = \frac{b}{d}$

b. $\frac{d}{b} = \frac{c}{a}$

c. $\frac{b}{a} = \frac{d}{c}$

d. $\frac{a+b}{b} = \frac{c+d}{d}$

e. $\frac{a-b}{b} = \frac{c-d}{d}$

Example 1

Complete the statement in three different ways. Justify each answer.
If $\frac{6}{9} = \frac{8}{12}$, then ___ .

Solution

$\frac{6}{8} = \frac{9}{12}$ *Switch the means.*

$\frac{12}{9} = \frac{8}{6}$ *Switch the extremes.*

$\frac{9}{6} = \frac{12}{8}$ *Invert the proportion.*

Try This

Complete the statement in five different ways. Justify each answer.
If $\frac{3}{7} = \frac{18}{42}$, then ___ .

Examples 2 and 3 illustrate the use of the properties of proportions.

First Five Minutes

(Quiz on previous lesson)

1. Find the value of x. $\frac{2x}{5} = \frac{3}{4}$ $\frac{15}{8}$

2. Express the ratio in simplest form. $\frac{3(x^2 - y^2)}{9(x - y)}$ $\frac{x+y}{3}$

☐ $1\frac{3}{4}''$

$1\frac{1}{4}''$

3. Find the actual dimensions using the scale 1 in. = 12 ft. $15' \times 21'$

4. If the actual dimensions of the gameroom are 18 ft by 24 ft, what are its dimensions in a scale drawing if the scale is 1 in. = 6 ft? $3'' \times 4''$

Lesson Opener

Review Theorem 6.1, Means-Extremes Products Theorem. Tell students that, according to this theorem, both equations ($\frac{a}{b} = \frac{c}{d}$ and $ad = bc$) are equivalent because either of them can be changed into the other by multiplying (or dividing) each side by bd.

Materials

student notebooks
investigative software

Teaching Notes

It may be less confusing to some students to see equivalent forms of a proportion with numerical values substituted in for the a, b, c, and d's. For example, if $\frac{2}{3} = \frac{4}{6}$, then $\frac{2}{4} = \frac{3}{6}$, $\frac{3}{2} = \frac{6}{4}$, etc.

Substitute numbers for variables in Theorem 6.2, e.g., $\frac{2}{3} = \frac{4}{6}$, $\frac{2}{4} = \frac{3}{6}$, etc.

Guided Practice

Chalkboard Examples

1. Determine whether each proportion is equivalent to $\frac{a}{b} = \frac{4}{5}$.

a. $\frac{a+b}{b} = \frac{2}{5}$ no

b. $\frac{a}{a+b} = \frac{4}{9}$ yes

Answer to Try This

$\frac{3}{18} = \frac{7}{42}$, $\frac{42}{7} = \frac{18}{3}$, $\frac{7}{3} = \frac{42}{18}$,

$\frac{10}{7} = \frac{60}{42}$, $-\frac{4}{7} = -\frac{24}{42}$

2. Use the proportion $\frac{y}{w} = \frac{x}{z}$ to complete each proportion.

a. $\frac{w}{y} = \frac{?}{x}$ $\frac{z}{x}$ **b.** $\frac{?}{z} = \frac{?}{x}$ w, y

Answer to Try This

a. $\frac{13}{5}$ **b.** $\frac{y+8}{8}$

3. Given: $\frac{AD}{DB} = \frac{AE}{EC}$

Prove: $\frac{AB}{AD} = \frac{AC}{AE}$ 1. $\frac{AD}{DB} = \frac{AE}{EC}$

(Given) 2. $\frac{DB}{AD} = \frac{EC}{AE}$

(Invert) 3. $\frac{DB+AD}{AD} = \frac{EC+AE}{AE}$

(Prop. of propor.) 4. $\frac{AB}{AD} = \frac{AC}{AE}$

(Segment Add.)

Answer to Try This

1. $\frac{AB}{AD} = \frac{AC}{AE}$ (Given) 2. $\frac{AB-AD}{AD} = \frac{AC-AE}{AE}$ (Prop. of Proportions)

3. $\frac{BD}{AD} = \frac{CE}{AE}$ (Segment Add.)

Class Exercise Answers

1. $\frac{3}{6} = \frac{8}{16}$ **2.** $\frac{9}{45} = \frac{5}{25}$

3. $\frac{18}{6} = \frac{12}{4}$ **4.** $\frac{7}{x} = \frac{y}{2}$

5. $\frac{8}{y} = \frac{7}{x}$ **6.** $\frac{4}{4} = \frac{y}{x}$

7. $\frac{9}{u} = \frac{16}{v}$, $\frac{v}{16} = \frac{u}{9}$, $\frac{9}{u} = \frac{v}{16}$, $\frac{25}{16} = \frac{u+v}{v}$, $\frac{-7}{16} = \frac{u-v}{v}$ **8.** $\frac{y}{x} = \frac{8}{4}$, $\frac{4}{8} = \frac{x}{y}$, $\frac{8}{y} = \frac{4}{x}$, $\frac{y+8}{8} = \frac{x+4}{4}$, $\frac{y-8}{8} = \frac{x-4}{4}$ **9.** $\frac{6}{n} = \frac{m}{8}$, $\frac{8}{m} = \frac{n}{6}$, $\frac{m}{6} = \frac{n}{8}$, $\frac{6+m}{m} = \frac{n+8}{8}$, $\frac{6-m}{m} = \frac{n-8}{n}$ **10.** $\frac{y}{9} = \frac{x}{5}$, $\frac{5}{x} = \frac{9}{y}$, $\frac{9}{x} = \frac{y}{5}$, $\frac{y+x}{x} = \frac{14}{5}$, $\frac{y-x}{x} = \frac{4}{5}$ **11.** $\frac{u}{3} = \frac{7}{v}$, $\frac{3}{u} = \frac{v}{7}$, $\frac{7}{u} = \frac{v}{3}$, $\frac{u+7}{u} = \frac{3+v}{3}$, $\frac{u-7}{u} = \frac{3-v}{v}$ **12.** $\frac{21}{4} = \frac{q}{r}$, $\frac{r}{q} = \frac{4}{21}$, $\frac{q}{21} = \frac{r}{4}$, $\frac{21+q}{q} = \frac{4+r}{r}$, $\frac{21-q}{q} = \frac{4-r}{r}$ **13.** Incorrect; if $\frac{3+4}{4} = \frac{6+4}{8}$, then $\frac{7}{4} = \frac{10}{8}$. But $56 \neq 40$.

Example 2

Use the proportion $\frac{x}{y} = \frac{5}{8}$ to complete each proportion.

a. $\frac{y}{8} = $ ___   **b.** $\frac{5}{x} = $ ___   **c.** $\frac{y}{x} = $ ___   **d.** $\frac{y+x}{x} = $ ___

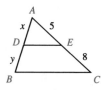

Solution

a. $\frac{y}{8} = \frac{x}{5}$ **b.** $\frac{5}{x} = \frac{8}{y}$ **c.** $\frac{y}{x} = \frac{8}{5}$ **d.** $\frac{y+x}{x} = \frac{13}{5}$

Try This

Use the proportion $\frac{x}{y} = \frac{5}{8}$ to complete each proportion.

a. $\frac{x+y}{x} = $ ___   **b.** $\frac{x+5}{5} = $ ___

Example 3

Given: $\frac{AD}{DB} = \frac{AE}{EC}$

Prove: $\frac{AB}{DB} = \frac{AC}{EC}$

Proof

Statements	Reasons
1. $\frac{AD}{DB} = \frac{AE}{EC}$	1. Given
2. $\frac{AD+DB}{DB} = \frac{AE+EC}{EC}$	2. Property of Proportions. Add the denominator to the numerator.
3. $\frac{AB}{DB} = \frac{AC}{EC}$	3. Segment Addition Postulate

Try This

Given: $\frac{AB}{AD} = \frac{AC}{AE}$

Prove: $\frac{BD}{AD} = \frac{CE}{AE}$

Class Exercises

Short Answer

Complete each statement by switching the means.

1. If $\frac{3}{8} = \frac{6}{16}$, then ___ .   **2.** If $\frac{9}{5} = \frac{45}{25}$, then ___ .   **3.** If $\frac{18}{12} = \frac{6}{4}$, then ___ .

Complete each statement by switching the extremes.

4. If $\frac{2}{x} = \frac{y}{7}$, then ___ .   **5.** If $\frac{x}{y} = \frac{7}{8}$, then ___ .   **6.** If $\frac{x}{4} = \frac{y}{4}$, then ___ .

Sample Exercises

Complete each statement in five different ways. Justify your answer.

7. If $\frac{9}{16} = \frac{u}{v}$, then ___ .   **8.** If $\frac{y}{8} = \frac{x}{4}$, then ___ .   **9.** If $\frac{6}{m} = \frac{n}{8}$, then ___ .

10. If $\frac{y}{x} = \frac{9}{5}$, then ___ .   **11.** If $\frac{u}{7} = \frac{3}{v}$, then ___ .   **12.** If $\frac{21}{q} = \frac{4}{r}$, then ___ .

Discussion

13. Suppose that $\frac{a}{b} = \frac{c}{d}$. One student concluded that $\frac{a+b}{b} = \frac{c+b}{d}$ by adding b to both sides of the equation. Do you think this reasoning is correct? Explain why or why not.

260 *Chapter 6 Similarity*

Exercises

A

Complete each statement in five different ways. Justify your answer.

1. If $\frac{7}{8} = \frac{14}{16}$, then ___.   **2.** If $\frac{4}{5} = \frac{36}{45}$, then ___.   **3.** If $\frac{5}{3} = \frac{125}{75}$, then ___.

4. If $\frac{x}{y} = \frac{7}{11}$, then ___.   **5.** If $\frac{u}{8} = \frac{v}{9}$, then ___.   **6.** If $\frac{5}{a} = \frac{7}{b}$, then ___.

Use the proportion $\frac{3}{4} = \frac{x}{y}$ to complete each proportion.

7. $\frac{3}{x} =$ ___   **8.** $\frac{y}{4} =$ ___   **9.** $\frac{7}{4} =$ ___

10. $\frac{x-y}{y} =$ ___   **11.** $\frac{y}{x} =$ ___   **12.** $\frac{y+x}{x} =$ ___

$\frac{LQ}{QM} = \frac{LR}{RN}$ **Prove each of the following.**

13. $\frac{LQ}{LR} = \frac{QM}{RN}$ **14.** $\frac{LM}{QM} = \frac{LN}{RN}$ **15.** $\frac{LM}{LQ} = \frac{LN}{LR}$

16. $\frac{LQ+QM}{QM} = \frac{LR+RN}{RN}$ **17.** $\frac{LQ+QM}{LQ} = \frac{LR+RN}{LR}$

B

Use the proportion $\frac{a}{b} = \frac{x}{y}$ to complete each proportion.

18. $\frac{a}{x} =$ ___   **19.** $\frac{y}{x} =$ ___   **20.** $\frac{y}{b} =$ ___

Use the proportion $\frac{c+d}{d} = \frac{u+v}{v}$ to complete each proportion.

21. $\frac{c}{d} =$ ___   **22.** $\frac{v}{u} =$ ___   **23.** $\frac{c+2d}{d} =$ ___

Find the value of x.

24. $\frac{x+3}{4} = \frac{9}{2}$ **25.** $\frac{x-2}{x} = \frac{3}{5}$ **26.** $\frac{2x-3}{3} = \frac{3x-7}{2}$

27. $\frac{x+2}{2} = \frac{9}{5}$ **28.** $\frac{6x-3}{3} = \frac{12}{2x}$ **29.** $\frac{x-3}{2} = \frac{2}{x}$

30. $\frac{x+2}{3} = \frac{4x}{6}$ **31.** $\frac{16}{4x} = \frac{4x}{9}$ **32.** $\frac{x+2}{6} = \frac{6}{x+2}$

$\frac{TU}{UV} = \frac{TX}{XW}$ **Use the figure to complete the table.**

	TU	UV	TV	TX	XW	TW
33.	14	16	—	—	24	—
34.	—	10	18	12	—	—
35.	12	—	26	—	21	—
36.	16	—	—	24	33	—
37.	—	—	21	12	—	28
38.	—	—	16	9	15	—
39.	10	18	—	—	—	42
40.	—	12	—	12	—	30
41.	—	—	26	—	24	39
42.	6	—	—	—	20	28

$\frac{a}{b} = \frac{c}{d}$ **Prove that each proportion is correct.**

43. $\frac{a}{c} = \frac{b}{d}$ **44.** $\frac{d}{b} = \frac{c}{a}$ **45.** $\frac{b}{a} = \frac{d}{c}$ **46.** $\frac{a+b}{b} = \frac{c+d}{d}$ **47.** $\frac{a-b}{b} = \frac{c-d}{d}$

Assignment Guide

Minimum: 1–52 e/o, 58–59, MR
Regular: 1–52 e/o, 58–59, MR
Advanced: 18–51 e/o, 53–59, MR

Applications
Exercises 48–52

Algebra
Exercises 24–32, 53–57

Lesson Closure

Review the five ways of obtaining equivalent forms of a given ratio.

Teacher's Resource Materials

Manipulatives 35
Practice Master 39
Technology: Calculator 6
Transparency 20

Exercise Answers

See Selected Answers for odd-numbered answers.

2. $\frac{4}{36} = \frac{5}{45}$, $\frac{45}{5} = \frac{36}{4}$, $\frac{5}{4} = \frac{45}{36}$, $\frac{9}{5} = \frac{81}{45}$, $\frac{-1}{5} = \frac{-9}{45}$ **4.** $\frac{x}{7} = \frac{y}{11}$, $\frac{11}{y} = \frac{7}{x}$, $\frac{y}{x} = \frac{11}{7}$, $\frac{x+y}{y} = \frac{18}{11}$, $\frac{x-y}{y} = \frac{-4}{11}$ **6.** $\frac{5}{7} = \frac{a}{b}$, $\frac{b}{a} = \frac{7}{5}$, $\frac{a}{5} = \frac{b}{7}$, $\frac{5+a}{a} = \frac{7+b}{b}$, $\frac{5-a}{a} = \frac{7-b}{b}$ **8.** $\frac{x}{3}$ **10.** $-\frac{1}{4}$

12. $\frac{7}{3}$ **14.** 1. $\frac{LQ}{QM} = \frac{LR}{RN}$ (Given) 2. $\frac{LQ+QM}{QM} = \frac{LR+RN}{RN}$ (Prop. of Proportions) 3. $\frac{LM}{QM} = \frac{LN}{RN}$ (Segment Addition Post.)

16. 1. $\frac{LQ}{QM} = \frac{LR}{RN}$ (Given) 2. $\frac{LQ+QM}{QM} = \frac{LR+RN}{RN}$ (Prop. of Proportions)   **18.** $\frac{b}{y}$

20. $\frac{x}{a}$ **22.** $\frac{d}{c}$ **24.** 15

26. 3   **28.** $-\frac{3}{2}$, 2

30. 2   **32.** -8, 4

48. A photographer enlarged a 6 in. × 10 in. photograph by multiplying each dimension by a factor of $\frac{3}{2}$. Use proportions to find the width x and length y of the enlarged photograph.

49. Repeat Exercise 48 using a factor of $\frac{5}{4}$.

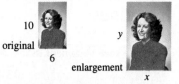

The $\frac{1}{4}$-in. line on the blueprint shown represents 12 ft.

50. If the distance measured from A to B is $2\frac{1}{2}$ in., what is the actual distance from A to B?

51. If the distance measured from C to D is $1\frac{5}{8}$ in., what is the actual distance from C to D?

52. If it costs $45 per foot to build a wall from A to B in this blueprint, what is the total cost of building the wall?

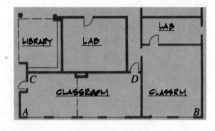

c

Given: $\triangle ABC$, $\frac{CD}{AD} = \frac{CE}{BE}$ Complete each statement.

53. If $CD = x$, $AD = x + 3$, $CE = x + 1$, and $BE = x + 5$; then
$CD =$ ___ , $AD =$ ___ , $CE =$ ___ , and $BE =$ ___ .

54. If $CD = 2x$, $AD = x + 3$, $CE = x + 5$, and $BE = x - 3$; then
$CD =$ ___ , $AD =$ ___ , $CE =$ ___ , and $BE =$ ___ .

55. If $CD = 3x$, $AD = x + 2$, $CE = x + 2$, and $BE = x - 1$; then
$CD =$ ___ , $AD =$ ___ , $CE =$ ___ , and $BE =$ ___ .

56. If $\frac{a}{b} = \frac{c}{d} = \frac{e}{f}$, then show that $\frac{a}{b} = \frac{a + c + e}{b + d + f}$.   **57.** Complete this generalization.
If $\frac{a}{b} = \frac{c}{d} = \frac{e}{f} = \frac{g}{h} = \ldots$, then $\frac{a}{b} = \frac{(a + \ldots)}{(b + \ldots)}$.

Critical Thinking

Decide whether each statement is always true, sometimes true, or never true. Explain your answer.

58. When two terms of the proportion $a : b = c : d$ are interchanged, the two ratios that result form a proportion.

59. If one term of the proportion $a : b = c : d$ is added to another term, the two ratios that result form a proportion.

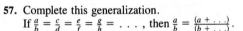

Mixed Review

$\overline{AB} \parallel \overline{DC}$, $AC = BD$, $m\angle BDC = 34$, $m\angle DAC = 84$
Find the measure of each angle.

1. $m\angle ACD$ **2.** $m\angle AEB$ **3.** $m\angle BEC$
4. $m\angle ADE$ **5.** $m\angle ABC$ **6.** $m\angle ABD$

$\triangle PQR$ is isosceles with legs $\overline{PQ}$ and $\overline{PR}$. $\overline{PT}$ is an altitude.
$m\angle PQR = 64°$, $m\angle RST = 44°$ **Find the measure of each angle.**

7. $m\angle PRT$ **8.** $m\angle QPR$ **9.** $m\angle SQT$
10. $m\angle PQS$ **11.** $m\angle QPT$ **12.** $m\angle PSQ$

13. Prove that $\triangle PQS \cong \triangle PRS$.   **14.** Prove that $\angle SQT \cong \angle SRT$.

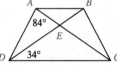

262   *Chapter 6   Similarity*

Enrichment
The Golden Rectangle

For centuries architects and artists have found the **golden rectangle** an especially pleasing form. You can find it in the front of the Parthenon in Athens and in vases from different periods of history. In nature, the spiral of the chambered nautilus shell fits within a golden rectangle.

The ratio of the length to the width distinguishes a golden rectangle from other rectangles. Imagine a square within the rectangle to the right whose sides are the same length as the width of the rectangle. The new rectangle formed has length and width in proportion to the original rectangle. That is, $\frac{1}{x} = \frac{x}{y}$. Because $y = 1 - x$, you can also express the proportion as follows. $\frac{1}{x} = \frac{x}{1 - x}$.

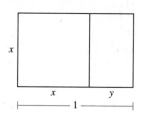

Exercises

1. State the product of the means and extremes for the proportion $\frac{1}{x} = \frac{x}{1 - x}$.
2. Express the solution above as a quadratic equation (that is, in the form $ax^2 + bx + c = 0$).
3. Use the formula $x = \frac{-b \pm \sqrt{b^2 - 4ac}}{2a}$ to solve the quadratic equation.
4. In the photograph of the vase above, measure the lengths and widths of several rectangles to the nearest millimeter. Use your calculator to compute the ratios of each length to width.
5. The ratio of the length to the width, $\frac{l}{w}$ or $\frac{1}{x}$, is the golden ratio. Use your answer to Exercise 3 to express the golden ratio as a decimal. How does your answer compare to the ratios in Exercise 4?

Enrichment

The Golden Rectangle

Exercise Answers
1. $x^2 = 1 - x$
2. $x^2 + x - 1 = 0$
3. $x = \frac{-1 + \sqrt{5}}{2}$ **4.** Answers may vary. **5.** ≈ 1.618

(Quiz on previous lesson)

1. Find the ratio of $x : y$ if
$3x = 4y$. **4 : 3**
2. Find the value of x if
$\frac{8}{x-4} = \frac{3}{5}$. **$\frac{52}{3}$**
3. A 50-m steel post is cut into
two parts in a ratio of 6 to 3.
How much longer is the larger
part than the smaller? **$\frac{50}{3}$**
4. If $\frac{a}{b} = \frac{c+d}{c}$, then $\frac{d}{c} = \frac{?}{b}$.
$a - b$

Lesson Opener

Give students a worksheet
showing a pair of similar triangles and a pair of congruent triangles. Ask students to use
rulers and protractors to list
characteristics of similar triangles and how they differ from
congruent triangles. You could
also have students use investigative software to produce
similar polygons and to study
their similarities and differences.

Key Questions

1. Are corresponding angles
congruent in similar triangles? **yes**
in congruent triangles? **yes**
2. Are corresponding sides congruent in similar triangles? **no**
in congruent triangles? **yes**
3. What is the ratio of each pair
of corresponding sides of
$\triangle ABC$ and $\triangle A'B'C'$ on the
worksheet? What is the ratio of
each pair of corresponding sides
of $\triangle DEF$ and $\triangle D'E'F'$?
Answers may vary.
4. What is the ratio of the
perimeters of the similar triangles? **Answers may vary.**
5. What generalization can be
made concerning sides and angles of similar triangles? **Sides
are proportional, angles are
congruent.**

OBJECTIVE: *Deduce information about the measures of sides and angles of two similar figures.*

6-3 Similar Polygons

You learned in Chapter 3 that triangles having the same size and shape are called congruent figures. In this lesson you will learn about triangles and other polygons that have the same shape but not necessarily the same size.

Polygon *WXYZ* is the same shape as polygon *ABCD*. Each side of *WXYZ* is double the length of the corresponding side of *ABCD*. That is, the ratio of the length of each side of *WXYZ* to its corresponding side of *ABCD* is 2. A characteristic of figures that have the same shape is that ratios of corresponding sides are equal. Two polygons that have the same shape are called **similar**.

The photograph of bacteria on the left has been enlarged by a factor of 10 to make it easier for scientists to study.

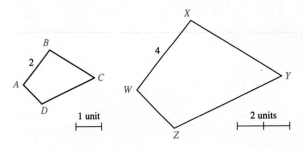

DEFINITION

Two polygons are similar (~) if their vertices can be matched so that

a. corresponding angles are congruent, and
b. ratios of lengths of corresponding sides are equal.

To indicate that polygon *ABCD* is similar to polygon *WXYZ*, write *ABCD* ~ *WXYZ*. When using this notation write corresponding vertices in the same order.

If *ABCD* ~ *WXYZ*, you know that

a. $\angle A \cong \angle W$, $\angle B \cong \angle X$, $\angle C \cong \angle Y$, $\angle D \cong \angle Z$, and
b. $\frac{AB}{WX} = \frac{BC}{XY} = \frac{CD}{YZ} = \frac{AD}{WZ}$

Conversely, if you know that all parts of *a* and *b* above are true, you can conclude that *ABCD* ~ *WXYZ*.

The ratio of lengths of corresponding sides of two similar polygons is called the **scale factor** between the similar polygons. Since $\frac{AB}{WX} = \frac{2}{4} = \frac{1}{2}$, the scale factor of *ABCD* to *WXYZ* is $\frac{1}{2}$. Since $\frac{WX}{AB} = \frac{4}{2} = 2$, the scale factor of *WXYZ* to *ABCD* is 2.

264 *Chapter 6 Similarity*

Example

$\overline{ABCDE} \sim JFGHI$ **Complete each statement.**

a. $m\angle J =$ ___   **b.** $m\angle G =$ ___   **c.** $\frac{ED}{IH} =$ ___

d. $x =$ ___   **e.** The scale factor of *JFGHI* to *ABCDE* is ___ .

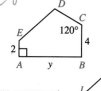 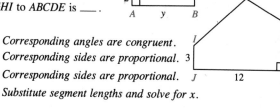

(handwritten: $y = 8$)

Solution

a. $m\angle J = 90$ **b.** $m\angle G = 120$ *Corresponding angles are congruent.*

c. $\frac{ED}{IH} = \frac{AE}{JI} = \frac{2}{3}$ *Corresponding sides are proportional.*

d. $\frac{AE}{JI} = \frac{BC}{FG}$ *Corresponding sides are proportional.*

   $\frac{2}{3} = \frac{4}{x}$ *Substitute segment lengths and solve for x.*

   $2x = 12$ or $x = 6$

e. The scale factor of *JFGHI* to $\frac{JI}{AE} = \frac{3}{2}$
ABCDE is $\frac{3}{2}$.

(handwritten: $\frac{y}{12} = \frac{2}{3}$ $3y = 24$ $y = 8$)

Try This

In polygon *ABCDE*, find *y*.

Class Exercises

Short Answer

Complete each statement.

1. If two polygons are similar, then corresponding ___ are congruent.
2. If two polygons are similar, then corresponding ___ are proportional.
3. If for two polygons corresponding angles are ___ and corresponding sides are ___ , then the polygons are similar.
4. If the scale factor between two similar triangles is one, then the triangles are ___ .

$\triangle ABC \sim \triangle XYZ$ **Complete each statement.**

5. $\angle A \cong$ ___   6. $\angle C \cong$ ___
7. $\frac{AC}{XZ} =$ ___   8. $\frac{XY}{AB} =$ ___

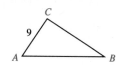

Sample Exercises

$\triangle RST \sim \triangle VUW$ **Complete each statement.**

9. $\angle R \cong$ ___   10. $\frac{RT}{VW} =$ ___
11. $x =$ ___   12. $y =$ ___

 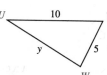

Discussion

Determine whether each statement is always true, sometimes true, or never true. Explain your answer.

13. If two triangles are congruent, then they are similar.
14. If two triangles are similar, then they are congruent.
15. Squares *ABCD* and *EFGH* are similar.
16. Isosceles triangles *ABC* and *DEF* are similar.
17. If corresponding sides of two rectangles are proportional, then the rectangles are similar.

Key Terms

similar
scale factor

Materials

student notebooks
rulers
protractors
investigative software

Teaching Notes

Emphasize that it is still necessary, as with congruent triangles, to name corresponding vertices of similar triangles in the same order. This will help in identifying corresponding sides and in writing ratios.

Restatement of the Definition of Similar Polygons: Two polygons are similar if there is a correspondence between the vertices such that (a) corresponding angles are congruent and (b) lengths of corresponding sides are proportional.

Guided Practice

Chalkboard Example

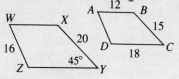

$ABCD \sim WXYZ$

Find each of the following.
1. scale factor of *ABCD* to *WXYZ* $\frac{3}{4}$ 2. $m\angle C$ 45 3. *WX* 16 4. *ZY* 24 5. *AD* 12

Answer to **Try This 8**

Class Exercise Answers

1. angles 2. sides
3. congruent, proportional
4. congruent

Exercises

A

RSTU ~ EFGH   Complete each statement.

1. ∠R ≅ ___   **2.** ∠S ≅ ___
3. ∠H ≅ ___   **4.** ∠G ≅ ___
5. $\frac{HG}{UT} = $ ___   **6.** $\frac{RU}{EH} = $ ___
7. $\frac{ST}{FG} = $ ___   **8.** $\frac{RS}{EF} = $ ___

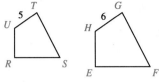

ABCDE ~ RSTUV   Complete each statement.

9. $m\angle E = $ ___   **10.** $m\angle A = $ ___
11. ∠T ≅ ___   **12.** $m\angle B = $ ___
13. x = ___   **14.** y = ___
15. UT = ___   **16.** UV = 20, DE = ___
17. $\frac{RS}{AB} = $ ___   **18.** $\frac{UV}{DE} = $ ___
19. The scale factor of ABCDE to RSTUV is ___ .

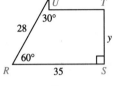

WXYZ ~ LPNM   Complete each statement.

20. $m\angle L = $ ___   **21.** $m\angle Y = $ ___
22. ∠M ≅ ___   **23.** ∠X ≅ ___
24. a = ___   **25.** b = ___
26. c = ___   **27.** If WZ = 12, LM = ___ .
28. The scale factor of WXYZ to LPNM is ___ .

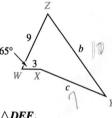
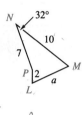

B

Find the coordinates of a point A so that △ABC ~ △DEF.

29.

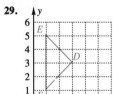
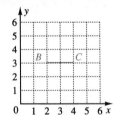

30.

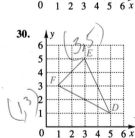
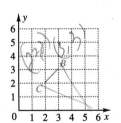

31. Plot points A(1, 1), B(7, 1), C(6, 3), and D(2, 3) and draw quadrilateral
ABCD. Then plot points A'(−3, 4) and B'(−3, 1). Find points C' and D'
so that A'B'C'D' is similar to ABCD.

△ABC ~ △DEF The scale factor of △ABC to △DEF is $\frac{3}{7}$.
Complete each statement.

32. If $AB = 15$, then DE = ___ .
33. If $EF = 42$, then BC = ___ .
34. $\frac{AB}{DE} =$ ___
35. If $DF = 56$, then AC = ___ .

36. In order to find the distance AB across a lake, a surveyor constructed △OCD similar to △OBA. He measured OB, OC, and CD directly to obtain the lengths shown. Find the length of AB.

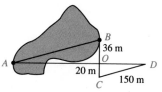

△ABC ~ △ADE

37. $m\angle A = 87$, $m\angle AED = 41$ Find $m\angle B$.
38. $AD = 8$, $AB = 12$, $AE = 14$ Find AC.
39. $AD = 9$, $AB = 13$, $AE = 14$ Find EC.
40. Prove that $\overline{DE} \parallel \overline{BC}$.

41. **Given:** $\overline{AB} \parallel \overline{DE}$
    Prove: △ABC ~ △DEC

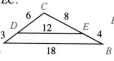

42. Keiko uses the sight marks to aim the ball. Suppose she misses the mark by 5 cm in a bowling alley that is 15 m long. If the mark is 2 m from the point A when the ball is released, by how much will she miss the pin?

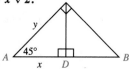

C

△ACD and △ABC are right triangles and $y = x\sqrt{2}$.
Complete each statement.

43. $CD =$ ___   44. $DB =$ ___
45. $BC =$ ___   46. $\frac{AB}{AC} =$ ___

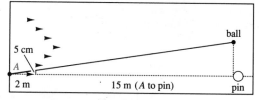

47. Prove that △ACD ~ △ABC.

Determine whether each statement is always true, sometimes true, or never true.

48. An equilateral triangle and an equiangular triangle are similar.
49. If an angle of one rhombus is congruent to an angle of another rhombus, the two rhombi are similar.
50. Two isosceles trapezoids are similar.
51. Two parallelograms that each have a 132° angle are similar.
52. Two rectangles, each with the property that two sides are twice the length of the other two sides, are similar.

Critical Thinking

53. An arithmetic progression is a sequence of the form x, $x + a$, $x + 2a$, $x + 3a$, ... Write the first five terms of each of these arithmetic progressions.
   a. $x = 3$, $a = 2$ **b.** $x = 4$, $a = 3$ **c.** $x = 2$, $a = 5$

54. Suppose the length of the sides of a triangle are the first three terms of an arithmetic progression. Show that the lengths of the sides of any similar triangle also form an arithmetic progression. (HINT: Assume that the lengths of the sides of one triangle are x, $x + a$, and $x + 2a$ and the lengths of the corresponding sides of the second triangle are y, $y + b$, and $y + c$ and show that $c = 2b$.)

Algebra Review

Write an equation and solve each problem.

1. In a triangle the second angle is 12° greater than the first angle. The third angle is 12° greater than the second angle. Find the measures of the three angles.

2. The measures of the angles of a triangle are in the ratio $4 : 5 : 6$. Find the measure of each angle.

3. The perimeter of a triangle is 39. If the ratio of the lengths of the sides is $3 : 4 : 6$, find the length of each side.

4. The vertex angle of an isosceles triangle has a measure 25 less than three times the measure of a base angle. Find the measures of the three angles.

5. The ratio of the measures of the angles of a quadrilateral is $2 : 4 : 7 : 11$. Find the measure of each angle.

Quiz

Express each ratio in the simplest form.

1. $\frac{AB}{CD}$ 2. $m\angle ACB : m\angle BAC$

3. CD to AD 4. $BC + CD : AC$

5. The width and length of a rectangle are in the ratio $2 : 3$. If the perimeter of the rectangle is 20, find the width and length.

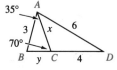

Given the proportion $\frac{x}{2} = \frac{7}{y}$, indicate whether the following proportions are true or false.

6. $\frac{2}{x} = \frac{y}{7}$ 7. $\frac{y}{2} = \frac{x}{7}$ 8. $7 : x = y : 2$ 9. $\frac{x + 2}{2} = \frac{y + 7}{y}$

quadrilateral $ABCD \sim$ quadrilateral $KLMN$ Complete each statement.

10. $\angle C \cong \angle$ ___

11. $AD = 20$, $BC = 32$, $LM = 24$ $KN =$ ___

12. The scale factor of $ABCD$ to $KLMN$ is ___ .

SIMILAR TRIANGLES

OBJECTIVE: *Use the AA Similarity Postulate to draw conclusions about triangles.*

6-4 AA Similarity Postulate

EXPLORE

Trace angles *A*, *B*, and *C* in this triangle. Then draw a large triangle *ABC* on dot paper so that the corresponding angles of the two triangles are congruent. Use a protractor if necessary.

Compare the ratios of corresponding sides of the two triangles.

State a generalization.

In order to prove that two triangles are similar using the definition of similarity, you must verify six relationships. You must establish that all three pairs of corresponding angles are congruent and that the three ratios of corresponding sides are equal.

In the Explore you may have discovered that if all three pairs of corresponding angles are congruent, then the two triangles are similar. In fact, knowing that two pairs of angles are congruent is sufficient to conclude similarity. Consider $\triangle ABC$ and $\triangle DEF$ in which two pairs of angles are congruent. You can use the Triangle Angle Sum Theorem to conclude that $m\angle C = 180 - (x + y)$ and $m\angle F = 180 - (x + y)$

Consequently, if two pairs of angles are congruent, all three pairs of angles are congruent.

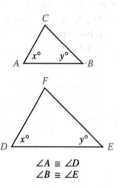

$\angle A \cong \angle D$
$\angle B \cong \angle E$

● **POSTULATE 19** AA Similarity

If two angles of one triangle are congruent respectively to two angles of another triangle, then the two triangles are similar.

Example 1
$\angle G \cong \angle J$, $\angle H \cong \angle K$
Find *x* and *y*.

Solution

$\triangle GHI \sim \triangle JKL$ *AA Similarity Postulate*

$\frac{x}{5} = \frac{7}{4}$ or $x = \frac{35}{4}$ *Ratios of corresponding sides are equal.*

$\frac{y}{6} = \frac{7}{4}$ or $y = \frac{21}{2}$

Try This

In the figure to the right, $JL = 12$.   Find *JK* and *KL*.

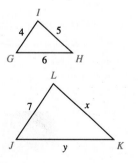

6-4   *AA Similarity Postulate*   **269**

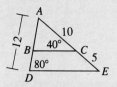

Materials

student notebooks
protractors
rulers
dot paper
investigative software

Teaching Notes

Note that AA Similarity is a postulate (accepted as true) not a theorem. It is probably the method of proving triangles similar used most often.

Emphasize the difference between the definitions of similar and congruent triangles. Corresponding angles of both must be congruent. Congruent triangles have congruent sides. Sides of similar triangles are proportional.

Guided Practice

Chalkboard Examples

1. Find $x : y$.

5 : 6

Answer to **Try This** 18, 15

2. What is the scale factor of $\triangle FED$ to $\triangle ABC$? $\frac{8}{5}$

Answer to **Try This** $\frac{75}{8}$

Enrichment

Example 3 Extension: Find the height of the school flagpole by using a meter stick perpendicular to the ground.

Example 2

$\angle A \cong \angle F$, $\overline{AB} \parallel \overline{EF}$, $BC = 4$, $AC = 5$, $DF = 8$ Find ED.

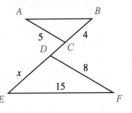

Solution

$\frac{BC}{ED} = \frac{AC}{FD}$

$\frac{4}{x} = \frac{5}{8}$

$5x = 32$

$x = \frac{32}{5}$

$\angle A \cong \angle F$ *When parallel lines are cut by a transversal, alternate interior angles are congruent so $\angle B \cong \angle E$. Therefore $\triangle ABC \sim \triangle FED$ by the AA Postulate.*

Try This

If $EF = 15$, find AB.

◆ **THEOREM 6.3**   Right Triangle Similarity

If an acute angle of one right triangle is congruent to an acute angle of another right triangle, then the triangles are similar.

Example 3

Application   A man 6 ft tall casts a shadow that is 11 ft 6 in. long. The end of his shadow coincides with the end of the shadow cast by a building 128 ft from the man. Find the height of the building.

Solution

Let x = height of the building.

$\frac{6}{11.5} = \frac{x}{139.5}$

$x = \frac{139.5(6)}{11.5}$

$x \approx 72.78$ ft   The building is about 73 ft high.

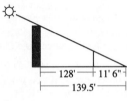

Try This

How tall would the building be if the man's shadow were 10 ft long?

Example 4

Given: $\triangle ABC$ is isosceles with base $\overline{BC}$. $\overline{DE} \perp \overline{BC}$, $\overline{FG} \perp \overline{BC}$

Prove: $\frac{DE}{FG} = \frac{BE}{CG}$

Proof

Statements	Reasons
1. $\triangle ABC$ is isosceles.	1. Given
2. $\angle B \cong \angle C$	2. Base $\angle$s of an isos. $\triangle$ are $\cong$.
3. $\overline{DE} \perp \overline{BC}$, $\overline{FG} \perp \overline{BC}$	3. Given
4. $\angle BED$ and $\angle CGF$ are rt. $\angle$s.	4. _?_
5. $\triangle BED$ and $\triangle CGF$ are rt. $\triangle$s.	5. Definition of rt. $\triangle$
6. $\triangle DEB \sim \triangle FGC$	6. Rt. $\triangle$ Similarity Theorem
7. $\frac{DE}{FG} = \frac{BE}{CG}$	7. Ratios of corr. sides of $\sim\triangle$s are =.

Solution

4. Definition of $\perp$ line segments

Class Exercises

Short Answer

Which of these statements about $\triangle DEF$ and $\triangle GHI$ are true?

1. If $m\angle E = 32$, $m\angle H = 32$, $m\angle D = 68$, and $m\angle G = 68$, then $\triangle DEF \sim \triangle GHI$.
2. If $m\angle F = m\angle I = 90$, $m\angle D = 35$, and $m\angle H = 50$, then $\triangle DEF \sim \triangle GHI$.
3. If $m\angle F = m\angle I = 115$, $m\angle E = 30$, and $m\angle H = 40$, then $\triangle DEF \sim \triangle GHI$.

State the measure of $\angle A$ that would make the given triangles similar.

4.

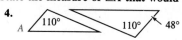

5.

6.

Sample Exercises

$\overline{BE} \parallel \overline{DF}$, $\overline{BC} \perp \overline{AC}$, $\overline{DE} \perp \overline{AE}$ **Complete each statement.**

7. $\triangle ABC \sim$ ___   8. $\triangle ADF \sim$ ___   9. $\frac{AE}{AC} =$ ___

10. Write a proportion that can be used to find x.
11. Find x.

Discussion

Determine whether each statement is always true, sometimes true, or never true. Draw pictures as needed and explain your answer.

12. Two right triangles are similar.   13. Two obtuse triangles are similar.
14. Two isosceles triangles with congruent vertex angles are similar.
15. Two isosceles right triangles are similar.

Exercises

A

Complete each statement.

1. $\triangle ABC \sim$ ___   2. The proportion ___ can be used to find x.
3. $x =$ ___   4. The proportion ___ can be used to find y.
5. $y =$ ___

$\overline{BC} \parallel \overline{DE}$ **Find x and y.**

6.

7.

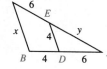

8.

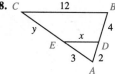

$\angle B \cong \angle Y$ (rt. $\angle$s)
$\angle A \cong \angle X$ by the sun's angle of inclination
$\triangle ABC \sim \triangle XYZ$ Measure the lengths of the shadows. Write a proportion to find the height of the flagpole.

Answer to Try This 82.8 ft

Class Exercise Answers

1. true   2. false   3. false
4. 48 or 22   5. 40 or 50
6. 46   7. $\triangle ADE$ 8. $\triangle ABE$
9. $\frac{4}{3}$ 10. $\frac{4}{3} = \frac{x}{9}$ 11. 12
12. Sometimes true, if at least one acute $\angle$ pair is $\cong$.
13. Sometimes true
14. Always true; base $\angle$s must be $\cong$ too since total measure = 180.   15. Always true; acute $\angle$s will be 45°.

Assignment Guide

Minimum: 1–37 e/o, 41, MR
Regular: 1–39 e/o, 41, MR
Advanced: 12–37 e/o, 38–43, MR

Applications

Exercises 17–19, 29

Algebra

Exercise 43

Lesson Closure

Ask students to use the definition of similar polygons to tell why the following statements are true.

1. Congruent triangles are *always* similar.
2. Regular polygons with the same number of sides are *always* similar.
3. Rectangles are *sometimes* similar.
4. Isosceles triangles are *sometimes* similar.

Teacher's Resource Materials

Enrichment Using
  Manipulatives 37
Practice Master 41
Technology: Computer
  Software 8
Transparency 22

Identify a pair of similar triangles and find x and y.

9.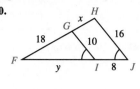

10.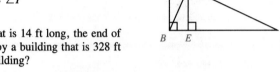

11.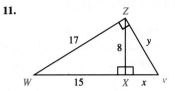

Prove that each pair of triangles is similar.

12. $\triangle ABC \sim \triangle DEC$ **13.** $\triangle ABC \sim \triangle BDC$ **14.** $\triangle BED \sim \triangle ADB$ **15.** $\triangle ADB \sim \triangle DEC$

16. Prove Theorem 6.3.
  Given: right triangles ABC and XYZ with
    $\angle A$ and $\angle X$ right angles, $\angle B \cong \angle Y$
  Prove: $\triangle ABC \sim \triangle XYZ$

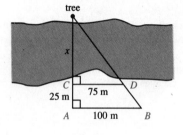

17. A person 5 ft 6 in. tall casts a shadow that is 14 ft long, the end of which lies at the end of the shadow cast by a building that is 328 ft away from the person. How tall is the building?

18. When a mirror is placed on the ground so that the top of a building can be seen beside a person standing by the mirror, $m\angle BMA = m\angle DMC$. A person 150 cm tall who is 6 m from the mirror observes the top of the tower when the mirror is 120 m from the tower. Find the height of the building.

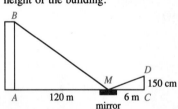

19. To find the distance x across a river, a surveyor located points A, B, C, and D through direct measurement. Find the distance x.

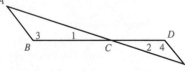

20. Given: $\angle 3 \cong \angle 4$
  Prove: $\triangle ABC \sim \triangle EDC$

21. Given: $\overline{AB} \parallel \overline{ED}$
  Prove: $\frac{AB}{ED} = \frac{BC}{DC}$

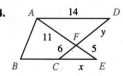

B

$ABCD$ **is a trapezoid with bases** $\overline{AD}$ **and** $\overline{BC}$. **Identify a pair of similar triangles and find x and y.**

22.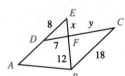

23.

24.

25. Rectangle *LMNO* coincides with rectangle *STUO* in such a way that $\overline{OL}$ lies on $\overline{OS}$ and $\overline{ON}$ lies on $\overline{OU}$. Show that when the diagonal from point *O* to point *T* passes through point *M*, the rectangles are similar.

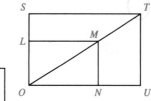

Use a straightedge and the diagonal test to determine whether the rectangles are similar.

26. 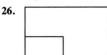   27. 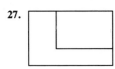   28.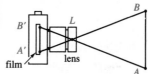

29. When a photograph is taken, the image formed on the film is similar to the object being photographed. Similar triangles help to explain this. If $\overline{AB}$ and $\overline{A'B'}$ are parallel, prove $\triangle LAB$ and $\triangle LB'A'$ are similar.

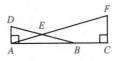

Suppose a slide projector and screen are set up as shown with the screen 20 ft from the projector. Assume *ABC* is similar to *A'B'C'* and these planes are parallel.

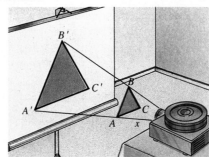

30. If the triangular cutout *ABC* is placed 2 ft in front of the projector, find the length of *A'B'* in terms of *AB*.
31. If the triangular cutout *ABC* is placed *x* ft in front of the projector, calculate the length *A'B'* in terms of the length *AB* and the distance *x*.
32. If *x* is halved, what happens to *A'B'*?
33. If *x* is doubled, what happens to *A'B'*?

34. **Given:** $\overline{BE}$ and $\overline{AD}$ are altitudes.
    Prove: $\frac{AD}{AC} = \frac{BE}{BC}$

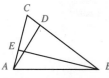

35. **Given:** $\triangle AEB$ is isosceles.
    Prove: $AD \cdot AF = CF \cdot BD$

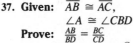

36. **Given:** *ABCD* is a parallelogram. $\overline{AE} \perp \overline{CD}, \overline{AF} \perp \overline{BC}$
    Prove: $AE \cdot CD = AF \cdot BC$

c

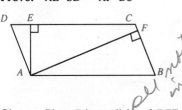

37. **Given:** $\overline{AB} \cong \overline{AC}$, $\angle A \cong \angle CBD$
    Prove: $\frac{AB}{BD} = \frac{BC}{CD}$

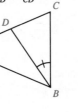

38. **Given:** Plane *P* is parallel to $\triangle DEF$.
    Prove: $\frac{AB}{DE} = \frac{BC}{EF} = \frac{AC}{DF}$.

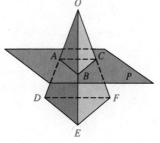

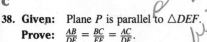

6-4   *AA Similarity Postulate*   **273**

26. yes   28. no   30. 10*AB*
32. doubled   34. 1. $\overline{BE}$ and $\overline{AD}$ are altitudes. (Given) 2. $\overline{AC} \perp \overline{BE}, \overline{BC} \perp \overline{AD}$ (Def. of altitude) 3. $\angle BEC$ and $\angle ADC$ are rt ∠s. (⊥ lines form rt. ∠s.) 4. $\triangle BEC$ and $\triangle ADC$ are rt. △s. (Def. of rt. △) 5. $\angle C \cong \angle C$ (Reflexive) 6. $\triangle BEC \sim \triangle ADC$ (Rt. △ Similarity) 7. $\frac{AD}{BE} = \frac{AC}{BC}$ (Def. of similar △s) 8. $\frac{AD}{AC} = \frac{BE}{BC}$ (Property of proportions.)
36. 1. *ABCD* is a parallelogram. (Given) 2. $AB = CD, AD = BC$ (Opp. sides of a ▱ are ≅) 3. $\angle D \cong \angle B$ (Opp. ∠s of a ▱ are ≅.) 4. $\overline{AE} \perp \overline{CD}, \overline{AF} \perp \overline{BC}$ (Given) 5. $\angle AED$ and $\angle AFB$ are rt. ∠s (⊥ lines from rt. ∠s.) 6. $\triangle AED$ and $\triangle AFB$ are rt. △s. (Def. rt. △) 7. $\triangle AED \sim \triangle AFB$ (Rt. △ Similarity) 8. $\frac{AE}{AF} = \frac{AD}{AB}$ (Side lengths of ∼ △s are proportional.) 9. $\frac{AE}{AF} = \frac{BC}{CD}$ (Substitution) 10. $AE \cdot CD = AF \cdot BC$. (Means/extremes)   38. 1. *P* ∥ $\triangle DEF$ (Given) 2. $\overline{AB} \parallel \overline{DE}$, $\overline{BC} \parallel \overline{EF}, \overline{CA} \parallel \overline{FD}$ (Coplanar lines in ∥ planes are ∥.) 3. $\angle OAB \cong \angle ODE, \angle OBC \cong \angle OEF, \angle OAC \cong \angle ODF$ (If ∥ lines are cut by a transversal, corr. ∠s are ≅.) 4. $\angle AOB \cong \angle DOE, \angle BOC \cong \angle EOF, \angle AOC \cong \angle DOF$ (Reflexive Property) 5. $\triangle AOB \sim \triangle DOE, \triangle BOC \sim \triangle EOF, \triangle AOC \sim \triangle DOF$ (AA Similarity) 6. $\frac{AB}{DE} = \frac{OB}{OE}, \frac{OB}{OE} = \frac{BC}{EF} = \frac{OC}{OF}, \frac{OC}{OF} = \frac{AC}{DF}$ (Sides of ∼ △s are proportional) 7. $\frac{AB}{DE} = \frac{BC}{EF} = \frac{AC}{DF}$ (Transitive)

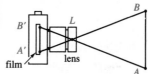

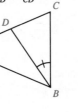

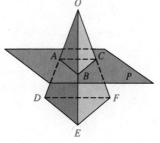

40. $\triangle AFC \sim \triangle AEB$ so $\frac{AF}{AE} = \frac{FC}{EB}$,
$\triangle BFC \sim \triangle BDA$ so $\frac{BF}{BD} = \frac{FC}{DA}$,
$\triangle CDA \sim \triangle CEB$ so $\frac{CD}{CE} = \frac{DA}{EB}$,
Then $\frac{AF}{BF} \cdot \frac{BD}{CD} \cdot \frac{CE}{AE} = \frac{AF}{AE} \cdot \frac{BD}{BF} \cdot \frac{CE}{CD}$
(Commutative Property) $= \frac{FC}{EB} \cdot \frac{DA}{FC} \cdot \frac{EB}{DA}$ (by above proportions) $= 1$.   **42.** $m\angle AJE = m\angle BAE = 108$, $m\angle JAE = m\angle BAE = 36$, $m\angle AEJ = m\angle BEA = 36$; so $\frac{EJ}{AE} = \frac{AE}{EB}$. $\triangle AEF$ is isos. so $AE = EF$. $\frac{EJ}{EF} = \frac{EF}{EB}$

Mixed Review Answers

1. If two triangles are equilateral, then they are similar.
2. If two triangles are not both equilateral, then they are not similar.   **3.** If two triangles are not similar, then they are not both equilateral.   **4.** If the triangles are similar, then they are congruent.   **5.** Any two similar triangles with scale, factor $\neq 1$ are not congruent.
6. Same counterexample as in 5.

Connections Answers

1. red: $-\sqrt{5}, 2\sqrt{2}, 3$
blue: $-2\sqrt{5}, 4\sqrt{2}, 6$
$\frac{\sqrt{5}}{2\sqrt{5}} = \frac{2\sqrt{2}}{4\sqrt{2}} = \frac{3}{6} = \frac{1}{2}$
3. $\frac{2\sqrt{5}}{4\sqrt{5}} = \frac{6}{12} = \frac{4\sqrt{2}}{8\sqrt{2}} = \frac{1}{2}$

39. $ABCD$ is a parallelogram. Find x. (HINT: Set up two proportions by using $\triangle AED$ and $\triangle AEB$ and triangles similar to them.)

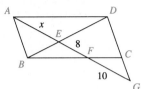

40. Given: $\overline{AD}$, $\overline{BE}$, and $\overline{CF}$ are altitudes.
Prove: $\frac{AF}{BF} \cdot \frac{BD}{CD} \cdot \frac{CE}{AE} = 1$
(HINT: Begin by writing three proportions using three pairs of similar right triangles.)

Critical Thinking

41. Trace pentagon $ABCDE$ and all its diagonals as shown in the figure to the right. Assume that all sides of $ABCDE$ are equal in length and all vertex angles are equal in measure. Label the angle measures of as many angles in your tracing as possible.

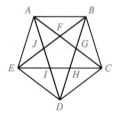

42. Show that $\triangle JAE \sim \triangle ABE$ and conclude that $\frac{EJ}{AE} = \frac{AE}{EB}$. Show that $AE = EF$ and write a proportion using EJ, EF, and EB.

43. Suppose that $AE = EF = 1$. Let $x = EJ$. Use the proportion from Exercise 42 to show that $\frac{x}{1} = \frac{1}{1+x}$. Show that $x = \frac{-1 + \sqrt{5}}{2}$.

Mixed Review

Any two equilateral triangles are similar.

1. Write the statement as a conditional.
2. Write the inverse of the statement.
3. Write the contrapositive of the statement

If two triangles are congruent, then they are similar.

4. Write the converse of the statement.
5. Show that the converse is false.
6. If the inverse is false, give a counterexample.

CONNECTIONS ◇◇

Transformations

Similarity as discussed in this lesson is related to concepts studied in algebra. Consider the transformation that associates each point (x, y) in the coordinate plane with the point $(2x + 2, 2y + 3)$ —the red triangle with the blue triangle.

1. Calculate the lengths of the sides of each triangle to show that the three ratios of corresponding sides are proportional.
2. Draw on graph paper the triangle whose vertices are $(-2, -1)$, $(4, -1)$, and $(2, 3)$. Then draw the triangle associated with it by the transformation above.
3. Show that the ratios of corresponding sides are proportional.

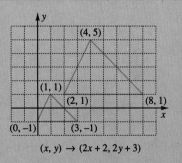

$(x, y) \rightarrow (2x + 2, 2y + 3)$

6-5 SAS and SSS Similarity Theorems

The AA Similarity Postulate provides what is probably the most often used method of showing that two triangles are similar, since it requires proving only two pairs of angles congruent.

However, there are other methods for proving triangles similar. The SAS Theorem below describes a comparison between two pairs of sides and one pair of included angles.

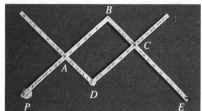

A mechanical linkage, called a pantograph, is used by draftsmen to enlarge or reduce drawings.

 THEOREM 6.4   SAS Similarity Theorem

If an angle of one triangle is congruent to an angle of another triangle and if the lengths of the sides including these angles are proportional, then the triangles are similar.

Given: $\angle C \cong \angle F, \frac{AC}{DF} = \frac{BC}{EF}$
Prove: $\triangle ABC \sim \triangle DEF$

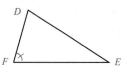

Plan   Suppose that $CA < FD$. Choose point U on $\overline{FD}$ so that $UF = AC$ and point V on $\overline{FE}$ so that $\angle 1 \cong \angle FDE$. Then $\triangle UVF \sim \triangle DEF$ by AA Similarity. Use this similarity to conclude that $\frac{UF}{DF} = \frac{VF}{EF}$. It is given that $\frac{AC}{DF} = \frac{BC}{EF}$ from which it can be concluded that $VF = BC$ (recall, $AC = UF$). Conclude that $\triangle UFV \cong \triangle ACB$ by SAS and that $\triangle ACB \sim \triangle UFV \sim \triangle DEF$.

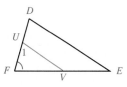

Example 1
Find the value of x for which $\triangle ABC \sim \triangle DEF$. State the theorem that justifies your answer.

Solution
$\frac{5}{7} = \frac{8}{x}$
$5x = 56$
$x = \frac{56}{5}$

The triangles are similar by the SAS Similarity Theorem.

Try This
Given: $\triangle ABC$ and $\triangle XYZ$ If $\angle A \cong \angle X$, state the proportion that must be true to conclude that $\triangle ABC \sim \triangle XYZ$ by SAS Similarity.

First Five Minutes

(Quiz on previous lesson)

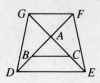

$\triangle ABC \sim \triangle ADE$

1. $\overline{BC}$ ___ $\overline{DE}$ Why? Corr. $\angle$s: $\angle ABC \cong \angle ADE$ **2.** $AB = 3$, $BD = x + 2$, $BC = 4$, $DE = 2x + 4$ Find x, BD, AD, and DE. 4, 6, 9, 12
3. Given: Isosceles trapezoid $DEFG$ with bases $\overline{GF}$ and $\overline{DE}$
Prove: $\triangle GAF \sim \triangle EAD$
1. Isos. trap. *DEFG* (Given)
2. $\overline{GF} \parallel \overline{DE}$ (Def. of a trap.)
3. $\angle GFA \cong \angle EDA$ (Alt. int. $\angle$s)
4. $\angle GAF \cong \angle EAD$ (Vert. $\angle$s)
5. $\triangle GAF \sim \triangle EAD$ (AA Similarity)

Lesson Opener

Review two methods to prove two triangles similar—Definition of Similar Polygons and AA Similarity Postulate. This section gives two other methods of proving triangles similar—the SAS Similarity Theorem and the SSS Similarity Theorem.

The following chart summarizes the various ways of proving triangles similar.

Similar Triangles

1. SSS—three pairs of corresponding sides proportional
2. SAS—two pairs of corresponding sides proportional and one pair of included angles ≅
3. AA—two pairs of corresponding angles ≅
4. Definition of similar triangles

Congruent Triangles

1. SSS—three pairs of corresponding sides congruent.
2. SAS—two pairs of corresponding sides congruent and one pair of included angles ≅.
3. ASA—two pairs of corresponding angles ≅ and one pair of included sides ≅.
4. Definition of congruent triangles

Materials

student notebooks
investigative software

Guided Practice

Chalkboard Examples

1. For what value of x is $\triangle ABC \sim \triangle DEF$ if $AC = 6$, $DF = 9$, and $AB = 7$? $\frac{63}{6}$

Answer to **Try This** $\frac{AB}{XY} = \frac{AC}{XZ}$

Example 2

Application: In the pantograph, P, D, and E are collinear, $AD = BC$, $AB = CD$, and $\frac{AB}{AP} = \frac{CE}{BC}$. How does PD compare to DE?

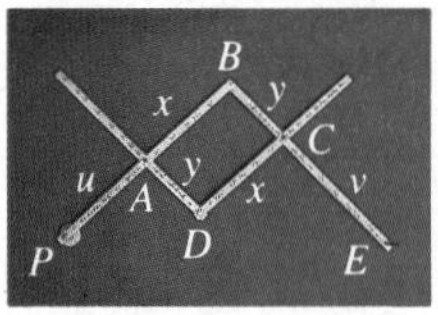

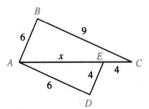

Solution

$ABCD$ is a parallelogram.	By construction opposite sides of $ABCD$ are congruent.
$\angle PAD \cong \angle B \cong \angle DCE$	If parallel lines are cut by a transversal, corresponding angles are congruent.
$\frac{x}{u} = \frac{v}{y}$	This is true by the pantograph construction.
$\triangle APD \sim \triangle CDE$	SAS Similarity Theorem
$\frac{PD}{DE} = \frac{u}{x}$ or $PD = \frac{u}{x} \cdot DE$	Corresponding sides of similar triangles are proportional.

Try This

In the pantograph shown, if $PA = 5$ cm and $AB = 10$ cm, find $\frac{DE}{PD}$.

The next theorem describes a situation where three pairs of sides of two triangles allow you to conclude that the triangles are similar.

◆ **THEOREM 6.5**   SSS Similarity Theorem

If corresponding sides of two triangles are proportional, then the two triangles are similar.

Given: $\frac{AC}{DF} = \frac{AB}{DE} = \frac{AB}{DE}$
Prove: $\triangle ABC \sim \triangle DEF$

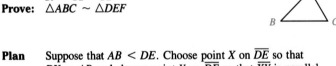

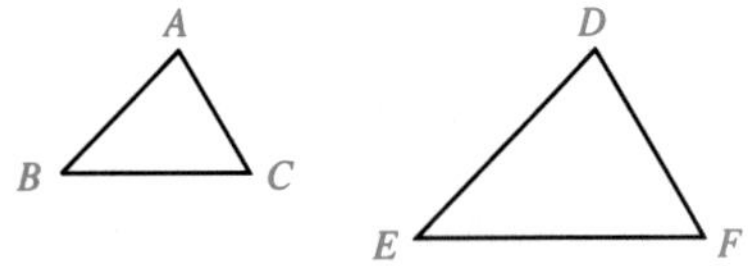

Plan   Suppose that $AB < DE$. Choose point X on $\overline{DE}$ so that $DX = AB$ and choose point Y on $\overline{DF}$ so that $\overline{XY}$ is parallel to $\overline{EF}$. It follows that $\angle 1 \cong \angle 2$ and $\triangle DXY \sim \triangle DEF$ by AA Similarity. Consequently, $\frac{DY}{DF} = \frac{XY}{EF}$. Use this proportion together with the given proportion to conclude that $AC = DY$, $AB = DX$, and $XY = BC$. It follows that $\triangle ABC \cong \triangle DXY$. Therefore, $\triangle ABC \sim \triangle DXY \sim \triangle DEF$.

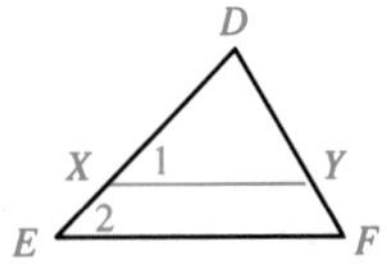

Example 3

Find the value of x for which $\triangle ABC \sim \triangle EDA$.

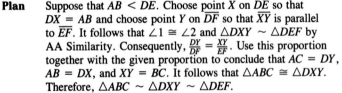

Solution

$\frac{6}{4} = \frac{9}{6} = \frac{x+4}{x}$ If $\frac{AB}{ED} = \frac{BC}{DA} = \frac{AC}{EA}$,
$\frac{3}{2} = \frac{x+4}{x}$ then the triangles are similar.
$3x = 2x + 8$
$x = 8$

Try This

If $EC = 3$ and the triangles are similar, show that the two triangles are isosceles.

Class Exercises

Short Answer

Determine whether the two triangles shown are similar. If so, state the postulate or theorem that justifies your answer.

1.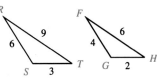

2.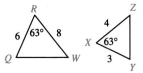

3.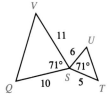

4.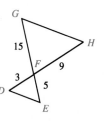

5.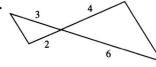

6.

7.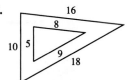

8.

9.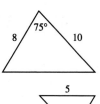

Sample Exercises

State whether you can conclude that $\triangle ABC \sim \triangle DEF$ from the given information.

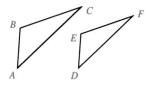

10. $\angle A \cong \angle D$, $\frac{AC}{DF} = \frac{AB}{DE}$

11. $\frac{DF}{AC} = \frac{DE}{AB} = \frac{EF}{BC}$

12. $\angle B \cong \angle E$, $\frac{EF}{BC} = \frac{AC}{FD}$

13. $\angle C \cong \angle F$, $\frac{AC}{BC} = \frac{DF}{EF}$

14. Given: $\triangle ABC$ and $\triangle DEF$, $\angle B \cong \angle E$, $AB = 6$, $DE = 2$, $BC = 4$
Find the length of $\overline{EF}$ for which $\triangle ABC \sim \triangle DEF$.

15. Given: $\triangle RST$ and $\triangle UVW$, $RS = 6$, $UV = 8$, $ST = 9$, $RT = 12$
Find lengths of $\overline{VW}$ and $\overline{UW}$ for which $\triangle RST \sim \triangle UVW$.

16. Given: $\triangle ABC$ and $\triangle DEF$, $DE = 6$, $EF = 3$, $DF = 9$, $AB = 4$, $BC = 2$
Find the length of $\overline{AC}$ for which $\triangle ABC \sim \triangle DEF$.

Discussion

17. Given: quadrilaterals $ABCD$ and $WXYZ$, $\frac{AB}{WX} = \frac{BC}{XY} = \frac{CD}{YZ} = \frac{AD}{WZ}$
Are the quadrilaterals similar? If so, give a convincing argument to support your answer. If not, give a counterexample.

6-5   SAS and SSS Similarity Theorems   **277**

---

2. Show that $\triangle CAB \sim \triangle MAL$.
1. $CA = 20$, $BA = 21$, $LA = 31.5$, $MA = 30$ (Given) 2. $20 \cdot 31.5 = 21 \cdot 30$ or $630 = 630$ (multiplication) 3. $CA \cdot LA = BA \cdot MA$ (Substitution) 4. $\frac{CA}{MA} = \frac{BA}{LA}$, (Prop. of Proportions)
5. $\angle CAB \cong \angle MAL$, (Vert. $\angle$s),
6. $\triangle CAB \sim \triangle MAL$ (SAS Similarity)

Answer to **Try This** $\frac{2}{1}$

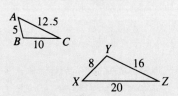

3. Is $\triangle ABC \sim \triangle XYZ$? Justify your answer. yes, by SSS Similarity

Answer to **Try This**
$x = 6 = AD = AE$, $BC = AC = 9$

Class Exercise Answers

1. yes, SSS   **2.** yes, SAS
3. no   **4.** yes, SAS
5. no   **6.** yes, SAS
7. yes, SSS   **8.** yes, SAS
9. no   **10.** yes   **11.** yes
12. no   **13.** yes   **14.** $\frac{4}{3}$
15. 12, 16   **16.** 6   **17.** The quadrilaterals are sometimes similar. Answers may vary. The measures of the angles can change while the side lengths remain constant and in proportion.

Assignment Guide
Minimum: 1–38 e/o, 41, AR
Regular: 1–40 e/o, 41, AR
Advanced: 15–38 e/o, 39–42, AR

Applications
Exercises 19–25, 33
Algebra
Algebra Review

Exercises

A

Find a value of x for which the triangles are similar. State the theorem that justifies your answer.

1.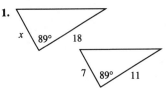

2.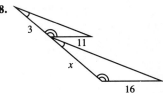

3.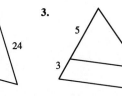

4.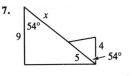

5.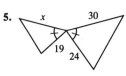

6.

7.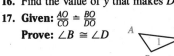

8.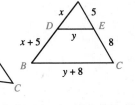

9.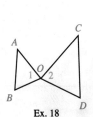

Draw and label figures for each exercise.

10. Given: $\triangle ABC$ and $\triangle DEF$ If $\angle B \cong \angle E$, state the proportion that must be true if $\triangle ABC \sim \triangle DEF$ by SAS Similarity.

11. Given: $\triangle UAZ$ and $\triangle RBN$ If $\angle U \cong \angle R$, state the proportion that must be true if $\triangle UAZ \sim \triangle RBN$ by SAS Similarity.

12. Given: $\triangle GHI$ and $\triangle KLM$ If $\angle I \cong \angle M$, state the proportion that must be true if $\triangle GHI \sim \triangle KLM$ by SAS Similarity.

13. Given: $\triangle XYZ$ and $\triangle UVW$ State the proportions that must be true if $\triangle XYZ \sim \triangle UVW$ by SSS Similarity.

14. $\triangle ADE \sim \triangle ABC$ Find AD and BD.

15. $y = 7$ Is $\triangle ADE \sim \triangle ABC$?

16. Find the value of y that makes $\overline{DE} \parallel \overline{BC}$.

17. Given: $\frac{AO}{CO} = \frac{BO}{DO}$
    Prove: $\angle B \cong \angle D$

Ex. 17

18. Given: $\frac{AB}{CD} = \frac{AO}{OC} = \frac{BO}{OD}$
    Prove: $\angle 1 \cong \angle 2$

Ex. 18

19. In the pantograph in Example 2, the ratio $\frac{PE}{PD}$ is called the magnification factor. If $PA = 5$ in. and $AB = 7$ in., what is the magnification factor of the pantograph?

278   *Chapter 6 Similarity*

The figure describes a camera with film width XY that is 35 mm and with focal length 50 mm. The scene has width AB.

20. What assumptions do you make about this figure that allow the conclusion $\triangle ALB \sim \triangle XLY$?
21. What is the width of the scene AB?
22. If the lens of the camera has a focal length of 100 mm, what is the width of the scene?

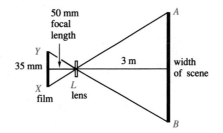

B

Use this figure for Exercises 23–25.

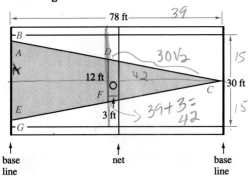

base line   net   base line

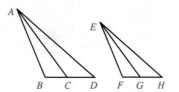

(handwritten notes)

$\frac{78}{2} = 39$

$\frac{42}{78} = \frac{12}{2x}$

$\frac{30}{2} = 15$ $2x = \frac{12 \cdot 78}{42}$

$x = 11.14$

see notes in note book

$15 - 11.14 = \approx 3.86 \text{ ft}$

23. Suppose that a tennis player standing 3 ft from the net at the center of the court can return all balls hit within 6 ft on each side of him. Then his opponent standing at the center of the base line would have to hit the ball outside the shaded region in order to hit a "winner." What assumptions do you make in order to ensure that $\triangle ACE \sim \triangle DCF$?
24. What is the distance AB from the corner of the shaded triangle to the corner of the singles court?
25. If the distance from the player to the net is 6 ft, will the distance AB increase or decrease? by how much?

Use the figure and the table to identify which triangles, if any, are similar.

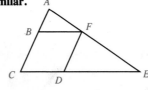

	AB	BC	CD	DE	FE	AF	BF	FD
26.	1	1	1	1	1	1	1	1
27.	3	6	6	3	6	3	3	5.2
28.	1	2	2	4	4	2	2	2
29.	8	16	24	3	20	4	8	18
30.	1	2	2	1	1	2	1.7	1
31.	4	10	10	2	4	8	6.5	4

32. **Given:** $\triangle ABD \sim \triangle EFH$
    C is the midpoint of $\overline{BD}$.
    G is the midpoint of $\overline{FH}$.

  Prove: $\triangle ABC \sim \triangle EFG$

6-5 SAS and SSS Similarity Theorems   **279**

20. $\angle Y \cong \angle B$, $\angle X \cong \angle A$, $\frac{LY}{LB} = \frac{LX}{LA}$ (or $\overline{XY} \| \overline{AB}$)
21. 2.1 m   22. 1.05 m
23. $\frac{DC}{AC} = \frac{FC}{EC} = \frac{DF}{AE}$
24. ≈ 3.86 ft
25. Increase by ≈ 0.74 ft.
26. $\triangle ABF \sim \triangle ACE \sim \triangle FDE$
27. $\triangle ABF \sim \triangle ACE$
28. $\triangle ABF \sim \triangle FDE$, $\triangle ABF \sim \triangle ACE$, $\triangle FDE \sim \triangle ACE$
29. none   30. $\triangle ACE \sim \triangle FDE$
31. none   32. 1. $\triangle ABD \sim \triangle EFH$ (Given) 2. $\frac{AB}{EF} = \frac{BD}{FH}$ (Sides of $\sim \triangle$s are proportional.) 3. $\angle B \cong \angle F$ (Corr. $\angle$s of $\sim \triangle$s are $\cong$.) 4. C is the midpoint of $\overline{BD}$. G is the midpoint of $\overline{FH}$ (Given) 5. $BC = CD$, $FG = GH$ (Def. of midpoint) 6. $BC + CD = BD$, $FG + GH = FH$ (Segment addition) 7. $BC + BC$ or $2BC = BD$, $FG + FG$ or $2FG = FH$ (Substitution) 8. $\frac{AB}{EF} = \frac{2BC}{2FG}$ (Substitution) 9. $\frac{AB}{EF} = \frac{BC}{FG}$ (Division) 10. $\triangle ABC \sim \triangle EFG$ (SAS Similarity)   33. $WY = 3XZ$ since $\triangle WOY \sim \triangle XOZ$ by SAS and $\frac{WY}{XZ} = \frac{OW}{OX} = 3$.
34. $ED = 2\sqrt{10}$, $DF = 2\sqrt{5}$, $EF = 2\sqrt{17}$, $CB = \sqrt{10}$, $AC = \sqrt{5}$, $AB = \sqrt{17}$.
35. $\frac{DE}{CB} = \frac{DF}{AC} = \frac{EF}{AB} = \frac{2}{1}$ so $\triangle ABC \sim \triangle FED$ and then $\angle DFE \cong \angle CAB$.
36. Answers may vary.
37. 1. $\angle A \cong \angle CBD$ (Given) 2. $\angle C \cong \angle C$ (Reflex.) 3. $\triangle ACB \sim \triangle BCD$ (AA Similarity) 4. $\frac{AC}{BC} = \frac{BC}{DC}$ (Lengths of corr. sides are proportional.) 5. $AC \cdot DC = BC \cdot BC$ (Property of proportions)
38. 1. $AC \cdot DC = BC \cdot BC$ (Given) 2. $\frac{AC}{BC} = \frac{BC}{DC}$ (Division) 3. $\angle C \cong \angle C$ (Reflexive Prop.) 4. $\triangle ACB \sim \triangle BCD$ (SAS Similarity Theorem) 5. $\angle A \cong \angle CBD$ (Corr. $\angle$s of $\sim \triangle$s are $\cong$.)

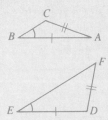

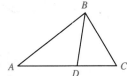

39. $\frac{AB}{AC} = \frac{DE}{DF}$ (since $AB = DE$ and $AC = DF$) and $\angle B \cong \angle E$ but triangles are not similar.

40. To prove $\overline{AB} \parallel \overline{A'B'}$, draw $\overline{AB}$ and $\overline{A'B'}$. $\angle AOB \cong \angle A'OB'$ (Reflexive Property) $\frac{OA'}{OA} = \frac{OB'}{OB}$ (given). By SAS Similarity Theorem $\triangle AOB \sim \triangle A'OB'$. Therefore $\angle BAO \cong \angle B'A'O$ (def. of similar triangles) so $\overline{AB} \parallel \overline{A'B'}$ (Postulate 14). Other pairs can be proved $\parallel$ similarly.

41. a. $AC_3 \cdot AC_4 = (AB_3)^2$, $AC_4 \cdot AC_5 = (AB_4)^2$ b. $AB_3 \cdot AB_4 = (AC_4)^2$, $AB_4 \cdot AB_5 = (AC_5)^2$

42. To show $\triangle AC_1B_1 \sim \triangle AB_1C_2$: $\angle A \cong \angle A$ (Theorem. 1.1) and $AC_1 \cdot AC_2 = (AB_1)^2 = AB_1 \cdot AB_1$ (given in Ex. 41 a) so $\frac{AC_1}{AB_1} = \frac{AB_1}{AC_2}$. Therefore by SAS Similarity Theorem, $\triangle AC_1B_1 \sim \triangle AB_1C_2$. To show $\triangle AB_1C_1 \sim \triangle AB_1C_2$, use the first equation of 41 b and an argument similar to the above. Use similar arguments for other triangles.

Algebra Review Answers

1. 3,−3   **2.** $\sqrt{6}, -\sqrt{6}$
3. 2,−2   **4.** 5,−5
5. −2,2   **6.** 3,−3
7. 4,−4   **8.** $-3 \pm 3\sqrt{3}$

Computer Activity Answers

Answers may vary.

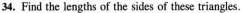

33. Proportional dividers are used to construct segments of proportional length. Two pieces of the same length are connected with a set screw. Suppose the set screw O is set so that $OW = OY = 3OX = 3OZ$. How does the length WY compare to the length XZ? Explain.

34. Find the lengths of the sides of these triangles.

35. Use the SSS Similarity Theorem to show that $\angle DFE \cong \angle CAB$.

36. Name the coordinates of points X, Y, Z so that $\triangle XYZ \sim \triangle ABC$.

37. Given: $\angle A \cong \angle CBD$
    Prove: $AC \cdot DC = BC \cdot BC$

38. Given: $AC \cdot DC = BC \cdot BC$
    Prove: $\angle A \cong \angle CBD$

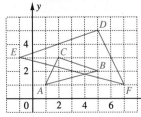

Ex. 34–36

C

39. Give a counterexample to show that this statement is false. If two sides of one triangle are proportional to two sides of another triangle and an angle of the first triangle is congruent to an angle of the second triangle, the triangles are similar.

40. Given: point O on lines $\overline{AA'}$, $\overline{BB'}$, $\overline{CC'}$, $\frac{OA'}{OA} = \frac{OB'}{OB} = \frac{OC'}{OC}$
    Prove: $\overline{AB} \parallel \overline{A'B'}$, $\overline{BC} \parallel \overline{B'C'}$, $\overline{AC} \parallel \overline{A'C'}$

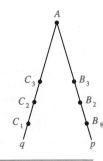

Critical Thinking

41. Suppose that lines p and q intersect at A and points $B_1, B_2, B_3, \ldots$ are on p and $C_1, C_2, C_3, \ldots$ are on q so that the following pattern of equations is true. State the next two equations in each of these patterns.
   a. $AC_1 \cdot AC_2 = (AB_1)^2$ **b.** $AB_1 \cdot AB_2 = (AC_2)^2$
      $AC_2 \cdot AC_3 = (AB_2)^2$ $AB_2 \cdot AB_3 = (AC_3)^2$

42. Use the equations in Exercise 41 to show that $\triangle AC_1B_1 \sim \triangle AB_1C_2 \sim \triangle AC_2B_2 \sim \triangle AB_2C_3 \sim \triangle AC_3B_3$. (HINT: Rewrite each equation as a proportion.)

Algebra Review

Solve.

1. $n^2 - 9 = 0$ **2.** $n^2 - 6 = 0$ **3.** $n^2 - 4 = 0$ **4.** $n^2 - 25 = 0$
5. $2n^2 - 8 = 0$ **6.** $(3n)^2 = 81$ **7.** $3n^2 + 9 = 2n^2 + 25$ **8.** $n^2 + 6n = 18$

Computer Activity

Computer Construction

Use a computer software program to complete the following constructions. Then measure the ratios of the segment lengths. Suggest theorems that you think could be proven.

a line parallel to   three parallel lines cut
a side of a triangle   by transversals

6-6 Segments Divided Proportionally

EXPLORE

Draw a segment *AB* and a point *X* between *A*
and *B*. Then draw a second segment *CD* parallel
to *AB*.

Using a straightedge only, devise a method for
constructing a point *Y* on *CD* so that $\frac{AX}{XB} = \frac{CY}{YD}$.

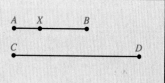

Segments *AB* and *CD* are **divided proportionally** by points *X* on *AB* and *Y*
on *CD* if $\frac{AX}{XB} = \frac{CY}{YD}$.

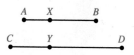

In the Explore you may have discovered a method of constructing a point *Y*
so that *AB* and *CD* are divided proportionally by *X* and *Y*.

◆ **THEOREM 6.6**   Triangle Proportional Segment Theorem

If a line parallel to one side of a triangle intersects the other two sides,
then it divides the two sides proportionally.

Given: $\triangle ABC$, $\overline{DE} \parallel \overline{BC}$
Prove: $\frac{AD}{DB} = \frac{AE}{EC}$

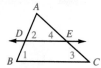

Proof

Statements	Reasons
1. $\overline{DE} \parallel \overline{BC}$	1. Given
2. $\angle 1 \cong \angle 2$, $\angle 3 \cong \angle 4$	2. If $\parallel$ lines are cut by a trans., corr. $\angle$s are $\cong$.
3. $\triangle ABC \sim \triangle ADE$	3. AA Similarity Theorem
4. $\frac{AB}{AD} = \frac{AC}{AE}$	4. Corr. sides of similar $\triangle$s are proportional.
5. $\frac{AB - AD}{AD} = \frac{AC - AE}{AE}$	5. Property of Proportions
6. $\frac{DB}{AD} = \frac{EC}{AE}$	6. Segment Addition Property
7. $\frac{AD}{DB} = \frac{AE}{EC}$	7. Property of Proportions

6-6   Segments Divided Proportionally   **281**

First Five Minutes

(Quiz on previous lesson)

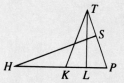

Given: Isosceles $\triangle TKP$ with
base $\overline{KP}$, $\overline{HS} \perp \overline{TP}$, $\overline{TL}$ is an
altitude to $\overline{KP}$.
Prove: $\triangle TKL \sim \triangle HSP$
1. Isos. $\triangle TKP$ (Given)
2. $\angle K \cong \angle P$ (Base $\angle$s of isos. $\triangle$
are $\cong$.) 3. $\overline{HS} \perp \overline{TP}$ (Given)
4. $\angle HSP$ is a rt. $\angle$ ($\perp$ lines form
rt. $\angle$s.) 5. $\triangle HSP$ is a rt. $\triangle$. (Def.
of rt. $\triangle$) 6. $\overline{TL}$ is an altitude to
$\overline{KP}$. (Given) 7. $\angle TLK$ is a rt. $\angle$
(Def. of alt.) 8. $\triangle TKL$ is a rt. $\triangle$.
(Def. of rt. $\triangle$) 9. $\triangle TKL \sim \triangle HSP$
(Rt. $\triangle$ Similarity)

Lesson Opener

This lesson presents four application theorems involving proportions: Triangle Proportional
Segment Theorem, converse
of Theorem 6.6, Parallels Proportional Segment Theorem,
and Triangle Angle Bisector
Theorem.

Materials

student notebooks
straightedges
investigative software

Teaching Notes

Point out that Theorem 6.7 is
the converse of Theorem 6.6.
Before discussing Theorem 6.9
review the definition of angle
bisector of a triangle.

Guided Practice

Chalkboard Examples

1. $\overline{DE} \parallel \overline{AC}$, $BD = 4$, $DA = 2$,
$BE = 7$, $DE = 6$
a. Find EC. $\frac{7}{2}$
b. Find AC. (HINT: Use similar
triangle concept.) 9
Answer to **Try This** $\frac{10}{3}$

2. $\overline{AD} \parallel \overline{BE} \parallel \overline{CF}$, $AB = 9$,
$BC = 18$, $DE = x$,
$EF = 24 - x$
a. $DE = \underline{\ 8\ }$ **b.** $EF = \underline{\ 16\ }$
Answer to **Try This** $3, \frac{15}{2}$

3. $\angle 1 \cong \angle 2$, $AC = 10$,
$BC = 15$, $AD = x$, $BD = 14 - x$ **a.** $AD = \frac{28}{5}$ **b.** $BD = \frac{42}{5}$
Answer to **Try This** $\frac{65}{17}, \frac{156}{17}$

Class Exercise Answers

1. yes **2.** yes **3.** no
4. $\frac{c}{d}$ **5.** $\frac{EC}{DB}$ **6.** $\frac{EC}{BC}$
7. $\frac{a}{b}$ **8.** $\frac{DE}{EF}$ **9.** 4, Triangle
Proportional Segment
10. 3, Triangle Angle Bisector
11. $\frac{15}{8}$, Parallels Proportional
Segment **12.** This will not work.

Example 1

Given: $\triangle ABC$ with $\overline{DE} \parallel \overline{AC}$
Find x.

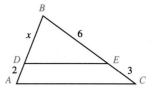

Solution

$\frac{x}{2} = \frac{6}{3}$ *This proportion is true by the Triangle*
$3x = 12$ *Proportional Segment Theorem.*
$x = 4$

Try This

Given: $\triangle ABC$ with $\overline{DE} \parallel \overline{AC}$ If $BE = 5$, find x.

The next theorem is the converse of Theorem 6.6. Its proof will be completed in Exercise 24.

◆ THEOREM 6.7

If a line divides two sides of a triangle proportionally, then the line is parallel to the third side.

◆ THEOREM 6.8   Parallels Proportional Segment Theorem

If three parallel lines intersect two transversals, then they divide the transversals proportionally.

Given: $\overline{AX} \parallel \overline{BY} \parallel \overline{CZ}$

Prove: $\frac{AB}{BC} = \frac{XY}{YZ}$

Plan   Draw the auxiliary segment $\overline{CX}$ intersecting $\overline{BY}$ at K. Apply Theorem 6.6 to $\triangle CAX$ to conclude that $\frac{CB}{BA} = \frac{CK}{KX}$. Then apply this theorem to $\triangle XCZ$ to conclude that $\frac{XK}{KC} = \frac{XY}{YZ}$. Use properties of proportions and equality to conclude that $\frac{AB}{BC} = \frac{XY}{YZ}$.

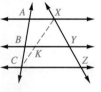

Example 2

$\overline{AD} \parallel \overline{BE} \parallel \overline{CF}$
EF is $\frac{3}{2}$ less than three times the length of DE.
Find DE and EF.

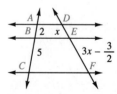

Solution

Let $DE = x$. Then $EF = 3x - \frac{3}{2}$.
$\frac{AB}{BC} = \frac{DE}{EF}$
$\frac{2}{5} = \frac{x}{3x - \frac{3}{2}}$
$6x - 3 = 5x$
$x = 3$
$DE = 3$ $EF = 3(3) - \frac{3}{2} = \frac{15}{2}$

Parallels Proportional Segment Theorem

Try This

If $\overline{EF}$ is three more than $\frac{3}{2}$ times as long as $\overline{DE}$, find DE and EF.

The Triangle Proportional Segment Theorem is used to prove the next theorem.

◆ **THEOREM 6.9** Triangle Angle Bisector Theorem

If a ray bisects an angle of a triangle, then it divides the opposite side into two segments whose lengths are proportional to the lengths of the other two sides.

Given: $\angle 1 \cong \angle 2$

Prove: $\dfrac{AD}{DB} = \dfrac{AC}{CB}$

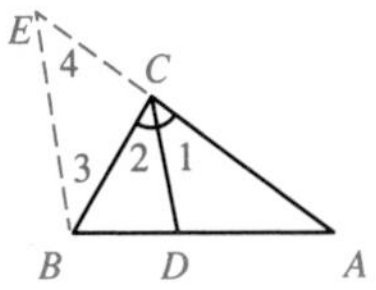

Plan Draw auxiliary segment $\overline{BE}$ parallel to $\overline{CD}$. Extend $\overline{AC}$ to point E. Use properties of parallel lines to conclude that $\angle 1 \cong \angle 4$ and $\angle 2 \cong \angle 3$, and conclude that $CE = CB$. Apply the Triangle Proportional Segment Theorem to show that $\dfrac{AD}{DB} = \dfrac{AC}{CE}$. By substitution $\dfrac{AD}{DB} = \dfrac{AC}{CB}$.

Example 3

If $\angle 1 \cong \angle 2$, find AD and DB.

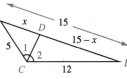

Solution

$\dfrac{x}{15-x} = \dfrac{5}{12}$ *Triangle Angle Bisector Theorem*

$12x = 75 - 5x$

$17x = 75$

$x = \dfrac{75}{17} = AD$ $BD = 15 - x = 15 - \dfrac{75}{17} = \dfrac{180}{17} \approx 10.59$

Try This

Use the figure to the right above.

If $AB = 13$, find AD and DB.

Three additional theorems also concern ratios in similar triangles.

◆ **THEOREM 6.10**

The lengths of bisectors of corresponding angles of two similar triangles are in the same ratio as the lengths of corresponding sides.

◆ **THEOREM 6.11**

The lengths of altitudes from corresponding vertices of similar triangles are in the same ratio as the lengths of corresponding sides.

◆ **THEOREM 6.12**

The lengths of medians from corresponding vertices of similar triangles are in the same ratio as the lengths of corresponding sides.

6-6 Segments Divided Proportionally   **283**

Assignment Guide

Minimum: 1–28 e/o, 31, MR

Regular: 1–30 e/o, 31, MR

Advanced: 13–28 e/o, 29–31, MR

Applications

Exercises 16–17, 22

Algebra

Exercise 30

Lesson Closure

Review the four application theorems involving proportions.

Teacher's Resource Materials

Enrichment Using Manipulatives 39

Practice Master 43

Quiz 12

Technology: Calculator 7

Transparency 24

Computer Software

See Computer Explorations 12–14, pages 645–647.

Exercise Answers

1. 9, Triangle Proportional Segment   **2.** $\frac{8}{3}$, Triangle Angle Bisector   **3.** 12, Parallels Proportional Segment

4. $\frac{144}{11}$, Triangle Angle Bisector

5. $\frac{81}{7}$, Parallels Proportional Segment   **6.** $\frac{40}{9}$, Triangle Proportional Segment

7. $\frac{3}{5}$ **8.** $\frac{8}{z}$ **9.** $\frac{40}{3}$

10. 5   **11.** $\frac{21}{5}$ **12.** 4

13. 8   **14.** $\frac{120}{11}, \frac{45}{11}$

15. $\frac{11}{4}$ **16.** 140 ft   **17.** The method works by the Triangle Proportional Segment Theorem.

18. 6, 24   **19.** 6, 2, $\frac{21}{2}$, $\frac{7}{2}$

20. $\frac{32}{3}$ **21.** 10   **22.** 288 ft

23. Plan: Extend lines CA and DB so that they intersect at a point E. $\triangle EAB \sim \triangle ECD$ by AA Similarity ($\angle E \cong \angle E$ by the Reflexive Property, $\angle EAB \cong \angle ECD$ because corresponding $\angle$s are congruent when parallel lines are cut by a transversal). Draw $\overrightarrow{EX}$. Where it intersects $\overline{CD}$ is point Y. We know that $\frac{EA}{EC} = \frac{EB}{ED}$. Also $\frac{EA}{EC} = \frac{AX}{CY}$ and $\frac{EB}{ED} = \frac{XB}{YD}$. By substitution, $\frac{AX}{CY} = \frac{XB}{YD}$. By a property of proportions (switching the means) $\frac{AX}{XB} = \frac{CY}{YD}$.   **24.** Given: $\frac{AB}{BC} = \frac{AE}{ED}$

Prove: $\overline{BE} \parallel \overline{CD}$

Proof: 1. $\frac{AB}{BC} = \frac{AE}{ED}$ (Given)
2. $\frac{BC}{AB} = \frac{ED}{AE}$ (Property of Proportions) 3. $\frac{AB + BC}{AB} = \frac{AE + ED}{AE}$ (Property of Proportions)
4. $\frac{AC}{AB} = \frac{AD}{AE}$ (Segment Addition Postulate) 5. $\angle A \cong \angle A$ (Reflexive Property)
6. $\triangle ABE \sim \triangle ACD$ (SAS Similarity Theorem) 7. $\angle ABE \cong \angle ACD$ (Definition of similar triangles)
8. $\overline{BE} \parallel \overline{CD}$ (If 2 lines are cut by a transversal so that corr. $\angle$s are $\cong$, the lines are $\parallel$.)

25. 1. Draw auxiliary segment $\overline{BE}$ parallel to $\overline{CD}$. Extend $\overline{AC}$ to E. (Through a point not on a given line, a line $\parallel$ the given line may be drawn.) 2. $\angle 1 \cong \angle 2$ (Given) 3. $\angle 1 \cong \angle 4$ (When 2 $\parallel$ lines are cut by a trans., corr. $\angle$s are $\cong$.) 4. $\angle 2 \cong \angle 4$ (Theorem 1.3) 5. $\angle 2 \cong \angle 3$ (When 2 $\parallel$ lines are cut by a trans, alt. int. $\angle$s are $\cong$.)
6. $\angle 3 \cong \angle 4$ (Theorem 1.3)
7. $\overline{CE} \cong \overline{CB}$ (Sides opposite $\cong$ angles are $\cong$.) 8. $\frac{AD}{DB} = \frac{AC}{CE}$ (Triangle Proportional Segment Theorem) 9. $\frac{AD}{DB} = \frac{AC}{CB}$ (Substitution)

Class Exercises

Short Answer

Determine whether segments $\overline{AB}$ and $\overline{CD}$ are divided proportionally.

1.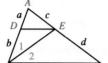

2.

3.

$\overline{BC} \parallel \overline{DE}$, $\angle 1 \cong \angle 2$ **Complete each statement.**

4. $\frac{a}{b} = $ ___

5. $\frac{AE}{AD} = $ ___

6. $\frac{AE}{AB} = $ ___

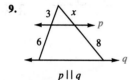

Line p, q, and r are parallel. Complete each statement.

7. $\frac{c}{d} = $ ___

8. $\frac{AB}{BC} = $ ___

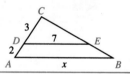

Sample Problems

Find x. State the theorem that justifies each answer.

9.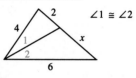

$p \parallel q$

10. 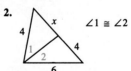 $\angle 1 \cong \angle 2$

11.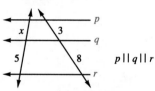

$p \parallel q \parallel r$

Discussion

12. Suppose that $\overline{DE}$ is parallel to $\overline{AB}$. One student claimed AB could be found by solving the proportion $\frac{3}{2} = \frac{7}{x}$. Discuss this method. Explain why this method does or does not work.

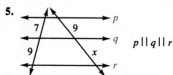

Exercises

A

Find x. State the theorem that justifies each answer.

1. 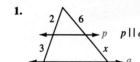 $p \parallel q$

2. $\angle 1 \cong \angle 2$

3. 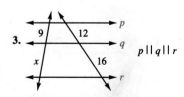 $p \parallel q \parallel r$

4. 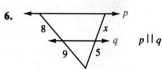 $\angle 1 \cong \angle 2$

5. $p \parallel q \parallel r$

6. $p \parallel q$

In the figure, $\overline{BE}$ bisects $\angle B$ and $\overline{DE} \parallel \overline{BC}$.

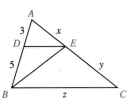

7. Use the Triangle Proportional Segment Theorem to complete the proportion $\frac{x}{y} =$ ___ .
8. Use the Triangle Angle Bisector Theorem to complete $\frac{x}{y} =$ ___ .
9. Combine the results of Exercises 7–8 to find z.
10. Find the length of $\overline{DE}$. **11.** If $y = 7$, find x.

Given $\triangle ADH$, $\overline{DF}$ bisects $\angle D$ and $p \parallel q \parallel r$. Find the indicated length and state the theorem applied.

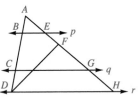

12. If $AB = 2$, $BD = 7$, and $EH = 14$, find AE.
13. If $AD = 12$, $DH = 15$, and $FH = 10$, find AF.
14. If $AC = 8$, $CD = 3$, and $AH = 15$, find AG and GH.
15. If $AF = 6$, $FH = 8$, $AC = 7$, and $DH = 13$, find CD.

B

16. In a new subdivision three trapezoidal lots are each 125 ft across the front. The lot lines on the side are all perpendicular to the front. What is the length of the property line across the back of each lot?
17. A carpenter wants to cut a $9\frac{1}{4}$ in.-wide board into five pieces equal in width. (NOTE: $9\frac{1}{4} \div 5 = 1\frac{17}{20}$, a unit that does not appear on a carpenter's ruler) Since he cannot divide $9\frac{1}{4}$ by 5 and measure directly, he places a ruler diagonally so that 10 units show across the board. Then he draws a horizontal line every 2 units. Explain why this method works.

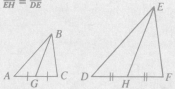

$ABCD$ is a trapezoid with bases $\overline{AB}$ and $\overline{CD}$, and $\overline{EF} \parallel \overline{AB}$.

18. If $\frac{AE}{ED} = \frac{1}{4}$ and $BC = 30$, find BF and FC.
19. If $\frac{BG}{BD} = \frac{3}{4}$, $AD = 8$, and $BC = 14$, find AE, ED, BF, and FC.
20. If $BG = 3$, $GD = 5$, and $GF = 4$, find CD.
21. If $AE = 2$, $ED = 3$, and $GF = 4$, find CD.

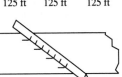

22. Two people walk away from each other at an angle, one moving straight ahead at 6 ft per second, the other moving straight ahead at 4 ft per second. After 5 seconds they are 24 ft apart. If they continue at the same angle and pace, how far apart will they be after 1 minute?
23. Prove that the construction you developed in the Explore is correct.
24. Prove Theorem 6.7.   **25.** Prove Theorem 6.9   **26.** Prove Theorem 6.10.
27. Prove Theorem 6.11   **28.** Prove Theorem 6.12.

C

29. In the pentagon-based pyramid on the left, $\overline{WX} \parallel \overline{BC}$, $\overline{XY} \parallel \overline{CD}$, $\overline{YZ} \parallel \overline{DE}$, $AW = 2$, $WB = 3$, and $AE = 6$. Find AZ and ZE.
30. If $\overline{DE} \parallel \overline{BC}$, show algebraically that $\overline{BF}$ cannot be the angle bisector of $\angle B$ in the figure on the right. (HINT: Obtain two equations involving x assuming that $\overline{DF}$ is the angle bisector. Show that the two equations imply different values for x, which is not possible.)

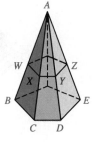

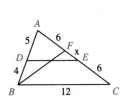

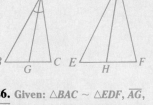

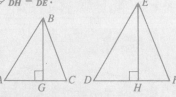

26. Given: $\triangle BAC \sim \triangle EDF$, $\overline{AG}$, $\overline{DH}$ are angle bisectors. Prove: $\frac{AG}{DH} = \frac{AB}{DE}$ Proof: $\angle B \cong \angle E$ (def. of similar $\triangle$s), $\angle BAG \cong \angle EDH$ (since $\angle BAC \cong \angle EDF$ and they are bisected), so $\triangle BAG \sim \triangle EDH$ (AA Similarity) $\Rightarrow \frac{AG}{DH} = \frac{AB}{DE}$.

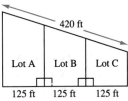

27. Given: $\triangle BAC \sim \triangle EDF$, $\overline{BG}$ and $\overline{EH}$ are altitudes. Prove: $\frac{BG}{EH} = \frac{AB}{DE}$ Proof: $\angle A \cong \angle D$ (def. of similar $\triangle$s), $\angle AGB \cong \angle DHE$ (All right $\angle$s are $\cong$.), $\triangle AGB \sim \triangle DHE$ (AA Similarity), so $\frac{BG}{EH} = \frac{AB}{DE}$

28. Given: $\triangle BAC \sim \triangle EDF$, $\overline{BG}$ and $\overline{EH}$ are medians. Prove: $\frac{BG}{EH} = \frac{AB}{DE}$ Proof: $\frac{AC}{AB} = \frac{DF}{DE}$ (by similarity), $AC = 2AG$, $DF = 2DH$ (G is midpt. of $\overline{AC}$, H is midpt. of $\overline{DF}$), so $\frac{2AG}{AB} = \frac{2DH}{DE}$ or $\frac{AG}{AB} = \frac{DH}{DE}$, also $\angle A \cong \angle D$ (similarity). So by SAS Similarity Theorem $\triangle BAG \sim \triangle EDH$ and then $\frac{BG}{EH} = \frac{AB}{DE}$. **29.** $\frac{12}{5}, \frac{18}{5}$

30. If $\overline{BF}$ were the bisector of $\angle B$, then $\frac{6+x}{6} = \frac{5}{4}$, $24 + 4x = 30$, $4x = 6$, $x = \frac{6}{4}$ or $\frac{3}{2}$, and $\frac{6}{x+6} = \frac{9}{12}$, $9x + 54 = 72$, $9x = 18$, $x = 2$, giving two different values for x.

31. a. never b. $\overline{AX} \| \overline{BB'}$ (Theorem 3.1), so $\frac{AB}{BC} = \frac{XB'}{B'C}$ (Theorem 6.6). Also, $\overline{B'Y} \| \overline{CZ}$ so by Theorem 6.6, $\frac{XB'}{B'C} = \frac{XY}{YZ}$. Put the two equations together to get $\frac{AB}{BC} = \frac{XY}{YZ}$.

Critical Thinking

31. Given: Planes $P_1 \| P_2 \| P_3$ and transversals p and q that are skew lines.
  a. Is $\overline{AX}$ always, sometimes, or never parallel to $\overline{CZ}$?
  b. Prove that $\frac{AB}{BC} = \frac{XY}{YZ}$.

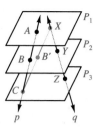

Mixed Review

1. If an airplane climbs 6000 ft while traveling 15 mi during its ascent, how many miles will it take to climb 33,000 ft?

2. At its current rate of ascent how high will the airplane be after 46 mi?

3. How many miles did the plane travel in climbing from 16,000 ft to 20,000 ft?

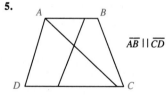

6000 ft

15 mi

Complete each statement. Use acute, right, obtuse, equilateral, isosceles, or scalene.

4. A right triangle may never have a(n) ___ angle.   **5.** An isosceles triangle is never ___ .

6. The acute angles of a(n) ___ triangle are complementary.   **7.** An equilateral triangle is always ___ .

Quiz

State if the two triangles are similar. If so, state a postulate or theorem that supports your answer. If not, write *triangles not similar*.

1.

10
6
2
5
4
12

2.

36°
36°
4
6
8

3.

3
5
58°
5
6
5
58°

4.

5.

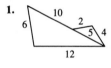

A   B

$\overline{AB} \| \overline{CD}$

D   C

6.

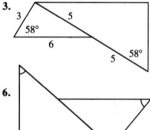

A   20   G r
B   3   F s
4   6
C   E u
2
D

If $r \| s \| u$, complete each proportion.

7. $\frac{AB}{BC} = \frac{?}{FE}$ **8.** $\frac{BD}{AB} = \frac{FD}{?}$

9. $\frac{CD}{BC} = \frac{?}{FE}$ **10.** $\frac{AG}{CE} = \frac{AD}{?}$

11. Find AD.   **12.** Find BF.

CRITICAL THINKING

Recognizing Quantifier Errors in Reasoning

Many reasoning errors occur in critical thinking because people do not know how to use the **quantifier** words *all*, *no*, and *some*. Consider these examples.

Example 1—All

Nino said, "All my friends dislike me." "You're wrong," said Tico, "All your friends like you a lot."

Since *all* means *every* member of a certain set, Tico could have negated Nino's statement by giving a counterexample, "You're wrong—I'm your friend and I like you."

Example 2—No

Jenny said, "No student from Lincoln High is friendly." "I don't agree," said Sara, "All of the ones I've met are really friendly."

Since *no* means *not one, or none* Sara found one example to contradict Jenny's statement and could say, "I disagree. I've met Sandy Sloan and she is very friendly."

Example 3—Some

Tip said, "Some theorems in geometry are easy to prove." "I disagree," said Bill, "Some theorems in geometry are not easy to prove."

Since *some* means *at least one*, Bill would have to say the following to negate Tip's statement, "I disagree. No theorem in geometry is easy to prove."

All, *no*, and *some* statements can be written in one of the following four forms.

I. All A are B.
II. No A is B.
III. Some A are B.
IV. Some A are not B.

Exercises

What would you have to do to prove that the statements in Exercises 1–4 are false?

1. Tom said, "All frogs are green."
2. Katy said, "No compact disk costs less than $10."
3. A teacher said, "Some students in our class are absent today."
4. A geometry student said, "Some triangles have two lines of symmetry."

Use statements I–IV above.

5. Give examples to explain why statements I and II are not negations of each other. Do the same for statements III and IV.
6. Which pairs from statements I, II, III, and IV are negations of each other? Give examples to explain why you think so.
7. What if-then statement means the same as statement I? statement II?
8. Which statement means the same as "Anytime an A is found to exist, it is guaranteed to be a B."? as "Anytime an A is found to exist, it is guaranteed not to be a B."?

Critical Thinking

Recognizing Quantifier Errors in Reasoning

Exercise Answers

Answers may vary.
1. Counterexample: "I've seen a brown frog."   **2.** Contradict: "I disagree, I paid $8.45 for a CD."   **3.** Negate: "No students are absent today."
4. Negate: "No triangles have two lines of symmetry."
5. (I) All people have brown hair. The negation of this statement is "Some people do not have brown hair." This is different from II, which is "No people have brown hair." (II) Some horses are green. The negation of this statement is "No horses are green." This is different from IV, which would be "Some horses are not green."
6. I and IV, II and III   **7.** If something is A, then it is B. If something is A, then it is not B.
8. I, II

CHAPTER SUMMARY

Vocabulary

extremes (6-1)   proportion (6-1)   scale factor (6-3)
means (6-1)   ratio (6-1)   similar polygons (6-3)

Key Ideas

1. The properties of proportions are used to change proportions into equivalent forms.
2. In similar polygons, the corresponding angles are congruent and the lengths of the corresponding sides are proportional.
3. Prove two triangles similar by AA, SAS, or SSS.
4. Prove two right triangles similar by showing a pair of acute angles congruent.
5. If a line is parallel to one side of a triangle and intersects the other two sides, then it divides those two sides proportionally.
6. Three parallel lines cut a pair of transversals proportionally.
7. If a ray bisects an angle of a triangle, then it divides the opposite side into segments whose lengths are proportional to the lengths of the other two sides.

CHAPTER REVIEW

6-1

Give each ratio in simplest form.

1. $\frac{3t}{15}$ **2.** 33 to 9   **3.** $16xy : 20x$ **4.** $\frac{45x^2 y}{18xy^2}$

5. If $3 : 5 = 7 : x$, then $x = \underline{\ ?\ }$.   **6.** If $2 : 6 = x : 18$, then $x = \underline{\ ?\ }$.
7. The measures of two supplementary angles are in a ratio $3 : 15$. What are the measures of the angles?
8. A 42-cm line segment is divided into two segments whose lengths are in a ratio of 5 to 9. How long is each segment?

6-2

Complete each statement and state which property of proportions you are using.

9. If $\frac{x}{y} = \frac{5}{7}$, then $7x = \underline{\quad}$.   **10.** If $\frac{8}{t} = \frac{4}{w}$, then $\frac{t}{8} = \underline{\quad}$.

11. If $\frac{3}{4} = \frac{x}{y}$, then $\frac{y}{4} = \underline{\quad}$.   **12.** If $\frac{x}{3} = \frac{4}{w}$, then $\frac{x-3}{3} = \underline{\quad}$.

Find the value of x.

13. $\frac{5}{4} = \frac{x-7}{8}$ **14.** $\frac{x+1}{4} = \frac{7}{2}$ **15.** $\frac{2}{5} = \frac{6}{x-4}$
16. $\frac{3x}{8} = \frac{9}{6}$ **17.** $\frac{x+2}{2} = \frac{16}{2x+4}$ **18.** $\frac{2x}{3} = \frac{4}{x-1}$

19. On a map, $\frac{1}{2}$ in. represents 2 mi. If the distance from a shopping mall to the high school is $\frac{3}{4}$ in. on the map, what is the distance in miles?
20. A 75 yd × 50 yd parking area was decreased in size by multiplying each dimension by a factor of $\frac{4}{5}$. Find the new length and width.

6-3

$\triangle ABC \sim \triangle DEF$

Complete each of the following.

21. $m\angle E = $ ___
22. $m\angle F = $ ___
23. $EF = $ ___
24. $AC = $ ___
25. The scale factor of $\triangle ABC$ to $\triangle DEF$ is ___ .

6-4

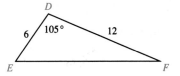

26. If $\angle R \cong \angle SWX$, then $\triangle SRU \sim$ __?__
    by the __?__ postulate.
27. **Given:** $\overline{RS} \| \overline{UT}$
    Prove: $\triangle WXS \sim \triangle VXU$
28. A person 5 ft 9 in. tall casts a $3\frac{1}{2}$-ft shadow, the foot of which lies at the end of the shadow cast by a tree 12 ft away. How tall is the tree?
29. If a person 6-ft tall casts a shadow 9 ft long, how long a shadow would a person 4 ft 6 in. tall cast?

6-5

State if the two triangles are similar. If so, state a theorem or postulate that justifies your answer. If not, write *triangles not similar*.

30.
31.
32.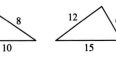

33. Given: $\triangle RST$ and $\triangle GHI$ If $\angle T \cong \angle I$, state the proportion that must be true if $\triangle RST \sim \triangle GHI$ by SAS Similarity.
34. Given: $\triangle WXY$ and $\triangle DEF$ State the proportions that must be true if $\triangle WXY \sim \triangle DEF$ by SSS Similarity.
35. Write a two-column proof.
    Given: $\square DFGI$
    Prove: $DE \cdot HJ = EJ \cdot GH$

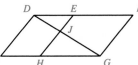

6-6

Find BC.

36.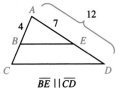

$\overline{BE} \| \overline{CD}$

37.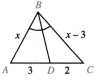

1. $\frac{t}{5}$ 2. $\frac{11}{3}$ 3. $4y : 5$
4. $\frac{5x}{2y}$ 5. $\frac{35}{3}$ 6. 6
7. 30°, 150°   8. 15, 27
9. 5y   10. $\frac{w}{4}$ 11. $\frac{x}{3}$
12. $\frac{4-w}{w}$ 13. 17   14. 13
15. 19   16. 4   17. −6, 2
18. −2, 3   19. 3 mi
20. 60 yd x 40 yd
21. 52   22. 23   23. 15
24. 8   25. $\frac{2}{3}$ 26. $\triangle SWX$,
AA   27. 1. $\overline{RS} \| \overline{UT}$ (Given)
2. $\angle RSU \cong \angle TUS$ (When ‖ lines
are cut by a trans., alt. int. $\angle$s
are $\cong$.) 3. $\angle WXS \cong \angle VXU$ (Vert.
$\angle$s $\cong$) 4. $\triangle WXZ \sim \triangle VXU$ (AA)
28. about 25.5 ft   29. $6\frac{3}{4}$ or 6
ft 9 in.   30. yes, SAS
31. triangles not similar
32. yes, SSS   33. $\frac{RT}{GI} = \frac{ST}{HI}$
34. $\frac{WX}{DE} = \frac{XY}{EF} = \frac{WY}{DF}$
35. 1. $\square DFGI$ (Given) 2. $\overline{DF} \| \overline{IG}$
(Def. $\square$) 3. $\angle FDG \cong \angle IGD$
(Trans. intersecting ‖ lines
forms $\cong$ alt. int. $\angle$s) 4. $\angle DJE \cong$
$\angle GJH$ (Vert. $\angle$s are $\cong$.)
5. $\triangle DJE \cong \triangle GJH$ (AA)
6. $\frac{DE}{GH} = \frac{EJ}{HJ}$ (Sides of $\sim\triangle$s are
proportional.) 7. $DE \cdot HJ =$
$EJ \cdot GH$ (Means/extremes)
36. $\frac{20}{7}$ 37. 6

Teacher's Resource Materials

Chapter 6 Tests

Test Answers

1. $\frac{5}{7}$ 2. $\frac{1}{2}$ 3. $\frac{7}{9}$
4. 6 5. 4 6. 18
7. $\frac{5}{7}$ 8. $\frac{x}{7}$ 9. $\frac{2}{3}$
10. 60 11. $\angle N$ 12. 8
13. yes, AA 14. not similar
15. yes, Rt. $\triangle$ Sim. 16. yes, SAS 17. yes, SSS
18. not similar
19. $\frac{CD}{DE}$ 20. 4 21. $\frac{16}{3}$
22. $\frac{AD}{DC}$ 23. $\frac{BD}{DC}$ 24. 8

CHAPTER TEST

Give each ratio in simplest form.

1. BD to BC 2. $CD:CB$ 3. $\frac{BC}{AB}$

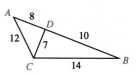

Find x in each proportion.

4. $x:12 = 8:16$ 5. $6:x = 9:6$ 6. $2:3 = 12:x$

Complete each statement.

7. If $\frac{3}{y} = \frac{7}{5}$, then $\frac{y}{3} =$ ___ .
8. If $7:4 = x:y$, then $\frac{y}{4} =$ ___ .
9. If $\frac{m}{2} = \frac{5}{3}$, then $\frac{m-2}{2} =$ ___ .

$ABCD \sim KLMN$ **Complete each statement.**

10. $m\angle B =$ ___
11. $\angle D \cong$ ___
12. $x =$ ___

Determine if each pair of triangles are similar. If so, state a theorem or postulate that supports your answer.

13.

14.

15.

16.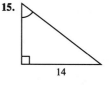

17.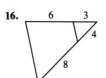

18.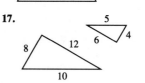

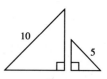

$\overleftrightarrow{CQ} \parallel \overleftrightarrow{DR} \parallel \overleftrightarrow{ES}$ **Complete each statement.**

19. $\frac{QR}{RS} =$ ___
20. If $CD = 2$, $DE = 5$, and $RS = 10$, then $QR =$ ___ .
21. If DE is twice CD and $QS = 16$, then $QR =$ ___ .

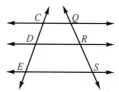

$\angle 1 \cong \angle 2$, $\angle 3 \cong \angle 4$ **Complete each statement.**

22. $\frac{AE}{EC} =$ ___
23. $\frac{AB}{AC} =$ ___
24. If $BD = 3$, $DC = 4$, and $AB = 6$, then $AC =$ ___ .

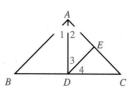

PREPARING FOR COLLEGE ENTRANCE EXAMS

1.

The ratio of the surface area of cube 1 to the surface area of cube 2 is

(A) 1 : 5   (B) 1 : 6   (C) 1 : 2
(D) 1 : 8   (E) 1 : 4

2. What is the next number in the sequence 1, 4, 9, 16, . . . ?

(A) 9   (B) 36   (C) 21
(D) 25   (E) 42

3.

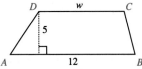

The area of trapezoid $ABCD = 55$. Find w.

(A) 9   (B) 10   (C) 11
(D) 12   (E) $\frac{55}{12}$

4. An item normally costs $10.00, but it has been marked down 10%. How much does it now cost?

(A) $9.00   (B) $7.50   (C) $5.00
(D) $4.00   (E) $1.00

5.

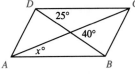

$ABCD$ is a parallelogram. Find x.

(A) 10   (B) 15   (C) 25
(D) 30   (E) 40

6. Solve for x. $x^2 - 36 = 0$

(A) 6, −6   (B) 5, −5   (C) 6, 0
(D) 6, 4   (E) 36

7. For any integer n, which of the following represents three consecutive odd integers?

(A) $n, n + 1, n + 2$
(B) $n + 1, n + 3, n + 5$
(C) $3n, 5n, 7n$
(D) $2n + 1, 2n + 3, 2n + 5$
(E) $2n, 2n + 2, 2n + 4$

8.

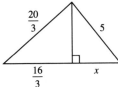

Find x.

(A) $\frac{10}{3}$ (B) $\frac{20}{3}$ (C) 3   (D) 4   (E) 5

9. In one week, sailboat production at four different factories was 8, 10, 5, 5. What was the average production per factory that week?

(A) 5   (B) 6   (C) 7   (D) 14   (E) 28

10.

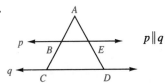

Which of the following is not necessarily true?

(A) $AB : AC = AE : AD$
(B) $\angle ACD \cong \angle ABE$
(C) $AB : BC = AE : ED$
(D) $AB : ED = AE : BC$
(E) $m\angle BED + m\angle CDA = 180$

11. On the moon, objects weigh only $\frac{1}{6}$ their earth weight. If an astronaut weighs 22 lb on the moon, how much does she weigh on earth?

(A) 66 lb   (B) 120 lb   (C) 124 lb
(D) 132 lb   (E) 148 lb

12. Three angles in a quadrilateral are 90, 145, and 80. The measure of the fourth angle is

(A) 25   (B) 45   (C) 115
(D) 205   (E) 225

CUMULATIVE REVIEW

Chapters 1–6

1. Points A, B, and C are collinear. If $AC = 9$, $BC = 10$, and $AB = 19$, which point is between the other two?

   a. A is between B and C.
   b. B is between A and C.
   c. C is between A and B.
   d. none of these

2. $\angle FED$ and $\angle FEG$ form a linear pair. If $m\angle FEG = x$, find $m\angle FED$.

   a. $x + 180$ **b.** $180 - x$
   c. 180 **d.** $90 - x$

3. What is the statement formed by negating both the hypothesis and the conclusion of a conditional called?

   a. converse   **b.** inverse
   c. contrapositive   **d.** biconditional

4. If $\overline{AB} \perp \overline{XY}$ at E, what conclusion can be drawn?

   a. $m\angle AEX + m\angle AEY = 180$
   b. $XE = EY$
   c. $m\angle AEB = 90$
   d. $AB = XY$

5. If $\overrightarrow{AC}$ is between $\overrightarrow{AB}$ and $\overrightarrow{AD}$, then ___ .

   a. $m\angle BAC = m\angle CAD$
   b. $m\angle CAB + m\angle DAB = m\angle CAD$
   c. $\overrightarrow{AB} \perp \overrightarrow{AD}$
   d. $m\angle BAC + m\angle CAD = m\angle BAD$

6. $\overline{RS}$ and $\overline{TU}$ intersect at V. If $m\angle RVT = 2x + 2$ and $m\angle RVU = x + 4$, find $m\angle RVT$.

   a. 58   **b.** 118   **c.** 62   **d.** 6

7. Which of the following statements is false?

   a. If one angle of a linear pair is a right angle, then the other angle is a right angle.
   b. If one angle of a linear pair is acute, then the other angle is obtuse.
   c. Perpendicular lines form congruent adjacent angles.
   d. If two angles are complements of congruent angles, then they are complementary.

8. If $l \parallel m$, then ___ .

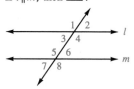

   a. $\angle 3 \cong \angle 5$.
   b. $\angle 1 \cong \angle 8$.
   c. $m\angle 1 + m\angle 5 = 180$.
   d. $m\angle 4 + m\angle 5 = 180$.

9. Find $m\angle 1$.

   a. 80   **b.** 150
   c. 100   **d.** 110

10. How many sides does a polygon have if the sum of the interior angles is 900?

   a. 6 sides   **b.** 7 sides
   c. 8 sides   **d.** 9 sides

11. $\triangle ABC \cong \triangle XYZ$. Which pair of angles are congruent?

   a. $\angle C \cong \angle Z$ **b.** $\angle B \cong \angle X$
   c. $\angle C \cong \angle X$ **d.** $\angle A \cong \angle Z$

12. $\overline{AE}$ and $\overline{BD}$ bisect each other at C. $\triangle ABC \cong \triangle DEC$ by which postulate?

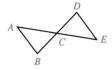

   a. SSS   **b.** ASA
   c. SAS   **d.** AAS

13. An equiangular triangle is both equilateral and ___ .
   a. right   **b.** isosceles
   c. scalene   **d.** obtuse

14. $\triangle RSU \cong \triangle WVT$

Which of these would not necessarily be true?

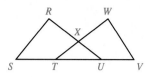

a. $\overline{RU} \cong \overline{WT}$
b. X is the midpoint of $\overline{WT}$.
c. $\overline{ST} \cong \overline{UV}$
d. $\overline{XR} \cong \overline{XW}$

15. $\overline{OM}$ is a median in $\triangle LON$. Which conclusion is correct?

a. $\angle 1 \cong \angle 2$
b. $\overline{OM} \| \overline{LN}$
c. $LM = MN$
d. all of the above

16. If $FGHI$ is a parallelogram, which conclusion is *not* correct?

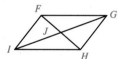

a. $\overline{FG} \cong \overline{IH}$
b. $m\angle FIH + m\angle IHG = 180$
c. $\overline{FH} \cong \overline{GI}$
d. $\overline{IJ} \cong \overline{JG}$

17. The altitude of a right triangle ___ .
a. may lie on the exterior of the triangle
b. may be congruent to the hypotenuse
c. may be a leg of the triangle
d. none of the above

18. Which quadrilateral has perpendicular diagonals?
a. rhombus
b. rectangle
c. parallelogram
d. all of the above

19. Find the length of the median of a trapezoid if the lengths of the bases are $2x$ and $3x + 15$, and the median is $2x + 20$.
a. 25
b. 50
c. $23\frac{1}{3}$
d. 70

20. What is the negation of $a \| b$?
a. $a \not\| b$
b. a and b intersect.
c. $a \perp b$
d. a and b are skew.

21. $\triangle ABC \sim \triangle DEF$, $AB = 8$, $AC = 10$, $DE = 12$
Find DF.
a. 30
b. $6\frac{2}{3}$
c. 15
d. 14

22. In $\triangle ABC$, $\angle 1 \cong \angle 2$, $AD = x + 2$, $DC = 3x - 3$, $AB = 8$, and $BC = 6$.
Find x.

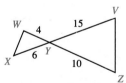

a. 3
b. 2
c. 7
d. 4

23. $\triangle WYX \sim \triangle ZYV$ by which postulate or theorem?

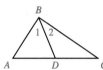

a. SSS
b. SAS
c. AA
d. The triangles are not similar.

24. The diagonals of a parallelogram make ___ .
a. 4 pairs of similar triangles
b. 6 pairs of similar triangles
c. 8 pairs of similar triangles
d. 12 pairs of similar triangles

Cumulative Review Answers

(Chapters 1–6)

1. c	**2.** b	**3.** b
4. a	**5.** d	**6.** b
7. d	**8.** b	**9.** c
10. b	**11.** a	**12.** c
13. b	**14.** b	**15.** c
16. c	**17.** c	**18.** a
19. d	**20.** a	**21.** c
22. b	**23.** b	**24.** a

Right Triangles

Chapter Overview

The first four lessons of this chapter are centered around a very important theorem—the Pythagorean Theorem. The remaining three lessons involve right-triangle trigonometry. This chapter, along with the preceding one, provides students with a good foundation for trigonometry, analytic geometry, and other higher-level math courses.

Objectives

7-1 ▪ Identify and apply proportions in right triangles.
7-2 ▪ Apply the Pythagorean Theorem.
7-3 ▪ Apply the converse of the Pythagorean Theorem.
7-4 ▪ Apply relationships in $45°-45°-90°$ and $30°-60°-90°$ right triangles.
7-5 ▪ Identify and use the tangent ratio.
7-6 ▪ Identify and apply the sine and cosine ratios.
7-7 ▪ Identify and apply the angle of elevation and angle of depression.

TEACHING CHAPTER 7

Cooperative Learning Opportunities

Group activities can be used to develop specific examples or instances that will reinforce new concepts. In Lesson 7-1, the important notion of geometric mean is introduced and explained. The **Try This**, after example 2, is a good spot for a brief three-person cooperative activity.

Assign students to groups of three. Each group should solve the **Try This** Exercise and make sure they all have the correct answer. Then each of the 3 students in the group should invent a problem asking for the geometric mean, and solve it. Students then pass their papers to another group member so that each exercise is checked by one other student.

A similar group activity can be used in the lessons on special triangles. After explaining the theorems and examples on pages 312 and 313, assign students to three-person groups as described above. Ask them to do the **Try This** exercises. After checking each other's results, have each student draw the special triangles and find the lengths of the unknown sides.

Multicultural Note: *Hypatia*

Diophantus lived at about 250 A.D. and is known for his work on equations having many solutions such as, $x + y = 10$. Hypatia lived in Alexandria about 150 years later and was renowned for her learning, especially in mathematics and science.

Hypatia, writing about Diophantus, posed this problem. Find a number that satisfies these two conditions: it is the sum of two squares; its square is the sum of two squares. Satisfying the first condition is easy. For example, $1 + 16 = 17$. Thus 17 is the sum of two squares. $17 \times 17 = 289$. Is 289 the sum of two squares? **Ans: Yes, 225 + 64**

Hypatia studied the class of numbers found using the formula $4n + 1$, where $n = 1, 2, 3, \ldots$ When $4n + 1$ is prime it is the sum of two squares.

For more information, see page 80 of **Multiculturalism in Mathematics, Science, and Technology**.

Alternative Assessment and Communication Ideas

A formal, graded class presentation by an individual or pair of students can be a good form of alternative assessment. **Theorem 7.6** (p. 308) on right, obtuse, and acute triangles is a good candidate for such a presentation. The material is not difficult but it is divided into several parts, requiring figures and inequalities. You will want to help

the student(s) prepare so that the presentation will set a high standard for others to follow.

The trigonometric ratios also offer the opportunity for individual reports and/or presentations. On page 321, discussion question 19 asks for a convincing argument that tan A increases as A increases. This idea, expanded

to the three basic trigonometric functions, could be used as the starting point for a report about the behavior of the trigonometric ratios as functions. Suggest that students draw a series of triangles showing what happens to the values of the tangent, sine, and cosine as angle values change.

Investigations and Projects

By drawing right triangles on graph paper, students can build an inductive argument for the **Pythagorean Theorem**. The figure shows a right triangle with legs 2 and 5. Squares are formed off each leg and off the hypotenuse. Have students compute the area of the hypotenuse square based on the square and triangles around it.

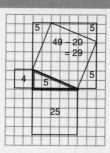

This demonstrates the **Pythagorean Theorem** without computing the length of the hypotenuse.

There are many proofs of the **Pythagorean Theorem** and students may follow this activity by researching and presenting other proofs. Perigal's dissection is particularly interesting.

Lesson	PACING CHART (DAYS)			Opening Activity	Cooperative Activity	Seat or Group Work
	1-Year Minimum	1-Year Regular	1-Year Advanced			
7-1	2	2	2	Chapter Opener: **TE** p. 294; Lesson Opener: **TE** p. 295	Lab Worksheet 7-1: *Laboratory Manual* p. 67	Try This Exercises
7-2	2	2	2	First Five Minutes 7-2: *FFM Transparency Masters* p. 23 or **TE** p. 301; Lesson Opener: **TE** p. 301	Explore: **SE** p. 301; ✂ Lab Worksheet 7-2A: *Laboratory Manual* p. 68; Lab Worksheet 7-2B: *Laboratory Manual* p. 69	Try This Exercise
7-3	2	2	2	First Five Minutes 7-3: *FFM Transparency Masters* p. 24 or **TE** p. 307; Lesson Opener: **TE** p. 307	Explore: **SE** p. 307	Try This Exercises
7-4	1	1	1	First Five Minutes 7-4: *FFM Transparency Masters* p. 24 or **TE** p. 312; Lesson Opener: **TE** p. 312	Explore: **SE** p. 312; ✂ Lab Worksheet 7-4A: *Laboratory Manual* p. 70; Lab Worksheet 7-4B: *Laboratory Manual* p. 71; ✂ Lab Worksheet 7-4C: *Laboratory Manual* p. 72	Try This Exercises
7-5	1	1	1	First Five Minutes 7-5: *FFM Transparency Masters* p. 25 or **TE** p. 319; Lesson Opener: **TE** p. 319	✂ Lab Worksheet 7-5: *Laboratory Manual* p. 74	Try This Exercises
7-6	1	1	1	First Five Minutes 7-6: *FFM Transparency Masters* p. 26 or **TE** p. 325; Lesson Opener: **TE** p. 326	✂ Lab Worksheet 7-6A: *Laboratory Manual* p. 75; ✂ Lab Worksheet 7-6B: *Laboratory Manual* p. 76	Try This Exercises
7-7	1	1	1	First Five Minutes 7-7: *FFM Transparency Masters* p. 27 or **TE** p. 331; Lesson Opener: **TE** p. 331	Critical Thinking: **SE** p. 335	Try This Exercises
Review	1	1	1			
Test	1	1	1			

FFM = First Five Minutes

Enrichment	Review/Assess	Reteach	Technology	Lesson
Careers: **SE** p. 300; ✄ Enrichment Using Manipulatives 7-1: *Enrichment* p. 40; BASIC 7-1: *Technology* p. B14	Class Exercises: **SE** p. 297; Algebra Review: **SE** p. 300	Practice Worksheet 7-1: *Practice and Mixed Review* p. 49	Computer Exploration 15: **SE** p. 648; Computer Exploration 16: **SE** p. 649; Computer Exploration 17: **SE** p. 650; Computer Exploration 18: **SE** p. 651; BASIC 7-1: *Technology* p. B14	**7-1**
Enrichment: **SE** p. 306; ✄ Enrichment Using Manipulatives 7-2: *Enrichment* p. 41; BASIC 7-2: *Technology* p. B15	Class Exercises: **SE** p. 302; Mixed Review: **SE** p. 306	Practice Worksheet 7-2: *Practice and Mixed Review* p. 50	BASIC 7-2: *Technology* p. B15; Lab Worksheet 7-2B: *Laboratory Manual* p. 69	**7-2**
Computer Activity: **SE** p. 311; ✄ Enrichment Using Manipulatives 7-3: *Enrichment* p. 42	Class Exercises: **SE** p. 309; Algebra Review: **SE** p. 311	Practice Worksheet 7-3: *Practice and Mixed Review* p. 51	Computer Activity: **SE** p. 311; Computer Exploration 19: **SE** p. 652; Calculator Worksheet 7-3: *Technology* p. CL8	**7-3**
Comparing Approaches in Geometry: **SE** p. 318; ✄ Enrichment Using Manipulatives 7-4: *Enrichment* p. 43; ✄ Lab Worksheet 7-4D: *Laboratory Manual* p. 73	Class Exercises: **SE** p. 314; Mixed Review: **SE** p. 317; Quiz: **SE** p. 317; Quiz: *Assessment* p. 91	Practice Worksheet 7-4: *Practice and Mixed Review* p. 52	Computer Exploration 20: **SE** p. 653; Computer Exploration 21: **SE** p. 654; Calculator Worksheet 7-4: *Technology* p. CL9	**7-4**
Calculator Investigation: **SE** p. 324	Class Exercises: **SE** p. 321; Mixed Review: **SE** p. 324	Practice Worksheet 7-5: *Practice and Mixed Review* p. 53	Calculator Investigation: **SE** p. 325; Computer Exploration 22: **SE** p. 655	**7-5**
Math Contest Problem: **SE** p. 330	Class Exercises: **SE** p. 326; Algebra Review: **SE** p. 330;	Practice Worksheet 7-6: *Practice and Mixed Review* p. 54	Calculator Worksheet 7-6: *Technology* p. CL10	**7-6**
Critical Thinking: **SE** p. 335	Class Exercises: **SE** p. 332; Mixed Review: **SE** p. 334; Quiz: **SE** p. 334; Quiz: *Assessment* p. 92	Practice Worksheet 7-7: *Practice and Mixed Review* p.55		**7-7**
	Summary & Review: **SE** p. 336–337	Mixed Review: *Practice and Mixed Review* p. 108		**Review**
Problem Solving: **SE** p. 339	Chapter 7 Test: **SE** p. 338; Chapter 7 Tests: *Assessment* p. 37–42; *MathTest*			**Test**

7

Right Triangles

A plane takes off at an angle of 20° and covers a ground distance of 15,000 ft. Find the altitude of the plane.

RIGHT TRIANGLE RELATIONSHIPS

OBJECTIVE: *Identify and apply proportions in right triangles.*

7-1 Right Triangle Proportions

In this section you will analyze the relationships among the triangles and segments formed when an altitude is drawn to the hypotenuse of a right triangle. To do this, the following idea is helpful.

When a, b, and x are positive numbers and $\frac{a}{x} = \frac{x}{b}$, x is called the **geometric mean** between a and b.

In order to prepare for finding the geometric mean between two numbers, you could review the process for writing a radical, such as $\sqrt{32}$, in simplest form. Recall that in such a radical, 32 is called the radicand. For a radical expression to be in simplest form, the following must be true.

- A radicand can have no factor (other than 1) that is a perfect square.
- A radicand cannot be a fraction.
- There can be no radicals in a denominator.

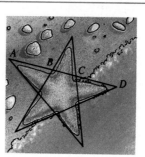

The idea of a geometric mean can be used to describe some relationships in a starfish. AB is the geometric mean between BC and AC.

Example 1

Simplify each radical. **a.** $\sqrt{32}$ **b.** $\sqrt{\left(\frac{16}{2}\right)}$

Solution

a. $\sqrt{32} = \sqrt{(16 \cdot 2)} = \sqrt{16} \cdot \sqrt{2} = 4\sqrt{2}$

b. $\sqrt{\left(\frac{16}{2}\right)} = \frac{\sqrt{16}}{\sqrt{2}} = \frac{4}{\sqrt{2}}$

$= \frac{4}{\sqrt{2}} \cdot \frac{\sqrt{2}}{\sqrt{2}}$ *Multiply by $\frac{\sqrt{2}}{\sqrt{2}}$ to remove the*

$= \frac{4\sqrt{2}}{2} = 2\sqrt{2}$ *radical from the denominator.*

Try This

Simplify $\frac{2}{\sqrt{5}}$.

The idea of the geometric mean is illustrated in the example below and used in the theorems that follow.

Example 2

Find the geometric mean between 3 and 6.

Solution

$\frac{3}{x} = \frac{x}{6}$ *Use the definition of geometric mean to write a proportion.*

$x^2 = 18$ *The product of the means equals the product of the extremes.*

$x = \sqrt{18} = \sqrt{9 \cdot 2} = \sqrt{9} \cdot \sqrt{2} = 3\sqrt{2}$

Try This

Find the geometric mean between 4 and 9.

Lesson Opener

Review the AA Similarity Postulate and special parts of right triangles, such as the hypotenuse, legs, and altitudes. Tell students that they will continue their study of ratio and proportion using lengths of sides and altitudes of right triangles. For example, if $a:b = c:d$, a and d are the extremes and b and c are the means. In this lesson, the means are equal. When b and x are positive numbers ($a:x = x:b$), x is the geometric mean (also called the mean proportional) between a and b.

In nature, the starfish illustrates the idea of a geometric mean. (See drawing.) Written symbolically, $BC:AB = AB:AC$.

Materials

student notebooks
calculators
investigative software

Teaching Notes

Point out that the geometric mean of two positive real numbers is the square root ($\sqrt{}$) of their product. For example, the geometric mean of 4 and 9 is $\sqrt{36}$ or 6.

NOTE: Because many of the problems in this chapter involve radicals, it may be helpful to review simplifying radical expressions.

In Example 2, explain that because the measures or lengths of segments cannot be negative, students can disregard the negative solution ($-3\sqrt{2}$).

Helpful Hint to Proving Theorem 7.1: First prove by the AA Similarity Postulate that the two smaller right triangles are similar to the larger right triangle (i.e., $\triangle ADC \sim \triangle ACB$ and $\triangle CDB \sim \triangle ACB$). Second prove by the transitive property that $\triangle ADC \sim \triangle CDB$.

Restatement of Theorem 7.2: The altitude to the hypotenuse is the geometric mean to the legs. Written symbolically, $AD{:}BD = BD{:}DC$ or $x{:}z = z{:}y$.

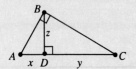

Restatement of Theorem 7.3: The measure of either leg of a right triangle is the geometric mean between the hypotenuse and the segment of the hypotenuse adjacent to that leg. Written symbolically,

Case 1: $\frac{DC}{BC} = \frac{BC}{AC}$ or $(BC)^2 = (DC)(AC)$; $\frac{y}{a} = \frac{a}{x+y}$ or $a^2 = y(x+y)$.

Case 2: $\frac{AD}{AB} = \frac{AB}{AC}$ or $(AB)^2 = (AD)(AC)$; $\frac{x}{c} = \frac{c}{x+y}$ or $c^2 = x(x+y)$.

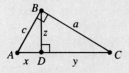

Key Terms

geometric mean
radical
radicand

Theorems 7.1, 7.2, and 7.3 present some right-triangle relationships that will be used later to prove other theorems about right triangles called the "altitude on the hypotenuse" theorems.

◆ THEOREM 7.1

The altitude to the hypotenuse of a right triangle forms two triangles that are similar to each other and to the original triangle.

Given: $\triangle ABC$ is a right triangle.
$\overline{CD}$ is the altitude to the hypotenuse $\overline{AB}$.

Prove: $\triangle ADC \sim \triangle CDB \sim \triangle ACB$

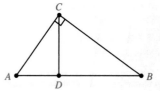

Proof The right angles in $\triangle ADC$, $\triangle CDB$, and $\triangle ACB$ are congruent. Also, since $\angle DCB$ and $\angle A$ are both complementary to $\angle ACD$, it follows that $\angle DCB \cong \angle A$. By the AA Similarity Postulates, $\triangle ADC \sim \triangle CDB$, Also, since $\angle A \cong \angle A$, it follows that $\triangle ADC \sim \triangle ACB$. By the properties of similarity, $\triangle ADC \sim \triangle CDB \sim \triangle ACB$.

◆ THEOREM 7.2

In a right triangle, the length of the altitude to the hypotenuse is the geometric mean between the lengths of the two segments on the hypotenuse.

Given: $\triangle ABC$ is a right triangle.
$\overline{CD}$ is an altitude to the hypotenuse $\overline{AB}$.

Prove: $\frac{x}{h} = \frac{h}{y}$

Proof From Theorem 7.1, we know that $\triangle ADC \sim \triangle CDB$. Since the ratios of corresponding sides of these similar triangles are equal, it follows that $\frac{x}{h} = \frac{h}{y}$.

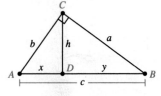

◆ THEOREM 7.3

In a right triangle with an altitude to the hypotenuse, each leg is the geometric mean between the length of the hypotenuse and the length of the segment of the hypotenuse adjacent to that leg.

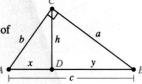

You will be asked to prove Theorem 7.3 in Exercise 45.

Example 3

Find the length of the altitude $\overline{FH}$ of right $\triangle EFG$.

Solution

$\frac{4}{FH} = \frac{FH}{16}$ *Theorem 7.2*

$FH^2 = 64$

$FH = 8$

Try This

Find HG if $EH = 5$ and $FH = 10$.

Example 4

Find the length of leg $\overline{AB}$ of right $\triangle ABC$.

Solution

$\frac{20}{AB} = \frac{AB}{15}$ *Use Theorem 7.3 to set up the proportion.*

$AB^2 = 300$

$AB = \sqrt{300} = 10\sqrt{3}$

Try This

Find the length of leg $\overline{BC}$ of right $\triangle ABC$.

Class Exercises

Short Answer

1. $\overline{EG}$ is the altitude to the hypotenuse in right $\triangle DEF$. Name three similar triangles.

Use Theorems 7.2 and 7.3 to complete these proportions.

2. $\frac{EG}{DG} = \frac{?}{EG}$ 3. $\frac{?}{DF} = \frac{DG}{?}$ 4. $\frac{EF}{GF} = \frac{?}{EF}$

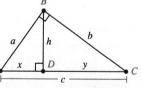

5. Simplify the radical. $\sqrt{27} = \sqrt{9 \cdot 3} = \underline{\ ?\ }$

Sample Exercises

6. Find the geometric mean between 3 and 9.

Complete each statement, write a proportion, and state a theorem that supports your answer.

7. h is the geometric mean between ___ and ___ .

8. a is the geometric mean between ___ and ___ .

9. b is the geometric mean between ___ and ___ .

10. If $x = 5$ and $y = 9$, find the lengths of the legs and the altitude of $\triangle ABC$.

Discussion

11. Suppose you wanted to find x, y, and z. Does it make any difference which variable you tried to find first? Explain your reasoning and discuss how to find the value of each variable.

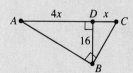

Common Errors

Some students may have problems naming similar triangles that overlap and, as a result, may set up proportions incorrectly. Suggest drawing the smaller triangles outside the larger triangle.

Guided Practice

Chalkboard Examples

1. Simplify each radical.

a. $8\sqrt{27}$ $24\sqrt{3}$

b. $\sqrt{21} \div \sqrt{14}$ $\frac{\sqrt{6}}{2}$

c. $1 \div \sqrt{2x}$ $\frac{\sqrt{2x}}{2x}$

d. $(4\sqrt{5})^2$ 80

e. $5\sqrt{4x} + 9\sqrt{9x}$ $37\sqrt{x}$

Answer to **Try This** $\frac{2\sqrt{5}}{5}$

2. Find the geometric mean between each pair of numbers.

a. 5 and 8 $2\sqrt{10}$

b. 1 and 2 $\sqrt{2}$

c. $\frac{2}{3}$ and $\frac{1}{2}$ $\frac{\sqrt{3}}{3}$

Answer to **Try This** 6

3. Find EF and FG. $6, 6\sqrt{3}$

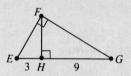

Answer to **Try This** 20

4. Find DC and AB. $8, 16\sqrt{5}$

Answer to **Try This** 10

Exercises

A

Simplify each radical.

1. $\sqrt{8}$ **2.** $\sqrt{48}$ **3.** $\frac{1}{\sqrt{2}}$ **4.** $\sqrt{\frac{3}{5}}$ **5.** $\frac{2}{3\sqrt{5}}$

Find the geometric mean between each pair of numbers.

6. 2 and 8   **7.** 9 and 16   **8.** 4 and 5   **9.** $\sqrt{3}$ and $\sqrt{5}$ **10.** 5 and 1.25

Use Theorems 7.2 and 7.3 to complete each proportion and find the values of x, y, or z.

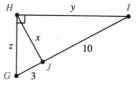

11. $\frac{3}{x} = \frac{x}{?}$ **12.** $\frac{3}{?} = \frac{?}{10}$

13. $\frac{13}{z} = \frac{z}{?}$ **14.** $\frac{?}{y} = \frac{y}{10}$

15. $\frac{10}{?} = \frac{?}{13}$ **16.** $\frac{13}{?} = \frac{?}{3}$

Find the length of the altitude of right $\triangle PQR$.

17. 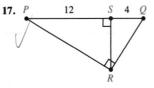   **18.** 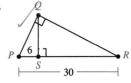   **19.**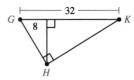

Find the length of each leg of right $\triangle GHK$.

20. 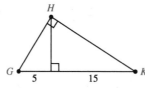   **21.** 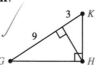   **22.**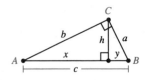

Complete each equation using Theorem 7.2 or 7.3.

23. Theorem 7.2: $h^2 = $ ___

24. Theorem 7.3: $a^2 = $ ___

25. Theorem 7.3: $b^2 = $ ___

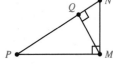

Find each of the following.

26. $PQ = 9$, $QN = 4$ Find MQ.

27. $QN = 3$, $MQ = 9$ Find PQ.

28. $PM = 12$, $PQ = 9$ Find PN.

29. $MN = 8$, $QN = 6$ Find PN.

30. $PN = 75$, $PQ = 72$ Find MN.

31. $MQ = 4$, $PQ = 10$ Find QN.

32. $PN = 13$, $PM = 12$ Find PQ.

33. $PN = 16$, $QN = 4$ Find QM.

34. How far is it across the lake?

B

35. If $EO = 4$ and $GH = 10$, find GO.
36. If $GH = 16$ and $EH = 12$, find EO.
37. If $EH = 16$ and $EG = 12$, find OH.
38. If $HO = 6$ and $EG = 4$, find OG.
39. If $EO = 8$ and $\frac{HO}{OG} = \frac{2}{1}$, find HO.
40. If $HO = 10$ and $OG = 8$, find $HE \cdot EG$.

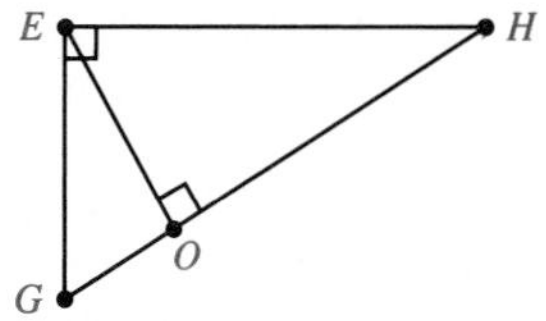

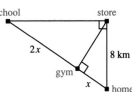

41. How far is it from home, past the gym, to school?

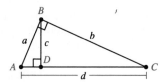

42. The altitude, $\overline{XR}$, to the hypotenuse of right $\triangle WXY$ divides the hypotenuse into segments that are 8 and 10 cm long. Find the length of the altitude.
43. A 12-cm long altitude of a right triangle divides the hypotenuse into two segments, one three times as long as the other. How long is the hypotenuse?
44. Use a ruler and compass to (a) construct a right triangle and (b) construct an altitude to its hypotenuse. Measure all segments to the nearest millimeter and verify that Theorems 7.2 and 7.3 hold for your triangle.
45. Prove Theorem 7.3.

Given: $\triangle ABC$ is a right triangle.
$\overline{CD}$ is an altitude to the hypotenuse $\overline{AB}$.

Prove: $\frac{y}{a} = \frac{a}{c}$ and $\frac{x}{b} = \frac{b}{c}$

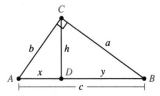

46. Use Theorem 7.3 to prove that if the altitude to the hypotenuse of a right triangle bisects the hypotenuse, then the right triangle is isosceles.
47. Use the information given below the starfish picture on page 295 to show that if $AB = CD$, then AC is the geometric mean between AB and AD. (HINT: Use the properties of proportions.)

C

48. Use Theorem 7.3 to find d. (HINT: Let x represent the length of one of the segments of the hypotenuse.)

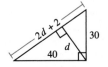

49. Given the information shown in the figure, prove that $cd = ab$. State in words the theorem you have proved.

Exercise Answers

1. $2\sqrt{2}$ 2. $4\sqrt{3}$
3. $\frac{\sqrt{2}}{2}$ 4. $\frac{\sqrt{15}}{5}$ 5. $\frac{2\sqrt{5}}{15}$
6. 4 7. 12 8. $2\sqrt{5}$
9. $\sqrt[4]{15}$ 10. $\frac{5}{2}$
11. 10, $x = \sqrt{30}$
12. x, $x = \sqrt{30}$
13. 3, $z = \sqrt{39}$
14. 13, $y = \sqrt{130}$
15. y, $y = \sqrt{130}$
16. z, $z = \sqrt{39}$
17. $4\sqrt{3}$ 18. $3\sqrt{5}$
19. 12 20. $GH = 10$, $HK = 10\sqrt{3}$ 21. $GH = 6\sqrt{3}$, $HK = 6$ 22. $GH = 16$, $HK = 16\sqrt{3}$ 23. xy
24. yc 25. xc 26. 6
27. 27 28. 16 29. $\frac{32}{3}$
30. 15 31. $\frac{8}{5}$ 32. $\frac{144}{13}$
33. $4\sqrt{3}$ 34. 9 km
35. 2 or 8 36. $3\sqrt{7}$
37. $\frac{64}{5}$ 38. 2
39. $8\sqrt{2}$ 40. $72\sqrt{5}$
41. $8\sqrt{3}$ km 42. $4\sqrt{5}$
43. $16\sqrt{3}$ cm 44. Check that students construct a rt. $\triangle$ and an alt. to its hyp. and that they verify Th. 7.2 and 7.3 using their $\triangle$s.

45. By Th. 7.1, $\triangle ACB$, $\triangle ADC$, and $\triangle CDB$ are similar. Because $\overline{DB}$ in $\triangle DCB$ corresponds to $\overline{CB}$ in $\triangle ACB$ and $\overline{CB}$ in $\triangle DCB$ corresponds to $\overline{AB}$ in $\triangle ACB$, $\frac{DB}{CB} = \frac{CB}{AB}$ or $\frac{y}{a} = \frac{a}{c}$. Because $\overline{AD}$ in $\triangle ACD$ corresponds to $\overline{AC}$ in $\triangle ACB$ and $\overline{AC}$ in $\triangle ACD$ corresponds to $\overline{AB}$ in $\triangle ACB$, $\frac{AD}{AC} = \frac{AC}{AB}$ or $\frac{x}{b} = \frac{b}{c}$.
46. Given $\triangle ABC$, prove $a = b$.

7-1 Right Triangle Proportions 299

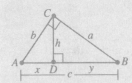

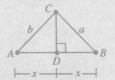

By Th. 7.2, $\frac{x}{b} = \frac{b}{2x}$ or $b^2 = 2x^2$, and $\frac{x}{a} = \frac{a}{2x}$ or $a^2 = 2x^2$. Therefore, $a^2 = 2x^2 = b^2$ and $a = b$.

47. Given AB is the geometric mean between BC and AC or $\frac{BC}{AB} = \frac{AB}{AC}$, prove $\frac{AB}{AC} = \frac{AC}{AD}$. If $CD = AB$, then all proportions can be written in terms of AB and BC. Given $\frac{BC}{AB} = \frac{AB}{AB + BC}$, prove $\frac{AB}{AB + BC} = \frac{AB + BC}{2AB + BC}$. $\frac{BC}{AB} = \frac{AB}{AB + BC}$ is equivalent to $(BC)^2 + AB \cdot BC = AB^2$. Add $(AB)^2 + AB \cdot BC$ to both sides of the equation to get $(BC)^2 + 2AB \cdot BC + (AB)^2 = 2(AB)^2 + AB \cdot BC$ or $(AC + BC)^2 = AB(2AB + BC)$. $(AC + BC)^2 = AB(2AB + BC)$ is equivalent to the proportion $\frac{AB}{AB + BC} = \frac{AB + BC}{2AB + BC}$.

48. 24 **49.** Let AD have length x and DC have length $d - x$. By Th. 7.2, $\frac{x}{c} = \frac{c}{d-x}$ or $x(d-x) = c^2$. By Th. 7.3, $\frac{x}{a} = \frac{a}{d}$ and $\frac{d-x}{b} = \frac{b}{d}$. Multiply the proportions: $\frac{x}{a} \cdot \frac{d-x}{b} = \frac{a}{d} \cdot \frac{b}{d}$ or $d^2 \cdot x(d-x) = a^2 b^2$. $x(d-x) = c^2$, so $d^2 c^2 = a^2 b^2$ or $cd = ab$. The product of the length of the alt. to the hyp. and the length of the hyp. equals the product of the lengths of the two legs.

50. a.

y $x - y$

x

$\frac{x}{y} = \frac{y}{x-y}$ b. The product of the means is one less than the product of the extremes for every set of triples circled. This holds true for every set of triples in the sequence.

Algebra Review Answers

1. 2 **2.** 45 **3.** $4a$
4. $5b$ **5.** $\frac{3}{4}$ **6.** $\frac{25}{2}$
7. $5a$ **8.** $\frac{b\sqrt{5}}{5}$ **9.** $\frac{\sqrt{3a}}{3}$
10. b **11.** $\frac{2c\sqrt{5}}{5}$ **12.** $\frac{6a\sqrt{7}}{7}$

Critical Thinking

50. Euclid, a Greek mathematician, described a segment divided into two parts so that "the greater part is the geometric mean between the whole and the lesser part."

  a. Draw a diagram and use variables to describe this situation.

  b. Test the triples circled in the Fibonacci sequence below to see if they are close to being possible lengths for Euclid's segment and its parts. Form a conjecture about this situation.

$$1, 1, \boxed{2, 3, 5}, 8, \boxed{13, 21, 34}, 55, \boxed{89, 144, 233}, \ldots$$

Algebra Review

Assume that a, b, and c are positive real numbers. Simplify each expression.

1. $(\sqrt{2})^2$ **2.** $(3\sqrt{5})^2$ **3.** $(2\sqrt{a})^2$

4. $(\sqrt{5b})^2$ **5.** $(\frac{\sqrt{3}}{2})^2$ **6.** $(\frac{5}{\sqrt{2}})^2$

7. $(\sqrt{5a})^2$ **8.** $\sqrt{\frac{b^2}{5}}$ **9.** $\frac{\sqrt{a}}{\sqrt{3}}$

10. $\frac{\sqrt{2b^2}}{\sqrt{2}}$ **11.** $\sqrt{\frac{4c^2}{5}}$ **12.** $\sqrt{\frac{36a^2}{7}}$

Careers

Architect

Architects design most of the structures we work and live in; every school, theater, and hospital was planned by an architect. Since rectangular windows, triangular roofs, and spiral staircases are common features of these structures, mathematics—especially geometry—plays an important role in an architect's training.

A project usually begins with a contract to design a particular type of building. A design is developed by the architect who prepares drawings and models showing how the building will look when it is completed. Thereafter, the architect oversees the construction of the building and works closely with contractors who provide plumbing, landscaping, and other components of the project. Often, the architect gets a percentage of the contruction budget as a fee.

Frank Lloyd Wright, one of the best-known American architects of the twentieth century, designed the Guggenheim Museum in New York pictured to the right.

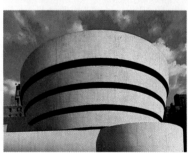

7-2 The Pythagorean Theorem

EXPLORE How does the sum of the areas of the squares on the legs of this right triangle compare to the area of the square on the hypotenuse? Make a generalization.

Use graph paper to decide if this generalization is true for right triangles with legs $a = 5$, $b = 12$, and $a = 8$, $b = 15$.

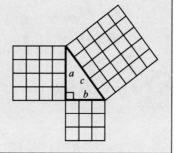

The Pythagorean Theorem is one of the most famous and useful theorems in plane geometry. It can be used to find the length of the third side of a right triangle when the lengths of two of the sides are known. It was named after the Greek mathematician Pythagoras who is thought to have given the first proof of the theorem around 500 BC. In the Explore, you may have "discovered" this famous theorem.

◆ **THEOREM 7.4** Pythagorean Theorem

In a right triangle, the square of the length of the hypotenuse equals the sum of the squares of the lengths of the legs.

Given: $\triangle ABC$ is a right triangle.
$\angle C$ is a right angle.
Prove: $a^2 + b^2 = c^2$

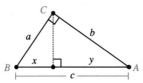

Proof

Statements	Reasons
1. $\triangle ABC$ is a right triangle. $\angle C$ is a right angle.	1. Given
2. Draw a perpendicular from C to $\overline{AB}$.	2. Theorem 2.9
3. $\frac{c}{a} = \frac{a}{x}, \frac{c}{b} = \frac{b}{y}$	3. Theorem 7.3
4. $a^2 = cx, b^2 = cy$	4. Product of mean equals product of extremes.
5. $a^2 + b^2 = cx + cy$	5. Addition Property
6. $a^2 + b^2 = c(x + y)$	6. Distributive Property
7. $a^2 + b^2 = c^2$	7. Segment Addition Postulate, Substitution

First Five Minutes

(Quiz on previous lesson)

1. Find the geometric mean between 3 and 27. 9
2. Find the geometric mean between 13 and 25. $5\sqrt{13}$

Find the missing values given right $\triangle ABC$.

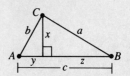

3. $y = 4$, $z = 25$ $a = 5\sqrt{29}$, $b = 2\sqrt{29}$, $c = 29$, $x = 10$
4. $b = 8$, $c = 16$, $y = 4$ $a = 8\sqrt{3}$, $x = 4\sqrt{3}$, $z = 12$
5. $x = 8$, $y = 8$, $z = 8$ $a = 8\sqrt{2}$, $b = 8\sqrt{2}$, $c = 16$

Lesson Opener

This lesson involves one of the most useful and well-known theorems in geometry, the Pythagorean Theorem, sometimes called the cornerstone of geometry. It is used to find the length of a third side of a right triangle when the lengths of two of the sides are known. Records show that Pythagoras was not the first to discover this well-known relationship; however, because of his active involvement in teaching the theorem, the Pythagorean Theorem was named in his honor.

One reason this theorem is so useful is because many everyday problems can be solved using it. (Exercises 39 and 41 are two examples.) Ask students to estimate the solutions to Exercise 39 and/or 41 before discussing the lesson content. Have them compare their estimated answers to the answers they obtain after learning how to apply the Pythagorean Theorem.

Extension

Point out that there are nearly 400 different proofs of the Pythagorean Theorem, one of which appears on page 299 of this text. Have students do research on some of these proofs. An excellent reference is an NCTM publication, *The Pythagorean Proposition*, by Elisha Scott Loomis. Many of the proofs are based upon an understanding of area, such as the example shown in the Explore. President Garfield was one person to discover a proof a few years prior to becoming President, around 1887.

Materials

student notebooks
straightedges
calculators
investigative software

The following example shows how to use the Pythagorean Theorem.

Example
Find the value of *a*.

Solution

$5^2 + a^2 = 13^2$ *Use the Pythagorean Theorem to write this equation.*
$25 + a^2 = 169$
$a^2 = 144$
$a = 12$ *Note that a = −12 is another solution to the equation, but the length of a segment must be a positive number.*

Try This
Find the value of *c* in the figure to the right.

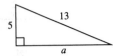

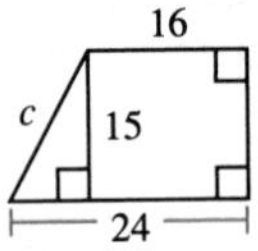

Class Exercises

Short Answer

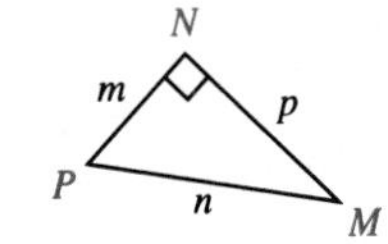

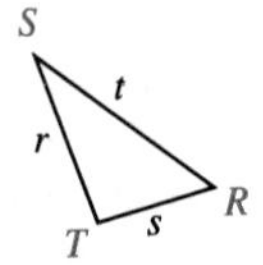

1. State the Pythagorean Theorem in your own words.
2. What equation gives the relationship of the sides in △*MNP*?
3. What information must you know about △*RST* to conclude that $r^2 + s^2 = t^2$.
4. Give an equation that can be solved to find the length of the hypotenuse of a right triangle with a 10-cm leg and a 24-cm leg.

Sample Exercises

Find the value of *x*.

5.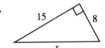

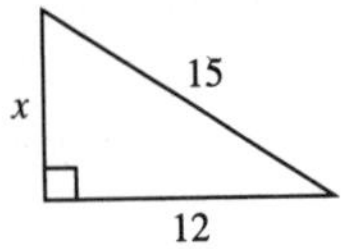

6.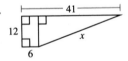

7.

8. Find the length of a diagonal of a square with side length $2\sqrt{2}$.
9. Find the perimeter of a rhombus with diagonals of 10 and 24 inches.

Discussion

10. If △*ABC* has sides with lengths 3, 4, and 5, why can you not conclude directly from the Pythagorean Theorem that it is a right triangle?

Determine whether each statement about the Pythagorean Theorem is always, sometimes, or never true.

11. It states a relationship among the sides of an obtuse triangle.
12. It states a relationship among the sides of an isosceles triangle.
13. It states a relationship among the sides of a scalene triangle.
14. It states a relationship among the sides of a right triangle.

Exercises

A

Find the value of x.

1.

2.

3.

4.

5.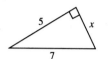

6.

Find each missing length. Express radicals in simplest form.

7. If $a = 6$ and $b = 8$, then $c =$ ___ .

8. If $c = 15$ and $a = 9$, then $b =$ ___ .

9. If $b = 2$ and $a = 2$, then $c =$ ___ .

10. If $c = \sqrt{15}$ and $a = \sqrt{10}$, then $b =$ ___ .

11. If $b = \sqrt{2}$ and $a = \sqrt{3}$, then $c =$ ___ .

12. If $a = 2\sqrt{3}$ and $c = 6$, then $b =$ ___ .

13. If the legs of an isosceles right triangle are 6 units long, find the length of the hypotenuse.

14. The length of a rectangle is 24 cm and the width is 10 cm. How long is the diagonal?

15. A television screen measures approximately 15.5 in. high and 19.5 in. wide. A television is advertised by giving the approximate length of the diagonal of its screen. How should this television be advertised?

Find each missing length x.

16.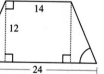

17.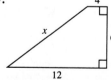

18.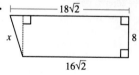

The length of the side of a square is given. Find the length of the diagonal of the square. Express radicals in simplest form.

19. $s = 2$ **20.** $s = 3$ **21.** $s = 4$ **22.** $s = 5$

Class Exercise Answers

1. Answers may vary.
2. $m^2 + p^2 = n^2$ **3.** $\angle T$ must be a right angle.   **4.** $10^2 + 24^2 = h^2$ **5.** 9   **6.** 17
7. 37   **8.** 4   **9.** 52 in.
10. The Pythagorean Theorem is an if-then statement: If the triangle is a right triangle, then the square of the hypotenuse equals the sum of the squares of the legs. The hypothesis must be satisfied before the conclusion is true.   **11.** never
12. sometimes
13. sometimes   **14.** always

Assignment Guide

Minimum: 1–27 e/o, 34–36, 53, MR
Regular: 13–47 e/o, 53–54, MR
Advanced: 23–55 e/o, MR

Applications
Exercises 15, 39–41, 44, 50, 52–53

Coordinate Geometry
Exercise 47

Constructions
Exercises 49, 51

Algebra
Exercises 25–35

Lesson Closure

Ask students to state the Pythagorean Theorem. Then have them use the theorem to complete the following table for right $\triangle ABC$. $m \angle C = 90$

	a	b	c
1.	5	12	_13_
2.	_8_	15	17
3.	1	_1_	$\sqrt{2}$
4.	5	$5\sqrt{3}$	10
5.	$3\sqrt{2}$	$3\sqrt{2}$	_6_

B

23. Look for a pattern in the answers to Exercises 19–22. Predict the formula for finding the diagonal of any square with side length s. Use the Pythagorean Theorem to show that your prediction is correct.

24. Find the length of each leg of an isosceles right triangle with hypotenuse 30 cm long.

Find the value of each variable.

25.
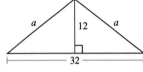

26.

27.

28.

29.

30.

31.
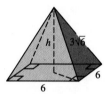

Cube

32.
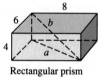

33.

Rectangular prism

34. The base of an isosceles triangle is $2x$ cm long. The altitude to the base is $3x$ cm long. Find the length of one other side of the triangle.

35. The hypotenuse of a right triangle is three times the length of a leg. The sum of the sides of the triangle is between 6 and 8. How long are the legs and the hypotenuse of the triangle if the length of the hypotenuse is an integer?

36. Find the altitude of an equilateral triangle with side length ten.

37. Find the perimeter of a rectangle that has diagonal length eight and a side of length five.

38. Find the perimeter of an isosceles trapezoid that has a base with length 10, another base with length 18, and height 8.

39. A 6-ft ladder is placed against a wall with its base 2 ft from the wall. How high above the ground is the top of the ladder?

40. A person travels 8 mi due north, 3 mi due west, 7 mi due north, and 11 mi due east. How far is that person from the starting point?

41. A door is 6 ft 6 in. high and 36 in. wide. Can a thin piece of plywood 7 ft wide be carried through the door?

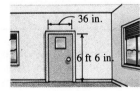

304   *Chapter 7   Right Triangles*

C

42. In $\triangle ABC$, a, b, and c are the lengths of the sides opposite vertices A, B, and C. If $a = 7$, $b = 8$, and $c = 9$, find the length of the altitude of the triangle from vertex C.

43. In isosceles $\triangle DEF$, $DE = EF = 25$ and $DF = 30$. Find the length of the altitude of the triangle from vertex F.

44. Will a fishing rod that collapses to a length of 80 cm fit into a suitcase with the dimensions shown?

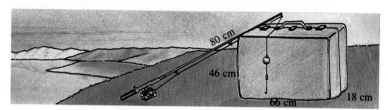

45. The faces of this triangular pyramid are equilateral triangles with side length 6. Find the altitude h of the pyramid.
(HINT: Point E is the intersection of the medians of $\triangle ADC$.)

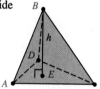

46. $\triangle ABC$ is a right triangle. Show that $AC^2 = AB^2 + BC^2$.

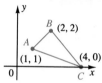

47. Mark and connect the points $(2, 4)$, $(-2, 2)$, $(4, 0)$, and $(-4, 4)$ on a coordinate grid. Find the perimeter of this quadrilateral and express it as simply as possible.

48. Find the length, to the nearest tenth, of the median m of this triangle. (HINT: Draw the altitude of the triangle from B.)

49. Use a straightedge and compass to construct a right triangle with hypotenuse equal to the length of this segment.

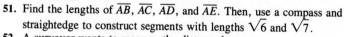

50. The 3-mi road from Cisco to Rockton forms a right angle with the 4-mi road from Rockton to Bayville. Emerson is on the straight road from Bayville to Cisco 2 mi from Bayville. Find the distance from Emerson to Rockton.

51. Find the lengths of $\overline{AB}$, $\overline{AC}$, $\overline{AD}$, and $\overline{AE}$. Then, use a compass and straightedge to construct segments with lengths $\sqrt{6}$ and $\sqrt{7}$.

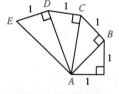

52. A surveyor wants to measure the distance between points A and B on rough land. She wants to find the actual horizontal distance AB. If the land is 0.75 m higher midway between the two stakes, and the measuring tape reads 27.0 m, use a calculator to find the actual distance AB.

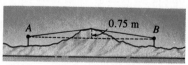

7-2 The Pythagorean Theorem **305**

Teacher's Resource Materials

Enrichment Using Manipulatives 41
Practice Master 45
Technology: BASIC 12
Technology: Computer Software 10
Transparency 26

Exercise Answers

1. 5 2. 25 3. 8
4. 4 5. $2\sqrt{6}$ 6. $\sqrt{19}$
7. 10 8. 12 9. $2\sqrt{2}$
10. $\sqrt{5}$ 11. $\sqrt{5}$
12. $2\sqrt{6}$ 13. $6\sqrt{2}$
14. 26 cm 15. ≈ 25 in.
16. 13 17. 10
18. $6\sqrt{2}$ 19. $2\sqrt{2}$
20. $3\sqrt{2}$ 21. $4\sqrt{2}$
22. $5\sqrt{2}$ 23. $d = \sqrt{2}s$, Answers may vary.
24. $15\sqrt{2}$ cm 25. 20
26. $\frac{20\sqrt{3}}{3}$ mi 27. $\sqrt{23}$
28. $4\sqrt{10}$ 29. $\frac{3\sqrt{5}}{5}$
30. $2\sqrt{15}$ 31. $8\sqrt{3}$
32. 6 33. $a = 10$, $b = 2\sqrt{29}$ 34. $\sqrt{10x}$ cm
35. $x = 1$, $y = 2\sqrt{2}$, $h = 3$
36. $5\sqrt{3}$ 37. $10 + 2\sqrt{39}$
38. $28 + 8\sqrt{5}$ 39. $4\sqrt{2}$ ft $\approx$ 5 ft 8 in. 40. 17 mi
41. yes 42. $\frac{8\sqrt{5}}{3}$
43. 24 44. yes 45. $2\sqrt{6}$
46. By the distance formula, $AB^2 = (2 - 1)^2 + (2 - 1)^2 = 1 + 1 = 2$, $BC^2 = (2 - 4)^2 + (2 - 0)^2 = 4 + 4 = 8$, $AC^2 = (4 - 1)^2 + (0 - 1)^2 = 9 + 1 = 10$, $2 + 8 = 10$, so $AB^2 + BC^2 = AC^2$. 47. $6 + 2\sqrt{5} + 2\sqrt{10} + 2\sqrt{2}$

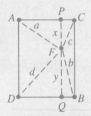
Critical Thinking

53. Four cities A, B, C, and D are located at the corners of a rectangle. If a
factory is built at any point F inside the rectangle, the builders claim that
the following relationship between the distances from the factory to the
cities holds. $a^2 + b^2 = c^2 + d^2$

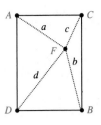

Draw two or three accurate rectangles and test this conjecture by
measuring to the nearest millimeter. If you think the conjecture is true,
give a convincing argument to support your conclusion.

54. A student looked at a right triangle and stated "b^2 can be found by
multiplying the sum of the other leg and the hypotenuse by the difference
of that leg and the hypotenuse." Test several cases and decide if this
generalization is true. If you think it is, give a convincing argument to
support your conclusion.

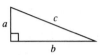

55. Give a general rule for finding the length of the diagonal of a cube when
you know the length of one of its sides.

Mixed Review

Complete each statement.

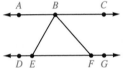

1. $\angle ABE$ and $\angle BEF$ are ___ angles.   **2.** If $\overleftrightarrow{AC} \parallel \overleftrightarrow{DG}$, then $\angle DEB \cong$ ___ .
3. If $\overleftrightarrow{AC} \parallel \overleftrightarrow{DG}$, $m\angle ABE = 60$, and $m\angle EBF = 50$, then $m\angle BFG =$ ___ .
4. If $\angle CBF$ is supplementary to ___, then $\overleftrightarrow{AC} \parallel \overleftrightarrow{DG}$.
5. $m\angle EBF + m\angle BFE =$ ___

6. Find the sum of the measures of the angles of $RSTUVW$.
7. If $RSTUVW$ is a regular hexagon, find the measure of each of its angles.
8. Find the sum of the measures of the exterior angles of $RSTUVW$.

Enrichment

Another Proof of the Pythagorean Theorem

The Hindu mathematician Bhaskara (1114–1185) was reported to have been
very excited when he used this figure to discover a proof of the Pythagorean
Theorem. He placed three copies of the right triangle as shown to form a
large square with a small square in the center.

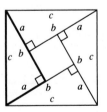

1. Use the variables given to express the side length and area of the small
square.
2. Write an equation relating the areas of the small and the four triangles to
the area of the large square.
3. Simplify the equation to prove the theorem!

OBJECTIVE: *Apply the converse of the Pythagorean Theorem*

7-3 The Converse of the Pythagorean Theorem

 **EXPLORE**

Cut a string or piece of yarn 12 in. long. At what two locations could you tie knots in the string so that it could be used to accurately form a right angle? Why does your method work?

When using the Pythagorean Theorem, you are given a right triangle and conclude a relationship among its side lengths. When using the *converse* of the Pythagorean Theorem, you are given a relationship among the side lengths and conclude that the given triangle is a right triangle. You may have used this idea in the Explore.

◆ **THEOREM 7.5**   Converse of the Pythagorean Theorem

If a triangle has side lengths a, b, and c, and $a^2 + b^2 = c^2$, then the triangle is a right triangle with right angle opposite the side of length c.

Given: $\triangle ABC$ with $a^2 + b^2 = c^2$

Prove: $\triangle ABC$ is a right triangle.

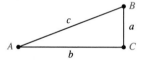

Plan   Draw a right triangle $\triangle PQR$ with $\angle Q$ a right angle, legs of lengths a and b, and hypotenuse length x. Use the Pythagorean Theorem to show that $x = c$. Then prove that the two triangles are congruent and use this to show that $\angle C$ is a right angle.

You will be asked to prove this theorem in Exercise 24.

Example 1
Is a triangle with sides 8, 15, and 17 a right triangle?

 Solution

 $8^2 + 15^2 = 289$, $17^2 = 289$

 Since $8^2 + 15^2 = 17^2$, a triangle with sides 8, 15, and 17 is a right triangle. *Theorem 7.4*

Try This

Is a triangle with sides 5, 6, and 8 a right triangle?

First Five Minutes

(Quiz on previous lesson)

Find the missing lengths given right $\triangle ABC$. $m\angle C = 90$

	a	b	c
1.	6	8	<u>10</u>
2.	5	<u>12</u>	13
3.	<u>9</u>	9	$9\sqrt{2}$
4.	5	$5\sqrt{3}$	<u>10</u>
5.	7	<u>24</u>	25

Lesson Opener

Review the definition of "converse." Then review classifying triangles by angles (acute, obtuse, right). Point out that sometimes the converse of a theorem is not necessarily true; however, the converse of the Pythagorean Theorem is not only true but is almost as important as the Pythagorean Theorem. The converse of the Pythagorean Theorem provides a standard way of showing that a triangle is a right triangle.

The Explore illustrates the converse of the Pythagorean Theorem and is similar to the process that was used by Egyptian "rope stretchers" to survey land. According to some historical notes, Egyptians obtained a right angle by forming a right triangle using certain lengths for sides. For example, they made 12 equally spaced knots in a rope and then stretched the rope to form a triangle having lengths 3, 4, and 5. The relationship between the lengths of the sides were always the same, $3^2 + 4^2 = 5^2$. Thus, $\triangle ABC$ was a right triangle and $\angle C$ was a right angle.

Teaching Notes

Emphasize that the converse of the Pythagorean Theorem provides a way of determining if a triangle is a right triangle, that is, if three lengths of the sides of a triangle are the lengths of the sides of a *right* triangle.

Point out that Pythagorean Triples are whole numbers. Although the numbers, 0.3, 0.4, and 0.5, satisfy the equation $a^2 + b^2 = c^2$, they are not by definition a Pythagorean Triple.

Encourage students to memorize the Pythagorean Triples that are given in the text because these triples are often found on standardized math tests. Have students complete the following table.

3,	*4,*	*5*	*5,*	*12,*	*13*
6,	8,	10	10,	24,	26
9,	12,	15	15,	36,	39
12	16	20	20	48	52
15	20	25	25	60	65
8,	15,	17	7,	24,	25
16,	30,	34	14,	48,	50
24	45	51	21	72	75
32	60	68	28	96	100

Before discussing Theorem 7.6, review the conditions that are necessary for a triangle to exist, that is, Theorem 5.23—the Triangle Inequality Theorem.

Key Terms

Pythagorean Triple

Consider the diagram below showing the result of increasing or decreasing the length c.

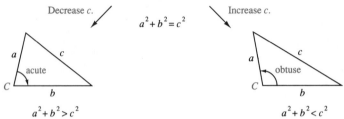

This diagram suggests the following convincing argument that the next theorem is true. If c is decreased, while keeping a and b the same, $a^2 + b^2$ will be greater than c^2 and $\angle C$ will be smaller and acute. If c is increased, while keeping a and b the same, $a^2 + b^2$ will be less than c^2 and $\angle C$ will be larger and obtuse.

These ideas are summarized in Theorem 7.6

◆ THEOREM 7.6

If $a < b < c$ are lengths of the sides of a triangle and
a. $a^2 + b^2 < c^2$, then the triangle is an obtuse triangle.
b. $a^2 + b^2 > c^2$, then the triangle is an acute triangle.

Example 2

Is a triangle with sides of lengths 2, 3, and 4 acute, right, or obtuse?

Solution

$2^2 + 3^2 = 4 + 9 = 13$
$4^2 = 16$
$2^2 + 3^2 < 4^2$, so the triangle is obtuse.   *Theorem 7.6*

Try This

Is a triangle with sides $\sqrt{3}$, $\sqrt{4}$, and $\sqrt{5}$ a right triangle? Explain.

A **Pythagorean Triple** is any three whole numbers a, b, and c that satisfy the equation $a^2 + b^2 = c^2$. Theorem 7.5 allows you to conclude that the numbers in a Pythagorean Triple are sides of a right triangle. Some commonly used Pythagorean Triples are (3, 4, 5), (5, 12, 13), (8, 15, 17), and (7, 24, 25). Any multiple of a Pythagorean Triple is also a Pythagorean Triple. For example, (6, 8, 10), (9, 12, 15), and so on, are multiples of (3, 4, 5) and are all Pythagorean Triples.

308   *Chapter 7   Right Triangles*

Class Exercises

Short Answer

1. State the Pythagorean Theorem in your own words.
2. State the converse of the Pythagorean Theorem in your own words.

Complete each statement.

3. If $r^2 + t^2 < s^2$, then $\angle S$ is ____.
4. If $r^2 + t^2 > s^2$, then $\angle S$ is ____.
5. If $r^2 + t^2 = s^2$, then $\angle S$ is ____.
6. The converse of the Pythagorean Theorem helps you tell if a triangle is ____.
7. If x, y, and z are a Pythagorean Triple, they satisfy the equation ____.

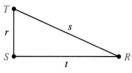

Sample Exercises

Which of these triples are sides of a right triangle?

8. (2, 3, 4)   9. (6, 8, 10)   10. (0.1, 0.4, 0.5)
11. (1, 1, 2)   12. ($\sqrt{2}$, $\sqrt{3}$, $\sqrt{5}$)   13. ($\frac{1}{3}$, $\frac{1}{4}$, $\frac{1}{5}$)

Classify each triangle as acute, right, or obtuse.

14. 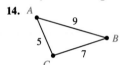   15. 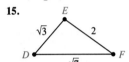   16.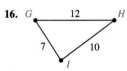

17. A rhombus has side length 5 and diagonal length $5\sqrt{2}$. Is the quadrilateral a square? Why or why not?
18. Certain side lengths and pairs of congruent angles are marked in the figure. How do you know that $\angle S$ is a right angle?

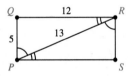

Discussion

Determine whether each statement is true or false. Give a convincing argument to support your decision.

19. The numbers $\sqrt{3}$, $\sqrt{4}$, and $\sqrt{7}$ do not form a Pythagorean Triple.
20. The converse of the Pythagorean Theorem allows you to conclude that the sum of the squares of the lengths of the legs of a right triangle is equal to the square of the length of the hypotenuse.
21. The numbers 0.3, 0.4, and 0.5 form a Pythagorean Triple.
22. If the sum of the squares of the lengths of the two shorter sides of a triangle is less than the square of the length of the longer side, the triangle is acute.

23. A student claimed that if each number in a Pythagorean Triple is multiplied by the same number, another Pythagorean Triple results. Use the triple (3, 4, 5) and discuss whether you think this is true. Give another example of a "family of triples."

7-3   The Converse of the Pythagorean Theorem   **309**

Guided Practice

Chalkboard Examples

1. Is a triangle with sides of the following lengths a right triangle?
a. 0.6, 0.8, 1 yes
b. $5n$, $12n$, $13n$ yes
c. 8, $8\sqrt{3}$, 16 yes

Answer to **Try This** no

2. Is a triangle with sides of the following lengths acute, obtuse, or right?
a. 0.2, 0.3, 0.4 obtuse
b. $\sqrt{7}$, $\sqrt{7}$, $\sqrt{14}$ right
c. $\sqrt{4}$, $\sqrt{5}$, $\sqrt{6}$ acute

Answer to **Try This** No, it is an acute triangle.

Class Exercise Answers

1.–2. Answers may vary.
3. obtuse   4. acute
5. right   6. a rt. △
7. $x^2 + y^2 = z^2$ 8. no
9. yes   10. no   11. no
12. yes   13. no
14. obtuse   15. right
16. acute   17. yes,
$5^2 + 5^2 = (5\sqrt{2})^2$ By the converse of the Pythagorean Th., the $\angle$ opp. the diagonal is a rt. $\angle$, so the rhombus is a square.   18. $5^2 + 12^2 =$ $25 + 144 = 169 = 13^2$ By the Converse of the Pythagorean Th., Q is a rt. $\angle$. $\triangle PQR$ and $\triangle PRS$ share $\overline{PR}$. $\angle QPR \cong \angle PRS$ and $\angle 1 \cong \angle 2$. By ASA Post., $\triangle PQR \cong \triangle RSP$. Because $\angle Q$ is a rt. $\angle$, $\angle S$ is also a rt. $\angle$.
19. True, a Pythagorean Triple is any three whole numbers a, b, and c that satisfy the equation $a^2 + b^2 = c^2$. $\sqrt{3}$, $\sqrt{4}$, and $\sqrt{7}$ are not whole numbers.
20. False, the Pythagorean Th., not its converse, states that the sum of the squares of the lengths of the legs of a rt. △ is equal to the square of the length of the hyp.

Exercises

A

Classify each triangle with the given side lengths as acute, right, or obtuse.

1. 4, 5, 7　　　　　**2.** 6, 8, 10　　　　　**3.** 0.4, 0.5, 0.6　　**4.** 0.9, 4.0, 4.1
5. $\sqrt{3}, \sqrt{2}, \sqrt{5}$　　**6.** $\sqrt{2}, \sqrt{3}, \sqrt{4}$　　**7.** 9, 10, 12　　　**8.** $\frac{3}{5}, \frac{4}{5}, 1$

Decide if ∠1 is acute, right or obtuse. Give reasons for your decision.

9. 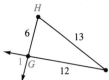　　**10.** 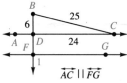　　**11.**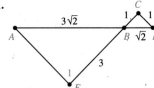

$\overrightarrow{AC} \parallel \overrightarrow{FG}$

12. 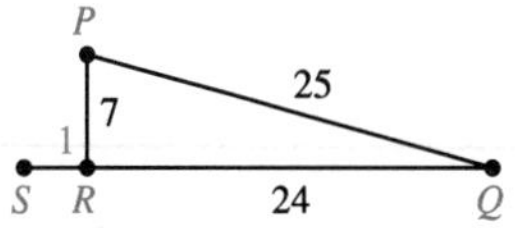 　　**13.** 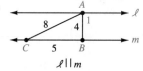　　**14.**

$\ell \parallel m$

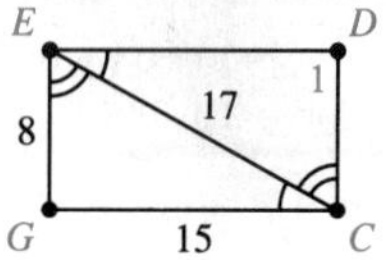

15. The sides of a triangle are 9, 40, and 41. Is the triangle a right triangle? Is a triangle with side lengths twice these a right triangle? Why or why not?

B

Classify each triangle with the given side lengths as acute, right or obtuse, or state that no conclusion can be made. Assume that n is a nonzero whole number.

16. $3n, 4n, 5n$　　**17.** $8n, 15n, 17n+1$　　**18.** $11n, 60n-1, 61n$

19. The shortest side of a triangle has length 14. The other sides have lengths $x + 1$ and $x + 3$. Find the value of x that would make the triangle a right triangle and give the length of each side.

20. The shortest side of a triangle has lengths x and $x + 1$. Find the value of x that would make the triangle a right triangle and give the length of each side.

21. A grounds crew was laying out a baseball diamond. They measured the distance from home plate to second base to check that the baseline angle at first base was a right angle. Find distance d.

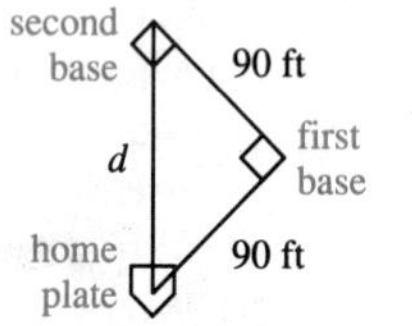

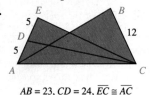

Decide if △ABC is right, acute, or obtuse. Explain.

22. 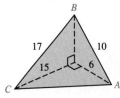　　**23.**

$AB = 23, CD = 24, \overline{EC} \cong \overline{AC}$

24. Prove Theorem 7.5.

25. Use Theorem 7.6 to decide if $\triangle ABC$ is an acute, obtuse, or right triangle.

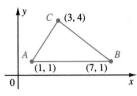

C

26. The sides of a triangle were given as m, $(\frac{m^2}{4} - 1)$, and $(\frac{m^2}{4} + 1)$, where m is an even number not equal to 2. Prove that it is a right triangle.

27. Prove that if n is an integer and $a = 2n + 1$, $b = 2n^2 + 2n$, and $c = 2n^2 + 2n + 1$, then a, b, c is a Pythagorean Triple.

28. Show that the 3–4–5 right triangle is the only right triangle with sides that are consecutive integers. (HINT: Use x, $x + 1$, and $x + 2$ to represent consecutive integers.)

29. Given: Right $\triangle ABC$ with leg lengths a and b, and hypotenuse length c.
$\triangle A'B'C'$ with side lengths $a + k$, $b + k$, and $c + k$ (where k is a positive integer).

 Prove: $\triangle A'B'C'$ is acute.

Critical Thinking

30. A teacher gave this easy method for finding a missing leg of a right triangle and it works whenever the other leg and the hypotenuse differ by one. "Just add 24 and 25. b is the square root of this sum." Use variables to prove that this method works.

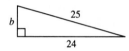

Algebra Review

Find the slope of each line.

1. $y = 3x + 1$ **2.** $y = -2x + 1$ **3.** $y = 5x$
4. $x + y = 7$ **5.** $3y + 6x = 2$ **6.** $y = -4$
7. $2y - 4x - 9 = 0$ **8.** $2y + x = 1$ **9.** $3x - 9y = 1$

Computer Activity

The following BASIC program produces some Pythagorean Triples.

```
10 FOR M = 2 TO 5
20 FOR N = 1 TO M-1
30 LET A = M*M-N*N
40 LET B = 2*M*N
50 LET C = M*M+N*N
60 PRINT A;" ";B;" ";C
70 NEXT N
80 NEXT M
90 END
```

1. What formula is used to produce the Pythagorean Triples? How does M relate to N?

2. Run the program. Change the program so it will produce more triples.

3. If n is a positive integer, then $(2n + 1, 2n^2 + 2n, 2n^2 + 2n + 1)$ is a Pythagorean Triple. Change the program so that it uses this formula to produce triples. Do the two programs produce the same triples? Describe any differences.

By SSS Post., $\triangle ABC \cong \triangle PQR$. Therefore, $\angle C \cong \angle Q$, $\angle C$ is a rt. $\angle$, and $\triangle ABC$ is a rt. $\triangle$.

26. $m^2 + (\frac{m^2}{4} - 1)^2 = m^2 + \frac{m^4}{16} - \frac{m^2}{2} + 1 = \frac{m^4}{16} + \frac{m^2}{2} + 1 = (\frac{m^2}{4} + 1)^2$
By the converse of the Pythagorean Th., the $\triangle$ is a rt. $\triangle$.

28. Solve $x^2 + (x + 1)^2 = (x + 2)^2$ for a positive integer x. $x^2 + x^2 + 2x + 1 = x^2 + 4x + 4$ or $x^2 - 2x - 3 = 0$, so $x = 3$ and $x = -1$. The only positive integer solution is 3, which makes 3, 4, 5 the only such triple.   **30.** Let x be the length of the unknown leg, d the length of the known leg, and $d + 1$ the length of the hyp. Prove $x = \sqrt{(d + 1) + d}$. By the Pythagorean Th., $x^2 + d^2 = (d + 1)^2$ or $x^2 + d^2 = d^2 + 2d + 1$. Simplifying, $x^2 = 2d + 1$ or $x = \sqrt{2d + 1} = \sqrt{d + (d + 1)}$. The method works.

Algebra Review Answers

1. 3   **2.** -2 **3.** 5
4. -1 **5.** -2 **6.** 0
7. 2   **8.** $-\frac{1}{2}$ **9.** $\frac{1}{3}$

Computer Activity Answers

1. $(M^2 - N^2) + (2MN)^2 = (M^2 + N^2)^2$, $M > N$ **2.** Extend the limit on M. For example, FOR M = 2 TO 7.

3.
```
10 FOR M = 2 TO 5
20 LET A = 2 * M + 1
30 LET B = 2 * M * M + 2 * M
40 LET C = 2 * M * M + 2 * M + 1
50 PRINT A; " "; B; " "; C
60 NEXT M
70 END
```
No, the new program misses some triples. Not all triples are of the form $(2n + 1, 2n^2 + 2n, 2n^2 + 2n + 1)$. The new program produces some larger triples.

OBJECTIVE: *Apply relationships in 45°–45°–90° and 30°–60°–90° right triangles.*

7-4 Special Right Triangles

 **EXPLORE** Construct three squares and three equilateral triangles of different sizes. Label each as shown.

Measure segments to the nearest millimeter. Find the ratios $\frac{c}{a}$ for each square. Find the ratios $\frac{c}{a}$ and $\frac{b}{a}$ for each triangle.

Recall that $\sqrt{2} \approx 1.414$ and $\sqrt{3} \approx 1.732$. What conjectures can you make about the two special triangles shown above in blue?

Certain special right triangles are frequently involved in applications of mathematics. One of these, an isosceles right triangle, has two 45° angles and is called a **45°–45°–90° triangle.** It is often necessary to find the length of the hypotenuse of a 45°–45°–90° triangle when the length of a leg is known. Theorem 7.7, proved using the Pythagorean Theorem, gives an efficient way to do this.

◆ **THEOREM 7.7**   45°–45°–90° Triangle Theorem

The length of the hypotenuse of a 45°–45°–90° triangle is $\sqrt{2}$ times the length of a leg.

Given: $\triangle ABC$ is a 45°–45°–90° triangle.
Prove: $c = a\sqrt{2}$.

Proof $\triangle ABC$ is a 45°–45°–90° triangle. Using the Pythagorean Theorem, $a^2 + a^2 = c^2$. Simplifying, it follows that $c^2 = 2a^2$, $c = \sqrt{2a^2}$, and $c = a\sqrt{2}$.

Example 1
Find the value of c.

    Solution
    $c = a\sqrt{2}$ *Theorem 7.7*
    $c = 5\sqrt{2}$ *Substitute 5 for a.*

Try This
Find the length of the diagonal of a square with side length 12 cm.

A special right triangle with a 30° and a 60° angle is called a **30°–60°–90° triangle.** The hypotenuse and the longer leg in a 30°–60°–90° triangle can be found when the shorter leg is known by using Theorem 7.8 below. Note that the shorter leg is opposite the 30° angle and the longer leg is opposite the 60° angle. The Pythagorean Theorem is used to prove Theorem 7.8.

 THEOREM 7.8 30°–60°–90° Triangle Theorem

In a 30°–60°–90° triangle, the length of the hypotenuse is 2 times the length of the shorter leg and the length of the longer leg is $\sqrt{3}$ times the length of the shorter leg.

Given: $\triangle ABC$ is a 30°–60°–90° triangle.

Prove: $c = 2a$
$b = a\sqrt{3}$

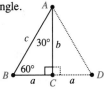

Plan Draw $\triangle ADC$ so that $\triangle ABC \cong \triangle ADC$. Show that $\triangle ABD$ is equiangular, and hence, equilateral. It follows that $c = 2a$. Then use the Pythagorean Theorem to show that $a^2 + b^2 = c^2 = 4a^2$. Finally, simplify to show that $b^2 = 3a^2$, or $b = a\sqrt{3}$.

The proof of this theorem will be called for in Exercise 41.

Example 2

Find the length of the hypotenuse and the longer leg.

Solution

Hypotenuse: $x = 2(6) = 12$ *hypotenuse* $= 2 \cdot$ *shorter leg*
Longer leg: $y = 6\sqrt{3}$ *longer leg* $= \sqrt{3} \cdot$ *shorter leg*

Try This

Find the length and diagonal length of the rectangle to the right.

Theorems 7.7 and 7.8 are summarized as follows.

Special Right Triangle Relationships

The ratio of side lengths opposite the 45°–45°–90° angles is $x : x : x\sqrt{2}$.

The ratio of side lengths opposite the 30°–60°–90° angles is $x : x\sqrt{3} : 2x$.

The Explore illustrates one way of introducing the 45°–45°–90° Triangle Theorem. Notice that each diagonal of a square is the hypotenuse of two isosceles right triangles.

Materials

student notebooks
investigative software

Teaching Notes

Point out that the 45°–45°–90° triangle is also called an isosceles right triangle.

Emphasize the importance of Theorems 7.7 and 7.8. Many proofs and exercises in the text, as well as questions that occur on standardized tests, require that students recognize these special right triangles, and apply their theorems in problem solving.

At the completion of the lesson on the 45°–45°–90° triangle, students should be able to find the hypotenuse given the measure of a leg and find the measure of a leg given the hypotenuse. The following chart summarizes both relationships.

leg	leg	hypotenuse
x	x	$x\sqrt{2}$
$\frac{x\sqrt{2}}{2}$	$\frac{x\sqrt{2}}{2}$	x

Remind students that radicals in simplest form do not have perfect-square factors under the radical sign nor do they have radicals in the denominator. Point out that in a 30°–60°–90° triangle, the longer leg is opposite the 60° angle and the shorter leg is opposite the 30° angle.

At the completion of the lesson on the 30°–60°–90° triangle, students should be able to derive the lengths of two unknown sides given a third side. The following chart summarizes the relationships.

Side Opp. 30° Angle	Side Opp. 60° Angle	Hyp.
x	$x\sqrt{3}$	$2x$
$\frac{x\sqrt{3}}{3}$	x	$\frac{2x\sqrt{3}}{3}$
$\frac{x}{2}$	$\frac{x\sqrt{3}}{2}$	x

Key Terms

45°–45°–90° triangle
30°–60°–90° triangle

Guided Practice

Chalkboard Examples

1. The perimeter of a square is 44. Find the length of a diagonal. $11\sqrt{2}$

Answer to **Try This**
$12\sqrt{2}$ cm ≈ 17 cm

2. Find the perimeter of the trapezoid ABCD. (HINT: Draw altitude $\overline{CE}$.) $44 + 8\sqrt{3}$

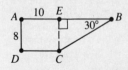

Answer to **Try This** diagonal
length = 10, length = $5\sqrt{3}$

Class Exercises

Short Answer

Complete each statement.

1. To find the length of the hypotenuse of a 45°–45°–90° triangle, multiply the length of one of the legs by ____ .
2. To find the length of the hypotenuse of a 30°–60°–90° triangle, multiply the length of the shorter leg by ____ .
3. To find the length of the longer leg of a 30°–60°–90° triangle, multiply the length of the shorter leg by ____ .

Sample Exercises

Find the value of x.

4.

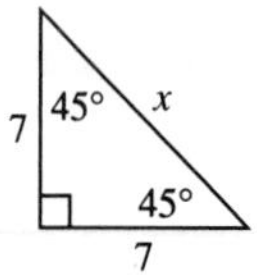

5.

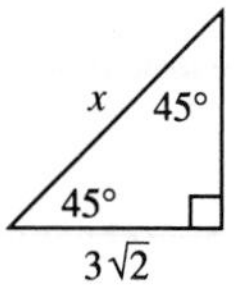

6.

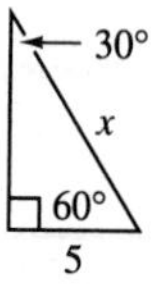

7.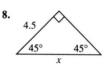

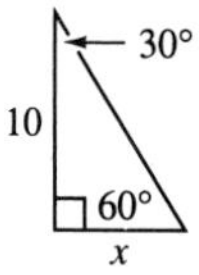

8.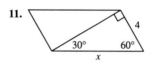

9.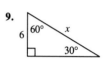

10.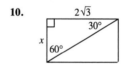

11.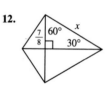

12.

13. The length of the hypotenuse of a 45°–45°–90° triangle is $5\sqrt{2}$. Find the length of a leg.
14. The length of the hypotenuse of a 30°–60°–90° triangle is 20. What is the length of the shorter leg?
15. The length of the longer leg of a 30°–60°–90° triangle is $4\sqrt{3}$. What is the length of the shorter leg?
16. The length of the hypotenuse of a 30°–60°–90° triangle is 10. Find the length of the two legs.
17. Find the length of the diagonal of a square with sides 8 cm long.
18. Find the length of the altitude of an equilateral triangle if a side is 10 mm long.
19. If the perimeter of a square is 64 cm, how long is its diagonal?

Discussion

20. Draw a 45°–45°–90° triangle and explain how to use variable expressions to give the relative lengths of the sides in terms of x. Do this for a 30°–60°–90° triangle in terms of y.

Discuss how to complete each statement. Explain your decision.

21. The length of a leg of a 45°–45°–90° triangle is ____ times the length of the hypotenuse.
22. The length of the hypotenuse of a 30°–60°–90° triangle is ____ times the length of the longer leg.
23. The length of the shorter leg of a 30°–60°–90° triangle is ____ times the length of the hypotenuse.
24. The length of the shorter leg of a 30°–60°–90° triangle is ____ times the length of the longer leg.

Exercises

A

Find the missing lengths to complete the table.

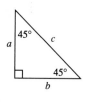

	a	b	c
1.	6	___	___
2.	___	10	___
3.	2.5	___	___
4.	___	$\sqrt{2}$	___
5.	___	___	$7\sqrt{2}$
6.	___	___	8

	a	b	c
7.	4	___	___
8.	$\frac{2}{3}$	___	___
9.	___	___	6
10.	___	___	$\frac{3}{4}$
11.	___	$5\sqrt{3}$	___
12.	___	9	___

Figure ABCD is a rectangle with the measures shown.

13. Find the length of the diagonal of rectangle ABCD.
14. Find the length of $\overline{AD}$.
15. Find the perimeter of rectangle ABCD.

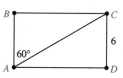

16. Find the length of a diagonal of a square with side length 10 cm.
17. Find the side length of a square with diagonal length 10 cm.
18. Find the length of the altitude of an equilateral triangle with side length 12 cm.

$\overline{AC} \perp \overline{DB}$, $m\angle BAD = 105$ **Complete each statement.**

19. $AC = $ ___   20. $BC = $ ___
21. $CD = $ ___   22. $AD = $ ___
23. $m\angle BAC = $ ___   24. $m\angle CDA = $ ___

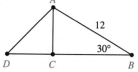

Class Exercise Answers

1. $\sqrt{2}$ 2. 2   3. $\sqrt{3}$
4. $7\sqrt{2}$ 5. 6   6. 10
7. $\frac{10\sqrt{3}}{3}$ 8. $\frac{9\sqrt{2}}{2}$ 9. 12
10. 2   11. 8   12. $\frac{7}{4}$
13. 5   14. 10   15. 4
16. short leg = 5, long leg = $5\sqrt{3}$ 17. $8\sqrt{2}$
18. $5\sqrt{3}$ 19. $16\sqrt{2}$
20.

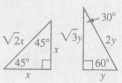

21. Theorem 7.5, $\frac{\sqrt{2}}{2}$
22. Theorem 7.6, $\frac{2\sqrt{3}}{3}$
23. Theorem 7.6, $\frac{1}{2}$
24. Theorem 7.6, $\frac{\sqrt{3}}{3}$

Assignment Guide
Minimum: 1–39 e/o, 48, MR
Regular: 7–24 e/o, 36–42, 48, MR
Advanced: 36–48, MR

Applications
Exercises 35, 42, 46

Lesson Closure

Review Theorems 7.7 and 7.8.

Teacher's Resource Materials

Enrichment Using
   Manipulatives 4
Practice Master 47
Quiz 13
Technology: Calculator 9
Transparency 28

Computer Software

See Computer Explorations 20 and 21, pages 653 and 654.

1. $6, 6\sqrt{2}$ 2. $10, 10\sqrt{2}$
3. $2.5, \frac{5\sqrt{2}}{2}$ 4. $\sqrt{2}, 2$
5. $7, 7$ 6. $4\sqrt{2}, 4\sqrt{2}$
7. $4\sqrt{3}, 8$ 8. $\frac{2\sqrt{3}}{3}, \frac{4}{3}$
9. $3, 3\sqrt{3}$ 10. $\frac{3}{8}, \frac{3\sqrt{3}}{8}$
11. $5, 10$ 12. $3\sqrt{3}, 6\sqrt{3}$
13. 12 14. $6\sqrt{3}$
15. $12 + 12\sqrt{3}$
16. $10\sqrt{2}$ cm
17. $5\sqrt{2}$ cm   18. $6\sqrt{3}$ cm
19. 6 20. $6\sqrt{3}$ 21. 6
22. $6\sqrt{2}$ 23. 60 24. 45
25. 90 26. 60 27. 45
28. 6 29. 6 30. $6\sqrt{2}$
31. $6\sqrt{3}$ 32. 6 33. 12
34. $6\sqrt{2}$ 35. $3\sqrt{3}$ m
36. $9\sqrt{2}$
37. $26 + 8\sqrt{2} + 6\sqrt{3}$
38. $4\sqrt{3}$ 39. $x = 3\sqrt{2}$,
$y = \frac{3\sqrt{2}}{2}, z = \frac{3\sqrt{6}}{2}$ 40. Legs
have length $\frac{10\sqrt{3}}{3}$ and 10, segments on hypotenuse have
length $\frac{5\sqrt{3}}{3}$ and $5\sqrt{3}$.
41. Construct $\triangle ACD$ such that
$\triangle ACD \cong \triangle ACB$ and the right
angles are adjacent.

$\triangle ABD$ is equiangular, since
$30° + 30° = 60°$. By Corollary
4.2a, $\triangle ABD$ is equilateral.
Therefore, $2a = c$. By the
Pythagorean Theorem,
$a^2 + b^2 = c^2$. Substitute $2a$ for
c: $c = 2a$, $a^2 + b^2 = 4a^2$ or
$b^2 = 3a^2$ and $b = \sqrt{3}a$.
42. $x = 2\sqrt{3}$ cm, $y = 4$ cm
43. 15 44. $\frac{\sqrt{3}}{3} \cdot s$
45. $AG = 8, AF = 4\sqrt{3}$
46. $AB = 80\sqrt{3}$ cm

Complete each statement.

25. $m \angle RTS = \underline{\quad}$ 26. $m \angle TRS = \underline{\quad}$
27. $m \angle TQR = \underline{\quad}$ 28. $TR = \underline{\quad}$
29. $TQ = \underline{\quad}$ 30. $QR = \underline{\quad}$
31. $TS = \underline{\quad}$ 32. $TP = \underline{\quad}$
33. $PS = \underline{\quad}$ 34. $PQ = \underline{\quad}$

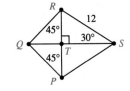

35. A ladder leaning against a wall makes a 60° angle with the ground. The
base of the ladder is 3 m from the building. How high above the ground
is the top of the ladder?

B

36. The perimeter of a square is 36. Find
the length of the diagonal of the square.
37. Find the perimeter of hexagon $RSTUVW$.

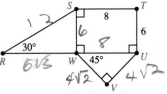

38. Find the length of an altitude of an equilateral triangle with perimeter 24.
39. Find lengths x, y, and z.

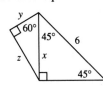

40. A right triangle has a 30° angle and altitude to the hypotenuse of 5 cm.
Find the length of its sides and of the segments on its hypotenuse.
41. Prove the 30°–60°–90° Triangle Theorem (Theorem 7.8).
42. The machine nut to the right has a regular hexagonal shape. Find the
distances x and y.

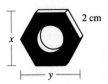

2 cm

C

43. The figure is a pyramid with a regular hexagonal base with center C.
$DB = 4$, $AB = 17$ Find the height h of the hexagonal pyramid.

44. An equilateral triangle has side length s. Find the distance to a vertex
from the point where its medians intersect.
45. A-$BCDE$ is a pyramid with a square base with center F. $\overline{AF}$ is the altitude
of the pyramid and $\overline{AG}$ is a perpendicular bisector of $\overline{ED}$. $m \angle AGF = 60$
If $BD = 8\sqrt{2}$, find AF and AG.

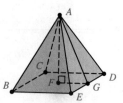

46. An architect is calculating the dimensions for a regular hexagonal window that must fit into an opening with height 120 cm. Find the distance AB from one corner of the opening to the opposite corner.

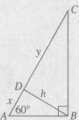

47. Show that the altitude to the hypotenuse of a $30°-60°-90°$ triangle divides the hypotenuse into two segments, one three times as long as the other.

Critical Thinking

48. Devise a formula for finding (a) the length of the altitude of an equilateral triangle with side length s, and (b) the area of an equilateral triangle with side length s.

Make and test a conjecture about how the area of an equilateral triangle changes as the length of its sides are doubled.

Mixed Review

Use $\square JKLM$ to determine whether each statement is always, sometimes, or never true.

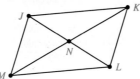

1. $\overline{MN} \cong \overline{NK}$ 2. $\overline{JL} \perp \overline{MK}$
3. $m\angle JKL + m\angle KLM = 90$ 4. $\angle MJK \cong \angle KLM$
5. If $m\angle J = 90$, then $JKLM$ is a rectangle.
6. If $\overline{JK} \cong \overline{KL} \cong \overline{LM} \cong \overline{JM}$, then $JKLM$ is a square.
7. $JKLM$ is a trapezoid.

Quiz

Complete each statement.

1. $\frac{y}{4} =$ ___   2. $\frac{y}{9} =$ ___
3. $\frac{z}{13} =$ ___   4. $x =$ ___
5. $y =$ ___   6. $z =$ ___

7. Find the geometric mean between 5 and 15.

Find x and/or y.

8.
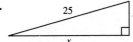

9.

10.

11. Is a triangle with sides 7, 9, and 11 an acute, right, or obtuse triangle?
12. Find the perimeter of a rhombus if the diagonals have lengths 16 and 30.

---

47. The altitude $\overline{BD}$ divides $\triangle ABC$ into two smaller $30°-60°-90°$ triangles, $\triangle ABD$ and $\triangle BCD$. By Theorem 7.6, $h = \sqrt{3}x$ and $y = \sqrt{3}h$. Substituting for h, $y = \sqrt{3} \cdot \sqrt{3}x = 3x$. y is three times as long as x.

48. a. By Theorem 4.6, the altitude bisects the vertex angle and the base. A $30°-60°-90°$ triangle is formed. By Theorem 7.8, $h = \sqrt{3} \cdot \frac{s}{2} = \frac{\sqrt{3}s}{2}$. **b.** Using the formula in a., the area of the triangle $= \frac{1}{2}$ base $\cdot$ height $= \frac{1}{2}s \cdot h = \frac{s}{2} \cdot \frac{\sqrt{3}s}{2} = \frac{\sqrt{3}s^2}{4}$. If s is doubled, the area will quadruple.

Mixed Review Answers

1. always   2. sometimes
3. never   4. always
5. always   6. sometimes
7. never

Quiz Answers

1. $\frac{3}{2}$ 2. $\frac{2}{3}$ 3. $\frac{3\sqrt{13}}{13}$
4. $2\sqrt{13}$ 5. 6
6. $3\sqrt{13}$ 7. $5\sqrt{3}$
8. 24   9. $4\sqrt{2}$
10. $x = 3\sqrt{3}, y = 6$
11. acute   12. 68

Comparing Approaches in Geometry

Symmetry and Metric Properties

Exercise Answers
1. $(6, 3)$ 2. $(6, -3)$
3. $(-6, -3)$ 4. $(-6, 3)$
5. $(0, 0)$ 6. $(4, 4\sqrt{3})$
7. $(3, 3\sqrt{3})$
8. $C(-3, 3\sqrt{3})$, $D(-6, 0)$,
$E(-3, -3\sqrt{3})$, $F(3, -3\sqrt{3})$

COMPARING APPROACHES IN GEOMETRY

Symmetry and Metric Properties

When a coordinate system is placed on a figure, it is important to name the coordinates of the vertices correctly. Often you will use symmetry properties as well as the relationships from Theorems 7.7 and 7.8. In this figure, review the reflectional symmetry of rectangles, equilateral triangles, and regular hexagons.

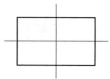

Lines of reflectional symmetry

Example

Suppose that an equilateral triangle ten units on a side is placed on coordinate system as shown. If $A(5, 0)$ is one vertex, find the coordinates of B and C.

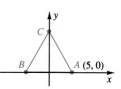

Solution

$B = B(-5, 0)$ *By symmetry, the x-coordinate of B is the opposite of the x-coordinate of A. All points on the x-axis have y-coordinate 0.*

$C = C(0, 5\sqrt{3})$ *All points on the y-axis have x-coordinate 0. The long leg of a 30°–60°–90° triangle is $\sqrt{3}$ times the short leg.*

Exercises

Suppose that a coordinate system is placed on a rectangle 12 units long and 6 units wide so that the *x*- and *y*-axes are both lines of symmetry as shown in this figure.

1. Find the coordinates of A.
2. Find the coordinates of B.
3. Find the coordinates of C.
4. Find the coordinates of D.

Suppose that an equilateral triangle 8 units on a side is placed on a coordinate system as shown.

5. Find the coordinates of C.
6. Use Theorem 7.8 to find the coordinates of B.

Suppose that a regular hexagon is placed on a coordinate system as shown.

7. Find the coordinates of B.
8. Use symmetry to find the coordinates of C, D, E, and F.

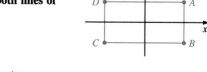

TRIGONOMETRIC RATIOS

OBJECTIVE: *Identify and use the tangent ratio.*

7-5 The Tangent Ratio

Trigonometry, which means *triangle measurement* in Greek, is the study of the relationships between the sides and angles of triangles. Trigonometry is a widely used part of mathematics. In sailing, surveying, photography, physics, and other situations, it serves daily as a valuable tool. The idea of similar triangles and the Pythagorean Theorem is used in this lesson to develop the trigonometry of right triangles.

This draftsman uses trigonometry in situations involving right triangles.

A **trigonometric ratio** is a ratio of the lengths of two sides of a right triangle. Consider the following ratio in the similar right triangles below.

$$\frac{\text{length of leg } \textit{opposite} \text{ the 60° angle}}{\text{length of leg } \textit{adjacent} \text{ to the 60° angle}}$$

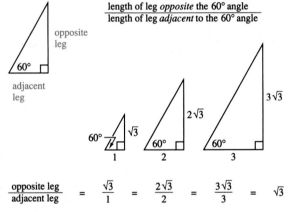

$$\frac{\text{opposite leg}}{\text{adjacent leg}} = \frac{\sqrt{3}}{1} = \frac{2\sqrt{3}}{2} = \frac{3\sqrt{3}}{3} = \sqrt{3}$$

Note that this ratio is the same in all three of the similar right triangles shown. The ratio of the length of the opposite leg to the length of the adjacent leg of a right triangle is called the **tangent ratio.** You can abbreviate this as tan 60° = $\sqrt{3}$. In general, the tangent of an acute angle of a right triangle is the following ratio.

$$\tan A = \frac{\text{length of opposite leg}}{\text{length of adjacent leg}} = \frac{a}{b}$$

First Five Minutes

(Quiz on previous lesson)

1. In a 30°–60°–90° triangle, the side opposite the 30° angle is __?__ the hypotenuse. **half**

2. In an isosceles right triangle, the ratio of the length of a leg to the length of the hypotenuse is __?__ . $\frac{1}{\sqrt{2}}$

3. Find the value of x. $\frac{15\sqrt{2}}{2}$

4. If *ABCD* is a square, find *BC*.

5. Use $\triangle ACB$.

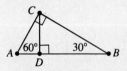

a. If *CD* = 7, find *CB* and *DB*. *CB* = 14, *DB* = 7$\sqrt{3}$

b. If *AC* = 30, find *AD* and *CD*. *AD* = 15, *CD* = 15$\sqrt{3}$

Lesson Opener

Point out that similar triangles and the Pythagorean Theorem will be used in the remaining three lessons of this chapter.

Materials

student notebooks
scientific calculators

Teaching Notes

Emphasize the importance of memorizing the tangent ratio. The tangent of an angle ($\angle A$) is abbreviated as tan A. If $m\angle A = 30$, then write tan 30°.

$$\text{tangent } \angle A = \tan A = \frac{\text{opposite leg } a}{\text{adjacent leg } b}$$

The trig table of values that appears on page 636 can be used to find decimal approximations for trig ratios and to find the measure of an angle, given a trig ratio. If a given value does not match any entry in the table, choose the closest value from the table.

Key Questions

1. What is the sin 34°? **0.5592**
2. What is the cos 18°? **0.9511**
3. What is the tan 45°? **1**
4. What is the sin 72°? **0.9511**
5. What is the cos 60°? **0.5**
6. What is $m\angle A$ if sin $A = 0.5592$? **34**
7. What is $m\angle A$ if cos $A = 0.2079$? **78**
8. What is $m\angle A$ if tan $A = 3.0777$? **72**
9. What is $m\angle A$ if cos $A = 0.5$? **60**
10. What is $m\angle A$ if tan $A = 1$? **45**

You will study other trigonometric ratios in Lesson 7-6. This example shows how to find the tangent ratio.

Example 1

Use right triangle ABC to find tan A and tan B.

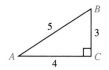

Solution

$\tan A = \frac{3}{4} = 0.75$ $\tan A = \frac{\text{opposite leg}}{\text{adjacent leg}}$

$\tan B = \frac{4}{3} \approx 1.33$ *Round to the nearest hundredth.*

Try This

Find tan A and tan B if $AB = 13$ and $AC = 12$.

Since ratios of corresponding sides of similar triangles are equal, the tangent ratio of an angle depends only on the size of the angle—not on the size of the triangle. For example, on page 319 you saw that tan 60° = $\sqrt{3}$, regardless of the size of the triangle. You can use the table on page 636 or a calculator with trigonometric functions to find decimal approximations of tangent and other trigonometric ratios.

Example 2

Write an equation and solve for x. Round to the nearest hundredth.

Solution

$\tan 54° = \frac{16}{x}$

$1.3764 \approx \frac{16}{x}$ *Read this value to the right of 54° under "tan" in the table or use a calculator.*

$x(1.3764) \approx 16$

$x \approx \frac{16}{1.3764}$ *Solve for x.*

$x \approx 11.6245 \approx 11.62$ *Use a calculator. Round to the nearest hundredth.*

Try This

What is the value of x if $\angle A$ is not given and $\angle B$ is 27°?

The following example shows how to use the tangent ratio to find the measure of an acute angle when the measures of the legs are given.

Example 3

Find the measure of $\angle R$.

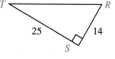

Solution

$\tan R = \frac{25}{14} \approx 1.786$

$m\angle R \approx 61°$ *Use a calculator or look in the "tan" column in the table for the number closest to 1.786. Read the angle that corresponds to this number.*

Try This

Find $m\angle T$ if $TS = 30$ and $RS = 12$.

Class Exercises

Short Answer

Use the right triangles below.

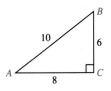
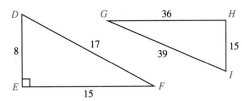

1. Give the length of the leg opposite each of these angles:
   $\angle A$, $\angle B$, $\angle D$, $\angle F$, $\angle G$, $\angle I$
2. Give the length of the leg adjacent to each of these angles:
   $\angle A$, $\angle B$, $\angle D$, $\angle F$, $\angle G$, $\angle I$
3. Use one of the triangles above and describe the tangent ratio in your own words.
4. Express the tangent of each of these angles as a ratio of whole numbers:
   $\angle A$, $\angle B$, $\angle D$, $\angle F$, $\angle G$, $\angle I$
5. Express the tangent of $\angle B$ as a decimal rounded to four places.
6. Use the table on page 636 to find the measure of $\angle B$ to the nearest degree.

Sample Exercises

Use the table on page 636 or a calculator to complete each of the following.

7. $\tan 34° \approx$ ___
8. $\tan 75° \approx$ ___
9. $\tan 5° \approx$ ___
10. $\tan$ ___ ≈ 2.6051
11. $\tan$ ___ ≈ 0.9657
12. $\tan$ ___ ≈ 0.6745

13. Find the width of rectangle $ABDE$.
14. Find the length of the altitude, CF, of $\triangle BCD$.

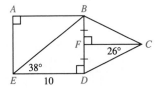

15. The long leg of a right triangle has length 12. The short leg has length 8. Find the measures of the acute angles of the triangle to the nearest degree.
16. A diagonal of a rectangle forms a 30° angle with the 25-cm base of the rectangle. What is the width of the rectangle?

Discussion

17. Compare the tangents of $\angle A$ and $\angle B$ in a 45°–45°–90° triangle ABC, where $\angle C$ is the right angle.
18. Discuss how the tangent of one acute angle of a right triangle compares to the tangent of the other acute angle of that triangle. Explain using examples.
19. How would you use figures like this to give a convincing argument that tan A decreases as $m \angle A$ decreases?

The tangent ratio, which never uses the length of the hypotenuse, is one of the three trigonometric ratios that is used to solve many practical problems involving right triangles. (See Exercises 29 and 36.) The sine and cosine ratios, which use the hypotenuse and a leg, are presented in the next lesson. NOTE: All three trigonometric ratios are based on right triangles.

Key Terms

trigonometry
trigonometric ratio
tangent ratio

Guided Practice

Chalkboard Examples

1. Find tan A and tan B if $BC = 5$ and $AB = 7$. (HINT: Use the Pythagorean Theorem to find AC.) $\tan A = \frac{5\sqrt{6}}{12}$, $\tan B = \frac{2\sqrt{6}}{5}$

Answer to **Try This** $\tan A = \frac{5}{12}$, $\tan B = \frac{12}{5}$

2. Find BC if $m \angle A = 32$ and $AC = 70$. ≈ 43.74

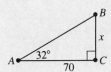

Answer to **Try This** ≈ 8.15

3. Find $m\angle T$ and $m\angle R$ if $TR = 17$, $TS = 15$, and $RS = 8$. $m\angle T \approx 28$, $m\angle R \approx 62$

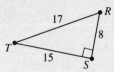

Answer to **Try This** ≈ 21

Class Exercise Answers

1. 6, 8, 15, 8, 15, 36   **2.** 8, 6, 8, 15, 36, 15

3. Answers may vary.

4. $\tan A = \frac{3}{4}$, $\tan B = \frac{4}{3}$, $\tan D = \frac{15}{8}$, $\tan F = \frac{8}{15}$, $\tan G = \frac{5}{12}$, $\tan I = \frac{12}{5}$

5. 1.3333   **6.** 53

7. 0.6745   **8.** 3.7321

9. 0.0875   **10.** 69°

11. 44°   **12.** 34°

13. ≈7.8   **14.** ≈8   **15.** 34 and 56   **16.** ≈14.43 cm

17. $\tan A = \tan B = 1$

18. They are reciprocals of each other.   **19.** Check students' drawings. As $m\angle A$ decreases, the length of a decreases and the length of b remains the same. As a result, the ratio $\frac{a}{b}$, or $\tan A$, decreases.

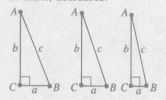

Assignment Guide

Minimum: 1–35 e/o, 43, MR
Regular: 18–41 e/o, 43, MR
Advanced: 30–43, MR

Applications

Exercises 29, 34–36, 40–41

Exercises

A

Express the tangents of $\angle A$ and $\angle B$ as ratios.

1.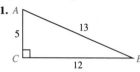

2.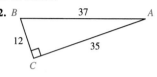

3.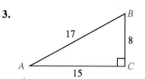

4. Express $\tan B$ for the triangle in Exercise 1 as a three-place decimal.

5. Express $\tan A$ for the triangle in Exercise 2 as a three-place decimal.

6. Express $\tan B$ for the triangle in Exercise 3 as a three-place decimal.

7. Find the measure of $\angle B$ for the triangle in Exercise 3 to the nearest degree.

Use the table on page 636 or a calculator to complete each statement.

8. $\tan 19° \approx$ ___   **9.** $\tan 35° \approx$ ___   **10.** $\tan 62° \approx$ ___

11. $\tan 89° \approx$ ___   **12.** $\tan$ ___ ≈ 0.5774 **13.** $\tan$ ___ ≈ 1.1918

14. $\tan$ ___ ≈ 0.2493 **15.** $\tan$ ___ ≈ 5.6713 **16.** $\tan$ ___ ≈ 1.0355

17. If $\tan G = 1$, then $m\angle G =$ ___ .

Write an equation and solve for s. Round to the nearest hundredth.

18.

19.

20.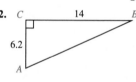

Find the measure of $\angle A$. Round to the nearest degree.

21.

22.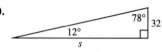

23.

24. Find $m\angle B$ in Exercise 21.   **25.** Find $m\angle B$ in Exercise 22.

26. Find $m\angle B$ in Exercise 23.

27. Find the width of rectangle $ABCD$.

28. Find the length of the altitude of this triangle.

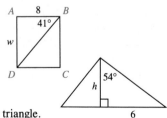

---

29. Find the height of the building.

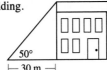

50°

⊢ 30 m ⊣

B

30. Write the tangents of the two acute angles of a 30°–60°–90° triangle as ratios in simplest form.

31. Find the altitude h to the base of an isosceles triangle with congruent sides of length 12 cm and base angles of 72°.

32. The length of a rectangle is 16. Its width is 10. Find the measure of each angle formed at the intersection of the diagonals. Round to the nearest degree.

33. Suppose $AB = 3$, $BC = 4$, and $AC = 5$ in △ABC. Use a calculator to find $m∠A$ and $m∠C$ to the nearest degree.

34. A landscape architect wants to build a bridge across a pond. He lays out $∠I$ to equal 44° and finds the length of $\overline{IH}$ to be 50 m. How far is it across the pond?

35. An airplane that climbs at a steady rate to reach an altitude of 30,000 ft covers 32 mi of ground distance. Find the measure of $∠T$, the angle of climb. You may wish to use a calculator.

T 32 mi   30,000 ft

36. A person 1000 ft from the base of the Washington Monument finds the angle the ground makes with the line of sight to the top of the monument to be about 29°. About how high is the monument?

37. If $m∠A$ is 43° and $BC = 20$, find AB.

38. If $BC = 7$ and $AB = 19$, find $m∠A$.

C

B A

39. Find the measures of the angles of a right triangle with leg lengths 9 and 40.

C

40. Molten gold is poured into a mold like this to form a brick. The "draft angle" $∠1$ is the degree of slant of the walls of the mold. The draft angle is 5° and the depth of the mold BE is 6 cm. How much wider is $\overline{AB}$ than $\overline{CD}$?

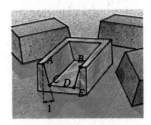

7-5   *The Tangent Ratio*   **323**

Lesson Closure

Review the two types of trig problems using a tangent ratio.

Teacher's Resource Materials

Practice Master 48
Transparency 29

Computer Software

See Computer Exploration 22, page 655.

Exercise Answers

1. $\tan A = \frac{12}{5}$, $\tan B = \frac{5}{12}$
2. $\tan A = \frac{12}{35}$, $\tan B = \frac{35}{12}$
3. $\tan A = \frac{8}{15}$, $\tan B = \frac{15}{8}$
4. 0.417   5. 0.343
6. 1.875   7. 62
8. 0.3443   9. 0.7002
10. 1.881   11. 57.2900
12. 30°   13. 50°   14. 14°
15. 80°   16. 46°   17. 45
18. 29.44   19. 8.40
20. 150.55   21. 50
22. 66   23. 25
24. ≈40   25. ≈24
26. ≈65   27. ≈6.95
28. ≈4.36   29. ≈35.75 m
30. $\tan 30 = \frac{\sqrt{3}}{3}$, $\tan 60 = \sqrt{3}$
31. ≈11.41 cm

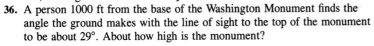

A 16 B

10

E

D C

32. $m∠AED = m∠BEC = 64$, $m∠AEB = m∠DEC = 116$
33. 53, 37   34. ≈48.28 m
35. ≈10   36. ≈550 ft
37. 21.45   38. ≈20
39. ≈77, ≈13   40. 1.05 cm

41. Suppose you are unable to measure $\overline{AC}$ or $\overline{BC}$ directly, but want to find the height of the tower. Find the height of the tower *DC* if the known measures are those shown in the diagram.

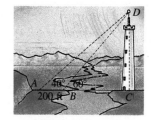

42. The diagonals of a rhombus are 5 cm and 12 cm long. Find the measures of the angles of the rhombus.

Critical Thinking

43. How would you use figures like those to the right to give a convincing argument that tan *A* increases as *m* ∠*A* increases? Do you think tan *A* could ever be as large as 100? Explain.

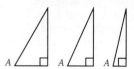

Mixed Review

Determine whether each pair of triangles is congruent by SSS, SAS, ASA, AAS, HA, or HL.

1.   **2.** 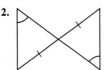   **3.**

Calculator Investigation

A calculator with trigonometric functions can be used instead of a table of trigonometric ratios to find the tangent of an angle. Here is a summary of how these calculator functions can be used.

- To use a calculator to find tan 42°

  Enter: 42 ⬚tan⬚   Display: 0.900404

- To use a calculator to find *m* ∠*A*, where tan *A* ≈ 1.4281

  Enter: 1.4281 ⬚2nd⬚ ⬚tan⬚   Display: 54.999095

1. Round the numbers on the display to give the tan 42° to the nearest ten-thousandth and *m* ∠*A* to the nearest degree.
2. Select a right triangle that has acute angles *A* and *B* with whole-number measures. Use a calculator to find tan *A*, tan *B*, and tan *A* · tan *B*. Do this for several different right triangles. Make a table to show your results. What did you discover? Can you prove that this is true?
3. Use your calculator to find the measures (to the nearest degree) of the acute angles in right triangles that have these Pythagorean Triples as side lengths. **a.** 3, 4, 5   **b.** 5, 12, 13   **c.** 8, 15, 17

OBJECTIVE: *Identify and apply the sine and cosine ratios.*

7-6 The Sine and Cosine Ratios

You have seen that the tangent ratio is the ratio of two legs of a right triangle. Two other useful trigonometric ratios, involving a leg and the hypotenuse of a right triangle, are the **sine** and **cosine** of an acute angle. These three ratios are given below for $\angle A$. They can also be given for $\angle B$. Note that the sine of $\angle A$ is usually abbreviated sin A and the cosine of $\angle A$ is usually abbreviated cos A.

The sine and cosine ratios are used in navigation to determine distances, establish locations, and chart a course.

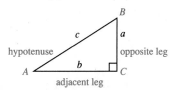

$$\tan A = \frac{\text{length of the opposite leg}}{\text{length of the adjacent leg}} = \frac{a}{b}$$

$$\sin A = \frac{\text{length of the opposite leg}}{\text{length of the hypotenuse}} = \frac{a}{c}$$

$$\cos A = \frac{\text{length of the adjacent leg}}{\text{length of the hypotenuse}} = \frac{b}{c}$$

Example 1

Write an equation and solve it to find an approximate value for x. Round to the nearest hundredth.

Solution

$\sin 56° = \frac{x}{24}$ *The sine is the ratio of the side opposite the angle to the hypotenuse*

$0.829 \approx \frac{x}{24}$ *Use a calculator or a table of trigonometric ratios. sin 56° ≈ 0.829*

$x \approx 0.829 \cdot 24$

$x \approx 19.896$ or 19.90 *Round to the nearest hundredth.*

Try This

Find the approximate value of y in the figure.

In Example 1, you were given the hypotenuse and the angle and used the sine and cosine ratios to find the legs. The next example gives the hypotenuse and a leg and uses the sine and cosine ratios to find the angle.

First Five Minutes

(Quiz on previous lesson)

Find the value of each variable. Use the trig table on page 636 or a calculator.

1.

≈**5.3**

2.

≈**62**

3.

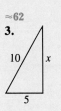

≈**8.7**

4.

x ≈ 22.0, y ≈ 15

5. Given rhombus *ABCD*, if $AC = 4$ and $BD = 10$, find $m\angle ABC$, $m\angle BCD$, $m\angle CDA$, and $m\angle DAB$.

$m\angle ABC = m\angle CDA \approx 43.6$,
$m\angle BCD = m\angle DAB \approx 136.4$

Lesson Opener

Begin the discussion of the sine and cosine functions by asking the Key Questions. Use the following 45°–45°–90° triangles.

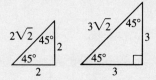

Key Questions

1. What is the ratio of a leg to the hypotenuse in each triangle? $\sqrt{2}:2$

2. What is the ratio of the other leg to the hypotenuse in each triangle? $\sqrt{2}:2$

3. What is the ratio of one leg to the other leg in each triangle and vice versa? 1

The ratios in Questions 1 and 2 are called sine ratios. Like the tangent ratio, both the sine and cosine ratios are formal ways of asking, "What is the ratio of the length of the opposite side to the length of the hypotenuse?" and "What is the ratio of the length of the adjacent side to the length of the hypotenuse?"

The sine and cosine ratios are two trigonometric ratios that are used to solve many practical problems involving right triangles. (See Exercises 35, 38, and 39.) Both the sine and cosine ratios use the hypotenuse and a leg.

Example 2

Find the measure of $\angle A$ to the nearest degree.

Solution

$\sin A = \frac{7}{16}$ *The sine is the ratio of opposite to hypotenuse.*

$\sin A = 0.4375$

$m\angle A \approx 26$ *sin 25° = 0.4256 and sin 26° = 0.4384*
   26° is the closer angle.

Try This

Use trigonometric ratios to find $m\angle B$ to the nearest degree.

In Example 3, an angle and a leg are given and the sine and cosine ratios are used to find the hypotenuse.

Example 3

Find the length of the hypotenuse, to the nearest hundredth.

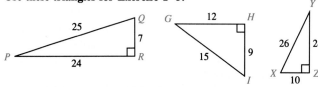

Solution

$\cos 28° = \frac{12}{h}$

$0.8829 \approx \frac{12}{h}$

$0.8829 \cdot h \approx 12$

$h \approx 12 \div 0.8829 \approx 13.59$

Try This

Find the length of the hypotenuse if $m\angle B = 74$ and $AC = 32$.

Class Exercises

Short Answer

Use these triangles for Exercise 1–5.

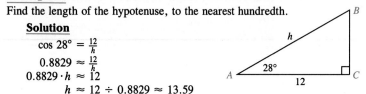

1. Name and give the length of the hypotenuse in each right triangle above.

2. Give the length of the leg opposite each of these angles.
   $\angle P, \angle Q, \angle G, \angle I, \angle X, \angle Y$

3. Give the length of the leg adjacent to each of these angles.
   $\angle P, \angle Q, \angle G, \angle I, \angle X, \angle Y$

4. Express the sine of each of these angles as a ratio.
   $\angle P, \angle Q, \angle G, \angle I, \angle X, \angle Y$

5. Express the cosine of each of these angles as a ratio.
   $\angle P, \angle Q, \angle G, \angle I, \angle X, \angle Y$

Sample Exercises

Use the table on page 636 or a calculator to complete each statement.

6. $\sin 13° \approx$ ___

7. $\cos 18° \approx$ ___

8. $\sin 87° \approx$ ___

9. $\cos 82° \approx$ ___

10. $\sin$ ___ ≈ 0.5736

11. $\cos$ ___ ≈ 0.7314

12. $\sin$ ___ ≈ 0.9816

13. $\cos$ ___ ≈ 0.2588

14. $\sin$ ___ ≈ 0.7986

15. $\sin$ ___ ≈ 0.5000

16. $\cos$ ___ ≈ 0.7071

17. $\cos$ ___ $= 0.5000$

18. Use $\triangle LMN$ to express $\sin L$ and $\cos M$ in decimal notation.

19. Use the table on page 636 or a calculator to find $m \angle L$ to the nearest degree.

20. Find x, y, and $m \angle C$.

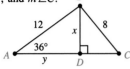

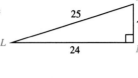

21. Find the height of the tree to the nearest foot.

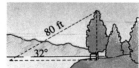

Discussion

22. In $\triangle FGH$, how does $\sin F$ compare to $\cos G$? Is this true for the other triangles above? State a generalization.

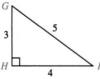

23. A student drew these pictures and asserted, "As the angle gets larger, the sine ratio increases and gets closer and closer to 1." Do you agree with this claim? Why or why not?

$\dfrac{a}{c} \longrightarrow 1$

Use *sine* or *cosine* to complete each statement. Give a convincing argument to support your answer.

24. As the angle gets larger, the ___ gets closer to 1 and the ___ gets closer to 0.

25. As the angle gets smaller, the ___ gets closer to 1 and the ___ gets closer to 0.

26. For what angle, if any, are the sine and cosine ratios equal? Explain your reasoning.

Materials

student notebooks
scientific calculators
investigative software

Teaching Notes

Emphasize the importance of memorizing the sine and cosine ratios. The sine and cosine of an angle ($\angle A$) are abbreviated as $\sin A$ and $\cos A$. If $m \angle A = 30$, then write $\sin 30°$ and $\cos 30°$.

sine $\angle A = \sin A = \dfrac{\text{opposite leg}}{\text{hypotenuse}}$

cosine $\angle A = \cos A = \dfrac{\text{adjacent leg}}{\text{hypotenuse}}$

Continue to stress that the value of a trigonometric ratio (sin, cos, tan) depends only on the *measure of an acute angle* in a right triangle and not on the *size* of the right triangle.

Key Terms

sine
cosine

Guided Practice

Chalkboard Examples

1. Find the approximate value of x and y. Round to the nearest hundredth. ≈ 19.90, ≈ 13.42

Answer to **Try This** ≈ 13.42

2. Find the $m \angle A$ and $m \angle B$ to the nearest degree. ≈24, ≈66

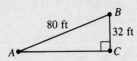
80 ft 32 ft

Answer to **Try This** ≈64

3. Find the length of the hypotenuse to the nearest hundredth. ≈13.95

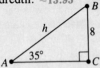
h 8 35°

Answer to **Try This** ≈33.29

Class Exercise Answers

1. $\overline{PQ}$, 25; $\overline{GI}$, 15; $\overline{XY}$, 26
2. 7, 24, 9, 12, 24, 10
3. P 24, Q 7, G 12, I 9,
X 10, Y 24   **4.** $\sin P = \frac{7}{25}$,
$\sin Q = \frac{24}{25}$, $\sin G = \frac{9}{15}$,
$\sin I = \frac{12}{15}$, $\sin X = \frac{24}{26}$,
$\sin Y = \frac{10}{26}$ **5.** $\cos P = \frac{24}{25}$,
$\cos Q = \frac{7}{25}$, $\cos G = \frac{12}{15}$,
$\cos I = \frac{9}{15}$, $\cos X = \frac{10}{26}$,
$\cos Y = \frac{24}{26}$
6. 0.2250   **7.** 0.9511
8. 0.9986   **9.** 0.1392
10. 35°   **11.** 43°
12. 79°   **13.** 75°
14. 53°   **15.** 30°
16. 45°   **17.** 60°   **18.** sin
$L \approx 0.28$, $\cos M \approx 0.28$
19. ≈16   **20.** ≈7.0534,
≈9.7082, 62   **21.** ≈42 ft
22. $\sin F = \cos G$, For any
$\triangle ABC$ with right $\angle C$, $\sin A =$
$\cos B$ and $\cos A = \sin B$.
23. Yes, a remains the same as
c gets close to a.   **24.** sine,
cosine **25.** cosine, sine
26. 45° angle, $\sin 45° = \cos 45°$
In a 45°–45°–90° triangle, legs
have equal length.

Exercises

A

Express the sine and cosine of $\angle A$ and $\angle B$ as ratios.

1.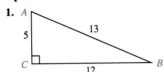
5 13 12

2.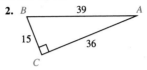
39 15 36

3.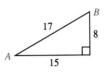
17 8 15

Find these sines and cosines using the table on page 636 or a calculator.

4. $\sin 32° \approx$ ___   **5.** $\cos 49° \approx$ ___   **6.** $\sin 75° \approx$ ___

Find the measure of the angle to the nearest degree. Use the table on page 636 or a calculator.

7. $\sin A \approx 0.6428$ **8.** $\cos B \approx 0.9613$ **9.** $\sin C \approx 0.9962$

Write and solve equations involving the sine ratio to find x and y. Round to the nearest hundredth.

10.
x 37° 35 53° y

11.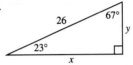
26 67° y 23° x

12.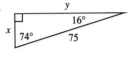
y 16° x 74° 75

13. Write an equation using the cosine ratio to find each of the lengths in Exercises 10–12.

Find the measure of $\angle A$ and $\angle B$ to the nearest degree.

14.
25 20 A C B

15.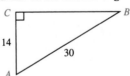
C 14 30 B A

16.
21 8 B C A

Find the length of the hypotenuse. Round to the nearest hundredth.

17.
B 18 47° A C

18.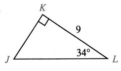
K 9 34° J L

19.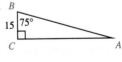
B 15 75° C A

20. Write two different equations, each of which could be used to find the length r of the slanted part of this roof.
Use one of the equations to find r to the nearest tenth.

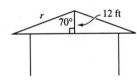
r 70° 12 ft

B

21. It is often helpful to know the trigonometric ratios for 30°, 45°, and 60° angles without looking at a table. Use the special triangles reviewed here to complete the following. Write as ratios. Copy and complete the table for your reference.

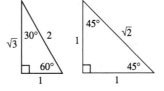

	30°	45°	60°
sin	$\frac{1}{2}$	——	——
cos	——	——	——
tan	——	——	——

22. The diagonal of a rectangle is 10. The length is 2 more than the width and the perimeter is 28. Find the measures of two angles of different sizes formed by a side and a diagonal.
23. The length of the altitude to the base of an isosceles triangle is 12 cm. The angle not congruent to the other two has measure 72°. Find the length of one of the congruent sides.
24. The length of a side of a rhombus is 24 cm. The smaller angle of the rhombus has measure 64°. Find the length of the shorter diagonal of the rhombus.
25. Given that $\angle B$ is an acute angle of a right triangle and $\sin B = \frac{5}{8}$, find $\cos B$ without referring to a table of trigonometric ratios or using a calculator.

Given $\triangle PQR$ with $\angle Q$ a right angle, decide whether each statement is always, sometimes, or never true.

26. Tan P is the reciprocal of tan R.
27. $\sin P = \sin R$
28. $\cos R = \sin P$
29. $\cos R = \tan P$

30. In this rhombus, $IK = 8$ and $m\angle LIJ = 44$. Find LJ and the perimeter of the rhombus.

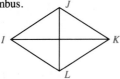

31. If $d = 4$ and $e = 12$, find a and the measure of $\angle B$.
32. If $m\angle BCD = 38$ and $d = 5$, find a and h.
33. If $b = 10$ and $m\angle A = 26$, find a and c.
34. If $b = 16$ and $e = 8\sqrt{3}$, find a and $m\angle B$.

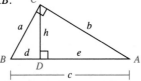

35. A cable is used to support a 245-m television tower. If the angle the cable makes with the ground is 78°, how long is the cable?

245 m

78°

7-6 The Sine and Cosine Ratios **329**

Assignment Guide
Minimum: 1–30 e/o, 41, AR
Regular: 10–39 e/o, 41, AR
Advanced: 21–41, AR

Applications
Class Exercise 21
Exercises 20, 35–36, 38–39

Algebra
Algebra Review

Lesson Closure

Review the sine, cosine, and tangent functions.

Teachers Resource Materials

Practice Master 49
Transparency 30

Exercise Answers

1. $\sin A = \cos B = \frac{12}{13}$, $\cos A = \sin B = \frac{5}{13}$ 2. $\sin A = \cos B = \frac{5}{13}$, $\cos A = \sin B = \frac{12}{13}$ 3. $\sin A = \cos B = \frac{8}{17}$, $\cos A = \sin B = \frac{15}{17}$ 4. 0.5299
5. 0.6561   6. 0.9659
7. 40   8. 16   9. 85
10. $x \approx 27.95$, $y \approx 21.06$
11. $x \approx 23.93$, $y \approx 10.16$
12. $x \approx 20.67$, $y \approx 72.09$
13. a. $x = 35 \cdot \cos 37°$, $y = 35 \cdot \cos 53°$ b. $x = 26 \cdot \cos 23°$, $y = 26 \cdot \cos 67°$
c. $x = 75 \cos 74°$, $y = 75 \cos 16$
14. $m\angle A \approx 53$, $m\angle B \approx 37$
15. $m\angle A \approx 62$, $m\angle B \approx 28$
16. $m\angle A \approx 68$, $m\angle B \approx 22$
17. 24.61   18. 10.86
19. 57.96   20. $\frac{12}{r} = \sin 20°$, $\frac{12}{r} = \cos 70°$, $r \approx 35.1$ ft

21. $\sin 45° = \frac{\sqrt{2}}{2}$, $\sin 60° = \frac{\sqrt{3}}{2}$,
$\cos 30° = \frac{\sqrt{3}}{2}$, $\cos 45° = \frac{\sqrt{2}}{2}$,
$\cos 60° = \frac{1}{2}$, $\tan 30° = \frac{\sqrt{3}}{3}$,
$\tan 45° = 1$, $\tan 60° = \sqrt{3}$

22. ≈37, ≈53　**23.** ≈14.83 cm

24. ≈25.44 cm　**25.** $\frac{\sqrt{39}}{8}$

26. always　**27.** sometimes

28. always　**29.** never

30. 3.23, 17.25　**31.** 8, 60

32. ≈8.12, ≈6.40　**33.** ≈4.88,
≈11.13　**34.** ≈9.24, 60

35. 250.47 m　**36.** ≈102.86 m

37. $\sin A = 0.6$, $\cos A = 0.8$,
$\sin B = 0.8$, $\cos B = 0.6$

38. ≈186.79 m　**39.** 60 km
east　**40.** Draw altitude ZW.
Let h represent its length.
$\sin Y = \frac{h}{x}$, $\sin X = \frac{h}{y}$, $x \cdot \sin Y =$
$x \cdot \frac{h}{x} = h = \frac{h \cdot y}{y} = y \cdot \sin X$

41. a. 1 b. 1 c. $(\sin x)^2 +$
$(\cos x)^2 = 1$ d. $\frac{\sin x}{\cos x} = \tan x$
e. By Pythagorean Theorem,
$a^2 + b^2 = c^2$. Divide through by
c^2: $\left(\frac{a}{c}\right)^2 + \left(\frac{b}{c}\right)^2 = 1$. $\frac{a}{c} = \sin A$,
$\frac{b}{c} = \cos A$, so $(\sin A)^2 +$
$(\cos A)^2 = 1$. $\tan A = \frac{a}{b} = \frac{\frac{a}{c}}{\frac{b}{c}} =$
$\frac{\sin A}{\cos A}$.

Algebra Review
Answers

1. −5, 5　**2.** 0　**3.** −4, 10

4. −11, −13　**5.** −1, 11

6. $-\frac{3}{7}$, 1　**7.** $-17\frac{1}{2}$, 16

8. −4, −2, 2, 4

Math Contest Problem
Answer

$\sqrt{521}$ ft ≈ 22.8 ft

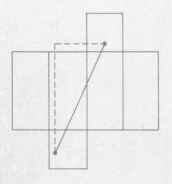

---

36. When flying, the string of a kite forms a straight line and makes a 36° angle with the ground. If the string is 175 m long, how high is the kite?

37. Find the sine and cosine of the acute angles of this right triangle.

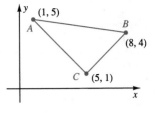

C

38. The area of the square base of an Egyptian Pyramid is 52,900 m². The faces of the pyramid make an angle of about 52° with the base. What is the shortest distance you would have to climb up a face to reach the top?

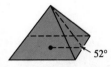

39. A boat at location P is directly east of lighthouse A. The navigator sights a lighthouse B at 53° south of the east-west direction. The boat then travels 60 km in a path 16° east of the north-south direction to point Q. It is then directly east of lighthouse B. How far is the boat from B?

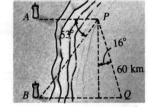

40. Given $\triangle XYZ$ with acute angles X and Y,
Prove that $x \sin Y = y \sin X$.
(HINT: Would it help to draw an altitude?)

Critical Thinking

41. Use a calculator to find the values of w and y.
　a. $(\sin 54°)^2 + (\cos 54°)^2 = w$　**b.** $(\sin 7°)^2 + (\cos 7°)^2 = y$
　c. Make a conjecture about $(\sin x°)^2 + (\cos x°)^2$, where x is the measure of any angle.
　d. Use a calculator to make a conjecture about how $\frac{\sin x°}{\cos x°}$ relates to $\tan x°$, where x is the measure of any angle.
　e. Draw a right triangle, label it using variables, and prove the the two relationships you discovered above are true.

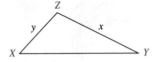

Algebra Review

Solve for x.

1. $|x| = 5$　**2.** $|x| = 0$　**3.** $|x - 3| = 7$　**4.** $|x + 12| = 1$

5. $|5 - x| = 6$　**6.** $|7x - 2| = 5$　**7.** $|4x + 3| = 67$　**8.** $|x^2 - 10| = 6$

Math Contest Problem

In a room 8 ft wide, 8 ft high, and 15 ft long—a bug crawls from the middle of the front wall, 1 ft above the floor, to the middle of the back wall, 1 ft below the ceiling. What is the shortest path? How far is it?

OBJECTIVE: *Identify and apply the angle of elevation and angle of depression.*

7-7 Angles of Elevation and Depression

Trigonometric ratios are often used to indirectly find lengths or distances that cannot be found by direct measurement. It is important to be able to identify special angles that are often used in these applications. For example, when an observer sights from a boat up to a plane, as shown in this picture, the angle the line of sight makes with the horizontal is called the **angle of elevation.**

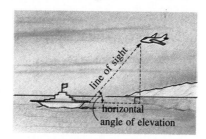

Example 1

Application An observer in an airport control tower sights an airplane at an angle of elevation 32°. The pilot reports the plane's altitude as 3.5 km. What is the airplane's horizontal ground distance *d* from the tower?

Solution

$$\tan 32° = \frac{3.5}{d}$$
$$d \tan 32° = 3.5$$
$$d = \frac{3.5}{\tan 32°} \approx \frac{3.5}{0.6248} \approx 5.6$$

The plane's ground distance from the airport is about 5.6 km.

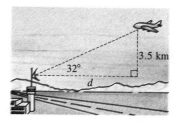

Try This

Solve the above problem if the angle of elevation is 24°.

When an observer sights downward, as from the plane to the boat in this picture, the angle the line of sight makes with the horizontal is called the **angle of depression.**

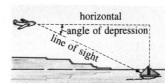

Example 2

Application An airplane pilot sights a life raft. The angle of depression is 26° and the plane's altitude is 3 km. What is the plane's distance *d* from the raft?

Solution

$$\sin 26° = \frac{3}{d}$$
$$d \sin 26° = 3$$
$$d = \frac{3}{\sin 26°} \approx \frac{3}{0.4384} \approx 6.84$$

The plane is about 6.8 km from the raft.

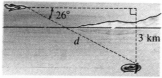

Try This

Solve the above problem if the angle of depression is 35°.

First Five Minutes

(Quiz on previous lesson)

Without using a trig table or calculator, find $m \angle A$.

1. $\tan A = 1$ 45
2. $\sin A = \frac{\sqrt{2}}{2}$ 45
3. $\cos A = \frac{1}{2}$ 60
4. $\sin A = \frac{\sqrt{3}}{2}$ 60
5. $\tan A = \sqrt{3}$ 60

Lesson Opener

Before discussing the concepts of angle of elevation or angle of depression, ask students to estimate how tall the tree is and how wide the river is.
≈18.66 m, ≈28.56 ft

75°
5 m

55°
20 ft

Teaching Notes

Emphasize that the angle of elevation or angle of depression is the angle between the line of sight and the *horizontal* line, not the *vertical* line. The figure shown may help some students who have difficulties distinguishing between these angles.

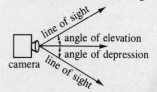

In the following illustration, the angle of depression is congruent to the angle of elevation because both angles are formed with respect to two horizontal lines that are parallel.

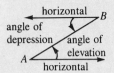

Key Terms

angle of depression
angle of elevation

Materials

student notebooks
scientific calculators

Guided Practice

Chalkboard Examples

1. What is the height of a tower if point P is 120 ft from the base of the tower and the measure of the angle of elevation to the top of the tower is 75? ≈**447.85 ft**

Answer to **Try This** ≈**7.9 m**

2. A kite flying on approximately 100 ft of string makes an angle of 40° with the ground. How high is the kite above the ground if the string is straight? ≈**64.28 ft**

Answer to **Try This** ≈**5.23 km**

Class Exercise Answers

1. 24° **2.** 47° **3.** sine
4. tangent **5.** ∠FAE, elevation **6.** ∠DCF, depression **7.** ∠DAE, depression
8. ∠BCF, elevation
9. ≈3998.81 m **10.** ≈1463.38 m
11. ≈587.70 ft

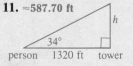

Class Exercises

Short Answer

A person standing on a cliff looks up to see a hot air balloon and then looks down to see a sailboat.

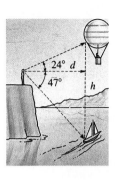

1. Find the angle of elevation.
2. Find the angle of depression.
3. Suppose you knew the height h of the cliff above the water. Which trigonometric function would you use to find the line-of-sight distance to the sailboat?
4. Suppose you knew the distance d to a point directly below the balloon. Which trigonometric function would you use to find the height of the balloon?

$\overleftrightarrow{AE}$ and $\overleftrightarrow{FC}$ are horizontal and $\overleftrightarrow{BD}$ is vertical. Name each angle and tell whether it is an angle of depression or an angle of elevation.

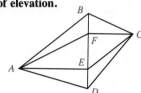

5. An observer at A sights F.
6. An observer at C sights D.
7. An observer at A sights D.
8. An observer at C sights B.

Sample Exercises

9. The angle of elevation of a helicopter from a ship is 35°. The altitude of the helicopter is 2800 m. How far is it from a buoy, directly below the helicopter, to the ship?
10. If the angle of depression of the ship from the helicopter is 29° and the water-surface distance from the helicopter to the ship is 2640 ft, find the altitude of the helicopter.

Draw a picture and solve each problem.

11. A person 1320 ft from a television tower sights its top. The angle of elevation is 24°. How tall is the tower?
12. A person in a hot air balloon that is directly over a school building sights her house. The angle of depression is 42°. The house is 1 mi from the school. Find the altitude of the balloon.

Discussion

Determine whether each statement is true or false. If true, give a convincing argument.

13. As you move farther away from a flagpole, the angle of elevation of its top increases.
14. If you look out the window of a tall building at a car, the angle of depression decreases as the car moves away from you.
15. If you look at a fountain from the windows of a tall building, the angle of depression decreases as you move to higher and higher floors of the building.
16. As an airplane flies toward you, its angle of elevation increases.
17. An object directly overhead has an angle of elevation of 90°.

Exercises

A

1. A monument casts a shadow 215 ft long when the angle of elevation of the sun is 52°. Find the height of the monument.
2. The angle of depression of a tree from the top of the monument in Exercise 1 is 78°. How far is the tree from the base of the monument?

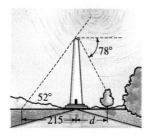

Draw a picture, then solve.

3. The angle of depression of a car from an air balloon basket is 40°. The balloon is directly over a water tower that is 5 km from the car. Find the altitude of the balloon.
4. A person on a building 180 ft high looked at a bench in a park below. The angle of depression was 24°. How far is the bench from the foot of the building?
5. The length of a guywire supporting a radio tower is 175 ft. The angle of elevation of the top of the radio tower from the foot of the guywire is 65°. How tall is the tower?

B

6. The Chrysler Building in New York is 1046 ft tall. A person stands half a mile away and views the top of the building. Find the angle of elevation of the top.
7. A Mission Control observer, 4.5 km from the launch pad, observes a space shuttle ascending. The angle of elevation of the shuttle is 38°. How far (air distance) is the shuttle from the observer?
8. A television tower 150 ft high casts a shadow 200 ft long. Find the angle of elevation of the sun.

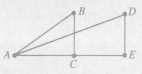

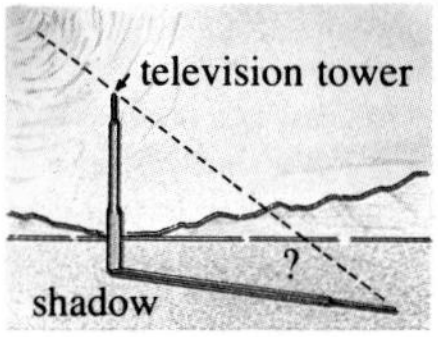

9. How far is the surface of the lake below the level land on the bank?

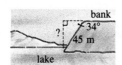

10. A ramp is 120 ft long and rises vertically 15 ft. Find the angle of elevation of the ramp.

C

11. A person on a bridge sights a boat at an angle of depression of 6°. The bridge is 96 ft above the water. If the boat is traveling 440 ft per minute, about how long will it take the boat to reach the bridge?

7-7 Angles of Elevation and Depression   **333**

---

12. ≈0.9 mi = 4752 ft

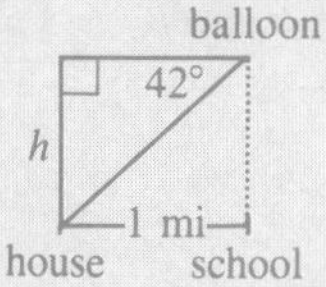

13. false   14. true,
$m \angle EDB > m \angle EDC$

15. false   16. true,
$m \angle BAC > m \angle DAE$

17. true

Assignment Guide

Minimum: 1–10, 14, MR
Regular: 2–12, 14, MR
Advanced: 6–14, MR

Applications

Class Exercises 1–17
Exercises 1–14

Lesson Closure

Ask students to give examples of an angle of elevation and an angle of depression.

Teacher's Resource Materials

Transparency 31
Practice Master 50
Quiz 14
Technology: Calculator 10

12. An observer at the top of a 50 m lighthouse sights two ships approaching, one behind the other. The angles of depression of the ships are 36° and 25°. Find the distance between the ships to the nearest meter.

13. A surveyor could not measure a distance ending directly under the top of a mountain so he marked two locations, *A* and *B*, 1000 m apart. He then measured the angle of elevation of the top of the mountain from each of these locations and drew this diagram. Find the height of the mountain. (HINT: Write and solve a pair of equations.)

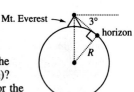

Critical Thinking

14. When the horizon is sighted from the top of the world's tallest mountain, Mt. Everest, the angle of depression is 3°. The height of Mt. Everest, to the nearest hundredth of a mile is 5.50 miles.

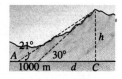

  a. How can you use this information to find the distance R from the center of the earth to the earth's surface (the radius of the earth)?
  b. Investigate how an error in measuring the angle of depression or the height of the mountain would affect the value of R. Explain your findings.

Mixed Review

$\triangle ABC \sim \triangle RST$ **Complete each of the following.**

1. $\angle B \cong$ ___ **2.** $\angle T \cong$ ___
3. $\frac{AB}{RS} = \frac{AC}{?}$ **4.** $\frac{?}{BC} = \frac{RT}{ST}$
5. $x =$ ___ **6.** $y =$ ___
7. The scale factor of $\triangle ABC$ to $\triangle RST$ is ___ .

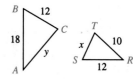

Quiz

Indicate whether each equation is true or false.

1. $\sin A = \frac{12}{13}$ **2.** $\cos B = \frac{5}{13}$
3. $\tan B = \frac{5}{13}$ **4.** $\tan A = \frac{12}{5}$

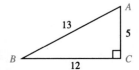

Find the indicated lengths to the nearest hundredth and angles to the nearest degree.

5.   **6.**   **7.**

8. A person in a lighthouse spots a boat. If he is 25 m above sea level and the angle of depression is 15°, find the distance from the boat to the foot of the lighthouse.

CRITICAL THINKING

Common Errors in Drawing a Conclusion

There are several common reasoning errors that are made every day in the critical thinking process. The ones described below often result in "proofs" which do not support the conclusion. Consider the following examples.

Example 1

Mr. Vasquez said, "All politicians are dishonest." Ms. Tsujimura said, "I agree with you. I've known a lot of politicians in my time, and none of them were honest."

This is an instance of *drawing a conclusion in the absence of a counterexample*. You have seen that a counterexample is a single example that shows a general statement to be false. In Example 1, the reasoning error was deciding a general statement to be true (all politicians are dishonest) just because a counterexample had not been found. This is similar to *drawing a conclusion from selected examples*, illustrated by the freshman who says, "The teachers in this school are strict—look at the ones I have this year."

Example 2

Jackie said, "The neighbors drive a big new car so they must be rich."

This is an example of *drawing a conclusion that does not follow from the supporting statements*. An expensive-looking car is, of course, not enough evidence to support the conclusion that those who drive it are rich.

Example 3

Rose decided she needed a job. Her mother asked why. Rose said, "I need to work to pay for a car." Her mother asked, "Why do you need a car?" Rose answered, "I need it to drive to my job."

This illustrates *drawing a conclusion by assuming it is true* (or *circular reasoning*). Notice that Rose used the assumption that she needed a job to convince her mother that she needed a job.

Exercises

Which reasoning error described above occurs in each situation? Explain.

1. Fred said, "My geometry teacher assigns a lot of homework. She must not like our class."
2. Janelle said to Samantha, "You joined our club because you're strange." Samantha asked, "Why do you think I'm strange?" Janelle responded, "You must be, or you wouldn't have joined our club."
3. Maurice said, "All four-sided figures are quadrilaterals." Su Ming agreed, "I've never seen a four-sided figure that wasn't a quadrilateral."
4. Niki said, "I've ordered two items from a bike catalog and they have both been of low quality. That company obviously sells only inferior items."
5. Victoria said, "I'm running for mayor." Marc asked her why. She answered, "I'm quite intelligent." When Marc asked Victoria how she knew she was intelligent, she responded, "I must be, otherwise I wouldn't be running for mayor."
6. Roger drew three right triangles, measured their sides, and found that the Pythagorean Theorem held for all of them. He concluded, "The Pythagorean Theorem must be true because I can't draw a triangle for which it doesn't hold."
7. Consider the advertisement below.

Which reasoning error occurs in the advertisement?

Critical Thinking

Common Errors in Drawing a Conclusion

Exercise Answers
1. drawing a conclusion that does not follow from the supporting statements   2. drawing a conclusion by assuming it is true   3. drawing a conclusion in the absence of a counterexample   4. drawing a conclusion from selected examples   5. drawing a conclusion by assuming it is true
6. drawing a conclusion in the absence of a counterexample
7. drawing a conclusion in the absence of a counterexample

CHAPTER SUMMARY

Vocabulary

angle of depression (7-7)
angle of elevation (7-7)
cosine ratio (7-6)
45°–45°–90° triangle (7-4)

geometric mean (7-1)
Pythagorean Triple (7-3)
sine ratio (7-6)
tangent ratio (7-5)

30°–60°–90° triangle (7-4)
trigonometric ratio (7-5)
trigonometry (7-5)

Key Ideas

1. The altitude to the hypotenuse of a right triangle
   a. forms two triangles that are similar to each other and to the original triangle.
   b. is the geometric mean between the length of the two segments on the hypotenuse.
2. The Pythagorean Theorem states that in a right triangle, the square of the length of the hypotenuse equals the sum of the squares of the lengths of the legs.
3. If a, b, and c are the lengths of the sides of a triangle (c being the longest side) and
   a. $a^2 + b^2 < c^2$, then the triangle is obtuse.
   b. $a^2 + b^2 > c^2$, then the triangle is acute.
   c. $a^2 + b^2 = c^2$, then the triangle is right.
4. In a 45°–45°–90° triangle with legs of length x, the hypotenuse has length $x\sqrt{2}$.
5. In a 30°–60°–90° triangle with shorter leg of length x, the hypotenuse has length $2x$ and the longer leg has length $x\sqrt{3}$.
6. In the right triangle shown to the right:
   a. $\tan A = \frac{a}{b}$
   b. $\sin A = \frac{a}{c}$
   c. $\cos A = \frac{b}{c}$

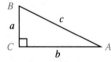

7. When an observer sights upward, the angle the line of sight makes with the horizontal is called the angle of elevation. When an observer sights downward, the angle the line of sight makes with the horizontal is called the angle of depression.

CHAPTER REVIEW

7-1

$\triangle ADC$ is a right triangle with altitude $\overline{DB}$.

1. If $AD = 6$ and $AB = 4$, find AC.
2. If $AB = 3$ and $BC = 8$, find BD.
3. If $BD = 6$ and $BC = 3$, find AC.
4. If $DC = 12$ and $BC = 6$, find AB.

7-2

$\angle U$ and $\angle S$ are right angles.

5. If $RU = 4$ and $UT = 6$, find RT.
6. If $RS = 8$ and $RT = 17$, find ST.
7. If $RT = 9$ and $RU = 5$, find UT.

8. Find the length of the altitude to the base of an isosceles triangle if the legs are 10 in. long and the base is 12 in. long.

7-3

Determine whether each triangle with the given side lengths is acute, obtuse, or right.

9. 4, 5, 8
10. 11, 60, 61
11. $2\sqrt{3}$, $4\sqrt{2}$, 6

7-4

Find x, y, and/or z.

12.
13.
14.

7-5

Use the table on page 636 or a calculator to complete each statement.

15. $\tan 23° \approx$ ___
16. $\tan 68° \approx$ ___
17. $\tan$ ___ ≈ 0.7421

18. Find x.
19. Find $m\angle 1$.

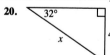
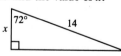

7-6

Write and solve an equation to find the value of x.

20.
21.
22.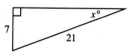

7-7

23. A person on top of a 150-ft tower looked at a car below. If the angle of depression was 32°, find the distance from the car to the foot of the tower?

1. 9   2. $2\sqrt{6}$ 3. 15
4. 18   5. $2\sqrt{13}$ 6. 15
7. $2\sqrt{14}$ 8. 8 in.
9. obtuse   10. right
11. acute   12. $7\sqrt{2}$
13. $x = 5$, $y = 10$ 14. $x = 4$, $y = 4\sqrt{3}$, $z = 4\sqrt{3}$
15. ≈ 0.4245 16. ≈ 2.4751
17. $\approx 37°$ 18. ≈ 2.9713
19. ≈ 55 20. $\sin 32° = \frac{4}{x}$, ≈ 7.5483 21. $\cos 72° = \frac{x}{14}$, ≈ 4.3262 22. $\sin x = \frac{7}{12}$, $\approx 19°$ 23. ≈ 240 ft

Teacher's Resource Materials

Chapter 7 Tests

Test Answers

1. AD, DC **2.** AC, DC
3. $3\sqrt{5}$ **4.** 10
5. $\sqrt{91}$ **6.** 7
7. obtuse   **8.** right
9. acute   **10.** $x = 12$,
$y = 24$ **11.** $x = 7$,
$y = 7\sqrt{2}$ **12.** $x = 5\sqrt{2}$,
$y = 5 + 5\sqrt{3}$ **13.** ≈ 0.9325
14. $\approx 72°$ **15.** ≈ 5.5919
16. ≈ 5.8737 **17.** $\approx 36°$
18. $\approx 22°$ **19.** false
20. ≈ 23.32 m   **21.** ≈ 2890.4 m

CHAPTER TEST

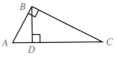

Complete each statement.

1. BD is the geometric mean between ___ and ___ .
2. BC is the geometric mean between ___ and ___ .
3. If $AD = 3$ and $DC = 15$, then $BD =$ ___ .

$\triangle ABC$ **is a right triangle with hypotenuse of length c and legs of length a and b. Complete each statement.**

4. If $a = 6$ and $b = 8$, then $c =$ ___ .
5. If $b = 3$ and $c = 10$, then $a =$ ___ .
6. If $a = 7$ and $c = 7\sqrt{2}$, then $b =$ ___ .

State whether each triangle with the given side lengths is acute, right, or obtuse.

7. 2, 4, 5   8. 5, 12, 13   9. $2\sqrt{3}$, 5, 6

Find the value of x and y.

10.
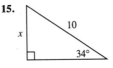

11.

12.
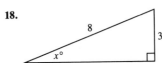

Use the table on page 636 or a calculator to complete each statement.

13. $\tan 43° \approx$ ___
14. $\tan$ ___ ≈ 3.0777

Use the table on page 636 or a calculator to find the indicated side lengths to the nearest hundredth and angles to the nearest degree.

15.

16.

17.
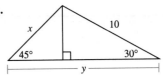

18.

19. Is the following statement true or false? As a plane flies toward an observer on the ground, its angle of elevation decreases.
20. The angle of elevation of the top of a tree from a point 21 m from its foot is 48°. Find the height of the tree.
21. A plane is flying at an altitude of 2,100 m. The angle of depression from the plane to a control tower is 36°. Find the distance from the control tower to the plane.

PROBLEM SOLVING

Simplify the Problem

Sometimes the numbers involved in a problem are so large that a direct solution is difficult and/or time-consuming. In such situations, the strategy Simplify the Problem is helpful. One method of simplifying a problem is to find a solution using a small number. Then, using a larger number, find another solution. After repeating the process several times, your results can be organized in a table and a pattern can be found.

Example 1

In a soccer tournament, there were a total of 32 teams. When a team lost, it was eliminated from the tournament and played no more games. To win the tournament, a team could not lose any games. How many games were needed to determine a champion?

Solution

Simplify the problem by considering a situation in which there were only two teams. In this case, one game would be necessary. If there were three teams, two games would be required (the winner of the first game meeting the team that had not yet played). The table below shows the pattern.

Number of teams	2	3	4	5	· · ·	32
Number of games	1	2	3	4	· · ·	31

31 games were needed.

Problem-Solving Strategies	
Draw a Diagram	Work Backward
Make a Table	Simplify the Problem
Look for a Pattern	

The problem-solving strategies that have been introduced up to this point in the book are presented in the chart.

Problems

Solve.

1. How many squares are in the figure below?

2. The figure below was made with 4 triangles, each having sides 1 m long. If a longer figure is made with 70 triangles, what will its perimeter be?

3. A warehouse has 16 identical desks to be distributed to 3 offices. Each office must receive at least 1 desk. In how many ways can the desks be distributed?

4. Ten houses are arranged in a circle. The phone company needs to connect each house. How many wires are needed if a separate wire is required for each pair?

Problem Solving   **339**

Circles

Chapter Overview

The basic vocabulary of circles and spheres is introduced in the first lesson of this chapter. Subsequent lessons cover theorems related to the tangents, secants, chords, arcs, and angles of circles.

Objectives

8-1 ▪ Apply basic definitions and concepts related to circles.

8-2 ▪ State and apply theorems regarding circles and tangents.

8-3 ▪ Calculate lengths related to common tangents to circles.

8-4 ▪ State and apply theorems about arcs and central angles.

8-5 ▪ State and apply theorems about chords of a circle.

8-6 ▪ State and apply theorems concerning measures of inscribed angles.

8-7 ▪ State and apply theorems concerning measures of angles formed by two chords or two secants.

8-8 ▪ State and apply theorems concerning measures of intersecting chords, secants, and tangents.

TEACHING CHAPTER 8

When starting a cooperative group activity, be sure to assign the students to groups. Students rarely self-select groups with a view toward the best learning environment, and some students may be left out altogether when groups are formed by choice.

Although cooperative learning is not tutoring, it is certainly a good idea to have a group in which not all of the students are having trouble with geometry. It may help to use paired learning as a way of familiarizing students with cooperative groups.

The **Class Exercises** for Lessons 8-2, 8-3, 8-5, 8-6, and 8-8 are well suited to cooperative pairs. No roles are needed. Have students discuss each question, find applicable definitions or theorems as needed, and agree on the answer to each exercise. If you are grading the activity, accept one paper from each pair.

Multicultural Note: *Benjamin Banneker*

Benjamin Banneker was an African-American surveyor, astronomer, and mathematician who was active at the time of the founding of the United States. He worked on the plans for the city of Washington, D.C., wrote almanacs, and made astronomical observations. Banneker taught himself how to calculate the positions of the planets and how to predict the dates of lunar and solar eclipses.

Almanacs used to contain a great deal of information about the times of the rising and setting of the sun, moon, and planets. In 1790 this information could be published for the whole country because most of the people lived on the east coast. Now you can find information about the sun and moon in most local papers.

You might ask students about the importance of the sunrise and moonlight to the people of 1790 as compared with today. You can also discuss with students how the time of sunrise differs in different parts of the country and how it changes from season to season. For more information, see page 25 of **Multiculturalism in Mathematics, Science, and Technology**.

Alternative Assessment and Communication Ideas

Drawing and measuring provides a hands-on method for students who might otherwise have difficulty with certain problems. Practical approaches can also help lead to a conceptual understanding.

In Lesson 8-2, Exercise 32 can be drawn at actual size. You probably

have a stencil with which to draw a circle with $\frac{3}{4}$ in. diameter. A ruler that

measures tenths of inches is also helpful. A careful figure gives a straight-line measure of x to be approximately 5.05 in.

In Lesson 8-3, Exercise 24 on page 354 can also be solved experimen-

tally. Circles with 10 cm radii will not fit on standard size paper. Students can draw circles with radii of 5 cm. This gives a triangle side of 27 cm. Doubling this gives 54 cm. The actual length is 54.6 cm. In Lesson 8-5, Exercise 28 can be done using this method.

Investigations and Projects

The circle, in its many forms, can be the subject for many kinds of projects. You might ask students to read up and prepare a report with display on the many different kinds of wheels. Why are particular sizes and materials suited to certain uses?

Another topic would be on gears. How do they work and where are they found? This could include cars, bicycles, watches, and machinery.

A third project could be on pipes and conduits of all kinds. Why is the circular shape used for these? Is it easier and more efficient to manufacture? Is it better suited to the flow of liquid?

Students might gather information on how pipes are made and used. Finally, you might ask: in what areas has modern technology moved beyond the wheel? Examples would be quartz time pieces without gears, digital watches, and magnetic trains.

Lesson	PACING CHART (DAYS)			Opening Activity	Cooperative Activity	Seat or Group Work
	1-Year Minimum	1-Year Regular	1-Year Advanced			
8-1	2	2	2	Chapter Opener: **TE** p. 340; Lesson Opener: **TE** p. 341	✂ Lab Worksheet 8-1A: *Laboratory Manual* p. 77; ✂ Lab Worksheet 8-1B: *Laboratory Manual* p. 78	Connections: **SE** p. 344
8-2	2	2	2	First Five Minutes 8-2: *FFM Transparency Masters* p. 28 or **TE** p. 345; Lesson Opener: **TE** p. 345	Explore: **SE** p. 345; ✂ Lab Worksheet 8-2: *Laboratory Manual* p. 79	Try This Exercises
8-3	1	1	1	First Five Minutes 8-3: *FFM Transparency Masters* p. 29 or **TE** p. 351; Lesson Opener: **TE** p. 351	Math Contest Problem: **SE** p. 354	Try This Exercises
8-4	2	2	2	First Five Minutes 8-4: *FFM Transparency Masters* p. 29 or **TE** p. 355; Lesson Opener: **TE** p. 355	✂ Lab Worksheet 8-4A: *Laboratory Manual* p. 80; ✂ Lab Worksheet 8-4B: *Laboratory Manual* p. 81	Try This Exercises
8-5	2	2	2	First Five Minutes 8-5: *FFM Transparency Masters* p. 30 or **TE** p. 360; Lesson Opener: **TE** p. 360	Explore: **SE** p. 360; ✂ Lab Worksheet 8-5A: *Laboratory Manual* p. 82; ✂ Lab Worksheet 8-5B: *Laboratory Manual* p. 83	Try This Exercises
8-6	1	1	1	First Five Minutes 8-6: *FFM Transparency Masters* p. 31 or **TE** p. 366; Lesson Opener: **TE** p. 366	Explore: **SE** p. 366 ✂ Lab Worksheet 8-6: *Laboratory Manual* p. 84	Try This Exercises
8-7	2	2	2	First Five Minutes 8-7: *FFM Transparency Masters* p. 32 or **TE** p. 373; Lesson Opener: **TE** p. 373	✂ Lab Worksheet 8-7: *Laboratory Manual* p. 85	Try This Exercises
8-8	1	1	1	First Five Minutes 8-8: *FFM Transparency Masters* p. 33 or **TE** p. 379; Lesson Opener: **TE** p. 379	Explore: **SE** p. 379 ✂ Lab Worksheet 8-8: *Laboratory Manual* p. 87	Try This Exercises
Review	1	1	1			
Test	1	1	1			

FFM = First Five Minutes

Enrichment	Review/Assess	Reteach	Technology	Lesson
Connections: **SE** p. 344; BASIC 8-1: *Technology* p. B16	Class Exercises: **SE** p. 342; Mixed Review: **SE** p. 344	Practice Worksheet 8-1: *Practice and Mixed Review* p. 56	BASIC 8-1: *Technology* p. B16	8-1
Career: **SE** p. 350; ✂ Enrichment Using Manipulatives 8-2: *Enrichment* p. 44	Class Exercises: **SE** p. 347; Mixed Review: **SE** p. 350	Practice Worksheet 8-2: *Practice and Mixed Review* p. 57		8-2
Math Contest Problem: **SE** p. 354; ✂ Enrichment Using Manipulatives 8-3: *Enrichment* p. 45	Class Exercises: **SE** p. 352; Algebra Review: **SE** p. 354	Practice Worksheet 8-3: *Practice and Mixed Review* p. 58		8-3
Enrichment: **SE** p. 359; ✂ Enrichment Using Manipulatives 8-4: *Enrichment* p. 46	Class Exercises: **SE** p. 357; Mixed Review: **SE** p. 358	Practice Worksheet 8-4: *Practice and Mixed Review* p. 59		8-4
✂ Enrichment Using Manipulatives 8-5: *Enrichment* p. 47	Class Exercises: **SE** p. 362; Algebra Review: **SE** p. 365; Quiz: **SE** p. 365; Quiz: *Assessment* p. 93	Practice Worksheet 8-5: *Practice and Mixed Review* p. 60		8-5
Computer Activity: **SE** p. 372; ✂ Enrichment Using Manipulatives 8-6: *Enrichment* p. 48	Class Exercises: **SE** p. 369; Algebra Review: **SE** p. 372	Practice Worksheet 8-6: *Practice and Mixed Review* p. 61	Computer Activity: **SE** p. 372	8-6
Biographical Note: **SE** p. p 378; BASIC 8-7: *Technology* p. B18	Class Exercises: **SE** p. 375; Mixed Review: **SE** p. 378	Practice Worksheet 8-7: *Practice and Mixed Review* p. 62	Calculator Worksheet 8-7: *Technology* p. CL11; BASIC 8-7: *Technology* p. B18	8-7
✂ Enrichment Using Manipulatives 8-8: *Enrichment* p. 49	Class Exercises: **SE** p. 381; Algebra Review: **SE** p. 384; Quiz **SE** p. 384; Quiz: *Assessment* p. 94	Practice Worksheet 8-8: *Practice and Mixed Review* p. 63	Calculator Worksheet 8-8: *Technology* p. CL12	8-8
Critical Thinking: **SE** p. 385	Summary & Review: **SE** p. 386–387	Mixed Review: *Practice and Mixed Review* p. 109		Review
Preparing for College Entrance Exams: **SE** p. 389	Chapter 8 Test: **SE** p. 388; Chapter 8 Tests: *Assessment* p. 43–48; *MathTest*			Test

8

Circles

A bicycle wheel has a radius
of 14 in. Find the diameter
and circumference of the
wheel.

TANGENTS, ARCS, AND CHORDS

OBJECTIVE: *Apply basic definitions and concepts related to circles.*

8-1 Basic Terms

A **circle** is the set of all points in a plane that are a given distance from a given point in the plane called the **center**. A **radius** of the circle is a segment with one endpoint the center and the other endpoint on the circle. The length of the radius is called *the radius* of the circle. A circle is named by its center. The circle below may be referred to as circle P ($\odot P$). In $\odot P$, $\overline{PA}$ is a radius and the radius is 5. All radii of a circle are congruent.

Congruent circles are circles that have congruent radii. So $\odot P$ and $\odot Q$ below are congruent.

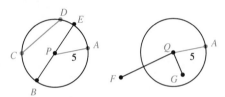

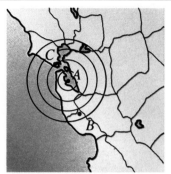

The distance from the airport is shown on this map by a set of circles with center A. If the radius of each successive circle represents an additional 10 mi, about how far are B and C from the airport at A?

A **chord** is a segment that joins two points on the circle. A **diameter** is a chord through the center of the circle. For $\odot P$, $\overline{CD}$ is a chord and $\overline{BE}$ is a diameter. Notice that a diameter is twice as long as a radius. Point F is *on the exterior of* the circle so $QF > 5$; point G is *on the interior of* the circle so $QG < 5$.

A line that contains a chord of the circle is a **secant**. A line in the plane of the circle that intersects the circle in exactly one point is a tangent to the circle. That point is the **point of tangency.** In the figure to the right, $\overleftrightarrow{RS}$ is a secant and $\overrightarrow{PQ}$ is a tangent with A the point of tangency for $\overrightarrow{PQ}$.

A polygon is **inscribed** in a circle if all its vertices are on the circle. A polygon is **circumscribed** about a circle if each of its sides is tangent to the circle. Two circles in the same plane with the same center are called **concentric** circles.

ABCD is an inscribed polygon.

EFGH is a circumscribed polygon.

concentric circles with center O

Point out that the circle does
not include any interior points
nor the center point.

Key Terms

circle
sphere
radius (radii)
chord
diameter
secant
tangent, point of tangency
inscribed/circumscribed
interior/exterior of a circle
tangent plane

Key Points

1. A circle is usually named by
its center, written symbolically
as $\odot O$.
2. The plural of radius is radii.
3. A diameter is also a chord.
4. Every diameter consists of
two radii and is twice as long
as any radius of a circle.

Class Exercise Answers

1. 8 **2.** $\overline{AE}$ and $\overline{CD}$ **3.** $\overline{BD}$
4. 16 **5.** $\overleftrightarrow{AE}$ **6.** line m
7. P **8.** $\overleftrightarrow{AB}$ **9.** $\overline{CD}$ or $\overline{AB}$
10. $\overleftrightarrow{RS}$ **11.** a. 24 b. $2\sqrt{5}$
c. $\sqrt{3}$ **12.** a. 12 b. $7\frac{1}{2}$ c. $\frac{5}{4}$
13. 3 cm **14.** 8 cm
15. No; it will intersect the circle at another point besides A.
16. A is not a point of tangency
for line m, but it may be a point
of tangency for another line.
17. Yes; it will contain a chord
of the circle through A.
18. No; if the ray were extended
in the opposite direction, it
would intersect the circle in a
second point. **19.** $\overline{AD}$ is not
tangent to the circle.

A **sphere** is the set of all points in space a given distance from a point called
the *center* of the sphere. The given distance is called the radius of the sphere.

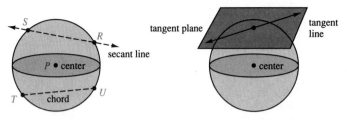

Chords, secants, and tangents of spheres are defined for spheres in a way
similar to the way they are for circles. A plane is *tangent to the sphere* and is
called a *tangent plane* if it contains exactly one point of the sphere.

Class Exercises

Short Answer

1. Find the length of the radius of $\odot P$.
2. Name two chords of $\odot P$ that are not diameters.
3. Name a diameter of $\odot P$.
4. Find the length of a diameter of $\odot P$.
5. Name a secant of $\odot P$.
6. Name a tangent of $\odot P$.
7. Name the point of tangency for the tangent plane to sphere O.
8. Name a secant of sphere O.
9. Name a chord of sphere O.
10. Name a line that is tangent to sphere O.

Sample Exercises

Complete each statement.

11. The diameter of a circle
  a. with radius 12 is ___. **b.** with radius $\sqrt{5}$ is ___. **c.** with radius $\frac{\sqrt{3}}{2}$ is ___.
12. The radius of a circle
  a. with diameter 24 is ___. **b.** with diameter 15 is ___. **c.** with diameter $\frac{5}{2}$ is ___.

The radius of $\odot C$ is 5 cm, the radius of $\odot A$ is 13 cm. Complete each statement.

13. $AB =$ ___ **14.** $AC =$ ___

Discussion

15. Is line m a tangent line? Why or why not?
16. Is point A a point of tangency? Why or why not?
17. Is line m a secant? Why or why not?
18. Is ray BC a tangent? Why or why not?
19. Explain why $ABCD$ is not a circumscribed polygon
for the circle shown.

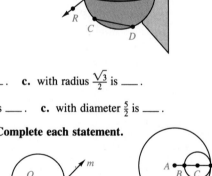

Exercises

A

1. Name a radius of ⊙*P*. Find its length.
2. Find the length of a radius of ⊙*Q*.
3. *BQ* = __?__
4. *CP* = __?__
5. Name a segment that is a chord of both circles.
6. What kind of triangle is △*PEF*?
7. Explain why △*PEQ* ≅ △*PFQ*.
8. Explain why △*GEQ* ≅ △*GFQ*.

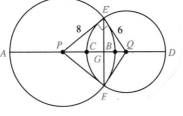

9. Name a triangle that is inscribed in a circle.
10. Name a triangle that is circumscribed about a circle.
11. Name a secant line and the circle for which it is a secant.
12. Name a tangent and the circle for which it is a tangent.

Point *P* lies outside ⊙*O*.

13. How many lines through *P* are tangents to ⊙*O*?
14. How many lines through *P* are secants for ⊙*O*?

Point *Q* lies inside ⊙*O*.

15. How many lines through *Q* are tangents of ⊙*O*?
16. How many lines through *Q* contain a diameter of ⊙*O*?

B

Draw a circle and then complete the figure as indicated.

17. Draw a segment in the interior of the circle that is not a chord.
18. Draw a segment that intersects the circle in two points, but is not a diameter, or chord.
19. Draw a line that is neither a secant nor a tangent line.
20. Draw a ray that intersects the circle in only one point but is not a tangent.
21. Draw a segment that has one endpoint on the circle but is not a chord.

Determine whether each statement is always, sometimes, or never true.

22. A chord is a diameter.
23. A secant to a circle is a tangent to the same circle.
24. A segment with one endpoint the center of a circle is a radius of the circle.
25. A line that passes through a point inside a circle is a secant for that circle.
26. A line that lies in a plane that is tangent to a sphere is a tangent line of the sphere.
27. A handle 0.41 cm in diameter is reduced to a diameter of 0.34 cm as shown to the right. Find the depth of cut.
28. Give a convincing argument that if a plane and a sphere intersect, the intersection is a single point, or a circle.

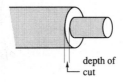

depth of cut

8-1 Basic Terms **343**

Assignment Guide
Minimum: 1–29 e/o, 34–35, MR
Regular: 1–35 e/o, MR
Advanced: 13–29 e/o, 30–35, MR

Applications
Exercises 27, 29

Coordinate Geometry
Exercises 17–21

Lesson Closure

Ask students to use a diagram to define the key words in the lesson.

Teacher's Resource Materials

Practice Master 51
Technology: BASIC 13
Technology: Computer
  Software 11
Transparency 32

Exercise Answers

1. $\overline{PA}$, $\overline{PB}$, $\overline{PE}$, $\overline{PF}$; 8   2. 6
3. 2   4. 4   5. $\overline{EF}$
6. isosceles   7. $\overline{PE} \cong \overline{PF}$
(radii of ⊙*P*), $\overline{QE} \cong \overline{QF}$ (radii of
⊙*Q*), $\overline{PQ} \cong \overline{PQ}$ (Reflex.),
△*PEQ* ≅ △*PFQ* (SSS)
8. $\overline{EQ} \cong \overline{QF}$ (radii of ⊙*Q*),
$\overline{GQ} \cong \overline{GQ}$ (Reflex.), *m*∠*EQG* =
m∠*GQF* (from Exercise 7,
CPCTC), △*GEQ* ≅ △*GFQ* (SAS)
9. △*ABC*   10. △*BCD*
11. $\overleftrightarrow{AC}$, $\overleftrightarrow{BC}$, $\overleftrightarrow{AB}$; the larger
circle   12. $\overrightarrow{CD}$; the smaller
circle   13. 2
14. infinitely many
15. none   16. 1

17.

18.

19.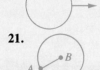

20.

21.

22. sometimes true

23. never true

24. sometimes true

25. always true

26. sometimes true

27. 0.035 cm   **28.** A plane tangent to a sphere intersects it in one point. If the sphere intersects a plane in more than one point, the distance from the center to any point is the same (equal radii). The perpendicular distance from the center to the plane at a point D is the same. Infinitely many right triangles can be formed, all congruent. The legs in the plane all have point D in common and are congruent. The intersection is a circle.   **29.** 0.297 in.

30. sometimes   **31.** never

32. sometimes   **33.** always

34. secant   **35.** 2

Mixed Review Answers

1. 105   **2.** 75   **3.** 25
4. 50   **5.** 50   **6.** 75
7. 3.6 cm   **8.** 5.8 cm

Connections Answers

1. $x^2 + y^2 = 4^2$
2. $x^2 + y^2 = 8^2$

---

29. A washer with a listed size of $\frac{9}{16}$ in. has an inside diameter B of 0.562 in. and an outside diameter A of 1.156 in. Find the width C of the washer.

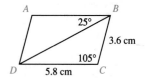

C

Use always, sometimes, or never to complete the statements below about a pair of concentric circles.

30. There ___ exists a line that is a tangent to one circle and a secant to the other circle.

31. There ___ exists a line that is a tangent to both circles.

32. A line that is a secant to one circle is ___ a secant for the other circle.

33. A line that intersects the inside of the small circle is ___ a secant for both circles.

Critical Thinking

Complete each statement to form a correct generalization.

34. A line that contains an interior point of a circle and is in the same plane as the circle is a ___ line.

35. Two circles can intersect each other in at most ___ points.

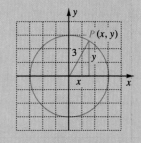

Mixed Review

ABCD is a parallelogram. Complete each statement.

1. $m\angle A =$ ___   **2.** $m\angle ABC =$ ___   **3.** $m\angle ABD =$ ___
4. $m\angle ADB =$ ___   **5.** $m\angle DBC =$ ___   **6.** $m\angle ADC =$ ___
7. $AD =$ ___   **8.** $AB =$ ___

CONNECTIONS ◇◇

Algebra and Geometry

A rectangular coordinate system of the plane allows you to connect geometry and algebra. See how a circle can be described using algebra.

The circle shown has radius 3 with center at the origin of a rectangular coordinate system. Point $P(x, y)$ is on the circle.

Point P and the origin are vertices of a right triangle with sides of length x, y, and 3. You can use the Pythagorean Theorem to obtain the equation $x^2 + y^2 = 3^2$.

Since the coordinates of each point on the circle satisfy this equation, it is called an equation of the circle.

Exercises

1. Write the equation of the circle with center (0, 0) and radius 4.
2. Write the equation of the circle with center (0, 0) and radius 8.

OBJECTIVE: *State and apply theorems regarding circles and tangents.*

8-2 Tangent Lines

Use a compass and straightedge to construct a line ℓ perpendicular to a radius of a circle. What kind of line is line ℓ?

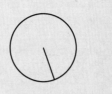

In the previous lesson, you learned that a line is tangent to a circle if it lies in the plane of the circle and intersects the circle in only one point. Theorem 8.1 and its converse Theorem 8.2 are about tangents to a circle.

◆ **THEOREM 8.1**

If a line is perpendicular to a radius of a circle at a point on the circle, then the line is tangent to the circle.

Given: Line *m* is ⊥ *PA* at *A*.

Prove: Line *m* is a tangent to ⊙*P*.

Proof Let *B* be any point on *m* other than *A*. Since *PA* ⊥ *m*, △*PAB* is a right triangle with hypotenuse *PB*. This means that *PB* > *PA* and *B* must be on the exterior of the circle. Therefore *B* cannot lie on the circle and point *A* is the only point of *m* that is on the circle. It follows that *m* is tangent to the circle.

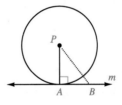

◆ **THEOREM 8.2**

If a line is tangent to a circle, then it is perpendicular to the radius at the point of tangency.

Given: Line *m* is tangent at point *A*.

Prove: Line *m* is ⊥ *OA*.

Proof Use an indirect proof. So assume that the desired conclusion is not true. That is, suppose *OA* is not ⊥ *m*. Then there exists a segment *OB* which is ⊥ *m*. If so, *OB* < *OA*. But *B* lies exterior to the circle since *m* is a tangent line. This means that *OB* > *OA*. Statements *OB* < *OA* and *OB* > *OA* are contradictory. Therefore the supposition is false and *m* is ⊥ *OA*.

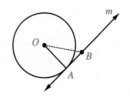

346 *Chapter 8 Circles*

Remind students that rays and segments contained in a tangent and intersecting the circle are also tangent to the circle.

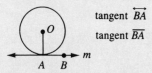

tangent $\overleftrightarrow{BA}$

tangent $\overline{BA}$

Emphasize that a tangent forms two right angles to a radius at the point of tangency.

NOTE: The proof for Theorem 8.2 is an indirect proof. Point out that Theorems 8.1 and 8.2 can be used to identify tangents to a circle. Stress that according to Corollary 8.3a only two tangents to a circle are possible from the same exterior point.

HINT: To prove Theorem 8.3 show that $\overline{OP}$ forms two congruent right triangles with tangent segments $\overline{PA}$ and $\overline{PB}$.

Key Terms

tangent segment

Guided Practice

Chalkboard Examples

1. Given tangent segments $\overline{PB}$ and $\overline{PA}$, radii $\overline{BO}$ and $\overline{AO}$, and $m\angle BPA = 38$, find $m\angle BOA$.
142

Answer to **Try This** 13

2. If $m\angle ABC = 30$ and $AB = 20$, find CB. (HINT: Use the 30°–60°–90° triangle ratio.)
$10\sqrt{3}$

Answer to **Try This** $\sqrt{176}$

Many theorems in geometry have interesting relationships with one another. In Exercises 18 and 19 you may decide to apply Theorem 8.2 to prove Theorem 8.3 and its corollary.

◆ THEOREM 8.3

The two tangent segments from an exterior point of a circle are congruent.

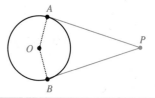

▶ COROLLARY 8.3a

The line through an external point and the center of a circle bisects the angle formed by the two tangents from the external point.

Example 1

$\overline{PA}$ and $\overline{PB}$ are tangent segments from P.
$PO = 17$, $OA = 8$, $m\angle APO = 28$.
Find   **a.** $m\angle POA$ **b.** PB

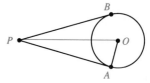

   Solution

   Let $PA = x$

   a. $m\angle POA = 90 - 28$ *Since PA is tangent, conclude*
   $\qquad\qquad\quad = 62$ *from Theorem 8.2 that $\overline{PA} \perp \overline{AO}$.*
   b. $8^2 + x^2 = 17^2$ *Use the Pythagorean Theorem.*
   $\qquad\quad x^2 = 17^2 - 8^2$
   $\qquad\qquad x = 15$
   $\qquad\quad PA = 15$
   Since $PB = PA$, $PB = 15$.

Try This

Find PO if $OA = 5$ and $PB = 12$.

Example 2

BC is tangent to $\odot A$ from B. $BC = 12$, $AC = 5$.   Find BD.

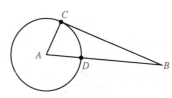

   Solution

   $AB^2 = 5^2 + 12^2$ *Apply the Pythagorean Theorem.*
   $AB^2 = 25 + 144 = 169$ *From Theorem 8.2 we know that*
   $\qquad\qquad\qquad\qquad$ *$\triangle ACB$ is a right triangle.*
   $AB = 13$, $BD = 13 - 5$ or $BD = 8$.

Try This

$BD = 8$ and the radius of the circle is 7.   Find BC.

Example 3

$\triangle ABC$ is a circumscribed triangle. Find $AB + BC + AC$.

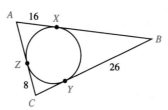

Solution

$AX = AZ = 16$
$BX = BY = 26$
$CY = CZ = 8$
These are tangent segments from exterior points.

$AB + BC + AC = (16 + 26) + (26 + 8) + (8 + 16)$
$\qquad\qquad\qquad = 100$

Try This

Find $AB + BC + AC$ if $BX = 21$, $CZ = 7$, and $AC = 22$.

Class Exercises

Short Answer

Consider the pair of concentric circles with center O and complete each statement.

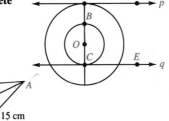

1. Suppose that p is tangent to the circle. Then $m\angle OAD = $ ___ .
2. Suppose that $m\angle OCE = 90$. Then q is ___ to the circle at C.
3. Suppose that q is tangent to the circle at C and that $p \parallel q$. Then $m\angle CAD = $ ___ .

AB and AD are tangent segments from A.
Complete each statement.

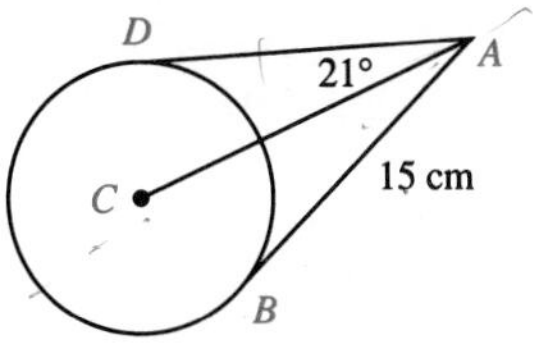

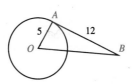

4. $AD = $ ___
5. $m\angle BAC = $ ___

Sample Exercises

6. If the radius of the circle to the right is 8 cm then $AC = $ __?__ .

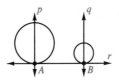

AB is a tangent segment from B. Complete each statement.

7. $m\angle OAB = $ ___
8. If $AB = 12$ and $OA = 5$, then $OB = $ ___ .
9. If $m\angle ABO = 25$, then $m\angle AOB = $ ___ .

Discussion

10. If r is tangent to both circles and if lines p and q pass through the centers of the circles and the points of tangency, give a convincing argument that p is parallel to q.
11. In the figure suppose that lines p and q pass through the centers of the circles and are perpendicular to line r at points A and B which are points on the circles. Give a convincing argument that r is tangent to both circles.

---

3. **Given:** isosceles $\triangle ABC$ with base $\overline{AC}$
Prove: $\overline{AZ} \cong \overline{ZC}$
1. isos. $\triangle ABC$ with base $\overline{AC}$ (Given) 2. $\overline{AB} \cong \overline{CB}$ (Def. isos. $\triangle$s) 3. $AX + XB = AB$, $CY + YB = CB$ (Seg. Add.) 4. $\overline{XB} \cong \overline{YB}$ (2 seg. from an ext. point of a $\odot$ are $\cong$.) 5. $XB = YB$ (Def. $\cong$ seg.) 6. $AX = CY$ (Subtraction) 7. $\overline{AX} \cong \overline{CY}$ (Def. $\cong$ seg.) 8. $\overline{AZ} \cong \overline{AX}$, $\overline{CY} \cong \overline{ZC}$ (2 seg. from an ext. point of a $\odot$ are $\cong$.) 9. $\overline{AZ} \cong \overline{ZC}$ (Transitive Property)

Answer to **Try This** 86

Class Exercise Answers

1. 90   **2.** tangent
3. 90   **4.** 15 cm   **5.** 21
6. 17 cm   **7.** 90   **8.** 13
9. 65   **10.** p and q both form right angles with $\overleftrightarrow{AB}$.
11. Line P passes through the center of the circle and point A. Therefore, p contains a segment CA which is a radius of the circle. By Theorem 8.1, r is tangent to the circle containing point A. Line q passes through the center of the circle and point B. Therefore q contains a segment DB which is a radius of the circle. By Theorem 8.1, r is tangent to the circle containing point B.

Assignment Guide

Minimum: 1–29 e/o, 33, MR
Regular: 1–33 e/o, 33, MR
Advanced: 14–29 e/o, 30–33, MR

Applications

Exercises 17, 32

Constructions

Exercises 20, 21

Algebra

Exercises 6, 7

Lesson Closure

Summarize by asking students to state and illustrate the three theorems and corollary involving tangent lines and segments.

Teacher's Resource Material

Enrichment Using
   Manipulatives 44
Practice Master 52
Transparency 33

Exercise Answers

See Selected Answers for odd-numbered exercises.

2. 10   **4.** 84   **6.** 10
8. 70   **10.** 4   **12.** 5
14. 1. ⊙*P* inscribed in *ABCD*, *m*∠*QPR* = 90 (Given)
2. *m*∠*BQP* = 90, *m*∠*BRP* = 90 (If a line is tan. to a ⊙, then it is ⊥ to the radius at the point of tan.) 3. *m*∠*QBR* = 90 (The sum of the measures of the ∠s of a convex polygon of *n* sides is (*n* − 2)180 4. $\overline{PQ} \cong \overline{PR}$ (Radii of a ⊙ are ≅.) 5. $\overline{BQ} \cong \overline{BR}$ (The 2 tan. seg. from an ext. point of a ⊙ are ≅.) 6. Draw aux. line *PB*. (2 points determine a line.)
7. *m*∠*QBP* = 45 (The line through an ext. point and the center of a ⊙ bisect the ∠ formed by the 2 tan. from the ext. point.) 8. *m*∠*QPB* = 45 (The acute ∠s of a rt. △ are comp.) 9. $\overline{PQ} \cong \overline{BQ}$ (Sides opp. ≅ ∠s are ≅.) 10. $\overline{BR} \cong \overline{BQ} \cong \overline{PQ} \cong \overline{PR}$ (≅ of seg. is trans.) 11. *PQBR* is a square. (Def. square)

Exercises

A

$\overline{XA}$ **and** $\overline{XB}$ **are tangent from the external point** *X*.

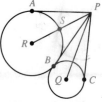

1. If *OA* = 7 and *XO* = 25, find *AX*.
2. If *XA* = 24 and *XO* = 26, find the radius of the circle.
3. *m*∠*AXO* = 32   Find *m*∠*AXB*.
4. *m*∠*AOX* = 48   Find *m*∠*AXB*.
5. *m*∠*AXB* = 38   Find *m*∠*AOB*.

$\overline{PA}$, $\overline{PB}$, **and** $\overline{PC}$ **are tangents to** ⊙*Q* **and** ⊙*R* **from an external point** *P*.

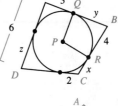

6. If *PA* = 10, find *PC*.
7. If *PA* = 15 and *AR* = 8, find *PS*.
8. If *m*∠*RPQ* = 35, find *m*∠*APC*.

ABCD **is a circumscribed quadrilateral with** *AD* = 6.

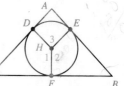

9. Find *x*.   **10.** Find *y*.
11. Find *z*.   **12.** Find *CD*.
13. Find the perimeter of *ABCD*.
14. **Given:** *m*∠*QPR* = 90
    Prove: *PQBR* is a square.

△*ABC* **is a circumscribed triangle.**

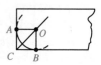

15. Prove that if ∠1 ≅ ∠2 ≅ ∠3, then △*ABC* is an equilateral triangle.
16. Prove that △*ABC* is an isosceles triangle with base $\overline{BC}$, if and only if ∠1 ≅ ∠2.

17. Suppose that a corner of a board is to be rounded off. An angle bisector $\overline{CO}$ is drawn, and *A* and *B* are points on the edge of the board so that $\overline{OA}$ and $\overline{OB}$ are perpendicular to the edges of the board. If a circle is drawn centered at *O* with radius $\overline{OA}$, why do you know that the two edges of the board are tangent to the drawn circle?

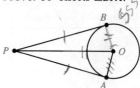

B

18. Prove Theorem 8.3.
    Given: $\overline{PA}$ and $\overline{PB}$ are tangent to ⊙*O*.
    Prove: *PA* = *PB*

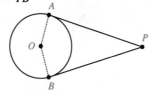

19. Prove Corollary 8.3a.
    Given: $\overline{PA}$ and $\overline{PB}$ are tangent to ⊙*O*.
    Prove: *OP* bisects ∠*BPA*.

20. Construct a circle and a line tangent to it.
21. Construct two circles with a common tangent.
22. **Given:** $\overline{PA}$ and $\overline{PB}$ are tangents from external point P.
    Prove: $\angle 1 \cong \angle 2$
23. **Given:** $\overline{PA}$ and $\overline{PB}$ are tangents from external point P.
    Prove: $\angle 3 \cong \angle 4$

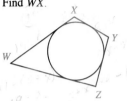

24. Given: circumscribed polygon $ABCD$
    $AB = 12$, $BC = 15$, $CD = 25$
    Find AD.

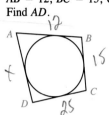

25. Given: circumscribed polygon $WXYZ$
    $XY = 8$, $YZ = 10$, $WZ = 21$
    Find WX.

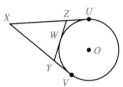

26. **Given:** $\overline{AD}$, $\overline{AB}$, and $\overline{BC}$ are tangents to $\odot O$.
    Prove: $AD + BC = AB$

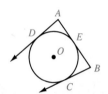

27. **Given:** $\overline{XU}$ and $\overline{XV}$ are tangents to $\odot O$.
    $XO = 17$, $OU = 8$, $ZW = WY$
    Find $XZ + YZ + XY$.

$\overline{AB}$, $\overline{BD}$, and $\overline{DE}$ are tangents to $\odot O$.
28. **Given:** $\overline{BO} \perp \overline{DO}$
    Prove: $\overline{AB} \parallel \overline{DE}$
29. **Given:** $\overline{AB} \parallel \overline{DE}$
    Prove: $\overline{BO} \perp \overline{DO}$

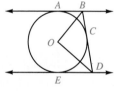

30. **Given:** $\overline{PA}$ and $\overline{PB}$ are tangents to $\odot O$.
    $\overline{AC}$ is a diameter.
    Prove: $\overline{BC} \parallel \overline{PO}$

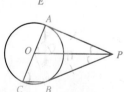

(handwritten notes) OC = DB, OA = AD, $\angle A \cong \angle A$, SAS ~ Theorem, $\triangle AOP \cong \angle ACB$, $\sim \triangle$'s $\cong$, $\overline{OP} \parallel \overline{CB}$

31. Suppose that quadrilateral $WXYZ$ is circumscribed about a circle. Prove that $XY + WZ = WX + YZ$.
32. Quality control in the manufacturing of machine parts often requires unusual methods of measurement. For example, in order to check that the angles A and B are correct on a part called a dovetail, circular plugs are inserted as shown. Then the distance x is measured with a micrometer. For the dovetail shown here, what should this distance equal?

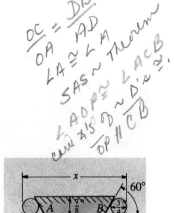

8-2 Tangent Lines   **349**

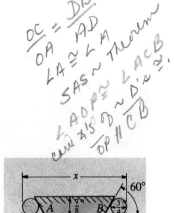

28. 1. $\overline{BO} \perp \overline{DO}$ (Given)
2. $m\angle OBD + m\angle ODB = 90$
(Acute $\angle$s of a rt. $\triangle$ are comp.)
3. $2(m\angle OBD + m\angle ODB) =$
180 (Mult.) 4. $2m\angle OBD +$
$2m\angle ODB = 180$ (Distr. Prop.)
5. $2m\angle OBD = m\angle ABC$,
$2m\angle ODB = m\angle EDC$ (The line
through an ext. point and the
center of a $\odot$ bisects the $\angle$
formed by the tangents from the
ext. point.) 6. $m\angle ABC +$
$m\angle EDC = 180$ (Subst.)
7. $\overline{AB} \parallel \overline{ED}$ (If 2 lines are cut by
a trans. and a pair of same-side
int. $\angle$s are supp., then the lines
are $\parallel$.) **30.** 1. Draw aux. line
AB. Let $D =$ intersec. of $\overline{AB}$ and
$\overline{OP}$. (2 points determine a line.)
2. $\overline{PA}$ and $\overline{PB}$ are tan. to $\odot O$.
(Given) 3. $\angle APO \cong \angle BPO$ (The
line through an ext. point and
the center of the $\odot$ bisect the $\angle$
formed by the 2 tan. from the
ext. point.) 4. $\overline{PA} \cong \overline{PB}$ (The 2
tan. seg. from an ext. point of $\odot$
are $\cong$.) 5. $\overline{PD} \cong \overline{PD}$ (Reflex.)
6. $\triangle PDA \cong \triangle PDB$ (SAS $\cong$ Post.)
7. $\overline{AD} \cong \overline{BD}$ (CPCTC) 8. $\overline{OA} \cong$
$\overline{OC}$ (Radii of a $\odot$ are $\cong$.)
9. $\frac{OC}{AO} = \frac{DB}{AD}$ (Lengths are in proportion.) 10. $\frac{AC}{AO} = \frac{AB}{AD}$ (Prop.
proportions) 11. $\angle A \cong \angle A$
(Reflex.) 12. $\triangle AOD \sim \triangle ACB$
(SAS $\sim$ Theorem) 13. $\angle AOD \cong$
$\angle ACB$ (Corr. $\angle$s of $\sim$ $\triangle$s are
$\cong$.) 14. $\overline{BC} \parallel \overline{PO}$ (If 2 lines are
cut by a transversal and a pair
of corr. $\angle$s are $\cong$, then the lines
are $\parallel$.) **32.** ≈ 5.049 in.

Mixed Review Answers

1. $\frac{u}{v} = \frac{7+y}{7}$ or $\frac{x+5}{5}$
2. $\frac{5}{5+x} = \frac{v}{u}$ 3. $\frac{x}{y} = \frac{5}{7}$
4. $\frac{14}{5}$ 5. $\frac{21}{5}$ 6. $\frac{12.6}{5}$

Critical Thinking

33. Suppose points $A_1, A_2, \ldots, A_n$ are arranged around a circle so
that for each i, $i = 1, 2, \ldots, n$, $m\angle A_iOA_{i+1} = \frac{360}{n}$ for all n.
Suppose tangent lines are drawn at each point A_i intersecting at
points $P_1, P_2, \ldots, P_n$. State a generalization about the kind of
polygon $P_1P_2 \ldots P_n$ is. Give a convincing argument that your
answer is correct.

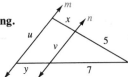

Mixed Review

$m \parallel n$ **Write a proportion involving each of the following.**
 1. u and v 2. x and u 3. x and y

Find y.
 4. $x = 2$ 5. $x = 3$ 6. $x = 1.8$

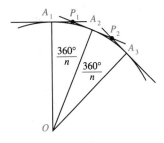

Career

Seismologist

An earthquake causes motions of the earth's surface, the site of which is the
focus of the earthquake. The focus is centered in rocks that have broken and
shifted position and most of the energy released in an earthquake travels from
the focus in seismic waves.

A seismologist studies and interprets data about earthquakes in an effort to
predict when and where they will take place. Seismologists locate
earthquakes by studying the time intervals between which the seismic waves
reach different seismographic stations. Circles are drawn on the map to show
the distance of the earthquake from each station; the epicenter of the
earthquake is located where the circles intersect.

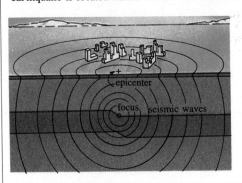

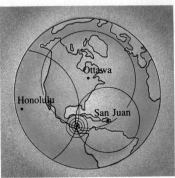

OBJECTIVE: *Calculate lengths related to common tangents to circles.*

8-3 Common Tangents and Tangent Circles

A line that is tangent to two coplanar circles is called a **common tangent** of the two circles. Common tangents are classified into two types. A common **external tangent** does not intersect the segment joining the centers of the two circles. A common **internal tangent** does intersect the segment joining the centers of the two circles.

A belt wrapped around two wheels transfers power from one wheel to the other. In this lesson you will learn how to calculate the length *AB* on such a belt linkage system.

In the figure to the right, line *MO* is a common external tangent to circles *P* and *Q*. Line *NO* is a common internal tangent to circles *P* and *Q*.

Two circles are called tangent circles if they intersect in exactly one point and they may be externally tangent or internally tangent.

In the figure below you can see that two tangent circles are called externally tangent if each lies in the exterior of the other. They are called internally tangent if one lies in the interior of the other.

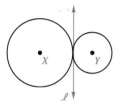   

Externally tangent circles   Internally tangent circles

The following example illustrates how similar triangles can be used to find unknown lengths in problems that involve common tangents.

Example 1

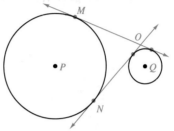

$\overline{RT}$ is a common tangent to $\odot P$ and $\odot Q$.
$QS = 7$, $ST = 24$, $RT = 48$

a. $x = PR = \underline{\ ?\ }$ **b.** $y = QT = \underline{\ ?\ }$

Solution

$\triangle PRT \sim \triangle QST$ *Both are right triangles with a common acute angle and so are similar by AA Similarity.*

a. $\frac{x}{48} = \frac{7}{24}$ or $x = PR = 14$ *Corresponding sides of similar triangles are proportional.*
b. $y^2 = 7^2 + 24^2$ or $y = QT = 25$ *Apply the Pythagorean Theorem.*

Try This
$z = PT = \underline{\ ?\ }$

First Five Minutes

(Quiz on previous lesson)

If $\overline{XY}$ is a tangent segment and $\overline{WX}$ is a radius of $\odot W$, find ZY.
6

Lesson Opener

This lesson involves the study of lines tangent to two or more circles and circles that are tangent.

Materials

student notebooks
compasses
straightedges

Teaching Notes

Circles may have common internal or external tangents. Circles may be internally or externally tangent, and may intersect in up to two points. The Pythagorean Theorem is useful for solving problems involving common tangents.

Guided Practice

Chalkboard Examples

1. If $QS = 4$, $ST = 4$, and $RT = 8$, find PQ. $4\sqrt{2}$

Answer to **Try This** 50

2. Suppose $\odot C$ is moved so that $DC = 20$. Find AB. $5\sqrt{15}$

Answer to **Try This** $10\sqrt{2}$

Example 2

$\overline{AB}$ is a common external tangent to circles *D* and *C* and *DC* = 13. Find *AB*.

Solution

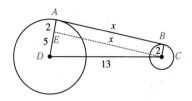

$13^2 = 5^2 + x^2$ *Draw $\overline{CE}$ to complete rectangle ABCE.*
  Apply the Pythagorean Theorem.

$x = AB = 12$

Try This

Suppose ⊙*C* is moved so that *DC* = 15. Find *AB*.

Class Exercises

Short Answer

State the number of external tangents and the number of internal tangents that exist for each pair of circles.

1.
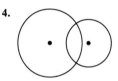
Disjoint circles

2.

Externally tangent circles

3.

Internally tangent circles

4.

Intersecting circles

5.

Concentric circles

6.

One inside the other

Sample Exercises

$\overline{AB}$ is a common tangent to ⊙*E* and ⊙*F*.

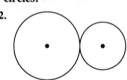

7. $EA = 10, FB = 3, CD = 12$ Find *EF*.
8. $EA = 10, FB = 3, CD = 12$ Find *AB*.
9. $EA = 10, FB = 2, CD = 5$ Find *AB*.

Complete each statement.

10. $ST =$ ___ **11.** $UV =$ ___

Discussion

12. $\overline{AB}$ is a common tangent between circles of equal radii. Give a convincing argument that *ABDC* is a rectangle.

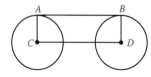

13. $\overline{AB}$ and $\overline{CD}$ are common tangents. Give a convincing argument that $\angle AEC \cong \angle BFD$.

Exercises

A

$\overline{AB}$ is a common tangent. $AE = 10$, $BD = 5$, $BC = 12$

1. Find AC.   2. Find AB.
3. Find CD.   4. Find ED.
5. If $AE = 9$, $BD = 3$, and $BC = 4$ find ED. Are the two circles tangent to each other?

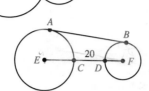

$\overline{AB}$ is a common tangent. $AE = 15$, $BF = 6$, $CD = 20$.

6. Find EF.
7. Find AB.
8. Find $AB + BF + EF + AE$.

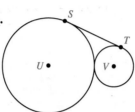

$\overline{ST}$ is a common tangent and the circles are tangent to each other.

9. If the radii are 9 and 4, find ST.
10. If the radii are 8 and 5, find ST.
11. If the radii are 9 and 3, find ST.
12. If $ST = 15$, $UV = 17$, and $VT = \frac{9}{2}$, find US.
13. If $ST = 24$, $UV = 25$, and $US = 16$, find VT.

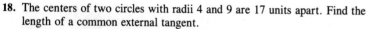

$\overline{AB}$ is a common tangent. $CA = 8$, $CP = 17$, $AP = 15$, $BD = 5$

14. Find PB.
15. Find PD.
16. Find AB.
17. Prove that $\angle PCA \cong \angle PDB$.

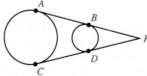

18. The centers of two circles with radii 4 and 9 are 17 units apart. Find the length of a common external tangent.
19. The centers of two circles with radii 5 and 7 are 14 units apart. Find the length of a common external tangent.

B

20. **Given:** $\overline{EF}$ and $\overline{GH}$ are common internal tangents.
    Prove: $\overline{EF} \cong \overline{GH}$

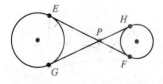

21. **Given:** $\overline{AB}$ and $\overline{CD}$ are common external tangents that intersect each other at P.
    Prove: $\overline{AB} \cong \overline{CD}$

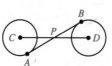

22. Prove that in the figure for Exercise 21, $ABDC$ is a trapezoid.

23. **Given:** $\overline{AB}$ is a common internal tangent of two disjoint congruent circles.
    Prove: $\overline{AB}$ and $\overline{CD}$ bisect each other.

8-3 Common Tangents and Tangent Circles   **353**

24. Three metal disks each with a radius of 10 cm are tangent to each other. The disks are enclosed by a metal frame that forms an equilateral triangle. What is the length of one side of the frame?

25. Suppose that four disks, each with radius 10 cm and arranged to form a square, are enclosed by a square metal frame similar to the figure. How does the length of a side of this square compare to the length of a side of the triangle in Exercise 24?

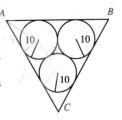

C

26. $\overline{DE}$ and $\overline{FG}$ are common tangents for the three circles. If the radii of the three circles are 8, 3, and 5 as shown, find BC.

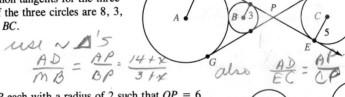

use ~ ∆'s $\frac{AD}{MB} = \frac{AP}{BP} = \frac{14 + x}{3 + x}$ *also* $\frac{AD}{EC} = \frac{AP}{CP}$

27. Construct ⊙O and ⊙P each with a radius of 2 such that $OP = 6$. Construct two circles that are tangent to both ⊙O and ⊙P.

28. After completing the constructions in Exercise 27, construct as many additional circles as you can that are tangent to both ⊙O and ⊙P.

Critical Thinking

29. Construct ⊙A, ⊙B, and ⊙C with equal radii such that $\triangle ABC$ is an equilateral triangle as shown. Next construct at least four circles that are tangent to all three circles. How many other circles that are tangent to all three circles do you think exist?

Algebra Review

Multiply.

1. $5(x - 2)$ 2. $4(x - 8)$ 3. $-6(y - 4)$ 4. $-12(y - 4)$
5. $6(2x - 3y - 8z)$ 6. $-9(3x - 2y - 5z)$ 7. $8(-2x - 6y + 7)$ 8. $15(2a + 4b - 8)$

Math Contest Problem

$\overline{AB}$ is a common tangent of ⊙C, ⊙D, ⊙E, and ⊙F. Suppose that $AC = 12$, $DB = 9$, and $AE = BF = 3$. If the midpoint of $\overline{EF}$ is the center of a circle that is tangent to both ⊙E and ⊙F, what are the possible values for its radius?

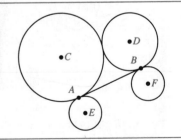

OBJECTIVE: *State and apply theorems about arcs and central angles.*

8-4 Arcs and Their Measure

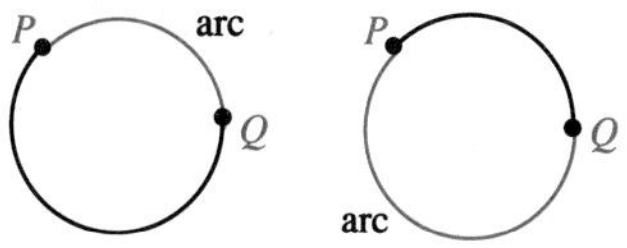

An **arc** of a circle consists of two points and a continuous part of a circle between them. Notice that any two given points on a circle determine two different arcs.

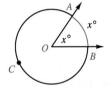

A **central angle** of a circle is an angle whose vertex is the center of the circle. $\angle ABC$ is a central angle of $\odot B$ in the figure shown.

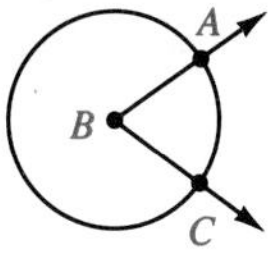

The sides of a central angle separate the circle into two different arcs. The endpoints and all the points on both the circle and the interior of the central angle are called a **minor arc.** The arc in the exterior of the central angle is called a **major arc.** Note that three letters are usually used to name a major arc. If the endpoints are the endpoints of a diameter then the circle is divided into two arcs called **semicircles.**

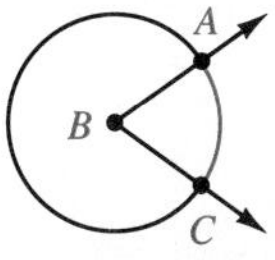

minor arc $\overset{\frown}{AC}$ 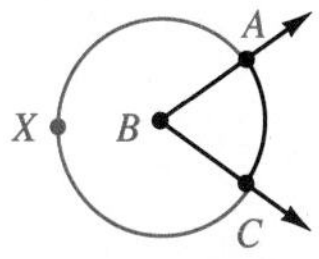   major arc $\overset{\frown}{AXC}$ 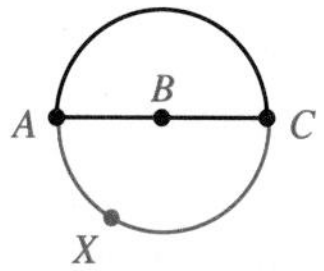   semicircle $\overset{\frown}{AXC}$

An arc, like an angle, is measured in degrees.

The measure of a minor arc is the measure of its central angle. $m\overset{\frown}{AB} = x$
The measure of a major arc is $360 - m$, where m is the measure of the central angle of its minor arc. $m\overset{\frown}{ACB} = 360 - x$

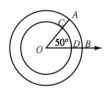

The measure of a semicircle is 180.

Congruent arcs are arcs with equal measure that lie in the same circle or in congruent circles. In the figure to the right $m\overset{\frown}{AB} = m\overset{\frown}{CD} = 50$. So two arcs with the same measure are not congruent unless they lie in congruent circles.

Example 1

Complete each statement.

a. $m\overset{\frown}{AB} =$ ___   b. $m\overset{\frown}{ACB} =$ ___

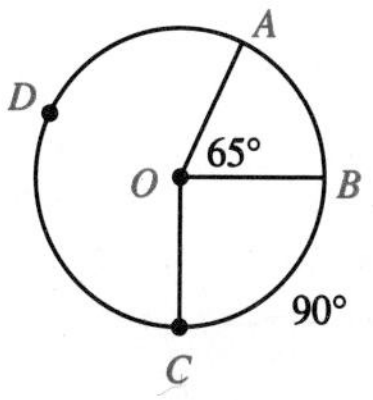

    Solution

    a. $m\overset{\frown}{AB} = 65$ b. $m\overset{\frown}{ACB} = 360 - 65 = 295$

Try This

Complete each statement.

a. $m\angle BOC =$ ___   b. $m\overset{\frown}{ADC} =$ ___

First Five Minutes

(Quiz on previous lesson)

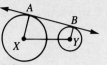

$\overleftrightarrow{AB}$ is tangent to $\odot X$ and $\odot Y$. If $XY = 50$, $AX = 24$, and $BY = 14$, find AB. $20\sqrt{6}$

Lesson Opener

Draw a circle on the chalkboard with several different central angles. Using a protractor, measure each angle. Point out that each central angle produces an arc whose degree measure is the same as its central angle.

Materials

student notebooks
protractors
compasses
straightedges
investigative software

Teaching Notes

Point out that minor arcs are named using two endpoints and major arcs and semicircles are named using three points.

Common Errors

The arc symbol "$\frown$" alone is used to name an arc. The "*m*" with the arc symbol refers to the *measure* of an arc.

Key Terms

arc
central angle
minor arc/major arc
semicircle
congruent arcs
midpoint of an arc

Guided Practice

Chalkboard Examples

1. Find $m\ \overset{\frown}{CAB}$ and $m\angle AOC$.
270, 155

Answer to **Try This** a. 90
b. 205

2. Find $m\overset{\frown}{DE}$ and $\overset{\frown}{ACD}$. 42, 197

Answer to **Try This** a. 162
b. $m\overset{\frown}{ED} = m\overset{\frown}{DC} = 42$

Class Exercise Answers

1. 8 **2.** $\overset{\frown}{AB}$, $\overset{\frown}{AC}$, $\overset{\frown}{AE}$, $\overset{\frown}{AD}$, $\overset{\frown}{BC}$, $\overset{\frown}{BD}$, $\overset{\frown}{BE}$, $\overset{\frown}{CD}$, $\overset{\frown}{CE}$, $\overset{\frown}{DE}$ **3.** $\overset{\frown}{ACD}$, $\overset{\frown}{ACE}$, $\overset{\frown}{BCE}$, $\overset{\frown}{CDA}$, $\overset{\frown}{CDB}$, $\overset{\frown}{BCA}$, $\overset{\frown}{DEB}$, $\overset{\frown}{DEC}$, $\overset{\frown}{EAC}$, $\overset{\frown}{EAD}$
4. none **5.** $\overset{\frown}{BC}$, $\overset{\frown}{ED}$ or $\overset{\frown}{BD}$, $\overset{\frown}{CE}$
6. $\angle COD$ **7.** $\overset{\frown}{ED}$, $\overset{\frown}{EC}$, $\overset{\frown}{EDB}$, $\overset{\frown}{EDA}$, $\overset{\frown}{EA}$, $\overset{\frown}{EAB}$, $\overset{\frown}{EAC}$, $\overset{\frown}{EAD}$
8. 67 **9.** 110 **10.** 81
11. 191 **12.** 279 **13.** 346
14. $m\overset{\frown}{BCD} = 177$ not 180.
15. Radii $\overline{OA}$, $\overline{OB}$, and $\overline{OC}$ divide $\triangle ABC$ into 3 $\triangle$s whose total $\angle$ measure is 540. $m\overset{\frown}{ACB} = m\angle AOC + m\angle BOC$, $m\overset{\frown}{AB} = m\angle AOB$, Subtract $m\angle A + m\angle B + m\angle C$ or 180. $540 - 180 = 360$ **16.** Central $\angle$s from center O are $\cong$. $\overline{OA}$, $\overline{OB}$, and $\overline{OC}$ are $\cong$. $\triangle AOB \cong \triangle AOC$ by SAS. $\overline{AB} \cong \overline{AC}$ by CPCTC, so $\triangle ABC$ is isos.

Assignment Guide

Minimum: 1–28 e/o, 31, MR
Regular: 1–30 e/o, 31, MR
Advanced: 8–28 e/o, 28–31, MR

Coordinate Geometry

Exercises 25–28

Algebra

Exercises 17–20

Lesson Closure

Review congruent arcs, chords, and central angles in the same or in congruent circles.

● **POSTULATE 20** Arc Addition Postulate

The measure of adjacent nonoverlapping arcs is the sum of the measures of the two arcs. That is, if C is on $\overset{\frown}{AB}$, then $m\overset{\frown}{AC} + m\overset{\frown}{CB} = m\overset{\frown}{AB}$.

This postulate applies to both minor arcs and major arcs. For example,
$m\overset{\frown}{AC} = m\overset{\frown}{AB} + m\overset{\frown}{BC}$, and
$m\overset{\frown}{DAC} = m\overset{\frown}{DAB} + m\overset{\frown}{BC}$
A point B on $\overset{\frown}{AC}$ is the *midpoint* of $\overset{\frown}{AC}$, if $m\overset{\frown}{AB} = m\overset{\frown}{BC}$.

Example 2

Find each measure. **a.** $m\overset{\frown}{AC}$ **b.** $m\overset{\frown}{AD}$

Solution
a. $m\overset{\frown}{AC} = 35 + 120$ **b.** $m\overset{\frown}{AD} = 360 - (35 + 120 + 42)$
$= 155$ $= 163$

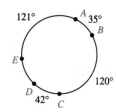

Try This

a. $m\overset{\frown}{BD} = \underline{\ ?\ }$ **b.** Show that D is the midpoint of $\overset{\frown}{CE}$.

Recall that a chord is a segment that joins two points on a circle. Theorem 8.4 and its converse, Theorem 8.5, describe a relationship between congruent chords and congruent minor arcs.

◆ **THEOREM 8.4**

In a circle or in congruent circles congruent chords have congruent minor arcs.

Given: $\overline{AB} \cong \overline{CD}$
Prove: $\overset{\frown}{AB} \cong \overset{\frown}{CD}$

Proof

Statements	Reasons
1. $\overline{AB} \cong \overline{CD}$	1. Given
2. Draw $\overline{OA}$, $\overline{OB}$, $\overline{OC}$, and $\overline{OD}$.	2. Two points determine a segment.
3. $\overline{OA} \cong \overline{OB} \cong \overline{OC} \cong \overline{OD}$	3. Radii of a circle are congruent.
4. $\triangle AOB \cong \triangle COD$	4. SSS Congruence Postulate
5. $\angle 1 \cong \angle 2$	5. Corr. parts of $\cong \triangle$'s are $\cong$.
6. $m\angle 1 = m\overset{\frown}{AB}$	6. Definition of measure of minor arc
7. $m\angle 2 = m\overset{\frown}{CD}$	7. Definition of measure of minor arc
8. $m\overset{\frown}{AB} = m\overset{\frown}{CD}$	8. Substitution

---

◆ **THEOREM 8.5**

In a circle or in congruent circles congruent minor arcs have congruent chords and congruent central angles.

Class Exercises

Short Answer

1. What is the radius of ⊙O?
2. Name a minor arc.
3. Name a major arc.
4. Name a semicircle.
5. Name two congruent arcs.
6. Name the central angle of $\overset{\frown}{CD}$.
7. Name two arcs with endpoint E.

Sample Exercises

8. Find $m\overset{\frown}{BC}$.   9. Find $m\overset{\frown}{CD}$.
10. Find $m\overset{\frown}{AC}$.   11. Find $m\overset{\frown}{ACD}$.
12. Find $m\overset{\frown}{AEC}$.   13. Find $m\overset{\frown}{ADB}$.

14. Explain why $\overline{BD}$ is not a diameter.

Discussion Exercises

15. Suppose that A, B, and C are points on a circle. Give a convincing argument that $m\overset{\frown}{ACB} + m\overset{\frown}{AB} = 360$.
16. Suppose that $m\overset{\frown}{AB} = m\overset{\frown}{AC}$. Give a convincing argument that $\triangle ABC$ is isosceles.

Exercises

A

Find each measure.

1. $m\overset{\frown}{BC}$ 2. $m\overset{\frown}{AC}$
3. $m\overset{\frown}{BAD}$ 4. $m\overset{\frown}{ADC}$
5. $m\angle BOC$ 6. $m\overset{\frown}{AE}$

7. Name a pair of congruent arcs.

$\overline{DF}$ is a tangent to ⊙O from the external point F and $m\angle OFD = 38$.
Find each measure.

8. $m\overset{\frown}{AB}$ 9. $m\overset{\frown}{AD}$ 10. $m\overset{\frown}{AC}$
11. $m\overset{\frown}{BC}$ 12. $m\overset{\frown}{ADC}$ 13. $m\overset{\frown}{ACD}$
14. $m\angle DOF$ 15. $m\overset{\frown}{ED}$ 16. $m\overset{\frown}{AE}$

B

Find each measure.

17. $m\angle AOB$ 18. $m\angle BOC$
19. $m\angle COD$ 20. $m\angle AOD$

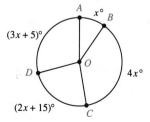

Teacher's Resource Materials

Enrichment Using
  Manipulatives 46
Practice Master 54
Transparency 35

Exercise Answers

1. 80   2. 165   3. 258
4. 195   5. 80   6. 110
7. $\overset{\frown}{AEC}$ and $\overset{\frown}{BAE}$ or $\overset{\frown}{AB}$ and $\overset{\frown}{CE}$ 8. 45   9. 140
10. 135   11. 90   12. 225
13. 220   14. 52
15. 52   16. 88   17. 34
18. 136   19. 83   20. 107
21. 1. $\overset{\frown}{AB} \cong \overset{\frown}{CD}$ (Given) 2. $\overset{\frown}{BC} \cong \overset{\frown}{BC}$ (Reflex.) 3. $m\overset{\frown}{AB} + m\overset{\frown}{BC} = m\overset{\frown}{BC} + m\overset{\frown}{CD}$ (Add.) 4. $m\overset{\frown}{AC} = m\overset{\frown}{BD}$ (Arc Add.) 5. $\overset{\frown}{AC} \cong \overset{\frown}{BD}$ (Def. ≅ arcs)   22. 1. $\overset{\frown}{AC} \cong \overset{\frown}{BD}$ (Given) 2. $\overset{\frown}{BC} \cong \overset{\frown}{BC}$ (Reflex.) 3. $m\overset{\frown}{AC} = m\overset{\frown}{AB} + m\overset{\frown}{BC}$, $m\overset{\frown}{BD} = m\overset{\frown}{BC} + m\overset{\frown}{CD}$ (Arc Add.) 4. $m\overset{\frown}{AB} + m\overset{\frown}{BC} = m\overset{\frown}{BC} + m\overset{\frown}{CD}$ (Trans.) 5. $m\overset{\frown}{AB} = m\overset{\frown}{CD}$ (Sub.) 6. $\overset{\frown}{AB} \cong \overset{\frown}{CD}$ (Def. ≅ arcs)
23. 1. ⊙O with tan. $\overline{CA}$ and $\overline{CB}$ (Given) 2. $\overline{OA} \perp \overline{CA}$, $\overline{OB} \perp \overline{CB}$ (If a line is tan. to a circle, then it is ⊥ to the radius at the point of tan.) 3. $m\angle OAC = m\angle OBC = 90$ (Def. ⊥) 4. $m\angle OAC + m\angle ACB + m\angle OBC + m\angle AOB = 360$ (sum of measures of ∠s of a quad. = 360) 5. $m\angle ACB = x$ (Given) 6. $90 + x + 90 + m\angle AOB = 360$ (Subst.) 7. $x + m\angle AOB = 180$ (Sub.) 8. $m\angle AOB = 180 - x$ (Sub.) 9. $m\overset{\frown}{AB} = 180 - x$ (Def. arc measure)
24. 1. ⊙O with tan. $\overline{CA}$ and $\overline{CB}$, $m\angle ACB = x$ (Given) 2. $m\angle AOB = 180 - x$ (See Ex. 23.) 3. $m\overset{\frown}{AB} = 180 - x$ (Def. arc measure) 4. $m\overset{\frown}{ADB} = 360 - (180 - x)$ (Def. major arc measure) 5. $m\overset{\frown}{ADB} = 180 + x$ (Sub.)

21. Given: $\widehat{AB} \cong \widehat{CD}$
  Prove: $\widehat{AC} \cong \widehat{BD}$
22. Given: $\widehat{AC} \cong \widehat{BD}$
  Prove: $\widehat{AB} \cong \widehat{CD}$

23. Given: ⊙O with tangents $\overline{CA}$ and $\overline{CB}$
   $m\angle ACB = x$
  Prove: $m\widehat{AB} = 180 - x$
24. Given: ⊙O with tangents $\overline{CA}$ and $\overline{CB}$
   $m\angle ACB = x$
  Prove: $m\widehat{ADB} = 180 + x$

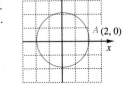

25. Find the coordinates of a point B above the x axis such that $m\widehat{AB} = 90$.
26. Find the coordinates of a point C below the x axis such that $m\widehat{AC} = 90$.
27. Find the coordinates of a point D in the quadrant I such that $m\widehat{AD} = 45$.
28. Find the coordinates of a point E in the quadrant III such that $m\widehat{AE} = 135$.

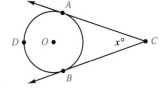

c

29. Given: △XYZ is a circumscribed triangle.
   $m\angle X = x$
   $m\angle Y = y$
  Prove: $m\widehat{AC} = x + y$

30. Given: $\overleftrightarrow{AB}$ is a tangent of ⊙O and ⊙O'.
   I is the midpoint of $\widehat{BID}$.
   J is the midpoint of $\widehat{AC}$.
   $\overleftrightarrow{CD}$ is the tangent of ⊙O'.
  Prove: $\overleftrightarrow{CD}$ is tangent to ⊙O.

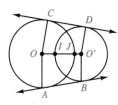

Critical Thinking

31. Complete the table below and discover a formula for the number of chords and arcs for n points on a circle.

number of points	2	3	4	5	· · ·	n
number of chords	1	3	6	—	· · ·	—
number of arcs	2	6	12	—	· · ·	—

Mixed Review

Lines m and n are parallel. Find each measure.

1. $m\angle 10$ **2.** $m\angle 9$
3. $m\angle 2$ **4.** $m\angle 6$
5. $m\angle 7$ **6.** $m\angle 8$

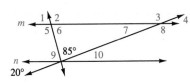

358 *Chapter 8 Circles*

Enrichment

The Earth as a Sphere

As you know, the earth is considered a sphere. This may seem strange since there are mountains on the earth's surface several miles high. However, if a scale model of the earth were made 8 ft in diameter it would be smoother than a finely polished bowling ball. The highest mountain would be represented by a projection of only 0.007 in. above the surface. The slight difference between the polar and equatorial diameters would also be negligible. Thus, for most purposes, the earth may be considered a sphere.

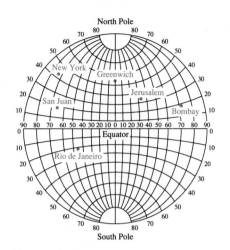

To locate a point on the earth, reference lines are needed (much like the grid used for locating points on a plane). Since the earth revolves from west to east on an axis through its poles, a series of circular arcs is drawn through the poles. These are called meridians.

The meridian through Greenwich, England, is arbitrarily chosen as the zero meridian. The other meridians are then defined in degrees both east and west from this meridian. New York City is near the meridian 74° W; Jerusalem is near the meridian 35° E. The degree measure associated with a point on the earth, along with the east or west designation, is called the longitude of the point.

To completely determine a point on the earth, another reference line is needed. This is the equator. A point is located by means of the arc, from the point to the equator, that is intercepted on the meridian passing through the point. Thus, if $m\overarc{PE} = 60$ $(m\angle POE = 60)$ the point P is said to have latitude 60° N. The latitude of New York City is about 41° N as shown in the figure. The equator has latitude 0° and the north pole has latitude 90° N.

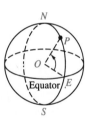

Longitude and latitude are used in many fields including astronomy, map making, and sailing. For example, to determine the location of a ship at sea, navigators first use an instrument called a sextant to calculate their latitude.

Exercises

Use the above figure to give the approximate latitude and longitude of each city.

1. Bombay
2. Rio de Janeiro
3. San Juan
4. Show that the radius of the circle of latitude 60° is half the radius of the earth.

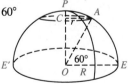

Enrichment

Exercise Answers

Answers may vary.
1. **18.56° N, 72.51° E**
2. **22.53° S, 43.17° W**
3. **18.29° N, 65.08° W**
4. $\triangle ACO$ **is a 30°–60°–90° triangle with** $m\angle CAO = 60$. $AC = \frac{1}{2}AO = \frac{1}{2}OE$

$\overline{MS}$ and $\overline{NP}$ are diameters in $\odot O$. Complete each statement.

1. $\overline{MO}$ is a ____ . radius
2. $\overline{XM}$ is a ____ . chord
3. $\angle SOT$ is a ____ . central angle
4. $\overset{\frown}{XM}$ is a ____ arc, $\overset{\frown}{XPM}$ is a ____ arc. minor, major
5. $m\angle POS = $ ____ 25
6. $m\angle TOS = $ ____ 75
7. $m\overset{\frown}{XM} = $ ____ 77.5
8. $m\overset{\frown}{PS} + m\overset{\frown}{ST} = $ ____ 100
9. $\overline{XM} \cong $ ____ $\overline{XP}$
10. $\overline{PN} \cong $ ____ $\overline{SM}$

Lesson Opener

The previous lessons dealt with some important relationships involving arcs, chords, and central angles in the same or in congruent circles. In this lesson, students apply several theorems about chords of a circle to solve practical problems carpenters and machinists face on the job. Encourage students to try to figure out how to find the center of a round table top.

Construction 10 in Chapter 9 could be used in this lesson as an optional Explore for Theorems 8.8 through 8.10.

OBJECTIVE: *State and apply theorems about chords of a circle.*

8-5 Chords of Circles

EXPLORE   Get a cardboard pizza platter from a pizza shop. Experiment and discover a way to find the center of the platter.

The midpoint of an arc bisects the arc. Any line or ray containing this midpoint is also said to bisect the arc. In this figure, point B and $\overrightarrow{OB}$ bisect $\overset{\frown}{AC}$.

◆ **THEOREM 8.6**

If a diameter is perpendicular to a chord, then it bisects the chord and its minor and major arcs.

Given: $\odot P$ with diameter $\overline{CD}$ and chord $\overline{AB}$
    $\overline{AB} \perp \overline{CD}$
Prove: $\overline{AE} \cong \overline{BE}$, $\overset{\frown}{AD} \cong \overset{\frown}{BD}$, $\overset{\frown}{AC} \cong \overset{\frown}{BC}$
Plan Draw $\overline{PA}$ and $\overline{PB}$ and use HL congruence to conclude that $\triangle APE \cong \triangle BPE$. Then conclude that $\overline{AE} \cong \overline{BE}$ and $\angle APE \cong \angle BPE$. Consequently $\overset{\frown}{AD} \cong \overset{\frown}{BD}$ and $\overset{\frown}{AC} \cong \overset{\frown}{BC}$.

Compare the hypotheses of Theorems 8.6 and 8.7. The hypothesis of each is part of the conclusion of the other.

◆ **THEOREM 8.7**

If a diameter bisects a chord that is not a diameter, then it is perpendicular to the chord and bisects its major and minor arcs.

Given: $\odot P$ has diameter $\overline{CD}$ bisecting chord $\overline{AB}$.
Prove: $\overline{CD} \perp \overline{AB}$, $\overset{\frown}{AD} \cong \overset{\frown}{BD}$, $\overset{\frown}{AC} \cong \overset{\frown}{BC}$
Plan Use SSS congruence to prove $\triangle APE \cong \triangle BPE$. Then use corresponding parts of congruent triangles are congruent to draw the final conclusion.

360   *Chapter 8   Circles*

Example 1

Refer to the figure to complete each statement.

a. $AD =$ ___   **b.** $OE =$ ___

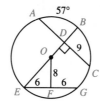

Solution

a. $AD = 9$ *$EB \perp AC$ means that EB bisects AC.*

b. $OE^2 = 6^2 + 8^2$ *OF bisects EG and hence $\perp$ it.*

      $= 100$ *Use the Pythagorean Theorem.*

   $OE = 10$

Try This

Find $m\overarc{AEC}$ in the figure to the right.

The proofs of the following theorems are completed in Exercises 30–32.

◆ **THEOREM 8.8**

The perpendicular bisector of a chord contains the center of the circle.

An electrician's drill bit has a shank end with six flat surfaces as shown to the right. These flat surfaces must be an equal distance from the rotating axis to ensure that the drill runs smoothly. How can a machinist determine that this is the case if the center of the drill is not known? To answer this question consider the distance from the center of a circle to a chord of the circle.

Recall that the distance from a point to a line is defined as the perpendicular distance from the point to the line. In this figure d is the perpendicular distance to $\overline{AB}$ from center P.

◆ **THEOREM 8.9**

In the same circle or in congruent circles congruent chords are equidistant from the center.

◆ **THEOREM 8.10**

In the same circle or in congruent circles, chords equidistant from the center are congruent.

Materials

student notebooks
compasses
protractors
straightedges
investigative software

Teaching Notes

Since this section contains five theorems, illustrate pictorially or symbolically what each theorem means before discussing its proof. This may help students solve problems like Exercises 24 and 33.

Continue to remind students that by definition the distance from a point to a line is the *perpendicular* distance. In the figure below the distance from $\overline{AB}$ to the center P is d.

Key Terms

bisector of an arc

Guided Practice

Chalkboard Examples

1. Find the length of the radius of a circle if a chord is 10 in. long and 12 in. from the center of the circle. (HINT: Draw a diagram.) 13

Answer to **Try This** 246

2. In $\odot O$, $AB = 10x + 13$ and $BE = 13x - 8$. Find the value of x. 7

Answer to **Try This** $z = 8$, $\overline{AB}$ and BE are equidistant from O and are congruent by Theorem 8.10.

Example 2

Refer to the figure to complete each statement:

a. $AB =$ ___   b. $x =$ ___

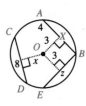

Solution

$AB = 8$ $\overline{OX} \perp \overline{AB}$ means that X is the midpoint of $\overline{AB}$.
$x = 3$ Since $\overline{AB}$ and $\overline{CD}$ are the same length, they are the same distance from the center.

Try This

Find z. Explain your answer.

Class Exercises

Short Answer

Complete each statement with a valid conclusion.

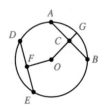

1. If $\overline{OC}$ is the perpendicular bisector of $\overline{AB}$, then ___ .
2. If $AB = DE$, then ___ .
3. If C is the midpoint of $\overline{AB}$ and G bisects $\overset{\frown}{AB}$, then ___ .
4. If $\overline{OF} \perp \overline{DE}$, then ___ .
5. If $\overline{OC} \perp \overline{AB}$, $\overline{OF} \perp \overline{DF}$, and $OC = OF$, then ___ .

Sample Exercises

   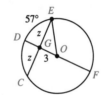

6. Find x.   **7.** Find y.   **8.** Find $m\angle EGO$.
9. Find $m\angle GEO$.   **10.** Find $m\overset{\frown}{CD}$.

Discussion

11. Explain how you can find the center of this circle in order to redraw a complete circle with a compass.

12. Would the following be the start of a proof of Theorem 8.9 or Theorem 8.10?

   Given: $OX = OY$
   Prove: $RS = TU$

13. Give a convincing argument that Theorem 8.10 is true.

Exercises

A

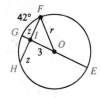

Complete each of the following.

1. $y = $ ___
2. $x = $ ___
3. $m\widehat{AD} = $ ___
4. $m\widehat{ABD} = $ ___
5. $m\angle FIO = $ ___
6. $m\widehat{GH} = $ ___
7. $m\widehat{HE} = $ ___
8. $m\widehat{FEH} = $ ___

9. Find FH.
10. Find $m\widehat{GF}$.
11. Find OD.
12. Find $m\angle ODB$.
13. Find $m\angle OBD$.
14. Find $m\widehat{FE}$.
15. If $m\widehat{GC} = 137$, then $m\widehat{AE} = $ ___ .

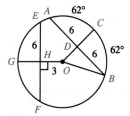

$m\widehat{AB} = m\widehat{CD} = 100$, $m\widehat{BD} = 40$, $\overline{OX} \perp \overline{AB}$, $\overline{OY} \perp \overline{CD}$
Find each measure.

16. $m\widehat{EB}$
17. $m\angle YOB$
18. $m\angle OYX$
19. $m\angle YXB$
20. $m\angle AOC$

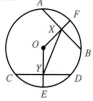

21. If $\overline{AB}$ is a diameter, $AB = 8$, and $m\angle ABC = 45$, how far is $\overline{BC}$ from the center of O?

B

22. Chords $\overline{PQ}$ and $\overline{RS}$ in a circle are equal in length. If $\overline{PQ}$ is distance $4x$ and $\overline{RS}$ is distance x^2 from the center, how far is each chord from the center?
23. $\overline{AB}$ and $\overline{CD}$ are both d units from the center of the circle. $AB = 2x + 7$ and $CD = 3x - 5$. What is the length of each chord?

16. 90   17. 90   18. 20
19. 70   20. 120   21. $2\sqrt{2}$
22. 0 (diameters) or 16
23. 31   24. If their lengths are =, they are equidist. from the center.   25. 1. $\overline{AD} \perp \overline{BC}$, $\overline{AD}$ is a diameter. (Given) 2. $\overline{AD}$ bisects $\widehat{BAC}$. (If a diameter $\perp$ a chord, it bisects the above chord's major arc.) 3. $\widehat{BA} \cong \widehat{AC}$ (Def. of bisector) 4. $\overline{BA} \cong \overline{AC}$ ($\cong$ arcs have $\cong$ chords.) 5. $\triangle ABC$ is isos. (Def. of isos. $\triangle$)   26. 1. $OX = OY$, $OY \perp \overline{AB}$, $\overline{OX} \perp \overline{CD}$ (Given) 2. $\overline{OX} \cong \overline{OY}$ (Def. = seg.) 3. $\overline{AB} \cong \overline{CD}$ (In the same $\odot$ chords equidist. from the center are $\cong$.) 4. $\widehat{AB} \cong \widehat{CD}$ (In a $\odot$, $\cong$ chords have $\cong$ minor arcs.) 5. $m\widehat{AB} = m\widehat{CD}$ (Def. $\cong$ arcs) 6. $m\widehat{AB} = m\widehat{AC} + m\widehat{BC}$, $m\widehat{CD} = m\widehat{AC} + m\widehat{AD}$ (Arc Add. Post.) 7. $m\widehat{AC} + m\widehat{AD} = m\widehat{AC} + m\widehat{BC}$ (Subst.) 8. $m\widehat{AD} = m\widehat{BC}$ (Sub.) 9. $\widehat{AD} \cong \widehat{CB}$ (Def. arc measure)
27. 24 in.   28. $\frac{5}{3}\sqrt{3}$
29. 1. $\odot P$, dia. $\overline{CD}$ bisects $\overline{AB}$. (Given) 2. $\overline{AE} \cong \overline{BE}$ (Def. bis.) 3. $\overline{PA} \cong \overline{PB}$ (Radii $\cong$ in same $\odot$.) 4. $\overline{PE} \cong \overline{PE}$ (Reflex.) 5. $\triangle APE \cong \triangle BPE$ (SSS) 6. $\angle AEP \cong \angle BEP$ (CPCTC) 7. $m\angle AEP + m\angle BEP = 180$ (Linear Pair Post.) 8. $m\angle AEP = m\angle BEP = 90$ (Div.) 9. $\overline{PD} \perp \overline{AB}$ (Def. $\perp$ lines) 10. $m\angle APD = m\angle BPD$ (CPCTC) 11. $\widehat{AD} \cong \widehat{DB}$ (Def. arc measure) 12. $\angle APC \cong \angle BPC$ ($\angle$s supp. to $\cong \angle$s are $\cong$.) 13. $\widehat{AC} \cong \widehat{BC}$ (Def. arc measure)

30. 1. $\overline{CD}$ is the $\perp$ bisector of $\overline{AB}$. $\odot P$ with chord $\overline{AB}$ (Given) 2. P is equidistant from A and B. (Def. center of circle) 3. $\overline{CD}$ contains P. (If a point is equidistant from the endpoints of a seg., it lies on the $\perp$ bisector of the seg.)   **31.** 1. $\overline{AB} \cong \overline{CD}$ (Given) 2. Draw $\overline{OT} \perp \overline{AB}$, $\overline{OS} \perp \overline{CD}$. (Through a given pt. not on a line there is exactly 1 line in the plane $\perp$ to the given line.) 3. $\angle ATO$ and $\angle CSO$ are rt. $\angle$s. ($\perp$ lines form rt. $\angle$s) 4. $\triangle ATO$ and $\triangle CSO$ are rt. $\triangle$s. (Def. rt. $\triangle$) 5. $\overline{OA} \cong \overline{OB} \cong \overline{OC} \cong \overline{OD}$ (Radii $\cong$.) 6. $\overline{OT}$ and $\overline{OS}$ are on dia. (Def. dia.) 7. $\overline{AT} \cong \overline{BT}$, $\overline{CS} \cong \overline{DS}$ (If a dia. is $\perp$ to a chord, then it bisects the chord.) 8. $AT = \frac{1}{2}AB$, $CS = \frac{1}{2}CD$ (Def. seg. bis.) 9. $\overline{AT} \cong \overline{CS}$ (Subst.) 10. $\triangle CSO \cong \triangle ATO$ (HL) 11. $\overline{OS} \cong \overline{OT}$ (CPCTC) 12. $OS = OT$ (Def. $\cong$ seg.)
32. 1. $OS = OT$ (Given) 2. $\overline{OS} \cong \overline{OT}$ (Def. $\cong$ seg.) 3. Draw $\overline{OA}$, $\overline{OB}$, $\overline{OC}$, $\overline{OD}$. (Between 2 pts. there is only 1 line.) 4. $\overline{OA} \cong \overline{OC} \cong \overline{OB} \cong \overline{OD}$ (Radii $\cong$.) 5. $\overline{OT} \perp \overline{AB}$, $\overline{OS} \perp \overline{CD}$ (Def. distance between point and line) 6. $\angle ATO$, $\angle BTO$, $\angle DSO$, $\angle CSO$ rt. $\angle$s ($\perp$ lines form rt. $\angle$s.) 7. $\triangle OAT$, $\triangle OBT$, $\triangle ODS$, $\triangle OCS$ rt. $\triangle$s (Def. rt. $\triangle$) 8. $\triangle OAT \cong \triangle OBT \cong \triangle ODS \cong \triangle OCS$ (HL) 9. $\overline{AT} \cong \overline{BT} \cong \overline{DS} \cong \overline{CS}$ (CPCTC) 10. $AT + TB = CS + SD$ (Add.) 11. $AB = CD$ (Seg. Add.) 12. $\overline{AB} \cong \overline{CD}$ (Def. $\cong$ seg.)

24. Often machine parts like the one shown here will work properly only if the groove is "centered." Why does measuring $\overline{AB}$ and $\overline{CD}$ tell you whether or not the groove is centered?

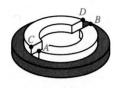

25. Given: $\overline{AD} \perp \overline{BC}$, $\overline{AD}$ is a diameter.
Prove: $\triangle ABC$ is isosceles.

26. Given: $\overline{OY} \perp \overline{AB}$, $\overline{OX} \perp \overline{CD}$, $OX = OY$
Prove: $\overline{AD} \cong \overline{BC}$

27. A chord is located 5 in. from the center of a circle with radius 13 in. Find the length of the chord.

28. An equilateral triangle with sides of length 10 is inscribed in a circle. Find the distance from the center of the circle to the side of the triangle.

29. Prove Theorem 8.7.
Given: $\odot P$ has diameter $\overline{CD}$ bisecting chord $\overline{AB}$.
Prove: $\overline{CD} \perp \overline{AB}$, $\overparen{DA} \cong \overparen{DB}$, $\overparen{AC} \cong \overparen{BC}$

30. Prove Theorem 8.8.
Given: $\odot P$ with chord $\overline{AB}$
$\overline{CD}$ is the $\perp$ bisector of $\overline{AB}$.
Prove: $\overline{CD}$ contains the center of $\odot P$.

31. Prove Theorem 8.9.
Given: $\overline{AB} \cong \overline{CD}$
Prove: $OS = OT$

32. Prove Theorem 8.10.
Given: $OS = OT$
Prove: $\overline{AB} \cong \overline{CD}$

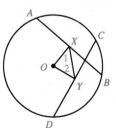

33. A part of an old wheel is found by an archeologist in a dig. The archeologist would like to determine how large the complete wheel was. How can she determine the radius of the complete wheel?

34. Given: $\overline{OX} \perp \overline{AB}$
$\overline{OY} \perp \overline{CD}$
$m\angle 1 = m\angle 2$
Prove: $AB = CD$

35. Given: $\overline{OX} \perp \overline{AB}$
$\overline{OY} \perp \overline{CD}$
$AB = CD$
Prove: $m\angle 1 = m\angle 2$

C

Circle O pictured is the set of all points in the coordinate plane whose coordinates satisfy the equation $x^2 + y^2 = 25$. The horizontal line consists of all points whose y-coordinate is 3.

36. Use the Pythagorean Theorem to find the length ED. Then find the length CD.

37. Use the results of Exercise 36 to find the coordinates of points C and D.

38. Use the distance formula to find the length of CD.

39. Solve the system of equations $x^2 + y^2 = 25$ and $y = 3$ to find the coordinates of points C and D.

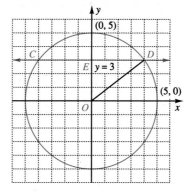

Critical Thinking

Complete each statement with the word *always*, *sometimes*, or *never*. Give a convincing argument to support each answer.

40. If AB and CD are parallel chords, then $ABCD$ is ___ a rectangle.

41. A line through the midpoint of a chord and its intercepted arc ___ passes through the center of the circle.

42. A line that is perpendicular to a chord ___ includes the center of the circle.

Algebra Review

Solve.

1. $4 + 3x = 28$ **2.** $5 + 4y = 37$ **3.** $5y - 9 = 21$ **4.** $4 - 3y = 13$

5. $10y - 7 = -12$ **6.** $6 - 8x = 18$ **7.** $8 - 2y = 22$ **8.** $3 - 6y = 15$

Quiz

Complete each statement with the most appropriate word.

1. A chord that contains the center of a circle is a ___ .

2. A ___ is a line that intersects the circle in exactly one point.

$\overline{AB}$ is tangent to $\odot E$.

3. If $AB = 8$ and $EB = 12$, find AE.

4. If $DC = 10$ and $AE = 13$, find EF.

5. If $m\angle ABE = 28$, find $m\widehat{AG}$.

6. Draw a pair of circles that have two common external tangents and no common internal tangents.

7. If $\overline{XY} \cong \overline{YZ}$ and $m\widehat{XY} = 105$, find $m\angle XTZ$.

8. Find $m\widehat{WX}$.   **9.** Find $m\angle XYZ$.

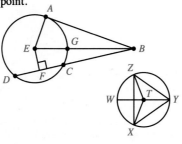

8-5 Chords of Circles **365**

---

33. Locate pt. A, B, and C on the inner arc. Find the $\perp$ bis. of $\overline{AB}$ and $\overline{BC}$. Their intersection is the center O of the circle. $\overline{OA}$ is the radius. **34.** 1. $m\angle 1 = m\angle 2$ (Given) 2. $\angle 1 \cong \angle 2$ (Def. $\cong$ seg.) 3. $\overline{OX} \cong \overline{OY}$ (Sides opp. $\cong$ $\angle$s are $\cong$.) 4. $\overline{OX} \perp \overline{AB}$, $\overline{OY} \perp \overline{CD}$ (Given) 5. $\overline{AB}$ and $\overline{CD}$ are equidist. from O. (Def. dist. of line from a pt.) 6. $\overline{AB} \cong \overline{CD}$ (In the same $\odot$ chords equidist. from the center are $\cong$.) 7. $AB = CD$ (Def. $\cong$ seg.) **35.** 1. $AB = CD$, $\overline{OX} \perp \overline{AB}$, $\overline{OY} \perp \overline{CD}$ (Given) 2. $OX = $ dist. $\overline{AB}$ to O, $OY = $ dist. $\overline{CD}$ to O (Def. dist. from a line to a pt.) 3. $OX = OY$ (In the same $\odot$, $\cong$ chords are equidist. from the center.) 4. $\overline{OX} \cong \overline{OY}$ (Def. $\cong$ seg.) 5. $\angle 1 \cong \angle 2$ (Base $\angle$s of isos. $\triangle$ are $\cong$.) 6. $m\angle 1 = m\angle 2$ (Def. $\cong$ $\angle$) **36.** $5^2 = 3^2 + ED^2$, $ED = 4$, $CD = 8$ **37.** $C(-4, 3)$, $D(4, 3)$ **38.** $CD = \sqrt{(4 - (-4))^2 + (3 - 3)^2} = 8$ **39.** $x^2 + 3^2 = 25$, $x = \pm 4$; $C(-4, 3)$, $D(4, 3)$ **40.** sometimes **41.** always **42.** sometimes

Algebra Review Answers

1. 8   **2.** 8   **3.** 6   **4.** -3
5. $-\frac{1}{2}$ **6.** $-\frac{3}{2}$ **7.** -7
8. -2

Quiz Answers

1. diameter   **2.** tangent
3. $4\sqrt{5}$ **4.** 12   **5.** 62
6.

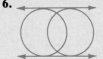

7. 150   **8.** 75   **9.** 75

1. If $\overline{AB} \cong \overline{CD}$, $OX = 6x - 9$ and $OY = 2x + 23$, find OX and OY. 39
2. If a diameter of $\odot O = 10$ and $CD = 8$, find OY. 3

3. Construct the center of the circle.

Lesson Opener

Review the definition of central angle before doing the Explore. You could repeat the activity using the circles below.

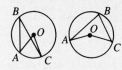

Key Questions

1. For each circle, compare the measures of $\angle AOC$ and $\angle ABC$. $m\angle ABC = \frac{1}{2}m\angle AOC$
2. What generalization(s) can you make from these results?

The measure of an inscribed angle is half the measure of the central angle which intercepts the same arc.

Materials

student notebooks
compasses
straightedges
protractors
investigative software

ANGLES AND SEGMENTS

OBJECTIVE: *State and apply theorems concerning measures of inscribed angles.*

8-6 Inscribed Angles

EXPLORE Construct a circle and an inscribed angle. Use a protractor to measure $\overset{\frown}{AC}$ and $\angle ABC$. What relationship do you discover?

An **inscribed angle** is an angle with vertex on a circle and sides that contain chords of the circle. In the figure, $\angle BAC$ is an inscribed angle and $\overset{\frown}{BC}$ is its **intercepted arc.**

◆ **THEOREM 8.11** Inscribed Angle Measure

The measure of an inscribed angle is half the measure of its intercepted arc.

Given: inscribed $\angle BAC$
Prove: $m\angle BAC = \frac{1}{2}m\overset{\frown}{BC}$

Plan Consider these three cases. In Case 1 the center of the circle is on one side of the inscribed angle. In Case 2 the center is in the interior of the angle and in Case 3 the center of the circle is in the exterior of the angle.

Case 1   **Case 2**   **Case 3**

$m\overset{\frown}{BC} = m\angle 3$ Use Case 1 for $\angle 1$ Use Case 1 for $\angle BAD$
$\quad = m\angle 1 + m\angle 2$ or   and $\angle 2$. Add angles   and $\angle 2$. Subtract angles
$m\overset{\frown}{BC} = 2m\angle 1$ and arcs.   and arcs.

In Case 1, the conclusion follows from the fact that $\angle 3$ is an exterior angle of $\triangle ABO$. This proof will be completed in Exercises 25, 26, and 27.

Example 1

Find each measure.

a. $m\angle CAB$
b. $m\angle CDB$

Solution

a. $m\angle CAB = 30$ *The measure of $\angle CAB$ is $\frac{1}{2}$ its intercepted arc BC.*
b. $m\angle CDB = 30$ *$\angle CDB$ has the same intercepted arc as $\angle CAB$.*

Try This

Find each measure.

a. $m\,\widehat{AD}$
b. $m\angle ACD$

Several corollaries to Theorem 8.11 are presented below. Their proofs follow directly from the theorem and you will be asked to prove them in Exercises 28, 29, and 30.

▶ **COROLLARY 8.11a**

If two inscribed angles intercept the same arc, then the angles are congruent.

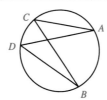

▶ **COROLLARY 8.11b**

If a quadrilateral is inscribed in a circle, then its opposite angles are supplementary.

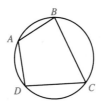

▶ **COROLLARY 8.11c**

An angle inscribed in a semicircle is a right angle. Also, if an inscribed angle is a right angle its intercepted arc is a semicircle.

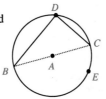

Teaching Notes

The measure of an inscribed angle whose sides intersect a circle is determined by the measure of its intercepted arc. Intercepted arcs are always in the interior of an angle. Remind students that two conditions are necessary for an angle to be inscribed: **a.** The vertex must be on the circle. **b.** Sides must be chords of the circle.

Before introducing Theorem 8.12, tell students to study the diagrams above the theorem. Point out that point B moves along the circle approaching point C, and finally merges with point C in diagram **e**. Thus, the side of $\angle C$ that was a chord becomes a tangent. If you applied Theorem 8.12 to diagrams **a–d**, $m\angle C = \frac{1}{2}m\widehat{AB}$.

Key Terms

inscribed angle
tangent-chord angle
intercepted angle

Guided Practice

Chalkboard Examples

Find each measure.

1. $m\widehat{CD}$, $m\widehat{AB}$, $m\widehat{BC}$, $m\widehat{AED}$, $m\angle CBD$, $m\angle AED$ 40, 48, 92, 180, 20, 90

Answer to **Try This** 92, 46

2. If $m\widehat{AB} = 57$, find $m\angle BAC$ and $m\angle BCA$. $61\frac{1}{2}$, $28\frac{1}{2}$

Answer to **Try This** 59, 112

Think about point B moving along the circle toward point C. The inscribed angle measure theorem continues to be true as $\overleftrightarrow{CB}$ moves to form a tangent at C. A **tangent-chord angle** has its vertex on a circle with one side tangent to the circle at the vertex and the other side containing a chord. Figure **e** shows a tangent-chord angle with intercepted arc AC.

 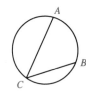 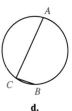 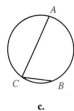 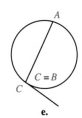

a.   b.   c.   d.   e.

In all five cases, $m\angle C = \frac{1}{2}m\overparen{AB}$.

This sequence of figures provides a convincing argument for the next theorem.

◆ **THEOREM 8.12**

The measure of a tangent-chord angle is half the measure of its intercepted arc.

Example 2

$\overleftrightarrow{BE}$ is tangent at B. Find each measure.
a. $m\angle ADC$
b. $m\angle BCD$

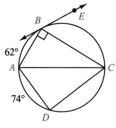

Solution

a. $m\angle ADC = 90$ *Opposite angles of an inscribed quadrilateral are supplementary.*

b. $m\angle BCD = m\angle DCA + m\angle BCA$
$= (\frac{1}{2})74 + (\frac{1}{2})62$
$= 37 + 31$
$= 68$

Try This

Find each measure.
a. $m\angle CBE$
b. $m\angle DAB$

368   *Chapter 8   Circles*

Class Exercises

Short Answer

1. Name two congruent inscribed angles.
2. Name two inscribed angles that are not congruent.
3. Name an angle that is not an inscribed angle.
4. Name a tangent-chord angle.
5. Name two inscribed angles that have measure 45.
6. Name two inscribed angles whose intercepted arc is $\widehat{AD}$.

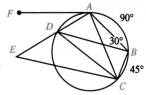

Sample Exercises

Find each measure.

7. $m\angle BDC$ 8. $m\angle BAC$ 9. $m\widehat{ADC}$
10. $m\angle ABC$ 11. $m\angle ADC$ 12. $m\angle FAD$

Discussion

$\overline{EC}$ is tangent at E.

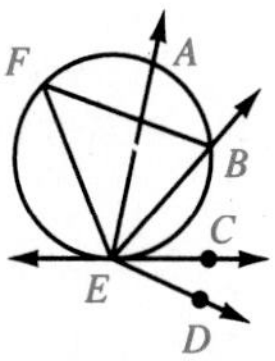

13. Explain why $\angle BED$ is not an inscribed angle.
14. Explain why $\angle CED$ is not a tangent-chord angle.
15. Explain why $\angle BFE \cong \angle BEC$.

16. Complete the proof. State a theorem (in if-then form) that you have proven.
   Given: $\overleftrightarrow{AB} \parallel \overleftrightarrow{CD}$. (Draw auxiliary line BD.)

Statements	Reasons
1. $\overleftrightarrow{AB} \parallel \overleftrightarrow{CD}$	1. ___
2. $\angle ABD \cong \angle BDC$	2. ___
3. ___	3. ___

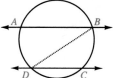

Exercises

A

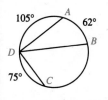

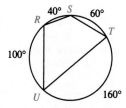

Find each measure.

1. $m\angle ADB$ 2. $m\widehat{BC}$ 3. $m\angle BDC$ 4. $m\widehat{AC}$
5. $m\angle R$ 6. $m\angle S$ 7. $m\angle T$ 8. $m\angle U$

Exercise Answers

1. 31 **2.** 118 **3.** 59
4. 180 **5.** 110 **6.** 130
7. 70 **8.** 50 **9.** 48
10. 105 **11.** 27 **12.** 40
13. 40 **14.** 60 **15.** 20
16. Points on the circle result in the same measure for $\angle ACB$, always intercepting $\widehat{AB}$.
17. $m\angle A = 135$, $m\angle B = 90$, $m\angle C = 45$, $m\angle D = 90$
18. $m\angle A = 87$, $m\angle B = 74$, $m\angle C = 93$, $m\angle D = 106$
19. 44 **20.** 45 **21.** 1. inscribed trap. $ABCD$ with $\overline{AB} \parallel \overline{DC}$ (Given) 2. $\widehat{AD} \cong \widehat{BC}$ (See Class Ex.16.) 3. $\angle ACD \cong \angle BDC$ (Def. arc measure) 4. $\widehat{AB} \cong \widehat{AB}$ (Reflex.) 5. $\widehat{DA} + \widehat{AB} = \widehat{CB} + \widehat{BA}$ (Add.) 6. $\widehat{DB} \cong \widehat{CA}$ (Seg. Add. Post.) 7. $\angle BCD \cong \angle ADC$ (Def. arc measure) 8. $\triangle ACD \cong \triangle BDC$ (ASA) 9. $\overline{BC} \cong \overline{AD}$ (CPCTC) 10. $ABCD$ is isos. (Def. isos. trap.)

8-6 Inscribed Angles **369**

22. 1. $\overline{AP}$ is a diameter of ⊙O. (Given)
2. $\overset{\frown}{ABP}$, $\overset{\frown}{ACP}$ are semicircles. (Def. semicircle) 3. ∠ABP, ∠ACP are right angles. (Cor. 8.11c) 4. $\overline{AB} \perp \overline{BP}$, $\overline{AC} \perp \overline{CP}$ (Def. ⊥ lines) 5. $\overline{PB}$, $\overline{PC}$ are tangent to ⊙A. (If a line is ⊥ to a radius of a ⊙ at a point on the circle, then the line is tangent to the circle.)
23. 1. $\overline{AB}$, $\overline{CB}$ are dia. ⊙X and ⊙Y are tan. at B. (Given)
2. m∠AEB = m∠CDB = 90 (An ∠ inscribed in a semi-circle is a rt. ∠.) 3. ∠AEB ≅ ∠CDB (All rt. ∠s are ≅.) 4. ∠ABE ≅ ∠DBC (Vert. ∠s are ≅.) 5. △AEB ~ △CDB (AA ~ Post.) 6. ∠1 ≅ ∠2 (Corr. ∠s of ~ △s are ≅.)
24. 1. △AEB ~ △CDB (See Exercise 23.) 2. $\frac{AE}{CD} = \frac{EB}{DB}$ (Sides of ~ △s are in proportion.) 3. $\frac{AE}{EB} = \frac{CD}{DB}$ (Properties of proportions) **25.** 1. inscribed ∠BAC (Given) 2. $\overline{OA} \cong \overline{OB}$ (Radii in same ⊙ ≅.)
3. ∠BAC ≅ ∠ABO (Isos. △ Th.) 4. m∠BAC = m∠ABO (Def. ≅ ∠s) 5. $m\overset{\frown}{BC}$ = m∠BOC (Def. arc measure) 6. m∠BOC = m∠BAC + m∠ABO (Ext. ∠ Theorem) 7. $m\overset{\frown}{BC}$ = m∠BAC + m∠ABO (Subst.) 8. $m\overset{\frown}{BC}$ = 2m∠BAC (Subst.) 9. m∠BAC = $\frac{1}{2}m\overset{\frown}{BC}$ (Div.)
26. 1. inscribed ∠BAC (Given)
2. $m\angle 1 = \frac{1}{2}m\overset{\frown}{BD}$, $m\angle 2 = \frac{1}{2}m\overset{\frown}{DC}$ (Case 1) 3. m∠BAC = m∠1 + m∠2 (∠ Add.) 4. m∠BAC = $\frac{1}{2}m\overset{\frown}{BD} + \frac{1}{2}m\overset{\frown}{DC}$ (Subst.) 5. m∠BAC = $\frac{1}{2}(m\overset{\frown}{BD} + m\overset{\frown}{DC})$ (Dist. Prop.) 6. m∠BAC = $\frac{1}{2}m\overset{\frown}{BC}$ (Arc Add. Post.)
27. 1. Inscribed ∠BAC (Given)
2. m∠BAD = $\frac{1}{2}m\overset{\frown}{BD}$, m∠CAD = $\frac{1}{2}m\overset{\frown}{CD}$ (Case 1) 3. m∠BAC = m∠BAD − m∠2 (Sub.) 4. m∠BAC = $\frac{1}{2}m\overset{\frown}{BD}$ − $\frac{1}{2}m\overset{\frown}{CD}$ (Subst.) 5. m∠BAC = $\frac{1}{2}(m\overset{\frown}{BD} − m\overset{\frown}{CD})$ (Dist. Prop.)
6. m∠BAC = $\frac{1}{2}m\overset{\frown}{BC}$ (Arc Add. Post.)

$\overleftrightarrow{CD}$ **is tangent at C. Find each measure.**

9. m∠CAB
10. m∠ABC
11. m∠ACB

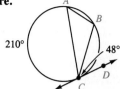

$\overrightarrow{AC}$ **bisects ∠BAD.** $m\overset{\frown}{CD} = 80$, $m\overset{\frown}{AD} = 160$
Find each measure.

12. m∠BAC   **13.** m∠BDC
14. m∠AEB   **15.** m∠ADB

16. Suppose that a harbor is too shallow for ships to enter inside the circular arc ACB, also known as the "danger circle." The navigator of a ship at location C measured ∠ACB and discovered it was equal to a published "danger angle." How did the ship's navigator know that the ship was on the danger circle?

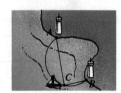

B

17. Suppose that $ABCD$ is a quadrilateral inscribed in a circle and that $\overline{AC}$ is a diameter of the circle. If m∠A is three times m∠C, what are the measures of all four angles?

18. If m∠A = 4x + 35, m∠B = 3x + 35, and m∠D = 7x + 15, find the measure of all four angles of quadrilateral $ABCD$.

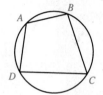

19. If m∠ABC = 3x + 5 and m∠ADC = 5x − 21, find the measure of these two angles.
20. If m∠BAD = 3x + 50, m∠ABC = 4x + 25, and m∠BCD = 7x + 30, find m∠ADC.

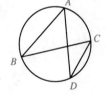

21. Prove that a trapezoid inscribed in a circle is an isosceles trapezoid.
22. Given ⊙A and a point P exterior to the circle, construct the circle with diameter $\overline{AP}$ and let B and C be the points at which the two circles intersect. Prove that $\overline{PB}$ and $\overline{PC}$ are tangent segments from the exterior point P.

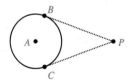

370 *Chapter 8 Circles*

23. Given: $\overline{AB}$ and $\overline{BC}$ are diameters.
$\odot X$ and $\odot Y$ are tangent at B.
Prove: $\angle 1 \cong \angle 2$

24. Given: $\overline{AB}$ and $\overline{BC}$ are diameters.
$\odot X$ and $\odot Y$ are tangent at B.
Prove: $\frac{AE}{EB} = \frac{CD}{DB}$

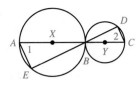

25. Prove Case 1 of Theorem 8.11.
Given: inscribed $\angle BAC$
Prove: $m\angle BAC = \frac{1}{2}m\widehat{BC}$

26. Use Case 1 to prove Case 2 of Theorem 8.11.
Given: inscribed $\angle BAC$
Prove: $m\angle BAC = \frac{1}{2}m\widehat{BC}$

27. Use Case 1 to prove Case 3 of Theorem 8.11.
Given: inscribed $\angle BAC$
Prove: $m\angle BAC = \frac{1}{2}m\widehat{BC}$

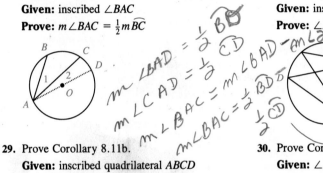

28. Prove Corollary 8.11a.
Given: inscribed $\angle$s ACB and ADB
Prove: $\angle ACB \cong \angle ADB$

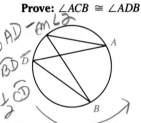

29. Prove Corollary 8.11b.
Given: inscribed quadrilateral $ABCD$
Prove: $\angle A$ and $\angle C$ are supplementary.

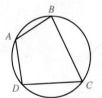

30. Prove Corollary 8.11c.
Given: $\angle BDC$ is inscribed in semicircle $\widehat{BDC}$.
Prove: $\angle D$ is a right angle.

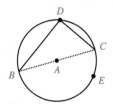

31. If $TV = 3$, $VS = 8$, $RV = 4$, find x.

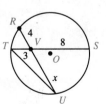

28. 1. $\angle ACB$, $\angle ADB$ inscribed $\angle$s (Given)
2. $m\angle ACB = \frac{1}{2}m\widehat{AB}$, $m\angle ADB = \frac{1}{2}m\widehat{AB}$ (inscribed $\angle$ measure)
3. $m\angle ACB = m\angle ADB$ (Trans.)
4. $\angle ACB \cong \angle ADB$ (Def. $\cong \angle$s)

29. 1. inscribed quad. $ABCD$ (Given) 2. $m\angle A = \frac{1}{2}m\widehat{BCD}$, $m\angle C = \frac{1}{2}m\widehat{BAD}$ (Theorem 8.11) 3. $m\angle A + m\angle C = \frac{1}{2}m\widehat{BCD} + \frac{1}{2}m\widehat{BAD}$ (Add.) 4. $m\angle A + m\angle C = \frac{1}{2}(m\widehat{BCD} + m\widehat{BAD})$ (Dist. Prop.) 5. $m\angle A + m\angle C = \frac{1}{2}(360) = 180$ (Arc Add. Post.) 6. $\angle A$, $\angle C$ are supp. (Def. supp. $\angle$s) 7. $m\angle B = \frac{1}{2}m\widehat{ADC}$, $m\angle D = \frac{1}{2}m\widehat{ABC}$ (Inscribed $\angle$ measure) 8. $m\angle B + m\angle D = \frac{1}{2}m\widehat{ADC} + \frac{1}{2}m\widehat{ABC}$ (Add.) 9. $m\angle B + m\angle D = \frac{1}{2}(m\widehat{ADC} + m\angle ABC)$ (Dist. Prop.) 10. $m\angle B + m\angle D = \frac{1}{2}(360) = 180$ 11. $\angle B$ and $\angle D$ are supp. (Def. supp. $\angle$s)   **30.** 1. $\widehat{BEC}$ is a semicircle. (Given) 2. $m\widehat{BEC} = 180$ (Def. semicircle) 3. $m\angle BDC = \frac{1}{2}(180)$ (Theorem 8.11)   4. $m\angle BDC = 90$ (Mult.) 5. $\angle BDC$ is a rt. $\angle$. (Def. rt. $\angle$)   **31.** 6   **32.** 1. $\overline{CD}$ is tan. to a $\odot$ at pt. D, $\overline{AD}$ contains the center of the $\odot$. (Given) 2. $m\angle BAD = m\angle BDC = \frac{1}{2}m\widehat{BD}$ (Theorems 8.11 and 8.12) 3. $\angle BAD \cong \angle BDC$ (Def. $\cong \angle$s) 4. $\angle C \cong \angle C$ (Reflex.) 5. $\triangle ACD \sim \triangle DCB$ (AA) 6. $\frac{AD}{DB} = \frac{AC}{DC}$ (Corr. sides of $\sim \triangle$s are proportional.) 7. $\frac{AD}{AC} = \frac{DB}{DC}$ (Prop. of proportions)

C

32. **Given:** $\overline{CD}$ is tangent to the circle at D and $\overline{AD}$ contains the center of the circle.

Prove: $\dfrac{AD}{AC} = \dfrac{DB}{DC}$

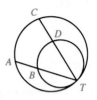

33. Suppose that a triangle is inscribed in each of two congruent circles. If a side and an adjacent angle of one is congruent to a side and an adjacent angle of the other prove that the two triangles are congruent.

Assume the two circles are tangent at T.

34. Prove that $\overline{AC}\|\overline{BD}$. (HINT: Draw the tangent line at point T.)
35. If $AB = 5$, $DT = 8$, and $CD = 6$, find BT.

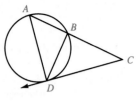

Critical Thinking

Complete each statement with the word *always*, *sometimes*, or *never*. Give a convincing argument that your answer is correct.

36. A quadrilateral that is inscribed in a circle with at least one diagonal a diameter is ___ a parallelogram.
37. A quadrilateral that is inscribed in a circle with both diagonals a diameter is ___ a rectangle.
38. If a triangle is inscribed in a circle to which a tangent line to the circle at one of the vertices forms a 60° tangent-chord angle with one side of the triangle, then the triangle is ___ an equilateral triangle.

Algebra Review

Find the LCM.

1. a^2b, ab^2 **2.** $3x^2$, $6xy$
3. $x + y$, $x - y$ **4.** $a + 1$, $a^2 - 1$
5. $8x^2y^2$, $12y^3$ **6.** $12xy^2$, $16x^3y$
7. $x^2 + 16$, $x - 2$ **8.** $x^2 - 2x + 1$, $1 - x^2$

Computer Activity

Use computer software to investigate the measure of an angle formed by two chords intersecting inside a circle.

Draw $\overline{BC}$ and $\overline{DE}$. Name the intersection of $\overline{BC}$ and $\overline{DE}$ point F.
Measure ∠CFD.
Measure ∠CAD and ∠BAE.

What generalization can you make about the measure of angle formed by two chords intersecting inside a circle?

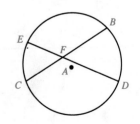

OBJECTIVE: *State and apply theorems concerning measures of angles formed by two chords or two secants.*

8-7 Angles of Chords, Secants, and Tangents

In the previous section you studied inscribed angles and tangent-chord angles. In both types of angles, the vertex of the angle is on the circle. In the angles formed by chords, secants, and tangents, vertices are either in the interior of the circle or on the exterior of the circle. Theorem 8.13 deals with the case in which the vertex is on the interior of the circle. This theorem also helps answer the question to the right.

If a ship's captain measures $\angle ACB$ and finds it to be greater than the published "danger angle" how would he know that he was located inside the "danger circle"?

◆ **THEOREM 8.13**

The measure of an angle formed by two chords intersecting inside a circle is one half the sum of the intercepted arcs.

Given: chords $\overline{AB}$ and $\overline{CD}$ intersecting at point X

Prove: $m\angle AXC = \frac{1}{2}(m\,\widehat{AC} + m\,\widehat{BD})$

Proof Draw $\overline{BC}$. Then $\angle AXC$ is an exterior angle of $\triangle XCB$ and hence $m\angle AXC = m\angle XCB + m\angle XBC$. Furthermore, $m\angle XCB = \frac{1}{2}m\,\widehat{BD}$ and $m\angle XBC = \frac{1}{2}m\,\widehat{AC}$. Therefore, $m\angle AXC = \frac{1}{2}(m\,\widehat{AC} + m\,\widehat{BD})$.

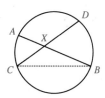

Example 1

Find $m\angle 1$.

Solution

$$m\angle 1 = \frac{1}{2}(m\,\widehat{AB} + m\,\widehat{ED})$$
$$= \frac{1}{2}(40 + 136)$$
$$= 88$$

Since $m\angle BCD = 105°$, you know that $m\,\widehat{BED} = 210$. So $m\,\widehat{ED} = 210 - (34 + 40) = 136$.

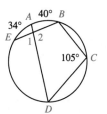

Try This

Find $m\angle 2$.

The next theorem deals with the measure of an angle whose vertex is outside the circle and whose sides intersect the circle. There are three cases. The sides are (1) both secants or (2) both tangents or (3) one secant and one tangent.

(Quiz on previous lesson)

1. Find $m\angle 1$ and $m\angle 2$. 80, 100

2. Find $m\angle BAC$, $m\,\widehat{BC}$, $m\angle COD$, and $m\angle FAD$. 15, 30, 50, 90

Lesson Opener

Angles previously studied include: (a) central angle—vertex at the center of a circle, (b) inscribed angle—vertex on the circle, and (c) tangent-chord angle—vertex on the circle. This lesson introduces four additional angles: (d) chord-chord angle—vertex inside but not at the center of a circle, (e) secant-secant angle—vertex outside a circle, (f) tangent-tangent angle—vertex outside a circle, (g) secant-tangent angle—vertex outside a circle.

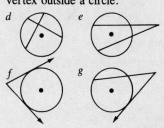

Materials

student notebooks
investigative software

Emphasize that the location of
the vertex of an angle is the
key to remembering how to
compute the measure of the angle.

Case 1—When vertex is at center of circle, angle equals measure of intercepted arc: central
angle.

Case 2—When vertex is inside
circle, angle equals half the sum
of measure of intercepted arc:
chord-chord angle.

Case 3—When vertex is on circle, angle equals half measure
of intercepted arc: inscribed angle, tangent-chord angle.

Case 4—When vertex is outside
circle, angle equals half difference of measure of intercepted
arcs: secant-secant angle,
tangent-tangent angle, secant-
tangent angle.

Guided Practice

Chalkboard Examples

1. Find $m\widehat{BCD}$. 150

Answer to **Try This** 92

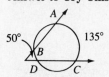

2. Find $m\widehat{BD}$. 35

Answer to **Try This** 52

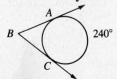

3. Find $m\angle ABC$. 60

Answer to **Try This** 100

◆ **THEOREM 8.14**

The measure of an angle formed by two secants, two tangents, or a
secant and a tangent drawn from a point in the exterior of a circle is
equal to half the difference of the measures of the intercepted arcs.

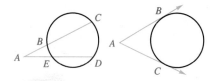

Example 2

Find

a. $m\angle CAE$ if $m\widehat{BD} = 10$ and $m\widehat{CE} = 50$.
b. $m\angle GAF$ if $m\widehat{GF} = 105$ and $m\widehat{GEF} = 255$.

Solution

a. $m\angle CAE = \frac{1}{2}(m\widehat{CE} - m\widehat{BD})$

$= \frac{1}{2}(50 - 10)$

$= 20$

b. $m\angle GAF = \frac{1}{2}(m\widehat{GEF} - m\widehat{GF})$

$= \frac{1}{2}(255 - 105)$

$= \frac{1}{2}(150) = 75$

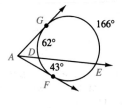

Try This

Find $m\angle GAE$ if $m\widehat{GE} = 166$ and $m\widehat{GD} = 62$.

Example 3

$\overline{AD}$ is a diameter and $\overline{GD}$ is tangent at D.
$m\widehat{AB} = 25$, $m\widehat{CD} = 40$ Find $m\angle AFB$.

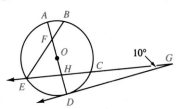

Solution

$m\angle EGD = \frac{1}{2}(m\widehat{ED} - m\widehat{CD})$ *Apply the tangent-secant form of Theorem 8.14.*

$10 = \frac{1}{2}(m\widehat{ED} - 40)$

$10 + 20 = \frac{1}{2}m\widehat{ED}$ *Use this fact in an application of Theorem 8.13*
to find $m\angle AFB$.

$m\widehat{ED} = 60$

$m\angle AFB = \frac{1}{2}(m\widehat{AB} + m\widehat{ED})$

$= \frac{1}{2}(25 + 60)$

$= 42.5$

Try This

Find $m\angle AHC$.

Class Exercises

Short Answer

Name an angle whose sides are as follows.

1. two secants of the circle
2. two tangents of the circle
3. a secant and a tangent of the circle
4. on intersecting chords of the circle

Tell what arc measures you would need to know to find each measure.

5. $m\angle BJF$ 6. $m\angle FGE$ 7. $m\angle AIC$ 8. $m\angle IHG$

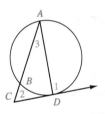

Sample Exercises

Find the measure of each numbered angle.

9.
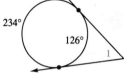
234°   126°   1

10.
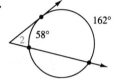
162°   58°   2

11.
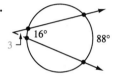
16°   88°   3

Discussion

12. This figure illustrates which one of the three cases of Theorem 8.14?
Draw figures that illustrate the other two cases and give a convincing
argument why each case is true.

Exercises

A

Find the measure of each numbered angle.

1.

42°   1   124°

2.

32°   2   20°

3.
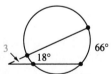
3   18°   66°

4. If $m\widehat{AC} = 39$ and $m\widehat{BD} = 73$, find $m\angle AED$.
5. If $m\angle AEC = 48$ and $m\widehat{AC} = 34$, find $m\widehat{BD}$.
6. If $m\angle BEC = 130$ and $m\widehat{AD} = 120$, find $m\widehat{BC}$.

8-7 Angles of Chords, Secants, and Tangents **375**

Class Exercise Answers

1. $\angle HGE$ 2. $\angle HIK$
3. $\angle IHG$ 4. $\angle BJH$, $\angle HJD$, $\angle DJG$, or $\angle GJB$ 5. $\widehat{BF}$, $\widehat{CD}$ 6. $\widehat{EF}$, $\widehat{CK}$ 7. $\widehat{AC}$, $\widehat{CDA}$ 8. $\widehat{AF}$, $\widehat{AC}$ 9. 54
10. 52   11. 36
12. Secant-tangent;
$m\angle 1 = m\angle 2 + m\angle 3$ (exterior $\angle$), so $m\angle 2 = m\angle 1 - m\angle 3 = \frac{1}{2}m\widehat{AD} - \frac{1}{2}m\widehat{BD} = \frac{1}{2}(m\widehat{AD} - m\widehat{BD})$.

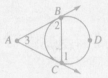

(Case 2) $m\angle 1 = m\angle 2 + m\angle 3$,
so $m\angle 3 = m\angle 1 - m\angle 2 = \frac{1}{2}m\widehat{BDC} - \frac{1}{2}m\widehat{BC} = \frac{1}{2}(m\widehat{BDC} - m\widehat{BC})$

(Case 3) $m\angle 2 = m\angle 1 + m\angle 3$,
so $m\angle 1 = m\angle 2 - m\angle 3 = \frac{1}{2}m\widehat{CD} - \frac{1}{2}m\widehat{BE} = \frac{1}{2}(m\widehat{CD} - m\widehat{BE})$

Assignment Guide

Minimum: 1–31 e/o, 39–40, MR
Regular: 1–36 e/o, 39–41, MR
Advanced: 17–31 e/o, 32–42, MR

Applications

Exercise 42

Algebra

Exercises 12, 15

Lesson Closure

Verify that students know how to
compute the measure of an angle
when the vertex is inside a circle
or at the center, on the circle, or
outside the circle.

Teacher's Resource Materials

Practice Master 57
Transparency 38
Technology: BASIC 14
Technology: Computer
 Software 12

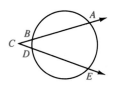

7. If $m\widehat{BD} = 15$ and $m\widehat{AE} = 85$, then find $m\angle ACE$.
8. If $m\angle ACE = 32$ and $m\widehat{BD} = 22$, find $m\widehat{AE}$.
9. If $m\angle ACE = 28$ and $m\widehat{AE} = 94$, find $m\widehat{BD}$.

$\vec{BA}$ and $\vec{BC}$ **are tangent to** $\odot X$.

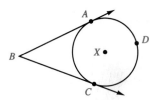

10. If $m\widehat{AC} = 160$, find $m\angle ABC$.
11. If $m\widehat{ADC} = 240$, find $m\angle ABC$.
12. If $m\widehat{AC} = b$ and $m\widehat{ADC} = 3b$, find $m\angle ABC$.

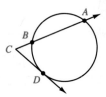

13. If $m\widehat{AD} = 165$ and $m\widehat{BD} = 63$, find $m\angle ACD$.
14. If $m\widehat{BD} = 55$ and $m\angle ACD = 43$, find $m\widehat{AD}$.
15. If $m\widehat{AD} = x$ and $m\widehat{BD} = y$, find $m\angle ACD$.

16. $\overleftrightarrow{AB}$ is tangent to $\odot O$. $m\widehat{AE} = 160$, $m\widehat{AD} = 50$, $m\widehat{DC} = 60$
Find $m\angle 1$ and $m\angle 2$.

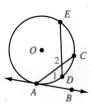

B

This design was drawn by using 16 points equally spaced around the circle. Find the measure of each angle.

17. $m\angle 1$ 18. $m\angle 2$
19. $m\angle 3$ 20. $m\angle 4$

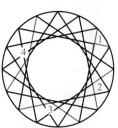

A diameter $\overline{AB}$ **and a chord** $\overline{CD}$ **intersect inside** $\odot O$ **at** X. **If** $m\widehat{AD} = 128$ **and** $m\angle AXD = 74$, **find each measure.**

21. $m\widehat{AC}$ 22. $m\widehat{CB}$ 23. $m\widehat{BD}$

In $\odot O$, $\overline{AC}$ **is a diameter and** $\overline{AE}$ **is a tangent.** $m\widehat{DC} = 30$, $m\angle AED = 30$ **Find each measure.**

24. $m\widehat{AB}$ 25. $m\widehat{BC}$ 26. $m\angle AXD$

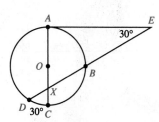

376 *Chapter 8 Circles*

27. Prove Theorem 8.14 for the case of two secant lines.

Given: $\overrightarrow{PA}$ and $\overrightarrow{PD}$ secants

Prove: $m\angle P = \frac{1}{2}(m\widehat{AD} - m\widehat{BC})$.

(HINT: Use the auxiliary line BD.)

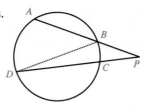

$m\widehat{AB} = 55$, $m\widehat{BD} = 40$, $\overline{AC}$ is a diameter and $\overrightarrow{PB}$ is tangent to the circle at B.

28. Find $m\angle P$.

29. Find $m\angle 2$.

30. Find $m\angle 1$.

31. Is $\overline{AD} \parallel \overrightarrow{PB}$? Explain.

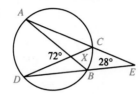

C

32. Given $m\angle AXD = 72$, $m\angle AED = 28$
Find $m\widehat{AD}$ and $m\widehat{CB}$.

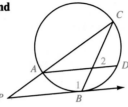

33. Given concentric circles centered at O. $\overline{AB}$ and $\overline{CD}$ are chords of the large circle that intersect at point E on the small circle.
$m\widehat{EF} = 80$, $m\widehat{AC} = 20$ Find $m\widehat{BD}$.

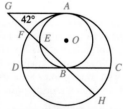

$\odot O$ is tangent to $\odot B$ at point A. $\overline{GA}$ is tangent to both circles at A and $\overline{CD}$ is tangent to $\odot O$ at B. $\overline{GA} \parallel \overline{CD}$, $m\angle AGB = 42$

34. Find $m\widehat{AH}$.

35. Find $m\widehat{AF}$.

36. Find $m\widehat{AE}$.

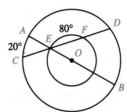

$\odot O$ is tangent to the larger circle at A. Chords $\overline{AE}$ and $\overline{CD}$ intersect at F on $\odot O$ and $\overline{CD}$ is tangent to $\odot O$.

37. If $m\angle EAB = 25$, find $m\angle AHF$.

38. If $m\angle DFE = 65$, find $m\angle BAE$.

39. If $m\angle DFE = 65$, find $m\widehat{BE}$.

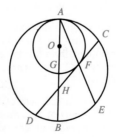

27. 1. Secants $\overrightarrow{PA}$ and $\overrightarrow{PD}$ (Given) 2. Draw aux. line $\overline{BD}$. (2 pts. determine a line.) 3. $m\angle ABD = m\angle BDP + m\angle P$ (The measure of an ext. $\angle$ of a $\triangle$ = the sum of the measures of its two remote int. $\angle$s.) 4. $\frac{1}{2}m\widehat{AD} = \frac{1}{2}m\widehat{BC} + m\angle P$ (The measure of an inscribed $\angle$ is half the measure of its intercepted arc.) 5. $m\angle P = \frac{1}{2}m\widehat{AD} - \frac{1}{2}m\widehat{BC}$ (Sub.) 6. $m\angle P = \frac{1}{2}(m\widehat{AD} - m\widehat{BC})$ (Dist. Prop.)

28. 35   **29.** 70   **30.** $117\frac{1}{2}$

31. No. For $\overline{AD} \parallel \overline{PB}$, $\angle 1$ must be supp. to $\angle 2$. But $m\angle 1 + m\angle 2 = 187\frac{1}{2}$.   **32.** $m\widehat{AD} = 100$, $m\widehat{CB} = 44$ **33.** 80

34. 132   **35.** 48   **36.** 96

37. 40   **38.** 25   **39.** 50

40. $\frac{1}{2}$ **41.** 2   **42.** If C is
on the circle, then $m\angle ACB =$
$\frac{1}{2}m\widehat{AB}$. If C is inside the circle,
then $m\angle ACB = \frac{1}{2}(m\widehat{AB} + m\widehat{DE})$
where D and E are the points
where $\overleftrightarrow{AC}$ and $\overleftrightarrow{BC}$ intersect the
circle. $m\angle ACB = \frac{1}{2}m\widehat{AB} +$
$\frac{1}{2}m\widehat{DE} > \frac{1}{2}m\widehat{AB}$

Mixed Review Answers

1. $x = 58, y = 16$ **2.** $x = 57,$
$y = 123$ **3.** $x = 43,$
$y = 18$ **4.** $x = 47, y = 24$
5. $\approx 36°$ **6.** $\approx 7°$

Critical Thinking

**Complete the following statements by considering
special cases and making generalizations.**

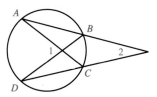

40. If $m\widehat{AD} = 2m\widehat{BC}$, then $m\angle 2 = $ ___ $m\widehat{BC}$.
41. If $m\widehat{AD} = 3m\widehat{BC}$, then $m\angle 1 = $ ___ $m\widehat{BC}$.

42. Reread the question asked in the caption under the map at the beginning
of the lesson. Give a convincing argument that if $m\angle ACB$ is greater than
the "danger angle," the captain will know that the ship was located inside
the danger circle.

Mixed Review

Determine the values of x and y so that each figure is a parallelogram.

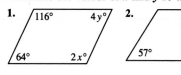   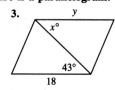   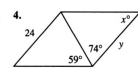

5. A tower 160 ft high casts a shadow 220 ft
long. Find the angle of elevation of the sun.

6. A ramp is 100 ft long and rises vertically
12 ft. Find the angle of elevation of the
ramp.

Biographical Note
Emmy Noether (1882–1935)

Emmy Noether has been recognized as the most creative abstract algebraist
of modern times. At the age of 31 she began to lecture on mathematics,
sometimes substituting for her father, a professor of mathematics at Erlangen
University in Germany. After years of unsuccessful attempts to overcome the
objections of those faculty members who wanted to exclude women from the
faculty, she won formal admission as an academic lecturer in 1919.

From 1930 to 1933 she was at the center of the mathematical activity at
Gottingen. When the Nazis came to power in 1933, Noether and many others
were prohibited from taking part in any academic activities. Within a year
she came to the United States and became professor of mathematics at Bryn
Mawr College.

The extent and significance of Noether's work cannot be judged from only
her writing. Many of her remarks and suggestions revealed her great insights
and influenced the work of students and colleagues.

OBJECTIVE: *State and apply theorems concerning measures of intersecting chords, secants, and tangents.*

8-8 Segments of Chords, Secants, and Tangents

 **EXPLORE** Construct on paper or on a computer screen $\odot O$ with diameter $\overline{AB}$ of length 4 and construct $\overline{CD}$ perpendicular to $\overline{OB}$ at its midpoint. Find $AE \cdot BE$ and $CE \cdot DE$. What do you discover?

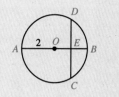

In the last lesson you studied how the measure of an angle formed (1) by chords intersecting in the interior of a circle, (2) by two secants from an external point, and (3) by a tangent and a secant from an external point are related to the measures of the intercepted arcs. In this lesson the same three situations are presented, but you will focus on lengths of chords and segments.

◆ **THEOREM 8.15**

If two chords intersect in a circle, then the product of the lengths of the segments of one chord equals the product of the lengths of the segments of the second chord.

Given: $\overline{AC}$ and $\overline{BD}$ are chords intersecting at P.

Prove: $AP \cdot PC = BP \cdot PD$

Plan You can prove that $\triangle ABP \sim \triangle DCP$ by the AA Similarity Theorem. Use the fact that ratios of lengths of corresponding sides in similar triangles are proportional to conclude $\frac{AP}{DP} = \frac{BP}{CP}$ and rewrite this equation.

Example 1

Find x if $RV = 3$, $TV = 7$, and $SV = 8$.

Solution

$RV \cdot VS = UV \cdot VT$
$3 \cdot 8 = x \cdot 7 \quad x = \frac{24}{7}$

Try This

Find y if $UV = 8$, $VT = 15$, and $RV = 7$.

The next theorem is about secants from an external point. The conclusion of the theorem is similar to that for Theorem 8.15.

Suppose that two secants from an external point P intersect a circle at points A, B, C, and D as shown to the right. $\overline{PA}$ and $\overline{PB}$ are called secant segments and $\overline{PC}$ and $\overline{PD}$ are called external segments.

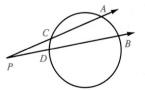

8-8 Segments of Chords, Secants, and Tangents   **379**

First Five Minutes

(Quiz on previous lesson)

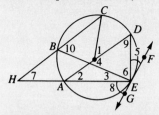

Points A, B, C, D, E on $\odot O$; diameter $\overline{AD}$, tangent $\overleftrightarrow{EF}$; $m\widehat{AB} = 30$, $m\widehat{BC} = 70$, $m\widehat{CD} = 80$, $m\widehat{DE} = 50$. Find each measure.

1. $m\angle 1$ 80 **2.** $m\angle 2$ 25
3. $m\angle 3$ 15 **4.** $m\angle 4$ 40
5. $m\angle 5$ 25 **6.** $m\angle 6$ 75
7. $m\angle 7$ 50 **8.** $m\angle 8$ 65
9. $m\angle 9$ 65 **10.** $m\angle 10$ 65

Lesson Opener

Begin by reviewing the definition of similar triangles, AA Similarity Postulate, and solving proportions. Point out that this lesson involves finding lengths of chords and segments rather than angle measure. A method that can be used to find lengths of segments when chords, secants, or tangents intersect is to establish a ratio of corresponding sides of similar triangles. (See the Explore.)

NOTE: Theorem 8.15 deals with intersecting chords at a point in the interior of a circle. Theorem 8.16 deals with intersecting secants from an exterior point. Theorem 8.17 deals with an intersecting tangent and secant from an exterior point.

Materials

student notebooks
compasses
straightedges
investigative software

Emphasize that the location of the *point of intersection* of two chords, two secant segments, or a tangent segment and a secant segment is the key to remembering how to find the lengths of segments of chords, secants, and tangents.

Case 1—Apply Theorem 8.15. When two chords intersect in a circle, then $a \cdot b = c \cdot d$.

Case 2—Apply Theorem 8.16. When two secant segments drawn to a circle intersect outside the circle, then $a(a + b) = c(c + d)$.

Case 3—Apply Theorem 8.17. When a tangent segment and a secant segment drawn to a circle intersect outside a circle, then $a(a + b) = c(c + 0)$ or $a(a + b) = c^2$.

Common Errors

Students frequently have difficulties determining and naming which triangles are similar and which angles are congruent. The use of colored chalk or overlays and extra practice may be helpful.

◆ THEOREM 8.16

If two secant segments are drawn to a circle from an exterior point, then the product of the lengths of one secant segment and its external segment equals the product of the lengths of the other secant segment and its external segment.

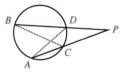

Given: $\overline{PA}$ and $\overline{PB}$ are secant segments from the external point P and intersect the circle at points C and D to form external segments $\overline{PC}$ and $\overline{PD}$.

Prove: $PA \cdot PC = PB \cdot PD$

Plan You can prove that $\triangle ADP \sim \triangle BCP$ by the AA Similarity Theorem. Ratios of corresponding sides in similar triangles are proportional so $\frac{PA}{PB} = \frac{PD}{PC}$. Rewrite this proportion to obtain the desired form.

Example 2

Find x in the figure to the right.

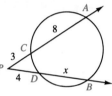

Solution

$$PA \cdot PC = PB \cdot PD$$
$$(8 + 3)3 = (x + 4)4$$
$$33 = 4x + 16$$
$$17 = 4x$$
$$x = \frac{17}{4}$$

Try This

If $PC = 7$, $PD = 9$, and $DB = 15$, find AC.

As the secant $\overline{PB}$ moves closer and closer to the position of tangent from P, the product $PB \cdot PD$ becomes $PB \cdot PB$. This result is stated in Theorem 8.17.

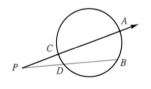
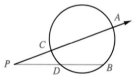
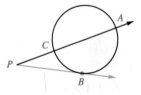

◆ THEOREM 8.17

If a tangent segment and a secant segment are drawn to a circle from an exterior point, then the square of the length of the tangent segment equals the product of the lengths of the secant segment and its external secant segment.

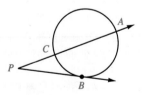

Example 3

Find x in the figure to the right.

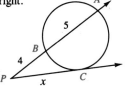

Solution

$PA \cdot PB = PC^2$
$(5 + 4)4 = x^2$
$36 = x^2$
$x = 6$

Try This

If $PC = 10$ and $PB = 6$, find AB.

Class Exercises

Short Answer

Complete each statement.

1.

$AP \cdot PB = $ ___

2.

$DP \cdot PC = $ ___

3.

$AP \cdot PB = $ ___

Sample Exercises

4. $AP = 8$, $BP = 6$, $CP = 5$ Find DP.
5. $AB = 11$, $AP = 6$, $DP = 7$ Find CP.
6. $EQ = 8$, $FQ = 6$, $GQ = 5$ Find HQ.
7. $EQ = 7$, $HQ = 9$, $GH = 6$ Find FQ.

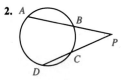

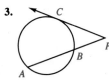

(handwritten notes:) $48 = 5x$ $48 = 5x$ $48 = x$ $9 \times 15 = 7x$ $135 = 7x$

Discussion

8. Imagine that points A, C, and D are fixed and that point B is moving clockwise around the circle. When B is near D is the value of $AX \cdot XB$ almost 1 or almost 0? Explain. If $\overline{CD}$ is a diameter, where would point B be located if $AX \cdot XB$ were exactly equal to one?

9. Give a convincing argument that for some locations of point B on the circles above $AX \cdot XB$ is greater than 10.

Incorrect: $5(7) = 6(4)$
Correct: $5(5 + 7) = 6(6 + 4)$

Guided Practice

Chalkboard Examples

1. If $RV = y$, $VS = 3y$, $UV = 12$, and $VT = 25$, find RV and VS. **10, 30**

Answer to **Try This** $\frac{120}{7}$

2. If $PC = 2$, $PA = 9$, and $PB = 12$, find PD. $\frac{3}{2}$

Answer to **Try This** $\frac{167}{7}$

3. If $PC = 8$ and $PA = 16$, find BA. **12**

Answer to **Try This** $\frac{32}{3}$

Class Exercise Answers

1. $DP \cdot PC$ **2.** $AP \cdot PB$
3. PC^2 **4.** $\frac{48}{5}$ **5.** $\frac{30}{7}$
6. $\frac{48}{5}$ **7.** $\frac{135}{7}$ **8.** Almost 0;
XB approaches 0. $AX \cdot 0 = 0$
When $AX \cdot XB = 1$, B is $\frac{1}{AX}$ from X.
9. For B sufficiently near
A, AX and XB can be made arbitrarily large so $AX \cdot XB$ can be made greater than 10.

Assignment Guide

Minimum: 1–21 e/o, 31a, MR
Regular: 1–25 e/o, 31, MR
Advanced: 14–21 e/o, 22–31, MR

Applications
Exercise 20

Algebra
Exercises 1–16, 19, AR

Exercises

A

Find x.

1.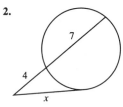

2.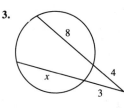

3.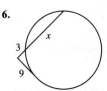

4.

5.

6.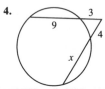

7. $AP = 12$, $PB = 7$, $PD = 11$ Find PC.
8. $AQ = 8$, $QC = 3$, $BQ = 5$ Find QD.
9. $AB = 9$, $BP = 10$, $PD = 18$ Find CD.
10. $AC = 12$, $AQ = 8$, $BQ = 5$ Find BD.
11. $AB = 8$, $AP = 17$, $CD = 7$ Find DP.
12. $BD = 18$, $AC = 14$, $CQ = 5$ Find BQ.
13. $AC = 15$, $BQ = 9$, $QD = 4$ Find AQ and CQ.

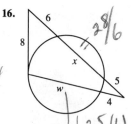

B

Find each variable.

14.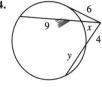

15.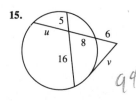

16.

17. Is the triangle in Exercise 16 equilateral, isosceles, or scalene?
   Explain your reasoning.

18. Prove Theorem 8.15.
   Given: $\overline{AC}$ and $\overline{BD}$ are chords intersecting at P.
   Prove: $AP \cdot PC = BP \cdot PD$

19. Find the lengths of chords $\overline{AB}$ and $\overline{CD}$.

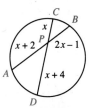

20. Suppose that $\overline{PA}$ and $\overline{PC}$ are both tangent to $\odot O$. Prove that $PC^2 = PB \cdot PD$.

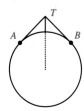

21. Suppose a radio tower T is 800 ft tall. Assuming that the diameter of the earth is 8000 mi, how far is it from the top of the tower to the horizon point A?

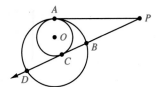

C

22. If $\overline{PB}$ and $\overline{PD}$ are secant segments and $PB = PD$, prove that $PA = PC$.

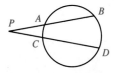

23. In the figure O is the center of two concentric circles. $\overline{RS}$ is tangent to the smaller circle. If $RX = 5$ and $RS = 30$, find XY.

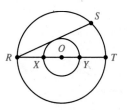

24. Suppose that two circles intersect at C and D and that point P is a point on $\overleftrightarrow{CD}$ exterior to both circles. $\overline{PA}$ and $\overline{PB}$ are tangent to the circles as shown. Prove that $\triangle APB$ is isosceles.

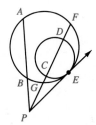

25. The two circles are tangent at E and $\overline{PE}$ is tangent to both circles at E. If $AP = 15$ and $PB = 6$, find $DP \cdot PC$. Explain your answer.

26. If $PF = 18$ and $PE = 5$, find $DP \cdot PC$. Explain your answer.

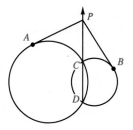

20. 1. $\odot O$ internally tan. to $\odot C$ at A, $\overline{PA}$ and $\overline{PC}$ tan. to $\odot O$ (Given) 2. $PA^2 = PB \cdot PD$ (If a tan. seg. and a secant seg. are drawn to a $\odot$ from an ext. pt., then the square of the length of the tan. seg. = the product of the lengths of the secant seg. and its ext. secant seg.) 3. $\overline{PA} \cong \overline{PC}$ (2 tan. seg. from an ext. pt. are $\cong$.) 4. $PA = PC$ (Def. $\cong$ seg.) 5. $PA^2 = PC^2$ (Square both sides.) 6. $PC^2 = PB \cdot PD$ (Subst.) **21.** $\approx 183,827.7$ ft or 34.8 mi **22.** 1. secants $\overline{PB}$ and $\overline{PD}$ (Given) 2. $PB \cdot PA = PD \cdot PC$ (If 2 secant seg. are drawn to a $\odot$ from an ext. pt., then the product of the lengths of one secant seg. and its ext. seg. = the product of the lengths of the other secant seg. and its ext. segment.) 3. $PB = PD$ (Given) 4. $PB \cdot PA = PB \cdot PC$ (Subst.) 5. $PA = PC$ (Div.) **23.** 40 **24.** 1. 2$\odot$s intersect at pt. C and D, P is on $\overleftrightarrow{CD}$. tan. $\overline{PA}$ and $\overline{PB}$ (Given) 2. $PD \cdot PC = PA^2$, $PD \cdot PC = PB^2$ (If a tan. seg. and a secant seg. are drawn to a $\odot$ from an ext. pt., then the square of the length of the tan. seg. = the product of the lengths of the secant seg. and its ext. secant seg.) 3. $PA^2 = PB^2$ (Trans.) 4. $PA = PB$ (Square roots) 5. $\overline{PA} \cong \overline{PB}$ (Def. $\cong$ seg.) 6. $\triangle PAB$ is isos. (Def. isos. $\triangle$) **25.** $AP \cdot PB = PE^2$, $PD \cdot PC = PE^2$ (Th. 8.17), $AP \cdot PB = PD \cdot PC$ (Trans.), $DP \cdot PC = 15 \cdot 6 = 90$ **26.** $DP \cdot PC = PE^2$ (Th. 8.17), $DP \cdot PC = 5^2 = 25$ **27.** $\frac{CG}{DG} = \frac{5}{7}$, $\frac{EG}{FG} = \frac{5}{7}$ **28.** 38

29. 1. ⊙s intersect at A and B. Chords $\overline{AF}$ and $\overline{BE}$ intersect at G. Chords $\overline{HI}$ and $\overline{EF}$ (Given) 2. Draw aux. line $\overline{BA}$. (2 pt. determine a line.) 3. $m \angle BEF = m \angle BAF$, $m \angle BCI = m \angle BAF$ (∠s intercepting the same arc have the same measure.) 4. $m \angle BEF = m \angle BCI$ (Trans.) 5. $\angle BEF \cong \angle BCI$ (Def. $\cong$ ∠s) 6. $\overline{CD} \parallel \overline{EF}$ (If 2 lines are cut by a trans. and corr. ∠s are $\cong$, then the lines are $\parallel$.)

30. 1. $m \angle BEF = m \angle BCI$ (Ex. 29) 2. $m \angle BEF = \frac{1}{2} m \widehat{BF}$ (The measure of an inscribed ∠ is half the measure of its intercepted arc.) 3. $m \angle BCI = \frac{1}{2}(m \widehat{HE} + m \widehat{BI})$ (The measure of an ∠ formed by 2 chords intersecting inside a circle is one half the sum of the intercepted arcs). 4. $\frac{1}{2} m \widehat{BF} = \frac{1}{2}(m \widehat{HE} + m \widehat{BI})$ (Subst.) 5. $\frac{1}{2}(m \widehat{BI} + m \widehat{IF}) = \frac{1}{2}(m \widehat{HE} + m \widehat{BI})$ (Arc Add. Post.) 6. $m \widehat{BI} + m \widehat{IF} = m \widehat{HE} + m \widehat{BI}$ (Mult.) 7. $m \widehat{FI} = m \widehat{EH}$ or $m \widehat{EH} = m \widehat{FI}$ (Sub.)   **31.** a. always true by Th. 8.16 b. sometimes true; true if $PC = PC'$ c. always true; $PC \cdot PD = PC' \cdot PD'$, $\frac{PC}{PC'} = \frac{PD'}{PD}$, $\angle P \cong \angle P$, $\triangle PCC' \sim \triangle PD'D$ by SAS $\sim$, $\triangle PCC' \sim \triangle PB'B$, $\triangle PD'D \sim \triangle PB'B$, $\triangle PB'B \sim \triangle PAA'$, $\triangle PD'D \sim \triangle PAA'$, $\frac{PD}{PA'} = \frac{PD'}{PA}$, $PD \cdot PA = PA' \cdot PD'$

Algebra Review Answers

1. $x^2 + 2x + 1$
2. $x^2 - 6x + 9$
3. $a^2 + 10a + 25$
4. $y^2 - 10y + 25$
5. $m^2 + m - 6$
6. $2a^2 + a - 3$
7. $3s^2 + 5s - 12$ 8. $r^2 - 25$

Quiz Answers

1. true   2. false
3. true   4. true   5. 64
6. 142   7. 99   8. 6
9. 31   10. 24   11. 17

384   *Chapter 8   Circles*

27. If $AG = 5$ and $BG = 7$, find $\frac{CG}{DG}$ and $\frac{EG}{FG}$.

28 If $m \angle BEF = 38$, find $m \angle BCI$.

29. Prove that $\overline{CD} \parallel \overline{EF}$.

30. Prove that $m \widehat{EH} = m \widehat{FI}$.

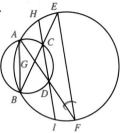

Critical Thinking

31. Suppose that $\overline{PD}$ and $\overline{PD}'$ are secants of all three circles. Decide whether or not each equation is always true, sometimes true, or never true. Give a convincing argument for each answer.

a. $PA \cdot PB = PA' \cdot PB'$
b. $PA \cdot PC = PA' \cdot PC'$
c. $PA \cdot PD = PA' \cdot PD'$

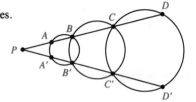

Algebra Review

Multiply.

1. $(x + 1)^2$ 2. $(x - 3)^2$ 3. $(a + 5)^2$ 4. $(y - 5)^2$
5. $(m + 3)(m - 2)$ 6. $(2a + 3)(a - 1)$ 7. $(s + 3)(3s - 4)$ 8. $(r - 5)(r + 5)$

Quiz

Determine whether each statement is true or false.

1. The measure of an inscribed angle is one half the measure of the intercepted arc.
2. If two inscribed angles in a circle are congruent, then they intercept the same arc.
3. If a right angle is inscribed in a circle, then its intercepted arc is a semicircle.
4. The measurement of an angle formed by two secants intersecting in the exterior of a circle is equal to one half the difference of the two intercepted arcs.

$\overline{DF}$ is tangent to ⊙T.

5. If $m \angle B = 32$, find $m \widehat{EC}$.
6. If $m \widehat{AD} = 76$, find $m \angle ADF$.
7. If $m \widehat{AE} = 28$ and $m \widehat{BD} = 170$, find $m \angle l$.
8. If $CF = 3$ and $BC = 9$, find DF.

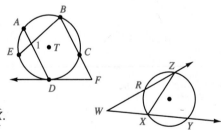

$\overline{WZ}$ and $\overline{WY}$ are secants.

9. If $m \widehat{ZY} = 88$ and $m \widehat{RX} = 26$, find $m \angle W$.
10. If $m \angle ZXY = 32$ and $m \angle W = 20$, find $m \widehat{RX}$.
11. If $WZ = 15$, $WR = 4$, and $WX = 3$, find XY.

CRITICAL THINKING

Venn Diagrams and Reasoning Patterns

Venn diagrams (see page 38) can be used to test whether an argument is logically correct. An if-then statement can be represented in terms of circles, which help illustrate the validity of arguments based on the conditional. Consider the following examples.

Example 1

If a student is taking geometry, then she recognizes triangles. $p \to q$

Bonnie is taking geometry. $\quad p$ (premise)

Bonnie recognizes triangles. $\quad q$ (conclusion)

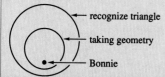

The outer circle defines those students that recognize triangles. The inner circle indicates that all of the students taking geometry recognize triangles. Since Bonnie is in the inner circle, she is automatically among those students that recognize triangles.

Example 2 *Assuming the Converse*

If a figure is a parallelogram, then it is a quadrilateral. $\quad p \to q$

Figure *ABCD* is a quadrilateral. $\quad q$

Figure *ABCD* is a parallelogram. $\quad p$

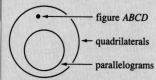

The Venn diagram shows that a point representing figure *ABCD* can be outside the parallelogram circle, so the reasoning pattern is invalid. Here, the converse of the original conditional is assumed.

Example 3 *Assuming the Inverse*

If a student worked hard, then he passed the course. $\quad p \to q$

Matthew did not work hard. $\quad \sim p$

Matthew did not pass the course. $\quad \sim q$

The Venn diagram shows that although Matthew did not work hard, the point representing him could still be inside the circle representing those who passed the course. The error in this case is assuming the inverse of the original conditional.

Exercises

Draw Venn diagrams to show each reasoning pattern and decide whether it is valid.

1. If you are over 21, then you can vote.

   Marika cannot vote.

   Marika is not over 21.

2. If you do not pay taxes, then you will go to jail.

   Peter paid his taxes.

   Peter went to jail.

3. If you have enough, then you must share.

   Theresa has enough.

   Theresa must share.

4. If you are a citizen, then you want power.

   If you want power, then you must vote.

   If you are a citizen, then you must vote.

5. If you are a doctor, then you have gone to college.

   Pat is not a doctor.

   Pat did not go to college.

6. If *x* is divisible by 4, then *x* is even.

   10 is even.

   10 is divisible by 4.

Exercise Answers

1. valid

2. Not valid; Peter may not be in jail or he may be in jail for another reason.

3. valid

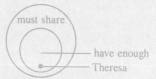

4. valid

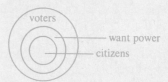

5. Not valid; Pat may be a college graduate and not be a doctor.

6. Not valid; 10 is not divisible by 4.

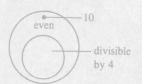

CHAPTER SUMMARY

Vocabulary

arc (8-4)
center (8-1)
central angle (8-4)
chord (8-1)
circle (8-1)
circumscribed polygon (8-1)
common tangents (8-3)

concentric circles (8-1)
congruent arcs (8-4)
congruent circles (8-1)
diameter (8-1)
inscribed angle (8-6)
inscribed polygon (8-1)
intercepted arc (8-6)

major arc (8-4)
minor arc (8-4)
radius (8-1)
secant (8-1)
semicircle (8-4)
sphere (8-1)
tangent (8-1)
tangent-chord angle (8-6)

Key Ideas

1. If a line is perpendicular to a radius of a circle at a point on the circle, then the line is tangent to the circle.
2. If a line is tangent to a circle, then it is perpendicular to the radius at the point of tangency.
3. In the same circle or congruent circles
   a. congruent chords have congruent minor arcs.
   b. congruent minor arcs have congruent chords and congruent central angles.
   c. congruent chords are equidistant from the center.
   d. chords equidistant from the center are congruent.
4. If a diameter is perpendicular to a chord, then it bisects the chord and its minor and major arcs.
5. If two inscribed angles intercept the same arc, then the angles are congruent.
6. The following are angle-arc relationships.

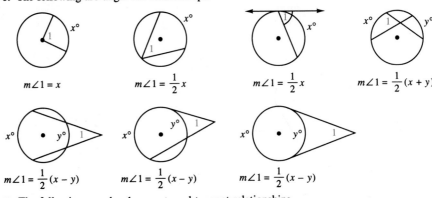

$$m\angle 1 = x \qquad m\angle 1 = \frac{1}{2}x \qquad m\angle 1 = \frac{1}{2}x \qquad m\angle 1 = \frac{1}{2}(x+y)$$

$$m\angle 1 = \frac{1}{2}(x-y) \qquad m\angle 1 = \frac{1}{2}(x-y) \qquad m\angle 1 = \frac{1}{2}(x-y)$$

7. The following are chord, secant, and tangent relationships.

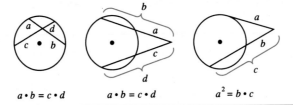

$$a \cdot b = c \cdot d \qquad a \cdot b = c \cdot d \qquad a^2 = b \cdot c$$

CHAPTER REVIEW

8-1

Determine whether each statement is true or false.

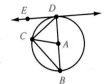

1. $\overline{BD}$ is a chord.
2. $\overline{BC}$ is a secant.
3. $\overline{CD}$ is a radius.
4. $\angle ACD$ is inscribed in $\odot A$.

8-2

$\overline{XW}$ and $\overline{XY}$ are tangent to $\odot P$ at W and Y.

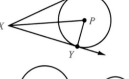

5. Find $m\angle PYX$.
6. If $XW = 10$, find XY.
7. If $m\angle WXY = 60$ and $XY = 6\sqrt{3}$, find PY.

8-3

8. If $WL = 6$, $LM = 8$, and $MY = 4$, find XM.
9. If $m\angle Y = 30$, $WL = 7$, and $WX = 8$, find XM.
10. Draw a pair of circles that have only one common internal tangent.

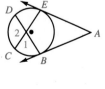

8-4

In $\odot I$, HF is a diameter.

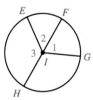

11. If $m\angle 1 = 43$, find $m\widehat{FG}$.
12. If $m\widehat{EF} = 53$, find $m\angle 3$.
13. If $m\widehat{HG} = 140$ and $\angle 1 = \angle 2$, find $m\widehat{HE}$.

8-5

In $\odot D$, $AB \perp DC$ and $\overline{AE} \cong \overline{EB}$.

14. If $AD = 26$ and $DE = 10$, find AB.
15. If $m\widehat{BC} = 45$ and $AE = 7$, find AD.
16. If $AB = 16$ and $AD = 9$, find DE.

8-6

$\overrightarrow{SW}$ is tangent at S. Determine whether each statement is true or false.

17. If $m\angle U = 103$, then $m\widehat{VRS} = 206$.
18. If $m\widehat{RU} = 150$, then $m\angle S = 150$.
19. If $m\angle WSR = 44$, then $m\widehat{RS} = 22$.

8-7

$\overrightarrow{AB}$ and $\overrightarrow{AE}$ are tangent at B and E. $m\widehat{CB} = 50$, $m\widehat{CD} = 30$, $m\widehat{DE} = 116$

20. Find $m\angle 1$.
21. Find $m\widehat{BE}$.
22. Find $m\angle A$.
23. Find $m\angle 2$.

8-8

24. Find x in the figure on the right.
25. Find x in the figure on the left.

 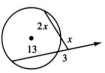

1. true
2. false
3. false
4. false
5. 90
6. 10
7. 6
8. 2
9. 3
10.

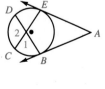

11. 43
12. 127
13. 140
14. 48
15. $7\sqrt{2}$
16. $\sqrt{17}$
17. true
18. false
19. false
20. 83
21. 164
22. 16
23. 97
24. 4
25. 4

Teacher's Resource Materials

Chapter 8 Tests

Test Answers

1. false   2. true   3. true
4. true   5. false   6. false
7. 24   8. 158   9. 18
10. 70   11. 118
12. 15   13. $5\sqrt{5}$
14. 25   15. 90   16. 8
17. 157   18. 80
19. center   20. congruent
21. perpendicular   22. 2
23. $\frac{11}{4}$ 24. $3\sqrt{5}$

CHAPTER TEST

Determine whether each statement is true or false.

1. A radius is a segment that joins two points on a circle.
2. Concentric circles have the same center.
3. Two circles are congruent if their radii are congruent.
4. If a line is perpendicular to a radius of a circle at a point on the circle, then the line is tangent to the circle.
5. If the measure of an arc in one circle is equal to the measure of an arc in another circle, the chords of these arcs are congruent.
6. If a quadrilateral is inscribed in a circle, then its opposite angles are complementary.

$\overline{AB}$ **is tangent at A.**

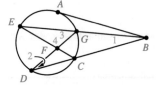

7. If $m\widehat{ED} = 48$, find $m\angle 3$.
8. If $m\widehat{DC} = 42$ and $m\angle 4 = 100$, find $m\widehat{EG}$.
9. If $m\widehat{ED} = 74$ and $m\widehat{GC} = 38$, find $m\angle 1$.
10. If $m\widehat{DEA} = 210$ and $m\widehat{AC} = 70$, find $m\angle ABD$.
11. If $m\angle 2 = 28$ and $m\angle 3 = 34$, find $m\angle 4$.

$\overline{LM}$ **is a common tangent.**

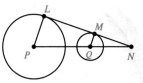

12. If $QM = 6$, $MN = 8$ and $LN = 20$, find PL.
13. If $PL = 5$ and $LN = 10$, find PN.
14. If $PL = 10$, $QM = 2$, and $LM = 20$, find LN.

$\overline{AD}$ **and $\overline{BD}$ are tangent to $\odot O$.**

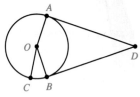

15. Find $m\angle OAD$.
16. If $BD = 8$, find AD.
17. If $m\angle BOC = 37$ and $m\angle AOB = 120$, find $m\widehat{AC}$.
18. If $\angle AOB$ is supplementary to $\angle ADB$ and $m\widehat{AB} = 100$, find $m\angle ADB$.

Complete each statement.

19. The perpendicular bisector of a chord contains the ___ of the circle.
20. In a circle, chords equidistant from the center are ___ .
21. If a diameter bisects a chord that is not a diameter, then it is ___ to the chord.

Find x in each figure.

22.   23.   24.

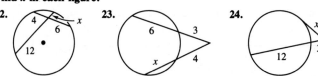

PREPARING FOR COLLEGE ENTRANCE EXAMS

Give the one correct answer for each question.

1. If $m = x + 7$ and $n = x - 12$, then $m - n$ is equal to which of the following?

(A) 5   (B) 19   (C) -5
(D) -19 (E) $2x - 5$

2. If $z < 0$, which of the following must be negative?

(A) z^2 (B) $-2z$ (C) $z + 1$
(D) $|z| - z$ (E) $\frac{z}{2}$

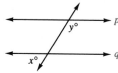

3. In the figure above, if $\overline{RS} \cong \overline{ST}$, then $m\angle RST =$

(A) 40   (B) 140   (C) 70
(D) 110   (E) 60

4. A long string of colored lanterns is prepared for a party. The colors of the lanterns form a repeating pattern starting with red, yellow, green, blue, white; red, yellow, green, blue, white, and so on. What color is the 37th lantern?

(A) red   (B) yellow   (C) green
(D) blue   (E) white

5. If the perimeter of a rectangular yard is 200 ft, which of the following could be the length of one of its sides?
I. 40 ft
II. 51 ft
III. 100 ft

(A) I only   (B) II only   (C) III only
(D) I and II only   (E) I, II, and III

6. If the sum of five consecutive integers is 50, what is the largest of these integers?

(A) 16   (B) 12   (C) 10
(D) 9   (E) Cannot be determined
from the information given.

7. A florist sells b bouquets of roses at d dollars per bouquet in h hours. Which of the following represents the amount of money received in two hours from the sale of roses?

(A) $\frac{2bd}{h}$ (B) $\frac{bd}{2h}$ (C) $2bdh$
(D) $\frac{2bh}{d}$ (E) $\frac{bh}{2d}$

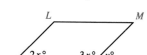

8. In the figure above, if $p \| q$, then $y - x =$

(A) 180   (B) 90   (C) 45
(D) 0   (E) Cannot be determined
from the information given.

9. If M is odd, which of the following CANNOT be a whole number?

(A) $\sqrt{M}$ (B) $\frac{M-1}{2}$ (C) $\frac{M^2}{2}$
(D) M^2 (E) $\frac{M}{5}$

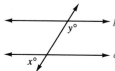

KLMN is a parallelogram.

10. In the figure above, what is the value of y?

(A) 36   (B) 60   (C) 72
(D) 108   (E) 45

11. If $x - y > 0$, which of the following MUST be true?

(A) $|x| > y$ (B) $-x > -y$
(C) $x > 0$ (D) $x^2 > y^2$ (E) $y < 0$

12. If 12 liters of pure alcohol are mixed with 8 liters of pure water, what percent of the resulting mixture is alcohol?

(A) $66\frac{2}{3}\%$ (B) 80%   (C) 40%
(D) 75%   (E) 60%

Constructions and Loci

Chapter Overview

Constructions have been introduced in the Explores and exercises of previous chapters. Some basic constructions are reviewed in the first lesson of this chapter, and more complex constructions are developed thereafter building on these. Concurrency theorems for triangles are discussed in Lesson 9-5. The final three lessons of this chapter deal with locus problems and their applications to the outside world.

Objectives

9-1 ■ Construct congruent segments, congruent angles, perpendicular bisectors, and angle bisectors.

9-2 ■ Construct the perpendicular to a given line from a given point on the line, and from a given point not on the line, and the parallel to a given line.

9-3 ■ Construct tangents to a circle.
Construct the center of a circle given the circle or arcs of the circle.

9-4 ■ Divide a given segment into *n* congruent parts and given two segments, construct their geometric mean.

9-5 ■ Apply the concurrency theorems for triangles, and distinguish among the circumcenter, the incenter, the centroid, and the orthocenter of a triangle.

9-6 ■ Solve simple locus problems.

9-7 ■ Solve compound locus problems.

9-8 ■ Solve construction problems.

Cooperative Learning Opportunities

Constructions in geometry should be done individually. It is necessary that each student have experience in constructing the angles, triangles, circles, and other figures. But many times a student will not completely understand how to complete a construction, will not be sure whether or not a construction is correct, or will not fully grasp why a construction accomplishes its objective. Cooperative groups can be used to check the practice and theory of constructions.

The constructions covered in the first two lessons can be reviewed in groups of three. In Lesson 9-1, have students do constructions 2, 3 and 4 individually. Assign students to groups of 3 and have them check that their constructions are the same. Then have students individually explain why their construction achieves its objective.

In Lesson 9-2, constructions 5, 6, and 7 can be treated in a similar way. Using this group work for two days at the beginning of the chapter will give students the start they need for the chapter.

Multicultural Note: *Egyptian Pi*

The Egyptians obtained a good approximation of π through the use of constructions. They assumed that a square of side 8 is equal in area to a circle of diameter 9. This relationship probably came through many careful measurements.

You might want to have students compare the areas of the two figures mentioned. The area of the circle is less than 1% smaller than that of the square. This difference would be difficult to detect experimentally.

Ask students to find the value of π based on the assumption that the given square and circle are equal in area. See who can get started without hints. The value is easily found by solving: $\pi \cdot 4.5^2 = 64$; $\pi = 3.16$.

Alternative Assessment and Communication Ideas

Since this chapter on constructions reviews a number of previously taught concepts, you can take this opportunity to check the understanding, and perhaps raise the grades, of some students who did not at first catch on to ideas of congruence or triangle relationships, for example.

For Lesson 9-1, Exercises 11 and 12, have one or two students prepare to do constructions and explain why each construction gives the desired congruence. They might use an overhead or the chalkboard. Ask them to explain the constructions and review why SAS and ASA establish congruence.

On page 399, Exercises 16, 17, and 18 may be treated in the same way. Ask the student working on 16 to review the special right triangle relationships and the students working on 17 and 18 to review quadrilaterals.

On page 403, Exercises 16 through 19 can be treated in a similar way.

Investigations and Projects

While studying loci, ask students to think about practical situations that use loci. Ask them to collect phrases that refer to locus and to explain just what kind of locus it might be. Some examples might include the following.

Radio commercial: within our listening area. **Weather report:** the storm will pass just north of the city. **Traffic report:** construction between exits 12 and 14. **Planning:** the arena will be in the downtown area. **Sports:** they played well inside the 20-yard line. **Politics:** no campaigning within 50 feet of the polling place.

After they have collected verbal expressions and perhaps pictures related to loci, have students create a display for the bulletin board. Each part of the display should contain a single expression, of the type listed above, along with a clear explanation of the locus referred to and perhaps some common misunderstandings about the locus.

Lesson	PACING CHART (DAYS)			Opening Activity	Cooperative Activity	Seat or Group Work
	1-Year Minimum	1-Year Regular	1-Year Advanced			
9-1	1	1	1	Chapter Opener: **TE** p. 390; Lesson Opener: **TE** p. 391	✂ Constructions 1–4: **SE** p. 391–392	Try This Exercise
9-2	2	2	2	First Five Minutes 9-2: **FFM Transparency Masters** p. 34 or **TE** p. 396; Lesson Opener: **TE** p. 396	Explore: **SE** p. 396; ✂ Constructions 5–7: **SE** p. 396–397; ✂ Lab Worksheet 9-2: **Labortary Manual** p. 89	Try This Exercise
9-3	1	1	1	First Five Minutes 9-3: **FFM Transparency Masters** p. 35 or **TE** p. 401; Lesson Opener: **TE** p. 401	Explore: **SE** p. 401; ✂ Constructions 8–10: **SE** p. 401–402	✂ Constructions 8–10: **SE** p. 401–402
9-4	2	2	2	First Five Minutes 9-4: **FFM Transparency Masters** p. 35 or **TE** p. 405; Lesson Opener: **TE** p. 405	Explore: **SE** p. 405; ✂ Constructions 11–13: **SE** p. 405–406	✂ Constructions 11–13: **SE** p. 405–406
9-5	1	1	1	First Five Minutes 9-5: **FFM Transparency Masters** p. 36 or **TE** p. 410; Lesson Opener: **TE** p. 410	Explore: **SE** p. 410; ✂ Lab Worksheet 9-5A: **Laboratory Manual** p. 90; ✂ Lab Worksheet 9-5B: **Laboratory Manual** p. 91; ✂ Lab Worksheet 9-5C: **Laboratory Manual** p. 93	Try This Exercise
9-6	2	2	2	First Five Minutes 9-6: **FFM Transparency Masters** p. 36 or **TE** p. 415; Lesson Opener: **TE** p. 415	Explore: **TE** p. 416; Enrichment: **SE** p. 419	Try This Exercises
9-7	1	1	1	First Five Minutes 9-7: **FFM Transparency Masters** p. 37 or **TE** p. 420; Lesson Opener: **TE** p. 420	Math Contest Problem: **SE** p. 423	Try This Exercises
9-8	1	1	1	First Five Minutes 9-8: **FFM Transparency Masters** p. 37 or **TE** p. 424; Lesson Opener: **TE** p. 424	Critical Thinking: **SE** p. 429	Try This Exercises
Review	1	1	1			
Test	1	1	1			
Cum. Review	1	1	1			

FFM = First Five Minutes

Enrichment	Review/Assess	Reteach	Technology	Lesson
Historical Note: **SE** p. 395; ✂ Enrichment Using Manipulatives 9-1: *Enrichment* p. 50	Class Exercises: **SE** p. 393; Algebra Review: **SE** p. 395	Practice Worksheet 9-1: *Practice and Mixed Review* p.64		**9-1**
Study Skills: **SE** p. 400	Class Exercises: **SE** p. 398; Mixed Review: **SE** p. 400	Practice Worksheet 9-2: *Practice and Mixed Review* p.65		**9-2**
Computer Activity: **SE** p. 404; ✂ Enrichment Using Manipulatives 9-3: *Enrichment* p. 51	Class Exercises: **SE** p. 402; Mixed Review: **SE** p. 404	Practice Worksheet 9-3: *Practice and Mixed Review* p.66	Computer Activity: **SE** p. 404	**9-3**
Connections: **SE** p. 409; ✂ Enrichment Using Manipulatives 9-4: *Enrichment* p. 52	Class Exercises: **SE** p. 407; Mixed Review: **SE** p. 409	Practice Worksheet 9-4: *Practice and Mixed Review* p.67		**9-4**
✂ Enrichment Using Manipulatives 9-5: *Enrichment* p. 53 ✂ Lab Worksheet 9-5D: *Laboratory Manual* p. 94	Class Exercises: **SE** p. 412; Algebra Review: **SE** p. 414; Quiz: **SE** p. 414; Quiz: *Assessment* p. 95	Practice Worksheet 9-5: *Practice and Mixed Review* p. 68	Computer Exploration 23: **SE** p. 656; Computer Exploration 24: **SE** p. 657; Computer Exploration 25: **SE** p. 658; Computer Exploration 26: **SE** p. 659; Calculator Worksheet 9-5: *Technology* p. CL13	**9-5**
Enrichment: **SE** p. 419; ✂ Enrichment Using Manipulatives 9-6: *Enrichment* p. 54	Class Exercises: **SE** p. 416; Mixed Review: **SE** p. 419	Practice Worksheet 9-6: *Practice and Mixed Review* p.69		**9-6**
Math Contest Problem: **SE** p. 423; Enrichment Using Manipulatives 9-7: *Enrichment* p. 55	Class Exercises: **SE** p. 421; Algebra Review: **SE** p. 423	Practice Worksheet 9-7: *Practice and Mixed Review* p.70		**9-7**
Discrete Math: **SE** p. 428; Critical Thinking: **SE** p. 429; Enrichment Using Manipulatives 9-8: *Enrichment* p. 56	Class Exercises: **SE** p. 425; Mixed Review: **SE** p. 427; Quiz: **SE** p. 427; Quiz: *Assessment* p. 96	Practice Worksheet 9-8: *Practice and Mixed Review* p.71		**9-8**
	Summary & Review: **SE** p. 430–431	Mixed Review: **Practice and Mixed Review** p. 110		**Review**
Problem Solving: **SE** p. 433	Chapter 9 Test: **SE** p. 432; Chapter 9 Tests: *Assessment* p. 49–54; *MathTest*			**Test**
	Cumulative Review: **SE** p. 434			**Cum. Review**

Review the basic compass and straightedge constructions that may already be familiar to students: duplicating a segment, duplicating an angle, bisecting a segment, bisecting an angle.

Answer

If the beam is segment AB, its perpendicular bisector can be constructed as follows. Use A as center and a radius greater than $\frac{1}{2} AB$ to mark an arc; use B as center and the same radius to mark another arc intersecting the first arc at C and D; draw $\overline{CD}$.

9

Constructions and Loci

A contractor wants to construct the perpendicular bisector of a beam shown on a blueprint. How can this be done using only a compass and straightedge?

BASIC CONSTRUCTIONS

OBJECTIVE: *Construct congruent segments, congruent angles, perpendicular bisectors, and angle bisectors.*

9-1 Segments, Angles, and Bisectors

In geometry, a **construction** is a geometric figure produced by using only a *compass* and *straightedge*. A compass is used to draw arcs and circles. A straightedge, which unlike a ruler has no measurement marks, is used to draw a line segment between two points. Basic constructions are used as a basis for more involved constructions.

CONSTRUCTION 1

Given a segment, construct a segment congruent to the given segment.

Given: $\overline{AB}$

Construct: a segment congruent to $\overline{AB}$

Procedure 1. Use a straightedge to draw $\overrightarrow{CE}$.
     2. Open your compass to radius AB.
     3. Placing the point of the compass at C, mark an arc intersecting $\overrightarrow{CE}$ at D.
     4. $\overline{CD}$ is congruent to $\overline{AB}$.

Proof $\overline{CD} \cong \overline{AB}$ since they are radii of congruent circles.

CONSTRUCTION 2

Given an angle, construct an angle congruent to the given angle.

Given: $\angle BAC$

Construct: an angle congruent to $\angle BAC$

Procedure 1. Draw ray $\overrightarrow{QM}$.
     2. Using A as center and any radius, mark an arc intersecting the sides of $\angle BAC$ at D and E.
     3. Using Q as center and radius $\overline{AD}$, mark an arc intersecting $\overrightarrow{QM}$ at R.
     4. Using R as center and $\overline{DE}$ as radius mark an arc intersecting the first arc at P.
     5. Draw $\overrightarrow{QP}$.
     6. $\angle PQR$ is congruent to $\angle BAC$.

Proof   By construction $\overline{QR} \cong \overline{AE} \cong \overline{QP} \cong \overline{AD}$ and $\overline{DE} \cong \overline{PR}$. Therefore $\triangle QPR \cong \triangle ADE$ by the SSS Postulate and $\angle PQR \cong BAC$ since corresponding parts of congruent triangles are congruent.

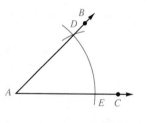

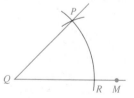

Lesson Opener

This lesson introduces four basic constructions that provide a foundation for more complex constructions later in the chapter. These constructions can be drawn using two simple tools—a compass and a straightedge. If available, use investigative software to illustrate the constructions.

Materials

student notebooks
compasses
straightedges
investigative software

Teaching Notes

In Construction 1, Step 3, point out that the lengths AB and CD are not measured by a ruler. In Construction 3, Step 2, show that the compass setting cannot be less than $\frac{1}{2}AB$ because if it were, the arcs would not intersect.

Key Terms

construction

Guided Practice

Chalkboard Examples

1. Given $\overline{AB}$ and $\overline{CD}$, construct a segment equal to $CD - AB$.

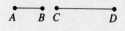

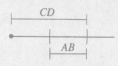

2. Construct an equilateral triangle with sides congruent to $\overline{AB}$ in Chalkboard Example 1.

Class Exercise Answers

1. Const. 1   **2.** Const. 2
3. Const. 2 and 4

4. 60°

5.

6.

7.

8.

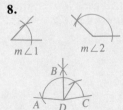

9. The lengths will not form a triangle. Theorem 5.23

CONSTRUCTION 3

Given a segment, construct the perpendicular bisector of the given segment.

Given: $\overline{AB}$

Construct: the perpendicular bisector of $\overline{AB}$

Procedure 1. Using A as center and a radius greater than $\frac{1}{2} AB$, mark an arc.
      2. Using B as center and the same radius, mark a second arc intersecting the first arc at points C and D.
      3. Draw $\overline{CD}$ intersecting $\overline{AB}$.
      4. $\overline{CD}$ is the perpendicular bisector of $\overline{AB}$.

Proof   Points C and D are equidistant from A and B. It follows that $\overline{CD}$ is the perpendicular bisector of $\overline{AB}$ from Theorem 4.7.

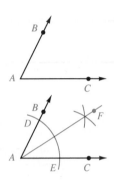

CONSTRUCTION 4

Given an angle, construct the bisector of the given angle.

Given: $\angle BAC$

Construct: the bisector of $\angle BAC$

Procedure 1. Using A as center and any radius, mark arcs intersecting the sides of $\angle BAC$ at points D and E.
      2. Using D and E as centers and the same (or larger) radius, mark arcs intersecting at F.
      3. Draw $\overline{AF}$.
      4. $\overline{AF}$ bisects $\angle BAC$.

Proof   Draw $\overline{DF}$ and $\overline{EF}$. Then $\triangle ADF \cong \triangle AEF$ by SSS. Thus $\angle DAF \cong \angle EAF$ since they are corresponding parts of congruent triangles.

Example 1

Given $\overline{AB}$ and $\overline{CD}$, construct a segment equal in length to $AB + CD$.

    Solution

    Use Construction 1 twice to construct a segment of length $AB + CD$.

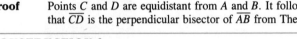

Try This

Construct a segment equal in length to $\frac{1}{2}(AB + CD)$.

Example 2

Construct an isosceles triangle with base $\overline{BC}$ and congruent sides $\overline{AB}$.

    Solution

    1. Draw $\overrightarrow{DX}$.
    2. Construct $DE = BC$.
    3. Using D as center and $\overline{AB}$ as radius, draw an arc.
    4. Using E as center and $\overline{AB}$ as radius, draw an arc intersecting the first arc at F.
    5. Draw sides $\overline{DF}$ and $\overline{EF}$.

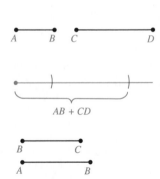

392   *Chapter 9   Constructions and Loci*

Class Exercises

Short Answer

1. Which construction would you use to construct a segment equal in length to the perimeter of a given triangle?
2. Which construction would you use to construct an angle equal in measure to the sum of the measures of the acute angles of a given obtuse triangle?
3. Which two constructions would you use to construct an angle equal in measure to the average measure of two given angles?

Sample Exercises

4. Use a ruler to draw a segment of length 2 cm. Construct an equilateral triangle with each side 2 cm long. What is the measure of each angle?
5. Use the triangle constructed in Exercise 4 to construct a 30° angle.
6. Use a ruler to draw segments of lengths 3 cm, 5 cm, and 6 cm. Construct a triangle using these three segments.
7. Draw two segments a and b of unequal length. Construct a segment of length $\frac{(a + b)}{2}$.
8. Draw an acute angle ($\angle 1$) and an obtuse angle ($\angle 2$). Construct an angle with a measure of $\frac{m\angle 1 + m\angle 2}{2}$.

Discussion

9. Try to construct a triangle with sides of lengths 3 cm, 5 cm, and 8 cm. What happens? Why?
10. Using only the construction for bisecting a segment, can you divide a segment into 4 equal parts? 6 equal parts? 8 equal parts? 12 equal parts? 16 equal parts? Explain.
11. Given $\triangle ABC$, suppose you constructed $\angle D \cong \angle A$, $\overline{DE} \cong \overline{AB}$, and $\overline{DF} \cong \overline{AC}$, then drew $\overline{EF}$. Would you have a triangle congruent to $\triangle ABC$? Explain.
12. Given $\triangle RST$, suppose you constructed $\overline{MN} \cong \overline{ST}$. Then, using M as center and RS as radius, suppose you drew an arc. Suppose next, using N as center and RT as radius, you drew an arc intersecting the first arc at P, then drew $\overline{PM}$ and $\overline{PN}$. Would you have constructed a triangle congruent to $\triangle RST$? Explain.

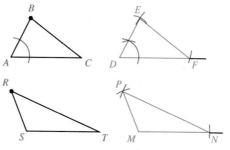

Exercises

A

Draw segments of length m and n and construct a segment of the given length. Label the constructed segment $\overline{AB}$.

•——— m ———• ⇒   •——————— n ———————•

1. $m + n$ 2. $2m + n$ 3. $2n - m$ 4. $\frac{m + n}{2}$

---

10. 4 yes, bisect the whole segment and then bisect each half; 6 no, need thirds; 8 yes, bisect the whole segment and then bisect each half and each quarter; 12 no, need thirds; 16 yes, bisect the whole segment and then bisect each half, each quarter, and each eighth.
11. By SAS, $\triangle DEF \cong \triangle ABC$.
12. By SSS, $\triangle PMN \cong \triangle RST$.

Assignment Guide
Minimum: 1–27 e/o, 30, AR
Regular: 1–27 e/o, 30, AR
Advanced: 19–30, AR

Constructions
Class Exercises 4–10
Exercises 1–12, 14–30
Algebra
Algebra Review

Lesson Closure
Review the four basic constructions.

Teacher's Resource Materials
Enrichment Using
   Manipulatives 50
Practice Master 59

Exercise Answers
See Selected Answers for odd-numbered exercises.
2.
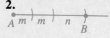

4.

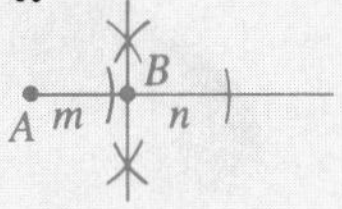

6.

8.

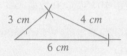

10. scalene obtuse △

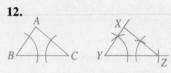

12.

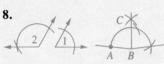

14.

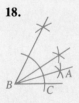

16.

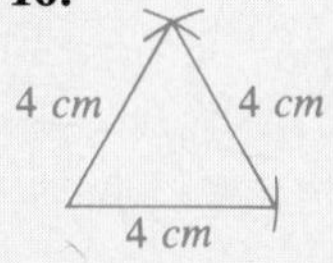

18.

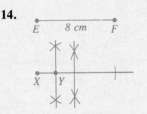

20.

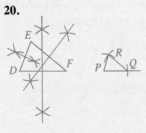

Trace angles 1 and 2 and construct an angle with the given measure. Label the constructed angle ∠ABC.

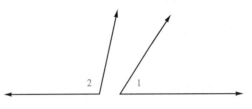

5. $m\angle 1 + m\angle 2$ **6.** $m\angle 2 - m\angle 1$
7. $180 - m\angle 2$ **8.** $\frac{m\angle 1 + m\angle 2}{2}$

9. Draw three segments of lengths 4.5 cm, 6 cm, and 7.5 cm. Construct a triangle with sides of these three lengths. What kind of triangle is it?
10. Draw three segments of lengths 3 cm, 4 cm, and 6 cm. Construct a triangle with sides these three lengths. What kind of triangle is it?

Trace △ABC.

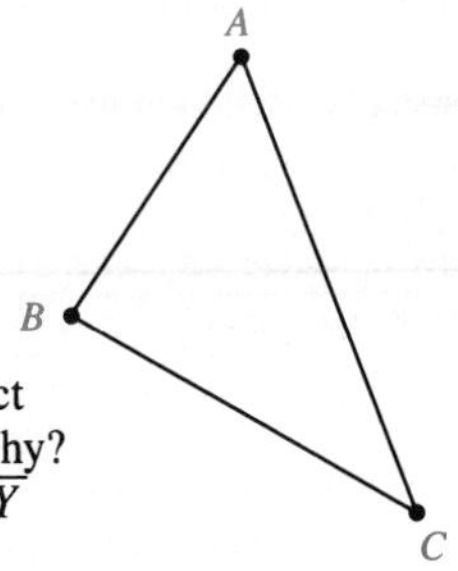

11. Use the SAS Postulate to construct △DEF congruent to △ABC.
12. Use the ASA Postulate to construct △XYZ congruent to △ABC.

13. Consider your solutions to Exercises 11 and 12. Is it easier to construct congruent triangles using the SAS Postulate or the ASA Postulate? Why?
14. Draw a segment $\overline{EF}$ approximately 8 cm long. Construct a segment $\overline{XY}$ whose length is $\frac{1}{4}EF$.
15. Draw an obtuse angle ABC. Construct an angle DBC with a measure that is $\frac{1}{4}m\angle ABC$.
16. Construct an equilateral triangle with each side 4 cm long.
17. Use the triangle constructed in Exercise 16 to construct a 30° angle.
18. Construct a 15° angle.

B

19. Draw a triangle ABC. Construct a triangle XYZ with sides twice the length of the sides of △ABC.
20. Draw a triangle DEF. Construct a triangle PQR with sides half the length of △DEF.

Construct an angle with the given measure.

21. 120° **22.** 105°
23. 75° **24.** 150°

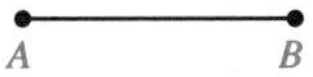

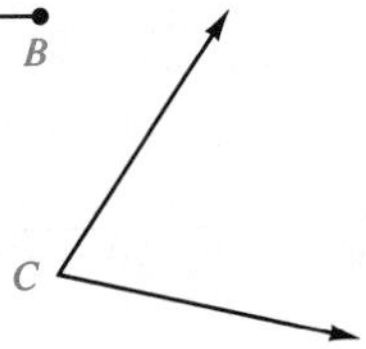

25. Construct an isosceles triangle with base $\overline{AB}$ and vertex ∠C.
26. Construct an isosceles triangle ABC given segments representing the perimeter and the base $\overline{BC}$.

$AB + BC + CA$

27. Draw an obtuse triangle ABC and use the ASA Postulate to construct a triangle DEF congruent to △ABC.

C

28. Construct a triangle *ABC* given ∠*A*, ∠*B*, and a segment representing the perimeter.
(HINT: Study the figure. Find the length of each side.)

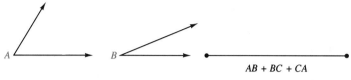
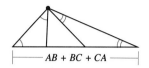

$$AB + BC + CA$$

$$AB + BC + CA$$

29. Construct an isosceles trapezoid *BCFE* given ∠*B* and the bases $\overline{BC}$ and $\overline{EF}$.

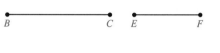

Critical Thinking

30. Draw three different triangles and label each triangle *ABC*. In the first triangle make ∠*A* acute, in the second triangle make ∠*A* a right angle, and in the third triangle make ∠*A* obtuse. In each triangle construct the angle bisector $\overline{AD}$ (*D* is on $\overline{BC}$) and the median $\overline{AM}$. Compare the lengths of $\overline{AD}$ and $\overline{AM}$. State a generalization. Test your generalization by drawing other triangles and comparing the lengths of the angle bisector and the median from the same vertex.

Algebra Review

Solve each inequality.

1. $3(y + 6) < 2y + 12$ **2.** $8 - \frac{3b}{5} \le -8$ **3.** $2(y + 5) > 4 + 15$

4. $5(n + 6) < 3n - 6$ **5.** $3x - \frac{4}{2} \ge \frac{2x}{4}$ **6.** $\frac{4x}{3} + \frac{2}{5} > 0$

Historical Note

Impossible Constructions

The geometricians of ancient Greece investigated what figures could be constructed with straightedge and compass. One of the construction problems they were not able to solve is the angle trisection problem, given below.

Given ∠*BAC*, you want to construct rays *AD* and *AE* (with points *D* and *E* in the interior of ∠*BAC*) so that ∠*BAD* ≅ ∠*DAE* ≅ ∠*EAC*.

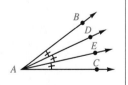

It was not until more recent times that proofs using modern abstract algebra eventually verified the impossibility of this construction and other constructions that had perplexed mathematicians over the centuries.

---

22. Answers may vary. Construct a 60° ∠, bisect it (30° ∠), duplicate 30° ∠ on top of 60° ∠ (90° ∠). Bisect the 30° ∠ (15° ∠) and duplicate 15° ∠ on top of 90° ∠ (105° ∠).

24.

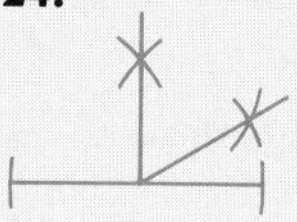

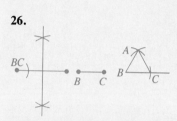

26.

28. Construct a seg. of length *AB* + *BC* + *CA* using Const. 1. At its endpoints, construct angles of measures $\frac{1}{2}m \angle A$ and $\frac{1}{2}m \angle B$ using Const. 2 and 4. Extend them to form a triangle. Construct isosceles triangles as shown in the figure. The inner triangle has angles congruent to ∠*A* and ∠*B* (Theorem 3.11) and has perimeter equal to *AB* + *BC* + *CA* (Theorem 4.2).

30. Construct the 3 △s using Const. 3 for the rt. ∠ in the rt. △. Construct the ∠ bis. $\overline{AD}$ in each △ using Const. 4. Bisect $\overline{BC}$ in each △ using Const. 3 and label the midpt. *M*. Draw $\overline{AM}$. Generalization: In a △, the length of the ∠ bis. is ≤ the length of the median from the same vertex.

Algebra Review Answers

1. $y < -6$ **2.** $b \ge \frac{80}{3}$
3. $y > \frac{9}{2}$ **4.** $n < -18$
5. $x \ge \frac{4}{5}$ **6.** $x > -\frac{3}{10}$

1. Locate the midpoint of $\overline{XY}$.

Const. 3

2. Bisect the obtuse angle of $\triangle ABC$.

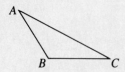

Const. 4

3. Construct $\overline{DE}$ with a measure that is three times the measure of $\overline{AB}$.

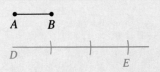

4. Construct an angle with a measure that is the sum of the measures of $\angle M$ and $\angle N$.

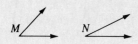

Lesson Opener

Use the Explore to introduce construction of perpendicular lines.

Materials

student notebooks
compasses
straightedges
investigative software

OBJECTIVE: *Construct the perpendicular to a given line from a point on the line and from a point not on the line, and the parallel to a given line.*

9-2 Perpendicular and Parallel Lines

EXPLORE

You can use paper folding to form a perpendicular from a point P to a line m by folding the paper so that line m is folded onto itself and the crease contains point P as shown below.

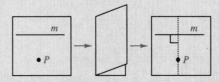

On three different pieces of paper, draw lines r, s, and t and mark a point P, as positioned in the figures below.

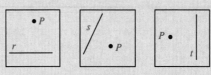

Fold the papers to form lines through P that are perpendicular to the lines r, s, and t. Label each perpendicular (crease) as horizontal, vertical, or neither.

The three constructions presented in this section apply definitions and theorems about perpendicular and parallel lines from previous chapters. The first construction is similar to bisecting an angle.

CONSTRUCTION 5

Given a point on a line, construct the perpendicular to the line at the given point.

Given: point P on m

Construct: the perpendicular to m at P

Procedure 1. Using P as center and any radius, draw arcs intersecting m at A and B.
2. Using A as center and any radius longer than $\overline{AP}$, draw an arc. Using B as center and the same radius draw an arc intersecting the first arc at C.
3. Draw $\overline{PC}$.
4. $\overline{PC}$ is perpendicular to m at P.

Proof By construction $\overline{PA} \cong \overline{PB}$ and $\overline{AC} \cong \overline{BC}$. Hence $\triangle CAP \cong \triangle CBP$ by SSS. Therefore, $\angle BPC$ is a right angle and $\overline{PC} \perp m$.

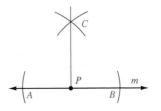

CONSTRUCTION 6

Given a point not on a line, construct the perpendicular to the line from the given point.

Given: point P not on m

Construct: the perpendicular to m from P

Procedure 1. Using P as center, draw an arc intersecting m at A and B.

2. Using A as center and a radius greater than $\frac{1}{2}AB$, draw an arc. Using B as center and the same radius, draw an arc intersecting the first arc at X.

3. Draw $\overrightarrow{PX}$.

4. $\overrightarrow{PX}$ is perpendicular to m.

Proof Since P and X are equidistant from A and B, $\overrightarrow{PX}$ is the perpendicular bisector of $\overline{AB}$. Therefore, $\overrightarrow{PX}$ is perpendicular to m.

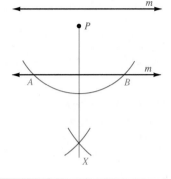

Example 1

Construct a 45° angle.

Solution

Construct a 90° angle by constructing a perpendicular. Bisect the 90° angle.

Try This

Construct a $22\frac{1}{2}°$ angle.

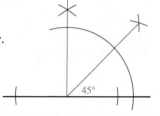

CONSTRUCTION 7

Given a point not on a line, construct the parallel to the given line through the given point.

Given: point P not on line m

Construct: the line through P parallel to m

Procedure 1. Draw any line through P intersecting m at A.

2. At P use Construction 2 to construct $\angle 2$ congruent to $\angle 1$. Label the line containing the ray (just constructed) n.

3. The line n contains P and is parallel to m.

Proof Since $\angle 1$ and $\angle 2$ are congruent corresponding angles, the lines are parallel.

Example 2

Construct a line through the midpoint of $\overline{AB}$ that is parallel to $\overline{BC}$.

Solution

Use Construction 3 to find the midpoint of side $\overline{AB}$. Use Construction 7 to construct the line through the midpoint D parallel to $\overline{BC}$. Line ℓ contains D and is parallel to $\overline{BC}$.

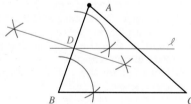

9-2 Perpendicular and Parallel Lines **397**

6.

7.

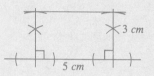

8.

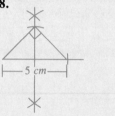

9.

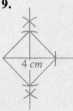

10. Const. 6   **11.** Const. 5
12. Const. 7   **13.** Yes; any pt.
equidist. between *A* and *B* is
on the ⊥ bis. of $\overline{AB}$.
14. Yes; construct ≅ ∠s on opp.
sides of the transversal.

Assignment Guide
Minimum: 1–20 e/o, 27, MR
Regular: 1–25 e/o, 27, MR
Advanced: 19–27, MR

Constructions
Class Exercises 4–12
Exercises 1–27

Lesson Closure

Review the three constructions.

Class Exercises

Short Answer

1. Which construction(s) would you use to construct the altitude from *A* to $\overline{BC}$?
2. Which construction(s) would you use to construct the altitude from *B* to $\overline{AC}$?
3. Which construction(s) would you use to construct a line through *A* parallel to $\overline{BC}$?

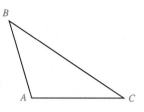

Sample Exercises

Construct each figure.

4. an isosceles right triangle with legs approximately 2 cm long
5. a square with perimeter equal to approximately 8 cm
6. a triangle with sides in the ratio of $1:1:\sqrt{2}$
7. a rectangle with sides approximately 3 cm and 5 cm long
8. an isosceles right triangle with a hypotenuse approximately 5 cm long
9. a square with a diagonal approximately 4 cm long

Draw a line *m* and mark a point *P* positioned approximately as shown. Construct the perpendicular to *m* through *P*.

10.   **11.**

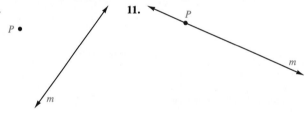

12. Draw a line *m* and mark a point *P* positioned approximately as shown. Construct the parallel to *m* through *P*.

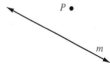

Discussion

13. Kris constructed the perpendicular from a point *P* not on *m* to *m*. She drew an arc intersecting *m* at points *A* and *B*. Kris said she could construct the perpendicular by increasing the radius and marking arcs above *m* rather than below *m*. Is she correct?
    Explain your reasoning.
14. Could Construction 7 be done using alternate interior angles rather than corresponding angles?
    Explain your reasoning.

Exercises

A

Draw line *m* and point *P* as shown. Construct the perpendicular to *m* from *P*.

1. P •

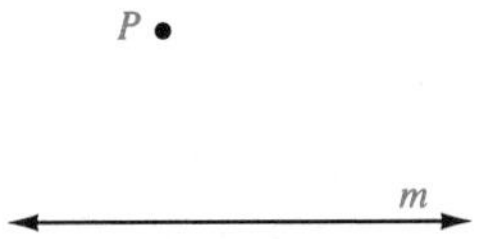

2.

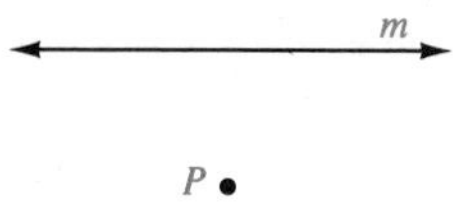

3. P •

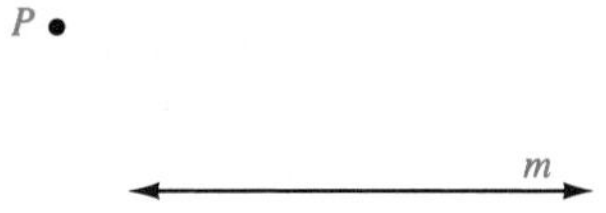

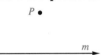

Draw line *m* and point *P* as shown. Construct the perpendicular to *m* at *P*.

4.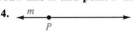

5.

6.

Draw line *m* and point *P* as shown. Construct the parallel to *m* through *P*.

7. P •

8.

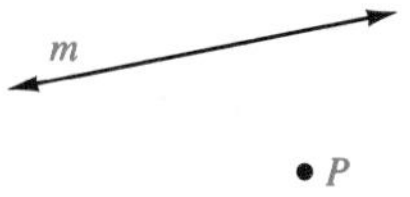

9.

10. Construct a 135° angle.   11. Construct a $157\frac{1}{2}°$ angle.

12. Draw a triangle *RST* with an obtuse angle at vertex *R*. Construct an altitude from *R* to $\overline{ST}$.

13. Draw a triangle *MNP*. Construct a line through *M* parallel to $\overline{NP}$.

14. Construct a right triangle *ABC* with $m\angle A = 90$. Construct the midpoint of the hypotenuse and label it *M*. Construct a line through *M* parallel to $\overline{AC}$.

15. Draw a segment $\overline{AB}$ and mark a point *P* positioned approximately as shown to the right. Construct a parallelogram with side $\overline{AB}$ and a vertex at *P*.

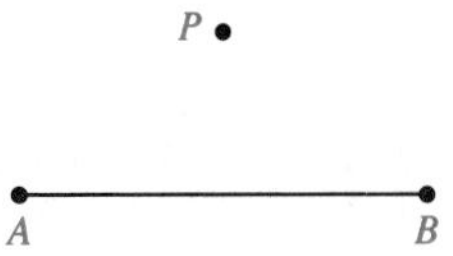

P •

Use segments approximately the length of m and n.

16. Construct a right triangle with legs of lengths *m* and *n*.

17. Construct a square given a side of length *n*.

18. Construct a rectangle with length *m* and width *n*.

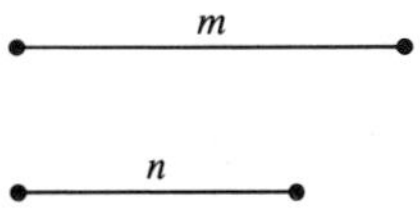

m

n

B

Use segments approximately the length of m and n above.

19. Construct a square with the diagonal of length *m*.

20. Construct a right triangle with leg length *n*.

21. Construct a square with perimeter equal to the given length.

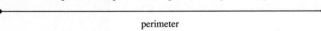

perimeter

22. Construct a rhombus *ABCD* with perimeter equal to the length shown in Exercise 21 and $m\angle A = 45$.

Teacher's Resource Materials

Practice Master 60
Transparency 40

Exercise Answers

Constructions may vary.
1.–3. Const. 6   **4.–6.** Const. 5
7.–9. Const. 7   **10.** Use Const. 5 to create two adj. 90° ∠s. Use Const. 4 to bisect one of the 90° ∠s. 45 + 90 = 135

11.

[figure]

12. Use Const. 6 to find the ⊥ line from *R* through $\overline{ST}$.

13.

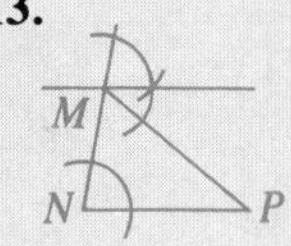

[figure with M, N, P]

14. Draw a line *AB* and construct a ⊥ ($\overline{AC}$) using Const. 5. Draw $\overline{CB}$ to make rt. △ *ABC*. Construct the ⊥ bis. of $\overline{CB}$ using Const. 5, intersecting $\overline{CB}$ at *M*. Construct a line ∥ $\overline{CA}$ through *M* using Const. 7.

15.

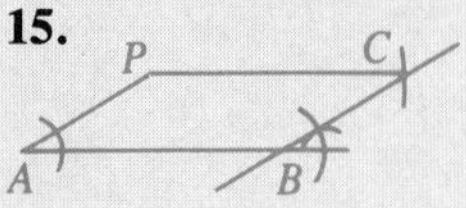

[figure with P, C, A, B]

16. Use Const. 5 to create ⊥ lines. Use Const. 1 to copy *m* as one leg and *n* as the other leg. Draw the hyp.   **17.** Draw a line *EF* = *n* using Const. 1. Use Const. 5 to construct ⊥ at *E* and *F*, then cut off line seg. $\overline{EH}$ and $\overline{FG}$ each = *n*. Connect *F* and *G* to make square *EFGH*.

18.

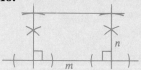

19. See Class Exercise 9.
20.

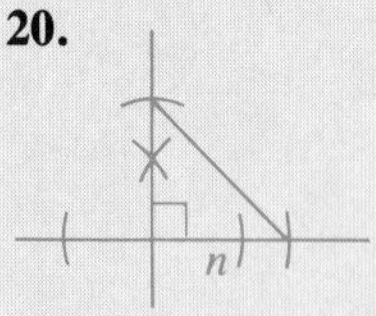

21. See Class Exercise 5.
22. Use Const. 3 to find the length of a side. Draw a ray. Use Const. 2 to copy the supp. of ∠A at the endpoint. Use Const. 1 to copy the length of a side on both rays of ∠A. Use Const. 2 to copy ∠A at the endpoint of one side. Use Const. 1 to copy the length of the third side. Draw the fourth side.
23.

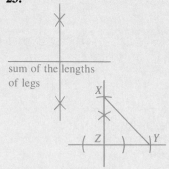

24. Draw a ray. Use Const. 1 to copy $\overline{BD}$ on the ray. Use Const. 3 to find ⊥ bis. of $\overline{BD}$. Use Const. 3 to bisect $\overline{AC}$. Use Const. 1 to copy $\frac{1}{2}AC$ on ⊥ bis. of $\overline{BD}$ from midpt. Draw sides from endpoints of $\overline{AC}$ and $\overline{BD}$.
25. Check students' work.
26. Check students' work.
27.

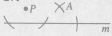

---

23. Construct an isosceles right triangle given the sum of the lengths of the legs.

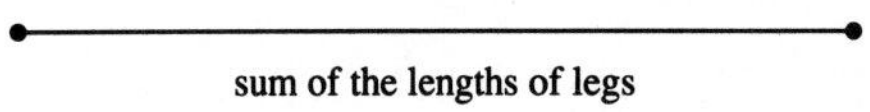

sum of the lengths of legs

C

List your procedure for each construction and explain why it works.

24. Construct a rhombus ABCD given lengths of diagonals $\overline{BD}$ and $\overline{AC}$.

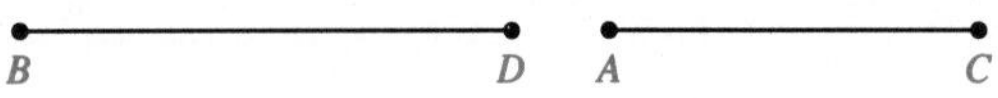

B   D   A   C

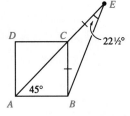

25. Construct a square ABCD given the sum of the lengths of the diagonal $\overline{AC}$ and side $\overline{BC}$. (HINT: Study the figure to the right.)

26. Construct a square ABCD given the sum and difference of the lengths of the diagonal $\overline{AC}$ and side $\overline{BC}$.

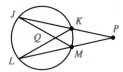

AC + BC   AC − BC

Critical Thinking

27. Draw a line m and a point P not on m. Using a compass, *not* a straightedge, construct another point A such that $\overrightarrow{PA}$ is parallel to m.

Mixed Review

1. $JP = 9$, $PK = 4$, $PL = 12$ Find PM.
2. $JQ = 5$, $QM = 4$, $KQ = 2$ Find QL.
3. $JK = 5$, $KP = 3$, $PL = 6$ Find ML.
4. $JM = 9$, $JQ = 6$, $KQ = 2$ Find KL.

Study Skills
Solving Construction Problems

The following procedures can be of help in solving construction problems that require a series of basic constructions.

1. Draw the "given" segments and angles.
2. Sketch the figure as it should appear when completed. Identify given parts.
3. Analyze the figure you have sketched to determine the sequence of constructions needed to complete the figure.
4. Construct the figure. Write out the sequence of steps you used.

Mixed Review Answers

1. 3   **2.** 10   **3.** 2   **4.** 11

OBJECTIVE: *Construct tangents to a circle and construct the center of a circle given the circle or arcs of the circle.*

9-3 Circles

Draw a circle with center O and radius r. For each of the three cases given below, state the relationship between $\overline{OP}$ and r.

1. From point P there exists only one tangent to circle O through P.
2. From point P there exist two tangents to circle O through P.
3. From point P there exist no tangents to circle O through P.

The following two constructions involve the first two cases in the Explore.

CONSTRUCTION 8

Given a point on a circle with center O, construct the tangent to the circle at the given point.

Given: point P on $\odot O$

Construct: the tangent to $\odot O$ at P

Procedure 1. Draw $\overrightarrow{OP}$.
2. Construct the perpendicular to $\overrightarrow{OP}$ at P. Label the line m.
3. Line m is the tangent to O at P.

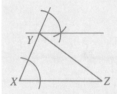

Proof Since m is perpendicular to radius $\overline{OP}$ at point P on $\odot O$, m is tangent to the circle.

CONSTRUCTION 9

Given a point outside a circle, construct a tangent to the circle from the given point.

Given: point P outside $\odot O$

Construct: a tangent to $\odot O$ from P

Procedure 1. Draw $\overline{OP}$.
2. Bisect $\overline{OP}$. Label the midpoint Q.
3. Using Q as center and $\overline{QP}$ as radius, draw circle Q. Label the points of intersection of $\odot Q$ and $\odot O$, X and Y.
4. Draw $\overrightarrow{PX}$.
5. $\overrightarrow{PX}$ is a tangent to $\odot O$ from P. The other tangent to $\odot O$ from P, which is not drawn, is $\overrightarrow{PY}$.

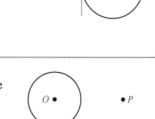

Proof Draw $\overline{OX}$. Since $\angle OXP$ is inscribed in a semicircle, it is a right angle. Therefore, $\overrightarrow{PX}$ is a tangent since it is perpendicular to radius $\overline{OX}$ at a point on the circle.

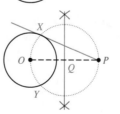

Guided Practice

Chalkboard Example

Draw a circle. Construct diameters $\overline{AC} \perp \overline{BD}$. Then construct tangents to the circle at points A, B, C, and D. Describe the results.

The tangents form a square.

Class Exercise Answers

1. Const. 8   **2.** Const. 9
3. Const. 10
4.

5. Const. 8   **6.** Const. 9
7. No; tangents are $\perp$ to radii drawn to the point of tangency. $\overline{AB}$ would be a diameter and tangents $\perp$ at A and B would be $\parallel$.

Assignment Guide

Minimum: 1–19 e/o, 23, MR
Regular: 5–21 e/o, 23, MR
Advanced: 11–24, MR

Constructions

Class Exercises 4–6
Exercises 1–24

Lesson Closure

Review the three constructions in the lesson.

CONSTRUCTION 10

Given a circle, construct the center of the circle.

Given: circle with unknown center

Construct: X so that X is the center of the circle

Procedure 1. Draw nonparallel chords $\overline{AB}$ and $\overline{CD}$.
    2. Construct perpendicular bisectors of $\overline{AB}$ and $\overline{CD}$. Label them p and q. Label the point of intersection of p and q point X.
    3. X is the center of the circle.

Proof   Since the perpendicular bisector of a chord contains the center of the circle, lines p and q both contain the center. Two lines intersect in only one point. Thus the center of the circle must be X, the point of intersection of the perpendicular bisectors of chords $\overline{AB}$ and $\overline{CD}$.

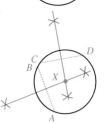

Example

Given arcs m and n of the same circle, find the center of the circle.

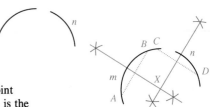

Solution

Draw chords $\overline{AB}$ and $\overline{CD}$. Construct the perpendicular bisector of each chord. The point of intersection of the perpendicular bisectors is the center of the arcs. X is the center of the arcs.

Class Exercises

Short Answer

1. Which construction would you use to construct a tangent to $\odot O$ at point X on $\odot O$?
2. Which construction would you use to construct a tangent to $\odot O$ from a point Y outside $\odot O$?
3. Which construction would you use to construct the center of $\overset{\frown}{ABC}$?

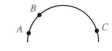

Sample Exercises

Draw each figure approximately the same as the one shown and complete the construction.

4. Construct a line that is parallel to $\overline{AB}$ and tangent to $\odot O$.
5. Construct tangents to $\odot O$ at points A and B.
6. Draw a circle with center M and a radius of 1 in. Mark a point P that is 2 in. from M. Construct a tangent from P to circle M.

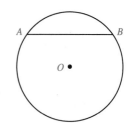

Discussion

7. If $\overrightarrow{PA}$ and $\overrightarrow{PB}$ are tangents to $\odot O$ with A and B on $\odot O$, is it possible for $\overline{AB}$ to contain the center of the circle? Explain your reasoning.

402   *Chapter 9   Constructions and Loci*

Exercises

A

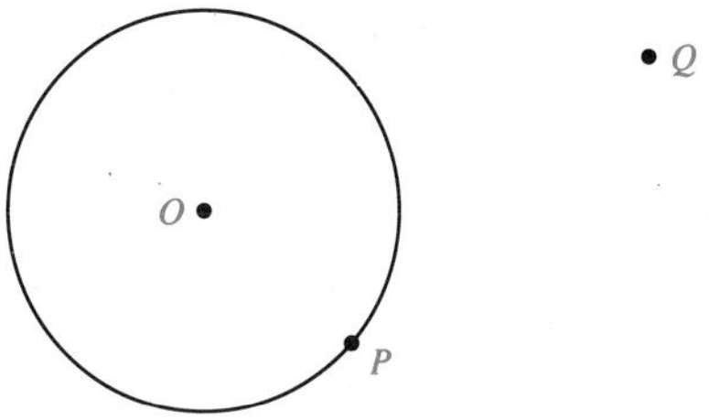

1. Draw a circle and mark a point P on the circle as shown to the right. Construct a tangent to the circle at P.
2. Draw a circle and mark a point Q outside the circle as shown to the right. Construct two tangents to the circle from Q.
3. Draw a circle with diameter $\overline{AB}$. Construct tangents to the circle at A and B.
4. Draw a circle and mark points P and Q on the circle. Construct $\triangle MPQ$ so that $\overline{MP}$ and $\overline{MQ}$ are tangent to the circle.
5. Draw a circle with a radius of 2 cm and mark a point P, 5 cm from the center. Construct two tangents from P to the circle.
6. Trace around a circular object such as a cup. Find the center of the circle.
7. Trace three arcs on the circumference of a circular object. Find the center of the arcs. Then use a compass to complete the circle.
8. Use a circular object to draw an arc that is about one third the circumference of the entire circle. Find the center of the arc. Then use a compass to complete the circle.
9. Draw a circle. Circumscribe a square about the circle.
10. Draw a circle with diameter $\overline{AB}$. Construct a tangent parallel to $\overline{AB}$.

B

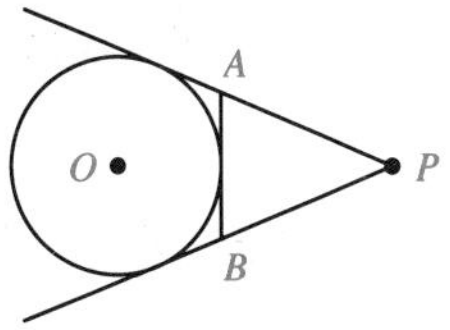

11. Draw a circle and a point P outside it. Construct isosceles triangle PAB with P as the vertex such that $\overline{PA}$, $\overline{PB}$, and $\overline{AB}$ are tangent to the circle. (HINT: Draw $\overline{OP}$ to determine the point of tangency for $\overline{AB}$.)
12. Draw a circle. Construct two tangents to the circle parallel to each other.
13. Draw a circle. Construct two tangents to the circle perpendicular to each other.
14. Mark three points on your paper that are not collinear. Construct a circle containing the three points.
15. Construct a rectangle with a length of approximately 5 cm and a width of approximately 3 cm. Circumscribe a circle about the rectangle.

Draw a circle and a line p approximately as shown.

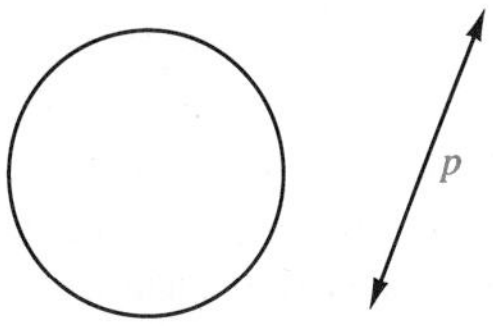

16. Construct a line tangent to the circle that is parallel to p.
17. Construct a line tangent to the circle that is perpendicular to p.
18. Draw a circle. Construct an equilateral triangle circumscribed about it.
19. Draw a circle. Construct a quadrilateral circumscribed about it.

C

Write a procedure for each construction and prove that it works.

20. Construct three congruent circles that are tangent to one another.
21. Draw an angle and mark a point P on the angle. Construct a circle tangent to the sides of the angle and containing P.
22. Draw two parallel lines and mark a point P between the lines as shown. Construct a circle that contains P and is tangent to the two lines.

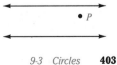

Teacher's Resource Materials

Enrichment Using
 Manipulatives 51
Practice Master 61
Transparency 41

Exercise Answers

See Selected Answers for odd-numbered exercises.

2. Const. 9   4. Draw $\overline{OP}$ and $\overline{OQ}$. Use Const. 8 to create tangents at P and Q. Label the point of intersection M. Draw $\overline{PQ}$.   **6. Const. 10**

8.

10. Draw ⊥ bis. of $\overline{AB}$. Use Const. 8 to find tangent at point of intersection of ⊥ bis. and circle. Tangent is ∥ to $\overline{AB}$.

12. Draw diameter $\overline{AB}$. Use Const. 8 to create tangents at A and B. The tangents are ∥.

14.

16. Use Const. 6 to draw ⊥ from center of circle to p. Use Const. 5 to draw ⊥ at intersection of ⊥ to p and of the circle. This ⊥ line is ∥ to p.

18.

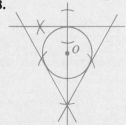

20.

1. Construct an equilateral △.
2. Bisect a side to get the radius of each circle. 3. Draw circles with centers at the vertices. The circles are ≅. They have ≅ radii equal to half the length of a side of the equilateral △. The circles are tangent at the midpt.

22.

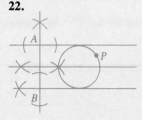

1. Construct ∥ lines. 2. Construct $\overline{AB}$ ⊥ to the ∥ lines. 3. Construct ⊥ bis. of $\overline{AB}$. 4. The distance from either ∥ line to the midpt. of $\overline{AB}$ is the radius of the circle. 5. Using the radius and P as the center, find the intersection of the circle where it intersects the ⊥ bis. of $\overline{AB}$. The point is the center of the tangent circle with the same radius. 6. Draw the circle.

24. Check students' work.

Mixed Review Answers

1. $\frac{2}{x} = \frac{x}{3}, x = \sqrt{6}$

2. $\frac{5}{y} = \frac{y}{3}, y = \sqrt{15}$

3. $\frac{5}{z} = \frac{z}{2}, z = \sqrt{10}$

4. $\frac{2}{z} = \frac{z}{5}, z = \sqrt{10}$

5. $\frac{2}{x} = \frac{x}{3}, x = \sqrt{6}$

6. $\frac{3}{y} = \frac{y}{5}, y = \sqrt{15}$

Computer Activity Answer

Check students' work.

$\frac{\text{area } \triangle RST}{\text{area } \triangle ABC} = \frac{1}{7}$

Critical Thinking

23. Consider circles Q and P with radii r_1 and r_2 respectively, as shown below. The dotted circle has radius $r_1 - r_2$. Study the figure and create a method for constructing a common external tangent $\overline{BC}$ to circles Q and P. (HINT: Begin by constructing a tangent from P to the dotted circle. Consider how to construct rectangle $BAPC$.)

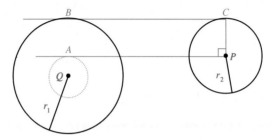

24. Create a method for constructing a common internal tangent to circles Q and P. (HINT: Begin by constructing a dotted circle with radius $r_1 + r_2$. Consider the method you devised in Exercise 23.)

Mixed Review

Complete each proportion and find x, y, and z.

1. $\frac{2}{?} = \frac{?}{3}$ 2. $\frac{?}{y} = \frac{y}{3}$ 3. $\frac{5}{?} = \frac{?}{2}$

4. $\frac{2}{z} = \frac{z}{?}$ 5. $\frac{2}{x} = \frac{x}{?}$ 6. $\frac{3}{?} = \frac{?}{5}$

Computer Activity

Triangle Ratios

Use computer software to complete the following construction.

1. Draw a triangle ABC.
2. Select a point D on $\triangle ABC$ so that AD is equal to $\frac{1}{3}AB$.
3. Select a point E on $\triangle ABC$ so that BE is equal to $\frac{1}{3}BC$.
4. Select a point F on $\triangle ABC$ so that CF is equal to $\frac{1}{3}CA$.
5. Draw $\overline{CD}$, $\overline{AE}$, and $\overline{BF}$.
6. Label the points of intersection R, S, and T.
7. Find the area of $\triangle ABC$.
8. Find the area of $\triangle RST$.
9. Find the ratio of the area of $\triangle RST$ to $\triangle ABC$.

Draw another triangle and repeat the steps above to see if the ratio of the areas is the same.

9-4 Special Segments

First Five Minutes

(Quiz on previous lesson)

1. Given circle O with diameter $\overline{XZ}$, construct tangents to the circle at points X and Z.

Const. 8

2. Find the center of the circle.

Const. 10

EXPLORE

Construct the triangle in *Figure 1* and determine the length of *x*. Extend *Figure 1* so it represents *Figure 2* and determine the length of *y*. Extend *Figure 2* to represent *Figure 3* and determine the length of *z*. If you were to extend the figure one more time, what would the length of the new hypotenuse be?

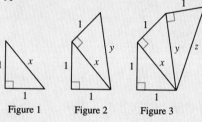

Figure 1   Figure 2   Figure 3

One question considered by mathematicians is, "Can a line segment of a given length be constructed?" Given the length of a single unit, for example, it is easy to construct a segment of length 5 units. The first construction in this section involves dividing a line segment into *n* congruent parts.

CONSTRUCTION 11

Given a segment, divide the segment into *n* congruent parts.

Given: segment *AB*

Construct: $\overline{AB}$ divided into three congruent segments

Procedure 1. Draw any ray $\overrightarrow{AC}$.

2. Using any radius, construct segments $\overline{AM}$, $\overline{MN}$, and $\overline{NP}$ such that $\overline{AM} \cong \overline{MN} \cong \overline{NP}$.

3. Draw $\overline{PB}$.

4. Construct lines through N and M that are parallel to $\overline{PB}$ and intersect $\overline{AB}$.

5. $\overline{AD} \cong \overline{DE} \cong \overline{EB}$ and points D and E divide $\overline{AB}$ into three congruent segments. To divide $\overline{AB}$ into *n* congruent parts, mark *n* congruent segments on $\overrightarrow{AC}$ and construct the parallel lines as described in the above procedure.

Proof   Consider a line through A parallel to the other parallel lines. Since the lines constructed parallel to $\overline{PB}$ cut off congruent segments on transversal $\overline{AP}$, they cut off congruent segments on transversal $\overline{AB}$. Therefore, $\overline{AD} \cong \overline{DE} \cong \overline{EB}$.

The proof can be generalized to dividing a segment into *n* congruent parts.

Lesson Opener

Use the Explore as an introduction to this lesson.

Materials

student notebooks
compasses
straightedges
investigative software

Teaching Notes

Demonstrate the three constructions on the chalkboard or on the computer using investigative software.

Guided Practice

Chalkboard Examples

1. Given segments of lengths *a*, *b*, and *c*, find the segment *x* such that $\frac{x}{a} = \frac{b}{c}$.

Const. 12

2. Given the unit segment shown, construct a segment with length $\sqrt{6}$.

1 *unit*

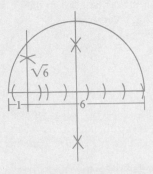

Class Exercise Answers

1. Const. 11   2. Const. 11
3. Const. 11   4. Const. 13
5. Const. 12   6. Const. 13
7. Given a seg. of length 1, use Const. 3 to bisect it and draw a ⊙ with $r = \frac{1}{2}$, with the seg. as dia. Draw a ⊙ with $r = \frac{1}{2}$ and center one of the endpt. of the original seg. Then connect one of the pt. where the $r = \frac{1}{2}$ ⊙ intesects the larger ⊙. Draw a △ with vertices this pt. and the endpt. of the unit seg. (dia.). It will be a 30°–60°–90° △ so, the longer leg will be $= \frac{\sqrt{3}}{2}$.
8.

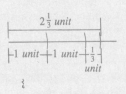

2$\frac{1}{3}$ unit

$\vdash$1 unit$\dashv$1 unit$\dashv$$\frac{1}{3}$$\dashv$
unit

CONSTRUCTION 12

Given three segments, construct a fourth segment so that the four segments are proportional.

Given: segments of lengths a, b, and c

Construct: a segment of length x such that $\frac{a}{b} = \frac{c}{x}$

Procedure 1. Draw an angle SPT.
    2. Copy segments a and b on $\overrightarrow{PT}$ so that $PA = a$ and $AB = b$. Copy c on $\overrightarrow{PS}$ so that $PC = c$.
    3. Draw $\overline{AC}$.
    4. Construct a line through B parallel to $\overline{AC}$. Label the point of intersection with $\overrightarrow{PS}$ as X.
    5. $\overline{CX}$ has length x such that $\frac{a}{b} = \frac{c}{x}$.

Proof $\overline{BX} \parallel \overline{AC}$ in $\triangle PBX$, so by the Triangle Proportional Segment Theorem, $\frac{PA}{AB} = \frac{PC}{CX}$ or $\frac{a}{b} = \frac{c}{x}$.

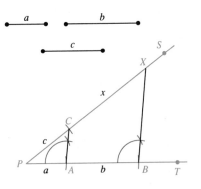

Example 1

Given segments of lengths a, b, and c, construct a segment of length x such that $\frac{a}{b} = \frac{x}{c}$.

Solution
Rewrite the proportion as $\frac{b}{a} = \frac{c}{x}$.
Using Construction 12, mark off segments of lengths b and a on $\overrightarrow{PA}$ and a segment of length c on $\overrightarrow{PX}$. Construct a line through A parallel to $\overline{BC}$. $\overline{CX}$ has length x.

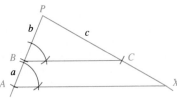

A procedure for constructing a segment that is the geometric mean between two given segments is based on properties of both circles and right triangles, as shown in Construction 13 below.

CONSTRUCTION 13

Given two segments, construct their geometric mean.

Given: segments a and b

Construct: geometric mean between a and b

Procedure 1. Draw $\overrightarrow{PM}$ and mark off $PA = a$ and $AB = b$.
    2. Construct the perpendicular bisector of $\overline{PB}$. Label the midpoint of $\overline{PB}$ as point O.
    3. Draw a semicircle using O as center and OB as radius.
    4. Construct the perpendicular to $\overline{PB}$ at A. Label the intersection with the semicircle point X.
    5. AX is the geometric mean between a and b.

Proof $\angle PXB$ is a right angle since it is inscribed in a semicircle. Therefore, $\overline{XA}$ is the altitude to the hypotenuse of a right triangle and XA is the geometric mean between PA and PB.

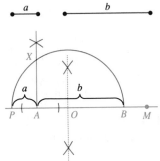

Example 2

Given the unit segment shown, construct a segment with length $\sqrt{3}$.

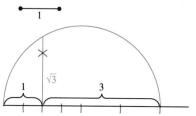

Solution

Use Construction 13, marking off segments representing one and three units.
$\frac{1}{x} = \frac{x}{3}$. Thus $x = \sqrt{3}$.

Class Exercises

Short Answer

1. Given a segment that represents the perimeter of an equilateral triangle, which construction(s) would you use to construct a segment the length of one side of the equilateral triangle?
2. Given a segment that represents the perimeter of a regular pentagon, which construction(s) would you use to construct a segment the length of one side of the regular pentagon?
3. Which construction(s) would you use to divide a 9-in. segment into four congruent segments?
4. Given a segment representing one unit, which construction(s) would you use to construct a segment of length $\sqrt{5}$?

Sample Exercises

5. Given segments of lengths 2 cm, 3 cm, and 5 cm, construct a segment of length x so that $\frac{2}{3} = \frac{5}{x}$.
6. Given segments of length a and b, construct a segment $x = \sqrt{ab}$.

Use the unit segment shown to the right.

7. Given the unit segment shown, construct a segment of length $\frac{\sqrt{3}}{2}$.
8. Given the unit segment shown, construct a segment of length $2\frac{1}{3}$ units.

one unit

9. Draw segments of lengths 2 cm and 8 cm. Construct the geometric mean of the two segments.

Discussion

10. Given segments with lengths a and b, discuss how you could use Construction 13 to find a segment of length x so that $\frac{a}{b} = \frac{b}{x}$.
11. Explain what would happen if you were to use an obtuse angle in completing Construction 11.

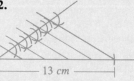

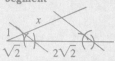
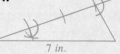
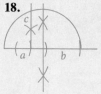

Exercises

A

1. Draw a segment 10 cm long. Use Construction 11 to trisect the segment.
2. Draw a segment 13 cm long. Use Construction 11 to divide the segment into five congruent segments.

Given three segments and a stated proportion, construct a segment of length x.

3. $\frac{a}{b} = \frac{c}{x}$ a ——— b —————— c ——————

4. $\frac{a}{b} = \frac{c}{x}$ a ——— b ——— c ——————

5. $\frac{x}{a} = \frac{b}{c}$ a ——— b ——— c ——————

6. $\frac{a}{x} = \frac{b}{c}$ a —————— b —————— c ——

7. Draw segments of lengths 2 in. and 4.5 in. and construct the geometric mean.

Use the unit segment to the right to construct a segment of the indicated length.

8. $\sqrt{2}$ 9. $\frac{\sqrt{2}}{2}$ 10. $\sqrt{5}$ 11. $2\sqrt{2}$

•———• one unit

B

12. Use the unit segment and the segments constructed in Exercises 8 and 11 to find the missing segment in the proportion $\frac{\sqrt{2}}{\sqrt{8}} = \frac{1}{x}$. Solve the proportion for x and compare x with the length of the segment you constructed.
13. Draw a segment 10 cm long and divide it into two segments with lengths in the ratio $1:2$.
14. Draw a segment 7 in. long. Divide it into two segments such that one segment is twice as long as the other.
15. Draw a triangle ABC with base $\overline{AC}$. Divide $\overline{AC}$ into two segments having the ratio of the adjacent sides, $\frac{AB}{BC}$.
16. Draw a segment 6 cm long and divide it into two segments with lengths in the ratio $2:3$.

a •———•

Use segments a and b to construct the required segment c.

17. $c = \frac{b^2}{a}$ 18. $c = \sqrt{ab}$ 19. $c = \sqrt{2ab}$

b •——————•

C

20. Given a unit segment and a segment m, construct a segment that represents $\frac{1}{m}$.

•———• one unit

21. Draw a line ℓ and two points P and Q, as shown below. Construct a circle that is tangent to ℓ and contains P and Q.
(HINT: Consider the figure on the right and use Construction 13.)

•——————• m

Critical Thinking

To find geometric solutions to an equation of the form $ax = b$ you can use Construction 12 and convert $ax = b$ to $\frac{a}{b} = \frac{1}{x}$. Using the unit segment shown to the right, construct a segment having a length that is a whole number greater than one. Then construct a segment that would represent the solution to the given equation. Use algebra to see if your constructed segment seems like a reasonable solution.

one unit

22. $2x = 3$ **23.** $3x = 10$ **24.** $4x = 3$

Mixed Review

$\overline{BE}$ bisects $\angle B$. $\overline{DE} \parallel \overline{BC}$

1. Complete the proportion $\frac{x}{y} = \frac{?}{?}$ in two different ways.
2. Find z.

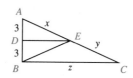

22. Check students' work. $x = \frac{3}{2}$
24. Check students' work. $x = \frac{3}{4}$

Mixed Review Answers

1. $\frac{x}{y} = \frac{3}{3}$, $\frac{x}{y} = \frac{6}{z}$ **2.** $z = 6$

Connections Answer

Based on Construction 13, the construction represents b as the geometric mean between x and y, resulting in the proportion $\frac{x}{b} = \frac{b}{y}$.

CONNECTIONS ◈

Geometric Constructions and Algebra

Geometric constructions played an important role in the history of algebra. As the early Arab mathematicians developed symbolic ways of solving algebra problems, they verified the results via constructions to make sure the results were really valid. Consider this equation.

$x + 1 = 3$

The mathematician can approach the solution of this equation algebraically by adding (-1) to each side of the equation and then adding to get $x = 2$. To find the solution geometrically the mathematician could start with a unit segment, copy it to get a segment three units long, and then mark off one unit on it so that the length of x, or 2 units, is the remaining portion of the segment.

Consider using geometric construction to solve the problem involving the system of equations $x + y = a$ and $xy = b^2$ where $b \le \frac{a}{2}$.

The values of a and b are given.
The first step is to draw a semicircle of radius $\frac{a}{2}$.
Next construct a line that is parallel to the diameter of the semicircle and b units from it. Since $b \le \frac{a}{2}$, b is either tangent to the circle or intersects it in two places. Construct the perpendicular from each of the points of intersection to the diameter. Either one of these points will divide the diameter into two segments with lengths x and y.

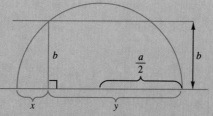

Explain why this construction solves the system of equations given above.

First Five Minutes

(Quiz on previous lesson)

1. Given the three segments, construct a segment of length x such that $\frac{2}{3} = \frac{5}{x}$.

Const. 12

2. Given the unit segment, construct a segment of length $2\sqrt{2}$.

1 *unit*

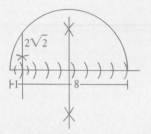

Lesson Opener

Have students use the Explore to discover Theorem 9.1.

Materials

student notebooks
compasses
straightedges
investigative software

Teaching Notes

Stress that the center of a circumscribed circle is the circumcenter of the polygon.
(HINT: **circum**scribed—**circum**center)

Explain that the center of an inscribed circle is the incenter of the polygon.
(HINT: **in**scribed—**in**center)

OBJECTIVE: *Apply the concurrency theorems for triangles and distinguish among the circumcenter, the incenter, the centroid, and the orthocenter of a triangle.*

9-5 Concurrency Theorems for Triangles

EXPLORE Draw a large acute triangle on a sheet of paper. Fold the paper to form creases representing the perpendicular bisector of each side of the triangle. What conclusion can you reach regarding the three perpendicular bisectors of the sides of the triangle?

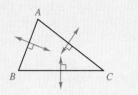

In this lesson you will use inductive reasoning to investigate properties that involve these lines. Consider the perpendicular bisectors below.

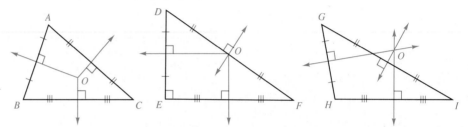

Three or more coplanar lines that have a point in common are called **concurrent lines.** In each triangle above, the three perpendicular bisectors are concurrent (at point O).

♦ **THEOREM 9.1**

The perpendicular bisectors of the sides of a triangle are concurrent in a point that is equidistant from the three vertices of the triangle.

The point that is equidistant from the vertices of a triangle is called the **circumcenter** of the triangle. It is the point of concurrency of the perpendicular bisectors of the sides of the triangle. O is the circumcenter of $\triangle ABC$ since $OA = OB = OC$. Circle O is circumscribed about $\triangle ABC$.

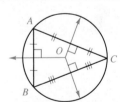

The next theorem involves the bisectors of the angles of a triangle. You can see in the figure to the right that the angle bisectors are concurrent at I. If you were to measure the distances from I to the sides of the triangle ($\overline{ID}$, $\overline{IF}$, $\overline{IE}$), you would discover the relationship stated in the following theorem.

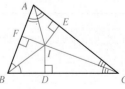

Key Terms

concurrent
circumcenter
incenter
centroid
orthocenter

◆ **THEOREM 9.2**

The bisectors of the angles of a triangle are concurrent in a point that is equidistant from the three sides of the triangles.

You will be asked to prove Theorems 9.1 and 9.2 in Exercises 23, 24 and 26.

The point of concurrency of the angle bisectors of a triangle is called the **incenter** of the triangle and is the center of the inscribed circle of the triangle. In the diagram to the right, I is the incenter of $\triangle ABC$ and $IF = IE = ID$.

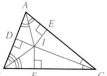

Example 1

Inscribe a circle in $\triangle ABC$.

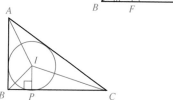

> **Solution**
>
> Bisect the angles to find the incenter I.
> Construct $\overline{IP}$ perpendicular to side $\overline{BC}$.
> Draw the inscribed circle with center I and radius $\overline{IP}$.

The medians of a triangle also have a special relationship. Study the medians of $\triangle ABC$. By using measurement to determine the ratios $\frac{AG}{AD}$, $\frac{CG}{CF}$, and $\frac{BG}{BE}$, you will discover the following theorem.

◆ **THEOREM 9.3**

The medians of a triangle are concurrent in a point that is two thirds of the distance from each vertex to the midpoint of the opposite side.

You will be asked for part of the proof of Theorem 9.3 in Exercise 25.

The point of intersection of the medians of a triangle is called the **centroid.** The centroid is the "center of gravity" of a triangle. That is, if you were to cut a triangle out of a firm substance, such as cardboard, the centroid would be the point at which you could balance the triangle.

Example 2

If G is the centroid of $\triangle ABC$ and $AG = 4$ cm, find AD and GD.

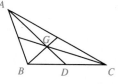

> **Solution**
>
> $AG = \frac{2}{3}AD$ *Theorem 9.3*
> $4 = \frac{2}{3}AD$
> $AD = 6$
> $GD = 6 - 4 = 2$

Try This

Find the length of the median $\overline{AD}$ of $\triangle ABC$ if $GD = 15$.

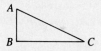

Consider the altitudes of the acute, right, and obtuse triangles below.

 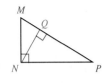 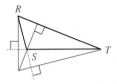

Observe that the three altitudes in each triangle are concurrent. This leads to Theorem 9.4, which you will be asked to prove in Exercise 27. The point of intersection of the lines containing the altitudes is the **orthocenter.**

◆ **THEOREM 9.4**

The lines that contain the altitudes of a triangle are concurrent.

Class Exercises

Short Answer

1. Name an altitude, an angle bisector, and a median of △ABC if $AZ = ZC$.

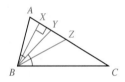

2. The lines p and q are perpendicular bisectors of sides $\overline{AB}$ and $\overline{AC}$ of △ABC. If $OA = 5$, find OB and OC.

3. What is the name of the center of the circle containing the vertices of a triangle?
4. What is the name of the center of the circle to which the sides of a triangle are tangent?
5. Name the point of concurrency of (a) the angle bisectors, (b) the medians, (c) the perpendicular bisectors of the sides, and (d) the altitudes of a triangle.

Sample Exercises

In △ABC, $\overline{AX}$, $\overline{BY}$, and $\overline{CZ}$ are medians. Complete each statement.

6. If $AZ = 3$, $ZB = $ ___ .   **7.** If $CG = 4$, $GZ = $ ___ .
8. If $AB = BY$, $BG = $ ___ .   **9.** If $CZ = BC$, $BX = $ ___ .

10. Draw an obtuse triangle. Construct the orthocenter of the triangle.
11. Draw a right triangle. Construct the circumcenter of the triangle.
12. Use a compass to circumscribe a circle about the triangle in Exercise 11.

Discussion

13. If you have an acute-triangle-shaped metal plate, which theorem will help you decide where to drill a hole in which to place a rod to balance the plate?
14. To circumscribe a circle about a triangle, which theorem can you use?

Exercises

A

1. Draw an acute triangle. Construct the centroid and label it G.
2. Draw a right triangle. Construct the orthocenter and label it H.
3. Draw an obtuse triangle. Construct the orthocenter and label it M.
4. Draw an obtuse triangle. Construct the circumcenter and the circumscribed circle.
5. Draw a right triangle. Construct the circumcenter and the circumscribed circle.
6. Draw an acute triangle. Construct the incenter and the inscribed circle.

Use your answers to Exercises 1–6. Draw sketches to indicate whether the point named is *inside*, *on*, or *outside* the triangle.

	acute △	right △	obtuse △
7. circumcenter	—	—	—
8. incenter	—	—	—
9. centroid	—	—	—
10. orthocenter	—	—	—

Assume G is the centroid of $\triangle ABC$. Complete each statement.

11. If $BE = 9$, $BG = $ ___ .   12. If $GC = 3$, $FC = $ ___ .
13. If $GE = 8$, $BE = $ ___ .   14. If $AD = 24$, $GD = $ ___ .
15. If $BE = 12$, $BG = $ ___ .   16. If $AG = 10$, $GD = $ ___ .
17. If $AG = x$, $GD = $ ___ .   18. If $BE = x$, $BG = $ ___ .

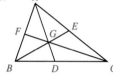

B

19. Prove that the median from the vertex angle of an isosceles triangle is also the angle bisector.
20. Prove that an altitude of an equilateral triangle is also a median.
21. If $\triangle ABC$ is an equilateral triangle with each side having length 5, find the length of the radius of the inscribed circle.
22. If $\triangle DEF$ is an isosceles right triangle with the legs having lengths 3, find the radius of the circumscribed circle.
23. Write a two-column proof for part of Theorem 9.1.

    Given: Lines r, s, and t are perpendicular bisectors of the sides of $\triangle ABC$ and are concurrent at point O.

    Prove: $OA = OB = OC$

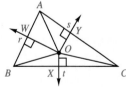

24. Write a two-column proof for part of Theorem 9.2.

    Given: $\overline{AI}$, $\overline{BI}$, and $\overline{CI}$ are angle bisectors concurrent at I. $\overline{DI}$, $\overline{EI}$, and $\overline{FI}$ are perpendicular to the sides of $\triangle ABC$.

    Prove: $DI = EI = FI$

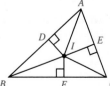

9-5 Concurrency Theorems for Triangles   **413**

4.

6. See Chalkboard Example 1.
8. acute △ inside, rt. △ inside, obtuse △ inside   **10.** acute △ inside, rt. △ on, obtuse △ outside   **12.** $4\frac{1}{2}$ **14.** 8
16. 5   **18.** $\frac{2}{3}x$
20. Given: equilateral $\triangle ABC$, alt. $\overline{AD}$ Prove: $\overline{AD}$ is median. 1. $\triangle ABC$ is equilateral; $\overline{AD}$ is alt. (Given) 2. $\overline{AB} \cong \overline{BC} \cong \overline{AC}$ (Def. equilateral △) 3. $m\angle B = m\angle C = 60$ (In an equilateral △ each ∠ has measure 60.)
4. $\angle B \cong \angle C$ (Def. $\cong$ ∠s)
5. $\triangle ABD \cong \triangle ACD$ (HA)
6. $\overline{BD} \cong \overline{DC}$ (CPCTC) 7. $\overline{AD}$ is a median. (Def. median)
22. $\frac{3\sqrt{2}}{2}$
24. 1. $\overline{AI}$, $\overline{BI}$, $\overline{CI}$ are ∠bis. (Given) 2. $\angle ICF \cong \angle ICE$, $\angle IAE \cong \angle IAD$, $\angle IBD \cong \angle IBF$ (Def. ∠bis.) 3. $\overline{DI}$, $\overline{EI}$, $\overline{FI}$ are ⊥ to sides of $\triangle ABC$. (Given)
4. $\angle IFC$, $\angle IEC$, $\angle IDA$, $\angle IEA$, $\angle IDB$, $\angle IFB$ are rt. ∠s and are $\cong$. (⊥ lines form $\cong$ rt. ∠s.)
5. $\overline{IB} \cong \overline{IB}$, $\overline{IC} \cong \overline{IC}$, $\overline{IA} \cong \overline{IA}$ (Reflex. Prop.) 6. $\triangle IFC \cong \triangle IEC$, $\triangle IDA \cong \triangle IEA$, $\triangle IDB \cong \triangle IFB$ (AAS) 7. $\overline{IF} \cong \overline{IE}$, $\overline{IE} \cong \overline{ID}$, $\overline{ID} \cong \overline{IF}$ (CPCTC) 8. $DI = EI = FI$ (Trans. Prop., Def. $\cong$ seg.)
26. 1. $\overline{DX}$, $\overline{EY}$, and $\overline{FZ}$ are ∠ bis. (Given) 2. $\frac{XF}{EX} = \frac{DF}{ED}$, $\frac{EZ}{ZD} = \frac{EF}{DF}$, $\frac{DY}{YF} = \frac{ED}{EF}$ (Triangle Angle Bisector Theorem) 3. $\frac{XF}{EX} \times \frac{EZ}{ZD} \times \frac{DY}{YF} = \frac{DF}{ED} \times \frac{EF}{DF} \times \frac{ED}{EF}$ (Mult. Prop. of =) 4. $\frac{DF}{ED} \times \frac{EF}{DF} \times \frac{ED}{EF} = 1$ (Algebra) 5. $\frac{XF}{EX} \times \frac{EZ}{ZD} \times \frac{DY}{YF} = 1$ (Subst.) 6. $\overline{DX}$, $\overline{EY}$, and $\overline{FZ}$ are concurrent. (Ceva's Theorem)

28. Yes, circumcenter, centroid, and orthocenter of a △ are collinear. The distance from the circumcenter to the centroid is one third the distance from the circumcenter to the orthocenter.

Algebra Review
Answers

1. $2a\sqrt{2}$ **2.** $2\sqrt{30}$
3. $-12\sqrt{x}$ **4.** $4\sqrt{3}$
5. $3\sqrt{3}$ **6.** $3x\sqrt{5xy}$
7. z^3 **8.** $40r\sqrt{r}$

Quiz Answers

1. Const. 3   **2.** Const. 4
3. Const. 6   **4.** Const. 7
5. Const. 11   **6.** Const. 9
7. false   **8.** true
9. true   **10.** false

C

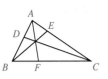

Italian mathematician Giovanni Ceva (1647–1736) stated the following condition for concurrency of lines, part of what is known as Ceva's Theorem. If $\frac{AD}{DB} \cdot \frac{BF}{FC} \cdot \frac{CE}{EA} = 1$, then $\overline{AF}$, $\overline{CD}$, and $\overline{BE}$ are concurrent. Use this part of Ceva's Theorem, the figure to the right, and the given information.

25. Prove the concurrency part of Theorem 9.3 (HINT: Use definition of median.)
   Given: $\overline{DX}$, $\overline{EY}$, and $\overline{FZ}$ are medians.
   Prove: $\overline{DX}$, $\overline{EY}$, and $\overline{FZ}$ are concurrent.

26. Prove the concurrency part of Theorem 9.2 (HINT: Use Theorem 6.9.)
   Given: $\overline{DX}$, $\overline{EY}$, and $\overline{FZ}$ are angle bisectors.
   Prove: $\overline{DX}$, $\overline{EY}$, and $\overline{FZ}$ are concurrent.

27. Prove Theorem 9.4 (HINT: Use similar triangles.)
   Given: $\overline{DX}$, $\overline{EY}$, and $\overline{FZ}$ are altitudes.
   Prove: $\overline{DX}$, $\overline{EY}$, and $\overline{FZ}$ are concurrent.

Critical Thinking

28. Draw a large acute triangle. Construct the circumcenter and label it O. Construct the centroid and label it G. Construct the orthocenter and label it H. Are O, G, and H collinear? What fraction of OH is OG? Is the same true for a right triangle? an obtuse triangle? State a generalization.

Algebra Review

Simplify. Assume all variables are nonnegative.

1. $\sqrt{8a^2}$ **2.** $\sqrt{120}$ **3.** $-\sqrt{144x}$ **4.** $\sqrt{27} + \sqrt{3}$
5. $\sqrt{75} - \sqrt{12}$ **6.** $\sqrt{45x^3y}$ **7.** $\sqrt{z^6}$ **8.** $\sqrt{1600r^3}$

Quiz

1. Draw a 5-in. segment. Construct the perpendicular bisector of the segment.
2. Draw an obtuse angle. Construct the angle bisector.
3. Draw a right triangle. Construct the altitude from the right angle to the hypotenuse.
4. Draw a line t and a point K not on line t. Construct $\overline{KL} \parallel t$.
5. Draw a 4-in. segment. Divide it into three equal parts by construction.
6. Draw $\odot T$ and a point X outside $\odot T$. Construct the tangents to $\odot T$ through X.

Indicate whether each statement is true or false.

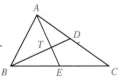

7. The three altitudes of a triangle are concurrent at the circumcenter.
8. The three medians of a triangle are concurrent at its center of gravity.
9. The angle bisectors of the triangle are concurrent at the incenter.
10. In $\triangle ABC$, if $\overline{BD}$ and $\overline{AE}$ are medians, then $TE = \frac{2}{3}AE$.

LOCUS

OBJECTIVE: *Solve simple locus problems.*

9-6 Simple Locus

A **locus** of points is a set of points and only those points that satisfy one or more conditions. The plural of locus is *loci*.

The set of points equidistant from the banks of a river can be described as a locus of points.

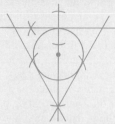

In geometry, the solution to a locus problem requires the drawing of a figure that satisfies specific conditions.

Consider the following problem.

Example 1

Determine the locus of points in the plane that are equidistant from points *A* and *B*.

Solution

Find a point that is equidistant from *A* and *B*.
Find other points equidistant from *A* and *B* and determine if the points form a familiar geometric figure. Draw the figure and write a description of it.

The locus of points in the plane equidistant from points *A* and *B* is the perpendicular bisector of the segment *AB*.

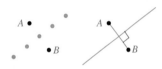

Try This

Determine the locus of points in space that are equidistant from points *A* and *B*.

To solve a locus problem, you will need to find the set of points defined by given conditions. You may find it helpful to use the strategy for solving locus problems outlined below.

Steps for Solving Locus Problems

1. Find a point that satisfies the given condition(s).
2. Find other points that satisfy the given condition(s).
3. Draw a figure that contains the points and, if possible, describe the figure in terms of a common geometric figure.
4. **a.** Make sure that every point in the described figure satisfies the given condition(s).
   b. Make sure that points not in the figure do not satisfy the given condition(s).

The solution to a locus problem consists of the figure and the description, as outlined in Step 3 of the steps for solving locus problems. Unless otherwise stated, the solution to a locus problem involves points that are coplanar only.

(Quiz on previous lesson)

1. Draw a circle. Construct a △ circumscribed about the circle.

2. Draw an acute △. Construct a circle inscribed in the △.
See Chalkboard Example in Lesson 9-5.

3. Draw an obtuse △. Construct an inscribed circle in the △ and a circumscribed circle about the △.
Use Const. 4 to bisect the vertex ∠s of the △ to find the incenter. Construct the ⊥ from the incenter to a side using Const. 6. The ⊙ centered at the incenter with radius the dist. from the incenter to a side is the inscribed ⊙. To construct the circumscribed ⊙, use Const. 3 to construct the ⊥ bis. of the sides (intersecting in the circumcenter). The ⊙ centered at the circumcenter with radius the dist. from the circumcenter to vertex (which are equidist.) is the circumscribed circle.

Lesson Opener

The term locus (plural loci, pronounced "low-sigh") is derived from a Latin word meaning place or location. Circle and sphere are defined in terms of a set of points or locus of points.

Materials

student notebooks
compasses
straightedges

Teaching Notes

Explore

If some students are unable to see that the $\perp$ bisector of $\overline{AB}$ is the only set of points equidistant from points A and B in Example 1, then have them construct several pairs of arcs with different radii, greater than half of $\overline{AB}$ above and below $\overline{AB}$. Ask students to connect the points of the locus, pointing out that all the points lie on a line that is perpendicular to $\overline{AB}$ and bisects $\overline{AB}$. The locus of points is the perpendicular bisector of $\overline{AB}$.

Discuss the differences and/or similarities between locus of points in a plane and in space. (NOTE: Use physical models whenever possible to explain locus of points in space.)

Key Terms

locus (loci)

Guided Practice

Chalkboard Examples

1. Describe the locus of points in a plane 5 in. from a circle that has a 7-in. radius. Draw a diagram.

2 circles with radii 2 in. and 12 in.

The following example illustrates how to use these four steps.

Example 2

Determine the locus of points that are 1 in. from a given point P.

Solution

Step 1 Find a point that is 1 in. from P. (point A)

Step 2 Find three other points that are 1 in. from P. (points B, C, and D)

Step 3 Draw the figure and write a description of it. The locus of points 1 in. from P is a circle with center P and a radius of 1 in.

Step 4 a. Is every point on the circle 1 in. from P? (yes)

b. Are there any points that are 1 in. from P that are not on the circle? (no)

Try This

Determine the locus of points in space that are 3 in. from a given point P.

The following example presents only the solution to the locus problem.

Example 3

Determine the locus of points that are 1 cm from a given line m.

Solution

The locus of points consists of two lines parallel to m and 1 cm from m.

Try This

Determine the locus of points in space that are 1 cm from a given line m.

Class Exercises

Short Answer

Determine whether the locus of points is best described by a point, a line, or a plane.

1. set of points equidistant from the ceiling and floor of a room
2. set of points of $\overline{AB}$ that are equidistant from A and B

3. set of points in a plane that are equidistant from sides $\overline{AB}$ and $\overline{CD}$ of rectangle $ABCD$

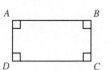

4. set of points in a plane that are equidistant from vertices A, B, and C of equilateral triangle ABC
5. set of points in space that are equidistant from vertices A, B, and C of equilateral triangle ABC
6. set of points that are equidistant from the front wall and the back wall of a room

Sample Exercises

7. Draw an angle.
   a. Find a point that is equidistant from the sides of the angle.
   b. Find three other points that are equidistant from the sides of the angle.
   c. Describe the set of points that are equidistant from the sides of the angle.
   d. Are there any points other than the figure you described that are equidistant from the sides of the angle?
8. Draw two parallel lines.
   a. Find a point that is equidistant from the two parallel lines.
   b. Find three other points that are equidistant from the two parallel lines.
   c. Describe the set of points that are equidistant from the two lines.
   d. Are there any points other than the figure you described that are equidistant from the parallel lines?

Determine the locus of points that satisfy the given conditions.

9. the locus of points that are equidistant from the vertices of a square
10. the locus of points that are equidistant from the bases of a parallelogram
11. the locus of points that are 5 cm from a circle with center P and a radius of 3 cm
12. the locus of the midpoints of congruent chords of a given circle

Discussion

Determine whether each statement is true or false. Explain your answer.

13. The locus of points 5 cm from a given line s is a line above s and a distance of 5 cm from s.
14. The locus of points equidistant from two intersecting lines is a line that bisects one of the angles formed by the intersecting lines.
15. The locus of points equidistant from two parallel lines is a line parallel to both.
16. Describe a line in space that is equidistant from all points on a circle.

---

2. Describe the locus of points in a plane that are equidistant from the sides of an angle. Draw a diagram.

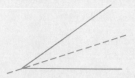

a line that bisects the angle

Answer to **Try This** a sphere with radius 3 in.

3. Describe the locus of points that are 2 in. from a given line m. Draw a diagram.

two lines parallel to m and 2 in. from m

Answer to **Try This** a cylinder with radius 1 cm

Class Exercise Answers

1. plane   2. pt.
3. line   4. pt.   5. line
6. plane
7.

c. the line that bisects the ∠
d. no
8. _____
   - - - - - - - - - -

c. ∥ line between the two lines
d. no 9. a pt. at intersection of diagonals   10. line between, and ∥ to, the bases
11. a circle with radius 8 cm
12. a circle concentric to the given circle   13. False; it is also the line 5 cm below s.
14. False; it is two such lines.
15. true   16. a line ⊥ to the plane of the circle containing the center of the circle

Exercises

A

Determine the locus of points that satisfy the given conditions.

1. the locus of points that are equidistant from the goal lines of a football field
2. the locus of points that are 3 cm from a circle with center P and a radius of 5 cm
3. the locus of the vertex of a right triangle with a given hypotenuse
4. the locus of the midpoints of all chords parallel to a given chord
5. the locus of the midpoints of radii of a given circle
6. the locus of the midpoints of chords drawn from a given point on a given circle
7. the locus of all cities that are 4 mi from a given railroad track that is straight

Determine the locus of points that satisfy the given conditions with respect to square $ABCD$.

8. the locus of points that are equidistant from sides $\overline{AB}$ and $\overline{CD}$
9. the locus of points that are equidistant from sides $\overline{AB}$ and $\overline{BC}$
10. the locus of points that are equidistant from the diagonals $\overline{AC}$ and $\overline{BD}$
11. the locus of points that are half the length of the diagonal $\overline{AC}$ from the intersection of the diagonals $\overline{AC}$ and $\overline{BD}$

Determine the locus of points in space that satisfy the given conditions.

12. the locus of points that are 3 cm from a point P
13. the locus of points that are equidistant from two parallel planes
14. the locus of points that are equidistant from two given points
15. the locus of lines that are perpendicular to a given line at a given point on the line

B

Determine the locus of points that satisfy the given conditions.

16. the locus of points that are a distance equal to the radius of a given circle from the circle
17. the locus of the centers of circles that are tangent to a given circle O at a given point P on circle O
18. the locus of the centers of all circles that have a given radius and that contain a given point P
19. the locus of midpoints of all possible segments $\overline{AD}$ of a $\triangle ABC$, given point D on side $\overline{BC}$

20. Describe the locus of the center of a ball bearing that rolls inside a circular plate.
21. Describe the locus of a doorknob as the door is opened and closed.
22. Describe the locus of points in space that are equidistant from the four vertices of a square.

Refer to the graph to the right.

23. Write an equation that describes the locus of points that are equidistant from A and B.
24. Write an equation that describes the locus of points that are equidistant from B and C.
25. Write an equation that describes the locus of points that are equidistant from A and C.
26. Determine the coordinates of the locus of points that are equidistant from A, B, and C.

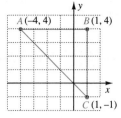

C

27. What is the locus of the midpoints of all chords formed by secants drawn to a circle from a given external point?
28. In rectangle $ABCD$, $\overline{AB}$ is twice as long as $\overline{BC}$. E is the midpoint of $\overline{CD}$. Describe the locus of midpoints of segments that have their endpoints on the sides of the rectangle and that are parallel to $\overline{AE}$. 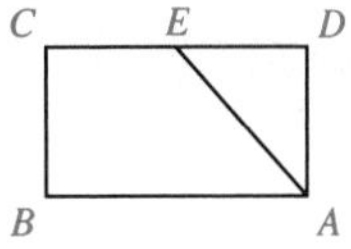
29. Describe the locus of the vertices of a $60°$ angle having rays that contain two given points A and B.

Critical Thinking

30. Suppose A and B are two points that are 4 in. apart. What is the locus of points P such that $AP + PB = 5$ in.? What happens to the figure if A and B are moved farther apart? What kind of figure is approximated as points A and B get closer and closer together?

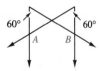

Mixed Review

Classify the triangle with the given side lengths as acute, right, or obtuse.

1. 5, 7, 9   2. 7, 10, 12
3. 3, 4, 7   4. 8, 15, 17
5. 2, 4, 5   6. 5, 12, 13

Enrichment

The Nine-Point Circle

Construct a triangle with sides of lengths 8 cm, 11 cm, and 15 cm. Then construct the following points.

a. Construct the midpoint s of the three sides of the triangle
b. Construct the points at which the three altitudes join the sides of the triangle Label the point of intersection of the three altitudes H.
c. Construct the midpoints of the segments joining H with the vertices of the triangle

How do the nine points you constructed in parts **a**, **b**, and **c** appear to be related?

---

16. the center of ⊙ and ⊙ with same center and radius equal to dia. of given ⊙   17. a line through O and P 18. ⊙ of radius equal to that of the ⊙, with center at P 19. line seg. ∥ to $\overline{BC}$ connecting midpt. of $\overline{AB}$ and $\overline{AC}$ 20. ⊙ concentric with, and with a smaller radius than, metal plate
21. arc of a circle
22. line ⊥ to plane of the square and containing pt. of intersect. of diag.
23. $x = -1.5$
24. $y = 1.5$ 25. $y = x + 3$
26. $(-1.5, 1.5)$ 27. arc from tangent to tangent, which includes the center of the ⊙ when the chord is a diameter
28. between $\overline{EB}$ and $\overline{EA}$, line seg. ∥ to $\overline{CD}$ and $\overline{BA}$ and midway between them; line seg. from B to midpt. of $\overline{BE}$ and from D to midpt. of $\overline{EA}$ 29. two connected major arcs of a circle
30. Figure approximated is an ellipse. The figure gets longer and narrower as A and B are moved apart. A circle is approximated as the points get closer together.

Mixed Review Answers

1. obtuse   2. acute
3. obtuse   4. right
5. obtuse   6. right

Enrichment Answer

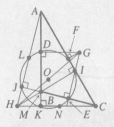

The points lie on a circle, the center of which is the midpoint of the segment between the circumcenter and the orthocenter.

(Quiz on previous lesson)

1. Describe the locus of pt. in a plane equidist. from the three vertices of a △. the circumcenter of the △

2. Describe the locus of pt. three units from both the *x*-axis and the *y*-axis. pt. at (3,3), (−3,3), (−3,−3), and (3,−3)

3. Describe the locus of pt. in space that are 10 units from a given pt. a sphere with radius 10 units

Lesson Opener

This lesson involves locus problems with more than one condition.

Materials

student notebooks
compasses
straightedges

Teaching Notes

Encourage students to follow the three steps in solving compound locus problems.

Key Terms

compound locus

Guided Practice

Chalkboard Examples

1. Describe the locus of pt. in a plane that are 3 cm from *m* and 6 cm from *P* on *m*. A, B, C, D, pt. of intersection of circle *P* with radius 6 cm and of two ∥ lines each 3 cm from *m*

OBJECTIVE: *Solve compound locus problems.*

9-7 Compound Locus

A locus problem that involves more than one set of conditions for defining a set of points is called a compound locus problem. The situation described in the caption under the photograph presents two sets of conditions for determining the locus of points of the area where most of the shots hit. The solution to a compound locus problem involves the identification of the points that satisfy all the given conditions. The following example presents a compound locus problem and its solution.

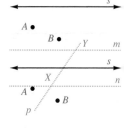

In a tennis match most of the shots were hit 3 ft from the base line and 5 ft from the side line. In what area were most of the shots hit?

Example 1

Determine the locus of points equidistant from points *A* and *B* and a given distance from line *s*.

> **Solution**
> Determine the locus of points equidistant from *A* and *B*. (line *p*)
> Determine the locus of points a given distance from line *s*. (lines *m* and *n*)
> Points *X* and *Y* satisfy both of the given conditions
>
> The solution to the problem is points *X* and *Y*.

The following steps can be used to solve compound locus problems.

Steps for Solving Compound Locus Problems

1. Determine the locus of points for the first condition.
2. Determine the locus of points for the second condition.
3. Determine the points that satisfy both conditions.

Example 2 uses the steps given above to solve a compound locus problem.

Example 2

Determine the locus of points equidistant from two concentric circles and equidistant from two secants that intersect at the center of the circles.

> **Solution**
> **Step 1** Determine the points equidistant from lines *m* and *n*. (lines *p* and *q*)
> **Step 2** Determine the points equidistant from the two concenteric circles. (dotted circle)
> **Step 3** Determine the intersection of the loci. (points *A*, *B*, *C*, and *D*)
>
> The solution to the problem is points *A*, *B*, *C*, and *D*.

Try This

Determine the locus of points equidistant from two concentric circles and equidistant from two parallel tangents to the smaller circle.

420 *Chapter 9 Constructions and Loci*

Example 3

Determine the locus of points equidistant from two parallel lines and equidistant from two points on one of the lines.

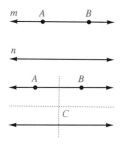

Solution

The solution consists of point C.

Try This

Determine the locus of points in space equidistant from two parallel lines and equidistant from two points on one of the lines.

Class Exercises

Short Answer

Determine whether each statement is true or false.

1. A circle and a line can intersect in zero, one, or two points.
2. A circle and a pair of intersecting lines must intersect in at least one point.
3. A circle and a pair of intersecting lines cannot intersect in more than four points.

State the number of points of intersection possible for the locus of points.

4. a line and a pair of intersecting lines
5. a line and a pair of parallel lines
6. a pair of intersecting lines and a pair of parallel lines

Sample Exercises

7. Consider the lines m and n and point P that is 1 cm from m and 2 cm from the intersection of m and n. Describe each locus.
    a. points equidistant from lines m and n
    b. points 3 cm from P
    c. points equidistant from lines m and n and 3 cm from P

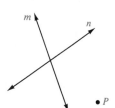

Draw a figure and describe the locus of points.

8. the locus of points 3 cm from circle Q and 1 cm from a line containing the center of the circle
9. the locus of points equidistant from two parallel lines that are 4 cm apart and 5 cm from a point P on one of the lines
10. the locus of points equidistant from the congruent sides of an isosceles triangle that are 5 cm long and form a 60° angle, and that are 1 cm from the base of the triangle

Discussion

Consider a circle Q with a radius of 5 cm and two lines m and n that are tangent to the circle from a point X that is 10 cm from Q. Circle P is concentric with circle Q and has a radius s.

11. For what values of s will circle P intersect lines m and n in four points?
12. For what values of s will circle P not intersect lines m and n?
13. For what values of s will circle P intersect lines m and n in two points?

---

2. Describe the locus of pt. in a plane that are equidist. from the sides of an acute ∠ and 5 in. from the vertex of the ∠. 2 pt. 5 in. from the vertex and on the ∠ bis.

Answer to **Try This** two pt. that are equidist. between the two circles and the two tangents

3. Describe the locus of pt. equidist. from two ∥ lines, m and n, and on the ⊥ bis. through P on m. a pt. halfway between m and n and on the ⊥ bis.

Answer to **Try This** a line ⊥ to the plane containing the two ∥ lines and equidist. between the two pt and the two ∥ lines

Class Exercise Answers

1. true   2. false   3. true
4. 1, 2   5. 0, 2
6. 2, 3, 4   7. a. the ∠ bis.
b. a circle with radius 3 cm
c. the four pt. at which the ∠ bis. intersect the circle with radius 3 cm and center P
8. 4 pt. if the radius of ⊙Q is < 4, 6 pt. if the radius = 4, 8 pt. if the radius > 4   9. J and K, each 5 cm from P and contained in the line 2 cm from the given ∥ lines   10. R and S, each 1 cm on either side of the base and also on the line containing the ∠ bis. of the vertex ∠
11. $s > 5, s \neq 15$
12. $s < 5$ 13. $s = 5$

Assignment Guide

Minimum: 1–20 e/o, 25, AR
Regular: 1–22 e/o, 25, AR
Advanced: 15–25, AR

Applications

Exercises 20–21

Constructions

Class Exercises 8–10
Exercises 3–14, 17–18

Algebra

Exercises 26, 27, AR

Exercises

A

Describe each of the following.

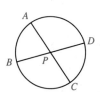

1. the locus of points equidistant from the diameters $\overline{AC}$ and $\overline{BD}$, that are 6 cm long, and intersect at P
2. the locus of points 2 cm from circle P
3. the locus of points equidistant from the diameters $\overline{AC}$ and $\overline{BD}$ and 2 cm from circle P
4. the locus of points equidistant from points A and B
5. the locus of points equidistant from lines m and n that intersect at A
6. the locus of points equidistant from lines m and n and equidistant from points A and B

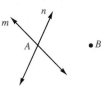

Draw a figure and describe the locus of points.

7. the locus of points 2 cm from a given line $\overleftrightarrow{AB}$ and equidistant from A and point C not on $\overleftrightarrow{AB}$
8. the locus of points 3 cm from $\overleftrightarrow{AB}$ and equidistant from parallel lines $\overleftrightarrow{BC}$ and $\overleftrightarrow{AD}$
9. the locus of points 4 cm from a point P and equidistant from two parallel lines each 1 cm from P
10. the locus of points 3 cm from P, equidistant from points P and A
11. the locus of points 3 cm from the vertex of a given angle and equidistant from the sides of the angle
12. Given equilateral triangle ABC, determine the locus of points which are distance BC from B and distance AC from C.

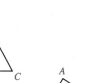

13. Given scalene triangle ABC, determine the locus of points equidistant from B and C and distance AD from $\overline{BC}$ where $\overline{AD}$ is an altitude of $\triangle ABC$.

14. Given rectangle $ABCD$, determine the locus of points equidistant from B and C and equidistant from sides $\overline{CB}$ and $\overline{CD}$ (extended).

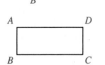

Draw a diagram to represent each of the different solutions possible.

15. Describe the locus of points equidistant from two given parallel lines and a given distance from a transversal intersecting the two lines.
16. Describe the locus of points a given distance from a given point and equidistant from two parallel secants.
17. Describe the locus of points a given distance from a given circle and equidistant from two intersecting chords.
18. Describe the locus of points equidistant from two concentric circles and equidistant from two parallel lines.

B

19. If the locus of points equidistant from M and N is the same as the locus of points equidistant from $\overrightarrow{PM}$ and $\overrightarrow{PN}$, what kind of triangle is PMN?
20. If the locus of points equidistant from vertices A, B, and C of $\triangle ABC$ is at the midpoint of side $\overline{AB}$, what kind of triangle is ABC?

21. The intersection of the set of points a given distance x from a given circle with a radius r and the set of points equidistant from two intersecting diameters of the given circle is four points. Is $x < r$, $r < x$ or $x = r$? Draw a diagram to illustrate your answer.
22. Draw a figure in which the intersection of the locus of points equidistant from two parallel lines, m and n, and the locus of points equidistant from two intersecting lines, p and q, is two points, A and B.

Describe the locus of points in space that satisfy the given conditions.

23. the locus of points 10 cm from P and 2 cm from a plane containing P
24. the locus of points equidistant from a ceiling and floor of a room and equidistant from two opposite walls of the room

C

25. How many points on the earth's surface are equidistant from New York and San Francisco and 1000 miles from the equator?
26. Write the equation of the line that represents the locus of points equidistant from the lines $y = 2x - 3$ and $y = 2x + 1$.
27. Write the equation of the lines that represent the locus of points equidistant from the lines $y = 4x + 1$ and $y = -4x + 1$.
28. Describe the locus of points in space such that for a given segment AB, every point P forms an angle APB such that $m\angle APB = 90$.

Critical Thinking

29. Consider line m and a point P located 4 cm from m. Find a point A such that A is 2 cm from m and 2 cm from P. Find a point B such that B is 3 cm from m and 3 cm from P. Find a second point that is 3 cm from m and 3 cm from P. Find two points that are 4 cm from m and 4 cm from P. Find two points that are 5 cm from both m and P.

Draw a smooth curve through all the points you determined. These points can be described as the locus of points that are equidistant from a given line m and a given point P. Such points form a parabola.

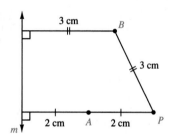

Algebra Review

Solve each inequality.

1. $3(y + 6) < 2y + 12$ 2. $2(y + 5) > y + 15$ 3. $5(n + 6) < 3n - 6$

Math Contest Problem

Draw a circle O with a diameter $\overline{AC}$. Extend $\overline{AC}$ to point D. As a point E on the circle moves from A to C, it traverses an arc of $x°$. Find an expression for $m\angle ECD$ in terms of x.

14. E, pt of intersection of $\perp$ bis. of $\overline{BC}$ and $\angle$ bis. of $\angle BCD$
16.

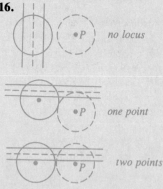

no locus

one point

two points

18.

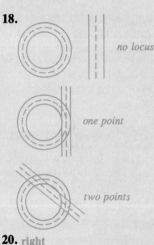

no locus

one point

two points

20. right
22.

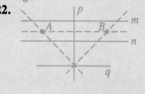

24. line ∥ to the walls, equidist. from the floor and ceiling, and equidist. from the walls
26. $y = 2x - 1$ 28. sphere with dia. $\overline{AB}$ and endpt. of $\overline{AB}$ deleted

Algebra Review Answers

1. $y < -6$ 2. $y > 5$
3. $n < -18$

Math Contest Problem Answer

$m\angle ECD = 180 - \frac{x}{2}$

1. Describe the locus of points in a plane 5 units from point P.

a circle with radius 5 units

2. Describe the locus of points in a plane equidist. from intersecting lines $\overleftrightarrow{AC}$ and $\overleftrightarrow{BD}$.

the ∠ bis. of ∠AOD, ∠DOC, ∠COB, ∠BOA where O is the pt. of intersec. of $\overleftrightarrow{AC}$ and $\overleftrightarrow{BD}$

Lesson Opener

This lesson involves construction problems that can be solved using locus concepts.

Materials

student notebooks
compasses
straightedges

Teaching Notes

Emphasize the importance of the solutions to Examples 1–2.

Guided Practice

Chalkboard Examples

1. Given vertex $\angle B$ and leg AB, construct an isos. $\triangle$.

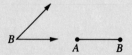

Copy $\angle B$. Mark off the length of $\overline{AB}$ on each ray of $\angle B$. Connect the endpoints.

Answer to **Try This** Copy BC. Construct ⊥ at C. Using radius $\overline{AB}$ and center B, make an arc. Point of intersection with ⊥ is A. Draw $\overline{AB}$.

OBJECTIVE: *Solve construction problems.*

9-8 Constructions and Loci

A construction problem requires the construction of a figure given the measures of parts of the figure. To solve the problem you must construct a locus of points based on the given information. The solution consists of the steps in the construction process together with the construction. Study the examples below.

Example 1

Construct right triangle ABC given the length of the hypotenuse $\overline{AB}$ and the measure of $\angle A$, an acute angle.

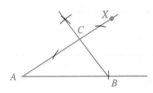

Solution

1. Copy $\angle A$.
2. Mark off $\overline{AB}$ on one ray of the angle.
3. Construct the perpendicular from B to $\overline{AX}$. Label the point of intersection of the perpendicular and $\overline{AX}$ point C.

Triangle ABC has right ∠ngle C, hypotenuse of length AB, and $\angle A$ the measure of the given acute angle. Therefore $\triangle ABC$ is the required triangle.

Try This

Construct a right triangle ABC with hypotenuse $\overline{AB}$ and side $\overline{BC}$.

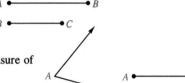

Example 2

Construct rhombus $ABCD$ given the measure of $\angle A$ and the length of diagonal $\overline{AC}$.

Solution

1. Copy $\angle A$ and bisect it.
2. Mark off $\overline{AC}$ on the bisector of $\angle A$.
3. Construct $\angle 2$ congruent to $\angle 1$ at C. Label the intersection with $\overline{AX}$ point D.
4. Construct $\overline{AB} \cong \overline{AD}$.

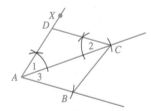

Figure $ABCD$ is a parallelogram since $\overline{AB} \parallel \overline{CD}$ ($\angle 2 \cong \angle 3$) and $\overline{CD} \cong \overline{AB}$. Since $\overline{AB} \cong \overline{AD}$, $ABCD$ is a rhombus.

Try This

Construct a rhombus $ABCD$ given $\angle A$ and side $AB = 3$ cm.

Class Exercises

Short Answer

Give the steps needed to complete each construction.

1. Construct an isosceles triangle given the vertex angle and one of the equal sides.
2. Construct an isosceles triangle given the base and the altitude to the base.
3. Construct a square given a diagonal.
4. Construct a rhombus given both diagonals.

Sample Exercises

Use $\angle 1$ and $\overline{AB}$ and $\overline{CD}$.

5. Construct an isosceles triangle with a base $\overline{CD}$ and an altitude $\overline{AB}$.
6. Construct an isosceles triangle with $\angle 1$ as the vertex angle and congruent sides of length AB.
7. Construct a rectangle $RSTV$ with $\overline{RS} \cong \overline{AB}$ and $\overline{ST} \cong \overline{CD}$.
8. Construct an isosceles triangle KLM with base $\overline{KL} \cong \overline{CD}$ and $\angle K \cong \angle L \cong \angle 1$.
9. Construct a square with the diagonal having length CD.

Discussion

10. Suppose you are constructing an equilateral triangle given the altitude $\overline{AP}$ and you have completed the first three steps in the construction process as follows.

   1. Construct a perpendicular to m at P.
   2. Mark off $\overline{PA}$ equal in length to the given altitude.
   3. Construct a 30° angle at point A.

   Describe two different methods you could use to complete the construction.

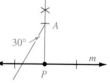

Exercises

A

1. Draw a line p. Construct the locus of points 2 cm from p.
2. Draw a segment $\overline{BC}$. Construct the locus of the vertices A of $\triangle ABC$ such that the altitudes from A to $\overline{BC}$ are each 3 cm in length.
3. Draw an angle A of approximately 60°. Construct a circle with a radius of 2 cm that is tangent to the sides of $\angle A$.

---

2. Given $AC = 5$ cm, construct a square with $\overline{AC}$ as a diagonal.

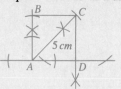

Answer to Try This

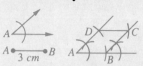

Class Exercise Answers

1. 1. Copy the vertex $\angle$. 2. Mark off seg. on the rays of the vertex $\angle$ that are the length of the given side. 3. Draw the base.
2. 1. Draw a line. 2. Mark off the length of the base on the line. 3. Construct the $\perp$ bis. of the base. 4. Mark off the length of the alt. on the $\perp$ bis. 5. Draw the sides.   **3.** 1. Construct the $\perp$ bis. of the diag. 2. On the $\perp$ bis., use the radius of half the length of the given diag. to mark off the endpoints of the other diag. 3. Draw the sides.
4. 1. Construct the $\perp$ bis. of each diag. 2. On the $\perp$ of one of the diag., use the radius of half the length of the other diag. to mark off the length of the second diag. 3. Draw the sides.
5. Copy $\overline{CD}$. Find $\perp$ bis. of $\overline{CD}$. Mark off length of $\overline{AB}$ on the $\perp$ bis. Draw $\overline{AC}$ and $\overline{AD}$.
6. Copy $\angle 1$. Mark off the length of $\overline{AB}$ on each ray of $\angle 1$. Connect the endpoints.
7.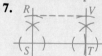
8.
9.

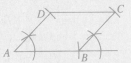

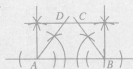

10. 1. Construct a 30° ∠ on the other side of $\overline{AP}$ from A. 2. Find the length of the seg. from P to the intersection of the 30° ∠ and line m. Mark off a ≅ seg. on the other side of P on line m. Draw the side from A.

Assignment Guide
Minimum: 1–17 e/o, 21, MR
Regular: 1–19 e/o, 21–22, MR
Advanced: 11–25, MR

Constructions
Class Exercises 5–9
Exercises 1–22

Lesson Closure

Review the steps in solving construction problems.

Teacher's Resource Materials

Enrichment Using Manipulatives 56
Practice Master 66
Quiz 18

Exercise Answers

See Selected Answers for odd-numbered exercises.

2.

4.

6.

Use ∠1 and the three segments given.

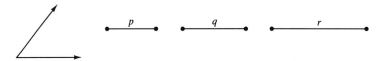

4. Construct a rhombus $ABCD$ with $m\angle A = m\angle 1$ and $AB = p$.
5. Construct a parallelogram $ABCD$ with $m\angle A = m\angle 1$, $AB = r$, and $BD = q$.
6. Construct an isosceles trapezoid $ABCD$ with the longer base $AB = r$, $m\angle A = m\angle 1$, and altitude p.
7. Construct an isosceles triangle ABC with $\angle A$ the vertex angle, altitude $AD = q$, and $m\angle B = m\angle 1$.
8. Construct a right triangle ABC with $m\angle A = 90$, the altitude $AD = q$, and $m\angle B = m\angle 1$.
9. Construct an isosceles triangle ABC with congruent sides $\overline{AB}$ and $\overline{AC}$ having length r and the altitude $\overline{CD}$ to the side $\overline{AB}$ having length p.
10. Construct a circle O with tangents $\overline{PA}$ and $\overline{PB}$ having length r and $m\angle APB = m\angle 1$. A and B are points of tangency.

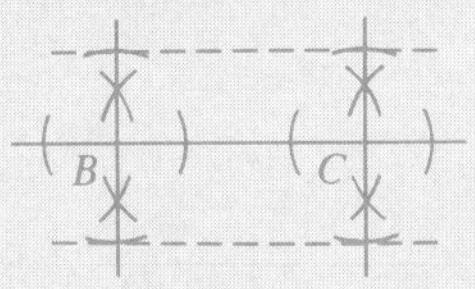

B

Use ∠1 and the three segments given above.

11. Construct an isosceles trapezoid $ABCD$ with the longer base $AB = q$, diagonal $AC = r$, and $m\angle CAB = m\angle 1$.
12. Construct a right triangle ABC with $m\angle B = 90$, leg $BC = q$, and the altitude $BD = p$.
13. Construct a right triangle ABC with $m\angle A = 90$, altitude $AD = p$, and median $AM = q$.
14. Construct a triangle ABC with base $BC = r$, side $AB = q$, and altitude $AD = p$.
15. Construct a triangle ABC with base $BC = r$, altitude $AD = p$, and median $AM = q$.
16. Construct a circle with radius q that is tangent to two congruent intersecting circles with radius p.
17. Construct an equilateral triangle given the radius p of its inscribed circle.

C

18. Construct a right triangle ABC given the sum of the legs $\overline{AB}$ and $\overline{AC}$ and acute angle B.
19. Construct a circle with radius r that is tangent to two congruent nonintersecting circles with a radius s.
20. Construct a circle that is tangent to a given circle at point P and contains a point Q outside the given circle.

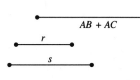

Critical Thinking

A rusty compass is one that is stuck and always has the same opening (radius). You can use your compass as a rusty compass by not changing its radius during the construction process. A collapsible compass is one that springs back together as soon as it is lifted from the paper.

You can use your compass as a collapsible compass by not using the same radius once you have drawn an arc.

21. Copy $\overline{AB}$ and bisect it using

$C \bullet$ $\bullet D$

   a. a collapsible compass
   b. a rusty compass with opening from C to D

22. Draw an acute angle and bisect it using

$A \bullet\!\!-\!\!-\!\!-\!\!-\!\!-\!\!-\!\!-\!\!-\!\!-\!\!\bullet B$

   a. a collapsible compass
   b. a rusty compass

Indicate whether each of the following constructions can be done with (a) a rusty compass, (b) a collapsible compass, (c) both a rusty compass and a collapsible compass, or (d) neither.

23. Construct the perpendicular to a line through a point on the line.
24. Construct the perpendicular to a line from a point not on the line.
25. Construct a parallel to a line through a given point not on the line.

Mixed Review

  1. What is the measure of each interior angle of a regular 10-sided polygon?
  2. If four angles of a pentagon have measures of 100°, 160°, 90°, and 150°, find the measure of the fifth angle.

Determine whether each statement is true or false.

  3. If a parallelogram is inscribed in a circle, it is a rectangle.
  4. If *ABCD* is a parallelogram, then its diagonals are congruent.
  5. If $m\angle A = 40$ in right triangle *ABC* and $m\angle D = 50$ in right triangle *DEF*, then the triangles are similar.

Quiz

Describe the locus of points that satisfy the given conditions.

  1. Given parallel lines *t* and *w* that are 6 cm apart, describe the locus of points equidistant from *t* and *w*.
  2. Given $\triangle ABC$, describe the locus of points equidistant from *A* and *B*.
  3. Given two distinct points *R* and *S* that are 4 in. apart, describe the locus of points 3 in. from *R* and 2 in. from *S*.
  4. Given $\angle M$, what is the locus of points equidistant from the sides of $\angle M$ and 3 m from the vertex *M*?

Complete the construction.

  5. Draw a segment having length *t* and an acute angle $\angle 1$. Construct a rhombus *ABCD* with $\angle A \cong \angle 1$ and $AC = t$.
  6. Draw two segments, *a* and *b*, having unequal lengths. Construct a right triangle with legs of lengths *a* and *b*.

8.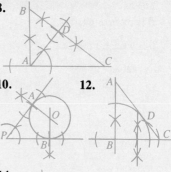

10.   **12.**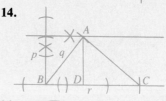

14.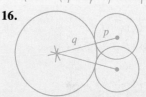

16.

18.

20.

22. Check students' work. **24.** c

Mixed Review Answers

1. 144°   **2.** 40°   **3.** T
4. F   **5.** T

Quiz Answers

1. a line ∥ to *t* and *w* and 3 cm from each **2.** the ⊥ bis. of $\overline{AB}$
3. two pt. of intersection of ⊙*R* and ⊙*S*
4. 2 pt. on the ∠ bis., 3 m from *M*
5.

6.

Exercise Answers

1. 96   **2.** 20   **3.** 20 outcomes

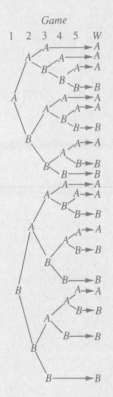

4. 70 outcomes, Check students' work

DISCRETE MATH

Tree Diagrams and Counting

A **tree diagram** is used to count the possibilities for an event. Consider how many different outfits are possible with 2 pairs of slacks and 3 shirts.

Slacks	Shirts	Outfits
black	white	black slacks and white shirt
	yellow	black slacks and yellow shirt
	red	black slacks and red shirt
blue	white	blue slacks and white shirt
	yellow	blue slacks and yellow shirt
	red	blue slacks and red shirt

For each of the 2 pairs of slacks you have 3 choices of shirts, so there are $2 \cdot 3$ or 6 possible choices. This illustrates the *Multiplication Principle:* If the first step can be done in n_1 ways, the second in n_2 ways, and the kth step in n_k ways—the number of different ways the entire procedure can be done is $n_1 \cdot n_2 \cdot n_3 \cdot \ldots \cdot n_k$. Tree diagrams are helpful if the counting of possibilities is complicated and the Multiplication Principle does not apply.

Example

In how many different ways can the Special Olympics series be played out if the A and B teams involved play until one of the teams has won two games?

Solution

Game 1	Game 2	Game 3	Winner
A	A		A
	B	A	A
		B	B
B	A	A	A
		B	B
	B		B

There are 6 different ways in which the series of games can be played out.

Exercises

Use the Multiplication Principle.

1. There are 12 flights from Chicago to New York and 8 flights from New York to Miami. How many different routings from Chicago to New York to Miami are possible?

2. There are 5 different routes . the stadium and 4 routes from store. How many different route take to the store via the stadium?

Make a tree diagram for each situation.

3. a five-game series in which one team must win three games to be called the champion

4. a seven-game World Series in which the of the two teams with 4 wins is the champ.

CRITICAL THINKING

Inductive Reasoning

Critical thinking is based on the consideration of evidence, patterns and relationships. **Inductive reasoning**, which plays an important role, involves forming a conclusion by working from a sequence of specific examples.

Consider the diagrams showing circles with interior regions formed by segments connecting points on the circles. What is the maximal number of regions formed in the interior of the circles by a given number of points? Counting in the first four circles the pattern of regions 1, 2, 4, and 8—you might guess that 5 points will result in 10 regions. You might form the conjecture that n lines cut the interior of a circle into $2n - 1$ regions. An extension of the drawings to the case with 5 points shows that the conjecture appears to hold. With 5 points, 16 regions are formed. However the extension to the case with 6 points shows that only 31 regions are formed. This case gives a counterexample which shows that the pattern formed by inductive reasoning was not valid for all cases.

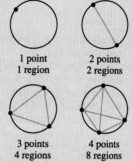

1 point
1 region

2 points
2 regions

3 points
4 regions

4 points
8 regions

Consider the pattern in the sums to the right. What conjecture is appropriate?

$$1 = 1$$
$$1 + 3 = 4$$
$$1 + 3 + 5 = 9$$
$$1 + 3 + 5 + 7 = 16$$
$$1 + 3 + 5 + 7 + 9 = 25$$

The sum for each series of odd numbers appears to be a square number. Thus one might conjecture: The sum of the first n odd numbers is n^2 or

$$\underbrace{1 + 3 + 5 + 7 + \ldots + (2n - 1)}_{n \text{ numbers}} = n^2$$

This conjecture is valid and can be proved using a method known as mathematical induction. In this case, it led to a valid result. Inductive reasoning is a powerful form of critical reasoning but the validity of the conjectures must be tested. It is not enough to form a conjecture on the basis of a few cases. If conjectures are to give us a useful generalization, they must be true for all cases.

Exercises

Make a 10 × 10 grid of numbers from 1 to 100 to form conjectures and test if they are valid. If a conjecture is not valid, give a counterexample.

1. Select any 3 × 3 array of numbers from the grid. What can you say about the sum of the numbers on the diagonals?
2. Select any 3 × 3 array of numbers from the grid. What can you say about the relationship of the number in the center to the sum of the numbers on the diagonal?
3. Select any 3 × 3 array of numbers from the grid. What can you say about the sums of numbers in the first row and numbers in the last row?
4. Select any 3 × 3 array of numbers from the grid. What can you say about the sums of numbers from opposite corners?
5. Select any 3 × 3 array of numbers from the grid. What can you say about the sum of the middle column and the sum of the middle row?

---

1. Const. 1   **2.** Const. 4
3. Const. 2
4.

5. Const. 6   **6.** Const. 5
7. Const. 7
8.

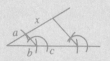

9.

10. Const. 9   **11.** Const. 8
12. Const. 10
13.

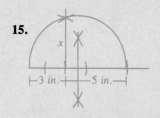

14.

15.

16. c   **17.** b   **18.** a
19. 9

CHAPTER SUMMARY

Vocabulary

construction (9-1)   concurrent lines (9-5)   orthocenter (9-5)
centroid (9-5)   incenter (9-5)
circumcenter (9-5)   locus (9-6)

Key Ideas

1. A construction is a geometric figure produced by using only a compass and straightedge.
2. Every triangle has the following concurrency properties.
   a. The perpendicular bisectors of the sides of the triangle intersect at a point that is equidistant from the vertices of the triangle.
   b. The bisectors of the angles of the triangle intersect at a point that is equidistant from the sides of the triangle.
   c. The medians of the triangle intersect at a point that is two thirds of the way from each vertex to the opposite side.
   d. The lines that contain the altitudes of the triangle are concurrent.
3. A locus of points is a set of points, and only those points, that satisfy one or more conditions.
4. When a locus of points must satisfy more than one condition, its location can be found from the intersection of the loci for each separate condition.

CHAPTER REVIEW

9-1

1. Draw a segment $\overline{AB}$ approximately 4 in. long. Construct a segment $\overline{CD}$ such that $\overline{AB} \cong \overline{CD}$.
2. Draw $\angle B$ whose measure is approximately 70°. Construct $\angle T$ such that $m\angle T = \frac{1}{2}m\angle B$.
3. Draw an obtuse angle. Construct an angle congruent to the obtuse angle.
4. Draw a segment $\overline{RS}$ approximately 8 in. long. Construct a segment $\overline{WY}$ whose length is $\frac{1}{4}RS$.

9-2

Copy the diagram to the right.

5. Construct a line through O perpendicular to $\overline{LN}$.
6. Construct a line through M perpendicular to $\overline{PO}$.
7. Construct a line through P parallel to $\overline{LN}$.
8. Construct a square with a diagonal approximately 5 cm long.
9. Construct a rectangle with sides approximately 4 cm and 6 cm long.

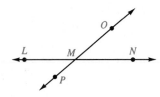

9-3

Draw a large ⊙T. Label a point U on ⊙T and a point X outside ⊙T.

10. Construct tangents to ⊙T from a point X.
11. Construct a tangent to ⊙T at a point U.
12. Draw a large ⊙A. Locate its center by construction.

9-4

13. Draw a segment that is approximately 9 in. long. By construction, divide this segment into five equal parts.
14. Construct the segment of length x given the segments of lengths a, b, and c and the proportion $\frac{a}{x} = \frac{b}{c}$.

15. Draw two segments that are approximately 3 in. and 5 in. long. Construct their geometric mean.

9-5

Choose the correct word to complete each statement.

16. The three altitudes of a triangle concur at a point called the ___ .
    a. circumcenter   **b.** incenter   **c.** orthocenter   **d.** centroid
17. The three angle bisectors concur at a point called the ___ .
    a. circumcenter   **b.** incenter   **c.** orthocenter   **d.** centroid
18. The point equidistant from the vertices of a triangle is called the ___ .
    a. circumcenter   **b.** incenter   **c.** orthocenter   **d.** centroid

19. In △ABC, medians $\overline{AD}$ and $\overline{CE}$ concur at point T. If AT = 6, then AD = __?__ .

9-6

Describe the locus of points that satisfy the given condition.

20. the locus of the centers of circles with radii 2 cm and passing through a given point T
21. the locus of points equidistant from sides $\overline{AB}$ and $\overline{CD}$ in rectangle ABCD

9-7

22. Point R is on line ℓ. What is the locus of points that are 3 cm from ℓ and 4 cm from R?
23. Points X and Y are 5 m apart. What is the locus of points 3 m from both X and Y?

9-8

Use the segments shown to the right.

24. Construct a rectangle with width a and length b.
25. Construct isosceles triangle RST with RS = RT = a and ST = b.

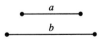

20. a circle with center T and radius 2 cm   21. a line parallel to $\overline{AB}$ and $\overline{CD}$ such that it is the perpendicular bisector of $\overline{AD}$ and $\overline{BC}$ 22. 4 points, the points of intersection of lines parallel, and 3 cm to, line l and of circle R with radius 4 cm
23. 2 points, the points of intersection of two circles, X and Y, with centers 5 m apart and with radii of 3 m
24.

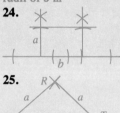

25.

Test Objectives

Item	Objective
1, 2, 6	9-1
7, 8, 18	9-2
9, 10, 11	9-3
3, 4, 12	9-4
15, 16, 17	9-5
19, 20, 21	9-6
22, 23, 24	9-7
5, 13, 14	9-8

Teacher's Resource Materials

Chapter 9 Tests

Test Answers

1. Const. 2   **2.** Draw $\overrightarrow{XZ}$. Use Const. 1 to mark off $2a$ on $\overrightarrow{XZ}$. Label the endpoint Y.
3. Const. 13   **4.** Const. 12
5. Use Const. 2 to copy $\angle 1$. Use Const. 1 to mark off length b on both rays of $\angle 1$. Connect the endpoints.   **6.** Const. 3
7. Const. 7   **8.** Const. 5
9. Const. 8   **10.** Const. 9
11. Const. 10   **12.** Const. 11
13. Construct $\perp$ lines. Use Const. 4 to bisect a 90° $\angle$.
14. Bisect $\angle ABC$. Construct a line $\| \overline{AB}$, a dist. x from $\overline{AB}$, inside $\angle ABC$. Q is its pt. of intersec. with bisector. Draw circle with radius x.   **15.** incenter
16. circumcenter   **17.** d
18. $\perp$ from S to $\overline{RT}$ **19.** two lines $\|$ to t and 3 cm from t
20. a concentric circle with radius $\frac{1}{2}$ the original circle
21. a diameter of the circle that is the $\perp$ bis. of the given chord   **22.** no locus, one point, or two points
23. four points   **24.** the intersection of two planes

CHAPTER TEST

Draw segments and an angle like those shown to the right.

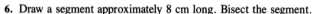

1. Construct an angle congruent to $\angle 1$.
2. Construct $\overline{XY}$ such that $XY = 2a$.
3. Construct the geometric mean between a and b.
4. Construct a segment of length x such that $\frac{x}{a} = \frac{b}{c}$.
5. Construct an isosceles triangle with vertex angle congruent to $\angle 1$ and legs of length b.

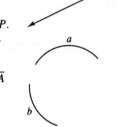

6. Draw a segment approximately 8 cm long. Bisect the segment.
7. Draw line m and point P as shown. Construct the parallel to m through P.
8. Draw a line ℓ with point W on line ℓ. Construct a line perpendicular to ℓ through W.
9. Draw $\odot A$ with point B on $\odot A$. Construct the tangent through B.
10. Draw $\odot Q$. Locate a point P not on $\odot Q$. Construct a tangent to $\odot Q$ from P.
11. Trace arcs a and b. Construct the center of the circle containing the arcs.
12. Draw a segment. Divide it into three equal parts by construction.
13. Construct a 45° angle.
14. Draw an angle ABC. Construct circle Q having radius x and tangent to $\overline{BA}$ and $\overline{BC}$.

State the name for the point described.

15. the point of concurrency of the angle bisectors of a triangle
16. the point that is equidistant from the vertices of a triangle
17. Which of the following are used to construct the orthocenter of $\triangle RST$?
    a. perpendicular bisectors   **b.** angle bisectors
    c. medians   **d.** altitudes
18. Draw a triangle like $\triangle RST$. Construct the altitude from point S.

Draw each locus of points in a plane and write its description.

19. the locus of points 3 cm from line t
20. the locus of the midpoints of all radii of a given circle
21. the locus of points within a circle that are equidistant from the ends of a chord
22. the locus of points equidistant from points A and B and 1.5 cm from point P
23. Lines ℓ and m intersect at W. Describe the locus of points equidistant from ℓ and m and 3 in. from W.
24. Describe the locus of points in a room equidistant from the ceiling and floor and equidistant from the front wall and back wall.

PROBLEM SOLVING

Make an Accurate Drawing

In some cases the answer to a problem can be found by making an accurate drawing or scale drawing. Study the example below in which a scale drawing is used to solve a problem.

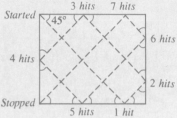

Example 1

An 8-ft by 12-ft pool table has a ball in the corner. Suppose the ball is struck and travels at a 45° angle with a side until it hits the side. The ball then rebounds off that side and travels at a 45° angle until it hits and rebounds off another side. How many times will the ball hit a side before it reaches a corner?

Solution

The scale drawing shows it will have three hits.

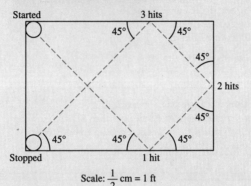

Scale: $\frac{1}{2}$ cm = 1 ft

Problem-Solving Strategies	
Draw a Diagram	Work Backward
Make a Table	Simplify the Problem
Look for a Pattern	Make an Accurate Drawing

The problem-solving strategies that have been introduced up to this point in the book are presented in the chart.

Problems

Use an accurate drawing or scale drawing to solve the problems below.

1. Suppose a ball travels as described in the example above on an 8-ft by 10-ft table. How many times will the ball hit a side before it reaches a corner?
2. Suppose a ball travels as described in the example above on a 6-ft by 8-ft table. How many times will the ball hit a side before it reaches a corner?
3. A pilot in a small plane maintains a constant ground speed of 120 mph. She travels due north for 30 min, then northeast for 10 min, then southeast for 45 min, and then southwest for 30 min. At that point how long will it take to fly straight home?
4. O is the intersection of the perpendicular bisectors of the sides of △ABC, G is the intersection of the medians, and H is the intersection of the altitudes. Observe that O, G, and H are collinear. What fraction of OH is OG? Try several triangles.

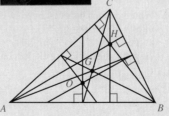

Problem Solving **433**

1.

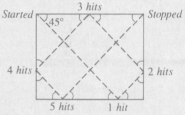

7 times

2.

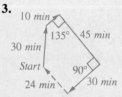

5 times

3.

24 min

4. $\frac{1}{3}$ Check students' work

CUMULATIVE REVIEW

Chapters 1–9

1. Line PQ is __?__ .

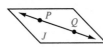

  a. a subset of plane J
  b. perpendicular to plane J
  c. coplanar with plane J
  d. both **a.** and **c.**

2. Two names for the same angle are __?__ .
  a. $\angle ABC$, $\angle CAB$ **b.** $\angle CBA$, $\angle BAC$
  c. $\angle ACB$, $\angle BCA$ **d.** $\angle BCA$, $\angle ABC$

3. An acute angle has a measure __?__ .
  a. greater than 90   **b.** less than 90
  c. equal to 90   **d.** both **a.** and **c.**

4. If E is the midpoint of $\overline{BD}$, then __?__ .

  a. $\overline{AE} \cong \overline{EC}$ **b.** $\overline{BE} \cong \overline{ED}$
  c. $\overline{AD} \cong \overline{CD}$ **d.** $\overline{AB} \cong \overline{BC}$

5. A triangle with no congruent sides is __?__ .
  a. equiangular   **b.** obtuse
  c. scalene   **d.** isosceles

6. Whenever $p \rightarrow q$ is true and p is true, what can you conclude?
  a. $q \rightarrow p$ is true   **b.** q is true
  c. $\sim q$ is true   **d.** both **a.** and **c.** are
                                   true

7. What is a conclusion arrived at through inductive reasoning?
  a. postulate   **b.** theorem
  c. generalization   **d.** deduction

8. Vertical angles are always __?__ .
  a. congruent   **b.** supplementary
  c. acute   **d.** obtuse

9. What type of angles are $\angle AOC$ and $\angle COB$?

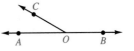

  a. complementary   **b.** supplementary
  c. a linear pair   **d.** both **b.** and **c.**

10. Two lines intersecting to form congruent right angles are __?__ .
  a. bisectors   **b.** vertical
  c. perpendicular   **d.** segment bisectors

11. Name a pair of alternate interior angles.

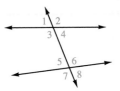

  a. 3 and 5   **b.** 2 and 3
  c. 5 and 4   **d.** 2 and 7

12. In $\triangle MKR$, find the measure of $\angle 1$.

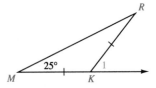

  a. 25   **b.** 50   **c.** 130   **d.** 60

13. $\triangle DKR$ is isosceles. If $m \angle K = 50$, find $m \angle D$.
  a. 50
  b. 55
  c. 65
  d. 60

14. Given that $\triangle STU \cong \triangle VWX$, then __?__ .
  a. $\angle S \cong \angle W$ **b.** $\angle T \cong \angle W$
  c. $\overline{TU} \cong \overline{VX}$ **d.** $\overline{US} \cong \overline{WX}$

15. These two triangles are congruent by __?__ .

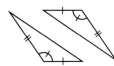

  a. ASA   **b.** SSS   **c.** SAS
  d. not enough information to tell

16. Given that $PR = PS$ and PQ bisects RS, you could prove $\triangle PRQ \cong \triangle PSQ$ by __?__ .

  a. SSS   **b.** ASA   **c.** AAS
  d. not enough information to tell

17. In a parallelogram opposite angles are __?__ .
  a. supplementary   **b.** congruent
  c. complementary   **d.** acute

18. In parallelogram $ABCD$, find $m\angle A + m\angle B$.
  a. 90   **b.** 180   **c.** 270   **d.** 360

19. The diagonals of a rhombus __?__ .
  a. bisect opposite angles
  b. are congruent
  c. intersect, forming a pair of acute angles
  d. all of the above

20. $\angle B \cong \angle C \cong \angle D \cong \angle E$ What is $BCDE$?
  a. trapezoid   **b.** rectangle
  c. square   **d.** rhombus

21. If the scale on a map indicates that 5 cm = 2 km, what would the actual length of a line segment shown on the map as 24 cm be?
  a. 9.6 km   **b.** 0.42 km
  c. 8 km   **d.** 60 km

22. If $\frac{p}{q} = \frac{x}{y}$, find $\frac{y}{q}$.
  a. $\frac{x}{p}$ **b.** $\frac{p}{x}$ **c.** $\frac{y}{x}$ **d.** $\frac{q}{y}$

23. Which of these polygons must be similar?
  a. two isosceles triangles
  b. two rectangles
  c. two parallelograms with 75° angles
  d. two regular octagons

24. The hypotenuse and one leg of a right triangle are 29 and 21. Find the length of the other leg.
  a. 1282   **b.** 36   **c.** 20   **d.** $15\sqrt{2}$

25. A triangle whose sides are 5, 10, and 13 is a(n) __?__ .
  a. obtuse triangle   **b.** acute triangle
  c. right triangle   **d.** impossibility

26. The shorter leg in a 30°–60°–90° triangle is 12. Find the length of the hypotenuse.
  a. $6\sqrt{3}$ **b.** 24   **c.** $12\sqrt{3}$ **d.** $2\sqrt{6}$

27. Find the measure of $\overset{\frown}{PQR}$.

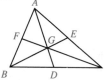

  a. 220   **b.** 290   **c.** 325   **d.** 140

28. If L and M are points on a circle, what is $\overline{LM}$?
  a. secant   **b.** radius
  c. chord   **d.** tangent

29. $\overline{LM}$ is tangent to $\odot R$ at M. If $m\angle MRS = 80$, find $m\overset{\frown}{MTS}$.

  a. 280   **b.** 220   **c.** 320   **d.** 40

30. G is the centroid of $\triangle ABC$. If $AD = 12$, find AG.

  a. 6   **b.** 8   **c.** 12   **d.** 24

31. Name the points of concurrency where the medians of a triangle meet.
  a. incenter   **b.** centroid
  c. orthocenter   **d.** circumcenter

1. d   **2.** c   **3.** b
4. b   **5.** c   **6.** b
7. c   **8.** a   **9.** d
10. c   **11.** c   **12.** b
13. c   **14.** b   **15.** c
16. a   **17.** b   **18.** b
19. a   **20.** b   **21.** a
22. a   **23.** d   **24.** c
25. a   **26.** b   **27.** b
28. c   **29.** a   **30.** b
31. b

Area and Perimeter of Polygons

Chapter Overview

This chapter gives students an opportunity to learn area formulas through exploration and inductive reasoning. The exercises then provide applications for these formulas. The first five lessons deal with polygons; the final two lessons cover circles and their related regions.

Objectives

10-1   ■ Apply formulas for the perimeter and area of rectangles.
10-2   ■ Apply formulas for the areas of parallelograms and triangles.
10-3   ■ Apply the formulas for the area of trapezoids and other quadrilaterals.
10-4   ■ Apply the formula for the area of a regular polygon.
10-5   ■ Apply theorems involving ratios of areas and perimeters of similar polygons.
10-6   ■ Apply formulas for the circumference and arc length of a circle.
10-7   ■ Apply formulas for finding the areas of circles, sectors, and segments.

TEACHING CHAPTER 10

Cooperative Learning Opportunities

One of the standard strategies for solving problems is, "break the problem into parts." Area exercises are well-suited to this strategy. Mistakes are sometimes made due to rushing. Cooperative groups can help insure checking at each step.

In Lesson 10-1, Exercises 27, 28, and 29 can be done by groups of three with the following role assignments.

Student A copies the figure, fills in the given dimensions, and adds any dividing lines that will be needed. Student B supplies dimensions as needed where they are not given. Student C performs the calculations and finds the area. The two students not involved in a particular task should watch and, after the working student is finished, point out anything further

that should be done. All on a team should agree on an answer. Roles should be rotated after each exercise is completed.

Other exercises that lend themselves to this approach are: p. 447, Exercises 30, 31, and 32; p. 452, Exercises 29, 30, and 31. In some of these the figure is not given in the text and role (A) becomes important.

Multicultural Note: *Aztec Land Records*

In 1519 when the Spaniards first saw the Aztec capital of Tenochtitlan, located on the site of present-day Mexico City, they marveled at its beauty, size, and complexity. The Aztec pyramid-temples demonstrated superior skill in engineering. The markets were visited by more than 50,000

customers a day. The city maintained a diverse population of farmers, merchants, military, priests, and nobility.

The Aztec used mathematics to keep records of farm land. It appears that the Aztec divided land into contiguous rectangles and triangles and then, without formulas, counted out square units called *quahuitls*.

As a related exercise, have students, with ruler and compass, draw on graph paper a triangle with sides 9, 8 and 6 and then count out units and partial units to find the area without using a formula.

For more information, see page 17 of **Multiculturalism in Mathematics, Science, and Technology.**

Alternative Assessment and Communication Ideas

The lessons in Chapter 10 build directly on one another and could form the basis of a small student portfolio. Such a portfolio might in turn provide the basis for a review of the chapter. The following steps might help students get started.

For each lesson, find a photo or illustration from a magazine that shows

the area discussed. Use these pictures and your own figure to present the main formula for that lesson.

Illustrate, solve and explain the following **Critical Thinking** exercises: p. 442, Exercise 42; p. 454, Exercise 45; p. 478, Exercise 50.

Review your portfolio and list at least four strategies for finding area of a particular figure. (These might include: dividing a figure into parts; connecting pieces to form a figure; finding the relationship to a larger figure containing the given figure; finding the appropriate formula.)

Investigations and Projects

Have students look up and explain a practical use of area. Students might collect information and pictures for a bulletin board display. Possible topics are described below.

Land measurement: acres. Land is described in acres and partial acres. What is an acre? What rectangular

measurements in feet would make up an acre? What portion of a square mile is an acre? What is the cost of an acre of land?

House and office measurement: square feet. How are square feet measured? What are some rental rates for office space by the square foot? What are some construction costs per square foot?

Cloth: square yards. How are amounts of cloth estimated and measured for furniture covering, drapes, curtains, and clothing?

TV monitors: inches and square inches. TV screens are identified with numbers such as 9, 16, 20, and 36 inch. What do these numbers measure? How might they be converted to area?

Lesson	PACING CHART (DAYS)			Opening Activity	Cooperative Activity	Seat or Group Work
	1-Year Minimum	1-Year Regular	1-Year Advanced			
10-1	2	2	2	Chapter Opener: **TE** p. 436; Lesson Opener: **TE** p. 437	Lab Worksheet 10-1A: *Laboratory Manual* p. 95; Lab Worksheet 10-1B: *Laboratory Manual* p. 96; ✂ Lab Worksheet 10-1C: *Laboratory Manual* p. 97	Try This Exercises
10-2	2	2	2	First Five Minutes 10-2: *FFM Transparency Masters* p. 38 or **TE** p. 443; Lesson Opener: **TE** p. 444	Explore: **SE** p. 443; ✂ Lab Worksheet 10-2A: *Laboratory Manual* p. 99; ✂ Lab Worksheet 10-2B: *Laboratory Manual* p. 100; Lab Worksheet 10-2C: *Laboratory Manual* p. 101	Try This Exercises
10-3	2	2	2	First Five Minutes 10-3: *FFM Transparency Masters* p. 39 or **TE** p. 449; Lesson Opener: **TE** p. 450	Explore: **SE** p. 449; ✂ Lab Worksheet 10-3A: *Laboratory Manual* p. 103; ✂ Lab Worksheet 10-3B: *Laboratory Manual* p. 105; ✂ Lab Worksheet 10-3C: *Laboratory Manual* p. 106	Try This Exercise
10-4	2	2	2	First Five Minutes 10-4: *FFM Transparency Masters* p. 40 or **TE** p. 455; Lesson Opener: **TE** p. 455	Explore: **SE** p. 455; Lab Worksheet 10-4: *Laboratory Manual* p. 107	Try This Exercise
10-5	1	1	1	First Five Minutes 10-5: *FFM Transparency Masters* p. 40 or **TE** p. 461; Lesson Opener: **TE** p. 461	Extension Activity: **TE** p. 462	Try This Exercise
10-6	2	2	2	First Five Minutes 10-6: *FFM Transparency Masters* p. 41 or **TE** p. 467; Lesson Opener: **TE** p. 467	Explore: **SE** p. 467; ✂ Lab Worksheet 10-6: *Laboratory Manual* p. 108	Try This Exercises
10-7	1	1	1	First Five Minutes 10-7: *FFM Transparency Masters* p. 41 or **TE** p. 473; Lesson Opener: **TE** p. 473	✂ Lab Worksheet 10-7: *Laboratory Manual* p. 109	Try This Exercises
Review	1	1	1			
Test	1	1	1			

FFM = First Five Minutes

MANAGING CHAPTER 10

Enrichment	Review/Assess	Reteach	Technology	Lesson
Biographical Note: **SE** p. 442; ✂ Lab Worksheet 10-1D: *Laboratory Manual* p. 98	Class Exercises: **SE** p. 439; Mixed Review: **SE** p. 442	Practice Worksheet 10-1: *Practice and Mixed Review* p.72		**10-1**
Enrichment: **SE** p. 448; ✂ Enrichment Using Manipulatives 10-2: *Enrichment* p. 57; BASIC 10-2: **Technology** p. B20; ✂ Lab Worksheet 10-2D: *Laboratory Manual* p. 98	Class Exercises: **SE** p. 445; Mixed Review: **SE** p. 448	Practice Worksheet 10-2: *Practice and Mixed Review* p. 73	Calculator Worksheet 10-2: *Technology* p. CL14; BASIC 10-2: *Technology* p. B20	**10-2**
✂ Enrichment Using Manipulatives 10-3: *Enrichment* p. 58	Class Exercises: **SE** p. 450; Mixed Review: **SE** p. 454	Practice Worksheet 10-3: *Practice and Mixed Review* p.74	Calculator Investigation: **SE** p. 454	**10-3**
Careers: **SE** p. 460; ✂ Enrichment Using Manipulatives 10-4: *Enrichment* p. 59	Class Exercises: **SE** p. 456; Algebra Review: **SE** p. 459	Practice Worksheet 10-4: *Practice and Mixed Review* p.75	Calculator Worksheet 10-4: *Technology* p. CL15	**10-4**
✂ Enrichment Using Manipulatives 10-5: *Enrichment* p. 60	Class Exercises: **SE** p. 462; Mixed Review: **SE** p. 466; Quiz: **SE** p. 466; Quiz: *Assessment* p. 97	Practice Worksheet 10-5 *Practice and Mixed Review* p.76	Computer Exploration 27: **SE** p. 660; Computer Exploration 28: **SE** p. 661	**10-5**
✂ Enrichment Using Manipulatives 10-6: *Enrichment* p. 61	Class Exercises: **SE** p. 469; Algebra Review: **SE** p. 472	Practice Worksheet 10-6: *Practice and Mixed Review* p. 77	Computer Activity: **SE** p. 472; Computer Exploration 27: **SE** p. 660; Computer Exploration 28: **SE** p. 661	**10-6**
✂ Enrichment Using Manipulatives 10-7: *Enrichment* p. 62; BASIC 10-7: **Technology** p. B21	Class Exercises: **SE** p. 475; Mixed Review: **SE** p. 478; Quiz: **SE** p. 478; Quiz: *Assessment* p. 98	Practice Worksheet 10-7: *Practice and Mixed Review* p.78	Calculator Worksheet 10-7: *Technology* p. CL16; BASIC 10-7: *Technology* p. B21	**10-7**
Critical Thinking: **SE** p. 479	Summary & Review: **SE** p. 480–481	Mixed Review: *Practice and Mixed Review* p. 111		**Review**
Discrete Math: **SE** p. 483	Chapter 10 Test: **SE** p. 482; Chapter 10 Tests: *Assessment* p. 55–60; *MathTest*			**Test**

10

Area and Perimeter of Polygons

The area of a tennis court is 2808 sq ft. Its length is 78 ft. Find the width and perimeter of the tennis court.

AREA AND POLYGONS

OBJECTIVE: *Apply formulas for the perimeter and area of rectangles.*

10-1 Perimeter and Area of Rectangles

A geometric figure, such as rectangle *EFGH* below, consists of the points that make up its sides, or boundary. The **perimeter** (*p*) of a polygon is the sum of the lengths of its sides. For a rectangle, perimeter = $2\ell + 2w$.

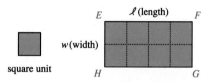

square unit

The perimeter and area of rectangular regions are important when building a wall or laying out a playing field.

A **region** includes the figure and its interior, as indicated by the shaded part inside rectangle *EFGH* above. The **area** (*A*) of a region is the number of square units contained in the region. By counting the number of square units in the rectangle above, you can see that the area of *EFGH* is 8 square units.

The following postulate ensures that a given region has exactly one area.

● **POSTULATE 21**

Every closed region has an area, which is a unique positive number.

The length of rectangle *EFGH* above gives the number of square units in each row. The width gives the number of rows of square units. You can use multiplication to find the total number of square units, as stated in the following postulate.

● **POSTULATE 22**

The area *A* of a rectangle is the product of its length ℓ and its width *w*.
$A = \ell w$

Since a square is a rectangle, the formula $A = \ell w$ can be used to find the area of a square. The length and width of a square are the same, so $A = s^2$.

10-1 Perimeter and Area of Rectangles **437**

4. What methods can be used to find the area of a square?

5. What is the total distance around each square, that is, what is the perimeter of each square?

6. What methods can be used to find the perimeter of a square?

Next, ask students to make several rectangles on the geoboard. Encourage students to make generalizations on patterns that develop in finding the perimeter and area of the rectangles.

Extension Activity

Using the geoboard, construct a rectangle and a square with the same area. Which has the smaller perimeter?

NOTE: In the student edition, the area of a rectangle (Postulate 22) is the starting point for the development of area formulas for special quadrilaterals, followed by the formula for the area of a square. It is also possible to begin with the area of a square and then move to the area of a rectangle, as illustrated above.

Stress the fact that perimeter is the distance *around* a closed plane figure, while area is the part of the plane *enclosed* by the figure.

Point out that since counting is not the easiest way to find the number of square units in a region (area), Postulate 22 gives a formula, which can be used with lengths and widths that are fractions or irrational numbers.

In the future, a specific unit of measure, such as square meters (m^2), will not always be stated. In such cases, it is understood that "units" are used for length and "square units" are used for area.

Example 1

Find the width of rectangle $ABCD$, if it has area 54 sq. units.

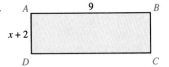

Solution

$9(x + 2) = 54 \qquad A = \ell w$
$9x + 18 = 54$
$\qquad 9x = 36$
$\qquad\; x = 4 \qquad$ The width is $4 + 2$, or 6.

Try This

Find the perimeter of $ABCD$ if the area is not given and $x = 11$.

The following two postulates give additional properties of area.

● **POSTULATE 23**

If two closed figures are congruent, then they have equal areas.

● **POSTULATE 24**

The area of a region is the sum of the areas of all its nonoverlapping parts.

Example 2

Find the area of $ABCDEF$.

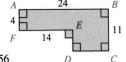 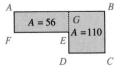

Solution

area $AGEF = 14 \cdot 4 = 56$
area $GBCD = 11 \cdot 10 = 110$
area $ABCDEF = 56 + 110 = 166$ square units $\qquad$ *Postulate 24*

Try This

Find the area of $ABCDEF$ if $BC = 13$ and $FE = 15$.

Example 3

Find the area of $GHIJKL$.

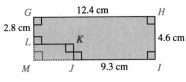

Solution

area $GHIM = (12.4)(4.6) = 57.04 \text{ cm}^2$
$LK = 12.4 - 9.3 = 3.1 \text{ cm}$
$LM = 4.6 - 2.8 = 1.8 \text{ cm}$
area $LKJM = (3.1)(1.8) = 5.58 \text{ cm}^2$
area $GHIJKL = 57.04 - 5.58 = 51.46 \text{ cm}^2$

Try This

Use a different method to find the area of $GHIJKL$.

Class Exercises

Short Answer

Complete each statement.

1. The perimeter of a rectangle with length a and width b is ___ .
2. The area of a rectangle with length a and width b is ___ .
3. The perimeter of a square with side length y is ___ .
4. The area of a square with side length y is ___ .
5. When the side length of a square is given in centimeters, the area is given in ___ .
6. Region C is made up of nonoverlapping regions A and B. If the area of region A is x and the area of region B is y, then the area of region C is ___ .
7. The area and perimeter of a rectangle with length 8 cm and width 6 cm are ___ and ___ .
8. Four rows of six squares each are put together to form a rectangle. Its area is ___ .

Sample Exercises

Find each missing value.

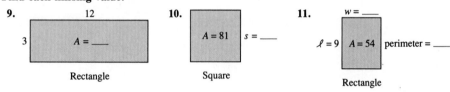

9. Rectangle, width 3, length 12, $A =$ ___

10. Square, $A = 81$, $s =$ ___

11. Rectangle, $w =$ ___, $\ell = 9$, $A = 54$, perimeter = ___

12. Find the area of *ABCDEFGH*.
Assume adjacent sides are perpendicular.

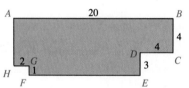

13. Use variables to express the area of a rectangle that has length x and width $x - 3$.
14. Use variables to express the length of the sides of a square that has area z.
15. Use variables to express the width of a rectangle that has area A and length ℓ.
16. It costs \$150 per sq ft to build a house. A planned rectangular house now has dimensions 70 ft by 40 ft. If the plan is changed to extend the dimensions to 72 ft by 42 ft, how much will the cost increase?

Discussion

17. Describe or draw as many rectangles as you can that have lengths and widths that are whole numbers and area 36 cm².
18. Describe or draw at least five different rectangles that have lengths and widths that are whole numbers and equal perimeters. How do the areas of the rectangles compare?
19. Do you think there is a rectangle with whole-number length and width that has the same number for its area as for its perimeter?

Point out that the formula for the area of a rectangle can also be expressed in terms of base and height. Since any side of a rectangle can be considered a base, the altitude to the base is a segment perpendicular to the line containing the base with endpoints on this line and the side opposite the base. The length of the base is also called the base (b) and the length of the altitude is called the height (h).

$$w \quad \boxed{A = \ell w} \quad \text{or} \quad b \quad \boxed{A = bh}$$
$$\ell \qquad\qquad\qquad h$$

Common Errors

Emphasize that the most common units for length and width are inches, feet, yards, and miles (customary), centimeters, meters, and kilometers (metric); for area, square inches, square meters, etc.

Tell students that many of the examples and exercises in this chapter require the use of the Pythagorean Theorem and similar figure concepts in finding a solution. Encourage the use of the calculator when solving these problems. Use diagrams to illustrate Postulate 23 and the converse of Postulate 23. Point out that the converse of Postulate 23 is false. For convenience, Postulate 24 is sometimes referred to as the Area Addition Postulate. It provides a method for finding areas of irregularly shaped figures by subdividing the nonoverlapping regions into areas that can be determined.

Guided Practice

Chalkboard Examples

1. Find the area of rectangle *ABCD* if *AD* = 8 and *AC* = 17. (HINT: Use the Pythagorean Theorem.) 120

Answer to **Try This** 44

2. Find the area of figure *ABCDEF* using the subtraction method. 166

Answer to **Try This** 177

3. Find the area of the shaded region. 116

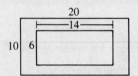

Answer to **Try This** Let *N* be intersection of $\overline{KJ}$ and $\overline{GH}$. Find area *GNKL* = 8.68 cm². Area *NHIJ* = 42.78 cm². Add both for area *GHIJKL*.

Class Exercise Answers

1. 2a + 2b   **2.** ab   **3.** 4y
4. y²   **5.** cm²   **6.** x + y
7. 48 cm², 28 cm   **8.** 24
9. 36   **10.** 9   **11.** 6, 30
12. 126   **13.** x² − 3x
14. √z   **15.** $\frac{A}{l}$
16. $33,600   **17.** 1 × 36, 2 × 18, 3 × 12, 4 × 9, 6 × 6
18. Given a fixed perimeter, a square is the rectangle with greatest area. The closer a rectangle is to being square, the greater its area.   **19.** yes, 3 × 6 and 4 × 4

Exercises

A

Refer to rectangle *ABCD* to complete the table.

	Length	Width	Area	Perimeter
1.	13	9	—	—
2.	12	12	—	—
3.	5√2	3√2	—	—
4.	—	7	63	—
5.	⏌	10	—	56
6.	x + 5	x	—	—
7.	y	—	y² − 5y	—

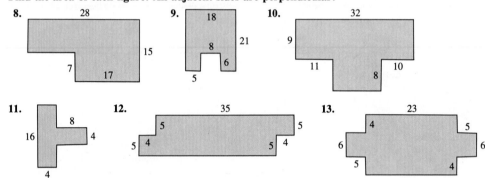

Find the area of each figure. All adjacent sides are perpendicular.

8. 28 7 17 15

9. 18 8 6 5 21

10. 32 9 11 8 10

11. 8 16 4 4

12. 35 5 5 4 5 4

13. 23 4 5 6 6 5 4

State a postulate that supports each statement.

14. You can find the area of a rectangular region by multiplying its length by its width.

15. You know that every closed region has one and only one positive number that can be called its area.

16. You can add the areas of regions that have only boundaries in common to find the total area of the combined region.

17. When you see two regions that have the same size and shape, you know they have the same area.

18. Jim needs to fertilize his rectangular yard which measures 10 m by 37 m. If one bag of fertilizer covers 180 m², approximately how many bags are needed to cover the yard?

B

Find the area of each rectangle.

19. 26 10

20. 45° 10

21. 60° 24

Determine whether each statement is always, sometimes, or never true.

22. Two squares with the same area have the same perimeter.
23. Two squares with the same perimeter have the same area.
24. The perimeter and the area of a given square are the same number.
25. Two rectangles with the same area have the same perimeter.
26. Two rectangles with the same perimeter have the same area.

Find the area of each shaded region. Assume adjacent lines are perpendicular.

27.

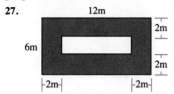

28.

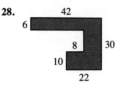

29.

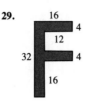

30. The dimensions of one lot for building a house are twice the dimensions of a second lot. How do the areas of the lots compare?
31. The width of a rectangular playing field is 60 yd. The area of the field is 7200 sq yd. How far is it diagonally across the field?
32. The ratio of the height of a wall to the length of the wall is 2:3. The area of the wall is 384 sq ft. What are the height and length of the wall?
33. Find the area of the roof of the building shown to the right. If you assume that 10% of the materials ordered are wasted in cutting, how many 4 ft by 8 ft plywood sheets should be ordered for this roof?
34. A fence was relocated to change the area of a rectangular field. The new length of the field is the old length, ℓ, increased by 6. The new width is 6 less than the old length. If the area of the new field is 108, what is its length and width?

C

35. *ADCB* and *MBNX* are rectangles. The area of *MBNX* is one third the area of *ABCD* and *M* is the midpoint of $\overline{AB}$. How does *BN* compare to *BC*?

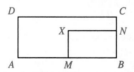

36. In this window pane, the vertices of the shaded square are the midpoints of the sides of the large square. Show that the area of the large square is twice the area of the shaded square.

37. A homeowner has 64 ft of fence that can be used to make a pen for rabbits. He wants to make a rectangular pen that gives the rabbits as much grass area as possible. What dimensions should he use for the pen?
38. The coordinates of the vertices of a rectangle are (3, 1), (1, 3), (5, 7), and (7, 5). Find the area and the perimeter of the rectangle.

Assignment Guide
Minimum: 1–30 e/o, 40–42, MR
Regular: 1–34 e/o, 40–42, MR
Advanced: 17–34 e/o, 35–42, MR

Applications
Exercises 18, 30–34, 36, 37
Coordinate Geometry
Exercise 38
Algebra
Class Exercises 13–15
Exercises 6, 7, 34
Teacher's Resource Materials

Practice Master 67
Transparency 44

Lesson Closure

Summarize the lesson by asking students to state whether each statement below is true or false. If false, explain why.

1. Two rectangles with the same area are congruent. false
2. Two squares with the same perimeter have the same area. true
3. Two squares with the same area have the same perimeter. true
4. If two figures have the same area, then they must be congruent. false
5. If two figures have the same area, then they must have the same perimeter. false

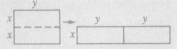
39. Give the dimensions of a rectangle that has perimeter 20 cm and area
21 cm². What do you think is the *greatest* possible area for a rectangle
with perimeter 20 cm?

Critical Thinking

40. A student claimed it is possible to keep the area of a rectangle the
same and change the perimeter and vice versa. Do you agree?
Support your conclusion.

41. *ABCD*, *IBHF*, and *EFGD* are all rectangles. Give a convincing
argument that regions *X* and *Y* have equal area no matter where *F* is
located on diagonal $\overline{BD}$.

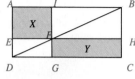

42. In the figure to the right, *D* is the center of the smaller of the
two squares. The larger square overlaps the smaller square in
quadrilateral *ABDE*. Find the area of *ABDE*. Give a convincing
argument that this area would be the same whether *B* trisects
$\overline{AC}$ or not.

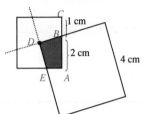

Mixed Review

Find each of the following.

1. $EF = 6, EG = 8$ Find *FG*.	**2.** $FG = 3, GH = 7$ Find *FH*.
3. $GH = 10, FH = 13$ Find *FG*.	**4.** $FG = 8, EG = 5$ Find *FE*.
5. $FE = 4, EH = 16$ Find *EG*.	**6.** $FE = 3, EH = 12$ Find *EG*.
7. $FE = 5, EH = 15$ Find *FG*.	**8.** $FE = 5, EH = 15$ Find *GH*.
9. $FH = 30, EH = 18$ Find *EG*.	**10.** $FH = 12, FE = 4$ Find *GH*.

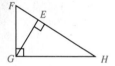

Biographical Note
Benjamin Banneker

Benjamin Banneker, a free black American born in 1731, was probably the
best-known black in early American history. He was a mathematician, an
astronomer, a surveyor, and a farmer.

Largely self-taught, Banneker, at an early age, built a remarkable clock
that kept almost perfect time for more than fifty years. President George
Washington was so impressed by Banneker's mathematical and engineering
abilities that he appointed Banneker to the Capital Committee in Washington
where he helped draw up plans that determined the borders of the District of
Columbia.

As an astronomer, Banneker published almanacs that were later used by
opponents of slavery as evidence of the abilities of blacks.

OBJECTIVE: *Apply formulas for the areas of parallelograms and triangles.*

10-2 Areas of Parallelograms and Triangles

 **EXPLORE** On lined paper, draw and cut three different parallelograms. Can you make one straight cut that will separate a parallelogram into two pieces that can be fitted together to form a rectangle? How do the areas of the parallelogram and rectangle compare?

The idea in the Explore suggests a way to develop a formula for finding the area of a parallelogram. To understand and use such a formula, you first need to be able to identify the base and altitude of a parallelogram. Any side of a parallelogram can be called a **base.** The length of this side is also called the base (*b*). For each base, a segment perpendicular to the line containing the base with endpoints on this line and the side opposite the base is called the **altitude.** The length of the altitude is called the **height** (*h*). Sometimes, as long as no confusion results, the height is also described as "the altitude."

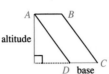

The diagram below shows region *R* being moved from the left side of the parallelogram to the right side.

You can use this procedure to give a convincing argument that the area of a parallelogram is the same as the area of a rectangle with the same base and height. This idea is the basis of Theorem 10.1.

◆ **THEOREM 10.1**

The area of a parallelogram equals the product of the base *b* and the height *h*. $A = bh$

Given: ▱ *ABCD* with base *b* and altitude *h*

Prove: $A = bh$

Plan Draw altitudes $\overline{AE}$ and $\overline{DF}$, forming right triangles *ABE* and *DCF*. Prove $\triangle ABE \cong \triangle DCF$ (area I = area III) using the HL Congruence Theorem. area *ABCD* = area II + area III (Postulate 24). By substitution, area *ABCD* = area II + area I = area rectangle *ADFE* = *bh*.

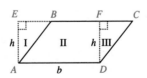

(Quiz on previous lesson)

1. Find the area and perimeter of a rectangle with sides $3\sqrt{2}$ cm and $4\sqrt{2}$ cm. A = 24 cm², p = 14√2 cm

2. Find the area and perimeter of square *WXYZ* if the area of square *ABCD* is 64 sq ft and if points *W*, *X*, *Y*, and *Z* are midpoints of $\overline{AB}$, $\overline{BC}$, $\overline{CD}$, and $\overline{DA}$. A = 32 sq ft, p = 16√2 ft

3. Stained glass will be installed in a rectangular window which is 5 ft by 4 ft. If the cost of the stained glass is $15 per square foot, find the cost of the stained glass for the window. $300

4. The Martinsons want to lease a rectangularly shaped shop that is located in the center of the shopping center. The dimensions of the shop are 50 ft by 75 ft. If the monthly cost to lease space in a shopping center is $0.38 per square foot, find the monthly cost for the Martinsons to lease the shop. $1425

5. A rectangular picture 10 cm by 20 cm of the LaPorte High School graduating class of 1990 was mounted in a frame 2 cm wide. Find the area of the frame. A = 136 cm²

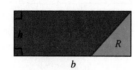

Review the HL Congruence
Theorem, the fact that the diagonals of a parallelogram divide
it into two congruent triangles,
and the 30°–60°–90° and
45°–45°–90° triangle relationships before discussing methods
for deriving formulas for the
area of parallelograms and triangles. It may be helpful to
draw several parallelograms on
the chalkboard and ask students
to identify the base and altitude
of the parallelograms before developing a formula for the area
of a parallelogram. Point out
that any side can serve as the
base and that each base has its
own corresponding altitude.

Next, use the Explore as an introduction to developing a formula for the area of a parallelogram that is based on the area
of a rectangle. Point out that
separating or rotating both
pieces of the parallelogram does
not change the area of the
figure. (See Page 31 on Transformations.)

Theorem 10.1 can be used to prove that parallelograms with equal bases and
equal altitudes have equal areas. You will be asked to complete this proof in
Exercise 36.

Example 1

Find each area.

a. $\square TWXY$
b. $\square PQRS$

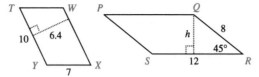

Solution

a. $A = bh = (10)(6.4) = 64$

b. $h = \frac{8}{2}\sqrt{2} = 4\sqrt{2}$
   $A = bh = (12)(4\sqrt{2}) = 48\sqrt{2}$ *In a 45°–45°–90° triangle with hypotenuse x, a leg has length $\frac{x}{2}\sqrt{2}$.*

Try This

Find the area of a parallelogram with base 15, side 10, and a 30° angle.

The following diagram demonstrates that two congruent triangles can be
combined to form a parallelogram.

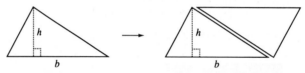

You can use this procedure to give a convincing argument that the area of the
triangle is half the area of the parallelogram. This idea is summarized in
Theorem 10.2.

◆ **THEOREM 10.2**

The area of a triangle equals half the product of the base b and the
height h. $A = \frac{1}{2}bh$

Given: $\triangle ABC$ with base b and altitude h
Prove: $A = \frac{1}{2}bh$

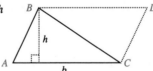

Plan Draw $\overline{BD} \parallel \overline{AC}$ and $\overline{BD} \cong \overline{AC}$, producing $\square ABDC$. Prove that
$\triangle ABC \cong \triangle DCB$ and that these triangles have equal areas. Then
show that area $\triangle ABC = \frac{1}{2}$ area $\square ABDC = \frac{1}{2}bh$.

Theorem 10.2 can be used to prove that triangles with equal bases and equal
altitudes have equal areas.

444   *Chapter 10   Area and Perimeter of Polygons*

Example 2

Find each area.

a. △GHI
b. △DEF

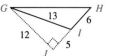

Solution

a. $A = \frac{1}{2}bh = \frac{1}{2}(6)(12) = 36$

b. $A = \frac{1}{2}bh$
$b = \frac{1}{2}(12) = 6$
$h = \frac{12}{2}\sqrt{3} = 6\sqrt{3}$
$A = \frac{1}{2}(6)(6\sqrt{3}) = 18\sqrt{3}$

In a 30°–60°–90° triangle, the side opposite the 30° angle is one half the hypotenuse. The side opposite the 60° angle is one half the hypotenuse times $\sqrt{3}$.

Try This

Find the area of a 45°–45°–90° triangle with hypotenuse 12.

Class Exercises

Short Answer

1. Name each base of △ABC and give its corresponding altitude.
2. Give three different pairs of segment lengths that can be multiplied to find area △ABC.
3. Find the area of a parallelogram with base 10 cm and height twice the base.
4. Find the area of a triangle with base 8 and height half the base.

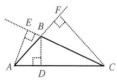

Sample Exercises

Find the area of each figure.

5.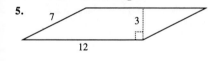

6.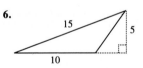

7.

8. A service station operator bought the parallelogram-shaped lot A and the adjoining lot B for \$6 per square foot. What was the total cost?

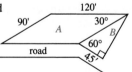

Discussion

9. Lines ℓ and m are parallel. Give a convincing argument that triangles EAF, EBF, and ECF all have the same area.
10. Do you think that if two parallelograms have the same area, they necessarily have equal bases and equal heights? If they have equal bases and equal heights, must they have equal areas? Explain.

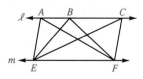

10-2 Areas of Parallelograms and Triangles **445**

Teaching Notes

Remind students that the base of a triangle is not always on the bottom and the altitude is not always inside the triangle.

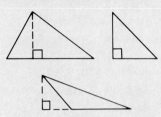

Chalkboard Examples

1. Find the area of parallelogram ABCD. $100\sqrt{3}$

Answer to **Try This** 75

2. Find the area of △ABC. $36\sqrt{3}$

Answer to **Try This** 36

Class Exercise Answers

1. base $\overline{AC}$, altitude $\overline{BD}$; base $\overline{AB}$, altitude $\overline{FC}$; base $\overline{BC}$, altitude $\overline{EA}$ 2. AC, BD; AB, FC; BC, EA 3. 200 cm² 4. 16 5. 36 6. 25 7. 32 8. \$42,922 9. All three triangles have a common base $\overline{EF}$, and their altitudes have the same length. 10. If they have the same area, then $b_1h_1 = b_2h_2$, but this does not mean that $b_1 = b_2$ or $h_1 = h_2$. However, if $b_1 = b_2$ and $h_1 = h_2$, then $b_1h_1 = b_2h_2$.

Assignment Guide

Minimum: 1–37 e/o, 42, 43, MR
Regular: 1–41 e/o, 42, 43, MR
Advanced: 17–43, MR

Applications
Exercises 17, 18, 32, 37

Coordinate Geometry
Exercise 35

Algebra
Exercises 4, 5, 8, 9, 40

Teacher's Resource Materials

Enrichment Using Manipulatives 57
Practice Master 68
Technology: Calculator 14
Technology: BASIC 15
Transparency 45

Lesson Closure

Summarize the lesson by asking students to state formulas for the area of a parallelogram (Theorem 10.1) and the area of a triangle (Theorem 10.2).

Then ask students to explain a method for deriving both formulas.

Exercise Answers

1. 151.2 m^2 **2.** 70 **3.** 6 cm
4. $x + 4$ **5.** $y^2 + 5y + 6$
6. 33.48 m^2 **7.** 7 cm **8.** t^2
9. $4x$ **10.** 70.2 **11.** 72
12. $\frac{25\sqrt{3}}{2}$ **13.** 153.6 **14.** 7
15. 16 **16.** The base of the △ is 2 × the base of the ▱.
17. $21{,}168\text{ m}^2$ **18.** \$108
19. $39\sqrt{3}$ **20.** $16\sqrt{3}$

Exercises

A

Use ▱ *JKLM* to find each missing value.

J
K
h
M
L
b

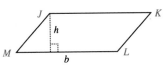

	b	h	A
1.	24 m	6.3 m	—
2.	$7\sqrt{2}$	$5\sqrt{2}$	—
3.	9 cm	—	54 cm^2
4.	x	—	$x^2 + 4x$
5.	$y + 2$	$y + 3$	—

Use △*PQR* to find each missing value.

Q
h
P
R
b

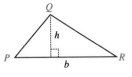

	b	h	A
6.	12.4 m	5.4 m	—
7.	10 cm	—	35 cm^2
8.	t	$2t$	—
9.	—	y	$2xy$

Find the area of each figure.

10.

9.2
7.8
18

11.

12√2
3√2

12.

10
30°

13. Find the area of a parallelogram with base 24, another side 8, and height 6.4.
14. Find the height of a parallelogram that has a base of 12 and an area of 84.
15. Find the base of a triangle that has a height of 12 and an area of 96.
16. A triangle and a parallelogram each have an area of 64 and a height of 4. How do their bases compare?
17. A surveyor was able to find the area of the quadrilateral-shaped plot of land using the following information: $\overline{FG} \parallel \overline{CD}$, $\overline{FC} \parallel \overline{BG}$, $\overline{CD}$ is the perpendicular bisector of $\overline{AB}$, $CD = AB = 168$ m. Find the area of *FGBC*.

F
A
G
C
E
D
B

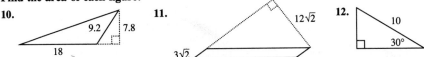

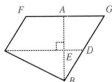

18. Find the cost of putting siding on the triangular region of the house to the right if siding costs 90 cents per square foot.

8 ft
30 ft

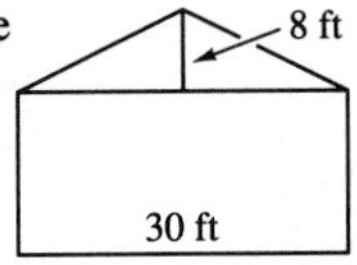

B

Find the area of each figure.

19.

6
60°
13

20.

8
60°
60°

21.

45°
24
10

446 *Chapter 10 Area and Perimeter of Polygons*

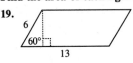

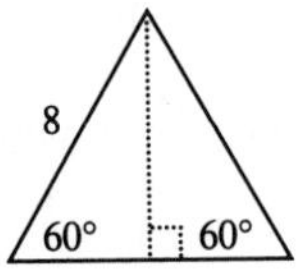

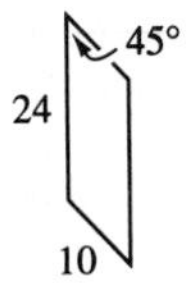

Find AB. Each quadrilateral is a parallelogram.

22.

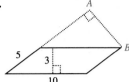

23.

24.

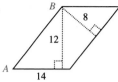

25. If area $\square ABCD$ = area $\square EFGH$ and $AB = 2EF$, how does this altitude to $\overline{AB}$ compare to the altitude to $\overline{EF}$?

26. The bases of two triangles are the same length. The altitude of the first triangle is 5 cm and the area of the second triangle is three times the area of the first. What is the altitude of the second triangle?

27. If the base and altitude of a triangle are doubled, what happens to the area of the triangle?

28. A triangle and a parallelogram have the same area. Give two possible descriptions of how their bases and altitudes might compare.

29. M is the midpoint of $\overline{RS}$. N is the midpoint of $\overline{MS}$. What is the area of the unshaded region? What is the ratio of the area of the shaded region to the area of $\triangle RST$?

30. Draw a triangle and a median. Show that the median divides the triangle into two regions with equal areas.

31. Draw a triangle and its three medians. Show that the six regions formed have equal areas.

32. A developer wanted to blacktop the shaded portion of this corner building site. How much will it cost if blacktopping costs $5 per square meter?

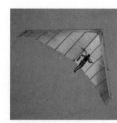

33. Find the area of a 30°–60°–90° right triangle if the hypotenuse has length 16.

34. Find the area of an equilateral triangle with side length 6.

35. Draw the triangle with coordinates $(2,2)$, $(8,4)$, and $(3,9)$ on a coordinate grid. Use the altitude with endpoints $(2,2)$ and $(6,6)$ to find the area of the triangle.

36. Prove that parallelograms with equal bases and equal heights have equal areas.

37. What is the area of this sail in terms of the length k of the keel? If 1 sq ft of sail is needed to support 1 lb of total weight, what length keel would be used for a 125-lb person and a 35-lb glider? What length keel is needed to support you and a 35-lb glider?

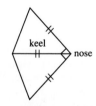

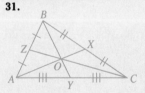

C

38. Prove that the area of an equilateral triangle with sides of length s is $A = s^2 \dfrac{\sqrt{3}}{4}$.

---

21. $120\sqrt{2}$ **22.** 6
23. $\frac{7}{4}$ **24.** 21   **25.** The alt. to $\overline{AB}$ is half the alt. to $\overline{EF}$.
26. 15 cm   **27.** The area is quadrupled.   **28.** (a) If their bases were = , the $\triangle$ would have 2 × the height of the $\square$. (b) If their heights were = , the $\triangle$ would have 2 × the base of the $\square$.   **29.** area of shaded region: $\frac{75}{2}$; area of unshaded region: $\frac{25}{2}$; ratio of shaded area of area of $\triangle RST$: $\frac{3}{4}$

30.

Since $\overline{BD}$ is a median, $AD = DC$. $\triangle ABD$ has the same height as $\triangle DBC$, since they share a vertex and their bases are on the same segment. Therefore, area of $\triangle ABD = \frac{1}{2}(AD)h$ = area of $\triangle DBC = \frac{1}{2}(DC)h$

31.

As in Ex. 30, the following pairs of $\triangle$s have = areas: (i) $\triangle ABX$ and $\triangle ACX$, (ii) $\triangle ABY$ and $\triangle CBY$, (iii) $\triangle ACZ$ and $\triangle BCZ$, (iv) $\triangle OYA$ and $\triangle OYC$, (v) $\triangle OXB$ and $\triangle OXC$, (vi) $\triangle OZA$ and $\triangle OZB$. By (i) and (v), area $(\triangle AOB)$ = area $(\triangle ABX)$ − area $(\triangle OXB)$ = area $(\triangle ACX)$ − area $(\triangle OXC)$ = area $(\triangle AOC)$. Similarly, area $(\triangle AOB)$ = area $(\triangle BOC)$. Since area $(\triangle ABC)$ = area $(\triangle AOB)$ + area $(\triangle AOC)$ + area $(\triangle BOC)$, conclude area $(\triangle AOB)$ = area $(\triangle AOC)$ = area $(\triangle BOC)$ = $\frac{1}{3}$ area $(\triangle ABC)$. By (iv), (v), and (vi), conclude each of the small $\triangle$s has area = $\frac{1}{6}$ area $(\triangle ABC)$.
32. $400   **33.** $32\sqrt{3}$
34. $9\sqrt{3}$

35. 20

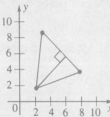

36. If $\square ABCD$ has base b_1 and height h_1, and $\square EFGH$ has base b_2 and height h_2, and $b_1 = b_2$, $h_1 = h_2$; then area $(\square ABCD) = b_1 h_1 = b_2 h_2 = $ area $(\square EFGH)$.

37. $\frac{k^2}{\sqrt{2}}$; about 15 ft   **38.** An equilat. $\triangle$ with side length s has an alt. of $\frac{\sqrt{3}}{2}s$. area $= \frac{1}{2}b \times h = \frac{1}{2}s \times \frac{\sqrt{3}}{2}s = \frac{\sqrt{3}}{4}s^2$. **39.** Let $b = AB = CD$ be the base length of the $\square$, and let h_1, h_2 be the heights of the shaded $\triangle$s. area of shaded region $= \frac{1}{2}h_1 b + \frac{1}{2}h_2 b = \frac{1}{2}(h_1 + h_2)b = \frac{1}{2}$ (height of $\square$)$b = \frac{1}{2}$ (area of $\square$)

40. (a) If the reg. octagon has side length a, then $x^2 + x^2 = a^2$ so $a = x\sqrt{2}$. $2x + a = s$, or $2x + x\sqrt{2} = s$, and $x = \frac{s}{2 + \sqrt{2}}$.

$\frac{s}{2 + \sqrt{2}} = \frac{s}{2 + \sqrt{2}} \times \left(\frac{2 - \sqrt{2}}{2 - \sqrt{2}}\right) = \frac{s(2 - \sqrt{2})}{4 - 2} = \frac{s}{2}(2 - \sqrt{2})$.

(b) $8(\sqrt{2} + 1)$ **41.** (a) $BE = \sqrt{2}$, $BH = \sqrt{3}$ (b) $\frac{\sqrt{3}}{2}$ (c) $\sqrt{2}$ (d) $\frac{\sqrt{2}}{4}$ **42.** yes, no

43. The area of $\triangle LMN$ is the sum of the areas of $\triangle LFM$, $\triangle MFN$, and $\triangle NFL$. $\triangle LMN$ is equilat., so $LM = MN = LN$. Thus area $\triangle LMN = \frac{1}{2}a \cdot LM + \frac{1}{2}b \cdot MN + \frac{1}{2}c \cdot LN = \frac{a + b + c}{2} \cdot LM$. This means that no matter where point F is inside $\triangle LMN$, $a + b + c = \frac{2}{LM} \cdot$ area $\triangle LMN$.

Mixed Review Answers

1. $5\sqrt{2}$ **2.** 20   **3.** 8
4. $7\sqrt{3}$ **5.** $6\sqrt{2}$
6. $16\sqrt{2}$

Enrichment Answers

1. 30   **2.** $\frac{\sqrt{3}}{4}t^2$

448   *Chapter 10   Area and Perimeter of Polygons*

---

39. *ABCD* is a parallelogram and *X* is any point inside. Prove that the area of the shaded region is one half the area of the parallelogram.

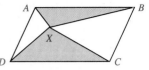

40. If triangles are cut off the corners of square *JKLM*, an octagon results.
  a. If $JK = s$, prove that when a regular octagon results, $x = \frac{s}{2}(2 - \sqrt{2})$.
  b. Use the figure and formula to find the area of a regular octagon whose side length is 2.

41. The length of an edge of the cube is 1.
  a. Find the length of $\overline{BE}$ and $\overline{BH}$.
  b. Find the area of $\triangle BEG$.
  c. Find the area of rectangle *BCHE*.
  d. Find the area of $\triangle BIC$.

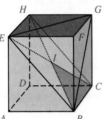

Critical Thinking

42. The ancient Babylonians used the formula $\frac{(a + c)(b + d)}{4}$ to find the area of a quadrilateral with side lengths a, b, c, and d. Does it work for rectangles? parallelograms? Explain.

43. How could you use the areas of triangles *LMN*, *LFM*, *MFN*, and *NFL* to prove that your hypothesis in Exercise 35 on page 79 is correct?

Mixed Review

Find each of the following.

1. $DE = 5$ Find *CE*.   **2.** $QR = 10$ Find *PR*.
3. $CE = 8\sqrt{2}$ Find *CD*.   **4.** $QR = 7$ Find *PQ*.
5. $PR = 12\sqrt{2}$ Find *QR*.   **6.** $CE = 32$ Find *DE*.

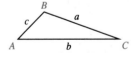

Enrichment
Heron's Formula

Heron of Alexandria (A.D. 75) is said to have discovered a formula that can be used to find the area of any triangle when its side lengths are known. In the formula, *a*, *b*, and *c*, are the lengths of the sides and $s = \frac{1}{2}(a + b + c)$.

1. Use Heron's Formula to find the area of a right triangle with sides of lengths 5, 12, and 13.
2. Develop a formula for the area of an equilateral triangle with side length *t*.

Heron's Formula

area $\triangle ABC = \sqrt{s(s-a)(s-b)(s-c)}$

448   *Chapter 10   Area and Perimeter of Polygons*

OBJECTIVE: *Apply the formulas for the area of trapezoids and other quadrilaterals.*

10-3 Areas of Trapezoids and Other Quadrilaterals

EXPLORE On lined paper, draw and cut out a trapezoid. Label its parallel segments and height as shown. Make a second trapezoid identical to the first. Can you put the trapezoids together to make a parallelogram? What is the area of the parallelogram? of the trapezoid?

You have seen that many area applications involve finding the area of a rectangle, a triangle, or a parallelogram. In this lesson you will see that the formula for finding the area of a trapezoid is also used in real-world situations.

In the Explore you may have discovered the formula for the area of a trapezoid. This formula, stated below, can also be found by dividing the trapezoid into two triangles.

◆ **THEOREM 10.3**

The area of a trapezoid equals half the product of the height h and the sum of the bases b_1 and b_2. $A = \frac{1}{2}h(b_1 + b_2)$

Given: trapezoid $ABCD$ with bases b_1 and b_2 and height h
Prove: $A = \frac{1}{2}h(b_1 + b_2)$

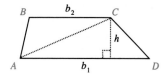

Proof Since $\overline{BC} \parallel \overline{AD}$, h is the height of both $\triangle ABC$ and $\triangle ACD$.

area of trapezoid $ABCD$ = area $\triangle ABC$ + area $\triangle ACD$
$= \frac{1}{2}b_1 h + \frac{1}{2}b_2 h$
$= \frac{1}{2}h(b_1 + b_2)$

Example 1
Find the area of the trapezoid.

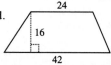

Solution
$A = \frac{1}{2}h(b_1 + b_2) = \frac{1}{2}(16)(42 + 24) = 8(66) = 528$

Try This
Find the area of a trapezoid with height 8.5 and bases 13.4 and 9.2.

(Quiz on previous lesson)
1. Find the area of parallelogram *WXYZ*. $36\sqrt{3}$

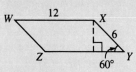

2. Several triangles with base $\overline{MN}$ and vertices *A*, *B*, *C*, and *D* have been drawn on dot paper. Which triangle has the largest area? Explain. All have equal area since all have base $\overline{MN}$ and the same height.

3. Suppose a farmer still needs to fertilize the shaded portion of his yard. Find the area of the shaded triangular region. 28.5

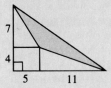

4. Find the area of $\triangle DXC$ if the area of parallelogram *ABCD* is 30 sq in. 15 sq in.

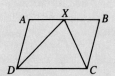

A quick review of the definition of trapezoid, isosceles, altitude/base of a trapezoid and rhombus may be helpful before beginning a discussion on finding areas of trapezoids and other quadrilaterals. Have students practice identifying various parts of trapezoids when they are not in standard position.

Materials

student notebooks
investigative software

Key Terms

perpendicular diagonals
kite

Alternate Explore

In deriving a formula for the area of a trapezoid, one method is simply to divide the trapezoid into two triangles and obtain a sum of the areas of the two triangles formed by the diagonal, each triangle having the same height, and a base that is one of the bases of the trapezoid. (See Theorem 10.3.) A second method is to take the original trapezoid $ABCD$ and trapezoid $WXYZ$ congruent to trapezoid $ABCD$ and form a parallelogram $AZWD$. Thus, the area of trapezoid $ABCD = \frac{1}{2}$ area of parallelogram $AZWD$.

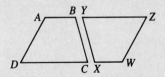

You can use formulas to find the areas of certain other quadrilaterals. A rhombus and a square have perpendicular diagonals. A figure with two distinct pairs of congruent, adjacent sides, often called a **kite,** also has perpendicular diagonals.

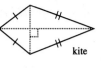

The area of any quadrilateral with perpendicular diagonals can be found as follows.

area $PQRS$ = area $\triangle PQS$ + area $\triangle RSQ$
$= \frac{1}{2}SQ \cdot PT + \frac{1}{2}SQ \cdot TR$
$= \frac{1}{2}SQ(PT + TR) = \frac{1}{2}SQ \cdot PR$

This procedure is summarized in Theorem 10.4, where $d_1 = SQ$ and $d_2 = PR$.

◆ **THEOREM 10.4**

The area of any quadrilateral with perpendicular diagonals d_1 and d_2 is half the product of the lengths of its diagonals. $A = \frac{1}{2}d_1 d_2$

Class Exercises

Short Answer

1. The area of a trapezoid is its __?__ times the average of its bases.
2. The area of a square is its diagonal squared and then divided by __?__ .
3. The area of a kite is __?__ the product of the lengths of its diagonals.
4. The area of a trapezoid is the same as the sum of the areas of two __?__ .

Sample Exercises

Find the area of each figure.

5.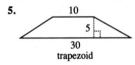

6.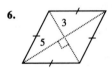

7.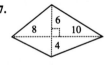

8. Find the area of a square with diagonal of length 6.

Discussion

9. A student claimed that the area of a trapezoid could be found simply by finding the product of the length of its median and its height. Do you think this is correct? Discuss how to give a convincing argument to support your conclusion.
(HINT: Consider Theorem 5.17.)

10. Any trapezoid $ABCD$ can be placed next to a trapezoid $CDFE$ congruent to it to form a parallelogram $ABEF$. How could you use this idea to give a convincing argument that the formula for the area of a trapezoid is correct?

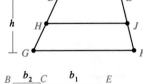

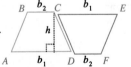

Exercises

A

Find the area of each figure. The figures in Exercises 1–4 are trapezoids.

1.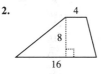
   11
   12
   39

2.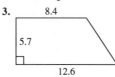
   4
   8
   16

3.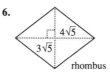
   8.4
   5.7
   12.6

4.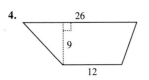
   26
   9
   12

5.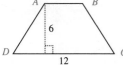
   6 4
   4 4
   kite

6.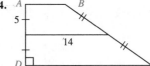
   $4\sqrt{5}$
   $3\sqrt{5}$
   rhombus

7. A trapezoid has bases 15 and 9 and height 7. Find its median and its area.
8. Find the area of a trapezoid if the sum of its bases is 36 and its altitude is 17.
9. A trapezoid has bases 12 and 8 and area 384. Find its height.
10. A trapezoid has median 16 and height 4.8. Find its area.
11. The lengths of the diagonals of a rhombus are 24 and 18. Find its area.
12. Find the area of a quadrilateral that has perpendicular diagonals with lengths 15.4 and 9.7.

Is enough information given in each diagram to find the area of trapezoid *ABCD*? If so, find the area. If not, tell what information you need to find the area.

13.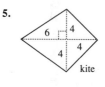
    A   B
    6
    D   C
      12

14.
    A   B
    5
         '14
    D   C

15.
    A 2   B
      6
    D   C
         16

16. The diagonals of a quadrilateral are perpendicular. What is the area of the quadrilateral if one diagonal has length 54 m and the other has length 72 m?
17. Find the area of the trapezoidal cross section of a dam if it is 180 m tall and has bases 20 m and 60 m long.

18. Find the length of the side of a square that has area equal to that of a rhombus with diagonals 9 and 8.

10-3 Areas of Trapezoids and Other Quadrilaterals   **451**

19. Ms. Gray pays 15 cents per square foot each month to lease space in a shopping center. Each store front is 50 ft wide.
 a. Find the monthly cost for her to lease store C.
 b. How much does the owner receive each month if all the stores are leased at this rate?

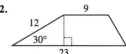

20. Find the length of the long diagonal of a kite with short diagonal 16 cm and area 144 cm².

Find the area of each trapezoid. Theorems 7.7 and 7.8 about special triangles may be helpful.

21. 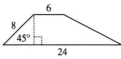   **22.**

B

23. Find the longer base of a trapezoid with shorter base 12, height 8, and area 128.

24. Find the height of a trapezoid with bases 16 and 21 and area 129.5.

25. One diagonal of a rhombus is 12 cm long and its area is 120 cm². Find the length of a side of the rhombus.

26. $BD = 10$ and $AB = 13$ in rhombus $ABCD$. Find its area.

27. Suppose the perimeter of rhombus $ABCD$ is 20 and $AC = 8$. Find the area of the rhombus.

28. Suppose $m\angle BAD = 60$ and $AB = 16$ in rhombus $ABCD$. Find the area of the rhombus.

29. $FGHI$ is a parallelogram and $IJ = FG$. Find GJ.

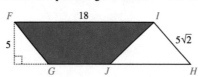

30. The ratio of the base to the height to the other base of a trapezoid is $2 : 3 : 4$. The area of the trapezoid is 117. Find the bases and the height.

Exercises 31–33 refer to these figures.

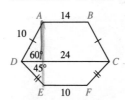
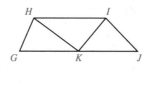

31. $\overline{AB}$, $\overline{DC}$, and $\overline{EF}$ are parallel. Find the area of hexagon $ABCFED$.

32. Find the area of rhombus $QSRT$ if $m\angle QSR = 50$ and the length of the shorter diagonal is 6. Use the table on page 636 or a calculator.

33. $GHIJ$ is a trapezoid and K is the midpoint of $\overline{GJ}$. Explain why the area of $GHIK$ is equal to the area of $HIJK$.

34. What is the effect on the area of a trapezoid if a base is doubled? a height is doubled? a median is doubled? both bases are doubled?

35. If *PQRS* is a trapezoid with bases $\overline{PQ}$ and $\overline{RS}$ and *X* is a point on $\overline{PQ}$, what is the ratio of the area of $\triangle RXS$ to the area of trapezoid *PQRS*?

36. Find the height of an isosceles trapezoid with 45° base angles and bases 8 and 14.

37. One base of a trapezoid is twice the other. The height is equal to the longer base and the area is 60. Find the height of the trapezoid.

38. A real estate agent estimated the area of a plot of land formed by regions *A*, *B*, *C*, and *D* between the road and the shore. What is the approximate area of this land?

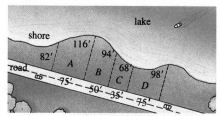

39. A city planner measured the distances shown from the old oak, the big rock, and the flag to the east-west line. Other distances along the line are shown. What is the area of the city park?

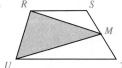

C

40. Find the length of the diagonals of a rhombus that has area 120 and perimeter 52.

41. Prove that the two trapezoids formed by the segment joining the midpoints of the bases of a given trapezoid have equal areas.

42. *RSTU* is a trapezoid and *M* is the midpoint of $\overline{ST}$. Prove that the area of the shaded region is one half the area of *RSTU*.

43. Suppose *NP* = 4 *LM*. How does the area of trapezoid *NLMP* compare to the area of triangle *LMO*?
Show that your answer is correct.

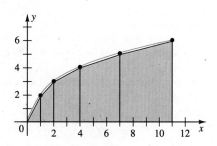

44. It is often necessary to find the area between a curve and the *x*-axis. Sometimes this area can be approximated by trapezoids. Find and add the areas of the shaded regions to estimate the area between this curve and the *x*-axis.

10-3 Areas of Trapezoids and Other Quadrilaterals **453**

30. shorter base $2\sqrt{13}$, longer base $4\sqrt{13}$; height $3\sqrt{13}$
31. $95\sqrt{3} + 110\ \ 85$
32. ≈ 38.6 **33.** $\triangle GHK$ and $\triangle KIJ$ have = bases and alt., and so have = areas. Area *GHIK* = area $\triangle GHK$ + area $\triangle HIK$, area *HIJK* = area $\triangle HIK$ + area $\triangle KIJ$. So, since area $\triangle KIJ$ = area $\triangle GHK$, the areas of the two quad. are = . **34.** The area increases but not necessarily by any fixed multiple; the area is doubled; the area is doubled; the area is doubled.
35. $\dfrac{RS}{PQ + RS} = \dfrac{1}{1 + \frac{PQ}{RS}}$ **36.** 3
37. $4\sqrt{5}$ **38.** $\approx 21,735$ sq ft
39. 18,744 m² **40.** longer diag. 24, shorter 10 **41.** Let *P* be midpt. of base $\overline{AB}$, let *Q* be midpt. of base $\overline{DC}$. The heights of *APQD* and *PBCQ* are the same. Then area of *APQD* = $\frac{1}{2}(AP + DQ)h$ and the area of *PBCQ* = $\frac{1}{2}(PB + QC)h$. These areas are equal, since *AP* = *PB* and *DQ* = *QC*. **42.** Let *h* be the heights of RSTU. Then the height of $\triangle RSM$ is $\frac{h}{2}$ and the height of $\triangle UMT$ is also $\frac{h}{2}$. Area $\triangle RSM$ + area $\triangle UMT = \frac{1}{2}RS\left(\frac{h}{2}\right)$ $+ \frac{1}{2}UT\left(\frac{h}{2}\right) = \frac{1}{2}(\frac{1}{2}(RS + UT)h) =$ $\frac{1}{2}$(area *RSTU*). So the remaining area, the shaded area, also has area = $\frac{1}{2}$(area *RSTU*).
43. Area *NLMP* is 5 times area $\triangle LMO$. If *LM* = *x*, then area *NLMP* = $\frac{x + 4x}{2}h = \frac{5x}{2}h$ and area $\triangle LMO = \frac{x}{2}h$. **44.** areas 1, 2.5, 7, 13.5, 22; sum is 46.
45. a. Draw a circle and an inscribed quad. Use a ruler to measure its sides. b. The sides of the quad. are 8, 6, $3\sqrt{10}$, and $\sqrt{10}$, respectively. area = 39 To check, note that diag. from $(-3, -4)$ to $(3, 4)$ is a dia. of the circle, hence by Cor. 8.11c, this dia. divides the quad. into 2 rt. $\triangle$s, with areas $\frac{1}{2}8 \cdot 6 = 24$, and $\frac{1}{2}(3\sqrt{10})(\sqrt{10})$ $= 15$, respectively. Therefore, area of quad. is 39.

c. The formula for the area depends only on the lengths of the sides of the quad. The side lengths of a quad. can be preserved while changing its area. (Consider a square with side s, and a rhombus with side s.) If the formula were valid for all quad., it would assign the same area to all quad. with $\cong$ sides, which is wrong. The restriction that a quad. have its vertices on a circle removes all ambiguity.
d. If the quad. is a rect., with a square as special case, then $c = a$ and $d = b$, and $s = a + b$. The formula then gives $A = \sqrt{baba} = \sqrt{b^2a^2} = ba$, which is the area of the rect. If $b = a$, then $A = a^2$, the area of square with side length a.

Mixed Review Answers

1. 90   2. 5   3. 5
4. 4   5. AD 6. 50
7. 150   8. 10   9. 5
10. 2

Calculator Investigation Answers

1. a. $a = c = 3$, $b = d = 4$, $p = q = 5$. Formula gives $A = \frac{1}{4}\sqrt{2500 - 196} = \frac{\sqrt{2304}}{4} = \frac{48}{4} = 12$. b. $a = 25$, $c = 15$, $b = d = 5\sqrt{2}$, $p = q = 5\sqrt{17}$. Formula gives $A = \frac{1}{4}\sqrt{722,500 - 562,500} = \frac{\sqrt{160,000}}{4} = \frac{400}{4} = 100$. c. $a = b = 5$, $c = d = 4\sqrt{5}$, $p = 8$, $q = 11$. Formula gives $\frac{1}{4}\sqrt{30,976 - 0} = \frac{176}{4} = 44$.
2. For a square with side length s, $a = b = c = d = s$ and $p = q = \sqrt{2}s$. The formula becomes $A = \frac{1}{4}\sqrt{4(2s^2)(2s^2) - (s^2 + s^2 - s^2 - s^2)^2} = \frac{\sqrt{16s^4}}{4} = \frac{4s^2}{4} = s^2$. For a rhombus with diag. d_1 and d_2, $p = d_1$, $q = d_2$, $a = b = c = d = \sqrt{(\frac{d_1}{2})^2 + (\frac{d_2}{2})^2}$ $A = \frac{1}{4}\sqrt{4d_1^2d_2^2 - (b^2 + d^2 - a^2 - c^2)^2} = \frac{\sqrt{4d_1^2d_2^2 - 0}}{4} = \frac{2d_1d_2}{4} = \frac{d_1d_2}{2}$

Critical Thinking

45. The following is a formula for finding the area of any quadrilateral that has all its vertices lying on a circle.

Area $= \sqrt{(s - a)(s - b)(s - c)(s - d)}$, where s is half the perimeter of the quadrilateral and a, b, c, and d are the lengths of its sides.

a. Explain how you could use measurement to see if the formula probably works.
b. Show that the formula works for the quadrilateral on the coordinate plane to the right.
c. Give a convincing argument that the formula does not work for a quadrilateral whose vertices are not all on a circle.
d. Show that the formula works when the quadrilateral is a square or a rectangle.

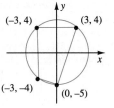

Mixed Review

$\overline{BD}$ and $\overline{CD}$ are tangents to $\odot O$. Complete each statement.

1. $m\angle OBD =$ ___
2. If $OD = 12$ and $AD = 7$, then the radius of the circle is ___.
3. If $BD = 5$, then $CD =$ ___.
4. If $BD = 8$ and $OB = 6$, then $AD =$ ___.
5. $ED \cdot$ ___ $= CD^2$.

Find each of the following.

6. $m\widehat{RS} = 30$, $m\widehat{TQ} = 70$ Find $m\angle RPS$.
7. $m\widehat{RT} = 170$, $m\widehat{SQ} = 130$ Find $m\angle SPQ$.
8. $TP = 8$, $PS = 5$, $RP = 4$ Find PQ.
9. $TS = 16$, $PS = 6$, $PQ = 12$ Find RP.
10. $PS = 2$, $TP = x$, $RP = 5$, $PQ = x - 3$ Find PQ.

Calculator Investigation

It has been claimed that the formula $A = \frac{1}{4}\sqrt{4p^2q^2 - (b^2 + d^2 - a^2 - c^2)^2}$ gives the area of any quadrilateral with side lengths a, b, c, d and diagonal lengths p, q.

1. Test the formula by using a calculator. Check to see if the formula works for
   a. a rectangle with width 3 cm and length 4 cm
   b. an isosceles trapezoid with one base 25 cm, another base 15 cm, height 5 cm, and sides $5\sqrt{2}$ cm
   c. a kite with diagonals 8 cm and 11 cm, a pair of sides 5 cm, and a pair of sides $4\sqrt{5}$ cm

2. Show how the formula can be simplified to give the standard formula for the area of a square. Do the same for a rhombus.

OBJECTIVE: *Apply the formula for the area of a regular polygon.*

10-4 Area of Regular Polygons

 **EXPLORE** Use a compass to construct a regular hexagon. Cut the hexagon into six equilateral triangles. Can you place the triangles together to form two trapezoids? a parallelogram? Suppose the height of each triangle is a and the length of each side is s. Use the formulas for the areas of a triangle, a trapezoid, and a parallelogram to describe three different ways of showing that the area of the hexagon is $3as$.

You learned in Chapter 3 that a regular polygon is both equiangular and equilateral. A circle can be inscribed in any regular polygon, such as *ABCDE*. Also, a circle can be circumscribed about any regular polygon.

The **center** of a regular polygon is the center of its circumscribed circle. The **apothem** of a regular polygon is the distance from the center of the polygon to a side. It is also the radius of a circle inscribed in the polygon. The **radius** of a regular polygon is the distance from the center of the polygon to a vertex. It is also the radius of the circumscribed circle.

Recall from Lesson 10-1 that the perimeter of a polygon is the sum of the lengths of the sides of the polygon. To find the area of a regular polygon with side length s, it seems reasonable to break it up into triangles. In the case of a regular pentagon, there are five congruent triangles with height a and area $\frac{1}{2}sa$, so the area of a pentagon $= 5(\frac{1}{2}sa) = \frac{1}{2}a(5s)$. But $5s$ is the perimeter, so the area of a pentagon $= \frac{1}{2}ap$.

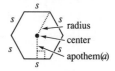

◆ THEOREM 10.5

The area of a regular polygon equals half the product of its apothem a and its perimeter p. $A = \frac{1}{2}ap$

Given: an n-sided regular polygon *ABCD* . . .
with apothem a, sides s, and perimeter p
Prove: area of *ABCD* $= \frac{1}{2}ap$

Proof Consider the congruent triangles formed by drawing all the radii. For each of these, $A = \frac{1}{2}sa$. Since there are n such triangles, the area of *ABCD* . . . $= n(\frac{1}{2}sa)$ or $\frac{1}{2}a(ns)$. Since $ns = p$, the area of *ABCD* . . . $= \frac{1}{2}ap$.

10-4 Area of Regular Polygons **455**

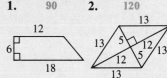
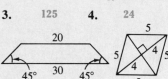
Lesson Opener

Review the definition of regular polygon, inscribed circle, and circumscribed circle before discussing how to find the area of a regular polygon.

In deriving a formula for the area of a regular polygon, inscribe a regular polygon in circle *O*. If all radii are drawn in pentagon *ABCDE*, the result is five congruent isosceles triangles. Since the area of a triangle $= \frac{1}{2}bh$ (also $\frac{1}{2}sa$ where s is the base and a is the apothem) and there are five triangles in the diagram, show students how to use algebra on the sum to derive a formula for finding the area of a regular polygon.

Materials

student notebooks
investigative software

Key Terms

apothem

The following example uses right triangle properties to find the apothem.

Example

Find the apothem and the area of this regular hexagon.

Solution

$m\angle AOC = 60$, so $m\angle AOB = 30$ *A central angle of a regular n-gon measures $\frac{360}{n}$.*

$a = 2\sqrt{3}$, $p = 6(4) = 24$ $\triangle AOB$ is a 30°–60°–90° triangle.
$A = \frac{1}{2}ap = \frac{1}{2}(2\sqrt{3})(24) = 24\sqrt{3}$

Try This

Find the apothem and area of a regular hexagon with 6-cm sides.

Class Exercises

Short Answer

Complete each statement.

1. The apothem of a regular polygon is the radius of its ___ circle.
2. The radius of a regular polygon is the radius of its ___ circle.
3. The perimeter of a regular hexagon with side length 8 is ___ .
4. The perimeter of a regular polygon with n sides, each of length s, is ___ .
5. The area of a regular octagon with perimeter 40 and apothem 6 is ___ .

Sample Exercises

6. Find the area of a regular pentagon with side 10 and apothem 6.9.
7. Find the area of a regular hexagon with side 5 and apothem $\frac{13}{3}$.

PQRSTU **is a regular hexagon.**

8. What is the measure of $\angle POQ$? How do you know?
9. What is the measure of $\angle VOQ$? Why?
10. What kind of triangle is $\triangle POV$?
11. Suppose $PO = 10$. Find PV and VO.
12. Suppose PQ is 16. Find PO, PV, and VO.

Discussion

13. Consider a polygon with an inscribed circle of radius r. As the number of sides of the polygon increases, give a convincing argument that the area of the polygon approaches $\frac{1}{2}rc$, where c is the circumference of the inscribed circle.

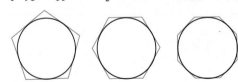

Exercises

A

Find the area of each regular polygon.

1.
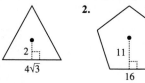
2
$4\sqrt{3}$

2.

11
16

3.
9.5
11

4.
$4\sqrt{2}$

5.

14.5
12

6.
$8\sqrt{3}$ 16

Find the measure of ∠1 and ∠2 in each regular polygon.

7.

1 2

8.

1
2

9.

1
2

Complete the table for the regular polygons to the right.

	Figure	r	s	p	a	A
10.	triangle	12	—	—	—	—
11.	triangle	—	$10\sqrt{3}$	—	—	—
12.	triangle	—	—	$24\sqrt{3}$	—	—
13.	square	—	16	—	—	—
14.	square	$8\sqrt{2}$	—	—	—	—
15.	square	—	—	—	$5\sqrt{2}$	—
16.	hexagon	10	—	—	—	—
17.	hexagon	—	—	—	$9\sqrt{3}$	—
18.	hexagon	—	6	—	—	—

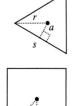

Determine whether each statement is true or false. If false, tell why.

19. An apothem of a regular polygon is a perpendicular bisector of a side.

20. An apothem of a regular polygon is the radius of the circumscribed circle.

21. A radius of a regular polygon bisects an angle of the polygon.

22. A radius of a regular polygon is a radius of the inscribed circle.

23. A radius of a regular polygon is always longer than an apothem.

24. Only regular polygons have apothems.

---

13. The area of the polygon is $\frac{1}{2}ap$, where a is the apothem and p the perimeter of the polygon. The apothem is also the radius of the inscribed circle. As the number of sides increases with the apothem kept constant, the difference between the perimeter of the polygon and the circumference of the circle becomes smaller and smaller, approaching zero. So the area of the polygon approaches $\frac{1}{2}rc$, where r is the radius ($a = r$) and c is the circumference.

Assignment Guide

Minimum: 1–37 e/o, 45, 46, AR
Regular: 1–42 e/o, 45, 46, AR
Advanced: 25–46, AR

Applications
Exercises 35, 37, 38
Algebra
Exercise 33, AR

Teacher's Resource Materials

Enrichment Using
  Manipulatives 59
Practice Master 70
Technology: Calculator 15
Transparency 47

Lesson Closure

In summary, ask students to state the formula for finding the area of a regular polygon and a method for deriving the formula.

1. $12\sqrt{3}$ **2.** 440   **3.** 313.5
4. 128   **5.** 696   **6.** $384\sqrt{3}$
7. 60, 30   **8.** 45, 45
9. 36, 54   **10.** $12\sqrt{3}$,
$36\sqrt{3}$, 6, $108\sqrt{3}$
11. 10, $30\sqrt{3}$, 5, $75\sqrt{3}$
12. 8, $8\sqrt{3}$, 4, $48\sqrt{3}$
13. $8\sqrt{2}$, 64, 8, 256
14. 16, 64, 8, 256
15. 10, $10\sqrt{2}$, $40\sqrt{2}$, 200
16. 10, 60, $5\sqrt{3}$, $150\sqrt{3}$
17. 18, 18, 108, $486\sqrt{3}$
18. 6, 36, $3\sqrt{3}$, $54\sqrt{3}$
19. true   **20.** False;
it is the radius of the inscribed
circle.   **21.** true   **22.** False;
it is a radius of the circumscribed circle.   **23.** true
24. true   **25.** $54\sqrt{3}$
26. $96\sqrt{3}$ **27.** $3\sqrt{2}$ cm,
$2\sqrt{6}$ cm   **28.** $20\sqrt{3}$ m,
$50\sqrt{3}$ m²   **29.** $27\sqrt{3}$
30. $\frac{3\sqrt{3}}{2}s^2$ **31.** 3, $2\sqrt{3}$
32. ≈613.9 cm²
33. side ≈ 16, apothem ≈ 11
34. $400 - 200\sqrt{3} \approx 53.6$
35. $(144\sqrt{2} + 72)$ ft²
36. ≈ 53.16 sq in.   **37.** $20.78
38. The hexagon has $\frac{2\sqrt{3}}{3}$ times
the area of the square.
39. area of triangle $= \frac{1}{2}\left(\frac{\sqrt{3}}{2}s\right)s$
$= \frac{\sqrt{3}s^2}{4}$, area of hexagon $=$
$\frac{1}{2}\left(\frac{\sqrt{3}}{2} \cdot \frac{s}{2}\right)3s = \frac{3\sqrt{3}s^2}{8}$,
ratio of areas $= \dfrac{\frac{\sqrt{3}}{4}s^2}{\frac{3\sqrt{3}s^2}{8}} = \frac{2}{3}$
40. $20\sqrt{3}$ ft, 5 ft   **41.** $1 + \sqrt{2}$
42. ≈17.5   **43.** The area is
multiplied by 4.

B

25. Find the area of a regular hexagon with apothem $3\sqrt{3}$.
26. Find the area of a regular hexagon with radius 8.
27. If the area of a regular hexagon is $36\sqrt{3}$ cm², find its apothem and the length of its side.
28. If the apothem of a regular hexagon is 5 m, find its perimeter and area.
29. An equilateral triangle and a regular hexagon are both inscribed in a circle with radius 6. Find the difference in their areas.
30. A side of a regular hexagon is s units long. Find the area of the hexagon.
31. A side of a regular hexagon is twice the square root of its apothem. Find the length of the apothem and the side.
32. The apothem of a regular pentagon is 13 cm. Find the area of the pentagon.
33. The perimeter of a regular pentagon is three more than seven times the approximate value of the apothem. The area of the pentagon is 440. Find the length of a side and an approximation for the apothem. You may wish to use a calculator.
34. A regular hexagon and a square are circumscribed about a circle with radius 10. How much more area does the square have?
35. A flower garden is to be made with a decorative brick border as shown by the shaded part of this figure. The inner square planting area is formed by connecting the midpoints of the 12-ft sides of the outer regular octagon. Find the area of the brick border.

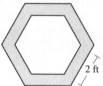

36. If each side of a five-pointed star measures 5 in., find the area of the star. (HINT: Connect some of the vertices of the star to form a pentagon.)
37. Approximately how much would it cost to replace this hexagonal window if glass costs $2 per square foot?

2 ft

C

38. If a square building and a regular hexagonal building have the same perimeter, how do the areas of their floors compare?
39. If an equilateral triangle and a regular hexagon have equal perimeters, prove that the ratio of their areas is 2 to 3.
40. The area of a regular hexagon is $50\sqrt{3}$ sq ft. Find its perimeter and apothem.
41. A side of a regular octagon is 2 units long. How long is its apothem?

a 2

42. Find the difference in area between an inscribed and a circumscribed octagon if the radius of the circle is 6.
43. If the radius of a circle is doubled, what is the effect on the area of an octagon circumscribed about the circle?

44. The figure to the right shows the intersection of a cube and the plane that is the perpendicular bisector of the segment joining one pair of opposite vertices of the cube. This plane contains the midpoints of the six sides of the cube. Find the area of this regular hexagonal region if the length of each side of the cube is 3 cm.

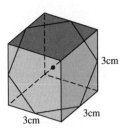

3cm

3cm

3cm

3cm

Critical Thinking

45. On a grid like those shown below, a "side" is a segment connecting a pair of dots. If one straight segment goes through more than two dots, it is still just one side. As shown below, four sides are the most possible for a convex polygon drawn on a 2×2 grid. Six sides are the most possible for a convex polygon on a 3×3 grid.

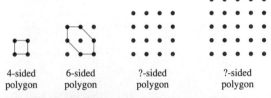

4-sided polygon

6-sided polygon

?-sided polygon

?-sided polygon

   Is it reasonable to use this information to predict the maximum number of sides possible on a 4×4 and a 5×5 grid? Explain. Then find the maximum number of sides for a convex polygon on a 4×4 and a 5×5 grid. Find the perimeter and area of each polygon. What patterns, if any, do you discover?

46. Devise a formula for finding the area of any n-sided regular polygon with radius 1 unit and show why it works.
    (HINT: You may want to consider trigonometric ratios.)

Algebra Review

Write an equation to solve each of the following.

1. Two trains leave town at the same time and travel in opposite directions. One travels 55 mph and the other travels 48 mph. In how many hours will the trains be 206 mi apart?

2. It takes Melissa 3 h to paint a certain area of a house. It takes Gayle 5 h to do the same job. How long would it take them, working together, to do the painting job?

3. Luis received grades of 85, 87, 91, and 89 on his chemistry tests. What must his grade be on the next exam if his average is to be at least 90?

4. There were 203 tickets sold for a school wrestling match. The price for students was $1.25. For nonstudents, the price was $2. The total amount of money collected was $310. How many of each type of ticket were sold?

Careers

Carpenter

Carpentry is the craft of cutting, joining, and finishing wood. A carpenter's work includes the design and assembly of cabinets, doors, wood floors, and other household items.

Carpenters often specialize in one of two broad areas. *Rough carpentry* involves working with frameworks for buildings and other large structures for which strength and stability are important. *Finish carpentry* includes the fitting of doors, window frames, and wood floors. A carpenter who has expertise in all areas of the field may want to go into business as a contractor and oversee work on a large project.

Because of the precision required in designing and assembling wood structures, carpenters must be able to read technical literature and blueprints. A thorough knowledge of geometry is important to carpenters as they interpret scale drawings, design structures with right angles, and construct wood floors to cover a specified area.

In the Middle Ages, apprentices worked with master craftsmen to learn the trade. In recent times, a combination of on-the-job training and courses of study at vocational schools provides training for many carpenters.

OBJECTIVE: *Apply theorems involving ratios of areas and perimeters of similar polygons.*

10-5 Ratios of Areas and Perimeters of Similar Polygons

An engineer who wants to decide whether it is more economical to put in two small heating ducts or one large one in a new building must compare the areas as well as the perimeters of two similar polygons.

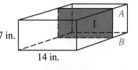

7 in.

14 in.

$$\frac{\text{perimeter of rectangle I}}{\text{perimeter of rectangle II}} = \frac{2 \cdot 7 + 2 \cdot 14}{2 \cdot 5 + 2 \cdot 10} = \frac{42}{30} = \frac{7}{5}$$

$$\frac{\text{area of rectangle I}}{\text{area of rectangle II}} = \frac{7 \cdot 14}{5 \cdot 10} = \frac{98}{50} = \frac{49}{25} = \left(\frac{7}{5}\right)^2$$

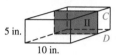

5 in.

10 in.

The cross-sectional area, which determines the amount of air moved, is about twice as large for the larger duct. But the perimeter of the larger duct, which determines the amount of material needed, is only $\frac{7}{5}$ that of the smaller duct. Since twice as much air is moved for only $\frac{7}{5}$ the cost, one large duct would be more economical than the two small ones.

Notice that in this example, the ratio of the perimeters is the same as the ratio of the sides, while the ratio of the areas is the *square* of the ratio of the sides.

◆ **THEOREM 10.6**

If two polygons are similar, then the ratio of their perimeters equals the ratio of the lengths of any pair of corresponding segments.

◆ **THEOREM 10.7**

If two polygons are similar, then the ratio of their areas equals the square of the ratio of the lengths of any pair of corresponding segments.

It is easy to show that the "segments" in the above theorems can be sides, radii, apothems, altitudes, medians, or diagonals.

Example

Find the ratio of the areas of these similar triangles by
a. computing areas   **b.** using Theorem 10.7.

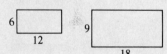

Solution

a. area of $\triangle I = \frac{1}{2}(5)(2.4) = 6$ area of $\triangle II = \frac{1}{2}(10)(4.8) = 24$
$\frac{\text{area of } \triangle I}{\text{area of } \triangle II} = \frac{6}{24} = \frac{1}{4}$

b. The scale factor of $\triangle I$ to $\triangle II$ is $1:2$.
$\frac{\text{area of } \triangle I}{\text{area of } \triangle II} = \left(\frac{1}{2}\right)^2 = \frac{1}{4}$

Try This

Find the ratio of the perimeters of the above triangles by computation and by using Theorem 10.6.

10-5   Ratios of Areas and Perimeters of Similar Polygons   **461**

First Five Minutes

(Quiz on previous lesson)

1. Find the area of a regular polygon with perimeter 36 in. and apothem $2\sqrt{3}$ in. $36\sqrt{3}$ sq in.
2. Find the length of the apothem and the radius of a square with 2-cm sides. 1 cm, $\sqrt{2}$ cm
3. Find the length of the radius, the apothem, the perimeter, and the area of a regular hexagon with 2-m sides. 2m, $\sqrt{3}$ m, 12 m, $6\sqrt{3}$ m²
4. Find the length of the radius, the apothem, the perimeter, and the area of an equilateral triangle with 2-m sides. $\frac{2\sqrt{3}}{3}$m, $\frac{\sqrt{3}}{3}$m, 6 m, $\sqrt{3}$ m²

Lesson Opener

Since this lesson involves some important relationships between the areas and the perimeters of similar polygons, ask students to draw two similar rectangles on grid paper.

6

12

9

18

Key Questions

1. What are the perimeters of rectangles A and B?
2. What are the areas of rectangles A and B?
3. What is the ratio of the perimeter of rectangle A to that of rectangle B?
4. What is the ratio of the area of rectangle A to that of rectangle B?
5. What is the ratio of the lengths of corresponding sides of rectangle A to rectangle B?

6. What generalizations can be made about the ratio of the perimeters of two similar polygons and the ratio of the lengths of any pair of corresponding segments?

7. What generalizations can be made about the ratio of the areas of two similar polygons and the ratio of the lengths of any pair of corresponding segments?

NOTE: If some students are still having difficulties understanding the relationships, repeat the activity using a different pair of similar polygons.

Materials

student notebooks
straightedges
grid paper
investigative software

Extension Activity

Have students contact a local newspaper and obtain a listing of display advertisement costs. Then have them compare samples of display ads with their costs to determine whether or not the cost of the ad was proportional to the area of the ad.

Teaching Notes

Emphasize that the concept of ratio of similarity applies to all corresponding segments of similar polygons and not only to corresponding sides. For all pairs of similar polygons, the ratio of similarity is equal to the ratio of any two corresponding segments determined by the figures, including altitudes, medians, angle bisectors, apothems, and radii.

Class Exercises

Short Answer

1. The ratio of a pair of corresponding sides of two similar triangles is $3:2$. Find the ratio of the perimeters of these triangles.

2. The ratio of a pair of corresponding sides of two similar quadrilaterals is $2:1$. Find the ratio of the areas of these quadrilaterals.

3. The ratio of the corresponding altitudes of a pair of similar triangles is $2:3$. Find the ratio of the areas of the two triangles.

4. The ratio of the areas of two similar triangles is $16:1$. Find the ratio of the perimeters of the two triangles.

Sample Exercises

Find the ratio of the areas and perimeters of similar figures I and II.

5.
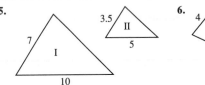

6.
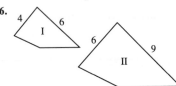

7. The ratio of the length of the hypotenuse of triangular sail I to the length of the hypotenuse of similar triangular sail II is $3:2$. The area of sail I is 24 sq ft. Find the area of sail II.

8. The ratio of the height of $\triangle CDE$ to the height of similar triangle $\triangle FGH$ is $3:5$. The perimeter of $\triangle FGH$ is 25 cm. Find the perimeter of $\triangle CDE$.

9. The areas of two regular hexagons are in the ratio $144:64$. Find the ratio of the side lengths of these polygons. Find the ratio of the perimeters of the polygons.

10. Find the length of the side and the apothem of pentagon II. How did you find these lengths.

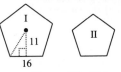

area of I: area of II = 12:9

Determine whether each statement is true or false. Explain your answers.

11. The ratio of the areas of two similar triangles is $9:4$, so the ratio of the lengths of corresponding sides of the triangles is $36:16$.

12. The ratio of the perimeters of any two regular polygons is the same as the ratio of the apothems of the polygons.

13. The ratio of the radii of two regular polygons with the same number of sides is $2:1$, so the ratio of the areas of these polygons is $4:1$.

14. A diagonal of one of two similar rectangles is three times the length of a diagonal of the other, so the area of the first rectangle is nine times the area of the other.

15. If you know that the perimeter of a figure is three times that of a second figure similar to it, then you know that any side of the first figure is three times the corresponding side in the second figure.

In each figure, $\overline{DE} \parallel \overline{CB}$. Find the ratio of the perimeters and areas of $\triangle ABC$
to $\triangle ADE$. How do you know?

16.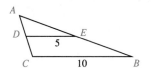

17.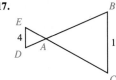

Discussion

18. Can you use Theorem 10.6 to conclude that the ratio of the perimeter
of triangle I to the perimeter of triangle II is 15 to 10? Explain.

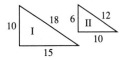

19. Suppose you have proved that Theorem 10.7 is true for similar triangles.
Give a convincing argument that the theorem is also true for similar
regular polygons.

Exercises

A

1. Find the ratio of the perimeters of these polygons using
Theorem 10.6. Then check the ratio by computing perimeters.
2. Find the ratio of the areas of these polygons using Theorem 10.7.
Then check the ratio by computing the areas.

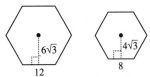

Complete the table for a pair of similar figures.

	Scale factor	Ratio of perimeters	Ratio of areas
3.	$1:2$	___	___
4.	$4:3$	___	___
5.	$a:b$	___	___
6.	___	$2:5$	___
7.	___	$1:4$	___
8.	___	$x:y$	___
9.	___	___	$9:16$
10.	___	___	$4:5$
11.	___	___	$p:q$

12. The lengths of the sides of two squares are 4 and 8. Find the ratio of
their perimeters.
13. Find the ratio of the areas for the squares in Exercise 12.
14. Two regular pentagons have side lengths in the ratio $13:20$. Find the
ratio of their perimeters.
15. Find the ratio of the areas of the pentagons in Exercise 14.
16. $\overline{BD} \parallel \overline{AE}$, $AC:BC = 3:2$
Find the ratios of the areas and perimeters of $\triangle ACE$ and $\triangle BCD$.

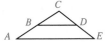

Assignment Guide
Minimum: 1–30 e/o, 39, 40, MR
Regular: 1–38 e/o, 39, 40, MR
Advanced: 19–40, MR

Applications
Exercises 19, 20, 25–29, 37, 38
Algebra
Exercises 5, 8, 11, 36
Teacher's Resource Materials

Enrichment Using
   Manipulatives 60
Practice Master 71
Quiz 19
Technology: Computer
   Software 15
Transparency 48

Computer Software

See Computer Explorations 27
and 28, pages 660 and 661.

Lesson Closure

Review Theorems 10.6 and 10.7.

5/6

17. The ratio of the areas of two regular pentagons is $25:36$. Find the ratio of their
   a. sides   **b.** apothems   **c.** radii
   d. diagonals   **e.** perimeters

18. Two regular hexagons have apothems of 6 cm and 15 cm. The area of the smaller hexagon is 126 cm². Find the area of the larger hexagon.

B

19. A billboard that is 6 ft by 10 ft costs $100 per week to rent. If the cost is the same per square foot, how much should a 9 ft by 15 ft billboard cost?

20. A box manufacturer makes cubical boxes 1 ft on a side. If he doubles the dimensions, how much new material does he need to make the larger cubical box?

21. Suppose $\triangle ABC$ is a right triangle and $\overline{CD} \perp \overline{AB}$. If $CD = 8$, $AD = 16$, and $BD = 4$, find these ratios.
   a. $\dfrac{\text{area of } \triangle ACD}{\text{area of } \triangle CDB}$ **b.** $\dfrac{\text{area of } \triangle ACD}{\text{area of } \triangle ABC}$

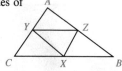

22. Suppose points X, Y, and Z are the midpoints of the sides of $\triangle ABC$. Find the ratio area of $\triangle XYZ$: area of $\triangle ABC$.

23. Two radii of similar regular polygons are in the ratio $5:4$. The sum of their perimeters is 20. Find the perimeters of these polygons.

24. The apothems of two similar regular polygons are in the ratio $3:5$. If the area of the larger polygon is 35 square units, find the area of the smaller polygon.

25. A builder has a small tract of land valued at $45,000 and wants to lay out a similarly shaped tract of land that is $2\frac{1}{2}$ times as large. If the large tract costs the same amount per acre as the small tract, what would you expect the large tract to cost?

26. The area of a rectangular TV screen with a 7-in. diagonal is 25 sq in. How long, to the nearest inch, would the diagonal be for a TV screen with an area of 121 sq in.?

27. A small carpet is 1 m long. A larger, similarly shaped carpet is 3 m long. The small carpet sold for $65. If the price of a carpet is directly proportional to its area, what would you expect the large carpet to cost?

28. A solar panel is 3 m long and 2 m wide. Find the dimensions of a similarly shaped panel that has four times the area of this panel.

29. A scale drawing of the rectangular floor of a gym shows dimensions 9 cm by 24 cm. The scale factor is 1 cm : 6 m. Find the area of the gym floor. You may want to use a calculator.

30. A is the right triangular region and B is the trapezoidal region adjacent to A. Find the ratio of the areas of regions A and B.

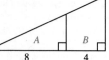

c

31. A square-based pyramid is "sliced" by a plane that intersects edge $\overline{PR}$ at point Q and is parallel to base A. The result is the square cross section B. If $PQ:QR = 1:3$, find the ratio area of B: area of A.

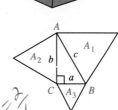

32. Suppose $\triangle ABC$ is a right triangle with hypotenuse c and legs a and b. Consider equilateral triangles on the sides of $\triangle ABC$ as shown. If the areas of these triangles are A_1, A_2, and A_3 as shown, show that $\frac{A_2}{A_1} + \frac{A_3}{A_1} = 1$.

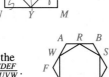

33. Points W, X, Y, and Z are the midpoints of the sides of square $KLMN$. Find $\frac{\text{area of } KLMN}{\text{area of } WXYZ}$.

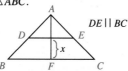

34. Points R, S, T, U, V, and W are the midpoints of the sides of regular hexagon $ABCDEF$. Find $\frac{\text{area of } ABCDEF}{\text{area of } RSTUVW}$.

35. Given a circle, find the ratio of the perimeter of a circumscribed square to the perimeter of an inscribed square. Find the ratio of their areas.

36. Determine x so that the area of $\triangle ADE = \frac{1}{2}$ area of $\triangle ABC$.

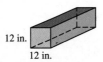

$DE \parallel BC$

37. A heating contractor made a duct with a square cross section with 12-in. sides. How long should one side of square duct be in order to have a cross section that carries twice as much air?

12 in.

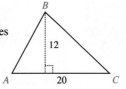

12 in.

38. If the amount of air carried by a 10-in. square duct is to be increased by 30%, what size square duct should be used? (Round to the nearest half inch.)

$.30(100) + 100 = 130$

$\sqrt{130} = ans$

Critical Thinking

39. How could you divide a triangle into three parts of equal area by drawing two lines parallel to a base? Trace this triangle, mark points on the altitude that make segments of selected lengths, and draw lines through them parallel to base $\overline{AC}$. Adjust your choices as needed to divide the triangle correctly. Generalize the procedure.

Exercise Answers

1. By Theorem 10.6, the ratio of perimeters $= \frac{12}{8} = \frac{3}{2}$. By computation, the ratio $= \frac{12 \times 6}{8 \times 6} = \frac{72}{48} = \frac{3}{2}$ 2. By Theorem 10.7, the ratio of the areas $= \left(\frac{12}{8}\right)^2 = \left(\frac{3}{2}\right)^2 = \frac{9}{4}$. By computation, the ratio $= \frac{\frac{1}{2}6\sqrt{3} \times 6 \times 12}{\frac{1}{2}4\sqrt{3} \times 6 \times 8} = \frac{216\sqrt{3}}{96\sqrt{3}} = \frac{9}{4}$ 3. 1:2, 1:4   4. 4:3, 16:9   5. $a{:}b$, $a^2{:}b^2$
6. 2:5, 4:25   7. 1:4, 1:16
8. $x{:}y$, $x^2{:}y^2$ 9. 3:4, 3:4
10. $2{:}\sqrt{5}$, $2{:}\sqrt{5}$
11. $\sqrt{p}{:}\sqrt{q}$, $\sqrt{p}{:}\sqrt{q}$
12. 1:2   13. 1:4
14. 13:20   15. 169:400
16. ratio of perimeters = 3:2, ratio of areas = 9:4
17. All ratios are 5:6.
18. 787.5 cm²   19. $225
20. 18 ft²   21. a. 4:1 b. 4:5
22. 1:4   23. $\frac{80}{9}$, $\frac{100}{9}$
24. $\frac{63}{5}$ sq units   25. $112,500
26. 15 in.   27. $585
28. 6 m by 4 m   29. 7776 m²
30. 4:5   31. 1:16   32. All equilateral triangles are similar. Using Theorem 10.7, $A_1{:}A_3 = c^2{:}a^2$ and $A_1{:}A_2 = c^2{:}b^2$. Then $\frac{A_2}{A_1} + \frac{A_3}{A_1} = \frac{b^2}{c^2} + \frac{a^2}{c^2} = \frac{a^2 + b^2}{c^2}$. By the Pythagorean Theorem, $a^2 + b^2 = c^2$, so $\frac{a^2 + b^2}{c^2} = \frac{c^2}{c^2} = 1$. This shows $\frac{A_2}{A_1} + \frac{A_3}{A_1} = 1$.
33. 2:1   34. 4:3
35. $\sqrt{2}{:}1$, 2:1   36. $\left(1 - \frac{\sqrt{2}}{2}\right)AF$
37. $12\sqrt{2}$ in.   38. 11.5 in. by 11.5 in.   39. Lines should intersect the altitude at $4\sqrt{6}$ and $4\sqrt{3}$ units from B.

40. Conjecture: The area is $\frac{1}{7}$ the area of ABC. Test by carefully drawing triangles and computing area directly.

Mixed Review Answers

1. alternate interior or congruent **2.** $\angle ABH$ **3.** 180 **4.** 65 **5.** 51 **6.** false **7.** true **8.** true

Quiz Answers

1. 48 **2.** 18 **3.** 36 **4.** $\frac{45}{2}$ **5.** $96\sqrt{3}$ **6.** 96 **7.** 6 **8.** 16:49 **9.** 20

40. Points A', B', and C' are points of trisection of the sides of $\triangle ABC$. What fraction of the area of $\triangle ABC$ is the area of the shaded region? Make a conjecture. Then devise a way of testing your conjecture to see if it might be true. (HINT: Consider computer software for geometry or small-grid graph paper.)

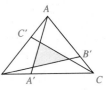

Mixed Review

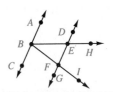

$\overleftrightarrow{AC} \parallel \overleftrightarrow{DG}$ **Complete each statement.**

1. $\angle ABF$ and $\angle BFG$ are ___ angles.
2. $\angle DEH$ and ___ are corresponding angles.
3. $m\angle ABF + m\angle BFE =$ ___
4. If $m\angle BFG = 100$ and $m\angle FBE = 35$, then $m\angle ABE =$ ___.
5. If $m\angle BEG = 47$ and $m\angle CBF = 82$, then $m\angle EBF =$ ___.

Determine whether each statement is true or false.

6. If two lines are cut by a transversal and a pair of alternate interior angles are supplementary, then the lines are parallel.
7. In a plane, two lines perpendicular to the same line are always parallel.
8. Two nonintersecting noncoplanar lines are called skew lines.

Quiz

Find the area of each figure.

1. rectangle

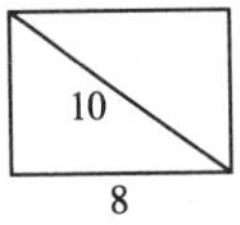

2. square

3. parallelogram

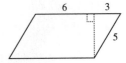

4. trapezoid

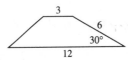

5. regular hexagon

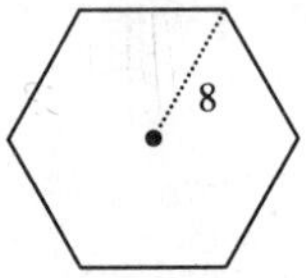

6. rhombus

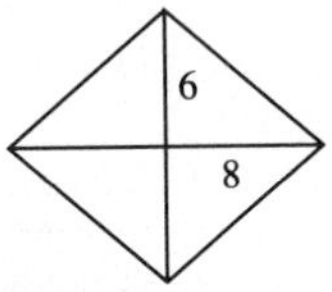

7. A trapezoid with area 42 has bases 4 and 10. Find its height.
8. Two similar polygons have sides in the ratio 4 : 7. What is the ratio of their areas?
9. Two similar regular polygons have apothems 4 and 5. If the perimeter of the smaller polygon is 16, find the perimeter of the larger polygon.

466 Chapter 10 Area and Perimeter of Polygons

AREA AND CIRCLES

OBJECTIVE: *Apply formulas for the circumference and arc length of a circle.*

10-6 Circumference and Arc Length

 **EXPLORE**

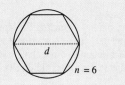

The perimeter of a regular polygon with n sides that is inscribed in a circle with diameter d can be found by using this formula. $\text{perimeter} = nd\sin(\frac{180}{n})°$

Use a calculator or a computer to show what happens to the perimeter as larger and larger values of n are used.

$n = 6$

When a computer graphics plotter draws "curved lines," the pen of the plotter really draws many short connected line segments that only appear to be curved.

As the number of sides of a regular polygon inscribed in a circle with diameter 1 increases, the perimeter of the polygon gets closer and closer to the length of the boundary or **circumference,** of its circumscribed circle. It approaches this as a limit, as suggested below.

 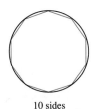

| 5 sides | 8 sides | 10 sides |

To look at this numerically, suppose the formula in the Explore is used to calculate the perimeter of regular polygons inscribed in a circle with diameter 1.

A Regular Polygon with Diameter 1

Number of sides	5	8	10	25	50	100
Perimeter	2.939	3.061	3.090	3.133	3.139	3.141

Notice that the perimeters seem to be approaching a limiting value. The following perimeters of 100-sided regular polygons inscribed in circles with different diameters were also calculated using the formula in the Explore.

Approximate Perimeters for 100-Sided Regular Polygons

Diameter of circumscribed circle	1	2	3	4	5
Perimeter	3.14	6.28	9.42	12.56	15.70
Ratio of perimeter to diameter	3.14	3.14	3.14	3.14	3.14

First Five Minutes

(Quiz on previous lesson)

Complete the table for a pair of similar figures.

	Scale Factor	Ratio of Perimeters	Ratio of Areas
1.	1:2	<u>1:2</u>	<u>1:4</u>
2.	<u>2:5</u>	2:5	<u>4:25</u>
3.	<u>3:4</u>	<u>3:4</u>	9:16
4.	<u>$x:y$</u>	$x:y$	<u>$x^2:y^2$</u>

Lesson Opener

The first five lessons in this chapter dealt with area and polygons. The remaining two lessons deal with area and circles. Since a formal development of deriving a formula for circumference and area of a circle requires the use of limits (a concept beyond the scope of this course), use an informal method of inscribing regular polygons in a circle with a diameter of 1, increasing the number of sides of the polygons each time. (See examples on page 467.) NOTE: As the number of sides of the regular polygon increases, the square root of the apothem becomes closer to the radius of the circle, the square root of the perimeter of the polygon becomes closer to an approximation of the circumference, and the square root of the area of the polygon approaches area of the circle. (See Lesson 10-7.)

Materials

student notebooks
investigative software

Point out that the distance around a polygon is called its perimeter, whereas the distance around a circle is called its circumference. The following point can be made.

The ratio of the circumference of a circle to its diameter is *always* the same for every circle. This ratio is defined as "pi," expressed by the Greek letter π, whose approximate value is 3.14 or $\frac{22}{7}$.

The circumference can also be expressed in terms of the radius r, since $d = 2r$. Therefore, $C = \pi d$ or $C = 2\pi r$.

Remind students that since the exact value for a circumference is given in terms of π, all decimal answers are approximations. Thus, students may need to use the symbol $\approx$, which means "is approximately equal to," when asked to approximate the answer. Otherwise, they should leave the answer in terms of π.

Point out that, like line segments, the length of an arc is a linear measurement, expressed in feet, meters, etc. Also, an arc length depends upon the circumference of the circle and the degree measure of the arc.

As you can see in the table, the ratio of the perimeter of the regular polygon to the diameter of its circumscribed circle, $3.14 : 1$, is always the same. This is also true for the ratio of the circumference of a circle to its diameter, as indicated in the following theorem.

◆ **THEOREM 10.8**

The ratio $\frac{C}{d}$ of the circumference C to the diameter d is the same for all circles.

The ratio $\frac{C}{d}$, which is the same for any circle, is denoted by π (the Greek letter pi). π is an irrational number, which means it cannot be written as an exact decimal. Note that π is the limiting value for the perimeter of regular polygons inscribed in circles with diameter 1. (See the first table.)

Some approximations of π are 3.14, $3\frac{1}{7}$ and 3.14159.

Since $\frac{C}{d} = \pi$ no matter what size the circle is, you can use this equation to derive the formula for finding the circumference of any circle. $\frac{C}{d} = \pi$, so $C = \pi d = 2\pi r$.

The circumference of a circle with radius r and diameter d is given by the formula $C = \pi d = 2\pi r$.

Example 1

Find the circumference of a circle with radius 8 cm.

> **Solution**
> $d = 2r$, so $d = 2 \cdot 8 = 16$
> $C = \pi d$
> $C = \pi \cdot 16$ or 16π cm   *Leave the answer in terms of π unless asked to give an approximate answer.*

Try This

Use $\pi \approx 3.14$ to find the approximate circumference of a circle with diameter 10 cm.

The **length of an arc** of a circle, ℓ, is a fractional part of the circumference of the circle. In this circle, 60° out of a possible 360° are cut by the angle, so ℓ is $\frac{60}{360}$ or $\frac{1}{6}$ of the circumference. You can describe the length of any arc using a ratio as in the following theorem.

◆ **THEOREM 10.9**

The ratio of the length of an arc of a circle, ℓ, to the circumference c equals the ratio of the degree measure of the arc, m, to 360.

$\frac{\ell}{C} = \frac{m}{360}$ or $\frac{\ell}{2\pi r} = \frac{m}{360}$

Example 2

Find the length of a 30° arc of a circle with a 10-cm radius.

Solution

$$\frac{\ell}{2\pi r} = \frac{m}{360}$$

$$\frac{\ell}{2\pi \cdot 10} = \frac{30}{360} \qquad \text{Replace } r \text{ with 10 and } m \text{ with 30.}$$

$$\frac{\ell}{20\pi} = \frac{1}{12}, \text{ so } \ell = \frac{5}{3}\pi \text{ cm}$$

Try This

Find the degree measure of an arc of length 6π of a circle with radius 9.

Class Exercises

Short Answer

Determine whether each statement is true or false.

1. The circumference of a circle circumscribed about a regular polygon can be approximated by the perimeter of the polygon as the number of its sides increases.
2. The ratio of the circumference to the diameter of a circle gets larger if the radius of the circle is increased.
3. The value of π is found by dividing the circumference of a circle by its radius.
4. π is represented exactly by the decimal 3.14.
5. The length of an arc and the degree measure of an arc are the same.
6. A formula for the circumference of a circle is $C = \pi d$.

Sample Exercises

7. Find the circumference of a circle with diameter 10.
8. Find the circumference of a circle with radius 8.
9. The diameter of a bike gear is 21 cm. Choose the more useful approximation for π, $\frac{22}{7}$ or 3.14, and find the circumference of the gear.
10. Find the length of an arc with measure 62 in a circle with diameter 14.
11. $\triangle ABC$ is an equilateral triangle and A is the center of a circle with radius 5. Find the length of $\widehat{EF}$ and $\widehat{ED}$.

Discussion

12. Do you think a regular polygon with 1000 sides has perimeter equal to the circumference of its circumscribed circle? Explain your reasoning.
13. The diameter of two circles may differ and the circumferences may differ. Discuss what property of the circles is always the same and why.
14. Without using any formulas, give a convincing argument that the information given about this figure cannot be correct.

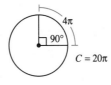

Two Methods for Finding the Length of an Arc:
(Refer to the figure on page 468 in the text.)

1. Suppose $r = 10$.
By definition
$C = \pi d$
$C = \pi \times 20$ or 20π
The 60° arc is $\frac{60}{360}$ or $\frac{1}{6}$ of the circle. $\therefore$ by definition, arc length $AB = \frac{1}{6} \times$ circumference
$$= \frac{1}{6} \times 20\pi$$
$$= \frac{20}{6}\pi \text{ cm}$$

2. By Theorem 10.9
$$\frac{\text{arc length}}{\text{circumference}} = \frac{\text{arc measure}}{360}$$
$$\frac{\ell}{20\pi} = \frac{60}{360}$$
$$\therefore \ell = \frac{20}{6}\pi \text{ cm}$$

NOTE: Method 2 involves setting up a proportion, which for some students is easier than Method 1.

Key Terms

circumference
pi, π
arc length

Guided Practice

Chalkboard Examples

1. If John's bicycle wheels are 40 cm in diameter, find the approximate distance that the bicycle moves forward during one revolution.

HINT: The distance covered in each revolution is the circumference of the bicycle wheel.

40π **cm** $\approx$ **125.6 cm**

Answer to **Try This** **31.4 cm**

2. For a circle of 24 cm radius, find the length of a 105° arc.

14π **cm** $\approx$ **44 cm**

Answer to **Try This** **120**

Exercises

A

Complete the table. Where appropriate, leave answers in terms of π.

	Radius	Diameter	Circumference
1.	4	—	—
2.	—	6	—
3.	—	—	8π
4.	—	—	16

5. Give an approximation to the circumference of a circle with radius 28 cm. Use $\frac{22}{7}$ for π.

6. Give an approximation to the circumference of a circle with radius 5 cm. Use 3.14 for π.

7. A circle has circumference 31.4 cm. Find its approximate diameter.

Complete the table.

	Radius	Degree measure of arc	Length of arc
8.	5	60	—
9.	8	—	4π
10.	$\frac{10}{\pi}$	—	2
11.	—	20	2π

12. A satellite is in orbit at a constant altitude of 300 mi. It is tracked by a ground station through an angle of 45°. How far, in miles, did the satellite travel?

13. The diameter of a bike wheel is 63 cm. How far does the bike move with one revolution of the wheel?

Find the perimeter of each figure. All arcs are arcs of circles.

14.   **15.**

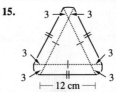

B

Find the circumference of each circle.

16.   **17.**   **18.**

Square   Equilateral triangle   Regular hexagon

19. If a gallon of paint covers 400 sq ft, how many gallons are required to paint a silo (excluding the roof) that is 10 ft in diameter and 50 ft high?

20. A round tower with a 10-m circumference is surrounded by a fence that is 2 m from the tower all around. How long is the fence?

21. On a large machine, the centers of two pulleys are 16 ft apart and the radius of each pulley is 24 in. How long a belt is needed to wrap around both pulleys?

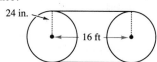

22. The large sprocket on the pedals of a bicycle has 50 teeth and the small sprocket on the wheel has 20 teeth. When the pedals make two complete revolutions, how many revolutions does the wheel make?

23. diameter $AB = 24$, $m\angle BAC = 18$
Find the length of $\overset{\frown}{BC}$.

24. If the radius of the circle is 6, find the length of $\overset{\frown}{UV}$.

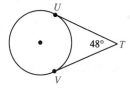

25. diameter $AD = 16$, measure of $\overset{\frown}{AC} = x$, measure of $\overset{\frown}{BD} = 2x$
Find the lengths of $\overset{\frown}{AC}$ and $\overset{\frown}{BD}$.

26. $PA = 12$, $PO = 13$
PA is tangent to $\odot O$ at A.
Find the circumference of the circle.

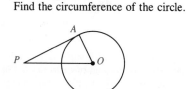

27. The proportion $\frac{\ell}{C} = \frac{m}{360}$ was given in Theorem 10.9. Use it to derive a formula for (a) finding ℓ when m and C are known and (b) finding m when ℓ and C are known.

28. Give a formula for finding the length of a semicircular arc of a circle with radius r.

29. Give a formula for finding the length of an arc intercepted by an angle of 90°.

C

30. Assume that the earth's equator is a perfect circle with radius 4000 mi and that a wire hoop is fitted tightly around it. Suppose a 40-ft piece of wire has been spliced into the hoop and the hoop is held equidistant from the earth's surface. What would be the distance between the hoop and the earth?

31. Four posts with 3-in. radii are bound together with a wire. Find the length of the shortest wire that will go around them.

3 in.

Critical Thinking

32. Suppose the curve *AB* is drawn on a graphics screen of a computer. Circles and segments of selected sizes can be moved around the screen. The circle diameters and segment lengths can be automatically determined at any time. Describe how you would estimate the length of the curve (a) using segments and (b) using circles. Include drawings of your procedures.

Algebra Review

Factor completely.

1. $10x^3 - 90x$ **2.** $m^4 - 625$ **3.** $8t^4 - 8$
4. $16y^2 + 16$ **5.** $5x^2 - 10x - 15$ **6.** $y^2x + 5yx + 6x$
7. $18 - 2x^2$ **8.** $st^2 - 64s$ **9.** $2x^2 + 5x - 12$

Computer Activity

The following is a program for calculating perimeters for regular polygons inscribed in a circle with diameter 1. It uses the formula given in the Explore.

Computer languages usually require angle or arc measures to be given in special units called *radians,* instead of degrees. A 180° arc of a circle with radius 1 has a measure of π radians. Note that this idea is used in line 30.

```
10 PRINT "HOW MANY SIDES FOR THE POLYGON?"
20 INPUT N
30 LET P = N*SIN(3.1415926/N)
40 PRINT "SIDES: "; N, "PERIMETER: "; P
50 LET N = N+1
60 IF N < 200 THEN 30
70 END
```

Exercises

1. Run the program. What can you say about the perimeters of polygons with greater and greater numbers of sides? Why is this true?
2. How can you change the program so that the perimeters produced are even closer to the circumference of the circumscribed circle?
3. How large must N be to produce a perimeter so close to the circumference of the circumscribed circle that it is correct to the hundred thousandth's place?

OBJECTIVE: *Apply formulas for finding the areas of circles, sectors, and segments.*

10-7 Areas of Circles, Sectors, and Segments

You have seen that, as the number of sides of a regular polygon inscribed in a circle increases, the perimeter of the polygon gets closer and closer to a fixed number called the circumference of the circle. In a similar way, as the number of sides of a regular polygon inscribed in a circle increases, its *area* gets closer and closer to a limiting value called the area of the circle. The apothem *a* of the regular polygon gets closer and closer to the radius *r* of the circle and the perimeter *p* of the polygon gets closer and closer to the circumference *C* of the circle.

A farmer might need to find the area of the circular field to calculate irrigation costs.

The variables in the formula for the area of a regular polygon can be replaced by their limiting values to produce a formula for the area of a circle.

$$\text{area of polygon} = \tfrac{1}{2}ap$$

$$\text{area of circle} = \tfrac{1}{2}rc \qquad \textit{Replace "polygon" with "circle," a with r, and p with c.}$$
$$\text{area of circle} = \tfrac{1}{2}r(2\pi r) \qquad \textit{Replace C with } 2\pi r.$$
$$\text{area of circle} = \pi r^2$$

◆ **THEOREM 10.10**

The area of a circle with radius r is given by the formula $A = \pi r^2$.

Example 1

Find the area of a circle with radius $5\sqrt{2}$.

Solution

$A = \pi r^2$
$A = \pi (5\sqrt{2})^2$
$A = 50\pi$ The area of the circle is 50π square units.

Try This

Find the radius of a circle that has area 64π.

A **sector** of a circle is a region formed by two radii and an arc of a circle. The region *HOJ* shaded in this circle is a sector. The region bounded by the radii and major arc *HIJ* is also a sector.

The area of sector *HOJ* is $\frac{60}{360}$ of the area of the whole circle, or $\frac{60}{360}(36\pi)$ square units. This suggests the following theorem.

10-7 Areas of Circles, Sectors, and Segments **473**

First Five Minutes

(Quiz on previous lesson)

Complete each table. Leave answers in terms of π where appropriate.

Radius	Diameter	Circum-ference
1. 8	<u>16</u>	<u>16π</u>
2. <u>9</u>	<u>18</u>	18π
3. <u>$6\sqrt{2}$</u>	$12\sqrt{2}$	<u>$12\sqrt{2}\,\pi$</u>

Radius	Degree Measure of Arc	Arc Length
4. 8	8	<u>$\frac{16\pi}{45}$</u>
5. 6	<u>90</u>	3π

Lesson Opener

Begin by reviewing some important concepts from the previous lesson.

1. As the number of sides of a regular polygon inscribed in a circle increases, the apothem gets closer and closer to becoming the radius of the circle.
2. As the number of sides of a regular polygon inscribed in a circle increases, the perimeter of the polygon gets closer and closer to a fixed number called the circumference of the circle.

(Introduce the following concept from this lesson.)

3. As the number of sides of a regular polygon inscribed in a circle increases, the area of the polygon gets closer and closer to a limiting value called the area of the circle. Thus the area of a polygon equals the area of a circle. Written symbolically, area of a polygon ($\frac{1}{2}ap$) → area of a circle (πr^2).

Materials

student notebooks
investigative software

Key Terms

area of a circle
sector of a circle
segment of a circle

Teaching Notes

Point out that the length of an arc is a fractional part of the circumference, whereas the area of a sector is a fractional part of the area of the circle. Keeping this in mind can help students derive the formulas for arc length and sector of a circle.

Remind students that arc lengths require linear measures and the area of a sector requires square units.

Emphasize that a sector of a circle is formed by two radii and an arc of a circle, whereas a segment of a circle is formed by an arc and its chord.

Guided Practice

Chalkboard Examples

1. Find the radius of the circle and the area of the shaded region. 5, $100 - 25\pi$

Answer to **Try This** 8

2. Find the area of each shaded sector. 4π, 18π

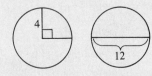

Answer to **Try This** $\frac{175\pi}{2}$

◆ **THEOREM 10.11**

The area of a sector, with arc degree measure m, of a circle with radius r is given by the formula $A = \frac{m}{360}(\pi r^2)$.

The formula can be rewritten as the proportion $\frac{A}{\pi r^2} = \frac{m}{360}$.

Example 2

Find the area of sector AOB.

Solution

$A = \frac{m}{360}(\pi r^2)$

$A = \frac{45}{360}(\pi\, 10^2)$

$A = \frac{100\pi}{8} = \frac{25\pi}{2}$

The area of sector AOB is $\frac{25\pi}{2}$ square units.

Try This

Find the area of the unshaded sector of circle O.

Example 3

Find the area of the blue region if $m\angle MON = 60$.

Solution

area of sector $MON = \frac{60}{360}(\pi\, 6^2) = 6\pi$

area of sector $POQ = \frac{60}{360}(\pi\, 3^2) = \frac{3}{2}\pi$

area of blue region $= 6\pi - \frac{3}{2}\pi = \frac{9}{2}\pi$

Try This

Find the area of the green region.

A **segment of a circle** is a region formed by an arc and its chord, as shown by the shaded area in the circle below. The area of the segment can be found by subtracting the area of $\triangle DOF$ from the area of sector DOF.

Example 4

Find the area of the shaded segment of circle O.

Solution

area of sector $DOF = \frac{60}{360}(64\pi)$

area of $\triangle DOF = \frac{1}{2}8(4\sqrt{3}) = 16\sqrt{3}$ $\triangle OEF$ is a 30°–60°–90° triangle, so $EF = 4$ and $EO = 4\sqrt{3}$.

area of segment $= \frac{60}{360}(64\pi) - 16\sqrt{3}$ area of shaded segment =

$= \frac{32\pi}{3} - 16\sqrt{3}$ area of sector DOF − area of $\triangle DOF$

Try This

Find the area of the shaded segment if $\angle DOF$ is a right angle.

Class Exercises

Short Answer

Complete each statement.

1. To find the area of a circle, square its radius and multiply by ___ .
2. The area of a sector of a circle with a 90° arc is ___ (fraction) of the area of the whole circle.
3. To find the area of a segment of a circle, you can subtract the area of a triangle from the area of a ___ .
4. The ratio of the area of a sector to the area of the whole circle equals the ratio of the measure of the arc of the sector to ___ .

Sample Exercises

5. Find the area of a circle with radius 5.
6. A circle has radius 9. Find the area of a sector of the circle with arc measure 30°.
7. Find the area of a circle with diameter 12.
8. Find the area of a sector of a circle with radius $\sqrt{7}$. The central angle of the sector is 120°.
9. Find the area of circle with radius 2. Find the area of a circle with radius twice as long. How does the area of the second circle compare with that of the first?

Discussion

10. When given the radius, a student concluded that the area of the circle was 12 square units and the area of the sector was 2 square units. Use only the information in the figure to give a convincing argument that the student's conclusion is incorrect.

11. A student concluded that the area of the shaded segment was less than 4 square units. Without finding its exact area, give a convincing argument that this conclusion is incorrect.

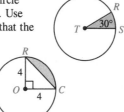

Exercises

A

Find the area of each circle with the given radius. Give your answers in terms of π.

1. 4   2. 6.5   3. 7   4. π 5. $\sqrt{5}$

Find the area of each circle with the given diameter.

6. 8   7. 9.5   8. 4π 9. $4\sqrt{2}$ 10. 98

Find the radius of each circle with the given area.

11. 121π 12. 289π 13. 8π 14. 100   15. 1.6π

---

3. Find area of the blue region if $\angle MON$ is a right angle. $\frac{27\pi}{4}$
Answer to **Try This** $\frac{45\pi}{2}$

4. Find the area of each shaded segment. $4\pi - 8, \frac{64\pi}{3} - 16\sqrt{3}$

Answer to **Try This** $16\pi - 32$

Class Exercise Answers

1. π 2. $\frac{1}{4}$ 3. sector
4. 360   5. 25π
6. $\frac{27\pi}{4}$ 7. 36π 8. $\frac{7\pi}{3}$
9. $4\pi, 16\pi$. The second area is 4 times the first.   10. A sector with arc measure 30 should have $\frac{30}{360} = \frac{1}{12}$ the area of the circle. The student claims the sector has $\frac{2}{12} = \frac{1}{6}$ the area. The student is incorrect.
11. area of segment =
$\frac{1}{4}\pi 4^2 - \frac{1}{2}4^2 = 16\left(\frac{\pi}{4} - \frac{1}{2}\right) =$
$4\pi - 8. \ 4\pi > 12$ so,
$4\pi - 8 > 4.$

Assignment Guide
Minimum: 1–41 e/o, 50, 51, MR
Regular: 1–46 e/o, 50, 51, MR
Advanced: 31–51, MR

Applications
Exercises 39, 41, 42, 44, 49, 50
Algebra
Exercise 40
Teacher's Resource Materials

Enrichment Using
   Manipulatives 62
Practice Master 73
Quiz 20
Technology: Calculator 16
Technology: BASIC 16
Technology: Computer
   Software 16
Transparency 50

Lesson Closure

Summarize the lesson by asking students to state formulas for the following.
circumference of a circle
arc length
area of a circle
area of a sector of a circle
area of a segment of a circle

Exercise Answers

1. 16π **2.** 42.25π **3.** 49π
4. π^3 **5.** 5π **6.** 16π
7. $\frac{361\pi}{16}$ **8.** $4\pi^3$ **9.** 8π
10. 2401π **11.** 11 **12.** 17
13. $2\sqrt{2}$ **14.** $\frac{10\sqrt{\pi}}{\pi}$
15. $0.4(\sqrt{10})$ **16.** 4π
17. 16π **18.** $\frac{5}{4}\pi$ **19.** $\frac{100}{\pi}$
20. $3.0625\,\pi$ **21.** 4π cm^2
22. $\frac{3}{8}\pi$ cm^2 **23.** 8π cm^2
24. ≈ 3.53 cm^2 **25.** 13.08 cm^2
26. 12.56 cm^2 **27.** 21.37 cm^2
28. $9\pi - 18$
29. $12\pi - 9\sqrt{3}$
30. $6\pi - 9\sqrt{3}$ **31.** $36, \frac{360}{n}$
32. $9{:}25$ **33.** $4{:}3$
34. area of inscribed circle = 4π cm^2, area of circumscribed circle = 8π cm^2 **35.** 90
36. $9 - \frac{9}{4}\pi$ **37.** $\frac{9}{2}\pi - 9$
38. $9 - \frac{9\pi}{4}$ **39.** $\frac{36}{25}$ times as much   **40.** $\frac{\pi}{4}d^2$

Find the area of each circle with the given circumference.

16. 4π **17.** 8π **18.** $\sqrt{5}\pi$ **19.** 20 **20.** 3.5π

Find the area of each shaded sector. Give your answer in terms of π.

21.   **22.**   **23.**

Find the approximate area of each sector. Use 3.14 for π.

24. central angle $45°$, radius 3 cm
25. central angle $15°$, radius 10 cm
26. central angle $160°$, diameter 6 cm
27. central angle $50°$, diameter 14 cm

Find the area of each shaded segment.

28.   **29.**   **30.**

B

31. If the area of a sector is one tenth the area of the circle, find the measure of the central angle of the sector. If the area of the sector is $\frac{1}{n}$ the area of the circle, find the measure of the central angle of the sector.

32. Two circles have radii 3 cm and 5 cm. Find the ratio of their areas.

33. The areas of two circles are in the ratio 16 to 9. Find the ratio of their radii.

34. Find the area of both the inscribed and circumscribed circles of a square whose sides are 4 cm.

35. Find the degree measure of the arc of a sector with area 36π if the area of the circle is 144π.

Find the area of the shaded regions in each square.

36.   **37.**   **38.**

39. A pipe 12 in. in diameter carries how many times as much water as a pipe 10 in. in diameter?

40. Write a formula for the area of a circle in terms of the diameter d of the circle.

476   *Chapter 10   Area and Perimeter of Polygons*

41. $\frac{13\pi}{16}$ sq in.   42. 21%
43. $\frac{1}{3}$ 44. ≈ 1761 m²
45. Shaded area = area of two
semicircles on legs − area of
semicircle containing △ABC +
area of △ABC = $\frac{1}{2}\pi\left(\frac{AB}{2}\right)^2$ +

$\frac{1}{2}\pi\left(\frac{BC}{2}\right)^2 - \frac{1}{2}\pi\left(\frac{AC}{2}\right)^2$ +
$\frac{1}{2}(AB)(BC)$ =
$\frac{1}{8}\pi(AC)^2 - \frac{1}{8}\pi(AC)^2$
$+ \frac{1}{2}(AB)(BC) = \frac{1}{2}(AB)(BC)$ =
area △ABC where the
Pythagorean Theorem has
been used.   46. area shaded
region = $\frac{1}{2}\pi\left(\frac{EF}{2}\right)^2 - \frac{1}{2}\pi\left(\frac{EG}{2}\right)^2$ −
$\frac{1}{2}\pi\left(\frac{GF}{2}\right)^2 = \frac{\pi}{8}[(EG + GF)^2 -$
$(EG^2 + GF^2)] = \frac{\pi}{8}(2EG \times GF)$
But △EHF is a right triangle,
with ∠H a right angle, so $\frac{EG}{GH}$ =
$\frac{GH}{GF}$ or EG × GF = GH². Area
shaded region = $\frac{\pi}{8}(2GH)^2$ =
$\frac{\pi}{4}GH^2 = \pi\left(\frac{GH}{2}\right)^2$ = area of circle
with $\overline{GH}$ as diameter.
47. $\frac{(\sqrt{3} - \frac{\pi}{2})r^2}{\sqrt{3}r^2} = 1 - \frac{\sqrt{3}\pi}{6}$

48. $\frac{4 - 4\pi + 2\sqrt{2}\pi}{\pi}$

41. The figure to the right represents the cross section of pipe $\frac{1}{4}$ in. thick that has an inside diameter of 3 in. Find the area of the shaded region.

C

42. Circles of equal radii are packed in a rectangle as shown. If you threw darts at this "target," what percent of the time would you expect to hit the shaded region? (Assume all darts hit the target.)

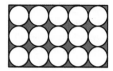

43. If $BC = 2AB$, what fraction of the circle is shaded?

44. A goat is tied to the corner of a house on a 33-m rope. There is a fence as shown. What is the total grazing area for the goat?

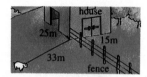

45. Given a right △ABC, its circumscribed circle, and semicircles on the two legs, show that the sum of the areas of the two shaded regions is equal to the area of △ABC.

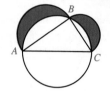

46. Given point G between E and F, and semicircles on $\overline{EG}$, $\overline{GF}$, and $\overline{EF}$ as shown, if $\overline{GH} \perp \overline{EF}$, show that the area of the shaded region is equal to the area of the circle with $\overline{GH}$ as diameter. (HINT: Consider the right triangle △EHF.)

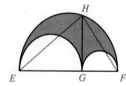

47. If △ABC is an equilateral triangle, what fraction of the triangle is shaded?

48. In the figure the small circle is tangent to four circular arcs. What fraction of the large circle is shaded?

10-7 Areas of Circles, Sectors, and Segments   **477**

49. $63 - 36\sqrt{3} \approx 0.646$
50. $\frac{1}{25}$ **51.** As long as similar figures are used, with one straight segment of appropriate length, it will work for any figure.

Mixed Review Answers

1. false   **2.** false
3. false   **4.** true   **5.** false

Quiz Answers

1. 64π **2.** 52π **3.** $6\sqrt{2}\pi$
4. 2π **5.** 6π **6.** $6\pi - 9\sqrt{3}$
7. $50\pi - 100$ **8.** $9\sqrt{3} - 3\pi$

49. Conduit for telephone cable is sized so that it carries three cables (each circular and tangent to the conduit and to each other) that are each 1 cm in radius. What fraction of the conduit is filled?

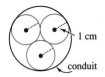

Critical Thinking

50. An official archery tournament target has four concentric rings and a center bull's eye. Each ring is 4.8 in. wide and the diameter of the bull's eye is 9.6 in. Draw a picture, analyze this situation, and estimate the probability of hitting the bull's eye. Then figure out the probability and compare it with your estimate. You may assume that every arrow shot hits the target.

51. The Pythagorean Theorem states that the sum of the areas of squares on the two legs of a right triangle equals the area of the square on the hypotenuse. What if figures other than squares were considered? Would the relationship still be true? Investigate this situation and support your conclusion. Try it with more than one type of figure.

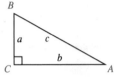

Mixed Review

Determine whether each statement is true or false.

1. If $ABDC$ is a rectangle, then $\overline{AD}$ is perpendicular to $\overline{CB}$.
2. If $\overline{AD} \cong \overline{CB}$, then $ABDC$ is a rhombus.
3. If $\overline{AD}$ is perpendicular to $\overline{CB}$, then $ABDC$ is a rhombus.
4. If $ABDC$ is a square, then $\angle ADC \cong \angle ADB$.
5. $\overline{AD} \cong \overline{CB}$ if $\overline{AB} \cong \overline{CD}$ and $\overline{AC} \cong \overline{BD}$

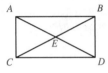

Quiz

1. Find the area of a circle with circumference 16π.
2. Find the circumference of a circle if the diameter is 52.
3. Find the circumference of a circle with area 18π.
4. Find the length of $\overarc{AB}$.
5. Find the area of sector ACB.
6. Find the area of the shaded segment.

Find the area of each shaded region. Assume the polygons are regular.

7.

8.

CRITICAL THINKING

Recognizing the Role of Propaganda

Propaganda is any systematic promotion of ideas to further a cause. The term comes from the Latin word meaning "propagate." Sometimes we make incorrect decisions because we react to propaganda that someone uses to persuade us to a point of view. Consider the following examples.

Example 1 *Jumping on the Bandwagon*
Ben saw this advertisement in a magazine.

"Olympic athletes choose Panther running shoes."

He felt that if Olympic athletes liked Panthers the best, they must be good running shoes. Ben bought two pairs of Panthers and later decided that he did not really like them.

Analysis
This form of propaganda tries to convince individuals that they will take on characteristics of others if they imitate their behavior.

Example 2 *Appealing to Authority or Testimony*
A television ad shows Bert Medico, an actor who plays a doctor on a soap opera, reading a report issued by the National Medical Doctors Association (NMDA). It describes the medical value of the pain reliever NoAche. A viewer likes Bert Medico, respects the NMDA, and goes to the store to buy NoAche. Later, she finds it upsets her stomach.

Analysis
In this situation, the fact that Bert plays a doctor on a soap opera carries over, as the viewer evaluates what Bert says during the ad. So it appears that the NMDA report on NoAche is accepted by a well-known doctor.

Example 3 *Avoiding the Question*
A congressman is asked if he is in favor of a plan to build a controversial highway. He responds, "I'm sure the people of this county will use wise judgement as they decide how to vote on this plan. I have always had great confidence in the decision-making process at our state and local levels."

Analysis
Listeners would think the congressman favors their view, as everyone likes to feel he or she uses good judgement in making decisions. The congressman did not actually state his position on the planned highway.

Example 4 *Transferring a Feeling*
A television ad for a sportscar shows a beautiful horse racing across a lush pasture as it shows the automobile. Marla watches the ad and tells a friend, "That car is a beauty—it can really fly."

Analysis
Marla equated the speed of the horse with the speed of the car in the advertisement. That is, she transferred her feelings about the horse to the car.

Exercises

1. Give another example of each of the above forms of propaganda.

Identify the type of propaganda involved in each situation.

2. Singh chose to buy a baseball because it had Babe Ruth's name on it.
3. Kara wanted to stay out later on weekends because, "All my friends get to stay out later."
4. When a store clerk was asked if an item had a guarantee, she said, "I have never had anyone bring one of those back because it did not work properly."
5. Think of another form of propaganda and give an example of its use.

Critical Thinking

Recognizing the Role of Propaganda

Exercise Answers
1. Answers may vary.
2. appeal to authority
3. jump on the bandwagon
4. avoid the question
5. Answers may vary.

CHAPTER SUMMARY

Vocabulary

altitude (10-2)	boundary (10-1)	radius of a regular polygon (10-4)
apothem (10-4)	circumference (10-6)	region (10-1)
area (10-1)	kite (10-3)	sector of a circle (10-7)
base (10-2)	perimeter (10-1)	segment of a circle (10-7)

Key Ideas

1. Every closed region has an area which is a unique positive number.
2. If two closed figures are congruent, then they have equal areas.
3. The area of a region is the sum of all of its nonoverlapping parts.
4. The following is a list of area formulas for polygonal and circular regions.

Rectangle $A = \ell w$	Triangle $A = \frac{1}{2}bh$	Regular polygon $A = \frac{1}{2}ap$
Square $A = s^2$	Trapezoid $A = \frac{1}{2}h(b_1 + b_2)$	Circle $A = \pi r^2$
Parallelogram $A = bh$	Rhombus $A = \frac{1}{2}d_1 d_2$	Sector $A = \frac{m}{360}(\pi r^2)$

5. The area of any quadrilateral with perpendicular diagonals is half the product of the length of its diagonals.
6. If two polygons are similar, then the ratio of their perimeters equals the ratio of any pair of corresponding sides.
7. If two polygons are similar, then the ratio of their areas equals the square of the ratio of the lengths of any pair of corresponding sides.
8. In a circle with radius r, length of an arc ℓ, and measure of the arc m, $\frac{\ell}{2\pi r} = \frac{m}{360}$.
9. The area of a segment of a circle can be found by subtracting the area of a triangle from the area of a sector.

CHAPTER REVIEW

10-1

1. If the area of a square is 64, find its perimeter.
2. Find the area of a rectangle with length 6 and diagonal 10.
3. Find the perimeter of a rectangle with width 3.2 and area 22.4.

10-2

4. Find the perimeter and area of a 30°–60°–90° triangle if the hypotenuse has a length of 20.
5. Find the area of a parallelogram with base 8 and height 4.2.

Find the area of each figure.

6.

3√2

3   4

7.

9   6

10

8.

6   6

6

480 Chapter 10 Area and Perimeter of Polygons

10-3

9. A trapezoid has an area of 28 cm² and bases 3 cm and 11 cm. Find its height.
10. Find the area of a rhombus with diagonals 4 and 10.
11. One diagonal of a kite is 4.3 cm long. The area is 13.33 cm. Find the length of the other diagonal.

10-4

Find the area of each regular polygon.

12. 8   13. [square] 5 m   14. [hexagon] 10

10-5

Two similar polygons have apothems of length 9 and 25. Determine whether each statement is true or false.

15. The ratio of their sides is 9 : 25.
16. The ratio of their areas is 3 : 5.
17. The ratio of their perimeters is 9 : 25.

18. Two similar polygons have perimeters 7 and 5. If the area of the smaller polygon is 75, find the area of the larger polygon.

10-6

19. Find the circumference of circle O.

20. A square with area 36 is inscribed in a circle. Find the circumference of the circle.
21. Find the length of a 70° arc of a circle with radius 10.

10-7

Find the area of each shaded region.

22. 6, 80°   23. [circle] 120°, 8

Chapter Review Answers
1. 32   2. 48   3. 20.4
4. perimeter = $30 + 10\sqrt{3}$, area = $50\sqrt{3}$ 5. 33.6   6. $\frac{21}{2}$
7. 120   8. $9\sqrt{3}$ 9. 4 cm
10. 20   11. 6.2 cm
12. $96\sqrt{3}$ 13. 100 m²
14. $150\sqrt{3}$ 15. true
16. false   17. true
18. 147   19. 12π
20. $6\sqrt{2}\pi$ 21. $\frac{35\pi}{9}$
22. 8π 23. $16\sqrt{3}$

Teacher's Resource Materials

Chapter 10 Tests

Test Answers

1. $24\sqrt{2}$ **2.** 60   **3.** 96
4. $40\sqrt{3}$ **5.** 18   **6.** $150\sqrt{3}$
7. 24   **8.** $\frac{25\pi}{9}$ **9.** 144
10. 96   **11.** $150\sqrt{3}$
12. $\frac{4\sqrt{3}}{3}$ **13.** $4\pi - 8$
14. $\frac{125\pi}{18}$ **15.** 4:5   **16.** 4:5
17. 16:25   **18.** $8\sqrt{5}$ cm
19. $\frac{10\pi}{3}$ **20.** 20   **21.** 6π

CHAPTER TEST

Find the area of each figure.

1. a rectangle with length 6 and width $4\sqrt{2}$
2. a rectangle with length 12 and diagonal 13
3. a rhombus with one diagonal 12 and perimeter 40
4. a parallelogram with sides 8 and 10 and an included angle of 60°
5. a 45°–45°–90° triangle with hypotenuse $6\sqrt{2}$
6. a regular hexagon with apothem $5\sqrt{3}$
7. an isosceles trapezoid with bases 4 and 12 and legs 5
8. a sector of a circle with circumference 10π and central angle 40°

Find the area of each figure.

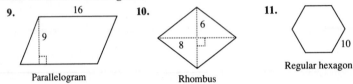

9. *(Parallelogram, base 16, height 9)*
10. *(Rhombus, diagonals 6 and 8)*
11. *(Regular hexagon, side 10)*

Parallelogram   Rhombus   Regular hexagon

Find the area of each shaded region.

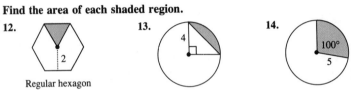

12. *(Regular hexagon, 2)*
13. *(Circle with radius 4, shaded region)*
14. *(Circle, 100°, radius 5)*

Regular hexagon

Two similar polygons have perimeters 40 and 50. Find each of the following.

15. the ratio of their sides
16. the ratio of their apothems
17. the ratio of their areas

18. Find the perimeter of a square if its area is 20 cm².

Find x.

19. *(circle with 60° angle, radius 10, arc x)*
20. *(circle, 10π, right angle, x)*
21. *(circle, radius 3, circumference = x)*

circumference = x

DISCRETE MATH

Geometric Probability

Geometry plays a role in many probability problems. Recall that the probability of an event that can occur in m ways out of n equally possible ways is the ratio $\frac{m}{n}$. For example, in rolling a die, the probability of the event that an even digit occurs is $\frac{3}{6}$. This is because there are three even digits (2, 4, 6) out of six possible outcomes (1, 2, 3, 4, 5, 6).

In the above example, the possibilities were finite and the problem could be solved by counting the desired outcomes. In other cases, we must measure the outcomes and compare the measures associated with the events.

Example 1

Consider the event of a number being chosen at random on the segment $\overline{AB}$ below. Find the probability that the number is between C and D.

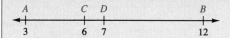

Solution

Since $AB = 9$ and $CD = 1$, the probability is $\frac{1}{9}$.

In other situations, the probability is determined by comparing the area of two regions.

Example 2

Find the probability that a dart hitting the dartboard below lands in one of the shaded areas.

All horizontal and vertical segments measure 1 ft.

Solution

The dartboard has an area of 7 sq ft. The shaded areas cover 2 sq ft. Thus, the probability that the dart lands in a shaded area is $\frac{2}{7}$.

Exercises

1. A point is chosen at random on $\overline{AE}$. Find the probability that the point is between C and D.

2. A point is chosen at random on $\overline{RS}$. Find the probability that the point is between T and U.

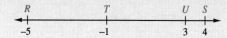

3. A point is chosen at random inside square $EFGH$. Find the probability that the point lies inside the shaded region.

4. Suppose a dart is thrown at a regular hexagonal dartboard with the design shown below. Find the probability that the dart hits one of the shaded regions.

5. If a point is chosen at random inside trapezoid $ABCD$, find the probability that it lies inside trapezoid $ABEF$. Find the probability that the point lies inside trapezoid $EFDC$.

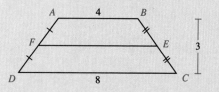

Discrete Math

Geometric Probability

Exercise Answers
1. $\frac{3}{8}$ 2. $\frac{4}{9}$ 3. $\frac{1}{2}$
4. $\frac{1}{3}$ 5. $\frac{5}{12}, \frac{7}{12}$

CHAPTER **11**

Surface Area and Volume

Chapter Overview

This chapter provides students with the opportunity to learn how to determine the area and volume of some very familiar solids. The first lesson includes a discussion of special properties of prisms and an informal development of the formulas for the lateral area and surface area of a prism. This approach is then continued throughout the chapter with other solids. Students should be encouraged to use a calculator when finding the volume or surface area of a solid.

Objectives

11-1 ■ Identify the bases, lateral faces, and edges of a prism and determine its lateral area and surface area.

11-2 ■ Identify the base, lateral faces, and edges of a pyramid and determine its lateral area and surface area.

11-3 ■ Determine the volume of a prism.

11-4 ■ Determine the volume of a pyramid.

11-5 ■ Find the surface area and volume of cylinders.

11-6 ■ Find the surface area and volume of cones.

11-7 ■ Find the surface area and volume of spheres.

11-8 ■ Compare the surface area and volume of similar solids.

TEACHING CHAPTER 11

Cooperative Learning Opportunities

Teachers sometimes find that geometry students have difficulty with solids. Students have different learning styles and models can help most students learn the facts and formulas for surface area and volume. These models can be effectively used in a cooperative setting.

Assign student groups of four the following roles: Student A is responsible for the models and returns them;

Student B supplies measurements; Student C does the calculations; Student D writes up and presents conclusions. Groups should remain the same for the whole chapter, with students alternating roles at each meeting.

The chapter is structured so that groups can be effectively used to reinforce any of the lessons. For example,

after the initial instruction for Lesson 11-2, distribute models of prisms and pyramids. Have students, with books closed, measure the various dimensions. They should then determine the formulas needed. Among the four in each group, they should remember or reconstruct the formulas. They then compute, check their work, and agree on conclusions.

Multicultural Note: *Srinivasa Ramanujan*

Srinivasa Ramanujan was born in southern India in 1887. His passion for mathematics led him to neglect his other subjects and, after his marriage in 1909, he found it difficult to support himself and his wife. But he used every spare moment to continue his mathematical work.

He sent his work on over 100 theorems to three mathematicians in England. One, G. H. Hardy, took the time to read it and immediately recognized its brilliance. He urged Ramanujan to come to England and there helped him continue his work in advanced number theory. Some of his work on pi, and on the sums of squares and cubes, relates to patterns

found when calculating areas and volumes. Ramanujan died in 1919 at the age of 32. More than 70 years later, his work is still an important source of new mathematical ideas.

For more information, see page 139 of **Multiculturalism in Mathematics, Science, and Technology**.

Alternative Assessment and Communication Ideas

In Chapter 11, almost all of the **Try This** exercises are similar to the preceding examples but do not provide a figure. They have several benefits as a review before a test or as an alternative assessment.

First, the student must understand the meaning of each term in order to draw a figure that accurately reflects the given information. Second, the example is directly in front of the student as a model. Third, they cover all of the main concepts and skills. Fourth, they are simple enough to be done by all the students.

If you hare having a quiz after Lesson 11-4, you might assign the **Try This** activities of the first four lessons to be done a day or two before the quiz, and even grade it as 25% of the quiz. This will give students a good review and a start toward a good grade on the quiz.

Investigations and Projects

Projects can be an opportunity for the more "hands-on" students to participate and to demonstrate skills that may surpass the skills of students who have a more theoretical inclination.

Have students collect or make models of as many of the shapes discussed in Chapter 11 as possible.

Possible manufactured articles include cans, balls, boxes, and cones. Students might paint or coat these to protect them and might also label some of the parts such as base and slant height.

You can ask that students construct some of the shapes not commonly found. They may work with cardboard, wood, or even metal. Again, ask students to be as neat as possible and to label their models. You may be able to add their models to your collection for future teaching.

Lesson	PACING CHART (DAYS)			Opening Activity	Cooperative Activity	Seat or Group Work
	1-Year Minimum	1-Year Regular	1-Year Advanced			
11-1	2	2	2	Chapter Opener: **TE** p. 484; Lesson Opener: **TE** p. 485	Explore: **SE** p. 485; ✂ Lab Worksheet 11-1A: *Laboratory Manual* p. 111; ✂ Lab Worksheet 11-1B: *Laboratory Manual* p. 113	Try This Exercises
11-2	2	2	2	First Five Minutes 11-2: *FFM Transparency Masters* p. 42 or **TE** p. 491; Lesson Opener: **TE** p. 491	Enrichment: **SE** p. 495	Try This Exercises
11-3	2	2	2	First Five Minutes 11-3: *FFM Transparency Masters* p. 43 or **TE** p. 496; Lesson Opener: **TE** p. 496	Lab Worksheet 11-3A: *Laboratory Manual* p. 115; Lab Worksheet 11-3B: *Laboratory Manual* p. 116	Try This Exercises
11-4	1	1	1	First Five Minutes 11-4: *FFM Transparency Masters* p. 44 or **TE** p. 501; Lesson Opener: **TE** p. 501	✂ Lab Worksheet: 11-4: *Laboratory Manual* p. 117	Try This Exercises
11-5	2	2	2	First Five Minutes 11-5: *FFM Transparency Masters* p. 45 or **TE** p. 506; Lesson Opener: **TE** p. 506	Explore: **SE** p. 506; Lab Worksheet 11-5A *Laboratory Manual* p. 119; ✂ Lab Worksheet 11-5B: *Laboratory Manual* p. 120; ✂ Lab Worksheet 11-5C: *Laboratory Manual* p. 121	Try This Exercises
11-6	2	2	2	First Five Minutes 11-6:: *FFM Transparency Masters* p. 46 or **TE** p. 511; Lesson Opener: **TE** p. 511	Explore: **SE** p. 511; Computer Activity: **SE** p. 516	Try This Exercises
11-7	1	1	1	First Five Minutes 11-7: *FFM Transparency Masters* p. 47 or **TE** p. 517; Lesson Opener: **TE** p. 517		Try This Exercises
11-8	1	1	1	First Five Minutes 11-8: *FFM Transparency Masters* p. 47 or **TE** p. 522; Lesson Opener: **TE** p. 522	✂ Lab Worksheet 11-8A: *Laboratory Manual* p. 123; Lab Worksheet 11-8B: *Laboratory Manual* p. 125	Try This Exercises
Review	1	1	1			
Test	1	1	1			

FFM = First Five Minutes

Enrichment	Review/Assess	Reteach	Technology	Lesson
Careers: **SE** p. 490; ✂ Enrichment Using Manipulatives 11-1: *Enrichment* p. 63; ✂ Lab Worksheet 11-1C: *Laboratory Manual* p. 114	Class Exercises: **SE** p. 487; Mixed Review: **SE** p. 490	Practice Worksheet 11-1: *Practice and Mixed Review* p. 79		**11-1**
Enrichment: **SE** p. 495; ✂ Enrichment Using Manipulatives 11-2: *Enrichment* p. 64	Class Exercises: **SE** p. 493; Algebra Review: **SE** p. 495	Practice Worksheet 11-2: *Practice and Mixed Review* p.80		**11-2**
✂ Enrichment Using Manipulatives 11-3: *Enrichment* p. 65	Class Exercises: **SE** p. 497; Mixed Review: **SE** p. 500	Practice Worksheet 11-3: *Practice and Mixed Review* p. 81	Calculator Investigation: **SE** p. 500; Calculator Worksheet 11-3: *Technology* p. CL17	**11-3**
Discrete Math: **SE** p. 505	Class Exercises: **SE** p. 502; Algebra Review: **SE** p. 504; Quiz: **SE** p. 504; Quiz: *Assessment* p. 99	Practice Worksheet 11-4: *Practice and Mixed Review* p.82		**11-4**
Math Contest Problem: **SE** p. 510; ✂ Enrichment Using Manipulatives 11-5: *Enrichment* p. 66	Class Exercises: **SE** p. 508; Algebra Review: **SE** p. 510	Practice Worksheet 11-5: *Practice and Mixed Review* p. 83		**11-5**
✂ Enrichment Using Manipulatives 11-6: *Enrichment* p. 67; BASIC 11-6: *Technology* p. B22	Class Exercises: **SE** p. 513; Mixed Review: **SE** p. 515	Practice Worksheet 11-6: *Practice and Mixed Review* p.84	Computer Activity: **SE** p. 516; BASIC 11-6: *Technology* p. B22	**11-6**
Historical Note: **SE** p. 521; ✂ Enrichment Using Manipulatives 11-7: *Enrichment* p. 68	Class Exercises: **SE** p. 519; Algebra Review: **SE** p. 521	Practice Worksheet 11-7: *Practice and Mixed Review* p.85		**11-7**
Critical Thinking: **SE** p. 527	Class Exercises: **SE** p. 524; Mixed Review: **SE** p. 526; Quiz: **SE** p. 526; Quiz: *Assessment* p. 100	Practice Worksheet 11-8: *Practice and Mixed Review* p.86		**11-8**
	Summary & Review: **SE** p. 528–529	Mixed Review: *Practice and Mixed Review* p. 112		**Review**
Problem Solving: **SE** p. 531	Chapter 11 Test: **SE** p. 530; Chapter 11 Tests: *Assessment* p. 61–66; *MathTest*			**Test**

11

Surface Area and Volume

A cylindrical storage tank has a diameter of 10 m and a height of 30 m. Find the volume of the tank.

PRISMS AND PYRAMIDS

OBJECTIVE: *Identify the bases, lateral faces, and edges of a prism and determine its lateral area and surface area.*

11-1 Surface Area of Prisms

EXPLORE

Fold a piece of paper into fourths. Unfold and tape the edges together as shown to construct a model of the lateral faces of a square-based prism.

1. By varying the number of folds, construct models with triangular, pentagonal, hexagonal, and octagonal bases.
2. How many pairs of parallel faces does each have?
3. Form a generalization.

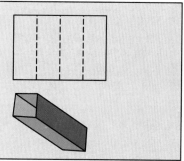

The models that you constructed in the Explore are examples of three-dimensional solids. A **polyhedron** is a solid made up of polygonal regions called **faces.** The sides and vertices of the faces are called, respectively, **edges** and **vertices** of the polyhedron. A **prism** is a polyhedron with a pair of identical faces, called **bases,** that lie in parallel planes. The vertices of these bases are joined to form parallelogram-shaped regions called **lateral faces.** Adjacent lateral faces share a common edge called a **lateral edge.** An **altitude** of a prism is a segment that is perpendicular to both bases with endpoints in the planes of the bases. The length of an altitude is called the **height**(*h*) of the prism.

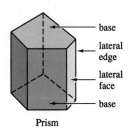

base
lateral edge
lateral face
base

Prism

As shown below, a prism is named by the shape of its bases. If the lateral edges of a prism are perpendicular to its bases, the prism is called a **right prism.** If the lateral edges are not perpendicular to the bases, the prism is an **oblique prism.**

Right triangular prism   Oblique pentagonal prism   Right trapezoidal prism

Imagine cutting a cube apart and laying its surface flat. The area of these six squares is called the surface area of the cube. This gives an idea of what is meant, in general, by the **surface area** of a solid.

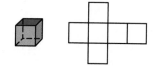

Use the Chapter Overview as an introduction to this chapter. Ask students to compare the contents of this chapter with content of the previous chapter. For example, Chapter 10 dealt with areas of two-dimensional figures (plane geometry), whereas this chapter deals with three-dimensional figures (solids).

Making paper models of these solids will help students visualize properties and better understand the formulas for finding the area and the volume of a solid. (See Explore.)

Key Questions

1. What are similarities of the five prisms? differences?
2. How many pairs of parallel sides does each prism have?
3. Can any generalization be made regarding the shape of the bases and the names of the prisms?

Materials

student notebooks
models of solids

Teaching Notes

Emphasize that a prism is named by the shape of its bases and that the faces that are not bases are called lateral faces. Explain that the bases of a prism are congruent to each other and that the lateral faces are parallelograms.

Point out that a regular prism is a right prism with bases that are regular polygons. A cube is an example of a regular prism in which all faces are squares.

To help students distinguish between a right prism and an oblique prism, point out that the lateral edges of a right prism are perpendicular to the bases and the lateral faces of a right prism are rectangular in shape. In an oblique prism, lateral edges are not perpendicular and lateral faces are not in the shape of a rectangle.

Point out that surface area (SA) is sometimes referred to as total area (TA). Remind students that surface area must be expressed in square units.

Stress that Theorem 11.1 applies only to right prisms. The p in both formulas refers to the perimeter of a base, not to a lateral face.

Important Facts to Remember About Prisms

• Lateral edges are congruent and parallel.
• Bases are congruent and are parallel polygonal regions.
• Lateral faces are in the shape of parallelograms.
• Edges of a right prism are perpendicular to the bases.
• Lateral faces of a right prism are in the shape of rectangles.
• Regular prisms are right prisms with bases that are regular polygons.
• The altitude of a prism is a segment perpendicular to both bases with endpoints in the planes of the bases. The measure of the altitude is called the height of the prism.
• The height of a right prism is the length of a lateral edge.
• The formula for finding the lateral area (LA) of a right prism is $LA = ph$.
• The formula for finding the surface area (SA) of a right prism is $SA = ph + 2B$ (where B stands for the area of a base).

The sum of the areas of the lateral faces of a prism is called the **lateral area** (LA) of the prism. When you add the area of the two bases to the lateral area, you obtain the **surface area** (SA) of the prism. For example, in this right prism the lateral area can be calculated by adding together the areas of the lateral faces.

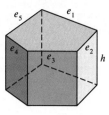

$LA = e_1h + e_2h + e_3h + e_4h + e_5h$
$LA = (e_1 + e_2 + e_3 + e_4 + e_5)h$
$LA = ph$ (The sum of the edge-lengths of one base is the perimeter, p.)

◆ THEOREM 11.1

The lateral area of a right prism is equal to the perimeter p of a base times the height h of the prism. $LA = ph$

The surface area is the sum of the lateral area and twice the area of a base B. $SA = ph + 2B$

Example 1

Find the lateral area and the surface area of the right triangular prism shown.

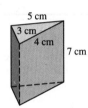

5 cm
3 cm
4 cm
7 cm

Solution
$LA = ph$
$\quad = (3 + 4 + 5) \cdot 7$
$\quad = 12 \cdot 7$
$\quad = 84 \text{ cm}^2$

$SA = LA + 2B$
$\quad = 84 + 2\left(\tfrac{1}{2} \cdot 3 \cdot 4\right)$ *The 3–4–5 triangular bases are right triangles.*
$\quad = 96 \text{ cm}^2$

Try This
Find the lateral area and the surface area of a right triangular prism whose base edges have lengths 5, 12, and 13 and whose height is 18.

Example 2

Find the lateral area and the surface area of the right equilateral triangular-based prism shown, if $AB = 14$ and $AD = 20$.

Solution
$LA = ph$
$\quad = (14 + 14 + 14) \cdot 20$
$\quad = 42 \cdot 20 = 840$

$SA = ph + 2B$
$\quad = 840 + 2\left(\tfrac{1}{2} \cdot 14 \cdot 7\sqrt{3}\right)$
$\quad = (840 + 98\sqrt{3})$

Try This
Find the lateral area and the surface area of a right regular hexagonal-based prism whose height is 12 cm and whose base edge-length is 5 cm.

Class Exercises

Short Answer

Name the bases and the lateral edges of each polyhedron that appears to be a prism. If it is not a prism, tell why.

1.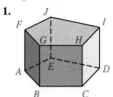
2.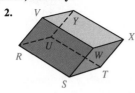
3.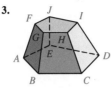

Determine whether each statement is true or false.

4. The lateral faces of a prism are always rectangles.
5. The least number of faces a prism can have is five.
6. An octagonal prism has six lateral faces and six lateral edges.
7. For any prism, the ratio of the number of base edges to the number of lateral edges is 2:1.
8. The surface area of a prism is equal to the perimeter of a base times the height of the prism.
9. The base of a right triangular prism will always be a right triangle.
10. A lateral edge of an oblique prism is an altitude of the prism.
11. Since all lateral faces of a prism are parallelograms, each lateral face of a right prism is a rectangle.
12. Each lateral face of a prism is a rectangular region.
13. A prism must have at least six base edges.

Sample Exercises

ABCD is a base of this right rectangular prism.

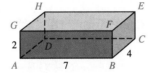

14. Find the height of the prism.
15. Find the perimeter of the base.
16. Find the lateral area of the prism.
17. Find the surface area of the prism.

A right prism whose bases are regular hexagons has base edges 3 m long and a height of 6 m.

18. Find the lateral area of the hexagonal prism.
19. Find the surface area of the hexagonal prism.

20. Sketch a prism with a square base.
21. Sketch a prism with a hexagonal base.

Discussion

22. Explain why face *BCEF* can be viewed as a base in the right rectangular prism above. What is the height if *BCEF* is the base?
23. Explain why, in the right rectangular prism above, you can correctly claim that its height is 4. What is the base relative to a height of 4?

---

polyhedron
prism (right/oblique)
faces (lateral)
edges (lateral)
bases
vertices
altitude (height-*h*)
lateral area (*LA*)
surface area (*SA*)

Common Errors

Sometimes when a prism is rotated, students may call the bottom face the base. For example:

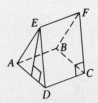

Incorrect: *ABCD* is a base.
Correct: △*AED* is a base.

To help students distinguish between a face and a base of a prism, remind them that the bases are parallel faces.

Guided Practice

Chalkboard Examples

1. Identify the following and then find the lateral area and surface area of the right equilateral triangular-based prism.

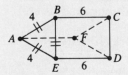

a. both bases **b.** lateral faces
c. lateral edges **d.** lateral area
e. surface area a. △*ABE*, △*FCD*
b. rectangles *BCDE, EDFA,* and
AFCB **c.** $\overline{BC}, \overline{ED}, \overline{AF}$ **d.** 72.
e. 72 + 8$\sqrt{3}$

2. Find the lateral area and the surface area of the cube.

LA = 36, *SA* = 54

Class Exercise Answers

1. bases: pentagons *ABCDE* and *FGHIJ*, lateral edges: $\overline{AF}$, $\overline{BG}$, $\overline{CH}$, $\overline{DI}$, $\overline{EJ}$ **2.** bases: parallelograms *RUYV* and *STXW*, lateral edges: $\overline{VW}$, $\overline{YX}$, $\overline{UT}$, $\overline{RS}$
3. not a prism because the bases are not identical
4. false **5.** true **6.** false
7. true **8.** false **9.** false
10. false **11.** true **12.** false
13. true **14.** 2 **15.** 22
16. 44 **17.** 100 **18.** 108 m²
19. 108 + 27√3 m²
20.

21.

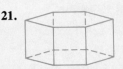

22. *BCEF* is also a rectangle and is identical to the opposite lateral face *ADHG*. The height would be 7. **23.** *BAGF* and *CDHE* are identical rectangles and opposite lateral faces. They can be chosen as bases. The height would be 4.

Assignment Guide
Minimum: 1–32 e/o, 37, MR
Regular: 7–35 e/o, 37–38, MR
Advanced: 20–39, MR

Applications
Exercises 19, 32–34
Algebra
Exercises 9, 26, 27

Exercises

A

Find the surface area of each right rectangular prism.

1.

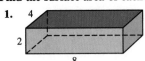

2.

3.

Complete the table. Refer to the right rectangular prism with dimensions ℓ, *w*, and *h* denoting length, width, and height respectively.

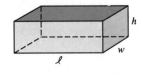

	ℓ	*w*	*h*	*LA*	*SA*
4.	26	5	20	—	—
5.	6	$2\frac{1}{2}$	$5\frac{2}{3}$	—	—
6.	6	—	2	40	—
7.	$5\sqrt{2}$	$4\sqrt{2}$	$3\sqrt{2}$	—	—
8.	2.5	3.8	—		44.2
9.	10x	7x	4x	—	—

Find the lateral area and the surface area of each right prism.

10.

Equilateral–triangular bases

11.

Isoceles right–triangular bases

12.

Trapezoidal bases

Decide whether each statement is always, sometimes, or never true.

13. The two bases of a prism can differ in their total number of edges.
14. A prism can have lateral faces that are hexagonal regions.
15. The bases of a right prism are isosceles trapezoids.
16. The altitude of a prism is longer than a lateral edge.
17. The altitude of a prism is shorter than a base edge.
18. If two prisms have equal surface areas, then the bases of the two prisms have equal areas.

19. Square cake pans 20 cm on an edge and 6 cm deep are to be coated on the inside with a non-stick material. If the amount of non-stick material available covers 100 m², how many pans can be coated?

B
20. Find the surface area of a right prism with equilateral triangular bases if all edges are two units long.
21. The perimeter of a base of a right prism is 37 cm and a lateral edge is 22 cm. Find the lateral area of the prism.

22. In a right hexagonal prism, one edge of a regular hexagonal base is 3 cm. If the height of the prism is 5 cm, find the lateral area of the prism.

23. The lateral faces of a cube are squares. Find the lateral area and the surface area of a cube whose base-edge length is 5 cm.

24. Find the lateral area of a right prism with pentagonal bases if its height is 10 cm and the sides of the bases are 2 cm, 3 cm, 4 cm, 5 cm, and 7 cm.

25. The length of a lateral edge of a right prism is 10 cm and its lateral area is 52 cm². Find the perimeter of the base.

26. The height of a right square-based prism is twice the length of a base edge. If the surface area is 490 square units, find the lengths of the edges of the prism.

27. If the lateral area of a right rectangular prism is 384 cm², its length is twice its width, and its height is twice its length, find the width of the prism.

28. An equilateral triangular-based prism 12 cm high has rectangular lateral faces and a lateral area of 288 cm². Find the surface area of the prism.

29. A right prism with a regular hexagonal base has a surface area of $96\sqrt{3}$ cm². Find the height of the prism if its base-edge length is 4 cm.

The figure to the right shows a prism in which all faces are parallelograms. Point O is the intersection of diagonals $\overline{AG}$ and $\overline{BH}$.

30. Prove that O is the midpoint of $\overline{AG}$ and $\overline{BH}$.
31. Explain why point O is also the midpoint of $\overline{DF}$.

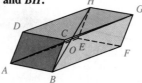

32. A commercial walk-in refrigerator with outside dimensions 8 ft by 24 ft by 7 ft is to be painted. Its walls, floor, and ceiling are each 3 in. thick. Inside, all four walls, the floor, and the ceiling are to be painted. Outside, only the four walls are to be painted. How many gallons of paint are needed if one gallon of paint covers 300 sq ft?

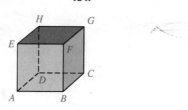

C

33. A school hall 12 ft high and 12 ft wide turns a 90° corner as shown in this top view. If $\overline{AB} \| \overline{CD}$, find CD.
34. In Exercise 33, can a pole 34 ft long be carried horizontally down the hall and around the corner? Explain.

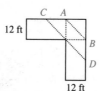

35. Suppose that the length of diagonal $\overline{AF}$ of a face of the cube to the right is 3 cm. Find the surface area of the cube.
36. Suppose that the length of diagonal $\overline{AG}$ of the cube is 5. Find the surface area of the cube.

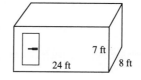

Lesson Closure

Summarize the lesson by reviewing the facts to remember about prisms.

Teacher's Resource Materials

Enrichment Using
  Manipulatives 63
Practice Master 74
Transparency 51

Exercise Answers

1. 112   **2.** 454   **3.** 216
4. *LA* = 1240, *SA* = 1500
5. *LA* = $96\frac{1}{3}$, *SA* = $126\frac{1}{3}$
6. *w* = 4, *SA* = 88
7. *LA* = 108, *SA* = 188
8. *h* = 2, *LA* = 25.2
9. *LA* = $136x^2$, *SA* = $276x^2$
10. *LA* = 144, *SA* = $144 + 18\sqrt{3}$
11. *LA* = $60 + 30\sqrt{2}$,
SA = $85 + 30\sqrt{2}$
12. *LA* = 133, *SA* = 169
13. never   **14.** never
15. sometimes   **16.** never
17. sometimes   **18.** sometimes
19. 1136   **20.** $12 + 2\sqrt{3}$
21. 814 cm²   **22.** 90 cm²
23. *LA* = 100 cm², *SA* = 150 cm²
24. 210 cm²   **25.** 5.2 cm
26. base edges 7, lateral edges 14   **27.** 4 cm
28. $288 + 32\sqrt{3}$ cm²
29. $2\sqrt{3}$ cm   **30.** 1. *ABCD*, *EFGH*, *ABFE*, *DCGH*, *AEHD*, *BFGC* are parallelograms. (Given) 2. $\overline{AB} \| \overline{EF}$, $\overline{EF} \| \overline{HG}$ (Def. of a parallelogram) 3. $\overline{AB} \| \overline{HG}$ (Substitution) 4. $\overline{AB} \cong \overline{EF}$, $\overline{EF} \cong \overline{HG}$ (Def. of a parallelogram) 5. $\overline{AB} \cong \overline{HG}$ (Substitution) 6. *ABGH* is a parallelogram.(Theorem 5.5) 7. $\overline{AG}$ bisects $\overline{BH}$. (Theorem 5.3) 8. *O* is the midpoint. (Def. of bis.)

31. Since $\overline{AD} \parallel \overline{GF}$ and $\overline{DG} \parallel \overline{AF}$, ADGF is a parallelogram. By Theorem 5.3, $\overline{DF}$ bisects $\overline{AG}$. The midpoint of $\overline{AG}$ is O, so O is also the midpoint of $\overline{DF}$.

32. ≈4.01 gal   **33.** $24\sqrt{2}$ ft

34. No; no pole longer than CD can be carried horizontally down the hall. $CD \approx 33.94 < 34$

35. 27 cm²   **36.** 50

37. The faces must be identical.

38. The faces must be parallelograms.

39. a. 42 sq units

b.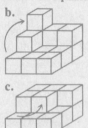

c.

Mixed Review

1. 9.58   **2.** 13.03
3. 18   **4.** 60   **5.** 9.14
6. 45

Critical Thinking

Give a counterexample by sketching a figure to show that each statement is false.

37. A solid with a pair of square faces that lie in parallel planes must be a prism.

38. A solid with a pair of congruent polygonal faces that lie in parallel planes must be a prism.

39. The solid to the right is made from 14 cubes glued together.

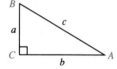

   a. Each square in this figure is one square unit. What is the surface area of the solid?
   b. How can you move one block and increase the surface area by two square units?
   c. How can you move one block and decrease the surface area by two square units?

Mixed Review

Use the table on page 636 or a calculator to find each of the following.

   1. If $m\angle A = 37$ and $c = 12$, find b to the nearest hundredth.
   2. If $m\angle B = 69$ and $a = 5$, find b to the nearest hundredth.
   3. If $a = 3$ and $b = 9$, find $m\angle A$ to the nearest degree.
   4. If $a = 2$ and $c = 4$, find $m\angle B$ to the nearest degree.
   5. If $m\angle B = 50$ and $b = 7$, find c to the nearest hundredth.
   6. If $a = b = 13$, find $m\angle B$ to the nearest degree.

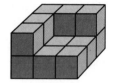

Careers

Geologist

Geology is the study of the earth. Geologists are scientists who try to explain the beginnings of the earth and its changes through time by studying soil, rocks, mountains, and other landforms. Subjects as diverse as fossils, glaciers, and volcanoes are included in the work of geologists.

There are several subfields of geology. Physical geology deals with the present condition of the earth. Dynamical geology deals with the processes that cause changes in the earth's composition and structure. Historical geology is the study of the events by which the earth achieved its current state. Economic geology includes such applications as the construction of dams and the preservation of the environment.

Geologists hold a variety of positions, most connected to companies that explore for oil, gas, or other minerals. Because geometry is so useful in the study of rock formations and mineral crystals, mathematics plays an important role in the training of many geologists.

OBJECTIVE: *Identify the base, lateral faces, and edges of a pyramid and determine its lateral area and surface area.*

11-2 Surface Area of Pyramids

The Great Pyramid was built in Egypt over two thousand years ago. With an original height of about 480 ft, the base of the pyramid covers an area greater than ten football fields. In this lesson, you will learn how to find the lateral area and surface area of pyramids.

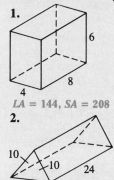

A **pyramid** is a polyhedron in which all faces but one have a vertex in common. The common vertex is called the *vertex* of the pyramid, and the face that does not contain the vertex is called the *base* of the pyramid. The remaining faces are called *lateral faces* and are always triangles. The segment from the vertex of the pyramid perpendicular to the base is called the *altitude* of the pyramid.

The length of the altitude is the *height* of the pyramid. Like a prism, a pyramid is named by its base. For example, a pyramid with a pentagonal base is called a pentagonal pyramid. If the base is a regular polygon and all lateral edges are congruent, the pyramid is called a **regular pyramid.** Most of the pyramids in this book are regular pyramids.

In a regular pyramid, all of the lateral faces are congruent isosceles triangles. The **slant height** of a regular pyramid is the height of any one of the lateral faces.

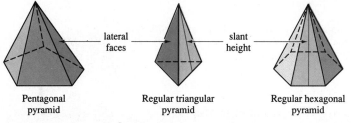

| Pentagonal pyramid | Regular triangular pyramid | Regular hexagonal pyramid |

A pyramid may be named by specifying its vertex and the vertices of its base. For example, the pyramid to the right is *V-PQRS*.

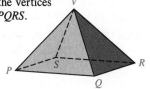

(Quiz on previous lesson)

Find the lateral area and the surface area of each prism.

1.

6

8

4

LA = 144, SA = 208

2.

10

10   24

12

LA = 768, SA = 864

3. A right prism has a square base with a perimeter of 24 cm and a height of 8 cm. Find the lateral area and the surface area of the prism. *LA = 192 cm², SA = 264 cm²*

4. If the lateral area of a right rectangular prism is 40 cm² with dimensions *l* = 6 cm and *h* = 2 cm, find the width and the surface area of the prism. *w = 4 cm, SA = 88 cm²*

Lesson Opener

Begin the lesson with a discussion of the photograph of The Great Pyramid, an example of a regular pyramid. Tell students that the Egyptians consistently built the bases of pyramids in the shape of a square. (NOTE: Use physical models of pyramids during this lesson.)

Materials

student notebooks
models of pyramids

Teaching Notes

Point out that the pyramid, like the prism, is named by the shape of its base, but a prism has two polygonal bases and a pyramid has only one.

Emphasize that the slant height is defined only for regular pyramids. Therefore, Theorem 11.2 applies only to regular pyramids.

Before discussing Example 2, review the definition of *apothem*, a line perpendicular from the center to a side of a regular polygon. Remind students that in every regular pyramid: the altitude, an apothem of the base, and an altitude of a lateral face form the sides of a right triangle.

Important Facts to Remember About Pyramids

• The altitude is a segment from the vertex perpendicular to the base. The measure of the altitude is the pyramid's height.
• A regular pyramid has a base that is a regular polygon.
• Lateral edges of a regular pyramid are congruent.
• Lateral faces of a regular pyramid are congruent isosceles triangles.
• The slant height of a regular pyramid is the height of any of the lateral faces.
• The formula for finding the lateral area (LA) of a regular pyramid is $LA = \frac{1}{2}pl$.
• The formula for finding the surface area (SA) of a regular pyramid is $SA = \frac{1}{2}pl + B$.

Key Terms

pyramid (regular)
base
lateral faces
altitude
slant height

The lateral area (*LA*) of a regular pyramid, like a prism, is equal to the sum of the areas of its lateral faces. The surface area (*SA*) is the sum of the lateral area and the area of its one base.

Consider a regular pyramid with a pentagonal base, slant height ℓ, and base edge e. The area of each lateral face is $\frac{1}{2}e\ell$. Therefore, the lateral area is

$$LA = 5 \cdot \frac{1}{2}e\ell$$
$$= \frac{1}{2}(5e)\ell$$
$$= \frac{1}{2}p\ell \quad \text{(since the perimeter of the base is } 5e\text{)}$$

◆ **THEOREM 11.2**

The lateral area of a regular pyramid is equal to half the product of the perimeter of the base p and the slant height ℓ. $LA = \frac{1}{2}p\ell$

The surface area of a regular pyramid is the sum of the lateral area and the area of the base B. $SA = \frac{1}{2}p\ell + B$

Example 1

Find the lateral area and surface area of the regular square pyramid to the right.

> **Solution**
> $LA = \frac{1}{2}p\ell$
> $\quad = \frac{1}{2} \cdot 40 \cdot 13$
> $\quad = 260$ square units
> $SA = 260 + 100 = 360$ square units

Try This

Find the lateral area and surface area of a regular square pyramid with base edge 6 and lateral edge $\sqrt{34}$.

Example 2

Find the lateral area and surface area of a regular hexagonal pyramid with slant height 11 cm and base edge 8 cm.

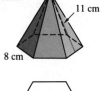

> **Solution**
> $LA = \frac{1}{2}p\ell$
> $\quad = \frac{1}{2} \cdot 48 \cdot 11$
> $\quad = 264$ cm²
> $SA = LA + B$
> $\quad = \frac{1}{2}p\ell + \frac{1}{2}ap$ *The apothem of a regular hexagon*
> $\quad = 264 + \frac{1}{2} \cdot 4\sqrt{3} \cdot 48$ *with side length 8 is $4\sqrt{3}$.*
> $\quad = 264 + 96\sqrt{3}$ cm²

Try This

Find the lateral area and surface area of a regular hexagonal pyramid if its slant height is 8 cm and the apothem of the base is 5 cm.

492   *Chapter 11   Surface Area and Volume*

Class Exercises

Short Answer

Which of the following polyhedra are pyramids? For those that are, name the base and the lateral edges.

1.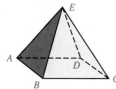

2.

3.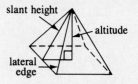

Determine whether each statement is true or false.

4. The least number of faces of a pyramid is five.

5. A pentagonal pyramid has five triangular faces.

6. The slant height of a regular pyramid is the height of one of its lateral faces.

7. The vertex of a pyramid is a vertex of each face of the pyramid.

8. The base of a pyramid is always a regular polygon.

Complete each statement.

9. The sum of the areas of the lateral faces of a regular pyramid is called the ___ of the pyramid.

10. All of the lateral faces of a regular pyramid form congruent ___ triangles.

The figure to the right is a regular square pyramid. Give a special name for each indicated segment.

11. $\overline{EF}$ **12.** $\overline{EG}$
13. $\overline{AE}$ **14.** $\overline{FG}$

Sample Exercises

Use pyramid E-$ABCD$ to complete each statement.

15. The perimeter of the base is ___ .

16. The slant height is ___ .

17. $LA =$ ___

18. $SA =$ ___

19. Sketch a pyramid with a triangular base.

20. Sketch a pyramid with a square base.

21. Find the surface area of a regular square pyramid with base diagonal 4 cm and slant height 3 cm.

Discussion

22. Can a pyramid have an isosceles trapezoid as its base? If not, why? If so, is the slant height of such a pyramid defined?

23. Give a convincing argument that the lateral area of a pyramid is always greater than the base area of the pyramid.

Common Errors

Sometimes students confuse the slant height, lateral edge, and altitude of a regular pyramid. Use the following illustration to point out that the slant height is defined only for regular pyramids.

Guided Practice

Chalkboard Examples

1. Find the lateral area and the surface area of the regular triangular pyramid. (HINT: Find the slant height.)

$LA = 36$, $SA = 36 + 16\sqrt{3}$

Answer to **Try This** $LA = 60$, $SA = 96$

2. Find the lateral area and the surface area of the rectangular pyramid. (NOTE: The pyramid has congruent lateral edges, but the pyramid is not regular.)

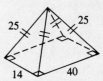

$LA = 936$, $SA = 1496$

Answer to **Try This** $LA = 80\sqrt{3}$ cm², $SA = 130\sqrt{3}$ cm²

Exercises

A

Find the lateral area and surface area of each regular pyramid.

1.
5

2.
9
4

3.
8
3

Complete the table below. The terms across the top of the table refer to the regular square pyramid shown to the right.

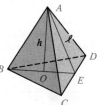

	altitude (h)	slant height (ℓ)	base edge (e)	LA	SA
4.	4	5	6	—	—
5.	24	—	14	—	—
6.	—	5	8	—	—
7.	$12x$	$13x$	$10x$	—	—
8.	—	x	x	—	—

9. Find the surface area of a regular triangular pyramid whose base-edge length is 5 in. and whose slant height is 8 in.
10. Find the surface area of a regular hexagonal pyramid whose base-edge length is 4 cm and whose slant height is 7 cm.

B

11. Find the slant height of a regular square pyramid with base-edge length 4 cm if its lateral area is 72 cm².
12. Find the surface area of a regular square pyramid with slant height 7 in. if its lateral area is 70 sq in.
13. Find the slant height of a regular hexagonal pyramid with base-edge length 6 cm and lateral area 198 cm².
14. Find the surface area of a regular hexagonal pyramid with slant height 6 m and lateral area 54 m².

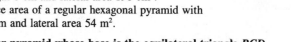

A-BCD is a regular pyramid whose base is the equilateral triangle BCD. Point E is the midpoint of side $\overline{CD}$ so that $\overline{BE}$ is an altitude of the base.

15. Find the surface area of the pyramid if each edge of the pyramid is 8 cm.
16. Find the surface area of the pyramid if $BC = 8$ in. and $AC = 5$ in.
17. Find the surface area of the pyramid if $BE = 12$ and $AE = 5$.
18. Find the surface area of the pyramid if $CD = 4\sqrt{3}$ and $AO = 4$. (HINT: Point O is the point of concurrency of the three altitudes of $\triangle BCD$.)

19. The surface area of a regular square pyramid is 48 cm². If the slant height is equal to the base-edge length, find the area of the base.
20. Find the slant height of a regular pyramid with base perimeter 20 cm and lateral area 70 cm².

21. A regular triangular pyramid with equilateral triangular lateral faces has edge length x. Find the surface area of this pyramid in terms of x.

C

22. A large container shaped like a regular hexagonal pyramid has an open top. If one hundred of these containers are to be painted, both inside and out, with a paint that covers 450 sq ft per gallon, how many gallons of paint must be purchased?

2 ft

3 ft

23. Suppose that a cube is sliced by a plane through points A, B, and C. Find the lateral area and surface area of pyramid D-ABC.
24. Find the surface area of pyramid D-ABC if $CD = 4$.

Critical Thinking

25. The pyramid to the right has a square base and two 45°–45°–90° triangular faces. Use a model or careful drawings to give a convincing argument that a cube can be divided into three identical pyramids like this one.
26. If the edges of the square face are one unit long, find the surface area of the pyramid described in Exercise 25. What assumptions are you making in doing this?

Algebra Review

Find the equation of the line through each pair of points.

1. (1, 1) and (2, 5)   2. (0, 9) and (3, 3)   3. (6, 8) and (−1, 8)
4. (−6, −7) and (12, 7)   5. (−4, 1) and (6, −2)   6. (1, 4) and (1, −7)

Enrichment
Euler's Formula

Use a sealed envelope to make the following model.

1. Construct an equilateral triangle ABC.
2. Cut along $\overline{DE}$, through C, parallel to $\overline{AB}$.
3. Fold back and forth along $\overline{AC}$ and $\overline{BC}$.
4. Let C' be the point on the reverse side corresponding to point C.
5. Open and pinch the envelope so that points D and E are joined and C and C' are separated. Tape along segment $\overline{CC'}$.

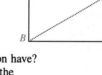

How many faces (F), edges (E), and vertices (V) does this polyhedron have? The equation $F - E + V = 2$ is called Euler's Formula. Verify that the polyhedron you have constructed satisfies this formula. How many other polyhedra can you find that satisfy the formula?

Teacher's Resource Materials

Enrichment Using Manipulatives 64
Practice Master 75
Transparency 52

Exercise Answers

1. $LA = 80$, $SA = 105$
2. $LA = 72$, $SA = 88$
3. $LA = 72$, $SA = 72 + \frac{27\sqrt{3}}{2}$
4. $LA = 60$, $SA = 96$
5. $l = 25$, $LA = 700$, $SA = 896$
6. $h = 3$, $LA = 80$, $SA = 144$
7. $LA = 260x^2$, $SA = 360x^2$
8. $h = \frac{\sqrt{3}x}{2}$, $LA = 2x^2$, $SA = 3x^2$
9. $60 + \frac{25\sqrt{3}}{4}$ sq in.
10. $84 + 24\sqrt{3}$ cm^2
11. 9 cm   12. 95 sq in.
13. 11 cm   14. $54 + \frac{27\sqrt{3}}{2}$ m^2
15. $64\sqrt{3}$ cm^2 16. $36 + 16\sqrt{3}$ sq in.   17. $108\sqrt{3}$
18. $12\sqrt{15} + 12\sqrt{3}$
19. 16 cm^2 20. 7 cm
21. $\sqrt{3}x^2$ 22. 5 gal
23. $LA = \frac{3s^2}{2}$, $SA = \frac{3s^2}{2} + \frac{\sqrt{3}s^2}{2}$
24. $24 + 8\sqrt{3}$
25. Check students' drawings.
26. $2 + \sqrt{2}$, The Pythagorean Theorem has been used twice.

Algebra Review Answers

1. $y = 4x - 3$
2. $y = -2x + 9$ 3. $y = 8$
4. $y = \frac{7}{6}x$ 5. $y = -\frac{3}{10}x - \frac{1}{5}$
6. $x = 1$

Enrichment Answers

$F = 4$, $E = 6$, $V = 4$; $4 - 6 + 4 = 2$; Euler's formula works for all polyhedra.

1. Find the lateral area and the surface area of the regular pyramid if $AB = 10$ cm and $BE = 12$ cm.

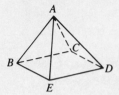

LA = 192 cm², SA = 336 cm²

2. If the slant height of the regular pyramid in Problem 1 above is 12 cm and each lateral edge is 15 cm, find the lateral area and the surface area.

LA = 432 cm², SA = 756 cm²

3. Find the surface area of a regular pyramid if the area of its square base is 25 cm² and if it has a slant height of 8 cm.

SA = 105 cm²

Lesson Opener

Stress that counting unit cubes to obtain the total number of cubic units that fits into a shoebox is the same as finding the volume of the box. Explain that the two formulas given to determine the volume of prisms are convenient and quicker methods of counting cubes.

Discuss various professions where people often have to determine the volume of an object shaped like a prism. For example, an engineer would need to find the volume of a building in order to design an appropriate air conditioning system. Ask for additional examples.

OBJECTIVE: *Determine the volume of a prism.*

11-3 Volume of Prisms

The **volume** of a solid is the number of cubic units contained in the solid. The right rectangular prism to the right is 8 cm long, 4 cm wide, and 2 cm high. It contains 64 cubic units, so its volume is 64 cm³.

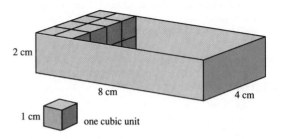

Notice that the volume of this rectangular solid can be calculated by multiplying the length by the width by the height. When calculating volume, always use the same unit of length for all three dimensions.

Imagine a prism with many thin layers of the polygonal base of the prism. You can see that the volume of the prism remains the same when the stack of layers slides as shown below.

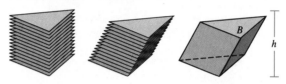

This observation suggests a postulate which can be applied to develop volume formulas.

● **POSTULATE 25**   Cavalieri's Principle

Let S and T be two solids and let X be a plane. If every plane parallel to X that intersects S or T intersects both S and T in a cross section having the same area, then

$$\text{volume of } S = \text{volume of } T.$$

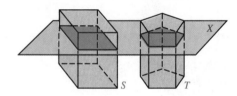

Cavalieri's Principle leads to this theorem and its corollary.

◆ **THEOREM 11.3**

The volume of any prism is the product of its height h and the area of its base B. $V = Bh$

▶ **COROLLARY 11.3a**

The volume of a right rectangular prism is the product of its length ℓ, its width w, and its height h. $V = \ell wh$

496   *Chapter 11   Surface Area and Volume*

Example 1

Find the volume of the rectangular prism shown.

Solution

$V = \ell wh$

$\quad = 7 \cdot 2.5 \cdot 9$ *Convert 25 mm to 2.5 cm.*

$\quad = 157.5 \text{ cm}^3$

Try This

Find the volume of a rectangular prism 4 ft long, 3 ft wide, and 18 in. high.

Example 2

Find the volume of the regular hexagonal prism shown.

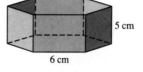

Solution

$B = \frac{1}{2} \cdot 3\sqrt{3} \cdot 36$ *First find the area of the base. The apothem of*

$\quad = 54\sqrt{3} \text{ cm}^2$ *a regular hexagon with side length 6 is $3\sqrt{3}$.*

$V = Bh$

$\quad = 54\sqrt{3} \cdot 5$

$\quad = 270\sqrt{3} \text{ cm}^3$

Try This

Find the volume of an equilateral triangular prism with base edge of length 4 cm and height 7 cm.

Class Exercises

Short Answer

Determine whether each statement is true or false.

1. The volume of any prism can be found with the formula $V = \ell wh$.
2. The volume of any prism can be found with the formula $V = Bh$.
3. A unit of volume is a cube one unit on a side.
4. The cubic inch and the cubic centimeter are two units of volume.
5. There are 27 cu ft in 1 cu yd.

Sample Exercises

Find the volume of each rectangular prism with the given dimensions.

6. $\ell = 9$ cm   7. $\ell = 4$ in.   8. $\ell = 12$ cm
    $w = 5$ cm $w = 3$ in. $w = 50$ mm
    $h = 3$ cm $h = 8$ in. $h = \;\;2$ cm

Discussion

9. If planes P and Q are parallel and the four triangular bases of these prisms are congruent, discuss how the volumes of these prisms compare. Explain your answer.

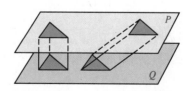

11-3 Volume of Prisms   **497**

Materials

student notebooks
models of prisms

Teaching Notes

Point out that the rectangular prism containing 64 cubic centimeters (64 cm³) has two layers, each with 4 × 8 or 32 cubes. The volume of the box can be determined by adding the volumes of both layers or by multiplying the length by the width by the height (Corollary 11.3a).

Continue to remind students that area is expressed in square units and that volume is expressed in cubic units. Area and volume are unique positive real numbers that indicate the number of units (square/cubic) that a given object contains.

Emphasize that in the illustration the two stacks have the same volume even if the stack of layers slides.

In discussing Cavalieri's Principle, point out that Bonaventura Cavalieri, an Italian mathematician, based his theory on the fact that all cross sections of a prism have equal areas. He used the same idea to compare the volumes of two solids.

Restatement of Cavalieri's Principle: If two solids have the same height and the same cross-sectional area at every level, then the two solids have the same volume.

Exercises

A

Find the volume of each prism. (Exercises 1—5 show right prisms.)

1.
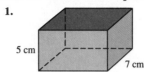
5 cm
5 cm
7 cm
8 cm

2.
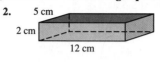
5 cm
2 cm
12 cm

3.
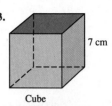
7 cm
Cube

4.

5
8   3

5.
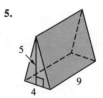
5
9
4

6.
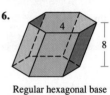
4
8
Regular hexagonal base

7. The base of a right prism is an equilateral triangle with sides of length
4 cm. The height of the prism is 9 cm. Find the volume of the prism.

8. A right regular prism has a hexagonal base. All sides of the prism are
5 cm long. Find the volume of the prism.

9. A right rectangular prism is 2 ft wide, 5 ft long and 18 in. high. Find
the volume of the prism in cubic feet.

10. Find the volume of a prism whose base has an area of 14 cm² and whose
height is 15 mm.

11. If the length of each side of a right rectangular prism is doubled, how
does the volume change?

12. If each edge of the base of a regular hexagonal prism is doubled
but the height stays the same, how does the volume change?

13. A landscape design specifies that topsoil to a depth
of 4 in. be spread over a field that is 76 yd by 32 yd.
How many cubic yards of topsoil should be ordered?

B

14. A silver ingot is molded into a bar shaped as shown. The ends are
parallel isosceles trapezoids. Find the volume of the ingot.

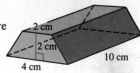
2 cm
2 cm
4 cm
10 cm

15. A right rectangular container is 5 cm wide and 12 cm long and contains water to a depth of 7 cm. A stone is placed in the water and the water rises 1.7 cm. Find the volume of the stone.

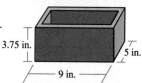

16. A box mold as shown in the illustration can be used for making bricks. If the walls of the mold are $\frac{1}{2}$ in. thick and the bottom is $\frac{3}{4}$ in. thick, what is the volume of a brick made with this mold?

3.75 in.
5 in.
9 in.

17. A heating engineer needs to find the volume of a building in order to design its heating system. Find the volume of the building shown to the right.

15 m
8 m
15 m
20 m

18. A right prism with a square base has a height of 8 cm and a volume of 128 cm³. Find the length of each edge of the base.

19. A prism with an isosceles right triangular base has a volume of 40 cu in. and a height of 5 in. Find the lengths of the edges of the base.

20. A prism with a regular hexagonal base and a height of 3 in. has a volume of $288\sqrt{3}$ cu in. Find the length of each edge of the base.

21. All edges of a right prism with a regular hexagonal base are equal in length. If the volume of the prism is $27\sqrt{3}$ cm³, find the length of each side.

c

22. A concrete retaining wall is 80 ft long and has a cross section as shown. How many cubic yards of concrete are used in constructing this wall?

2 ft 2 ft
7 ft
2 ft
2 ft 6 ft

23. An engineer's plan shows a canal with a trapezoidal cross section that is 8 ft deep and 14 ft across at the bottom with walls sloping outward at an angle of 45°. The canal is 620 ft long. A contractor bidding for the job estimates the cost to excavate the canal at $1.75 per cu yd. If the contractor adds 10% profit, what should the bid be?

24. If a square-based right prism has base edges a units long and a height of b units, find the volume of the prism.

b
a

25. If all edges of an equilateral triangular based right prism are s units long, find the volume of the prism.

Exercise Answers

1. 280 cm³   2. 120 cm³
3. 343 cm³   4. 60
5. 90   6. $192\sqrt{3}$
7. $36\sqrt{3}$ cm³
8. $\frac{375\sqrt{3}}{2}$ cm³   9. 15 cu ft
10. 21 cm³   11. The volume is multiplied by eight.
12. The volume is multiplied by four.   13. 270.2 cu yd
14. 60 cm³   15. 102 cm³
16. 96 cu. in.   17. 3450 m³
18. 4 cm   19. 4 in., 4 in., $4\sqrt{2}$ in.   20. 8 in.
21. $\sqrt[3]{18}$ cm   22. ≈ 74.1 cu yd
23. about $7779.85
24. a^2b cubic units
25. $\frac{\sqrt{3}}{4}s^3$ cubic units
26. Yes; it is a prism. To calculate the volume, it must be assumed that the treads and risers of the steps are of uniform size and meet at right angles. 1 cu yd

Mixed Review Answers

1. 176   2. 168   3. 24
4. 18 sq. in.

1.

0.25 m	24.125 m²
0.5 m	12.5 m²
0.75 m	9.125 m²
1 m	8 m²
1.25 m	7.925 m²
1.5 m	8.5 m²
1.75 m	9.554 m²
2 m	11 m²

2. 1.25 m

3.

0.2 m	30.08 m²
0.4 m	15.32 m²
0.6 m	10.72 m²
0.8 m	8.78 m²
1 m	8 m²
1.2 m	7.88 m²
1.4 m	8.21 m²
1.6 m	8.87 m²
1.8 m	9.813 m²
2 m	11 m²

4. 1.2 m; the actual minimum
surface area occurs when $x = \sqrt[3]{1.5} \approx 1.14$ m.

Critical Thinking

26. Use the definition of a prism to explain whether or not you think these concrete steps with the landing at the top form a prism. What assumptions do you need to make to calculate the number of cubic yards of concrete needed for these steps? If you can order only a whole number of cubic yards of concrete, how much should you order?

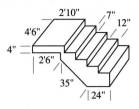

Mixed Review

Find the area of each quadrilateral.

1.
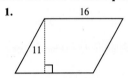
Parallelogram

2.
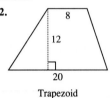
Trapezoid

3.
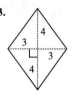

4. The diagonal of a square is 6 in. long. Find its area.

Calculator Investigation

A box manufacturer wants to produce an open box with the following characteristics: the volume must be 2 m³ and the length must be twice the width. What dimensions will minimize the amount of material required?

If x represents the width of the box, then $2x$ represents the length. If h represents the height of the box, then
$$V = \ell wh$$
$$2 = 2x \cdot x \cdot h = 2x^2 h$$
$$\text{so } h = \frac{1}{x^2}.$$

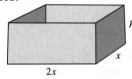

To minimize the amount of material needed, the manufacturer must consider the surface area of the box.

$$SA = \text{area of base} + 2(\text{area of front}) + 2(\text{area of side})$$
$$= 2x^2 + 2 \cdot 2xh + 2xh = 2x^2 + 4x\frac{1}{x^2} + 2x\frac{1}{x^2} = 2x^2 + \frac{6}{x}$$

Given any width x this formula can be used to calculate the surface area of the box.

1. Use a calculator to find the surface area of the box when $x = 0.25$ m, 0.5 m, 0.75 m, 1 m, 1.25 m, 1.5 m, 1.75 m, and 2 m. Make a table showing these widths and the corresponding surface areas.
2. Which of these widths corresponds to the least surface area?
3. Prepare another table, this time calculating the surface area of the box using widths from 0.2 m to 2 m in increments of 0.2 m.
4. Which width corresponds to the least surface area now? What dimensions do you think will minimize the surface area of the box?

OBJECTIVE: *Determine the volume of a pyramid.*

11-4 Volume of Pyramids

How would you find the volume of the solid the right? You could find the volume of each of the six small pyramids and add these volumes to that of the shaded cube. The goal of this lesson is to develop a method for finding the volume of a pyramid.

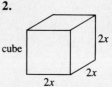

It can be shown that pyramids with congruent bases and equal heights have equal volumes. Using this fact, you can conclude that the pyramids below have equal volumes—each has one third the volume of the prism in the middle.

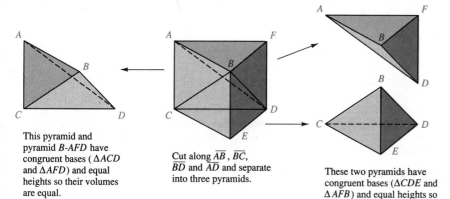

This pyramid and pyramid *B-AFD* have congruent bases (△*ACD* and △*AFD*) and equal heights so their volumes are equal.

Cut along $\overline{AB}$, $\overline{BC}$, $\overline{BD}$ and $\overline{AD}$ and separate into three pyramids.

These two pyramids have congruent bases (△*CDE* and △*AFB*) and equal heights so their volumes are equal.

The above figures suggest the following theorem.

◆ **THEOREM 11.4**

The volume of a pyramid is one third the product of the area of the base *B* and the length of the altitude *h*. $V = \frac{1}{3}Bh$

Example 1

Find the volume of the regular pyramid shown to the right.

Solution

$V = \frac{1}{3}Bh$

$= \frac{1}{3} \cdot 64 \cdot 11$ *Since the base is a square, $B = 8^2 = 64$.*

$= \frac{704}{3} \text{ cm}^3$

Try This

Find the volume of a square pyramid with 8.5 cm base edges and height 9 cm.

First Five Minutes

(Quiz on previous lesson)
Find the volume of each prism.

1.

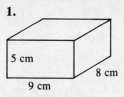

360 cm³

2.

cube

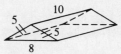

8x³

3.

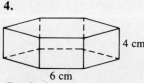

120

4.

4 cm

6 cm

Regular hexagonal prism

216√3 cm³

Lesson Opener

Point out that the volume of a pyramid is related to the volume of a prism having the same base area and altitude (height).

If a triangular prism is cut into three triangular pyramids of equal volume, the volume of the prism equals the sum of the volumes of three pyramids. The volume of each pyramid is $\frac{1}{3}$ the volume of the prism.

NOTE: The formula for finding the volume of a pyramid ($V = \frac{1}{3}Bh$) is for any pyramid, not just for regular pyramids.

Example 2

Find the volume of the regular pyramid shown to the right.

Solution

$V = \frac{1}{3}Bh$

$\quad = \frac{1}{3}\left(\frac{1}{2}\cdot 48\cdot 4\sqrt{3}\right)\cdot 12$

$\quad = 384\sqrt{3}$ cm³

The area of the base can be found using the formula $A = \frac{1}{2}ap$.

Try This

Find the volume of a pyramid with a height of 8 cm and an equilateral triangular base with base edges of 5 cm.

Class Exercises

Short Answer

Determine whether each statement is true or false.

1. Pyramids with congruent bases and equal altitudes have equal volumes.
2. The volume of a pyramid with a square base cannot be equal to the volume of a pyramid with a triangular base.
3. Two pyramids with equal volumes have equal altitudes.
4. If two pyramids have equal volumes and bases equal in area, then their altitudes are equal.

Sample Exercises

Find the volume of each pyramid.

5.

area of base = 51

6.

square base

7.

area of base = 65

8. A square pyramid has a volume of 135 cm³ and a height of 5 cm. Find the length of an edge of its base.

Discussion

9. A polygon with area B lies in plane M. Line p is parallel to and 4 in. above M and line q is parallel to and 8 in. above M. If P is any point on p and Q is any point on q, explain how the volumes of the pyramids with the polygonal base and vertices P and Q compare.

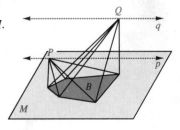

Exercises

A

1. Find the height of the pyramid to the right.
2. Find the area of the base of the pyramid.
3. Find the volume of the pyramid.
4. Find the surface area of the pyramid assuming opposite faces are congruent.

Find the volume of each regular pyramid.

5.

6.

7.

8. The area of the base of a pyramid is 62 sq in. and the height of the pyramid is 42 in. Find its volume.
9. A pyramid has a base with area 27 cm² and a height of 12 cm. Find its volume.
10. A pyramid has a right triangular base with legs 3 cm and 7 cm long. If the height of the pyramid is 10.3 cm, find its volume.
11. The height of a pyramid is 14 cm and the base is a right triangle having a hypotenuse of 13 cm and a leg of 12 cm. Find its volume.
12. A pyramid has a base area of 288 sq in. and a height of 2 ft. Find its volume.
13. The regular pyramid to the right with square base has base edges of length 10 and a slant height of 13. Find the height of the pyramid.
14. Find the volume of the pyramid described in Exercise 13.

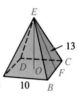

B

15. A regular pyramid with a square base 16 cm on a side has a slant height of 17 cm. What is the volume of the pyramid?
16. A pyramid has a volume of 48 cm³ and a base area of 14 cm². Find its height.
17. Find the height of a pyramid if its volume is 2500 cm³ and the base is an equilateral triangle 15 cm on a side.
18. The volume of a pyramid is 336 cu in. and its base is a right triangle having one leg 0.5 ft long and another leg 1 ft long. Find its height.
19. The bases of the two pyramids to the right have equal area. How do their volumes compare?
20. Two square pyramids have equal heights. The edge of a side of one base is 3 and of the other base is 2. How do their volumes compare?
21. Find the volume of a pyramid whose height is 14 cm and whose base is a rhombus with diagonals 6 cm and 8 cm.
22. Prove that if the base of a pyramid is a parallelogram, then the plane determined by the vertex of the pyramid and a diagonal of the base will divide the pyramid into two pyramids that have the same volume.

11-4 Volume of Pyramids **503**

Assignment Guide

Minimum: 1–26 e/o, 29, AR
Regular: 1–27 e/o, 29, AR
Advanced: 15–30, AR

Algebra

Exercise 28, AR

Lesson Closure

Review the formula for finding the volume of a pyramid.
Theorem 11.4: $V = \frac{1}{3}Bh$

Teacher's Resource Materials

Enrichment Using
    Manipulatives 65
Practice Master 77
Quiz 21
Technology: BASIC 17
Technology: Calculator 17

Exercise Answers

1. 8   2. 144   3. 384
4. 384   5. $4583\frac{1}{3}$
6. $2592\sqrt{3}$ 7. $3456\sqrt{3}$
8. 868 cu. in.   9. 108 cm³
10. 36.05 cm³   11. 140 cm³
12. $\frac{4}{3}$ cu ft   13. 12
14. 400   15. 1280 cm³
16. $10\frac{2}{7}$ cm   17. $\frac{400\sqrt{3}}{9}$ cm
18. 28 in.   19. The volume of the taller pyramid is twice the volume of the shorter pyramid.   20. The pyramid with a base edge of 2 has $\frac{4}{9}$ the volume of the pyramid with a base edge of 3.   21. 112 cm³

22. The two pyramids formed will have the same height since they share a vertex and their bases are in the same plane. Prove that the area of the bases of the pyramids are equal. A diagonal of a parallelogram divides the base into two triangles. By Theorem 5.2, the opposite sides of a parallelogram are congruent. The third side of each triangle is the shared diagonal. By SSS Postulate, the triangles are congruent and have equal area.

23. The heights of the pyramids are in the ratio $\frac{9}{10}$.

24. $\frac{9}{2}$ cm³   **25.** $\frac{9}{2}$ cm³

26. $AB = 3\sqrt{2}$ cm, $BC = 3\sqrt{2}$ cm, $AC = 3\sqrt{2}$ cm, $AD = 3$ cm, $BD = 3$ cm, $CD = 3$ cm; $FH = 3\sqrt{2}$ cm, $FG = 3\sqrt{3}$ cm, $HG = 3$ cm, $EH = 3$ cm, $EF = 3$ cm, $EG = 3\sqrt{2}$ cm

27. $\frac{256\sqrt{2}}{3}$ cm³

28. $\frac{h}{x} = \frac{k}{y}$ = tangent of acute angle at bottom of triangle; $B_1 = 4x^2$, $B_2 = 4y^2$; $x = \frac{h}{k}y$, so $B_1 = 4 \cdot \frac{h^2}{k^2}y^2 = \frac{h^2}{k^2}B_2$. Dividing through by B_2 gives the proportion $\frac{B_1}{B_2} = \frac{h^2}{k^2}$.   **29.** The volume of the double pyramids is $\frac{2}{3}$ the volume of the hexagonal prism.

30. For the faces to be equilateral, the height would have to be zero.

Algebra Review Answers

1. $x = 1$, $y = 3$ **2.** $x = 4$, $y = 1$ **3.** $p = 1$, $q = -1$

Quiz Answers

1. $LA = 168$, $SA = 222$, $V = 189$ **2.** $LA = 27.04$, $SA = 40.56$, $V = 17.576$

3. $LA = 240$, $SA = 384$, $V = 384$ **4.** $LA = 288$, $SA = 288 + 192\sqrt{3}$, $V = 576\sqrt{3}$ **5.** true

6. false   **7.** true

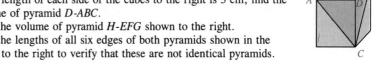

23. The base of one pyramid is a rectangle with sides 5 cm and 8 cm long and the base of another pyramid is a square with sides 6 cm long. If the volumes of the two pyramids are equal, compare their heights.

24. If the length of each side of the cubes to the right is 3 cm, find the volume of pyramid $D\text{-}ABC$.

25. Find the volume of pyramid $H\text{-}EFG$ shown to the right.

26. Find the lengths of all six edges of both pyramids shown in the cubes to the right to verify that these are not identical pyramids.

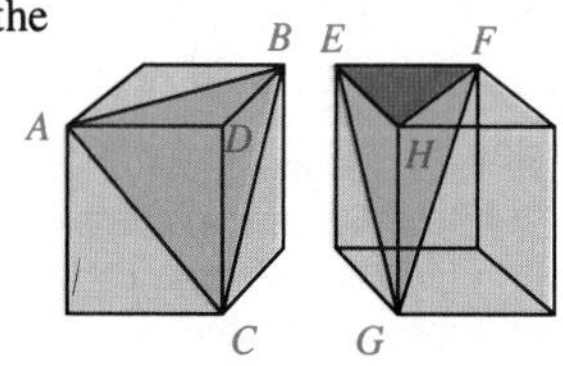

C

27. All edges of a square pyramid are 8 cm long. Find the volume of the pyramid.

28. A right square-based pyramid is cut by a plane parallel to the base to form a second square-based pyramid. The heights of the two pyramids are h and k and the edges of the bases are $2x$ and $2y$. Prove that $\left(\frac{h}{k}\right)^2 = \frac{B_1}{B_2}$.

Critical Thinking

29. How do the volumes of these solids seem to compare? What assumptions do you make in arriving at your conclusion?

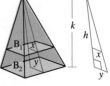

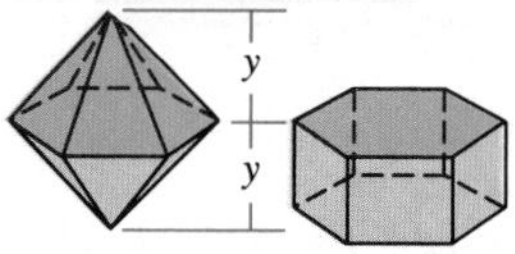

30. Why is it not possible for a regular hexagonal pyramid to have equilateral triangular faces?

Algebra Review

Solve each system of equations.

1. $x + y = 4$
$y = 2x + 1$

2. $x + y = 5$
$5x - 3y = 17$

3. $7p + 5q = 2$
$8p - 9q = 17$

Quiz

Find the lateral area, surface area, and volume of each solid.

1. a right rectangular prism with length 9, width 3, and height 7

2. a cube with edges 2.6

3. a square pyramid with base area 144 and height 8

4. a regular hexagonal prism with height 6 and base apothem $4\sqrt{3}$

Determine whether each statement is true or false.

5. In a prism, the lateral faces are parallelograms.

6. A pentagonal pyramid has 15 edges.

7. A triangular prism has six vertices.

DISCRETE MATH

Levels of Tolerance

In manufacturing processes, companies are interested in producing products that satisfy a certain standard. The standard could be a fixed diameter for a car axle, the number of raisins in a box or the width of a 1×8 piece of lumber. In reality, the specified number is not always achieved; but rather the actual value is the specified target number plus or minus an acceptable amount, the tolerance.

Suppose an individual on an assembly line in a factory producing bulldozers is supposed to make 15 rock guards per day. The tolerance that has been set for this target number is 2 rock guards. That is, actual production between 13 and 17 rock guards is acceptable for a given day. Look at the production graphs for three individuals at the plant.

The first worker A always keeps production within the target (red line) plus or minus the tolerance levels shown by the parallel dotted lines (blue). Worker B occasionally overproduces, but never falls under the target number. Worker C always stays within the band of expectation indicated by the tolerance lines.

Such methods of production supervision allow factories to monitor the amount and quality of production, and also have applications in other situations.

Exercises

1. What are the positive and negative aspects of each of the three different production patterns shown above?
2. If all other factors were equal, which of the workers would you hire? Explain your reasoning.
3. The graph to the right shows the average speed on a state highway where the speed limit is 55 mph. The tolerance lines show the possible error rates for a radar gun set at 55 mph. What decisions would you make if you were a policeman who had to determine which day to set up a radar trap? if you were a motorist? if you were a person who studied human behavior?
4. The graph to the right shows the production of boats in a boat factory where the target number is 8 boats and the tolerance level is 2. What can you say about production in this factory? What factors might lead to this pattern of production?
5. Select a situation similar to the ones above where it is possible for you to obtain information. Collect some data and determine an acceptable target number and tolerance level. Then collect more data and graph your results on a production chart. Explain any special features you notice.

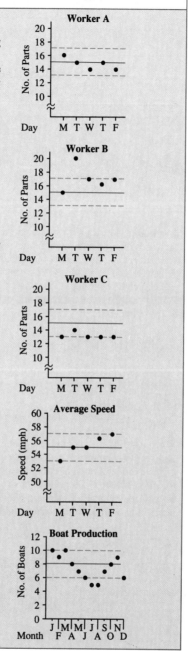

Exercise Answers

1. Answers may vary. Worker A shows a predictable output but may not be able to work faster if needed. Worker B produces more than the standard but the output is less predictable. Worker C produces steadily but the level of output is just barely acceptable. **2.** Answers may vary. Worker B consistently meets or exceeds the target level of production.

3. Answers may vary. The policeman will give out more tickets on Friday. A motorist will be less likely to be caught speeding on Monday. A psychologist will want to observe the behavior every day of the week.

4. Answers may vary. Production is high in the winter and early spring when buyers are more likely to be placing orders for the coming vacation season. It tapers off and drops below the tolerance level in summer probably because customers have already bought boats. Production rises in the fall anticipating increased demand but drops sharply over the winter vacation season. **5.** Answers may vary.

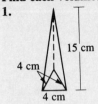
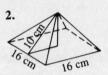
CYLINDERS, CONES, AND SPHERES

OBJECTIVE: *Find the surface area and volume of cylinders.*

11-5 Surface Area and Volume of Cylinders

EXPLORE Examine a can of fruit or vegetables. Estimate the area of the paper label that wraps the can.

Check your estimate by cutting the label with a single cut, laying it flat to form a rectangle, and measuring the rectangle.

A **cylinder,** like a prism, has congruent bases in a pair of parallel planes. But the bases of a cylinder are circular regions, rather than polygons. The segment joining the centers of the bases is called the axis of the cylinder. When the axis of a cylinder is perpendicular to the bases, the cylinder is called a **right cylinder.** Otherwise it is called an **oblique cylinder.** A segment joining the planes of the bases and perpendicular to both is an altitude of the cylinder and the length of an altitude is the height of the cylinder.

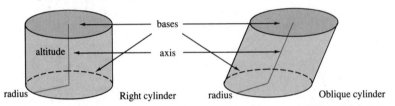

When a cylinder (without the top and bottom) is cut and laid flat you obtain a rectangle whose height is the height of the cylinder and whose length is the circumference of the circular bases. The area of this rectangle is the *lateral area* of the cylinder. By adding the area of the bases to the lateral area we obtain the *surface area* of the cylinder.

◆ **THEOREM 11.5**

The lateral area of a right cylinder is equal to the circumference of the base ($2\pi r$) times the height h. $LA = 2\pi rh$

The surface area of a right cylinder is equal to the lateral area ($2\pi rh$) plus the area of the bases ($2\pi r^2$). $SA = 2\pi rh + 2\pi r^2$

Example 1

Find the lateral area and the surface area of a cylinder with height 35 cm and diameter 18 cm.

Solution

$LA = 2\pi rh$
$\quad = 2\pi \cdot 9 \cdot 35$ *With diameter 18 cm, the radius is 9 cm.*
$\quad = 630\,\pi \text{ cm}^2$ *Substitute 9 for r and 35 for h.*

The lateral area is 630 cm².

$SA = 2\pi rh + 2\pi r^2$
$\quad = 2\pi \cdot 9 \cdot 35 + 2\pi \cdot 9^2$ *Substitute 9 for r and 35 for h.*
$\quad = 630\pi + 162\pi$
$\quad = 792\pi \text{ cm}^2$

The surface area is 792π cm².

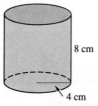

Try This

Find the lateral area and the surface area of the cylinder to the right.

The shape of a prism with many sides approximates the shape of a cylinder. The greater the number of sides to the prism, the closer the approximation. Based on this comparison, you could conclude that the volume of a cylinder, like a prism, is found by multiplying the area of the base by the height.

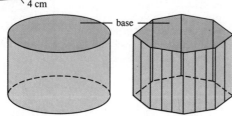

◆ **THEOREM 11.6**

The volume of a right cylinder is the product of π, the radius r squared, and the height h. $V = \pi r^2 h$

Example 2

Find the volume of a cylinder with diameter 12 cm and altitude 5 cm.

Solution

$V = \pi r^2 h$
$\quad = \pi \cdot 6^2 \cdot 5$ *Substitute 6 for r and 5 for h.*
$\quad = 180\pi \text{ cm}^3$

The volume of the cylinder is 180π cm³.

Try This

Find the radius of a cylinder with altitude 4 cm and volume 100π cm³.

---

2. Find the height of a right cylinder with radius 2 cm and volume 16π cm³. *4 cm*

Answer to **Try This** *5 cm*

Assignment Guide
Minimum: 1–21 e/o, 27, AR
Regular: 1–25 e/o, 27, AR
Advanced: 13–28, AR

Applications
Exercises 8–9, 13–14, 16–20, 24–28

Algebra
Algebra Review

Lesson Closure

Review the important facts to remember about cylinders.

Teacher's Resource Materials

Enrichment Using
   Manipulatives 67
Practice Master 78
Transparency 54

Class Exercises

Short Answer

Complete each statement.

1. The bases of a cylinder are ___ .
2. The perpendicular distance between the bases of a cylinder is called the ___ .
3. A cylinder is a right cylinder if its axis is ___ to the bases.
4. The altitude of the cylinder to the right is ___ .
5. The radius of the cylinder is ___ .

Sample Exercises

6. Find the lateral area of the cylinder to the right.
7. Find the area of one base of the cylinder.
8. Find the surface area of the cylinder.
9. Find the volume of the cylinder.
10. Sketch a cylinder.

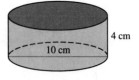

Discussion

11. Is an axis of a cylinder never, sometimes, or always also an altitude of the cylinder? Explain.
12. If the altitude of a right cylinder is doubled, how does the volume of the cylinder change? Explain.
13. If the radius of the base of a right cylinder is doubled how does the volume of the cylinder change? Explain.

Exercises

A

Find the lateral area, the surface area, and the volume of each right cylinder.

1.   6, 4

2.   8, ⊢ 4 ⊣

3.   4.5 cm, 2 cm

Complete the table.

	r	h	LA	SA	V
4.	8	6	—	—	—
5.	10	7	—	—	—
6.	5	—	—	—	100π
7.	—	4	—	—	64π

8. A cylindrical tank is 17 ft high and has a base radius of 10 ft. How many cubic feet are contained in the tank?

9. How many cubic yards are contained in the tank in Exercise 8?

10. What is the altitude of a right cylinder with radius 4 cm and volume 64π cm³?

11. What is the total surface area of a cylinder of altitude 8 cm and volume 200π cm³?

12. What is the lateral area of a cylinder of radius 5 cm and volume 100π cm³?

B

13. A right cylindrical water tank 18 ft in diameter contains water to a depth of 8 ft. What volume of water must be added to raise the water level to 12 ft?

14. A right cylindrical tank is 8 ft in diameter and 20 ft tall. How many gallons of paint are needed to paint the tank if one gallon covers 200 sq ft?

15. Find the surface area and the volume of a right cylinder that is 20 in. in diameter and 3 ft high.

16. A marble column in the shape of a right cylinder is 9 m high and 80 cm in diameter. If 1 m³ of marble weighs 300 kg, find the weight of the column.

17. Water is running into a right cylindrical tank at the rate of 5 cu ft per min. How long will it take to fill a tank 8 ft in diameter and 5 ft high?

18. A cylindrical hole with diameter 8 in. is cut through a cube 10 in. on a side. Find the surface area of this solid, shown to the right.

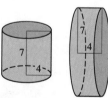

19. Find the volume of the solid in Exercise 18.

20. A copper pipe 8 in. long has an inside diameter of 0.5 in. and an outside diameter of 0.65 in. Find the volume of the copper in this piece of pipe.

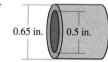

0.65 in.   0.5 in.

21. If the radius of a right cylinder is doubled, is its volume doubled? Explain why or why not.

22. If the altitude of a right cylinder is doubled is its surface area doubled? Explain why or why not.

C

23. A 4×7 rectangle can be rotated about the long side to generate a cylinder. It also can be rotated about the short side to generate a cylinder. Find the ratio of the volumes of these cylinders.

7

4

7

4

24. A case is tightly packed with six cylindrical tin cans. Find the ratio of the volume of the box to the combined volumes of the tin cans.

1. $LA = 48\pi$, $SA = 80\pi$, $V = 96\pi$
2. $LA = 32\pi$, $SA = 40\pi$, $V = 32\pi$
3. $LA = 18\pi$ cm², $SA = 26\pi$ cm²,
$V = 18\pi$ cm³   4. $LA = 96\pi$,
$SA = 224\pi$, $V = 384\pi$
5. $LA = 140\pi$, $SA = 340\pi$,
$V = 700\pi$ 6. $h = 4$,
$LA = 40\pi$, $SA = 90\pi$
7. $r = 4$, $LA = 32\pi$, $SA = 64\pi$
8. 1700π cu ft   9. 62.963π cu yd
10. 4 cm   11. 130π cm²
12. 40π cm²   13. 324π cu ft
14. 3.02 gal   15. $SA =$
920π sq. in., $V = 3600\pi$ cu in.
16. 1357 kg
17. about 50 min
18. $(600 + 48\pi)$ sq in.
19. $(1000 - 160\pi)$ cu in.
20. 0.345π cu in.
21. No; if r is doubled, V is
quadrupled.   22. No; if h is
doubled, the lateral area is doubled but the surface area is not.
23. $\frac{4}{7}$ 24. $\frac{4}{\pi}$
25. $SA = (232 + 6\pi)$ cm²,
$V = (160 - 4\pi)$ cm³
26. $SA = \frac{177\pi + 9 + 9\sqrt{5}}{8}$ sq in.,
$V = \left(\frac{27\pi}{8} + \frac{27}{32}\right)$ cu in.   27. If
r and h are each doubled, then
the surface area is quadrupled.
The volume is multiplied by 8.
28. All other things being equal,
it is more efficient to have one
large tank because it takes less
material to contain the same
volume.

2. $m = 0$

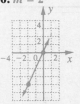

4. $m = \frac{2}{3}$

6. $m = 2$

8. $m = 2$

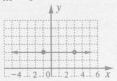

Math Contest Problem Answer

31.25π cu in.

---

25. Find the surface area and volume of this solid casting.

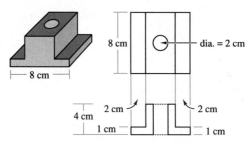

8 cm   dia. = 2 cm

4 cm   2 cm   2 cm

1 cm   1 cm

8 cm

26. Find the surface area and volume of this bearing washer.

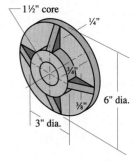

1½" core   ¼"

¾"   6" dia.

⅜"   3" dia.

Critical Thinking

27. Isabella claimed that if the radius and the altitude of one of these cylindrical tanks are each doubled the surface area of the tank is quadrupled but the volume is eight times greater. Verify that Isabella is correct.

28. Given that surface quadruples but volume is eight times greater if all the dimensions are doubled, does it seem more efficient to build one large tank or several smaller tanks? Explain.

Algebra Review

Graph the lines containing these points and find each slope.

1. (4, 0), (5, 7)   **2.** (3, 2), (−1, 2)   **3.** (−4, 2), (2, −3)   **4.** (3, 0), (6, 2)

5. (0, 5), (−4, −3)   **6.** (0, 0), (−2, −4)   **7.** (0, 2), (4, −3)   **8.** (1, 6), (−2, 0)

Math Contest Problem

Find the volume of the cylinder cut on a slant.

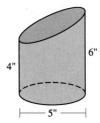

6"

4"

5"

OBJECTIVE: *Find surface area and volume of cones.*

11-6 Surface Area and Volume of Cones

 **EXPLORE** Take a circular piece of construction paper and cut from it a pie-shaped piece as shown. Join the two free edges and tape them together to form a cone-shaped hat. Is the radius of the base of the hat less than, equal to, or greater than the radius of the original disk?

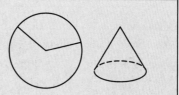

A **cone**, like a pyramid, has a vertex and a base. However its base is a circle instead of a polygon. The axis of a cone is the segment joining the vertex and the center of the base. If the axis of a cone is perpendicular to the base, the cone is called a **right cone.** Otherwise, it is called an **oblique cone.** The axis of a right cone is also its altitude. The length of the altitude is the height of the cone.

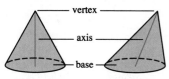

Right cone   Oblique cone

In a right cone, the distance from the vertex to the base along the surface of the cone is called the **slant height** (ℓ). The surface of the cone excluding the base is called the **lateral surface.**

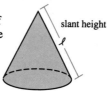

slant height
ℓ

The Explore demonstrates that a cone can be cut along a line on the lateral surface and laid flat on a plane to form a sector of a circle. The radius of this sector is ℓ —the slant height of the cone. Also, the arc length of the sector is $2\pi r$—the circumference of the base of the original cone.

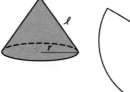

$2\pi r$

Based on this demonstration, you obtain the following proportion.

(area of sector) : (area of circle) = (circumference of base) : (circumference of circle of radius ℓ)

$$\frac{A}{\text{area of circle of radius }\ell} = \frac{2\pi r}{2\pi\ell} \text{ or } \frac{A}{\pi\ell^2} = \frac{r}{\ell}$$

You can solve this proportion to obtain the equation $A = \pi r\ell$ for the area of the lateral surface.

11-6   Surface Area and Volume of Cones   **511**

First Five Minutes

(Quiz on previous lesson)

Complete the table for the cylinder shown.

	r	h	LA	SA	V
1.	5	4	40π	90π	100π
2.	3	12	72π	90π	108π
3.	$\frac{1}{2}$	400	400π	$400\frac{1}{2}\pi$	100π
4.	2	4	16π	24π	16π

Lesson Opener

Review the definition of a sector of a circle. Point out that in the Explore, the remaining portion of the circular piece of paper is called a sector of a circle.

Materials

student notebooks
models of cones

Teaching Notes

Stress that a cone is like a pyramid because both have one base and a vertex. They differ in the shape of their bases. A cone has a circular base whereas the base of a pyramid is a polygon.

Emphasize that if the axis of a cone is also an altitude, then the cone is a right cone. Otherwise, it is called an oblique cone. (NOTE: Unless indicated, the term cone refers only to a right circular cone.)

Emphasize that slant height applies only to regular pyramids and right cones.

Point out that the formulas for a cone are closely related to the formulas for a pyramid.

	Pyramid	Cone
LA	$\frac{1}{2}p\ell$	$\pi r\ell$
SA	$\frac{1}{2}p\ell + B$	$\pi r\ell + \pi r^2$
V	$\frac{1}{3}Bh$	$\frac{1}{3}\pi r^2 h$

Point out that a cone can be thought of as a pyramid with an infinite number of lateral faces: where the slant height of a cone corresponds to the slant height of a pyramid, the lateral surface of a cone corresponds to the lateral faces of a pyramid, and the circumference of the base of a cone corresponds to the perimeter of the base of a pyramid.

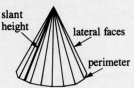

Point out that Theorems 11.7 and 11.8 refer to a right cone only. (NOTE: The volume of any cone is $V = \frac{1}{3}Bh$.)

◆ THEOREM 11.7

The lateral area of a right cone is equal to the product of π, the radius r, and the slant height ℓ. $LA = \pi r\ell$

The surface area of a right cone is equal to the sum of the lateral area ($\pi r\ell$) and the area of the base (πr^2). $SA = \pi r\ell + \pi r^2$

Example 1

Find the lateral area and surface area for the cone to the right.

Solution

$LA = \pi r\ell$
$\quad = \pi \cdot 5 \cdot 13 \qquad$ *Substitute values for r and ℓ.*
$\quad = 65\pi$

$SA = \pi r\ell + \pi r^2$
$\quad = \pi \cdot 5 \cdot 13 + \pi 5^2$
$\quad = 65\pi + 25\pi$
$\quad = 90\pi$

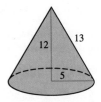

Try This

If the surface area of a cone with base radius 5 cm is 100π cm², find the slant height.

You will recall that a pyramid and a prism with congruent bases and congruent altitudes have volumes that are related by the fraction $\frac{1}{3}$. The same relationship holds between the volume of a cone and a cylinder with congruent bases and congruent altitudes.

◆ THEOREM 11.8

The volume of a right cone is one third the product of π, the radius r squared, and the height h. $V = \frac{1}{3}\pi r^2 h$

Example 2

Find the volume of the cone to the right.

Solution

$V = \frac{1}{3}\pi r^2 h$
$\quad = \frac{1}{3}\pi \, 8^2 \cdot 15 \qquad$ *Substitute values for r and h.*
$\quad = 320\pi$

Try This

If the base radius is doubled and the altitude is divided in half, how does the volume of the cone change?

Class Exercises

Short Answer

Complete each statement.

1. The base of a right cone is a ___ .
2. The ___ of a cone is the segment from the vertex to the center of the base.
3. The height of a right cone is the length of its ___ .
4. If a sector of a circle is cut from a piece of poster board and taped together to form a hat, the assembled hat is a model of the ___ surface of a cone.
5. Given a right cone and a right cylinder with equal heights and congruent bases, the ___ of a right cone is $\frac{1}{3}$ the ___ of a right cylinder.
6. The lateral area of a right cone is always $\overset{(> \text{ or } <)}{\underline{}}$ the area of its base.

Sample Exercises

7. Find the height of the cone to the right.
8. Find the radius of the cone.
9. Find the slant height of the cone.
10. Find the lateral area of the cone.
11. Find the surface area of the cone.
12. Find the volume of the cone.
13. Sketch a cone.

Discussion

14. Given a right cone with base radius r and slant height ℓ, does there always exist a right cone with base radius $2r$ and slant height $\frac{\ell}{2}$? Explain.
15. Suppose a pie-shaped wedge is cut from a circular piece of construction paper with edges brought together to form a cone-shaped hat. Suppose the angle of the cut is increased. Give a convincing argument that explains the effect on **a.** the radius, **b.** the altitude, and **c.** the slant height of the resulting cone.

Exercises

A

Find the lateral area (LA), the surface area (SA), and the volume (V) of each cone.

1.

2.

Important Facts to Remember About Cones

- A cone has a vertex and a circular base.
- The axis of a cone is a segment from the vertex to the center of the base.
- The axis of a right cone is also its altitude.
- The length of the altitude is the height of the cone.
- The slant height, which applies only to a right cone, is the distance from the vertex to the base along the lateral surface of a cone.
- The formula for finding the lateral area of a right cone is $LA = \pi r \ell$.
- The formula for finding the surface area of a right cone is $SA = \pi r \ell + \pi r^2$.
- The formula for finding the volume of right cone is $V = \frac{1}{3}\pi r^2 h$.

Key Terms

cone (right/oblique)
lateral surface
slant height

Guided Practice

Chalkboard Examples

1. The lateral area of a cone with slant height 15 cm is 180π cm². Find the radius, height, and surface area. *$r = 12$ cm, $h = 9$ cm, $SA = 324\pi$ cm²*

Answer to **Try This** *15 cm*

2. The volume of a cone with a radius 15 cm is 600π cm³. Find the height, slant height, lateral area, and surface area. *$h = 8$ cm, $\ell = 17$ cm, $LA = 255\pi$ cm², $SA = 480\pi$ cm²*

Answer to **Try This** *The volume is doubled.*

Complete the table.

	r	h	ℓ	LA	SA	V
3.	8	6	—	—	—	—
4.	10	7	—	—	—	—
5.	5	—	—	50π	—	—
6.	—	4	—	—	—	100π

7. If the volume of a right cone is 72π, find its surface area if its height and radius are equal.

8. If the base radius of a cone is 5 cm and its height is 12 cm, find the surface area and volume of the cone.

9. Which holds more, a cone-shaped drinking cup with a 6-in. base diameter or a cylindrical drinking cup of the same height with a 4-in. diameter? Explain.

10. What would the diameter of the cone-shaped cup be if it held an amount equal to the cylindrical-shaped cup?

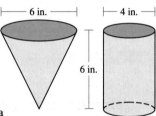

11. Find the lateral area of a cone that has a base radius of 5 cm and a volume of 100π cm³.

12. If the radius and height of a cone are doubled, how does the volume change?

13. If the radius of a cone is doubled and its height is halved, how does the volume change?

B

14. How many gallons of paint are needed to paint an open conical shaped tank that has an 8-ft base radius and is 15 ft tall if one gallon covers 200 sq ft?

15. A container consists of a right cylinder of diameter 4 cm and height 8 cm topped by a right cone of height 6 cm. Find the volume of this container.

16. Find the surface area of the container pictured to the right.

17. Find the volume of the toy top pictured to the right.
18. Find the surface area of the top.

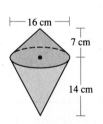

19. A cone-shaped tank with base diameter 10 ft and altitude 8 ft is being filled with water at the rate of 18 cu ft per min. How long will it take to fill the tank?

20. How many cubic inches of graphite are there in the wood pencil?

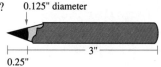
0.125" diameter
3"
0.25"

C

21. This solid is formed by cutting a cone with a slice parallel to the base of the cone. Find its volume and surface area. (HINT: Use similar triangles to find the height of the original cone.)

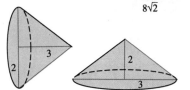
5√2
45°
8√2

22. The legs of a right triangle have lengths of 2 and 3. Cones are formed by revolving the triangles about the shorter and longer sides. Find the ratio of volumes and the ratio of surface areas of these two solids.

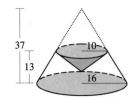
3
2
2
3

23. This solid is formed by cutting a cone with a plane parallel to the base, and then boring a cone-shaped cut into the resulting solid. If the height of the original cone is 37 units, the height of the resulting solid is 13 units, and the height of the cone that has been bored out is 5 units, how many cubic units of volume does the resulting solid have?

37
13
10
16

Critical Thinking

24. Suppose you have a cylindrical container and a conical container with the same base diameter and height. Suppose you fill the cylindrical container with water and then you insert the cone like a lid, forcing some of the water to be displaced. After removing the conical-shaped lid, how full would the cylindrical tank be?

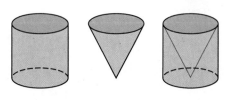

25. The following implication is true. If a cone and a cylinder have the same base diameter and same altitude, then the volume of the cone is $\frac{1}{3}$ the volume of the cylinder.
State the converse of this implication. Do you think that the converse is true? Give a convincing argument that your answer is correct.

Mixed Review

1. Find the length of the diagonal of a square if each side has a length of $5\sqrt{2}$ cm.
2. Tell whether 3, 18, and 22 could be the lengths of the sides of a triangle.
3. How many diagonals does a six-sided convex polygon have?
4. The measures of two vertical angles are $6x$ and $4x + 20$. Find the measures

11-6 Surface Area and Volume of Cones   **515**

11-6 Surface Area and Volume of Cones   **515**

Computer Activity

The BASIC program below can be used to approximate the volume of a cone. For simplicity, consider a right circular cone of radius 1 and height 10.

One way to approximate its volume is with a stack of 10 cylindrical discs, each of equal height.

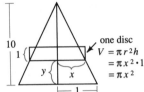

one disc
$V = \pi r^2 h$
$= \pi x^2 \cdot 1$
$= \pi x^2$

To determine the volume of one of these discs, look at a disc y units above the base of the cone. As shown above, $V = \pi x^2$. x can be found in terms of y using similar triangles.

$$\frac{10 - y}{x} = \frac{10}{1}$$
$$x = \frac{10 - y}{10}$$

so, $V = \pi(\frac{10 - y}{10})^2$.

Substituting $y = 0, 1, 2, \ldots , 9$ and adding the corresponding volumes gives an approximation of the volume of the cone.

More generally, if n discs are used instead of 10, each will have a height of $\frac{10}{n}$ and a volume of $\pi(\frac{10 - y}{10})^2 \cdot \frac{10}{n}$. In the program below, 3.14159 is used for π.

```
10 LET Y = 0
20 LET V = 0
30 PRINT "HOW MANY DISCS ARE TO BE USED?";
40 INPUT N
50 FOR I = 0 TO N − 1
60 LET Y = I * 10/N
70 LET V = V + 3.14159 * ((10 − Y)/10) ↑ 2 * (10/N)
80 NEXT I
90 PRINT "THE VOLUME OF THE DISCS IS"; V
100 END
```

Exercises

1. Use the formula $V = \frac{1}{3}\pi r^2 h$ to find the volume of the cone described above.
2. Run the program with N = 10 to find an approximation to the volume of the cone.
3. How does the approximation compare to the actual volume of the cone?
4. Run the program with other values for N. What happens as N gets larger and larger?
5. Change the program to approximate the volume of a cone with radius 1 and height 15.

516   *Chapter 11   Surface Area and Volume*

OBJECTIVE: *Find the surface area and volume of spheres.*

11-7 Surface Area and Volume of Spheres

From basketballs to marbles to the earth itself, spherical shapes are found all around us. A **sphere** is a set of points in space that are a given distance, called the **radius,** from a given point, called the **center.**

The next theorem states the formula for both the surface area and volume of a sphere.

◆ **THEOREM 11.9**

The volume of a sphere is $\frac{4}{3}$ the product of π and the radius r cubed.
$V = \frac{4}{3}\pi r^3$

The surface area of a sphere is four times the product of π and the radius r squared. $SA = 4\pi r^2$

The Cavalieri Principle can be used to explain the volume formula for a sphere. To understand the volume formula for a sphere, consider a sphere of radius r and a cylinder with base radius r and height $2r$ with a double cone carved from it as shown below. Consider a cross section of both the sphere and the carved out cylinder that is a distance b from the center of the sphere.

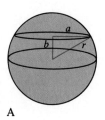
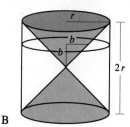

A   B

Use the Pythagorean Theorem to show that distance a in the figure is
$a^2 = r^2 - b^2$.

First Five Minutes

(Quiz on previous lesson)
Complete the table for the cone shown.

	1	2	3
r	3	12	5
h	4	5	$5\sqrt{3}$
ℓ	5	13	10
LA	15π	156π	50π
SA	24π	300π	75π
V	12π	240π	$\frac{125\sqrt{3}}{3}\pi$

Lesson Opener

Ask students to name some objects that have a spherical shape. Have students state any similarities/differences a sphere has compared to a circle, a cylinder, and a prism.

Review the formula for the area of a circle ($A = \pi r^2$), the volume of a cylinder ($V = \pi r^2 h$), and Cavalieri's Principle.

Materials

student notebooks
models of spheres

Teaching Notes

Point out that Theorem 11.9 is followed by an informal discussion on how the volume formula for a sphere can be derived. (NOTE: Cavalieri's Principle is used in the derivation of the volume formula for a sphere.)

Remind students that in solids A and B, a cross section of both the sphere and the cylinder is like a plane that intersects both A and B at a distance b from the center of the sphere. Each plane that intersects and is parallel to the base of the cylinder will intersect the cylinder in a circle. Likewise, the plane intersects the sphere in a circle.

Tell students that the formula for finding the surface area of a sphere is given in Theorem 11.9 with no discussion in the lesson on how the formula was derived. The proof of the formula requires the concept of limits, which is covered in higher-level math courses. (NOTE: An extension activity for more advanced and/or honor students could involve an investigation of how to derive the formula for the area of a sphere using the volume formula.)

Important Facts to Remember About Spheres

• A sphere is a set of points in space that are a given distance (radius) from a given point (center).
• The formula for finding the surface area of a sphere is $SA = 4\pi r^2$.
• The formula for finding the volume of a sphere is $V = \frac{4}{3}\pi r^3$.

Key Terms

sphere
radius of a sphere
center of a sphere

Compare the areas of the two cross sections.

 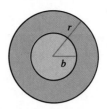

area of cross section A $= \pi a^2$ area of cross section B $= \pi r^2 - \pi b^2$
$$= \pi(r^2 - b^2)$$
$$= \pi a^2$$

The cross section areas of sphere A and solid B are equal. Thus the Cavalieri Principle indicates that the volume of solids A and B are equal. The volume of solid B, and therefore of sphere A, is

volume of sphere $= \pi r^2(2r) - 2(\frac{1}{3}\pi r^2)r$
$$= 2\pi r^3 - \frac{2}{3}\pi r^3$$
$$= \frac{4}{3}\pi r^3$$

Example 1

Find the volume and surface area of a sphere of radius 4 cm.

Solution

$V = \frac{4}{3}\pi r^3$
$\quad = \frac{4}{3}\pi 4^3$ *Substitute 4 for r in each formula.*
$\quad = \frac{256}{3}\pi$ cm³

$SA = 4\pi r^2$
$\quad = 4\pi 4^2$
$\quad = 64\pi$ cm²

Try This

Find the volume and surface area of a sphere of radius 5 cm.

Example 2

If the surface area of a sphere is 36π cm², find its volume.

Solution

$SA = 4\pi r^2$ *Use the formula for SA and solve for r.*
$36\pi = 4\pi r^2$
$9 = r^2$
$3 = r$

$V = \frac{4}{3}\pi r^3$
$\quad = \frac{4}{3}\pi 3^3$ *Substitute 3 for r.*
$\quad = 36\pi$ cm³

Try This

If the volume of a sphere is 972π cm³, find its surface area.

Class Exercises

Short Answer

Determine whether each statement is true or false.

1. A sphere is contained in a plane.
2. A sphere is to space as a circle is to a plane.
3. A sphere with center O and radius 4 consists of all points that are a distance less than or equal to 4 units from O.

Sample Exercises

4. Find the volume of a sphere with radius 2 cm.
5. Find the surface area of a sphere with radius 6 cm.
6. Find the surface area of a sphere with radius $\frac{9}{2}$ ft.
7. Find the volume of a sphere with radius $\frac{3}{4}$ yd.
8. If the volume of a sphere is 12π, find the radius of the sphere.
9. If the surface area of a sphere is 64π, find its volume.

Discussion

10. For a sphere, can the number of square units of surface area ever be greater than the number of cubic units of volume? Explain.

Exercises

A

Find the surface area and volume of each sphere.

1.
2.

Complete the table.

	r	SA	V
3.	2	——	——
4.	6	——	——
5.	8	——	——
6.	——	9π	——
7.	——	——	288π

8. Find the surface area of a sphere of radius 9 cm.
9. Find the volume of a sphere of radius $\frac{3}{2}$ cm.
10. Find the volume of a sphere of radius 2π.
11. Find the radius of a sphere whose surface area is 16π cm².
12. Find the volume of a sphere whose surface area is 16π cm².

11-7 Surface Area and Volume of Spheres   **519**

Guided Practice

Chalkboard Examples

1. Find the surface area and the volume of a sphere with a diameter of 6 cm.
$SA = 36\pi$ cm², $V = 36\pi$ cm³

Answer to **Try This**
$SA = 100\pi$ cm², $V = \frac{500\pi}{3}$ cm³

2. The surface area of a sphere is 144π. Find the radius. 6

Answer to **Try This** 324π cm²

Class Exercise Answers

1. false   2. true
3. false   4. $\frac{32\pi}{3}$ cm³
5. 144π cm²   6. 81π sq ft
7. $\frac{9\pi}{16}$ cu yd   8. $\sqrt[3]{9}$
9. $\frac{256\pi}{3}$ 10. If the radius is less than 3 units long, then the number of square units of surface area is greater than the number of cubic units of volume.

Assignment Guide

Minimum: 1–25 e/o, 28, AR
Regular: 1–27 e/o, 28, AR
Advanced: 19–29, AR

Applications
Exercises 26–27

Algebra
Exercises 24, 27, AR

Lesson Closure

Review the important facts to remember about spheres.

Exercise Answers

1. $SA = 196\pi$, $V = \frac{1372\pi}{3}$
2. $SA = 400\pi$, $V = \frac{4000\pi}{3}$
3. $SA = 16\pi$, $V = \frac{32\pi}{3}$
4. $SA = 144\pi$, $V = 288\pi$
5. $SA = 256\pi$, $V = \frac{2048\pi}{3}$
6. $r = \frac{3}{2}$, $V = \frac{9\pi}{2}$ **7.** $r = 6$,
$SA = 144\pi$ **8.** 324π cm²
9. $\frac{9\pi}{2}$ cm³   **10.** $\frac{32\pi^4}{3}$
11. 2 cm   **12.** $\frac{32\pi}{3}$ cm³
13. $\frac{352\sqrt{11}}{3}\pi$ cm³   **14.** $\frac{3}{4}$
15. 12π **16.** 64π cm²
17. $\frac{256\pi}{3}$ cm³   **18.** $\frac{6}{\pi}$
19. $\frac{8800}{3}\pi$ **20.** 720π
21. $\frac{5}{6}$ **22.** $\frac{5}{3}$ **23.** none of
these   **24.** 3 ft
25. The surface area of the
sphere is equal to $4\pi r^2$. The lateral area of the cylinder is
equal to $2\pi rh = 2\pi r \cdot 2r = 4\pi r^2$. Both the surface area of
the sphere and the lateral area
of the cylinder are $4\pi r^2$.
26. ≈117.5 cu ft   **27.** $\frac{3}{2}$
28. It is only sometimes true.
If the radius of the hole is so
large that the surface area of
the hole is less than the surface
area removed at the two ends,
the surface area will decrease.
29. It will remain as one solid.
The holes do not join to form
a cut.

---

13. Find the volume of a sphere whose surface area is 176π cm².
14. Find the radius of a sphere whose volume is $\frac{9}{16}\pi$.
15. Find the surface area of a sphere whose volume is $4\pi\sqrt{3}$.

A cube whose edge length is 8 cm on a side is circumscribed about a sphere.

16. Find the surface area of the sphere.
17. Find the volume of the sphere.
18. Find the ratio of the volume of the cube to the volume of the sphere.

B

A plane that passes through the center of a sphere divides the sphere into two identical sets, each called a hemisphere.

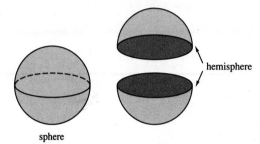

hemisphere

sphere

Assume that the solid is a right cylinder capped by two hemispheres.

19. Find the volume of the solid shown.
20. Find the surface area of the solid shown.
21. Find the ratio of the volume of the hemispheres to the volume of the cylinder portion.
22. If the radius of the solid is doubled find the ratio of the volume of the hemispheres to the volume of the cylinder portion.
23. If the radius of the above solid is doubled, is the surface area increased by a factor of 2, 4, 8, or none of these?

24. If the number of square feet of surface area of a sphere is equal to the number of cubic feet of volume of the sphere, find the radius of the sphere.
25. A sphere is inscribed in a cylinder. Show that the surface area of the sphere is equal to the lateral area of the cylinder.

C

26. A spherical tank whose radius to the outer surface is 15 ft is made of steel $\frac{1}{2}$ in. thick. How many cubic feet of steel are used in the construction of this tank?

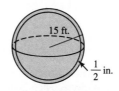

27. A can of tennis balls contains three balls. Find the ratio of the volume of the can to the volume of the three balls.

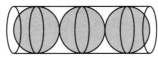

Critical Thinking

28. If a hole is drilled through the center of a sphere the volume of the resulting solid, shown to the right, appears less than the volume of the original sphere. However the surface area of the resulting solid seems to increase. Is that always or sometimes true? Explain.

29. Visualize a sphere centered at the origin of a three-dimensional coordinate system. If holes are drilled into the sphere along the x axis, y axis, and z axis, will the sphere be cut into two pieces, four pieces, eight pieces, or will it remain as one solid? Explain.

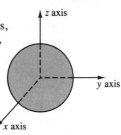

Algebra Review

Solve and graph.

1. $3 < x$ and $x < 7$
2. $-2 < x$ and $x < -1$
3. $-3x - 6 > 4$ or $x + 3 > 8$
4. $-4x + 2 > 16$ or $x - 7 > 2$
5. $3 < x + 2 < 5$
6. $-4 \leq x - 3 < 1$
7. $-6 < 4x - 6 \leq 18$
8. $-17 \leq 5x + 6 < -3$

Historical Note

A Greek mathematician named Apollonius (225 B.C.) observed that if a right cone is cut by a plane as shown, the cross section that results is an ellipse. His work made it possible for Kepler (1609) to show that the orbits of the earth and other planets are approximately ellipses.

11-7 Surface Area and Volume of Spheres   **521**

(Quiz on previous lesson)

1. Find the volume of a sphere with diameter 4 cm. $\frac{32}{3}\pi$ cm³

2. Find the surface area of a sphere with radius 9 cm.
324 cm²

3. If the surface area of a sphere is 64π, find the volume.
$\frac{256}{3}\pi$

4. If the volume of a sphere is 12π, find the surface area.
$12\sqrt[3]{3}\pi$

Lesson Opener

Review the definition of similarity. Emphasize that solids, like polygons, can be similar if they are the same shape but not necessarily the same size. Ask students to give examples of similar solids.

Materials

student notebooks

Teaching Notes

In discussing the figures of the three cubes, stress the fact that all corresponding edge lengths must be in the same proportion for two solids to be similar. Corresponding faces must be similar polygons.

If some students appear to be having difficulties understanding the relationships between similarity and ratios of area and volume of similar solids, other examples may be helpful. For example, it is easy to see that all spheres are similar and that all circles are similar.

OBJECTIVE: *Compare the surface area and volume of similar solids.*

11-8 Volume and Surface Area of Similar Solids

A small scale model is usually prepared for large construction projects. These models may be constructed with cardboard and light balsa wood, even though the full-size structure could not be completed with these light materials. As an object is enlarged, the linear dimensions, area, and volume of the object increase at different rates. This explains why the materials used must change as objects get larger.

Consider the case of the cubes below.

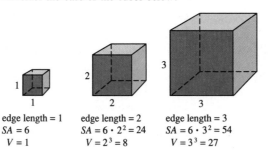

edge length = 1	edge length = 2	edge length = 3
$SA = 6$	$SA = 6 \cdot 2^2 = 24$	$SA = 6 \cdot 3^2 = 54$
$V = 1$	$V = 2^3 = 8$	$V = 3^3 = 27$

The ratios of edge lengths, surface areas, and volumes of the cubes above can be recorded in a table so that you can formulate a generalization.

edge length	surface area	volume
2:1	4:1	8:1
3:1	9:1	27:1
3:2	9:4	27:8
$a:b$	$a^2:b^2$	$a^3:b^3$

The generalization reached is that surface area increases at a rate proportional to the square of the length and volume increases at a rate proportional to the cube of the length.

These observations are true not only for cubes but for any solids that are identical in shape, that is, *similar solids.*

522   *Chapter 11   Surface Area and Volume*

Exercises

A

Suppose that the cylinders to the right are similar.

1. Find the ratio of the diameters of the cylinders.
2. Find the ratio of the surface areas of the cylinders.
3. Find the ratio of the volumes of the cylinders.
4. If the area of a base of the small cylinder is 50 cm², find the area of a base of the larger cylinder.
5. If the volume of the large cylinder is 512 cm³, find the volume of the small cylinder.

Suppose the two right rectangular prisms to the right are similar.

6. Find the ratio of the base perimeters of the two prisms.
7. Find the ratio of the surface areas of the prisms.
8. If the volume of the large prism is 54 cm³, find the volume of the small prism.
9. If the surface area of the small prism is 100 cm², find the surface area of the large prism.

10. A trough is made similar to the one to the right but 60 units long. What will the height of the larger trough be?
11. What will the ratio of the volumes of these two troughs be?
12. How much more paint will be needed to paint the larger trough, if both troughs are painted inside and outside?
13. Find the ratio of the weights of the two troughs.
14. If the surface area of the larger trough is 18 sq ft, find the surface area of the smaller trough.

B

15. Given two similar cylinders, the smaller with radius a and height h and the larger with radius $3a$, find the height of the larger cylinder.
16. Verify that Theorem 11.10 holds for the cylinders in Exercise 15.
17. Spherical fuel tanks of two different sizes are available. The diameter of the larger one is 1.5 times the diameter of the smaller one. If the cost of construction of the larger tank is 2.5 times the cost of the smaller one, which tank is the better buy? Explain.
18. The larger tank in Exercise 17 should have supporting legs how much larger in diameter than the smaller tank in order to have the strength rating of the smaller tank? (Assume that the strength of a post is proportional to its cross-sectional area.)

C

19. A certain filter system is packed with spherical particles that absorb unwanted materials from liquids that are drained through the filter. The effectiveness of the filter depends on how much surface area of these particles is exposed. The particles come in two sizes—1 cm in diameter (or 1 per cubic centimeter) and 0.5 cm in diameter (or 8 per cubic centimeter). Which size is more effective? Explain.

These observations can be summarized in the following theorem.

◆ THEOREM 11.10

If the lengths of two corresponding parts of two similar solids are in a ratio of $a:b$, then

  a. the ratio of any corresponding lengths is $a:b$,
  b. the ratio of corresponding surface areas is $a^2:b^2$,
  c. the ratio of corresponding volumes is $a^3:b^3$.

Example 1

Two cylinders are similar with diameters 6 units and 9 units respectively.

  a. Find the ratio of the circumference of their bases.
  b. Find the ratio of their lateral areas.
  c. Find the ratio of their volumes.

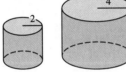

Solution

  a. $6:9$ or $2:3$ *Circumferences are corresponding lengths.*
  b. $6^2:9^2$ or $36:81$ or $4:9$ *Lateral areas are corresponding areas.*
  c. $6^3:9^3$ or $216:729$ or $8:27$

Try This

If the height of the smaller cylinder is 8, find the surface area of the larger cylinder. Assume that the cylinders are similar.

The following example illustrates Theorem 11.10.

Example 2

Two similar prisms have edge lengths in a ratio of 2 to 5. The volume of the smaller prism is 40 cm³. Find the volume of the larger prism.

Solution

$$\text{ratio of volumes} = \frac{8}{125}$$
$$\frac{8}{125} = \frac{40}{x}$$
$$8x = 125 \cdot 40$$
$$x = 625$$

Thus, the volume of the larger prism is 625 cm³.

Try This

If the surface area of the larger prism is 825 cm², find the surface area of the smaller prism. Assume that the prisms are similar.

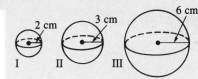

	Ratio of radii	Ratio of SA	Ratio of V
I to II	2:3	4:9	8:27
I to III	1:3	4:36	8:216
II to III	1:2	9:36	27:216

Key Terms

similar solids

Guided Practice

Chalkboard Examples

1. Suppose that two similar pyramids have base perimeters in the ratio of 2:1.
a. Find the ratio of the lateral areas of the pyramids. 4:1
b. Find the ratio of the surface area of the pyramids. 4:1
c. Find the ratio of the volume of the pyramids. 8:1

Answer to **Try This** 160π

2. If two cubes have volumes that are in the ratio of 125 to 343, find the ratio of their areas. 25:49

Answer to **Try This** 297 cm²

Class Exercise Answers

1. false   2. true   3. true
4. false   5. true
6. doubled   7. 4 to 9
8. 8 to 125   9. 9 to 16
10. 5400π cm³   11. 180π cm²
12. 2058 cm³   13. 8, 4, The weight increases faster than the strength of the stem.
14. larger bar

Assignment Guide

Minimum: 1–17 e/o, 21, MR
Regular: 1–19 e/o, 21, MR
Advanced: 15–22, MR

Applications

Class Exercises 13–14
Exercises 10–14, 17–22

Lesson Closure

Review Theorem 11.10.

Teacher's Resource Materials

Practice Master 81
Quiz 22

Exercise Answers

1. 8 to 5   **2.** 64 to 25
3. 512 to 125   **4.** 128 cm²
5. 125 cm³   **6.** 3 to 2
7. 9 to 4   **8.** 16 cm³
9. 225 cm²   **10.** 8 units
11. 64 to 1   **12.** 16 times as
much paint   **13.** 64 to 1
14. $\frac{9}{8}$ sq ft   **15.** 3h
16. length: a, h to 3a, 3h or 1:3;
surface area: $2\pi ah + 2\pi a^2$ to
$18\pi ah + 18\pi a^2$ or 1:9; volume:
$\pi a^2 h$ to $27\pi a^2 h$ or 1:27
17. The larger tank has (1.5)³ or
3.375 times the volume of the
smaller tank. The larger tank
has a lower price per unit
capacity, making it the better
buy.   **18.** Diameter of leg
should increase by $\sqrt{3.375}$
times.

Class Exercises

Short Answer

Determine whether each statement is t

1. If the edge length of a cube doubles
   doubles.
2. If the radius of a sphere triples, then
   times greater.
3. If the edge length of a cube triples,
   greater.
4. If the edge length of a cube doubles
   greater.
5. If the linear dimensions of a solid ar
   becomes four times greater.

Complete each statement.

6. If the linear dimensions of a solid ar
   greater.
7. If two similar solids have correspond
   the ratio of their surface areas is ___
8. If two similar solids have correspond
   the ratio of their volumes is ___ to _
9. If two similar cylinders have radii in
   their heights is ___ to ___ .

Sample Exercises

10. The diameters of two similar cylinde
    volume of the smaller cylinder is 160
    larger cylinder.
11. The altitudes of two similar cones ar
    area of the larger cone is 500π cm².
    cone.
12. Suppose the ratio of the radii of two
    the smaller sphere is 48π cm³. What

Discussion

13. Suppose that one apple is twice the d
    and therefore the weight, of the large
    smaller apple. The cross-sectional ar
    strength, of the larger apple is __?__ ti
    does this explain the fact that when a
    off the tree?

14. A company manufactures bars of soa
    shape. The edges of the larger bar ar
    edges of the smaller bar. If the small
    larger bar costs $1.89 per bar, which

Quiz Answers

1. $LA = 90\pi$, $SA = 140\pi$,
$V = 225\pi$ **2.** $LA = 156\pi$,
$SA = 300\pi$, $V = 240\pi$
3. $SA = 36\pi$, $V = 36\pi$
4. 49π   **5.** 15   **6.** 4:25
7. 8:125

---

20. A brand of cereal comes in boxes of two sizes that are similar in
    shape and have a ratio of edge lengths as shown to the right. Suppose
    the two boxes are filled with an equal density. If the small box costs
    $0.73 and the large box costs $2.12, which one is the better buy?

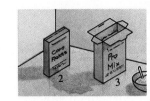

Critical Thinking

21. A long piece of grass will bend under its own weight. On the other hand,
    lumber 2 in. by 4 in. by 8 ft, called a stud, is used for support in
    building a house. The support does not bend under its own weight. But
    suppose that each dimension of a stud increases continuously at the same
    rate. Explain how we know that a support increased in size will
    eventually bend under its own weight.

22. Explain why large, heavy animals like elephants and rhinos have short
    stubby legs.

Mixed Review

Find each of the following.

1. $TO = 9$, $OU = 10$, $OV = 15$ Find OW.
2. $TO = x$, $OU = 2x$, $OV = 4$, $OW = 8$ Find TO.
3. $m\widehat{TW} = 38$, $m\widehat{VU} = 72$ Find $m\angle TOV$.
4. $m\angle TOW = 40$, $m\widehat{VU} = 65$ Find $m\widehat{TW}$.

$\overline{SR}$ and $\overline{TR}$ are tangents to $\odot P$.

5. Find $m\angle PSR$.
6. If $SP = 6$ and $PR = 8$, find SR.
7. If $m\widehat{SQ} = 75$, find $m\angle SRP$.
8. If $PR = 9$ and $QR = 4$, find SR.
9. If $PR = 8$ and $TR = 4$, find PQ.

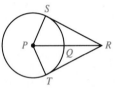

Quiz

1. Find the lateral area, surface area, and volume of a right circular cylinder
   with radius 5 and height 9.
2. Find the lateral area, surface area, and volume of a right circular cone
   with base area 144π and height 5.
3. Find the surface area and volume of a sphere with diameter 6.
4. A right circular cone has lateral area 35π and slant height 5. Find the
   area of the base.

A cone has radius 4 and height 6. A similar cone has radius 10.

5. Find the height of the larger cone.
6. Find the ratio of the areas of the cones.
7. Find the ratio of the volumes of the cones.

CRITICAL THINKING

Making and Supporting Decisions

In previous Critical Thinking lessons, the focus has been on individual topics, such as the following.

- Understanding the situation
- Dealing with assumptions
- Checking logic
- Understanding different patterns of reasoning

Now, consider all of these skills relative to the following situation.

A shipment of eight identical boxes, each assumed to contain the same top secret equipment, was delivered to Sonia, the manager of the secret equipment warehouse. They were marked, "TOP SECRET Do not open under any circumstances." As she was loading them to be taken to their destination, Sonia received a message that one box was missing a very small, but vital, part. Since she could not open the boxes, how could Sonia best determine which box had the missing part?

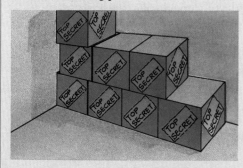

Answer the questions in each step below to use the process of critical reasoning.

1. Understand the situation.

   a. What is the situation about?
   b. What conclusion, decision, or solution is required?
   c. Are there any questions you could ask to clarify the problem?

2. Deal with the data/evidence/assumptions.

   a. Make a list of the most important evidence and data. Is other data needed?
   b. Which evidence is opinion, not fact? Which is not relevant?
   c. What assumptions are made? What other assumptions could be made?

3. Go beyond the data/evidence/assumptions.

Sonia decided to use the precision balances at a nearby aerospace laboratory. The scale operator allowed two free weighings and then charged $50 per weighing thereafter. Furthermore, Sonia did not have any funds at her disposal.

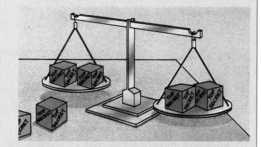

4. State and support your conclusion/decision/solution.

Write a paragraph detailing your solution to Sonia's problem. Describe one process she could have used to find the desired box without spending any money.

5. Apply the conclusion/decision/solution.

Two weeks after the above situation occurred, Sonia received a shipment of 12 boxes containing top secret equipment. Again, one box was missing a very small part. Sonia needed to use the precision balances to determine which box had the missing part. What is the least number of weighings necessary in this case?

Exercise Answers
1. a. There were eight identical-looking boxes, one of which was missing a small part. Sonia had to find the box with the missing part without opening any of the boxes. **b.** Sonia needs to determine which box has the missing part. **c.** Answers may vary.
2. a. There are eight identical-looking boxes; each box is assumed to have the same contents; one box is missing a very small part; Sonia cannot open the boxes. Answers may vary. **b.** Answers may vary. **c.** Answers may vary.   **4.** Weigh six of the boxes, three on each pan. If the scale balances, weigh the two remaining boxes, one on each pan. The lighter box is the box without the part. If the scale does not balance with three on each pan, take the lighter group of three boxes and weigh two of the boxes, one on each pan. If the scale balances, then the third box (the box not on the scale) is the box with the missing part. If the scale does not balance, then the lighter box is the box with the missing part.
5. three weighings

CHAPTER SUMMARY

Vocabulary

altitude (11-1)	lateral face (11-1)	right cone (11-6)
cone (11-6)	oblique cone (11-6)	right cylinder (11-5)
cylinder (11-5)	oblique cylinder (11-5)	right prism (11-1)
edges (11-1)	oblique prism (11-1)	slant height (11-2)
faces (11-1)	polyhedron (11-1)	sphere (11-7)
height (11-1)	prism (11-1)	surface area (11-1)
lateral area (11-1)	pyramid (11-2)	vertices (11-1)
lateral edge (11-1)	regular pyramid (11-2)	volume (11-3)

Key Ideas

1. A polyhedron is a solid made up of polygonal regions called faces. The sides and vertices of the faces are called the edges and vertices of the polyhedron.

2. The following chart summarizes formulas for lateral area, surface area, and volume.

Solid	LA	SA	V
Right prism	ph	$ph + 2B$	Bh
Regular pyramid	$\frac{1}{2}pl$	$\frac{1}{2}pl + B$	$\frac{1}{3}Bh$
Right cylinder	$2\pi rh$	$2\pi rh + 2\pi r^2$	$\pi r^2 h$
Right cone	πrl	$\pi rl + \pi r^2$	$\frac{1}{3}\pi r^2 h$
Sphere	—	$4\pi r^2$	$\frac{4}{3}\pi r^3$

3. The volume of a right rectangular prism is the product of its length, width, and height.

4. If two similar solids have lengths of sides in a ratio of $a:b$, then the following statements are true.
   - The ratio of any corresponding lengths is $a:b$.
   - The ratio of corresponding surface areas is $a^2:b^2$.
   - The ratio of corresponding volumes is $a^3:b^3$.

CHAPTER REVIEW

11-1

1. How many vertices, edges, and faces does a hexagonal prism have?
2. Find the lateral area and surface area of a right rectangular prism with length 3 cm, width 6 cm, and height 2 cm.
3. Find the lateral area and surface area of a right regular hexagonal prism with base edges of length 6 and a height of 5.

11-2

4. Find the lateral area and surface area of a regular triangular pyramid with a slant height of 6 and base edges of length 5.
5. A regular pentagonal pyramid has a lateral area of 60 cm and a slant height of 4 cm. Find the length of an edge of the pyramid's base.

11-3

6. Find the volume of a right pentagonal prism with a base area of 30 and a lateral edge of length 7.
7. Find the volume of a right triangular prism whose height is 9 and whose base is a right triangle with legs 12 and 5.
8. The volume of a cube is 64 cu in. Find the surface area of the cube.

11-4

9. Find the volume of a regular hexagonal pyramid if the perimeter of the base is 48 in. and the altitude is 5 in.
10. Find the volume of a regular square pyramid with slant height 10 and base edges of length 12.
11. The volume of a regular pentagonal pyramid is 126 cm³. If its base area is 42 cm², find the height of the pyramid.

11-5

12. Find the volume of the right cylinder to the right.

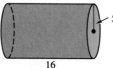

5

16

13. The area of the base of a right cylinder is 49π and its height is 4.2. Find the lateral area, surface area, and volume of the cylinder.
14. Find the volume of a right cylinder if it has a height of 3 and a lateral area of 30π.

11-6

15. A right cone has a height of 8 and a slant height of 17. Find the lateral area, surface area, and volume of the cone.
16. Find the volume of a right cone if the circumference of the base is 6π and the altitude is 7.

11-7

17. Find the surface area of a sphere with radius 7.
18. Find the volume of a sphere with diameter 4.
19. Find the surface area of a sphere if its volume is 36π.

11-8

Two similar cylinders have heights in a ratio of 3 to 4.

20. Find the ratio of the circumferences of their bases.
21. Find the ratio of their lateral surface areas.
22. Find the ratio of the diameters of their bases.
23. Find the ratio of their volumes.

24. Two similar prisms have surface areas in a ratio of 4 to 9. If the volume of the smaller prism is 40, find the volume of the larger prism.

Chapter Review
Answers

1. 12 vertices, 18 edges, 8 faces
2. $LA = 36$ cm², $SA = 72$ cm²
3. $LA = 180$, $SA = 180 + 108\sqrt{3}$ 4. $LA = 45$, $SA = 45 + \frac{25\sqrt{3}}{4}$ 5. 6 cm
6. 210   7. 270   8. 96 sq in.
9. $160\sqrt{3}$ cu in.   10. 384
11. 9 cm   12. 400π
13. $LA = 58.8\pi$, $SA = 156.8\pi$, $V = 205.8\pi$ 14. 75π
15. $LA = 255\pi$, $SA = 480\pi$, $V = 600\pi$ 16. 21π
17. $SA = 196\pi$ 18. $V = \frac{32\pi}{3}$
19. 36π 20. 3:4   21. 9:16
22. 3:4   23. 27:64   24. 135

Teacher's Resource Materials

Chapter 11 Tests

Test Answers

1. true   2. false
3. true   4. false   5. false
6. $16 + 8\sqrt{29}$ 7. 96
8. 96 cm²   9. 250π sq in.
10. 36π   11. 96   12. 78
13. 1920π   14. $\frac{32\pi}{3}$ m³
15. 60   16. $\frac{500\pi}{3}$
17. 125:512   18. 162
19. 15   20. $\frac{32\pi}{3}$ 21. 144π
22. $80\sqrt{3}$ 23. 96π   24. π

CHAPTER TEST

Determine whether each statement is true or false.

1. The lateral faces of a pyramid are triangles.
2. The volume of any prism can be found with the formula $V = \ell wh$.
3. The surface area of a prism is the sum of its lateral area and twice the area of a base.
4. The lateral area of a pyramid with height 4 and base perimeter 6 is 24.
5. If the ratio of the diameters of two similar cylinders is 3 to 5, the ratio of their volumes is 9 to 25.

Find the surface area of each solid.

6. a regular square pyramid with height 5 and base edges of length 4
7. a right triangular prism with base edges of lengths 6, 8, and 10 and height 2
8. a cube with edge length 4 cm
9. a cylinder with height 20 in. and diameter 10 in.
10. a sphere with diameter 6

Find the volume of each solid.

11. a right rectangular prism with length 4, width 3, and height 8
12. a regular pentagonal pyramid with base area 26 and height 9
13. a right cone with slant height 26 and base circumference 48π
14. a sphere with radius 2 m
15. a triangular prism with base area 10 and height 6

16. A sphere has a surface area of 100π. Find its volume.
17. Two similar solids have heights in a ratio of 5 to 8. Find the ratio of their volumes.
18. Two similar cones have volumes in a ratio of 8 to 27. If the surface area of the smaller cone is 72, find the surface area of the larger cone.

Find the volume of each solid.

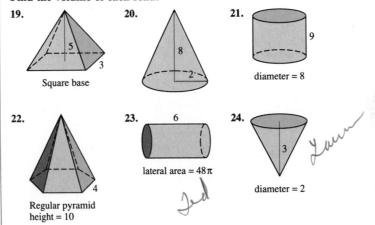

19.
5
3
Square base

20.
8
2

21.
9
diameter = 8

22.
4
Regular pyramid
height = 10

23.
6
lateral area = 48π

24.
3
diameter = 2

PROBLEM SOLVING

Guess, Check, Revise

Some problems can be solved by guessing a solution, checking the guess, and, if necessary, using information gained to revise the guess.

Example

A company received an electric bill of $108 for one month. The bill showed that 1440 kilowatt hours (kWh) were used. The manager of the company wanted to cut the electric bill exactly in half the next month. How many kilowatt hours could the company use to have a bill only half as large?

Electric Bill

$$\begin{aligned} \text{1st 600 kWh @ 4¢ each} &= \$\ 24 \\ \text{next 840 kWh @ 10¢ each} &= \$\ 84 \\ \text{Total} &= \$108 \end{aligned}$$

Solution

The desired number of kilowatt hours must be greater than 600, since $24 is less than half of $108.

Guess: 800 kWh 600 kWh @ 4¢ each = $24
         200 kWh @ 10¢ each = $20
             Total = $44

Since $44 is less than $54 (half of $108), the guess of 800 kWh was too low. The next guess should be higher.

Guess: 900 kWh 600 kWh @ 4¢ each = $24
         300 kWh @ 10¢ each = $30
             Total = $54

900 kWh results in a bill of $54–the amount of electricity that could be used.

Problem-Solving Strategies

Draw a Diagram	Simplify the Problem
Make a Table	Make an Accurate Drawing
Look for a Pattern	Guess, Check, Revise
Work Backward	

The problem-solving strategies that have been introduced up to this point in the book are presented in the chart.

Problems

1. At a banquet in a Chinese restaurant, 65 dishes were served. Every two guests shared a dish of rice between them; every three guests shared a dish of noodles; and every four guests shared a dish of meat. How many people were at the banquet if there were no extra dishes?

2. Renee accidentally hit the button on her clock radio that makes it go on and off repeatedly. The buzzer went on at exactly 7:00 AM. Then it went on and off at regular intervals. At 7:09 AM the buzzer was off, at 7:17 AM it was on, and at 7:58 AM it was on. Was the buzzer on or off at 9:00 AM?

3. Roosevelt's and Central High's bands have a combined total of 385 students. Roosevelt's and Riverside High's bands have a combined total of 320 students. Central's band has 65 more members than Riverside's. Roosevelt's band has 70 more members than Riverside's. How many members are in each school's band?

4. Is there a cube with whole-number side lengths that has the same volume as surface area? If so, what is the length of each side?

Problem Answers
1. 60 people 2. off
3. Roosevelt 195 members, Riverside 125 members, Central 190 members 4. yes, 6

Coordinate Geometry

Chapter Overview

Although coordinate geometry has been used throughout this book, this chapter provides a more rigorous and detailed treatment of the subject. The first five lessons cover basic topics related to lines, slopes, and distances. Lesson 12-6 covers equations and graphs of circles. The use of coordinate geometry in proofs is introduced in the final two lessons of the chapter.

Objectives

12-1 ■ Graph a point given its coordinates and determine the coordinates of a point given its graph.
Apply the midpoint formula.

12-2 ■ Find the slope of a line given coordinates of two points on the line.

12-3 ■ Given the slopes of two lines, determine whether the two lines are parallel, perpendicular, or neither.

12-4 ■ Graph a line given its equation.
Write an equation of a line in slope-intercept form, point-slope form, and two-point form.

12-5 ■ Apply the distance formula.

12-6 ■ Given the equation of a circle, determine the center and radius of the circle and vice versa.

12-7 ■ Choose an appropriate placement of a figure on a coordinate system for proving theorems.

12-8 ■ Prove theorems using the coordinate plane.

Cooperative Learning Opportunities

As a review of Lessons 12-1 through 12-4, assign students in pairs and try the following. Have a number of cards prepared, each one indicating a point and a slope. One student in each pair selects a card and then draws a line through the given point and with the given slope. The second student draws a line perpendicular to the given line, through the given point.

A second exercise proceeds in the same way but in addition to drawing a graph of the line, each student also writes the equation of the line. They then check each other's work. This activity can be done as a cooperative quiz in which the one paper is collected and the grade is for both students in the pair.

In Lesson 12-5, the same procedure can be used to find the distance between two points, with the second student finding the midpoint.

Multicultural Note: *Descartes*

Rene Descartes (1596–1650) was a genius with wide ranging interests. He had a firm belief in the power of the mind and said that he would be guided by, "clear and distinct ideas." He looked for unifying concepts that would connect branches of science and mathematics.

Descartes had a keen interest in all branches of science, and in particular, mechanics, optics, and biology. It is said that he was a first rate physicist and only incidentally a mathematician, although he is considered the founder of analytic geometry. Thus he brought to the study of geometry a concern with measurement and with the uses of mathematics and science. His key idea leading to the conjunction of algebra and geometry was that equations can be represented by curves. He did not use the coordinate systems as we know them, but his insights and work showing that equations can be shown visually opened vast new horizons to mathematicians.

Alternative Assessment and Communication Ideas

Students generally enjoy creating mathematical problems. If they also supply solutions then they will sharpen their skills and reinforce concepts as they enjoy thinking up new exercises.

For Lessons 12-1 through 12-5 have students write one exercise that simply requires the use of the formula or rule presented in that lesson. Have them also write an exercise that is an application of the formula or rule. Most of the lessons contain several applications that can be used to generate ideas. Students should work out their exercises and provide you with the answers. You may grade the exercises based on whether they do exemplify the material of the lesson.

You may also check to see that the answers are correct.

After the exercises are written, they might serve as the basis for an oral or written student presentation, or you can compile their problems to form a practice worksheet. Students will enjoy seeing problems they wrote on an assignment.

Investigations and Projects

As an illustration of coordinate systems, you might encourage students to collect different kinds of maps in which locations can be found according to a grid of some kind.

Road maps usually include a grid of numbers along one dimension and letters along another. In some cities, the streets are set up to form a grid that allows a person to find locations based on numbers. Trail maps for hiking and boating maps have other methods for finding locations.

A related project is to have a student or group of students gather information about how a grid is used to create a billboard advertisement based on a small picture.

A third topic to consider is the preparation of pictures and designs obtained from students holding colored cards at football games. Students might look into computer programs that generate these graphics.

Lesson	PACING CHART (DAYS)			Opening Activity	Cooperative Activity	Seat or Group Work
	1-Year Minimum	1-Year Regular	1-Year Advanced			
12-1	2	2	2	Chapter Opener: **TE** p. 532; Lesson Opener: **TE** p. 533	Explore: **SE** p. 533; ✂ Lab Worksheet 12-1: *Laboratory Manual* p. 127	Try This Exercises
12-2	2	2	2	First Five Minutes 12-2: *FFM Transparency Masters* p. 48 or **TE** p. 538; Lesson Opener: **TE** p. 538	✂ Lab Worksheet 12-2: *Laboratory Manual* p. 128	Try This Exercises
12-3	1	1	1	First Five Minutes 12-3: *FFM Transparency Masters* p. 48 or **TE** p. 542; Lesson Opener: **TE** p. 542	Explore: **SE** p. 542; ✂ Lab Worksheet 12-3A: *Laboratory Manual* p. 129; ✂ Lab Worksheet 12-3B: *Laboratory Manual* p. 132	Try This Exercises
12-4	1	1	1	First Five Minutes 12-4: *FFM Transparency Masters* p. 49 or **TE** p. 546; Lesson Opener: **TE** p. 546	Explore: **SE** p. 547; Lab Worksheet 12-4A: *Laboratory Manual* p. 131; ✂ Lab Worksheet 12-4B: *Laboratory Manual* p. 132	Try This Exercises
12-5	2	2	2	First Five Minutes 12-5: *FFM Transparency Masters* p. 49 or **TE** p. 552; Lesson Opener: **TE** p. 552	Statistics: **SE** p. 632	Try This Exercises
12-6	1	1	1	First Five Minutes 12-6: *FFM Transparency Masters* p. 49 or **TE** p. 557; Lesson Opener: **TE** p. 557	Calculator Worksheet 12-6: *Technology* p. CL19	Try This Exercises
12-7	1	1	1	First Five Minutes 12-7: *FFM Transparency Masters* p. 50 or **TE** p. 561; Lesson Opener: **TE** p. 561		Try This Exercises
12-8	1	1	1	First Five Minutes 12-8: *FFM Transparency Masters* p. 50 or **TE** p. 567; Lesson Opener: **TE** p. 567	Critical Thinking: **SE** p. 571	Exercise 1: **SE** p. 569
Review	1	1	1			
Test	1	1	1			

FFM = First Five Minutes

Enrichment	Review/Assess	Reteach	Technology	Lesson
Biographical Note: **SE** p. 537; ✂ Enrichment Using Manipulatives 12-1: *Enrichment* p. 69	Class Exercises: **SE** p. 535; Algebra Review: **SE** p. 537	Practice Worksheet 12-1: *Practice and Mixed Review* p. 87		**12-1**
✂ Enrichment Using Manipulatives 12-2: *Enrichment* p. 70	Class Exercises: **SE** p. 539; Mixed Review: **SE** p. 541	Practice Worksheet 12-2: *Practice and Mixed Review* p.88	Computer Activity: **SE** p. 541	**12-2**
✂ Enrichment Using Manipulatives 12-3: *Enrichment* p. 71; BASIC 12-3: *Technology* p. B24	Class Exercises: **SE** p. 544; Algebra Review: **SE** p. 546	Practice Worksheet 12-3: *Practice and Mixed Review* p. 89	Computer Activity: **SE** p. 546; BASIC 12-3: *Technology* p. B24	**12-3**
	Class Exercises: **SE** p. 549; Algebra Review: **SE** p. 551; Quiz: **SE** p. 551	Practice Worksheet 12-4: *Practice and Mixed Review* p. 90	Calculator Worksheet 12-4: *Technology* p. CL18	**12-4**
Connections: **SE** p. 556; ✂ Enrichment Using Manipulatives 12-5: *Enrichment* p. 72; BASIC 12-5: *Technology* p. B25	Class Exercises: **SE** p. 553; Mixed Review: **SE** p. 555	Practice Worksheet 12-5: *Practice and Mixed Review* p.91	BASIC 12-5: *Technology* p. B25	**12-5**
✂ Enrichment Using Manipulatives 12-6: *Enrichment* p. 73	Class Exercises: **SE** p. 558; Mixed Review: **SE** p. 560; Quiz: **SE** p. 560; Quiz: *Assessment* p. 101	Practice Worksheet 12-6: *Practice and Mixed Review* p. 92	Calculator Worksheet 12-6: *Technology* p. CL19	**12-6**
Enrichment: **SE** p. 566; ✂ Enrichment Using Manipulatives 12-7: *Enrichment* p. 74	Class Exercises: **SE** p. 562; Algebra Review: **SE** p. 565	Practice Worksheet 12-7: *Practice and Mixed Review* p.93		**12-7**
✂ Enrichment Using Manipulatives 12-8: *Enrichment* p. 75; Critical Thinking: **SE** p. 571	Class Exercises: **SE** p. 568; Mixed Review: **SE** p. 570; Quiz: **SE** p. 570; Quiz: *Assessment* p. 102	Practice Worksheet 12-8: *Practice and Mixed Review* p.94		**12-8**
	Summary & Review: **SE** p. 572–573	Mixed Review: *Practice and Mixed Review* p. 113		**Review**
Preparing for College Entrance Exams: **SE** p. 575	Chapter 12 Test: **SE** p. 574; Chapter 12 Tests: *Assessment* p. 67–72; *MathTest*			**Test**

12

Coordinate Geometry

An air-traffic control screen shows two jets with coordinates (17, 42) and (71, 100). Find the coordinates of a helicopter located at the midpoint of the segment between the two jets.

SEGMENTS AND LINES

OBJECTIVES: *Graph a point given its coordinates and determine the coordinates of a point given its graph. Apply the midpoint formula.*

12-1 Coordinates and Midpoints

 **EXPLORE**

Draw a coordinate system and graph the points A, B, C, and D as shown on the right. On a second paper trace the axes and mark the same four points. Flip the tracing paper over the x-axis and mark the traced points on your original graph. Label these points A', B', C', and D'. Compare the coordinates of A', B', C', and D' with the coordinates of A, B, C, and D. What conclusion can you draw? Repeat the process, this time flipping the tracing paper over the y-axis.

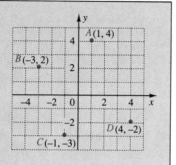

Recall that the plane containing a **rectangular coordinate system** is called the **coordinate plane.** The coordinate system consists of a horizontal number line, the **x-axis**, and a vertical number line, the **y-axis.** The intersection of the axes is called the **origin.** The x- and y-axes divide the coordinate plane into four **quadrants,** identified as quadrants I, II, III, and IV.

Points in the coordinate plane are determined by ordered pairs of numbers. The first number in an ordered pair, the **x-coordinate,** is called the **abscissa;** the second number, the **y-coordinate,** is called the **ordinate.** In the graph shown, the point M has an x-coordinate of 2 and a y-coordinate of 1. The notation $P(x, y)$ names the point P with coordinates (x, y).

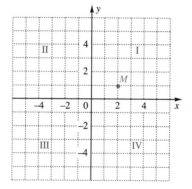

Example 1
a. Name the coordinates for each point.
   1. point A **2.** point B **3.** point F

b. Name the point for each pair of coordinates.
   1. (3, 2)   **2.** (−1, 4)   **3.** (1, −2)

   Solution
   a. 1. (2, 4)   **2.** (0, 4)   **3.** (−4, 1)
   b. 1. point P **2.** point C **3.** point L

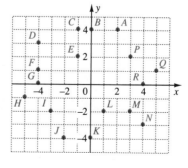

Try This
Name the coordinates of a point halfway between the given points.
a. the origin and point B **b.** the origin and point G

Key Terms

coordinate plane
origin
x-axis
y-axis
Cartesian coordinate system

Common Errors

Remind students to be careful
to substitute the correct values
in the Midpoint Formula.

Guided Practice

Chalkboard Examples

1. In which quadrant, if any, is
point *F*? **II**
In which quadrant are abscissas
and ordinates negative? **III**
In which quadrant, if any, is
point *K*? **none, on the *y*-axis**

Answer to **Try This** a. **(0, 2)**
b. **(−2, 0)**

2. Find the coordinates of the
midpoint of $\overline{AB}$ if *A* has coordinates (*a*, *b*) and *B* has coordinates (*a*, 3*b*). **(*a*, 2*b*)**

Answer to **Try This** **(1, 2)**

3. If *AB* = *BC* and point *A* has
coordinates (2*m*, 3*n*) and point
B has coordinates (*m*, −*n*), find
the coordinates of point *C*.
(0, −5*n*)

Answer to **Try This** **(−1, −1)**

In a rectangular coordinate system, the midpoint of a segment
can be determined when the coordinates of the endpoints of the
segment are known. In the graph to the right, observe that for
the horizontal segment $\overline{MN}$, the *x*-coordinate of the midpoint is
half the sum of the *x*-coordinates of the endpoints. For the
vertical segment $\overline{PQ}$, the *y*-coordinate of the midpoint is half
the sum of the *y*-coordinates of the endpoints.

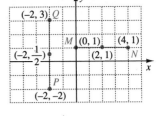

This idea can be used to find the midpoint of a segment that is
oblique to the *x*- and *y*-axes, as is the case with segment $\overline{AB}$ in
the graph to the right. The midpoint of segment $\overline{AB}$ with
coordinates *A*(−3, −2) and *B*(5, 3) is *M*, which has
coordinates $M\left(1, \frac{1}{2}\right)$.

This leads to the following theorem, which you will be asked
to prove in Exercise 36.

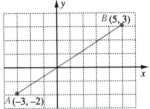

◆ **THEOREM 12.1**

If the coordinates of the endpoints of the segment $P_1 P_2$ are $P_1(x_1, y_1)$ and
$P_2(x_2, y_2)$, then the coordinates of the midpoint of $\overline{P_1 P_2}$ are $\left(\frac{x_1 + x_2}{2}, \frac{y_1 + y_2}{2}\right)$.

Example 2

Find the coordinates of the midpoint *M* of $\overline{AB}$ if *A* has coordinates (−4, −2)
and *B* has coordinates (8, 4).

Solution

$x = \frac{-4 + 8}{2} = 2 \quad y = \frac{-2 + 4}{2} = 1 \quad$ *Theorem 12.1*
$x = 2 \qquad\qquad y = 1$

The coordinates of *M* are (2, 1).

Try This

Find the coordinates of the midpoint *M* of $\overline{AB}$ if *A* has coordinates (5, −1)
and *B* has coordinates (−3, 5).

Example 3

M is the midpoint of $\overline{AB}$. Find the coordinates of *A* if *M* has coordinates
(2, 1) and *B* has coordinates (10, 5).

Solution

$2 = \frac{x_1 + 10}{2} \qquad 1 = \frac{y_1 + 5}{2} \qquad$ *Theorem 12.1*
$4 = x_1 + 10 \qquad 2 = y_1 + 5$
$x_1 = -6 \qquad\quad y_1 = -3$

The coordinates of *A* are (−6, −3).

Try This

M is the midpoint of $\overline{AB}$. Find the coordinates of *B* if *M* has coordinates
(−3, 1) and *A* has coordinates (−5, 3).

534   *Chapter 12   Coordinate Geometry*

Class Exercises

Short Answer

Name the coordinates of each point.

1. point A 2. point B 3. point C

Name the quadrant in which each point lies.

4. $(-4, 9)$ 5. $(8, -1)$ 6. $(-3, -5)$

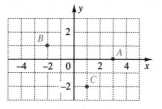

7. Find the coordinates of a point one unit directly "above" a point with coordinates $(4, 7)$.

8. Find the coordinates of a point one unit directly "below" a point with coordinates $(-2, -5)$.

9. If the y-axis is the perpendicular bisector of $\overline{AB}$ and A has coordinates $(-4, 2)$, what are the coordinates of B?

10. If the x-axis is the perpendicular bisector of $\overline{AC}$ and A has coordinates $(-4, 2)$, what are the coordinates of C?

11. What is the x-coordinate of every point on the y-axis?

12. What is the y-coordinate of every point on the x-axis?

Sample Exercises

Find the midpoint of each segment with the following endpoints.

13. $A(6, 2)$, $B(4, 10)$ 14. $C(1, 6)$, $D(4, -3)$
15. $M(-3, 6)$, $N(-1, -9)$ 16. $X(1, 5)$, $Y(-5, -1)$

Discussion

17. The midpoint of $\overline{AB}$ has coordinates $(2, 3)$ and A is at the origin. How can you find the coordinates of B? Give the coordinates of B.

18. Points B and C trisect $\overline{AD}$ such that $AB = BC = CD$, A is at the origin, and B has coordinates $(1, 3)$. How can you find the coordinates of point D? Give the coordinates of D.

Exercises

A

Complete the table by finding the missing point or coordinates.

Point	Coordinates
1. A	—
2. C	—
3. —	$(-1, 3)$
4. —	$(5, 2)$

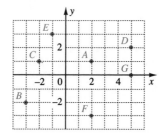

Name the quadrant that contains each point.

5. point A 6. point B 7. point C
8. point D 9. point E 10. point F

12-1 Coordinates and Midpoints   **535**

Exercise Answers

1. (2, 1)　　**2.** (−2, 1)
3. E　　**4.** D　　**5.** I
6. III　　**7.** II　　**8.** I
9. II　　**10.** IV　　**11.** $\left(\frac{5}{2}, \frac{1}{2}\right)$
12. $\left(2, \frac{-1}{2}\right)$　　**13.** $\left(\frac{1}{2}, -2\right)$
14. (−2, 0)　　**15.** (2, 6)
16. (1, 0)　　**17.** (2, 1)
18. $\left(-5, -\frac{7}{2}\right)$　　**19.** $\left(\frac{1}{2}, \frac{-1}{2}\right)$
20. $\left(\frac{7}{2}, \frac{-3}{2}\right)$　　**21.** $\left(\frac{a}{2}, \frac{b}{2}\right)$
22. $\left(\frac{a}{4}, \frac{b}{4}\right)$
23. (2, 3), (1, −1), (−3, 1)

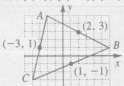

24. (9, 1)　　**25.** (−2, 8)
26. (9, 5)　　**27.** (4, −3)
28. (50, 30)　　**29.** (90, 45)
30. (45, 90)
31. parallelogram

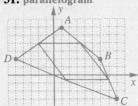

32. (7, 6), which is the midpoint of $\overline{BC}$　　**33.** $\left(2, \frac{-5}{2}\right)$, which is the midpoint of $\overline{MP}$
34. $\left(-\frac{3}{2}, 4\right)$　　**35.** $\left(-1, -\frac{3}{2}\right)$

Determine the coordinates of the midpoint of each segment.

11.

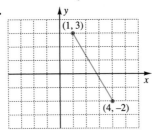

(1, 3)
(4, −2)

12.

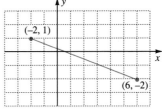

(−2, 1)
(6, −2)

13.

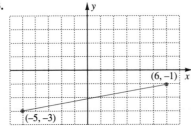

(6, −1)
(−5, −3)

14.

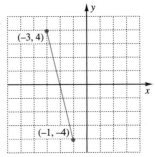

(−3, 4)
(−1, −4)

Determine the coordinates of the midpoint of the segment with the given endpoints.

15. $A(-3, 2), B(7, 10)$　　**16.** $M(-7, 4), N(9, -4)$　　**17.** $K(-1, -2), L(5, 4)$
18. $R(-3, -5), S(-7, -2)$　　**19.** $E(-4, 2), F(5, -3)$　　**20.** $P(7, -3), Q(0, 0)$
21. $X(a, b), Q(0, 0)$　　**22.** $Y\left(\frac{a}{2}, \frac{b}{2}\right), Q(0, 0)$

23. Graph the points $A(-2, 5), B(6, 1)$, and $C(-4, -3)$. Draw $\triangle ABC$. Find the midpoints of $\overline{AB}, \overline{BC},$ and $\overline{AC}$.

M **is the midpoint of** $\overline{AB}$. **Find the coordinates of each point.**

24. $A(1, 1), M(5, 1)$　　Find B.　　　　**25.** $A(-2, -6), M(-2, 1)$　　Find B.
26. $A(-5, -3), M(2, 1)$　　Find B.　　　**27.** $M(0, 0), B(-4, 3)$　　Find A.

B

28. A soccer field is 100 yd long and 60 yd wide. Suppose coordinates are assigned to the corners of the field as pictured to the right. Find the coordinates of the center of the field.

29. A baseball player is halfway between first base and second base. Suppose home plate is the origin, first base has coordinates (90, 0) and second base has coordinates (90, 90). Find the coordinates of the player's position.

30. A baseball player is halfway between second base and third base. Refer to the coordinates given in Exercise 29 and determine the coordinates of the player's position.
(HINT: Find the coordinates of third base.)

31. Graph the points $A(1, 6), B(6, 2) C(8, -3)$, and $D(-5, 2)$. Find the midpoints of $\overline{AB}, \overline{BC}, \overline{CD},$ and $\overline{DA}$. Connect the midpoints to form a quadrilateral. What kind of quadrilateral does it appear to be?

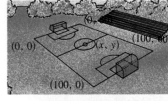

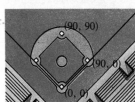

32. Triangle ABC has vertices $A(-4, -3)$, $B(8, 0)$, and $C(6, 12)$. A line is drawn parallel to base $\overline{AB}$ and bisecting $\overline{AC}$. Find the coordinates of the point where the line intersects $\overline{BC}$.

33. Triangle MNP has vertices $M(6, -2)$, $N(-8, 4)$, and $P(-2, -3)$. A line is drawn parallel to base $\overline{MN}$ and bisecting $\overline{NP}$. Find the coordinates of the point where the line intersects $\overline{MP}$.

34. Suppose the coordinates of A and B are $(-4, 6)$ and $(6, -2)$. Find the coordinates of X on $\overline{AB}$ such that $AX = \frac{1}{4}AB$.

35. Suppose the coordinates of A and B are $(-7, -2)$ and $(5, -1)$. Find the coordinates of a point C on $\overline{AB}$ such that $AC = \frac{1}{2}AB$.

C

36. Prove Theorem 12.1.

   Given: $P_1(x_1, y_1)$, $P_2(x_2, y_2)$, $P_1M = P_2M$

   Prove: The coordinates of M are $\left(\frac{x_1 + x_2}{2}, \frac{y_1 + y_2}{2}\right)$.

   (HINT: Draw the auxiliary lines indicated in the figure.)

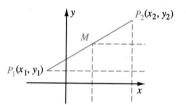

37. Consider the points $P_1(x_1, y_1)$ and $P_2(x_2, y_2)$. Find the coordinates of the points that trisect $\overline{P_1P_2}$.

Critical Thinking

38. Consider a three-dimensional coordinate system with an x-axis, a y-axis, and a z-axis. Suppose that a cube with each edge 4 units long is placed as shown in the diagram. Find the coordinates of points A, B, C, and D. Find the coordinates of the center of the cube.

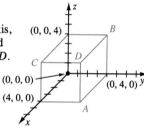

Algebra Review

Simplify.

1. $(3x^2yz^4)^2$ 2. $(-2x^6y^2)^3$ 3. $[(-n)^{15}]^2$

Solve.

4. $-25 = \frac{4x}{5} + 3x$ 5. $\frac{3}{4x} + \frac{1}{4} = 8$ 6. $\frac{1}{2}(4x - 6) = 6x + 5$

1. The coordinates of P_1 and P_2 are (x_1, y_1) and (x_2, y_2). (Given)
2. $\overline{P_2C} \parallel y$-axis, $\overline{P_1C} \parallel x$-axis (Construction) 3. C has coordinates (x_2, y_1) (Definition of rectangular coordinates)
4. $\overline{MA} \parallel \overline{P_2C}$, $\overline{MB} \parallel \overline{P_1C}$ (Construction) 5. $P_1M = P_2M$ (Given)
6. $P_1A = AC$, $CB = BP_2$ (Triangle Proportional Segment Theorem)
7. A is the midpt. of $\overline{P_1C}$, B is the midpt. of $\overline{P_2C}$. (Def. of midpt.) 8. $P_1A = \frac{1}{2}P_1C$, $CB = \frac{1}{2}CP_2$ (Midpt. Theorem)
9. $P_1C = x_2 - x_1$, $CP_2 = y_2 - y_1$ (Length of vertical and horizontal lines) 10. $P_1A = \frac{x_2 - x_1}{2}$, $CB = \frac{y_2 - y_1}{2}$ (Subst.) 11. A has x-coordinate $x_1 + \frac{x_2 - x_1}{2} = \frac{x_1 + x_2}{2}$, B has y-coordinate $y_1 + \frac{y_2 - y_1}{2} = \frac{y_1 + y_2}{2}$ (Length of vertical and horizontal lines)
12. M has coordinates $\left(\frac{x_1 + x_2}{2}, \frac{y_1 + y_2}{2}\right)$ (Definition of rectangular coordinates)

37. $\left(\frac{x_1 + 2x_2}{3}, \frac{y_1 + 2y_2}{3}\right)$, $\left(\frac{2x_1 + x_2}{3}, \frac{2y_1 + y_2}{3}\right)$

38. $A(4, 4, 0)$, $B(0, 4, 4)$, $C(4, 0, 4)$, $D(4, 4, 4)$; center of cube $(2, 2, 2)$

Algebra Review Answers

1. $9x^4y^2z^8$ 2. $-8x^{18}y^6$
3. n^{30} 4. $-\frac{125}{19}$ 5. $\frac{3}{31}$
6. $x = -2$

First Five Minutes

(Quiz on previous lesson)

1. Find the midpoints of the sides of a triangle with vertices $A(-4, 4)$, $B(5, -1)$, and $C(6, 5)$. $\overline{AB}: \left(\frac{1}{2}, \frac{3}{2}\right)$, $\overline{BC}:$ $\left(\frac{11}{2}, 2\right)$, $\overline{AC}: \left(1, \frac{9}{2}\right)$

2. The endpoints of the diameter of circle O are $(-5, 2)$ and $(6, -13)$ Find the coordinates of the center of circle O. $\left(\frac{1}{2}, -5\frac{1}{2}\right)$

3. A square has vertices at coordinates $(2, 4)$, $(2, -3)$, and $(6, 4)$. Find the coordinates of the fourth vertex. $(6, -3)$

Lesson Opener

Introduce the concept of slope with a discussion of the roofs in the pictures, which have different degrees of steepness. Ask students to give other examples of slopes, such as the grade of a road or the incline of a wheelchair ramp.

Materials

student notebooks
graph paper
investigative software

Teaching Notes

Emphasize that slope can be found by using the coordinates of any two points on the line. Students may determine slope in two ways:

$$\frac{\text{change in the } y\text{-coordinates}}{\text{change in the } x\text{-coordinates}}$$

or

$$\frac{\text{change in vertical distance}}{\text{change in horizontal distance}}$$

OBJECTIVE: *Find the slope of a line given coordinates of two points on the line.*

12-2 Slope of a Line

The degree of steepness, or **slope,** of each roof pictured is different.

The slope of a line or a segment depends on its steepness, or the rate at which it rises or falls. Consider the examples below.

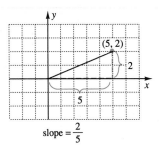 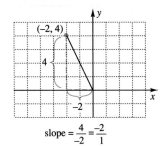

$$\text{slope} = \frac{2}{5} \qquad \text{slope} = \frac{4}{-2} = \frac{-2}{1}$$

The slope of a line is determined by the change in the vertical distance $(y_2 - y_1)$ divided by the change in the horizontal distance $(x_2 - x_1)$.

■ DEFINITION

If P_1 and P_2 have coordinates (x_1, y_1), (x_2, y_2) respectively and $x_2 - x_1 \neq 0$, then the slope m of a line containing $\overline{P_1P_2}$ is $m = \frac{y_2 - y_1}{x_2 - x_1}$

There are two special cases of slope: the slope of a horizontal line and the slope of a vertical line.

Observe that for the segment in the graph to the right
$m = \frac{-2 - (-2)}{5 - (-3)} = \frac{0}{8} = 0$
If a line is horizontal, then $y_2 = y_1$ and
$m = \frac{y_2 - y_1}{x_2 - x_1} = \frac{0}{x_2 - x_1} = 0$
The slope of a horizontal line is zero.

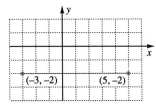

538   *Chapter 12   Coordinate Geometry*

Observe that for the segment in the graph to the right
$$m = \frac{3 - (-1)}{2 - 2} = \frac{4}{0}$$
If a line is vertical, then $x_2 = x_1$.

Since the denominator of m is 0, the slope is undefined. The slope of a vertical line is undefined. This is why the definition of slope includes the condition that $x_2 - x_1 \neq 0$.

Example
Find the slope of each segment. State whether the slope is positive, negative, zero, or undefined.

a. $\overline{AB}$ **b.** $\overline{BC}$ **c.** $\overline{AC}$

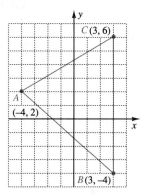

Solution
a. $m = \frac{-4 - 2}{3 - (-4)} = \frac{-6}{7}$
     The slope of $\overline{AB}$ is negative.

b. $m = \frac{6 - (-4)}{3 - 3} = \frac{10}{0}$
     The slope of $\overline{BC}$ is undefined.

c. $m = \frac{6 - 2}{3 - (-4)} = \frac{4}{7}$
     The slope of $\overline{AC}$ is positive.

Try This
Find the slope of each of the medians of $\triangle ABC$.

Class Exercises

Short Answer
Indicate if the slope of each line is positive, negative, zero, or undefined.

1. The line rises to the right.
2. The line is parallel to the x-axis.
3. The rise of the line is zero.
4. The line falls to the right.
5. The line is perpendicular to the x-axis.
6. For changes in the vertical distance there is no change in the horizontal distance.

Sample Exercises
Find the slope of the line containing the given points.

7. $A(1, 2)$, $B(3, 7)$ 8. $C(-2, 5)$, $D(7, 5)$
9. $S(-2, 6)$, $T(4, -2)$ 10. $X(-4, -3)$, $Y(-4, -8)$

Discussion
11. Explain how you would estimate the slope for each of the lines ℓ, m, and n. What general guidelines would you give for estimating the slope of a line?

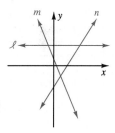

Point out that a rising line ($\overline{AB}$) yields a positive slope, a falling ($\overline{CD}$) line yields a negative slope, a horizontal line ($\overline{EF}$) has a zero slope, and a vertical line ($\overline{GH}$) has no slope.

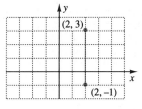

Emphasize that a slope of 0 is not the same as no slope.

Key Terms
slope

Guided Practice

Chalkboard Example
Find the slope of each side of a triangle with vertices $A(3, 0)$, $B(0, 6)$, and $C(-3, 0)$. slope of $\overline{AB} = -2$, slope of $\overline{BC} = 2$, slope of $\overline{AC} = 0$

Answer to **Try This** $\frac{-1}{7}$, $\frac{-16}{7}$, 2

Class Exercise Answers
1. positive   2. 0   3. 0
4. negative   5. undefined
6. undefined   7. $\frac{5}{2}$ 8. 0
9. $\frac{-4}{3}$ 10. undefined
11. ℓ is nearly horizontal, so its slope is about 0. n rises to the right a bit more quickly than it goes across, so its slope is somewhat larger than 1. m drops a bit more than its rightward motion, so its slope is somewhat less than -1.

Exercises

A

Find the slope of each segment.

1. $\overline{AB}$ 2. $\overline{HN}$ 3. $\overline{AC}$
4. $\overline{MC}$ 5. $\overline{GJ}$ 6. $\overline{LQ}$
7. $\overline{HG}$ 8. $\overline{MB}$ 9. $\overline{MG}$

Find the slope of the line containing the given points.

10. $(0, 0)$, $(4, 6)$ 11. $(3, 5)$, $(9, 2)$
12. $(-7, 2)$, $(5, 2)$ 13. $(4, -2)$, $(-6, -5)$
14. $(-2, 5)$, $(6, -3)$ 15. $(-2, 10)$, $(-6, -4)$
16. $(0, 2)$, $(4, 1)$ 17. $(5, 0)$, $(0, -5)$
18. $(4\frac{1}{2}, -2)$, $(-2\frac{1}{4}, 1\frac{1}{3})$ 19. $(a, -b)$, $(b, -a)$

20. $\triangle ABC$ has coordinates $A(-2, 4)$, $B(6, 2)$, and $C(0, -4)$.

   a. Find the coordinates of the midpoints D, E, and F.
   b. Determine the slopes of $\overline{AB}$, $\overline{BC}$, and $\overline{AC}$.
   c. Determine the slopes of $\overline{DE}$, $\overline{DF}$, and $\overline{FE}$.
   d. What observation can you make about the slopes in **b** and **c**?

B

21. The vertices of a quadrilateral are $R(1, 4)$, $S(3, 2)$, $T(4, 6)$, and $U(2, 8)$. Graph the points and find the slope of each side. Which sides have equal slopes? What kind of quadrilateral is $RSTU$?
22. The vertices of a quadrilateral are $E(-2, 3)$, $F(4, 3)$, $G(4, -1)$ and $H(-2, -1)$. Graph the points and find the slope of each side. Which two sides have undefined slopes? What kind of quadrilateral is $EFGH$?

Estimate the slope of the indicated line to the nearest integer.

23. p 24. q 25. r 26. s 27. t

28. Points $A(-4, -2)$, $B(-1, 1)$, and $C(3, x)$ are collinear. Solve for x. (HINT: Since A, B, and C are collinear, the slope of $\overline{AB}$ is equal to the slope of $\overline{BC}$.)

29. The slope of a drainage pipe is $\frac{1}{15}$ and the horizontal distance from one end to the other is 100 ft. Find the number of feet the tile drops.

30. An airplane descends at the steady rate of 6 ft per 100 ft (horizontal distance) traveled. If its altitude is 30,000 ft before starting its decline, find its altitude after traveling a horizontal distance of 50,000 ft.
31. Find the slope of a line that crosses the x-axis at 6 and the y-axis at −2.
32. Find the slope of a line that crosses the x-axis at −6 and the y-axis at 2. How is the slope of this line related to the slope of the line in Exercise 32?
33. A line with a slope of −3 crosses the x-axis at $(8, 0)$. At what point does it cross the y-axis?

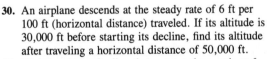

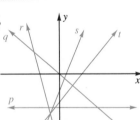

34. Find the slope of a line if its x-coordinate is always twice the y-coordinate.

35. A line contains the points $R(-5, -3)$, $S(-1, -1)$ and $T(5, x)$. Solve for x.

36. A line contains the points $X(-1, 8)$, $Y(1, 4)$ and $Z(x, -4)$. Solve for x.

37. A line with slope -1 contains the points $(5, -2)$ and $(x, -8)$. Solve for x.

38. A line with slope $\frac{3}{5}$ passes through the point $(2, 1)$. Find the coordinates of three more points on the line.

39. The vertices of $\triangle ABC$ are $A(4, 6)$, $B(-1, 2)$, and $C(2, -4)$. Find the slope of each median of the triangle.

C

40. $\triangle ABC$ has vertices $B(-6, -3)$ and $C(8, -4)$. The slope of $\overline{AB}$ is $\frac{1}{2}$. The slope of AC is -2. Find the coordinates of point A.

41. Three points A, B, and C are collinear if the slope of $\overline{AB}$ equals the slope of $\overline{BC}$. Use this fact in the following proof.

Given: $\triangle AXY$ with $A(0, 0)$, slope of $AY = \frac{1}{2}$
$DEFG$, $HIJK$, and $LMNP$ are squares with coordinates $D(4, 0)$, $H(10, 0)$, and $L(18, 0)$.

Prove: F, J, and N are collinear.

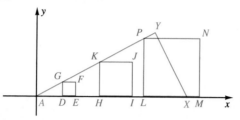

Critical Thinking

42. A line can be thought of as generated by a moving point with the rate of change in the y-coordinate divided by the rate of change in the x-coordinate as a constant. If that constant is $-\frac{1}{2}$ and the point passes through the point $(-4, 2)$, find the coordinates at which the point crosses the x-axis and the y-axis.

Mixed Review

1. $KXTR$ is a rhombus whose diagonals intersect at Q. If $m\angle KQX = 5x + 15$ and $m\angle KRT = 6x + 25$, find $m\angle RTX$.

2. If $PQ = 3x + 3$, $RS = 4x - 12$, $PS = 4x + 9$, and $QR = 6y - 5$, find the values of x and y that make $PQRS$ a parallelogram.

Computer Activity

Investigating Slopes of Lines

Use computer software to graph vertices $A(3, 3)$, $B(7, -1)$, $C(4, -4)$, and $D(0, 0)$ of rectangle $ABCD$. Compare slopes of opposite sides of the rectangle. Compare slopes of adjacent sides. What do you observe?

30. 27,000 ft   **32.** $\frac{1}{3}$; same
34. $\frac{1}{2}$ **36.** 5   **38.** Answers
may vary. Any 3 pt. on the line
$y = \frac{3}{5}x - \frac{1}{5}$ **40.** $\left(\frac{24}{5}, \frac{12}{5}\right)$
42. $(0, 0)$, $(0, 0)$

Mixed Review Answers

1. 65   **2.** $x = 15$, $y = 12\frac{1}{3}$

Computer Activity Answer

Opposite sides have equal slopes. Adjacent sides have slopes whose product is -1.

First Five Minutes

(Quiz on previous lesson)

1. Find the slope of a line containing points (6, −6) and (4, −3). $\frac{-3}{2}$

2. Find the slope of a line containing points (0, a) and (b, 0). $-\frac{a}{b}$

3. Find the missing coordinate of $P(\underline{\hspace{1cm}}, 6)$, a point on line m whose slope is $\frac{-5}{2}$. Line m contains point $R(7, -4)$. 3

Lesson Opener

Begin by asking students to graph points $A(0, 0)$, $B(3, 5)$, $C(10, 5)$, and $D(7, 0)$; and to draw $\overline{AB}$, $\overline{BC}$, $\overline{CD}$, and $\overline{AD}$.

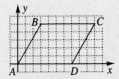

Key Questions

1. What is the special name for quadrilateral $ABCD$? parallelogram

2. What is true about opposite sides of $ABCD$? parallel

3 Find the slopes of $\overline{AB}$, $\overline{BC}$, $\overline{CD}$, $\overline{AD}$. $\frac{5}{3}$, 0, $\frac{5}{3}$, 0

4. What generalization can be made concerning slopes of lines that are parallel? equal

(NOTE: The above activity can be repeated using a rhombus and computing the slopes of the diagonals. The results would yield Theorem 12.3.)

Materials

student notebooks
graph paper
investigative software

OBJECTIVE: *Given the slopes of two lines, determine whether the two lines are parallel, perpendicular, or neither.*

12-3 Slopes of Parallel and Perpendicular Lines

 **EXPLORE** Draw a coordinate system and a line $\overline{AB}$ as shown to the right. Use a compass and straightedge to construct the following.

a. Construct a line through the origin that is parallel to $\overline{AB}$. Find the slope of this line and compare its slope to the slope of $\overline{AB}$.

b. Construct a line through the origin that is perpendicular to $\overline{AB}$. Find the slope of this line and compare its slope to the slope of $\overline{AB}$.

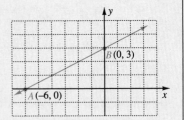

The slopes of parallel lines and the slopes of perpendicular lines have special relationships, which you may have discovered in the Explore. Consider the slopes of the pair of parallel lines in each graph below.

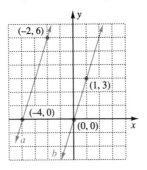

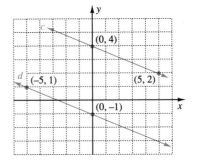

The slope of $a = \frac{3}{1}$ and the slope of $b = \frac{3}{1}$. Observe that the slope of $a =$ the slope of b.

The slope of $c = -\frac{2}{5}$ and the slope of $d = -\frac{2}{5}$. Observe that the slope of $c =$ the slope of d.

These observations lead to the following theorem.

◆ **THEOREM 12.2**

Two nonvertical lines are parallel if and only if their slopes are equal.

Theorem 12.2 is true only if neither line is parallel to the y-axis. This is because, as you learned in the previous lesson, the slope of a vertical line is undefined. If two parallel lines are vertical, then the slopes are both undefined.

542 *Chapter 12   Coordinate Geometry*

Example 1

$\overline{AB}$ contains the points $(0, 0)$ and $(3, 2)$. Suppose $\overline{AB} \parallel \overline{CD}$.
Find the slope of $\overline{CD}$.

Solution

slope of $\overline{AB} = \frac{2-0}{3-0} = \frac{2}{3}$ *Definition of slope*

slope of $\overline{CD} = \frac{2}{3}$ *Theorem 12.2*

Try This

$\overline{AB}$ contains the points $(0, 0)$ and $(-2, 5)$. Suppose $\overline{AB} \parallel \overline{CD}$.
Find the slope of $\overline{CD}$.

Consider the slopes of the pair of perpendicular lines in each graph below.

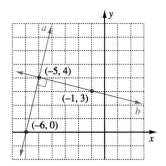   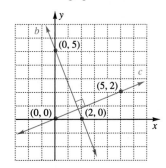

The slope of $a = 4$ and the slope of $b = -\frac{1}{4}$.   The slope of $b = -\frac{5}{2}$ and the slope of $c = \frac{2}{5}$.
Observe that $4 \cdot -\frac{1}{4} = -1$.   Observe that $-\frac{5}{2} \cdot \frac{2}{5} = -1$.

◆ THEOREM 12.3

Two nonvertical lines are perpendicular if and only if the product of their
slopes is -1.

You will be asked to complete part of the proof of Theorem 12.3 in Class
Exercise 13.

Example 2

Given $A(2, 5)$, $B(-1, -1)$, $C(-1, 4)$, and $D(9, -1)$, show that $\overline{AB} \perp \overline{CD}$.

Solution

slope of $\overline{AB} = \frac{-1-5}{-1-2} = \frac{-6}{-3} = \frac{2}{1}$ *Definition of slope*

slope of $\overline{CD} = \frac{-1-4}{9-(-1)} = \frac{-5}{10} = -\frac{1}{2}$ *Definition of slope*

Since $\frac{2}{1} \cdot -\frac{1}{2} = -1$, $\overline{AB} \perp \overline{CD}$.   *Theorem 12.3*

Try This

The points $R(-2, 3)$, $S(-1, 0)$, and $T(-4, -1)$ are the vertices of a
triangle. Show that $\angle S$ is a right angle.

Class Exercises

Short Answer

Given the slopes of lines a and b, determine whether the lines are parallel, perpendicular, or neither.

1. slope of $a = \frac{1}{2}$, slope of $b = 2$
2. slope of $a = -5$, slope of $b = \frac{1}{5}$
3. slope of $a = 0$, slope of $b = \frac{0}{5}$
4. slope of a undefined, slope of $b = 0$
5. slope of $a = \frac{2}{3}$, slope of $b = -\frac{2}{3}$
6. slope of $a = 2$, slope of $b = \frac{6}{3}$
7. slope of $a = \frac{3}{4}$, slope of $b = -\frac{12}{9}$

Sample Exercises

8. Find the slope of a line parallel to the line containing the points $(2, 3)$ and $(-4, 5)$.
9. Find the slope of a line perpendicular to the line containing the points $(2, 3)$ and $(-4, 5)$.
10. Show that $(3, 9)$, $(7, 5)$, $(4, -1)$, and $(0, 3)$ are the coordinates of the vertices of a parallelogram.
11. Show that $A(4, 6)$, $B(5, 1)$, and $C(2, 4)$ are the coordinates of the vertices of a right triangle.
12. Triangle ABC has vertices with coordinates $A(-1, 6)$, $B(3, 3)$, and $C(x, 7)$. If ABC is a right triangle with $m\angle B = 90$, find the value of x.

Discussion

13. **Given:** $p \perp q$
    Prove: (slope of p)(slope of q) $= -1$

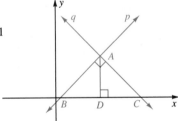

Let B and C be the points of intersection of the x-axis with p and q, respectively. Let $\overline{AD}$ be the altitude of $\triangle ABC$.
Answer the following questions to develop a convincing argument that the product of the slopes of lines p and q equals -1.

a. How can the slopes of p and q be expressed in terms of the segments $\overline{AD}$, $\overline{BD}$, and $\overline{DC}$?
b. What are the products of the slopes?
c. What relationship exists between the altitude $\overline{AD}$ and the segments $\overline{BD}$ and $\overline{CD}$ on the hypotenuse?
d. How can the expressions in **b** and **c** be used to show the product of the slopes is -1?

Exercises

A

Given coordinates for the points A, B, C, and D, determine whether $\overrightarrow{AB}$ and $\overrightarrow{CD}$ are parallel, perpendicular, or neither.

	A	B	C	D
1.	$(3, 5)$	$(7, -1)$	$(-4, 4)$	$(0, -2)$
2.	$(4, 7)$	$(8, -1)$	$(0, 1)$	$(-4, -1)$
3.	$(-2, -3)$	$(4, -1)$	$(5, -2)$	$(6, 1)$
4.	$(5, 2)$	$(10, 4)$	$(-6, 2)$	$(-4, -3)$

5. Show that $(3, 9)$, $(7, 5)$, $(3, -3)$, and $(-1, 1)$ are the coordinates of the vertices of a parallelogram.

6. Show that $(7, 9)$, $(10, -3)$, and $(2, -5)$ are the coordinates of the vertices of a right triangle. Find the coordinates of the right angle.

7. Show that $(-3, -3)$, $(-1, -2)$, $(1, -6)$, and $(-1, -7)$ are the coordinates of the vertices of a rectangle.

8. Show that $(10, 2)$, $(8, 8)$, $(-1, 5)$, and $(1, -1)$ are the coordinates of the vertices of a rectangle.

9. Find the value of y so that $(1, 2)$, $(3, 1)$, $(0, -4)$, and $(-2, y)$ are the coordinates of the vertices of a parallelogram.

10. Find the value of x so that $(1, 4)$, $(3, 5)$, $(-3, 12)$, and $(x, 13)$ are the coordinates of the vertices of a rectangle.

$\triangle ABC$ has vertices $A(-1, 4)$, $B(-3, -4)$, and $C(5, 2)$.

11. Find the slope of the altitude to $\overline{BC}$.

12. Find the slope of the altitude to $\overline{AC}$.

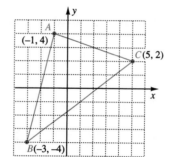

B

13. A triangle has vertices with coordinates $A(5, 1)$, $B(-1, 7)$, and $C(1, -3)$. If R is the midpoint of $\overline{AB}$, S is the midpoint of $\overline{BC}$, and T is the midpoint of $\overline{AC}$, find the slopes of $\overline{RS}$, $\overline{ST}$, and $\overline{RT}$.

14. The vertices of right triangle ABC have coordinates $A(-2, 0)$, $B(6, 4)$, and $C(x, 0)$. Find the value of x.

15. ABC is a right triangle with coordinates $A(-4, 1)$ and $C(2, -1)$. What point on the y-axis will make $m\angle B = 90$?

16. Find the value of y so that the line through $(-4, -3)$ and $(8, y)$ is parallel to the line through $(4, -4)$ and $(3, 5)$.

17. Find the value of y so that the line through $(-2, -1)$ and $(10, y)$ is perpendicular to the line through $(6, -2)$ and $(5, 7)$.

18. Find the value of a so that the line through $(7, 1)$ and $(4, 8)$ is parallel to the line through $(2, a)$ and $(a, -2)$.

19. Find the value of b so that the line through $(2, 3)$ and $(4, -5)$ is perpendicular to the line through $(4, -5)$ and (b, b).

20. Given the points $A(-3, 2)$, $B(4, -2)$ and $C(0, 6)$, find D so that $\overrightarrow{AB} \| \overrightarrow{CD}$ and D is on the x-axis.

21. Given the points $A(0, 4)$ and $B(-5, 1)$, and $\overline{AB} \perp \overline{AC}$, find the point at which $\overline{AC}$ crosses the x-axis.

Exercise Answers

1. $\overline{AB} \| \overline{CD}$　　**2.** $\overline{AB} \perp \overline{CD}$

3. neither　　**4.** $\overline{AB} \perp \overline{CD}$

5. Slope from $(3, 9)$ to $(7, 5)$ is -1; slope from $(7, 5)$ to $(3, -3)$ is 2; slope from $(3, -3)$ to $(-1, 1)$ is -1; slope from $(-1, 1)$ to $(3, 9)$ is 2; opp. sides are $\|$ so figure is a $\square$.

6. Slope from $(7, 9)$ to $(10, -3)$ is -4; slope from $(2, -5)$ to $(10, -3)$ is $\frac{1}{4}$; the right angle is at $(10, -3)$.　　**7.** Slope from $(-3, -3)$ to $(-1, -2)$ is $\frac{1}{2}$; slope from $(-1, -2)$ to $(1, -6)$ is -2; slope from $(1, -6)$ to $(-1, -7)$ is $\frac{1}{2}$; slope from $(-1, -7)$ to $(-3, -3)$ is -2; consec. sides are $\perp$ so fig. is a rect.

8. Slope from $(10, 2)$ to $(8, 8)$ is -3; slope from $(8, 8)$ to $(-1, 5)$ is $\frac{1}{3}$; slope from $(-1, 5)$ to $(1, -1)$ is -3; slope from $(1, -1)$ to $(10, 2)$ is $\frac{1}{3}$; consec. sides are $\perp$ so fig. is a rect.

9. $y = -3$　　**10.** $x = -1$

11. $-\frac{4}{3}$　　**12.** 3　　**13.** slope of $\overline{RS} = 1$, slope of $\overline{ST} = -1$, slope of $\overline{RT} = -5$　　**14.** $x = 6$ ($\angle C$ is a rt. $\angle$.) or $x = 8$ ($\angle B$ is a rt. $\angle$.)　　**15.** $(0, 3)$ or $(0, -3)$

16. $y = -111$　　**17.** $y = \frac{1}{3}$

18. $a = 5$　　**19.** $b = -8$

20. $\left(\frac{21}{2}, 0\right)$　　**21.** $\left(\frac{12}{5}, 0\right)$

22. a. 16 b. yes c. 4

23. $(1, -1)$　　**24.** $(6, -1)$

25. slope of $\overline{AB} = 0$, slope of $\overline{BC} = \frac{e-b}{d}$, slope of $\overline{CD} = 0$, slope of $\overline{DA} = \frac{e-b}{d}$. Opp. sides are $\|$, so $ABCD$ is a $\square$.

26. a. $\frac{4}{3}$ b. $\frac{-3}{4}$　　**27.** $-\frac{c}{d}$

Algebra Review Answers

1. -4　　**2.** 35　　**3.** 24

4. -32　　**5.** 41　　**6.** 66

7. -8　　**8.** 25　　**9.** 18

10. -7

Computer Activity Answer

1. $\frac{1}{2}$　　**2.** -2　　**3.** -2

First Five Minutes

(Quiz on previous lesson)

1. If $(-2, -3)$ and $(4, -1)$ are points on line m and $(5, -2)$ and $(6, 1)$ are points on line n, is $m \parallel n$? Explain. No; slopes are not equal.

2. If $(5, 2)$ and $(10, 4)$ are points on line p and $(-6, 2)$ and $(-4, -3)$ are points on line q, is $p \perp q$? Explain. Yes; product of the slopes = -1.

3. Find x so that $(1, 4)$, $(3, 5)$, $(-3, 12)$, and $(x, 13)$ are the coordinates of the vertices of a rectangle. $x = -1$

Lesson Opener

Introduce the lesson by asking students to recall from Algebra I that the graph of a linear equation written in the standard form $Ax + By = C$ is a line.

Materials

student notebooks
grid paper
investigative software

Teaching Notes

Remind students that for every line in the coordinate plane there is a distinct equation which can be written in several forms.
standard: $Ax + By = C$
slope-intercept: $y = mx + b$
point-slope: $y - y_1 = m(x - x_1)$
two-point:
$y - y_1 = \frac{y_2 - y_1}{x_2 - x_1} \cdot (x - x_1)$

Key Terms

standard form
slope-intercept form
point-slope form
two-point form

22. $\overline{AB}$ and $\overline{CD}$ are roof lines of a house, with A at the center of the house, as shown in the figure to the right. $\overline{AM}$ and $\overline{CN}$ are vertical supports for the roof.

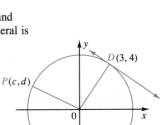

    a. If $AM = 9$, $CN = 8$, and $EB = 36$, how long should $\overline{ND}$ be if the slopes of the roof lines $\overline{AB}$ and $\overline{CD}$ are to be equal?
    b. Does EN equal ND?
    c. How long is $\overline{DB}$?

C

23. $ABCD$ is a rhombus with vertices $A(-3, 6)$, $B(5, 7)$, and $C(9, 0)$. Find the coordinates of D.

24. $ABCD$ is a parallelogram with vertices $A(3, 6)$, $B(5, 9)$, and $C(8, 2)$. Find the coordinates of D.

25. Quadrilateral $ABCD$ has vertices $A(a, b)$, $B(c, b)$, $C(c + d, e)$ and $D(a + d, e)$. Find the slope of each side. What kind of quadrilateral is $ABCD$?

Critical Thinking

26. A circle with center at the origin contains the point $D(3, 4)$. Find each of the following.

    a. the slope of the radius $\overline{OD}$.
    b. the slope of the tangent to the circle at point D.

27. Suppose $P(c, d)$ represents any point of the circle. Write an expression in terms of c and d for the slope of the tangent to the circle at point P as P moves around the circle.

Algebra Review

Evaluate each of the following.

1. $3a + 4a + 10$ if $a = -2$
2. $q - 3 + 17$ if $q = 21$
3. $\frac{-36}{p} + 3(p + 7)$ if $p = 4$
4. $3x + 5 + 4x - 2$ if $x = -5$
5. $5 + b[b(3 + 2b) + 4]$ if $b = 2$
6. $\frac{-121}{n} + n(3 + 6) - 2n$ if $n = 11$
7. $x\sqrt{x} - x^2$ if $x = 4$
8. $4a^3 - 2a^2 + a - 1$ if $a = 2$
9. $|y| - 2y + y^2$ if $y = -3$
10. $\frac{1 - y}{2} - \sqrt{y}$ if $y = 9$

Computer Activity

More on Slopes of Lines

1. Use computer software to plot the points $(1, 1)$ and $(3, 2)$. Find the slope of the line m through these points.
2. Draw a line n through $(3, 2)$ perpendicular to m. Predict the slope of line n and check your answer with the computer.
3. Draw a line through $(1, 1)$ parallel to n. Predict and check its slope as above.

OBJECTIVES: *Graph a line given its equation. Write an equation of a line in slope-intercept form, point-slope form, and two-point form.*

12-4 Equations of Lines

 **EXPLORE**

The relationship between Celsius and Fahrenheit degree measures can be represented by a straight line graph. Use the table of values to the right to draw a graph representing the relationship between the Celsius and Fahrenheit scales. Let Celsius be represented by the horizontal axis and Fahrenheit by the vertical axis. Estimate the temperature in degrees Celsius when the temperature is 0° Fahrenheit.

C	F
-10	14
-5	23
0	32
5	41
10	50

A relationship that can be represented by a straight line graph is called a linear relationship. The relationship between Fahrenheit and Celsius degree measures is an example of a linear relationship.

A linear relationship can be represented by an equation written in different forms. Three forms of linear equations considered in this lesson are as follows.

slope-intercept form   *point-slope* form   *two-point* form

Recall that the y-intercept of a line is the y-coordinate of the point where the line intersects the y-axis. It is often denoted by the letter b.

◆ **THEOREM 12.4** Slope-Intercept Form

An equation of the line that has slope m and y-intercept b is $y = mx + b$.

Example 1

Write an equation of a line that contains the point $(0, 4)$ and has slope $\frac{1}{2}$. Graph the line.

Solution

$m = \frac{1}{2}, b = 4$

$y = \frac{1}{2}x + 4$

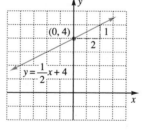

Try This

Write an equation of a line that contains the point $(0, -3)$ and has slope -2. Graph the line.

When the equation of a line is written in the form $Ax + By = C$, where A and B are both not zero, it is said to be in standard form. If the equation of a line is written in standard form you can determine the slope and y-intercept of the line. You can do this by solving the equation for y and writing the equation in the slope-intercept form, as illustrated in the following example.

12-4 Equations of Lines **547**

Chalkboard Examples

1. Find the slope and y-intercept of the following equations.
a. $y = \frac{2}{3}x$ **b.** $y = 6$
c. $y = x$ **d.** $x = 6$
$\frac{2}{3}$, 0; 0, 6; 1, 0; undefined, none

Answer to Try This
$y = -2x - 3$

2. Find the equation of a line containing the point $(-2, 4)$ and having a slope of -3. (HINT: Graph the line to find the y-intercept.) $y = -3x - 2$

Answer to Try This $\frac{5}{2}$, -5

3. Find the slope and y-intercept of the line whose equation is $-2x - 3y = 9$. $-\frac{2}{3}$, -3

Answer to Try This
$y + 5 = \frac{4}{3}(x - 2)$

4. Find the equation of a line containing the points $(5, -2)$ and $(-1, -6)$.
$y + 2 = \frac{2}{3}(x - 5)$

Answer to Try This
$y = -\frac{6}{5}x + 4$ or $y - 4 = -\frac{6}{5}x$ or $y + 2 = -\frac{6}{5}(x - 5)$

Assignment Guide

Minimum: 1–52 e/o, 57, AR
Regular: 1–56 e/o, 57, AR
Advanced: 16–51 e/o, 52–57, AR

Applications
Exercises 34–36
Algebra
Class Exercises 1–15
Exercises 1–56, AR

Lesson Closure

Summarize the lesson by asking
students to state the following
forms for equations of lines:
standard form, slope-intercept
form, point-slope form, two-
point form.

**Teacher's Resource
Materials**

Practice Master 85
Quiz 23

Example 2

Determine the slope and y-intercept of the line $3x + 4y = 12$.
Graph the line.

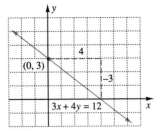

    Solution

    $3x + 4y = 12$
        $4y = -3x + 12$
         $y = -\frac{3}{4}x + 3$
        $m = \frac{-3}{4}$ *m represents the slope.*
        $b = 3$ *b represents the y-intercept.*

Try This

Determine the slope and y-intercept of the line $5x - 2y = 10$. Graph the line.

Given a point on a line and its slope, you can write an equation of a line in
the following form.

◆ **THEOREM 12.5**   Point-Slope Form

    An equation of the line that passes through point (x_1, y_1) and has slope m
    is $y - y_1 = m(x - x_1)$.

Example 3

Write an equation of a line that contains
the point $(-4, 3)$ and has slope $-\frac{2}{3}$.
Graph the line.

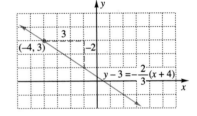

    Solution

    $x_1 = -4, y_1 = 3, m = -\frac{2}{3}$
    $y - 3 = -\frac{2}{3}(x - (-4))$
    $y - 3 = -\frac{2}{3}(x + 4)$

Try This

Write an equation of a line that contains the point $(2, -5)$ and has slope $\frac{4}{3}$.

Given coordinates of two points on a line, you can determine an equation of
the line by finding the slope of the line and using the point-slope form.

Example 4

Find an equation of a line that contains the points $(-3, 6)$ and $(1, 2)$.

    Solution

    $m = \frac{6 - 2}{-3 - 1} = -1$ *Definition of slope*
    $x_1 = 1, y_1 = 2$
    $y - 2 = -1(x - 1)$ *Substitute in point-slope form*

Try This

Find an equation of a line that contains the points $(5, -2)$ and $(0, 4)$.
Graph the line.

Class Exercises

Short Answer

State the slope and y-intercept of each line.

1. $y = 2x - 4$ **2.** $y = -\frac{3}{4}x + 10$ **3.** $y = 0.2x + 5$

4. $x = -7$ **5.** $x + y = -8$ **6.** $y = 4$

7. Does the line $y = \frac{1}{2}x$ contain the origin?

8. Does the line $y = \frac{3}{4}x - 5$ contain the origin?

Sample Exercises

9. Write an equation of a line that has slope $\frac{2}{3}$ and y-intercept -2.

10. Graph the equation of the line $y = \frac{3}{4}x - 5$.

11. Find the slope and y-intercept of the line $2y - x = 5$.

12. Find an equation of a line that contains the point $(1, -3)$ and has slope 2.

13. Find an equation of the line that contains the points $(0, -4)$ and $(6, 0)$.

Discussion

14. Explain how you can find an equation of a line that is perpendicular to the line $y = -2x + 3$ through the point $(1, 1)$.

15. Triangle ABC has vertices with coordinates $A(1, 2)$, $B(-2, 3)$, and $C(4, -7)$.
Explain how you can find an equation of the line containing the median $\overline{AM}$.

Exercises

A

Write the equation of each line in the form $y = mx + b$.

1. $m = 2$, $b = 3$ **2.** $m = -4$, $b = 5$ **3.** $m = -\frac{3}{4}$, $b = -\frac{1}{2}$

4. $m = -0.2$ **5.** $m = 0$ **6.** $m = 0$
     y-intercept $= -2.5$ y-intercept $= -2$ y-intercept $= 0$

Determine the slope and y-intercept of each line and graph the equation.

7. $y = x + 4$ **8.** $y = -2x - 3$ **9.** $y = -\frac{3}{2}x + 3$

10. $x = 5$ **11.** $y = -1$ **12.** $y = \frac{3}{2}x - 4$

13. $x + 2y = 4$ **14.** $y - 4 = -2x$ **15.** $5 - 3x = 2y$

Write an equation of each line given the slope and a point on the line.

16. $m = -3$, $P(-2, 1)$ **17.** $m = \frac{2}{3}$, $P(0, 0)$ **18.** $m = -\frac{1}{2}$, $P(4, 3)$

19. $m = 0$, $P(-2, -3)$ **20.** $m = \frac{3}{2}$, $P(-3, -4)$ **21.** $m = -\frac{5}{2}$, $P(0, 4)$

22. $m = 5$, $P(2, 4)$ **23.** $m = -2$, $P(0, 0)$ **24.** $m = 0$, $P(5, 0)$

Find an equation of the line that contains the given points.

25. $(0, 0)$, $(4, 3)$ **26.** $(-2, 1)$, $(5, -3)$ **27.** $(0, 0)$, $(-3, -3)$

28. $(5, 2)$, $(-3, 2)$ **29.** $(1, 3)$, $(-4, -2)$ **30.** $(-2, 4)$, $(4, -2)$

31. $(2, 4)$, $(-2, -4)$ **32.** $(0, 3)$, $(0, 9)$ **33.** $(4, 0)$, $(-2, 0)$

12-4 Equations of Lines   **549**

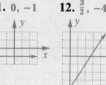

21. $y - 4 = -\frac{5}{2}x$

22. $y - 4 = 5(x - 2)$

23. $y = -2x$ **24.** $y = 0$

25. $y = \frac{3}{4}x$ or $y - 3 = \frac{3}{4}(x - 4)$

26. $y - 1 = -\frac{4}{7}(x + 2)$ or $y + 3 = -\frac{4}{7}(x - 5)$

27. $y = x$ or $y + 3 = x + 3$

28. $y - 2 = 0$ **29.** $y - 3 = x - 1$ or $y + 2 = x + 4$

30. $y - 4 = -(x + 2)$ or $y + 2 = -(x - 4)$

31. $y - 4 = 2(x - 2)$ or $y + 4 = 2(x + 2)$

32. $x = 0$ **33.** $y = 0$

34. a. 0.5 **b.** 0 **c.** The spring stretches another inch.

35. a. 0.1 **b.** $5.50

36. a. $y = 1.05x$ **b.** 1.05 **c.** yes   **37.** $\frac{1}{2}$ **38.** $-\frac{3}{4}$

39. $-\frac{3}{2}$ **40.** $\frac{5}{2}$

41. $y - 2 = \frac{1}{2}(x - 4)$

42. $y - 4 = \frac{3}{4}(x + 3)$

43. $y = -3x$ **44.** $y - 5 = -3(x + 1)$ **45.** $(4, 1)$

46. $y = \frac{3}{4}x - 3$ **47.** $\frac{25}{2}$

48. $y - 4 = \frac{5}{2}(x - 4)$ or $y + 1 = \frac{5}{2}(x - 2)$ **49.** $\overline{AC}$: $y + 4 = -2(x - 6)$ or $y - 2 = -2(x - 3)$; $\overline{BD}$: $y - 2 = 2(x - 6)$ or $y + 4 = 2(x - 3)$

50. $y + 2 = -(x - 6)$

51. $x = \frac{13}{4}$

B

34. Suppose for every ounce of weight added to a spring the spring stretches an additional 0.5 in. The relationship between the weight (x) and the length of the stretch (y) is given by the equation $y = 0.5x$.

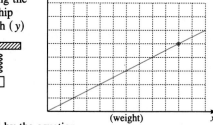

a. Find the slope of the line.

b. Find the y-intercept.

c. If the weight is doubled from 2 units to 4 units, how much is the spring stretched because of the additional weight?

35. Suppose the cost in dollars of a taxi is represented by the equation $C = 0.10d + 0.50$, where C is the cost of the taxi and d is the number of tenths of miles traveled.

a. Find the slope of the line.

b. Find the cost if the taxi travels 5 mi.

36. Suppose a gallon of gasoline costs $1.05.

a. Write an equation that represents the relationship between cost (y) and gallons (x).

b. Find the slope of the graph of the line.

c. Does the line contain the origin?

Find the slope of the line that is perpendicular to the given line.

37. $y = -2x + 3$ **38.** $y = \frac{4}{3}x + 6$

39. $2x - 3y = 6$ **40.** $12x + 30y = 18$

41. Find an equation of the line that contains the point $(4, 2)$ and is perpendicular to the line $y = -2x - 4$.

42. Consider a circle with center at the origin. Find an equation of the line that is tangent to the circle at the point $(-3, 4)$ on the circle.

43. The vertices of a triangle have coordinates $A(0, 0)$, $B(2, 4)$, and $C(-4, 2)$. Find an equation of the line that contains the altitude to $\overline{BC}$.

44. Find an equation of the line that contains the altitude $\overline{AD}$ of $\triangle ABC$ with vertices that have coordinates $A(-1, 5)$, $B(-7, -3)$, and $C(5, 1)$.

45. Find the point of intersection of the line $x - 3y = 1$ and the line containing the points $(1, 7)$ and $(6, -3)$.

46. If the x- and y-intercepts of a line are $(4, 0)$ and $(0, -3)$, find an equation of the line.

47. Find the area of a triangle formed by the x-axis, the y-axis, and the line $y = x - 5$.

48. Find an equation of the line that contains the median $\overline{AD}$ of $\triangle ABC$ with vertices that have coordinates $A(4, 4)$, $B(6, 2)$, and $C(-2, -4)$.

49. Find an equation of each of the lines that contain the diagonals of rectangle $ABCD$ with vertices that have coordinates $A(6, -4)$, $B(6, 2)$, $C(3, 2)$, and $D(3, -4)$.

50. Find an equation of the line that is the perpendicular bisector of the segment $\overline{AB}$ with endpoints that have coordinates $A(10, 2)$ and $B(2, -6)$.

51. If the line containing the points $E(x, 3)$ and $F(2, 0)$ is parallel to the line containing the points $D(2, 8)$ and $C(-3, -4)$, find x.

C

52. A diagonal of a square lies on the line $3x - 5y = 14$. One vertex is at $(0, 4)$. Find an equation of the line that contains the other diagonal.

53. The equations of two adjacent sides of a parallelogram are $x + 2y = 0$ and $3x + y + 3 = 0$. One vertex has coordinates $(8, -7)$. Find an equation of each of the lines that contain the other two sides of the parallelogram.

54. Find the distance between two parallel lines with equations $y = -1x + 10$ and $y = -1x + 15$.
    (HINT: Draw an accurate diagram.)

55. The coordinates of $\triangle ABC$ are $A(0, 0)$, $B(6, 0)$, and $C(4, 6)$. $\overline{AD}$ is an altitude to $\overline{BC}$. Find the coordinates of D.

56. The coordinates of the vertices of a triangle are $(0, 0)$, $(18, 0)$, and $(6, 12)$. Find the coordinates of the centroid.

Critical Thinking

57. Identify two variables that you think have some relationship, such as a person's height and weight or the number of "at bats" and the number of "hits" for a baseball player. Collect data and graph the ordered pairs.

   a. Draw a line that appears to most closely fit the data.
   b. Determine the slope and the y-intercept of the line.

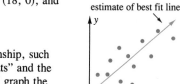
estimate of best fit line

Algebra Review

Simplify.

1. $\sqrt{27} + \sqrt{3}$ 2. $\sqrt{75} - \sqrt{12}$ 3. $\sqrt{108} + 3\sqrt{3}$

Quiz

Use the points $W(-3, 6)$, $X(5, -8)$, $Y(-3, 4)$, and $Z(-1, 5)$.

1. Point W is in quadrant __?__ and point X is in quadrant __?__ .
2. State the coordinates of the midpoint of $\overline{WZ}$.
3. State the coordinates of the midpoint of $\overline{YZ}$.
4. Find the slope of $\overleftrightarrow{WY}$.
5. Find the slope of the line that is perpendicular to $\overline{XZ}$.
6. Use the form $y = mx + b$ to write an equation of the line that passes through X and Y.

7. A line with slope $-\frac{1}{2}$ passes through the points $(4, -2)$ and $(6, y)$. Find y.
8. State the slope and y-intercept of the line $-3x + 4y = 12$. Graph the line.
9. Write an equation of the line that is parallel to the line $y = -5x + 3$ and contains the point $(2, -8)$.

---

52. $y - 4 = -\frac{5}{3}x$
53. $y + 7 = -\frac{1}{2}(x - 8)$ and $y + 7 = -3(x - 8)$
54. $\frac{5\sqrt{2}}{2}$ 55. $(5.4, 1.8)$
56. $(8, 4)$ 57. Answers may vary. (NOTE: See Fitting a Line to a Set of Data on p. 291.)

Algebra Review Answers

1. $4\sqrt{3}$ 2. $3\sqrt{3}$ 3. $9\sqrt{3}$

Quiz Answers

1. II, IV   2. $\left(-2, \frac{11}{2}\right)$
3. $\left(-2, \frac{9}{2}\right)$ 4. undefined
5. $\frac{6}{13}$ 6. $y = -\frac{3}{2}x - \frac{1}{2}$
7. $y = -3$ 8. $m = \frac{3}{4}, b = 3$
9. $y = -5x + 2$

First Five Minutes

(Quiz on previous lesson)

1. Find the slope and y-intercept of the line $2y - x = 5$.
$\frac{1}{2}, \frac{5}{2}$

2. Find the slope and y-intercept of the line $y - 4 = -2x$.
$-2, 4$

3. Find the slope and y-intercept of the line containing points $(-2, 4)$ and $(4, -2)$.
$-1, 2$

4. Find the equation of the line that contains the point $(4, 2)$ and is perpendicular to the line $y = -2x - 4$. $y = \frac{1}{2}x$

Lesson Opener

Before discussing the development of the distance formula, it might be helpful for students to review the definition of distance, absolute value, and the Ruler Postulate in Lesson 1-2. Tell students that finding the distance between two points is merely finding the length of the segment joining the two points. When a segment is either horizontal or vertical, find its length by simply counting the spaces from one endpoint to the other endpoint.

Point out that to find the distance or length of any nonvertical or nonhorizontal segment, draw a right triangle and then use the Pythagorean Theorem. Another method is to use the distance formula, which is derived from the Pythagorean Theorem.

Materials

student notebooks
grid paper
rulers
investigative software

USING THE DISTANCE FORMULA

OBJECTIVE: *Apply the distance formula.*

12-5 The Distance Formula

The distance formula, which you used in previous chapters to find the distance between two points in the coordinate plane, is restated and proved here as a theorem.

◆ **THEOREM 12.6** Distance Formula

The distance d between points $P_1(x_1, y_1)$ and $P_2(x_2, y_2)$ is given by the formula $d = \sqrt{(x_2 - x_1)^2 + (y_2 - y_1)^2}$.

Given: points $P_1(x_1, y_1)$ and $P_2(x_2, y_2)$

Prove: $P_1P_2 = \sqrt{(x_2 - x_1)^2 + (y_2 - y_1)^2}$

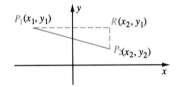

Proof Let R be the intersection of a line through P_1 parallel to the x-axis and a line through P_2 parallel to the y-axis. It follows that $\angle R$ is a right angle and that R has coordinates (x_2, y_1). $P_1R = |x_2 - x_1|$ and $P_2R = |y_2 - y_1|$ since the segments are parallel to the x- and y-axes, respectively. Since $\triangle P_1RP_2$ is a right triangle, by the Pythagorean Theorem $(P_1P_2)^2 = (P_1R)^2 + (P_2R)^2$. Substitution and algebra result in the following equations.

$$(P_1P_2)^2 = (|x_2 - x_1|)^2 + (|y_2 - y_1|)^2$$
$$(P_1P_2)^2 = (x_2 - x_1)^2 + (y_2 - y_1)^2$$
$$P_1P_2 = \sqrt{(x_2 - x_1)^2 + (y_2 - y_1)^2}$$

Example 1
Find the distance between $A(2, 3)$ and $B(-3, -2)$.

Solution
$$AB = \sqrt{(-3 - 2)^2 + (-2 - 3)^2} \quad \textit{Distance Formula}$$
$$AB = \sqrt{25 + 25} = \sqrt{50}$$
$$AB = 5\sqrt{2}$$

Try This
Find the distance between $C(-1, 6)$ and $D(8, -2)$.

552   *Chapter 12   Coordinate Geometry*

Given the coordinates of the vertices of a triangle, you can use the distance formula to classify the triangle as scalene, isosceles, or equilateral.

Example 2

Determine whether $\triangle ABC$ is scalene, isosceles, or equilateral.

Solution

$AB = \sqrt{(8 - (-2))^2 + (7 - 0)^2} = \sqrt{149}$ *Distance*

$BC = \sqrt{(0)^2 + (7 - (-5))^2} = \sqrt{144}$ *Formula*

$AC = \sqrt{(8 - (-2))^2 + (-5 - 0)^2} = \sqrt{125}$

$\triangle ABC$ is scalene.   *Definition of scalene triangle*

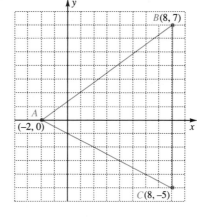

Try This

Determine whether $\triangle ABC$ with vertices $A(-2, 5)$, $B(1, -1)$, and $C(4, 2)$ is scalene, isosceles, or equilateral.

Class Exercises

Short Answer

1. Find the length of $\overline{AB}$ if A has coordinates $(6, -3)$ and B has coordinates $(-1, -3)$.
2. Find the length of $\overline{CD}$ if C has coordinates $(-2, -4)$ and D has coordinates $(-2, -1)$.
3. Find the distance between the points $(0, 0)$ and $(3, 4)$.
4. Does the segment from point $(2, 2)$ to point $(3, 4)$ have the same length as the segment from point $(0, 0)$ to point $(1, 1)$?
5. Does the segment from point $(0, 0)$ to point $(3, 4)$ have the same length as the segment from point $(0, 0)$ to point $(-3, -4)$?
6. Given the coordinates of the vertices of a triangle, how many times must you apply the distance formula to find the perimeter of the triangle?

Sample Exercises

Find the distance between the given points.

7. $(6, -1)$, $(-2, -1)$ 8. $(-1, 4)$, $(-6, 2)$

9. Determine whether $\triangle ABC$ with vertices $A(6, 1)$, $B(-2, -3)$, and $C(0, 3)$ is scalene, isosceles, or equilateral.
10. Given the points $A(-4, 13)$, $B(-2, 7)$, and $C(2, -5)$, use the distance formula to determine if B is between A and C.
    (HINT: If B is between A and C, then $AB + BC = AC$.)

Discussion

11. Consider triangle ABC with vertices $A(-1, -6)$, $B(5, 2)$, and $C(-3, -2)$. Use the distance formula to answer the following questions.
    a. Why is the triangle a right triangle?   **b.** Which sides are the legs?
    c. Is the triangle an isosceles right triangle?   **d.** What is the area of $\triangle ABC$?

12-5   The Distance Formula   **553**

Exercises

A

Find the distance between the given points.

1. $(-4, 5)$, $(6, 5)$ **2.** $(3, 2)$, $(3, -8)$ **3.** $(4, 5)$, $(-3, -2)$ **4.** $(-2, 5)$, $(5, -2)$
5. $(4, 0)$, $(0, -6)$ **6.** $(1, 2)$, $(-7, 3)$ **7.** $(-5, 3)$, $(0, -4)$ **8.** $(6, -2)$, $(7, 3)$

Determine whether $\triangle ABC$ is scalene, isosceles, or equilateral.

9. $A(4, 5)$, $B(5, -2)$, $C(1, 1)$ **10.** $A(-6, 2)$, $B(1, 7)$, $C(6, 3)$
11. $A(10, -5)$, $B(-2, 1)$, $C(7, 4)$ **12.** $A(1, 1)$, $B(-3, 5)$, $C(\frac{2}{3} - 1, \frac{2}{3} + 3)$

Use the distance formula to determine if the triangle is a right triangle.

13. $A(1, 4)$, $B(-2, -2)$, $C(10, -8)$ **14.** $A(5, 7)$, $B(8, -5)$, $C(-4, -4)$

15. Is it easier to use the definition of slope or the distance formula to determine whether a triangle is a right triangle?

Use the distance formula to determine if B is between A and C.
(HINT: If B is between A and C, then $AB + BC = AC$.)

16. $A(-3, -3)$, $B(0, -2)$, $C(6, 8)$ **17.** $A(1, -2)$, $B(4, 3)$, $C(10, 12)$

18. Is it easier to use the definition of slope or the distance formula to determine if three points are collinear?

B

19. Graph and label at least four points that satisfy the condition that the distance from the point $(1, 2)$ is 5 units.
20. Given $\triangle ABC$ with vertices $A(2, 6)$, $B(3, -5)$, and $C(-1, 7)$, find the length of the median $\overline{AD}$.
21. Given a trapezoid with vertices at points $(4, 0)$, $(8, 0)$, $(0, 2)$, and $(0, 4)$, find the length of the median. (HINT: Graph the trapezoid and determine which segment is the median.)
22. The distance between the points $(1, 2)$ and $(x, 8)$ is 10. Find x.
23. Given isosceles $\triangle ABC$ with $AC = BC$ and vertices with coordinates $A(-1, 4)$, $B(-3, -2)$, and $C(x, -1)$, find x.
24. Rectangle $ABCD$ has vertices $A(0, 0)$, $B(2, 1)$, $C(4, -3)$, and $D(2, -4)$ and is inscribed in a circle. Find the length of the diameter of the circle.
25. Find the length of the diameter of the circle circumscribed about a right triangle with vertices $(8, 0)$, $(5, 2)$, and $(2, -9)$.
26. Find the area of a $\triangle ABC$ with coordinates $A(3, 4)$, $B(-3, -5)$, and $C(6, 2)$.
27. Find the area of $\triangle ABC$ with vertices $A(-3, -4)$, $B(3, 4)$, and $C(-5, 0)$.
28. Find the area of $ABCD$ with vertices $A(-2, 3)$, $B(3, 8)$, $C(8, 3)$ and $D(3, 2)$.
29. Assign a coordinate system for a baseball diamond and a point A in the field as follows: $C(0, 0)$, $D(90, 0)$, $E(90, 90)$, $A(280, 20)$, $B(0, 90)$. If a right fielder throws the baseball from point A to third base (point B), how far does the ball travel?
30. If a baseball player picks up the ball halfway between second base (point E) and third base (point B) and throws the ball to first base (point D), how far has the ball been thrown?

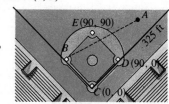

31. In a championship high school soccer match, the winning goal was kicked by Maya from a point 10 yd behind the midfield strip and 5 yd from the sideline. How far was Maya from the center of the goal when she kicked the winning goal?

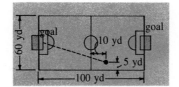

32. In a championship high school basketball game, Vonetta made the winning shot from a point even with the foul line and 10 ft to the side of the foul line. How far was she from the basket?

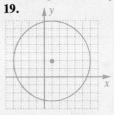

c

33. Find the coordinates of the point equidistant from the points $(3, 11)$, $(9, 5)$, and $(7, -1)$.

34. Find the coordinates of the point that is equidistant from the points $(0, 6)$ and $(10, 0)$ and lies on the line $y = x$.

35. Given $\triangle ABC$ with vertices $A(5, 2)$, $B(1, 5)$, and $C(-1, 1)$, find the length of the altitude $\overline{AD}$.

36. Consider a three-dimensional coordinate system with an x-axis, a y-axis, and a z-axis. A cube with each edge 4 units is placed as shown in the figure to the right.
  a. Find the length of $\overline{OP}$.
  b. Find a formula for the length of the diagonal $\overline{OP}$ in a cube with one vertex at the origin and edges on the x- and y-axes.
  (HINT: Let P have coordinates (x_1, y_1, z_1).)

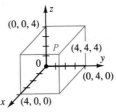

Critical Thinking

37. You can estimate the distance between points $A(x_1, y_1)$ and $B(x_2, y_2)$ by using the following formula.

$$d = \text{maximum}(|x_1 - x_2|, |y_1 - y_2|) + \tfrac{1}{3}\text{minimum}(|x_1 - x_2|, |y_1 - y_2|)$$

Use the distance formula and the formula for estimating distance between points, given above, to calculate the lengths of several segments. On the basis of these trials, what would be the greatest percent of error one could expect using the estimate formula?

Mixed Review

$\overline{AC}$ is a secant. $\overline{AD}$ is a tangent. $m\widehat{BC} = 100$, $m\angle CBD = 100$, $m\widehat{BD} = 60$

1. Find $m\angle ABD$.
2. Find $m\angle BCD$.
3. Find $m\angle CAD$.
4. Find $m\angle EDC$.

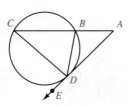

12-5 The Distance Formula **555**

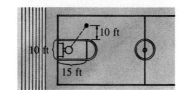

Connections

Exercise Answers

1. With 0 h of training an average of 18 h were lost from the job due to machine-related accidents.　**2.** About 12 h
3. With 0 h spent studying, the average grade was 45. For every increase of 1 h in study time, the average increase in test score was 3.5. In theory, about 15.7 h of studying would result in a score of 100.

CONNECTIONS

Coordinate Geometry and Statistics

The equation of a line is often used in statistics to explain the behavior of the values of one variable in terms of the values of another variable. Consider the graph below. The equation of the line is $y = -1.5x + 18$.

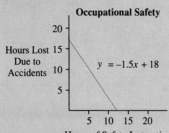

Occupational Safety

Hours Lost Due to Accidents

$y = -1.5x + 18$

Hours of Safety Instruction

This equation results from finding a "line of best fit" for the data shown on the graph. This line is called the **linear regression line.** The horizontal axis relates the number of hours spent in safety training prior to using a machine in the factory. The value of y represents the number of hours lost from the job due to machine-related accidents in the first year on the job.

The value of the slope of the regression line tells us that for every increase of 1 h in training, the average decrease in hours lost due to an accident related to the training area is 1.5 h, or 1 h and 30 min.

Exercises

Refer to the graph above.

1. What is the significance of the y-intercept of 18?
2. How much training, at least in theory, would result in the elimination of the accidents targeted by the training program?
3. Refer to the graph below. Write a short paragraph telling what this equation tells about the relationship between number of hours spent studying geometry and grades on a test on coordinate geometry.

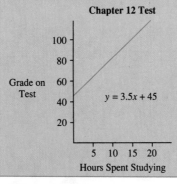

Chapter 12 Test

Grade on Test

$y = 3.5x + 45$

Hours Spent Studying

OBJECTIVE: *Given the equation of a circle, determine the center and radius of the circle and vice versa.*

12-6 The Equation of a Circle

In Chapter 8, the definition of a circle was given as the set of all points in a plane a given distance from a fixed point called the center. A circle can be represented in various ways in the coordinate plane. One way to develop an equation of a circle is by using the distance formula, as demonstrated below.

An equation of a circle can be used to graph a circle on a computer screen.

Consider the circle to the right with center at the origin and a radius of 5 units.

Using the distance formula you obtain the following.
$$5 = \sqrt{(x - 0)^2 + (y - 0)^2} \quad \text{or} \quad x^2 + y^2 = 5^2$$

If r units is used for the radius rather than 5 units, you have the following equation of a circle with center at the origin and a radius of r units.
$$x^2 + y^2 = r^2$$

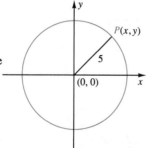

Now consider the circle to the right, which also has a radius of 5 units but has its center at $(-2, 3)$ rather than at the origin. The distance formula is used to find the distance between the point $(-2, 3)$ and the general point $P(x, y)$ in developing the following equation.
$$5 = \sqrt{(x - (-2))^2 + (y - (3))^2} \quad \text{or}$$
$$(x - (-2))^2 + (y - (3))^2 = 5^2$$

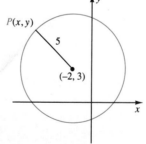

The development presented above leads to the following theorem, which gives an equation of a circle that has its center at (h, k) and radius r units.

◆ THEOREM 12.7

An equation of the circle with center (h, k) and radius r is
$(x - h)^2 + (y - k)^2 = r^2$.

12-6   *The Equation of a Circle*   **557**

Point out that since the converse of Theorem 12.6 is true, students can easily find the center and radius of a circle, given the equation. But it may be necessary to rewrite the given equation in the appropriate form. (See Example 2.)

HINT: All points whose coordinates satisfy the equation $(x - h)^2 + (y - k)^2 = r^2$ $(r > 0)$ lie on the circle with center (h, k) and radius r. All points whose coordinates satisfy the inequality $(x - h)^2 + (y - k)^2 > r^2$ $(r > 0)$ lie outside the circle with center (h, k) and radius r. All points whose coordinates satisfy the inequality $(x - h)^2 + (y - k)^2 < r^2$ $(r > 0)$ lie inside the circle with center (h, k) and radius r.

Guided Practice

Chalkboard Examples

1. Find the equation of a circle with center $(-5, 5)$ and radius $\sqrt{6}$. Find the equation of a circle with center $(0, 0)$ and radius $2\sqrt{3}$. $(x + 5)^2 + (y - 5)^2 = 6$, $x^2 + y^2 = 12$

Answer to **Try This**
$(x - 4)^2 + (y + 1)^2 = 16$

2. Find the center and radius of the circle whose equation is $x^2 + y^2 = 121$. Find the center and radius of the circle whose equation is $(x + 11)^2 + (y - 5)^2 = 8$. $(0, 0), 11; (-11, 5), 2\sqrt{2}$

Answer to **Try This** $(-3, 7), 5\sqrt{2}$

Example 1

Write an equation of the circle with center $(3, -2)$ and radius 6.

    Solution

    $(x - h)^2 + (y - k)^2 = r^2$ *Theorem 12.6*

    $(x - 3)^2 + (y - (-2))^2 = 6^2$ *Substitution*

    $(x - 3)^2 + (y + 2)^2 = 36$

Try This

Write an equation of the circle with center $(4, -1)$ and radius 4.

Example 2

Find the center and radius of the circle. $(x - 2)^2 + (y + 6)^2 = 20$

    Solution

    $(x - 2)^2 + (y - (-6))^2 = (\sqrt{20})^2$ *Rewrite in standard form.*

    The circle has center $(2, -6)$, radius $\sqrt{20}$ or $2\sqrt{5}$.   *Theorem 12.6*

Try This

Find the center and radius of the circle. $(x + 3)^2 + (y - 7)^2 = 50$

Class Exercises

Short Answer

Find the center and radius for each circle.

1. $x^2 + y^2 = 100$
2. $(x - 2)^2 + (y - 4)^2 = 81$
3. $(x - 1)^2 + (y + 1)^2 = 16$
4. $(x + 3)^2 + y^2 = 72$
5. $x^2 + (y + 2)^2 = 18$
6. $(x + 6)^2 + (y - (-4))^2 = 40$

Sample Exercises

Write an equation of the circle with the given center and radius.

7. $(0, 0); 6$ 8. $(-2, 3); \sqrt{12}$ 9. $(-3, 0); 3\sqrt{5}$

Sketch the graph of each circle.

10. $(x - 3)^2 + y^2 = 1$ 11. $(x + 2)^2 + (y - 1)^2 = 4$

12. For what value of r does the circle $(x - 3)^2 + (y + 4)^2 = r^2$ contain the origin?

Discussion

13. Consider a circle tangent to the x- and y-axes with radius 4 units.
    a. Explain why there is more than one such possible circle.
    b. Sketch each possible circle on the same coordinate system.
    c. Write an equation for each of the possible circles.

Exercises

A

Write an equation of each circle with the given center and radius.

1. $(0, 0)$; 5   **2.** $(0, 2)$; 3   **3.** $(-5, 0)$; 4
4. $(2, 3)$; 6   **5.** $(-3, -4)$; 4   **6.** $(-3, 5)$; 2
7. $(-1, 3)$; $2\sqrt{3}$ **8.** $(3, -6)$; $\sqrt{10}$ **9.** (a, b); c

Find the center and radius of each circle.

10. $x^2 + y^2 = 25$ **11.** $x^2 + y^2 = 20$
12. $x^2 + (y - 3)^2 = 12$ **13.** $(x + 6)^2 + y^2 = 45$
14. $(x + 4)^2 + (y - 2)^2 = 10$ **15.** $(x - a)^2 + (y - b)^2 = 36$

16. Sketch the graph of $(x - 2)^2 + (y + 1)^2 = 9$.
17. Sketch the graph of $(x + 1)^2 + y^2 = 4$.
18. For what value of r does the circle $(x + 5)^2 + (y - 12)^2 = r^2$ contain the origin?

B

19. Write an equation of the circle with center $(-4, 0)$ that contains the origin.
20. Write an equation of the circle with center $(3, 4)$ that contains the origin.
21. Write an equation of the circle with center $(4, -2)$ that contains the point $(0, 5)$.
22. Write an equation of the circle with center $(-2, 3)$ that contains the point $(3, 3)$.

Write an equation of each circle given the endpoints of a diameter.

23. $(-4, 0)$ and $(2, 0)$ **24.** $(3, 6)$ and $(3, -2)$ **25.** $(3, 6)$ and $(-5, 6)$

26. Write an equation of the line that is tangent to the circle $x^2 + y^2 = 25$ at the point $(-3, 4)$.
27. Write an equation of the line that contains the centers of the circles $(x + 4)^2 + (y - 2)^2 = 36$ and $(x - 5)^2 + (y + 3)^2 = 17$.
28. Write an equation of the circle with center at $(-5, -5)$ and tangent to both the x-axis and the y-axis.
29. Write an equation of a circle that has the same center as the circle $(x + 4)^2 + (y - 3)^2 = 9$ and is tangent to the y-axis.

Given the circle $x^2 + y^2 = 49$, determine if each line is a tangent to the circle, secant to the circle, or neither.

30. $x = 5$ **31.** $y = 9$ **32.** $x = -7$ **33.** $y = x$

Given the circle $(x + 4)^2 + (y - 3)^2 = 25$, determine if each line is tangent to the circle, secant to the circle, or neither.

34. $y = -2$ **35.** $y = -x$ **36.** $x = 1$ **37.** $y = 9$

38. A circle with radius of 2 units is tangent to the x-axis at the point $(6, 0)$. Is there more than one circle that satisfies these conditions? Write an equation for each possible circle.

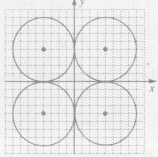
Assignment Guide

Minimum: 1–40 e/o, 47, MR
Regular: 1–46 e/o, 47, MR
Advanced: 16–40 e/o, 41–47, MR

Algebra
Class Exercises 7–9, 12
Exercises 1–9, 19–46

Lesson Closure

Summarize the lesson by asking students to state the following:

1. distance formula
$$\sqrt{(x_2 - x_1)^2 + (y_2 - y_1)^2}$$

2. equation of a circle with center at the origin and radius r
$$x^2 + y^2 = r^2$$

3. equation of a circle with center (h, k) and radius r
$$(x - h)^2 + (y - k)^2 = r^2$$

Teacher's Resource
Materials

Enrichment Using
  Manipulatives 74
Practice Master 87
Technology: Calculator 18

Exercise Answers

See Selected Answers for
odd-numbered exercises.

2. $x^2 + (y - 2)^2 = 9$

4. $(x - 2)^2 + (y - 3)^2 = 36$

6. $(x + 3)^2 + (y - 5)^2 = 4$

8. $(x - 3)^2 + (y + 6)^2 = 10$

10. $(0, 0), 5$ **12.** $(0, 3),$
$2\sqrt{3}$ **14.** $(-4, 2), \sqrt{10}$

16.

18. 13 **20.** $(x - 3)^2 +$
$(y - 4)^2 = 25$

22. $(x + 2)^2 + (y - 3)^2 = 25$

24. $(x - 3)^2 + (y - 2)^2 = 16$

26. $y - 4 = \frac{3}{4}(x + 3)$ or
$3x - 4y + 25 = 0$

28. $(x + 5)^2 + (y + 5)^2 = 25$

30. secant   **32.** tangent

34. tangent   **36.** tangent

38. Yes: $(x - 6)^2 + (y - 2)^2 =$
4, and $(x - 6)^2 + (y + 2)^2 = 4$

40. $(x + 5)^2 + (y + 10)^2 =$
125 **42.** $(x - 4)^2 +$
$(y - 2)^2 = 32$ **44.** 4

46. $(x - 1)^2 + (y - 3)^2 +$
$(z - 2)^2 = 35$

Mixed Review Answers

1. 7900 sq yd   **2.** 576π m²

Quiz Answers

1. false   **2.** true   **3.** false

4. true   **5.** true

6. $(x + 3)^2 + (y - 5)^2 = 28$

7. $x^2 + (y + 1)^2 = 9$

---

39. Suppose the intersection of the circles shown is the origin and each circle has diameter 8 cm. Write an equation of each of the four circles.

40. Write an equation of the circle that contains the points $(-10, 0)$, $(0, 0)$, and $(0, -20)$.

C

41. Find the area of the ring formed by the concentric circles defined by the equations $(x - 2)^2 + (y + 6)^2 = 25$ and $(x - 2)^2 + (y + 6)^2 = 36$.

42. Find an equation of the circle that has its center on the line $y = \frac{1}{2}x$ and contains the points $(0, 6)$ and $(0, -2)$.

43. Write an equation of the circle with center at $(1, 7)$ and tangent to the line $x + 3y = 12$.

44. Find the length of a tangent segment from the point $(6, 4)$ to the circle $x^2 + y^2 = 36$.

45. Suppose a sphere with center at $(0, 0, 0)$ contains the point $P(4, 4, 4)$ in a three-dimensional coordinate system. Write an equation that represents the sphere.

46. Write an equation of a sphere that has its center at $(1, 3, 2)$ and contains the point $(4, -2, 3)$.

Critical Thinking

47. In the equation of the circle $x^2 + y^2 = 16$ the coefficients of x^2 and y^2 are 1. Suppose the coefficients are not 1. Sketch the following equations. Conjecture the effects if the coefficients are not 1.

a. $x^2 + 2y^2 = 16$ **b.** $2x^2 + y^2 = 16$

c. $x^2 + 4y^2 = 16$ **d.** $4x^2 + y^2 = 16$

(HINT: Determine the points at which the curves cross the *x*- and *y*-axes.)

Mixed Review

1. Find the area of a rectangular field whose length is 100 yd and width is 79 yd.

2. Find the area of a circular pond with a diameter of 48 m.

Quiz

Determine whether each statement is true or false.

1. If $R(-3, 6)$ and $S(4, 2)$, then $RS = \sqrt{17}$.

2. If $A(4, -3)$ and $B(-2, -1)$, then $AB = 2\sqrt{10}$.

3. The circle with equation $(x - 4)^2 + (y + 3)^2 = 9$ has its center at $(-4, 3)$.

4. The length of the radius of the circle $(x - 2)^2 + y^2 = 16$ is 4.

5. The line $y = 5$ is tangent to the circle $x^2 + y^2 = 25$.

Write the equation of each circle with the given center and radius.

6. center $(-3, 5)$, radius $2\sqrt{7}$ **7.** center $(0, -1)$, radius 3

COORDINATE PROOFS

OBJECTIVE: *Choose an appropriate placement of a figure on a coordinate system for proving theorems.*

12-7 Organizing Proofs

In geometry, statements and theorems can be proved using a variety of methods. Some theorems can be easily proved using coordinates. An important part of a coordinate proof is choosing the coordinates of the figure. Consider the following theorem.

The diagonals of a rectangle are congruent.

Note the placement of the figure below used in the coordinate proof of the theorem.

Given: *RSTV* is a rectangle.

Prove: $TR = VS$

Proof Let $R(0, 0)$, $S(a, 0)$, and $V(0, b)$ be the coordinates of three vertices of the rectangle. The coordinates of T will be (a, b). From the distance formula you obtain the following.

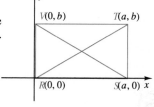

$$VS = \sqrt{(0 - a)^2 + (b - 0)^2} = \sqrt{a^2 + b^2}$$
$$TR = \sqrt{(a - 0)^2 + (b - 0)^2} = \sqrt{a^2 + b^2}$$

Therefore, $VS = TR$ and the diagonals of a rectangle are congruent.

A second possible placement for the rectangle is shown to the right, with $R(-a, 0)$, $S(a, 0)$, $T(a, b)$, and $V(-a, b)$ as coordinates of the vertices of the rectangle. In this case from the distance formula you obtain

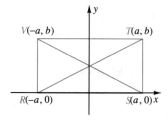

$$VS = \sqrt{(-a - a)^2 + (b - 0)^2} = \sqrt{4a^2 + b^2}$$
$$TR = \sqrt{(a - (-a))^2 + (b - 0)^2} = \sqrt{4a^2 + b^2}$$

Therefore, $VS = TR$ and, again, the diagonals of a rectangle are congruent.

In most cases a theorem can be proved by positioning the figure in any of several ways. Consider the following theorem.

The median to the base of an isosceles triangle is perpendicular to the base.

In proving this theorem, let $\triangle RTS$ be an isosceles triangle with $RT = TS$ and median $\overline{TV}$. Consider the two different positions presented for proving that median $\overline{TV}$ is perpendicular to the base of $\triangle RTS$.

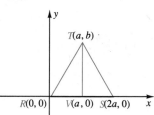

In the placement on the left $\overline{RS}$ is on the *x*-axis so that R has coordinates $(0, 0)$ and S has coordinates $(2a, 0)$. Since $RT = TS$, you can assign T the coordinates (a, b). Since $\overline{TV}$ is a median, V has coordinates $(a, 0)$. It follows that $\overline{TV}$ is a vertical line and hence it is perpendicular to $\overline{RS}$.

First Five Minutes

(Quiz on previous lesson)

1. What is the equation of a circle with center (0, 0) and radius 4? $x^2 + y^2 = 16$

2. What is the equation of a circle with center $(-4, 2)$ and radius $\sqrt{10}$?
$(x + 4)^2 + (y - 2)^2 = 10$

3. Find the center and radius of the circle $(x - 2)^2 + (y + 1)^2 = 9$. $(2, -1), 3$

4. Write an equation of a circle with center $(-2, 3)$ that contains the point (3, 3).
$(x + 2)^2 + (y - 3)^2 = 25$

Lesson Opener

The last two sections of this chapter are about coordinate proofs, that is, proving theorems using coordinate geometry. Some students may find that a coordinate proof is easier than the two-column proof, especially if their algebraic skills are good.

NOTE: Do not assume more than what is given in the hypothesis of the theorem. For example, if the hypothesis is about a triangle, do not assume the triangle to be right, isosceles, equilateral, etc., unless indicated.

Materials

student notebooks
grid paper

Teaching Notes

Emphasize that the placement of a geometric figure in a coordinate plane is an important step in the planning of a coordinate proof.

Listed below is one set of coordinates for some basic geometric figures.

Scalene triangle: $A(0, 0)$, $B(a, 0)$, $C(b, c)$

Isosceles triangle with vertex C and base $\overline{AB}$: $A(0, 0)$, $B(2a, 0)$, $C(a, b)$

Equilateral triangle: $A(0, 0)$, $B(2a, 0)$, $C(a, a\sqrt{3})$

Right triangle with legs $\overline{AB}$ and $\overline{AC}$, and hypotenuse $\overline{BC}$: $A(0, 0)$, $B(a, 0)$, $C(0, b)$

$30°-60°-90°$ triangle with legs $\overline{AC}$ and $\overline{AB}$, and hypotenuse $\overline{BC}$: $A(0, 0)$, $B(a, 0)$, $C(0, a\sqrt{3})$

$45°-45°-90°$ triangle with legs $\overline{AC}$ and $\overline{AB}$, and hypotenuse $\overline{BC}$, $m\angle B = m\angle C = 45$: $A(0, 0)$, $B(a, 0)$, $C(0, a)$

Quadrilateral: $A(0, 0)$, $B(a, 0)$, $C(b, c)$, $D(d, f)$

Parallelogram: $A(0, 0)$, $B(a, 0)$, $C(a+b, c)$, $D(b, c)$

Rectangle: $A(0, 0)$, $B(a, 0)$, $C(a, b)$, $D(0, b)$

Square: $A(0, 0)$, $B(a, 0)$, $C(a, a)$, $D(0, a)$

Trapezoid: $A(0, 0)$, $B(a, 0)$, $C(b, c)$, $D(f, c)$ (NOTE: $b \neq f$, $b \neq a + f$)

Isosceles trapezoid: $A(0, 0)$, $B(a, 0)$, $C(a-b, c)$, $D(b, c)$

In the second possible placement, shown on the right, $\overline{TS}$ is placed on the x-axis and $\overline{TR}$ is placed on the y-axis, with the coordinates indicated. Since $\overline{TV}$ is a median, V has coordinates (a, a). To prove the theorem with this placement, you must show that the product of the slope of $\overline{TV}$ and the slope of $\overline{RS}$ is -1.

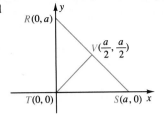

Example 1

$\triangle ABC$ is an equilateral triangle with coordinates $A(0, 0)$ and $B(2a, 0)$. Determine the coordinates of C without introducing any new letters.

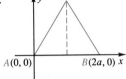

Solution

x-coordinate of $C = a$ $\frac{1}{2}$ *the length of* $\overline{AB}$
y-coordinate of $C = a\sqrt{3}$ *Altitude of equilateral* $\triangle$ *is* $a\sqrt{3}$.
C has coordinates $(a, a\sqrt{3})$.

Try This

Determine the coordinates of C for coordinates $B(a, 0)$ and $A(0, 0)$.

Example 2

Set up a coordinate system to prove the following statement.
The medians to the congruent sides of an isosceles triangle are congruent.

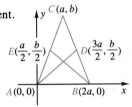

Solution

Given: isosceles $\triangle ABC$, $AC = BC$
       $\overline{BE}$ and $\overline{AD}$ are medians.
Prove: $BF = AD$

Try This

Set up a coordinate system to prove the following statement.
The medians to any two sides of an equilateral triangle are congruent.

Class Exercises

Short Answer

Supply the missing coordinates.

1. *ABCD* is a square.

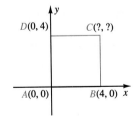

2. *ABCD* is a rectangle.

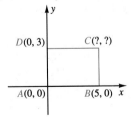

3. *ABCD* is a rhombus.

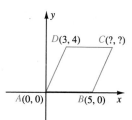

4. △*ABC* is isosceles.

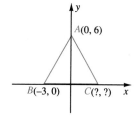

5. *ABCD* is a parallelogram.

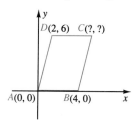

6. *ABCD* is an isosceles trapezoid.

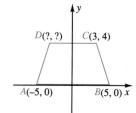

Sample Exercises

Supply the missing coordinates without introducing any new letters.

7. *CDEF* is a parallelogram.

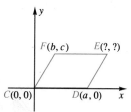

8. △*RST* is an isosceles triangle.

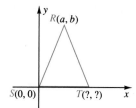

Set up a coordinate system that could be used to prove each statement.

9. The diagonals of a square are congruent.

10. The opposite sides of a parallelogram are congruent.

Discussion

11. Which placement below is better for proving the following statement.
The diagonals of an isosceles trapezoid are congruent? Justify your choice.

a.

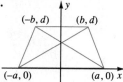

b.

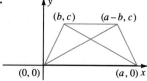

Chalkboard Examples

1. Supply the missing coordinates of the parallelogram without introducing any new letters.
$(a + b, c)$

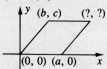

Answer to **Try This** $\left(\frac{a}{2}, \frac{a\sqrt{3}}{2}\right)$

2. Set up a coordinate system to prove the following statement. The two nonparallel sides of an isosceles trapezoid are congruent.

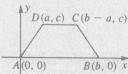

Answer to **Try This**

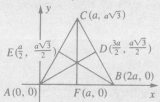

Class Exercise Answers

1. $(4, 4)$ **2.** $(5, 3)$
3. $(8, 4)$ **4.** $(3, 0)$
5. $(6, 6)$ **6.** $(-3, 4)$
7. $(b + a, c)$ **8.** $(2a, 0)$
9.

10.

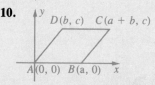

11. Computing is easier with *a*.

Assignment Guide
Minimum: 1–13 e/o, 16, AR
Regular: 1–15 e/o, 16, AR
Advanced: 3–13 e/o, 14–16, AR
Algebra
Class Exercises 7–11
Exercises 1, 2, 8–15, AR

Lesson Closure

Review the steps for setting up
coordinate proofs.

Teacher's Resource Material

Enrichment Using
   Manipulatives 75
Practice Master 88
Technology: Calculator 19

Exercise Answers

1. $C(p + m, n)$
2. $V(b - a, c)$
3.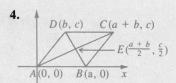
4.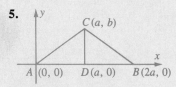
5.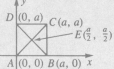
6.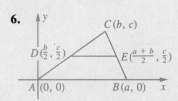

Exercises

A

Supply the missing coordinates for each figure without introducing any new letters.

1. *ABCD* is a rhombus.

2. *RSTV* is a parallelogram.

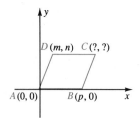

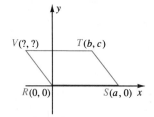

Set up a coordinate system that could be used to prove each statement.

3. The diagonals of a square bisect each other.

4. The diagonals of a parallelogram bisect each other.

5. The altitude of an isosceles triangle bisects the base.

6. The segment joining the midpoints of two sides of a triangle is one half
   the length of the third side.

7. The diagonals of a rhombus are perpendicular.

B

Supply the missing coordinates for each figure without introducing any new letters.

8. *ABCD* is a rhombus.

9. △*ABC* is an equilateral triangle.

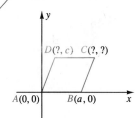

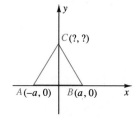

10. *KLMN* is a parallelogram.

11. △*DEF* is an isosceles triangle with base $\overline{DF}$.

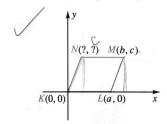

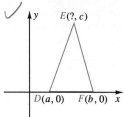

564   *Chapter 12   Coordinate Geometry*

12. Consider quadrilateral *ABCD* with coordinates shown to the right. Determine the coordinates of the midpoints *E*, *F*, *G*, and *H* of sides $\overline{AB}$, $\overline{BC}$, $\overline{CD}$, and $\overline{DA}$, respectively.

13. Use the distance formula to show that $GF = HE$ and $HG = EF$.
Is *EFGH* a parallelogram? Why or why not?

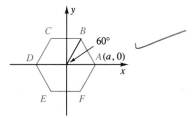

C

14. *ABCDEFGH* is a regular octagon with coordinates for *A* as shown. Determine the coordinates for points *B*, *E*, and *F*. Show that $\overline{AB} \parallel \overline{EF}$.

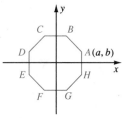

15. *ABCDEF* is a regular hexagon with coordinates for *A* as shown. Determine the coordinates for *B*, *D*, and *E* and show that $\overline{AB} \parallel \overline{DE}$.

Critical Thinking

16. Kelly, Maria, and Yoshie were trying to prove the following theorem. If *M* is the midpoint of side $\overline{AB}$ of equilateral triangle *ABC*, then the sum of the distances from *M* to sides $\overline{AC}$ and $\overline{BC}$ is equal to the length of the altitude.

Each student used a different placement of the triangle, as shown below.

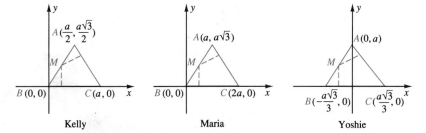

Kelly   Maria   Yoshie

Which placement makes the proof the easiest? Explain your choice.

Algebra Review

Simplify.

1. $\frac{3a^2}{4a^6}$ **2.** $(3x^2)^2$ **3.** $\frac{-6a^2b^3}{2ab^2}$

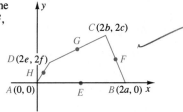

7.

8. $C(\sqrt{a^2 - c^2} + a, c),$
$D(\sqrt{a^2 - c^2}, c)$

9. $C(0, \sqrt{3}a)$ **10.** $N(b - a, c)$

11. $E\left(\frac{a + b}{2}, c\right)$

12. $E(a, 0)$, $F(a + b, c)$,
$G(b + e, c + f)$, $H(e, f)$

13. $GF =$
$\sqrt{(b + e - (a + b))^2 + (c + f - c)^2} =$
$\sqrt{(e - a)^2 + f^2}$; $HE =$
$\sqrt{(e - a)^2 + (f - 0)^2} =$
$\sqrt{(e - a)^2 + f^2}$ so $GE = HE$;
$HG = \sqrt{(b + e - e)^2 + (c + f - f)^2} =$
$\sqrt{b^2 + c^2}$, $EF =$
$\sqrt{(a + b - a)^2 + (c - 0)^2} =$
$\sqrt{b^2 + c^2}$ so $HG = EF$. *EFGH* is
a ▱ because opp. sides are ≅.

14. $B(b, a)$, $E(-a, -b)$,
$F(-b, -a)$, slope of $\overline{AB} =$
$\frac{b - a}{a - b} = -1$; slope of $\overline{EF} =$
$\frac{-a + b}{-b + a} = -1$, so $\overline{AB} \parallel \overline{EF}$.

15. $B\left(\frac{a}{2}, \frac{\sqrt{3}a}{2}\right)$, $D(-a, 0)$,

$E\left(-\frac{a}{2}, -\frac{\sqrt{3}a}{2}\right)$; slope of $\overline{AB} =$

$\frac{\frac{\sqrt{3}a}{2}}{\frac{a}{2} - a} = -\sqrt{3}$, slope of $\overline{DE} =$

$\frac{-\frac{\sqrt{3}a}{2}}{-\frac{a}{2} + a} = -\sqrt{3}$ **16.** Maria's
is easiest. The fractions are
more manageable; however,
they will all work.

Algebra Review
Answers

1. $\frac{3}{4a^4}$ **2.** $9x^4$ **3.** $-3ab$

Enrichment Answers

1. $y = \frac{1}{2}x^2 + \frac{1}{2}$

2. $y = \frac{1}{6}x^2 + \frac{3}{2}$

3. $y = \frac{1}{2}x^2 + \frac{5}{2}$

4. $y = \frac{1}{6}x^2 + \frac{7}{2}$ **5.** $y = \frac{1}{8}x^2$

6. $y = \frac{1}{8}(x - 3)^2 - \frac{233}{4}x + \frac{9}{80}$

7. The coefficient of x^2 decreases. **8.** The y-intercept is no longer 0. **9.** As $|a|$ decreases the parabola becomes flatter.

10. As b changes, the vertical position of the parabola changes.

Enrichment

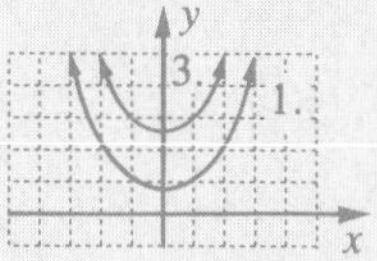

Equations for Parabolas

In a Critical Thinking exercise in Chapter 9 you found the locus of points that are equidistant from a given line and a given point not on the line. The locus of points define a particular curve called a **parabola.** The coordinate plane and the distance formula can be used to develop equations for parabolas when the line and the point are given.

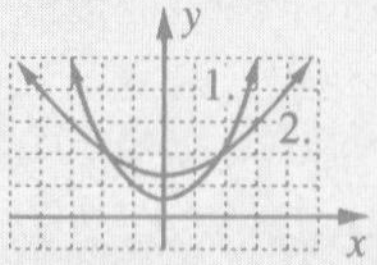

Example

Determine an equation of the parabola that is equidistant from $y = 0$ (x-axis) and from the point $(0, 2)$.

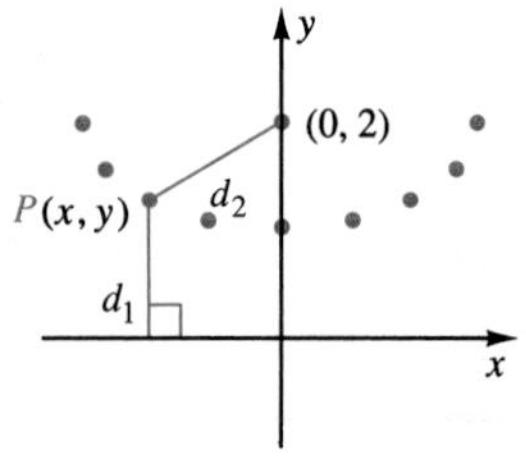

Solution

Let $P(x, y)$ be the general point that is equidistant from the line $y = 0$ (x-axis) and $(0, 2)$.

$d_1 = y - 0 = y$

$d_2 = \sqrt{(x - 0)^2 + (y - 2)^2}$

Since $d_1 = d_2$, then

$y = \sqrt{(x - 0)^2 + (y - 2)^2}$

$y^2 = (x - 0)^2 + (y - 2)^2$ *Square both sides of the equation.*

$y^2 = x^2 + y^2 - 4y + 4$ *Remove the parentheses.*

$4y = x^2 + 4$ *Addition Property of Equality*

$y = \frac{1}{4}x^2 + 1$ *Multiplication Property of Equality*

Thus $y = \frac{1}{4}x^2 + 1$ is the equation of the parabola that is equidistant from the x-axis and the point $(0, 2)$.

Exercises

Determine an equation for the parabola defined by each pair of lines and points.

1. $y = 0$ (x-axis), $(0, 1)$ 2. $y = 0$ (x-axis), $(0, 3)$ 3. $y = 2$, $(0, 3)$
4. $y = 2$, $(0, 5)$ 5. $y = -2$, $(0, 2)$ 6. $y = -2$, $(3, 2)$
7. Compare the equations from Exercises 1 and 2 and the equations from Exercises 3 and 4. What seems to be the effect on the equation when the point gets farther away from the line?
8. Compare the equations from Exercises 5 and 6. What seems to be the effect on the equation when the point is off the y-axis but the same distance from the line?
9. For the equations in Exercises 1 and 2, choose numbers for x and find the corresponding values for y. Use the same set of axes and graph the ordered pairs (x, y). Describe the change in the graph $y = ax^2 + b$ as $|a|$ changes.
10. For the equations in Exercises 1 and 3, choose numbers for x and find the corresponding values for y. Use the same set of axes. Graph the ordered pairs (x, y). Describe the change in the graph $y = ax^2 + b$ as b changes.

566 *Chapter 12 Coordinate Geometry*

OBJECTIVE: *Prove theorems using the coordinate plane.*

12-8 Proving Theorems

As you prove theorems using coordinate geometry, keep in mind how the placement of the figure can influence the difficulty of completing the proof.

Example 1

Use coordinates to prove the following theorem.

The diagonals of a rectangle are congruent.

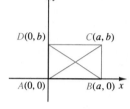

Solution

Given: $ABCD$ is a rectangle with coordinates $A(0, 0)$, $B(a, 0)$, $C(a, b)$, $D(0, b)$ and diagonals $\overline{AC}$ and $\overline{BD}$.

Prove: $AC = AD$

Proof

Statements	Reasons
1. $ABCD$ is a rectangle with coordinates $A(0, 0)$, $B(a, 0)$, $C(a, b)$, $D(0, b)$ and diagonals $\overline{AC}$ and $\overline{BD}$.	1. Given
2. $AC = \sqrt{(a - 0)^2 + (b - 0)^2}$	2. Distance Formula
3. $AC = \sqrt{a^2 + b^2}$	3. Properties of numbers
4. $BD = \sqrt{(a - 0)^2 + (0 - b)^2}$	4. Distance Formula
5. $BD = \sqrt{a^2 + b^2}$	5. Properties of numbers
6. $AC = BD$	6. Substitution Property of Equality

Example 2

Use coordinates to prove the following statement.

The median to the base of an isosceles right triangle is perpendicular to the base.

Solution

Given: Isosceles right triangle ABC has coordinates $A(0, 0)$, $B(2a, 0)$, and $C(0, 2a)$. $BM = MC$.

Prove: $\overline{AM} \perp \overline{BC}$

Proof

Statements	Reasons
1. Isosceles right triangle ABC has coordinates $A(0, 0)$, $B(2a, 0)$, $C(0, 2a)$	1. Given
2. The coordinates of M are (a, a).	2. Midpoint Formula
3. slope of $\overline{AM} = \frac{a - 0}{a - 0} = 1$	3. Definition of slope
4. slope of $BC = \frac{2a - 0}{0 - 2a} = -1$	4. Definition of slope
5. (slope of $\overline{AM}$) $\cdot$ (slope of $\overline{BC}$) $= 1 \cdot -1 = -1$	5. Properties of numbers
6. $\overline{AM} \perp \overline{BC}$	6. Two nonvertical lines are perpendicular if and only if the product of their slopes is -1.

12-8 Proving Theorems   **567**

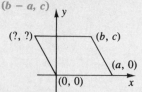
Lesson Opener

Coordinate geometry is used to prove theorems about polygons.

Materials

student notebooks
grid paper

Teaching Notes

The placement of figures on the coordinate plane can affect the ease of proving theorems.

Guided Practice

Chalkboard Examples

1. Use coord. to prove: The diag. of a sq. are $\perp$. 1. Sq. *ABCD* has coord. $A(0, 0)$, $B(0, a)$, $C(a, a)$, $D(a, 0)$. (Given) 2. slope of $\overline{AC} = 1$ and $\overline{BD} = -1$ (Def. of slope) 3. (slope of $\overline{AC}$) $\cdot$ (slope of $\overline{BD}$) $= -1$ (Prop. of no.) 4. $\overline{AC} \perp \overline{BD}$ (Th. 12.3)

2. Use coord. to prove the diag. of a $\square$ bisect each other. 1. $\square ABCD$ has coord. $A(0, 0)$, $B(a, 0)$, $C(a + b, c)$, $D(b, c)$.

Diag. intersect at $E\left(\frac{a + b}{2}, \frac{c}{2}\right)$.

(Given) 2. $AE = CE = \frac{1}{2}\sqrt{(a + b)^2 + c^2}$ (Dist. Form.)
3. $DE = BE = \frac{1}{2}\sqrt{(b - a)^2 + c^2}$ (Dist. Form.) 4. The diag. of a $\square$ bisect each other. (Def. bis.)

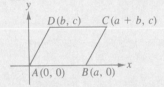
Class Exercises

Short Answers

Refer to square *ABCD* to the right.

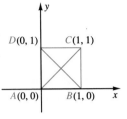

1. Use the distance formula to find AC.
2. Use the distance formula to find BD.
3. Compare AC and BD.
4. What conclusion can you state?
5. Find the slope of $\overline{AC}$.
6. Find the slope of $\overline{BD}$.
7. Find the product of the slopes of $\overline{AC}$ and $\overline{BD}$.
8. What conclusion can you state?

Sample Exercises

9. **Given:** parallelogram *ABCD* with coordinates as shown
   Prove: $AD = BC$, $AB = CD$

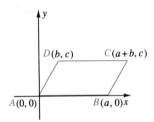

10. **Given:** isosceles $\triangle XYZ$ with $XZ = YZ$ and medians $\overline{XM}$ and $\overline{YN}$
    Prove: $XM = YN$

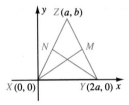

11. Use coordinate geometry to prove the following theorem.
    The opposite sides of a parallelogram are equal in length.

Discussion

12. Suppose you had to prove the following theorem.
    The diagonals of a square are perpendicular.

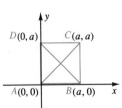

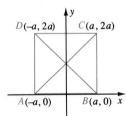

a. For each placement above, what must you show to be able to conclude that the diagonals are perpendicular?
b. Which placement do you think makes this task easier? Explain your choice.

Exercises

A

1. **Given:** $\triangle RST$ with coordinates as shown.
   M and N are midpoints.
   Prove: $MN = \frac{1}{2}RS$

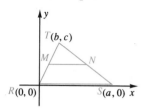

2. **Given:** $ABCD$ is a parallelogram with
   coordinates $A(0, 0)$, $B(a, 0)$, $C(c, b)$
   and $D(c - a, b)$.
   Prove: $\overline{AC}$ and $\overline{BD}$ bisect each other.

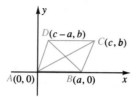

3. **Given:** $ABCD$ is an isosceles trapezoid
   with coordinates $A(0, 0)$, $B(a, 0)$,
   $C(a - b, c)$, and $D(b, c)$.
   Prove: $AC = BD$

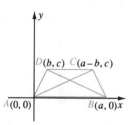

4. **Given:** quadrilateral $ABCD$ with coordinates
   $A(0, 0)$, $B(a, 0)$, $C(b, b)$, and $D(0, a)$
   Prove: $\overline{AC} \perp \overline{BD}$

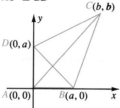

5. Use coordinates to prove the following theorem.
   The diagonals of a rhombus are perpendicular.

B

6. **Given:** Circle with center at the origin has chord $\overline{AB}$ with coordinates
   $A(0, a)$ and $B(a, 0)$. Line m is the $\perp$ bisector of $\overline{AB}$.
   Prove: m contains the center of the circle.

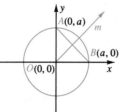

Prove each theorem using coordinates.

7. The median of a trapezoid is half the sum of the lengths of the bases.
8. The midpoint of the hypotenuse of a right triangle ABC is equidistant from
   the vertices. (HINT: Assign the vertices $A(0, 0)$, $B(a, 0)$, and $C(0, b)$.)
9. If the diagonals of parallelogram $ABCD$ are congruent, the parallelogram is a rectangle.
10. The medians to the congruent sides of an isosceles triangle are congruent.

C

11. The quadrilateral formed by joining the midpoints of the sides of a
    quadrilateral is a parallelogram.
12. The quadrilateral formed by joining the midpoints of the sides of an
    isosceles trapezoid is a rhombus.

8. 1. rt. △ABC with coord. $A(0, 0)$, $B(a, 0)$, $C(0, b)$ (Given) 2. Midpt. M of $\overline{BC}$ has coord. $\left(\frac{a}{2}, \frac{b}{2}\right)$ (Midpt. Th.)

3. $BM = \sqrt{\left(\frac{a}{2}\right)^2 + \left(\frac{b}{2}\right)^2}$,

$CM = \sqrt{\left(\frac{a}{2}\right)^2 + \left(\frac{b}{2}\right)^2}$;

$AM = \sqrt{\left(\frac{a}{2}\right)^2 + \left(\frac{b}{2}\right)^2}$

(Dist. Form.) 4. $AM = BM = CM$ (Subst. Prop.)

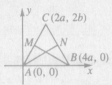

10. 1. Isos. △ABC with med. $\overline{BM}$ and $\overline{AN}$ (Given) 2. M midpt. of $\overline{AC}$; N of $\overline{BC}$ (Def. med.) 3. M has coord. (a, b); N has $(3a, b)$ (Midpt. Th.) 4. $BM = \sqrt{9a^2 + b^2}$, $AN = \sqrt{9a^2 + b^2}$ (Dist. Form.) 5. $BM = AN$ (Trans. Prop.) 6. $\overline{BM} \cong \overline{AN}$ (Def. $\cong$ seg.)

12.
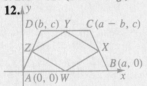

1. Isos. trap. with midpt. W, X, Y, Z (Given) 2. W has coord. $\left(\frac{a}{2}, 0\right)$; X, $\left(a - \frac{b}{2}, \frac{c}{2}\right)$; Y, $\left(\frac{a}{2}, c\right)$; Z; $\left(\frac{b}{2}, \frac{c}{2}\right)$ (Midpt. Th.)

3. $WX = \sqrt{\left(\frac{a}{2} - \frac{b}{2}\right)^2 + \left(\frac{c}{2}\right)^2}$;

$XY = \sqrt{\left(\frac{a}{2} - \frac{b}{2}\right)^2 + \left(\frac{c}{2}\right)^2}$;

$YZ = \sqrt{\left(\frac{a}{2} - \frac{b}{2}\right)^2 + \left(\frac{c}{2}\right)^2}$;

$ZX = \sqrt{\left(\frac{a}{2} - \frac{b}{2}\right)^2 + \left(\frac{c}{2}\right)^2}$

(Dist. Form.)
4. $WX = XY = YZ = ZX$ (Subst. Prop.) 5. $WXYZ$ is a rhom. (Def. rhom.)   **14.** Answers may vary.

Mixed Review Answers

1. 96 cm², 64 cm³

2. 78π cm², 90π cm³

---

13. Consider the cube shown to the right. Prove that the triangle OAB is equilateral. (HINT: Set up a three-dimensional coordinate system with O at the origin, $\overline{OD}$ on the x-axis, $\overline{OC}$ on the y-axis, and $\overline{OE}$ on the z-axis. Assign coordinates to O, A, and B.)

Critical Thinking

14. Consider two methods for proving the following theorem.
The diagonals of a rhombus are perpendicular.
One proof method is based on procedures developed in previous chapters (for example, using congruent triangles); the other method is based on the use of coordinates. Which proof method do you think is easier for proving the theorem given above? Explain your choice.

15. Consider the two proof methods described in Exercise 14. Indicate which method you think is easier to use for proving the following theorem.
The quadrilateral formed by joining the midpoints of the sides of a quadrilateral is a parallelogram.
Explain your choice.

Mixed Review

1. Find the surface area and volume of a cube with each edge 4 cm.
2. Find the surface area and volume of a cylinder 10 cm high with a circular base 6 cm in diameter.

Quiz

State the coordinates of point T without introducing any new letters.

1. square

2. isosceles trapezoid

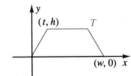

3. equilateral triangle

4. rectangle

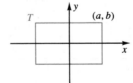

5. Use coordinate geometry to prove the following statement.
The median of a trapezoid is one half as long as the sum of its bases.

CRITICAL THINKING

Making and Supporting Decisions

Apply your critical thinking abilities to solving the following situation. It takes nine days to cross the Dryasdust Desert on foot. A messenger must deliver a secret written message to the other side of the desert, where no food and water is available, and then return. One person can carry enough food and water to last for 12 days. Food and water may be buried in plastic sacks in the desert and collected for use on the way back. There are two messengers available to carry out the task. How quickly can the two messengers get the message delivered without either messenger suffering from lack of food and water?

1. Understand the Situation
   - a. What is the situation about?
   - b. What conclusion, decision, or solution is required?
   - c. Are there any questions which would clarify the situation?
2. Deal with the Data/Evidence/Assumptions
   - a. Make a list of the most important evidence/data. Are other data needed?
   - b. What evidence is opinion, not fact? Which data are not relevant?
   - c. What assumptions are made? What other assumptions could be made?
3. Modify the Data/Evidence/Assumptions
   - a. Try the situation with deserts requiring less days to cross.
   - b. Develop a method of recording the positions of the messengers and the amount of food available.
   - c. Is there any sense to having one of the other messengers return to base and then head back out to meet the other messenger returning?
4. State and Support your Conclusion/Decision/Solution
   Write a paragraph, with an accompanying diagram, describing your solution to this situation.
5. Apply the Conclusion/Decision/Solution
   What is the widest desert that can be crossed by the two messengers if they are not allowed to bury food for the return trip?

Quiz Answers

1. (x, x) **2.** $(w - t, h)$
3. $(4h, 0)$ **4.** $(-a, b)$
5. 1. trap. $ABCD$ with coord. $A(0, 0)$, $B(a, 0)$, $C(d, c)$, $D(b, c)$, $\overline{EF}$ med. of $ABCD$. (Given) 2. E midpt. of $\overline{AD}$, F midpt of $\overline{CX}$ (Def. med.) 3. E has coord. $\left(\frac{b}{2}, \frac{c}{2}\right)$; F has coord. $\left(\frac{a+d}{2}, \frac{c}{2}\right)$. (Midpt. Th.)
4. $EF = \frac{1}{2}(a + d - b)$, $AB = a$, $DC = d - b$ (Dist. Form.); $EF = \frac{a+d-b}{2}$ (Dist. Form.)
5. $EF = \frac{1}{2}(AB + DC)$ (Subst.)

Critical Thinking

Making and Supporting Decisions

Exercise Answers

It takes 9 days to deliver the message. (18 days for the total trip)

The first messenger goes out, delivers the message, and starts his return trip. The second messenger sets out on the same day as the first, but after 3 days, buries 6 days worth of food and returns, then immediately sets out again. After 12 days (3 days into the return journey), the first messenger meets the second and they travel together sharing the food. After 3 days, this runs out and they dig up the food buried earlier. This is just enough food to make it back.

The widest desert that could be crossed by two messengers without burying food takes 8 days to cross. (16 days for the total trip)

Chapter Review
Answers

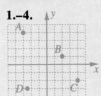

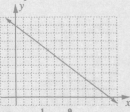
CHAPTER SUMMARY

Vocabulary

abscissa (12-1)   quadrants (12-1)   x-axis (12-1)
coordinate plane (12-1) rectangular coordinate system (12-1) x-coordinate (12-1)
ordinate (12-1)   slope (12-2)   y-axis (12-1)
origin (12-1)   slope-intercept form (12-4)   y-coordinate (12-1)
point-slope form (12-4) standard form (12-4)

Key Ideas

1. Given two points with coordinates $A(x_1, y_1)$ and $B(x_2, y_2)$ the coordinates of the midpoint of $\overline{AB}$ are
   $\left(\frac{x_1 + x_2}{2}, \frac{y_1 + y_2}{2}\right)$.
2. Given two points with coordinates $A(x_1, y_1)$ and $B(x_2, y_2)$ where $x_1 - x_2 \neq 0$ the slope of $\overline{AB}$ is
   $\frac{y_1 - y_2}{x_1 - x_2}$.
3. Given two points with coordinates $A(x_1, y_1)$ and $B(x_2, y_2)$ the distance from A to B is
   $\sqrt{(x_1 - x_2)^2 + (y_1 - y_2)^2}$.
4. The slope of a horizontal line is zero.
5. The slope of a vertical line is undefined.
6. Two nonvertical lines are parallel if their slopes are equal.
7. Two nonvertical lines are perpendicular if the product of their slopes is -1.
8. The graph of any equation that can be written in the form $ax + by = c$, with a and b not both zero, is a line. Other forms for equations of lines include:
   a. slope-intercept form $y = mx + b$ where m is the slope and b is the y-intercept.
   b. point-slope form $y - y_1 = m(x - x_1)$ where (x_1, y_1) is a point on the line and m is the slope.
9. The equation of a circle with center (h, k) and radius r is
   $(x - h)^2 + (y - k)^2 = r^2$.
10. To prove a theorem using coordinate geometry, place and label the given geometric figure on coordinate axes in a position that helps to simplify work.

CHAPTER REVIEW

12-1

Graph each point on the same set of axes.

1. $A(-3, 4)$ 2. $B(2, 1)$ 3. $C(4, -2)$ 4. $D(-2\frac{1}{2}, -3)$

5. Find the coordinates of the midpoint of the segment having endpoints $X(-2, 5)$ and $Y(-6, 1)$.
6. One endpoint of $\overline{RS}$ is $R(4, -3)$ and the midpoint of $\overline{RS}$ is $M(-3, 5)$. Find the coordinates of point S.

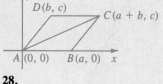

12-2

Find the slope of the line that contains the given points.

7. $A(3, 4)$, $B(-2, 7)$ **8.** $D(4, 6)$, $E(-2, 6)$

9. $X(-4, -2)$, $Y(-6, 4)$

10. A line with slope $\frac{1}{5}$ passes through the points $(-1, 6)$ and $(4, y)$. Find y.

12-3

For the given coordinates, determine whether $\overline{LM} \parallel \overline{PQ}$, $\overline{LM} \perp \overline{PQ}$, or neither.

11. $L(3, 4)$, $M(5, -1)$, $P(-3, 7)$, $Q(-8, 5)$

12. $L(-2, 4)$, $M(5, -1)$, $P(0, 8)$, $Q(7, 3)$

13. The coordinates of the vertices of $\triangle ABC$ are $A(4, 6)$, $B(-2, 1)$, and $C(2, -2)$. Find the slope of the altitude to side $\overline{AC}$.

12-4

State the slope and y-intercept. Graph the line.

14. $3x + 2y = 10$ **15.** $y = -2$ **16.** $(y - 3) = -\frac{3}{4}(x - 8)$

Write the equation of the line for the given conditions. Use $y = mx + b$ form.

17. a line that contains the point $P(-3, 4)$ and has slope $\frac{1}{6}$

18. a line that contains the points $(4, 3)$ and $(-2, -15)$

12-5

Find the distance between each pair of points.

19. $(-4, -1)$, $(-4, 3)$ **20.** $(-2, 3)$, $(3, -2)$

21. Determine whether $\triangle ABC$ is scalene, isosceles, or equilateral if the coordinates of the vertices are $A(-3, 2)$, $B(5, 1)$, and $C(1, -6)$.

12-6

Find the center and radius of each circle.

22. $(x + 2)^2 + (y - 4)^2 = 16$ **23.** $(x - 1)^2 + y^2 = 20$

Write the equation of the circle described.

24. center at $(-3, 2)$ and radius 9

25. center at $(4, 7)$ and contains the point $(2, 11)$

12-7

26. Without introducing any new letters, find the coordinates of points A and B for the rectangle shown to the right.

27. Set up a coordinate system that could be used to prove the statement. A diagonal of a parallelogram forms two congruent triangles.

12-8

Prove the following by methods of coordinate geometry.

28. The segment joining the midpoints of two sides of a triangle is parallel to the third side of the triangle.

29. The diagonals of an isosceles trapezoid are congruent.

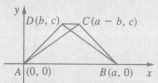

1. $\triangle ABC$ with coord. $A(0, 0)$, $B(a, 0)$, $C(b, c)$ (Given) 2. D is the midpt. of $\overline{AC}$, E is the midpt. of $\overline{CB}$. (Given) 3. D has coord. $\left(\frac{b}{2}, \frac{c}{2}\right)$; E has coord. $\left(\frac{a+b}{2}, \frac{c}{2}\right)$. (Midpt. Th.) 4. slope of $\overline{DE} = 0$, slope of $\overline{AB} = 0$ (Def. slope) 5. $\overline{DE} \parallel \overline{AB}$ (2 nonvertical lines $\parallel$ if their slopes are =.)

29.

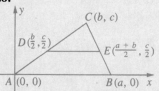

1. $ABCD$ is an isos. trap. with coord. $A(0, 0)$, $B(a, 0)$, $C(a - b, c)$, $D(b, c)$, diag. $\overline{AC}$ and $\overline{BD}$ (Given)
2. $AC = \sqrt{(a - b)^2 + c^2}$, $BD = \sqrt{(b - a)^2 + c^2}$ (Dist. Form.) 3. $(a - b)^2 = (b - a)^2$ (Prop. real numbers)
4. $\sqrt{(a - b)^2 + c^2} = \sqrt{(b - a)^2 + c^2}$ (Subst.)
5. $AC = BD$ (Subst. Prop.)
6. $\overline{AC} \cong \overline{BD}$ (Def. $\cong$ seg.)

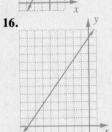

CHAPTER TEST

1. Give the coordinates for point P.
2. Give the coordinates for point S.
3. Give the point for $(-4, 2)$.

Use the points $A(-2, 6)$, $B(4, -2)$, and $C(4, -6)$.

4. Find the coordinates of the midpoint of $\overline{AB}$.
5. Find the coordinates of the midpoint of $\overline{AC}$.
6. Find the slope of $\overline{AB}$.
7. Find the slope of $\overline{AC}$.
8. Find the slope of $\overline{BC}$.
9. Find BC.
10. Find AC.
11. One endpoint of $\overline{RS}$ is $R(-5, 2)$ and the midpoint of $\overline{RS}$ is $(-1, 5)$. Find the coordinates of S.
12. Determine whether the lines $3x + 2y = 6$ and $6y = 4x + 12$ are parallel, perpendicular, or neither.
13. Determine whether the lines $2x + 5y = 8$ and $5y = -2x + 4$ are parallel, perpendicular or neither.
14. Find the slope of a line that is parallel to the line $3 + 2y = 5x$.
15. Graph $y = 2x + 5$.
16. Graph $y - 2 = \frac{3}{2}(x + 6)$.
17. Graph $x = 3$.
18. Write the equation of the line in the form $y = mx + b$ when $m = 3$ and $b = 9$.
19. Write an equation of the line given the slope $m = -\frac{1}{3}$ and point $P(-1, 3)$ on the line.
20. Write the equation of a line through the points $(6, 2)$ and $(0, -4)$.
21. Determine whether $\triangle RST$ is scalene, isosceles, or equilateral if $R(-4, 1)$, $S(5, 4)$, and $T(2, -2)$.
22. Write the equation of a circle with center $(5, 3)$ and radius 4.
23. Write the equation of a circle with center $(-2, -3)$ and radius 6.
24. State the center and radius of the circle with equation $(x - 3)^2 + (y + 5)^2 = 4$.
25. Without introducing any new letters, give the coordinates for A and B in the rhombus to the right.
26. $\triangle ABC$ is an equilateral triangle with coordinates $A(0, 0)$ and $B(5, 0)$. Determine the coordinates of C without using any new letters.
27. Set up a coordinate system to prove that opposite sides of a parallelogram are congruent.
28. Use coordinate geometry to prove the diagonals of a square are perpendicular.
29. Use coordinate geometry to prove that in an isosceles triangle, the medians to the legs are congruent.
30. Use coordinate geometry to prove that the diagonals of a rectangle are congruent.

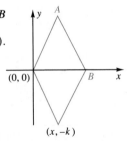

PREPARING FOR COLLEGE ENTRANCE EXAMS

Each question consists of two quantities, one in Column A and one in Column B. Compare the two quantities and choose

A if the quantity in Column A is greater;
B if the quantity in Column B is greater;
C if the two quantities are equal;
D if the relationship cannot be determined from the information given.

Column A	Column B

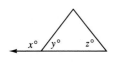

1. x $y + x$

$x = 0.01$

2. x^2 x^3

---

3. $0.3 \times 10{,}000$ 30×100

The figure is a cube.

4. AC BD

$x = 2$

5. $3x^2$ $\dfrac{2x^3 + 4x^2}{x + 2}$

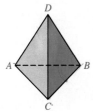

6. $m\angle ABC$ $m\angle ADC$

Column A	Column B
	$5 + x = 9$
	$5 + y = 9$

7. x y

$x = 2$

8. $\dfrac{1}{x}$ $\dfrac{1}{\frac{1}{x}}$

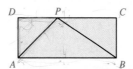

ABCD is a rectangle.

9. perimeter of ADP perimeter of APB

---

10. 0 $x^2 + 1$

11. area of rectangle   area of parallelogram

---

12. area of shaded circle   area of outer ring

27.

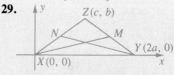

28.

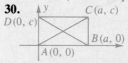

1. *ABCD* is a square with coord. $A(0, 0)$, $B(a, 0)$, $C(a, a)$, $D(0, a)$; $\overline{AC}$ and $\overline{DB}$ are diag. (Given) 2. slope of $\overline{AC} = 1$, slope of $\overline{DB} = -1$ (Def. of slope) 3. slope of $\overline{AC} \cdot$ slope of $\overline{DB} = 1 \cdot -1$ (Mult. Prop. of =) 4. $\overline{AC} \perp \overline{DB}$ (Th. 12.3)

29.

1. Isos. $\triangle XYZ$ with coord. $X(0, 0)$, $Y(2a, 0)$, $Z(a, b)$, med. $\overline{XM}$ and $\overline{YN}$ (Given) 2. M midpt. of $\overline{YZ}$, N midpt. of $\overline{XZ}$. (Def. med.) 3. M has coord. $\left(\frac{3a}{2}, \frac{b}{2}\right)$. N has coord. $\left(\frac{a}{2}, \frac{b}{2}\right)$. (Midpt. Th.) 4. $XM =$
$$\sqrt{\left(\frac{3a}{2}\right)^2 + \left(\frac{b}{2}\right)^2} = \frac{\sqrt{9a^2 + b^2}}{2}.$$
$$YN = \sqrt{\left(2a - \frac{a}{2}\right)^2 + \frac{b^2}{2}}$$
$$= \frac{\sqrt{9a^2 + b^2}}{2} \text{ (Dist. Form.)}$$
5. $XM = YN$ (Trans. Prop.)

30.

1. Rect. *ABCD* with coord. as shown (Given)
2. $AC = \sqrt{(a - 0)^2 + (c - 0)^2}$; $BD = \sqrt{(0 - a)^2 + (c - 0)^2}$ (Dist. Form.) 3. $AC = BD$ (Subst. Prop.) 4. $\overline{AC} \cong \overline{BD}$ (Def. $\cong$ seg.)

College Entrance Exam Answers

1. B	**2.** A	**3.** C
4. C	**5.** A	**6.** D
7. C	**8.** B	**9.** B
10. B	**11.** C	**12.** A

CHAPTER 13

Transformations

Chapter Overview

In this chapter, students are encouraged to explore the properties of four basic transformations—reflections, translations, rotations, and dilations. The first four lessons cover the major theorems related to these transformations and their compositions. The last three lessons contain ideas that allow the concepts of congruence and similarity to be generalized.

Objectives

13-1	▪ Find the reflection image of a figure and lines of symmetry of a figure.
13-2	▪ Find the image of a figure under a translation.
13-3	▪ Find the rotation image of a figure.
13-4	▪ Find the image of a figure under a composition of transformations.
13-5	▪ Use properties of isometries.
13-6	▪ Find the image of a figure under a dilation.
13-7	▪ Use dilations to draw conclusions about figures.

TEACHING CHAPTER 13

Cooperative Learning Opportunities

Some students have trouble with the composition of transformations. You can use a cooperative group quiz to review transformations and also to start on the composition of mappings.

Assign students to groups of four. They should then draw the following roles by picking from numbered cards: (1) draw the figure; (2) draw the reflection image; (3) draw the transla-tion image; (4) draw the rotation im-age. You might do this with two or three problems so that students in the group remain occupied and get practice with different kinds of trans-formations. If so, have students alternate roles for each exercise. You might also use different exercises for each group so that groups will not look at each other's work. An example follows.

(1) On graph paper, draw the triangle with vertices $(-2, 2)$, $(-4, 2)$, and $(-2, 4)$.
(2) Reflect the figure over the y-axis.
(3) Translate the figure 4 units down.
(4) Rotate the figure 90° clockwise about the right-angle vertex.

Use correct papers to explain the composition of transformations.

Multicultural Note: *Sonya Kovalevsky*

Sonya Kovalevsky (1850–1891) was initially self taught. She learned trigonometry from a text written by a neighbor and calculus by studying pages that were used as a temporary wall covering in her home. When she finally began to study calculus with a teacher, her exceptional ability was immediately recognized. At the age of 18 she left Russia to study at universi-ties in Germany.

Although women were not permitted to attend classes, Kovalevsky was tu-tored by outstanding mathematicians and earned her doctorate. She made important contributions to several ar-eas of advanced mathematics and was awarded a major prize for her paper, "On the Rotation of a Solid Body About a Fixed Point."

Based on mathematical calculations, Kovalevsky concluded that the rings of the planet Saturn are egg-shaped with one axis of symmetry rather than el-lipses with two axes of symmetry. Her mathematical approach to astronomy was a model for other scientists.

For more information, see page 99 of **Multiculturalism in Mathematics, Science, and Technology**.

Alternative Assessment and Communication Ideas

The discussion questions (in **Class Exercises**) in Chapter 13 can lead to more general conclusions. The analy-ses required may be difficult for class discussion but could be used for a written alternative assessment. In Les-son 13-1, the discussion question asks whether certain quadrilaterals are unchanged under reflections. Ask, in general, what properties of line seg-ments and angles are preserved in a reflection transformation.

Similar generalizations can be pursued following the discussion questions in Lessons 13-2, 13-3, and 13-4. You can then ask for a list of the properties that are left unchanged by the three transformations and their compositions. These properties in-clude distance, parallelism, perpendicularity, angle measure, betweenness, collinearity, and congru-ence.

Investigations and Projects

The graphics displayed on TV and in video games make frequent use of the transformations discussed in Chapter 13. Ask students to watch for these, particularly in the standard openings of programs and other shows in which corporate logos or advertising images are shown.

Students, individually or in small groups, may want to tape these graphic transformations and then edit them so as to demonstrate individual transformations. You might help them interpose commentary explaining the transformations.

A second project is related to symme-try and left-handedness. Left-handed students might be particularly interested; or you might suggest pairs with a left- and right-handed student working together. The project would be to examine everyday items in which a lack of symmetry works to the disadvantage of left-handed people.

Lesson	PACING CHART (DAYS)			Opening Activity	Cooperative Activity	Seat or Group Work
	1-Year Minimum	1-Year Regular	1-Year Advanced			
1-1	2	2	2	Chapter Opener: **TE** p.576; Lesson Opener: **TE** p. 577	Explore: **SE** p. 577; ✂ Lab Worksheet 13-1A: *Laboratory Manual* p. 133; ✂ Lab Worksheet 13-1B: *Laboratory Manual* p. 134; ✂ Lab Worksheet 13-1C: *Laboratory Manual* p. 135	Try This Exercises
13-2	2	2	2	First Five Minutes 13-2: **FFM** *Transparency Masters* p. 51 or **TE** p. 583; Lesson Opener: **TE** p. 583	✂ Lab Worksheet 13-2: *Laboratory Manual* p. 136	Try This Exercises
13-3	1	1	1	First Five Minutes 13-3: **FFM** *Transparency Masters* p. 52 or **TE** p. 588; Lesson Opener: **TE** p. 588	Explore: **SE** p. 588; Lab Worksheet 13-3A: *Laboratory Manual* p. 137; ✂ Lab Worksheet 13-3B: *Laboratory Manual* p. 138	Try This Exercises
13-4	2	2	2	First Five Minutes 13-4: **FFM** *Transparency Masters* p. 52 or **TE** p. 594; Lesson Opener: **TE** p. 594		Try This Exercises
13-5	1	1	1	First Five Minutes 13-5: **FFM** *Transparency Masters* p. 53 or **TE** p. 600; Lesson Opener: **TE** p. 600		Try This Exercises
13-6	1	1	1	First Five Minutes 13-6: **FFM** *Transparency Masters* p. 54 or **TE** p. 605; Lesson Opener: **TE** p. 605	Discrete Math: **SE** p. 609	Try This Exercises
13-7	1	1	1	First Five Minutes 13-7: **FFM** *Transparency Masters* p. 55 or **TE** p. 610; Lesson Opener: **TE** p. 610	Critical Thinking: **SE** p. 615	Try This Exercises
Review	1	1	1			
Test	1	1	1			
Cum. Review	1	1	1			

FFM = First Five Minutes

Enrichment	Review/Assess	Reteach	Technology	Lesson
Enrichment: **SE** p. 582; ✂ Enrichment Using Manipulatives 13-1: *Enrichment* p. 76	Class Exercises: **SE** p. 579; Mixed Review: **SE** p. 582	Practice Worksheet 13-1: *Practice and Mixed Review* p.95		**13-1**
Connections: **SE** p. 587; ✂ Enrichment Using Manipulatives 13-2: *Enrichment* p. 77	Class Exercises: **SE** p. 585; Mixed Review: **SE** p. 587	Practice Worksheet 13-2: *Practice and Mixed Review* p.96		**13-2**
✂ Enrichment Using Manipulatives 13-3: *Enrichment* p. 78; ✂ Lab Worksheet 13-3C: *Laboratory Manual* p. 139	Class Exercises: **SE** p. 590; Algebra Review: **SE** p. 593	Practice Worksheet 13-3: *Practice and Mixed Review* p.97	Computer Activity: **SE** p. 593	**13-3**
✂ Enrichment Using Manipulatives 13-4: *Enrichment* p. 79	Class Exercises: **SE** p. 596; Algebra Review: **SE** p. 599; Quiz: **SE** p. 599; Quiz: *Assessment* p. 103	Practice Worksheet 13-4: *Practice and Mixed Review* p.98		**13-4**
Biographical Note: **SE** p. 604; ✂ Enrichment Using Manipulatives 13-5: *Enrichment* p. 80	Class Exercises: **SE** p. 602; Mixed Review: **SE** p. 604	Practice Worksheet 13-5: *Practice and Mixed Review* p.99		**13-5**
Discrete Math: **SE** p. 609; ✂ Enrichment Using Manipulatives 13-6: *Enrichment* p. 81	Class Exercises: **SE** p. 606; Mixed Review: **SE** p. 608	Practice Worksheet 13-6: *Practice and Mixed Review* p. 100	Calculator Worksheet 13-6: *Technology* p. CL20	**13-6**
Critcal Thinking: **SE** p. 615; ✂ Enrichment Using Manipulatives 13-7: *Enrichment* p. 82	Class Exercises: **SE** p. 612; Algebra Review: **SE** p. 614 Quiz: **SE** p. 614 Quiz: *Assessment* p. 104	Practice Worksheet 13-7: *Practice and Mixed Review* p. 101		**13-7**
	Summary & Review: **SE** p. 616–617	Mixed Review: *Practice and Mixed Review* p. 114		**Review**
Problem Solving: **SE** p. 619	Chapter 13 Test: **SE** p. 618; Chapter 13 Tests: *Assessment* p. 73–78; *MathTest*			**Test**
	Cumulative Review: **SE** p. 620–621; End-Year Test: *Assessment* p. 111–116			**Cumulative**

Chapter Opener

Ask students to give examples of the two other types of symmetry: translational symmetry (e.g., a strip of postage stamps) and rotational symmetry (e.g., an asterisk).

Answer

Answers may vary. Some other examples of reflectional symmetry are the wings of a butterfly, the letter "A", and a valentine heart.

13

Transformations

This geodesic dome and its reflection are an example of reflectional symmetry. Describe other examples of this type of symmetry.

MAPPINGS

OBJECTIVE: *Find the reflection image of a figure and lines of symmetry of a figure.*

13-1 Reflections and Line Symmetry

 **EXPLORE** Draw a line ℓ and a $\triangle ABC$ on one side of ℓ. Place a sheet of tracing paper over the line and triangle and trace them. Then, flip the tracing paper over and line up the tracing of ℓ with ℓ and locate the points on the other side of ℓ corresponding to A, B, and C. Label these points A', B', and C'.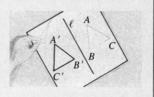

A correspondence between points of the plane is a **mapping.** A mapping which establishes a one-to-one correspondence between points in the plane is called a **transformation.** The mapping illustrated in the Explore establishes a one-to-one correspondence between points in the plane by reflecting them in a line. A transformation T maps a point P to its **image** under T, usually indicated by P'. Point P is called the **preimage** of P'.

■ DEFINITION

A **reflection in line** ℓ is a transformation that maps every point P of the plane to a point P' of the plane such that

a. if point P is on ℓ then it is mapped to itself,
b. if point P is not on ℓ then ℓ is the perpendicular bisector of $\overline{PP'}$.

In the Explore, A' is the image of A in the reflection in line ℓ. A' is called the **reflection image** of A in line ℓ.

Example 1
Find the reflection image in line m of each of the following.
a. R **b.** S' **c.** T **d.** V **e.** $\overline{RS}$ **f.** $\triangle RST$

> **Solution**
> **a.** R' **b.** S **c.** T' **d.** W **e.** $\overline{R'S'}$ **f.** $\triangle R'S'T$

Try This
Find the reflection image in line m of each of the following.
a. U **b.** W **c.** $\overline{TV}$

The reflection image of a point in the x-axis or the y-axis can be described using the coordinates of the point. This is illustrated in the following example.

Key Terms

mapping
transformation
image
preimage
reflection
symmetry

Guided Practice

Chalkboard Examples

1.

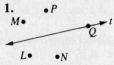

What is the reflection image in line t of points M, N, and Q? *L, P, Q*

Answer to **Try This** a. *U'* b. *V* c. *T'W*

2.

Find the vertices of the reflection image of $\triangle ABC$ if the line of reflection is the x-axis. (3, −3), (4, 1), (1, −2)

Answer to **Try This** *in x-axis, (1, 1); in y-axis, (−1, −1)*

3. Draw a regular hexagon and identify all lines of symmetry.

Answer to **Try This**

a.   b.

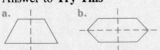

Class Exercise Answers

1. *P*   2. *Q*   3. $\overline{QR}$ 4. $\overline{DE}$
5. $\triangle SDE$ 6. *C*   7. $\overline{SD}$
8. (3, 1)   9. (4, 3)
10. (1, 2)   11. (2, 3)
12. (5, −1), (−5, 1)

Example 2

Find the coordinates of the reflection image of point P in each of the coordinate axes.

Solution

Reflection in x-axis: Image of $P\,(3, 2)$ is $(3, -2)$.
Reflection in y-axis: Image of $P\,(3, 2)$ is $(-3, 2)$.

Try This

Find the coordinates of the reflection image of point Q in each of the coordinate axes.

The reflection image of a figure is found by reflecting each point of the figure. Notice that the reflection image of the letter H in line m is again the letter H.

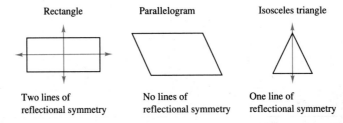

■ DEFINITION

A line ℓ is called the **line of reflectional symmetry** for a figure if the figure coincides with its reflection image in ℓ. The figure is said to have **reflectional symmetry** in line ℓ.

Example 3

Draw a rectangle, a parallelogram, and an isosceles triangle and identify all lines of reflectional symmetry for each figure.

Solution

Rectangle	Parallelogram	Isosceles triangle

Two lines of reflectional symmetry

No lines of reflectional symmetry

One line of reflectional symmetry

Try This

Draw each of the following.

a. quadrilateral that has exactly one line of symmetry
b. a hexagon that has exactly two lines of symmetry

Class Exercises

Short Answer

Complete each statement.

1. The reflection image in line ℓ of *A* is ___ .
2. The reflection image in line ℓ of *B* is ___ .
3. The reflection image in line ℓ of $\overline{BC}$ is ___ .
4. The reflection image in line ℓ of $\overline{SE}$ is ___ .
5. The reflection image in line ℓ of △*DSE* is ___ .
6. The reflection image in line ℓ of ___ is *R*.
7. The reflection image in line ℓ of ___ is $\overline{DS}$.

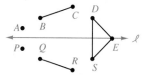

Sample Exercises

Complete the following chart showing the coordinates of the given points reflected in the indicated axes.

Point	Image in *x*-axis	Image in *y*-axis
8. (3, −1)	___	(−3, −1)
9. (−4, 3)	(−4, −3)	___
10. (1, −2)	___	(−1, −2)
11. (−2, 3)	(−2, −3)	___
12. (5, 1)	___	___
13. (2, −3)	___	___
14. (3, −4)	___	___
15. ___	(−2, −2)	___
16. (*x*, −*y*)	___	___
17. (−*x*, *y*)	___	___
18. (−*x*, −*y*)	___	___

19. What generalization can you state about the relationship between the coordinates of a point and those of its reflection image in the *x*-axis? the *y*-axis?

Determine whether each line appears to be a line of symmetry for each figure. Then trace the given polygon and draw its reflection image about each of the red lines.

20.   21. 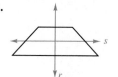   22.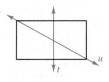

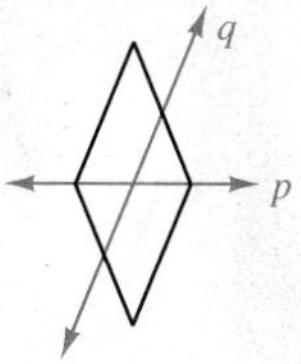

Discussion

23. The reflection image in ℓ of a pair of parallel segments is a pair of parallel segments. Give a convincing argument, using this information, to explain why the reflection image of a parallelogram is a parallelogram. Do you think that the reflection image of a rectangle is always a rectangle? Explain.

13-1 Reflections and Line Symmetry   **579**

---

13. (2, 3), (−2, −3)
14. (3, 4), (−3, −4)
15. (−2, 2), (2, 2)
16. (*x*, *y*), (−*x*, −*y*)
17. (−*x*, −*y*), (*x*, *y*)
18. (−*x*, *y*), (*x*, −*y*)
19. Reflection in the *x*-axis maps (*x*, *y*) to (*x*, −*y*); reflection in the *y*-axis maps (*x*, *y*) to (−*x*, *y*).
20. *p* yes, *q* no

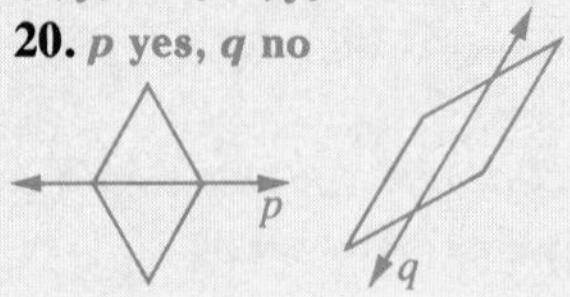

21. *r* yes, *s* no

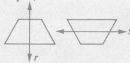

22. *t* yes, *u* no

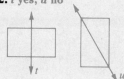

23. Opp. sides of a □ are ∥. Reflection in a line carries ∥ seg. to ∥ seg. So, opp. sides of a □ are reflected to ∥ seg. The opp. sides of the reflection image of a □ are ∥, hence the reflection image of a □ is a □. The reflection image of a rect. is always a rect. because ⊥ seg. are reflected to ⊥ seg.

Assignment Guide
Minimum: 1–37 e/o, 43, MR
Regular: 1–46 e/o, MR
Advanced: 15–30 e/o, 31–46, MR

Applications
Exercises 41–44

Coordinate Geometry
Class Exercises 8–19
Exercises 9–14, 31–35, 39, 40

Algebra
Class Exercises 16–18
Exercises 31–35, 39, 40

Exercise Answers

1. *H*   **2.** *B*   **3.** $\overline{CB}$
4. $\triangle HGF$ **5.** $\overline{XW}$ **6.** *U*
7. $\overline{TS}$
8. *XWVUTSR*   **9.** (−1, 2)
10. (−4, 2)   **11.** (−2, −1)
12. (−4, 2), (−4, −1)
13. (−3, 1), (−4, 2)
14. (−1, 2), (−3, 1)
15.   **16.**

17.   **18.**

19. no lines of symmetry
20.   **21.**

22.   **23.**

24. Some possiblities are a line, a circle, or infinitely many lines equally spaced.

25.   **26.**

Exercises

A

Complete each statement.

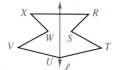

1. The reflection image in ℓ of *A* is ___.
2. The reflection image in ℓ of *G* is ___.
3. The reflection image in ℓ of $\overline{FG}$ is ___.
4. The reflection image in ℓ of $\triangle ABC$ is ___.

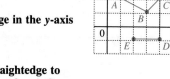

5. The reflection image in ℓ of $\overline{RS}$ is ___.
6. The reflection image in ℓ of *U* is ___.
7. The reflection image in ℓ of ___ is $\overline{VW}$.
8. The reflection image in ℓ of *RSTUVWX* is ___.

Find the reflection image in the *y*-axis of each of the following.

9. point *A*   **10.** point *C*   **11.** point *E*

Find the coordinates of the endpoints of the reflection image in the *y*-axis of each segment.

12. $\overline{CD}$ **13.** $\overline{BC}$ **14.** $\overline{AB}$

Trace each figure. Use tracing paper or a compass and straightedge to draw as accurately as possible the reflection image in line *p* of each figure.

15.   **16.**   **17.**

Trace each figure and draw all the lines of reflectional symmetry.

18.   **19.**   **20.**

21. Draw a hexagon with exactly one line of symmetry.
22. Draw a quadrilateral with exactly four lines of symmetry.
23. Draw a triangle with exactly three lines of symmetry.
24. Draw a figure with an infinite number of lines of symmetry.

B

Trace each figure and draw its reflection image in line *p*.

25. 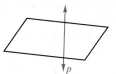   **26.**   **27.**

28. The reflection image of the word HIDE in a horizontal line is again the word HIDE. Print five other words for which this is true.
29. The reflection image of the word WOW in a vertical line is again the word WOW. Print five other words for which this is true.
30. Can you decode this message? How does the decoding relate to a line reflection?

The reason this
looks so strange is
that it was written
using a mirror.

The reflection image in the line $y = x$ of point $P(x, y)$ is point $P'(y, x)$. Use the definition of reflection in a line to find the coordinates of the reflection image in $y = x$ of each point.

31. point $A(4, 2)$
32. point $B(2, -3)$
33. point $C(1, 1)$

Find the coordinates of the reflection image in the line $y = -x$ of each point.

34. point $A(4, 2)$
35. point $C(1, 1)$

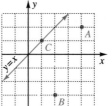

36. Points L and N are on the same side of line p and L' is the reflection image of L. If M is the intersection of line p and $\overline{L'N}$, prove that $m\angle 1 = m\angle 2$.
37. If L' is the reflection image of L in line p and M is a point on line p, prove that $LM = L'M$.

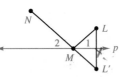

C

38. If A and B are two points and A' and B' are their reflection images in line ℓ, prove that $\overline{AB} \cong \overline{A'B'}$.
39. If the line with equation $y = x$ is reflected in the x-axis, what would the equation of its reflection be?
40. If the line with equation $y = 2x$ is reflected in the y-axis, what would the equation of its reflection image be?
41. Two cities are positioned on the same side of a straight river. A bridge is to be built. Where should the bridge B be built so that the length of the highway, $AB + BC$, is as small as possible?

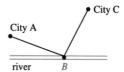

42. If cities D and E are 1 km and 2 km from the river respectively and XX' is 6 km, how far from X should the bridge B be placed so that $DB + BE$ is as small as possible?

Critical Thinking

43. Passengers in a rowboat at A decide they want to row to the north shore to pick fruit and then row to the south shore to pick corn before proceeding to island I for a picnic. Trace this figure with points A and I as shown and figure out how to locate points B and C so that the trip $AB + BC + CI$ is the least possible distance.

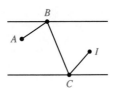

13-1   Reflections and Line Symmetry   **581**

27.

28. Answers may vary.
29. Answers may vary.
30. "The reason this looks so strange is that it was written using a mirror." The message may be read by reflecting it in a vertical line.   31. (2, 4)
32. (−3, 2)   33. (1, 1)
34. (−2, −4)   35. (−1, −1)
36. Label point of intersection of line p and $\overleftrightarrow{LL'}$ as X. 1. L' is the reflection image of L in line p. (Given) 2. Line p is the ⊥ bis. of $\overline{LL'}$. (Definition of reflection image) 3. $\overline{LX} \cong \overline{L'X}$ (Definition of bis.) 4. M is on line p. (Given) 5. $\overline{LM} \cong \overline{L'M}$ (Points on the ⊥ bis. of a segment are equidistant from endpoints.) 6. $\overline{MX} \cong \overline{MX}$ (Reflexive Prop. of $\cong$) 7. $\triangle LMX \cong \triangle L'MX$ (SSS Postulate) 8. $\angle 1 \cong \angle L'MX$ (Corr. parts of $\cong$ $\triangle$s are $\cong$.) 9. $\angle 2 \cong \angle L'MX$ (Vertical Angle Theorem) 10. $\angle 1 \cong \angle 2$ (Substitution) 11. $m\angle 1 = m\angle 2$ (Definition of $\cong$ $\angle$s)
37. 1. L' is the reflection image of L in line p. (Given) 2. Line p is the ⊥ bis. of $\overline{LL'}$. (Definition of reflection image) 3. M is on line p. (Given) 4. $\overline{LM} \cong \overline{L'M}$ (Points on the ⊥ bis. of a segment are equidistant from endpoints.)   38. (i) If A is on line ℓ and if B is also on ℓ, B' is B and $\overline{AB}$ is the same as $\overline{A'B'}$. (ii) If A is on line ℓ and B is not on ℓ, A is on the ⊥ bis. of $\overline{BB'}$ so $\overline{AB} \cong \overline{AB'}$ and $\overline{A'B'}$ is $\overline{AB'}$. (Theorem 4.8) (iii) If A is not on line ℓ and if B is on line ℓ, B' is B and B is on the ⊥ bis. of $\overline{AA'}$. (iv) If neither A nor B is on line ℓ, then let X be the point of intersection of $\overleftrightarrow{AA'}$ and ℓ and let Y be the point of intersection of $\overline{BB'}$ and ℓ. Draw lines as shown.

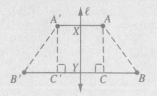

$\overline{AA'}$ and $\overline{BB'}$ are both $\perp$ to ℓ,
$\overline{AA'} \parallel \overline{BB'}$ and $\overline{AA'} \perp \overline{AC}$,
$\overline{AA'} \perp \overline{A'C'}$, $\overline{BB'} \perp \overline{AC}$, and
$\overline{BB'} \perp \overline{AC'}$. Now $\overline{AC} \cong \overline{A'C'}$
($\parallel$ lines are equidistant at all
points.) and since
$\overline{CY} \cong \overline{AX} \cong \overline{A'X} \cong \overline{C'Y}$ and
$\overline{BY} \cong \overline{B'Y}$, $\overline{BC} \cong \overline{B'C'}$. Finally,
$\angle ACB \cong \angle A'C'B'$ (All right $\angle$s
are $\cong$.) So $\triangle ACB \cong \triangle A'C'B'$
(SAS Post.) and hence,
$\overline{AB} \cong \overline{A'B'}$. (Corr. parts of $\cong \triangle$s
are $\cong$.)   **39.** $y = -x$
40. $y = -2x$ **41.** Reflect one
city about the line formed by
the river. Draw a line connecting the reflection image to the
other city. The bridge should be
built where that line intersects
the river.   **42.** 4 km
43. Reflect I about the south
shoreline and reflect that
reflection image about the north
shoreline. Draw a line connecting A to this new reflection image. The intersection of this
line with the north shoreline is
point B. Draw a line connecting
B to the original reflection image of I. The intersection of this
line with the south shoreline is C.
44. 7 (5 directly, 2 in the mirror)   **45.** If $A'B'C'D'$ is a
rhombus, then $ABCD$ is a parallelogram. The converse is true.
The original implication is not.
46. Yes; each follows from the
other since the reflec-tion image
of a line segment has the same
length as the original segment.

Mixed Review Answers

1. true   **2.** true   **3.** false
4. false   **5.** false   **6.** false

Enrichment Answers

1. 6 ft   **2.** $\frac{8\sqrt{3}}{3}$ m

---

44. A small restaurant has a mirror on one wall and a partition to block
off part of the restaurant for private parties. How many of the tables
can the restaurant manager, standing at the cashier stand, see from
direct vision or from reflection in the mirror? Explain your answer.

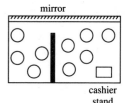

mirror

cashier
stand

**Suppose that quadrilateral $A'B'C'D'$ is the reflection image of
quadrilateral $ABCD$.**

45. State the converse of the following conditional.
If $ABCD$ is a parallelogram, then $A'B'C'D'$ is a rhombus.
Is this converse true? Is the original implication true?
46. Does each statement follow logically from the other?
(a) $ABCD$ is a rhombus.   (b) $A'B'C'D'$ is a rhombus.
Explain your answer.

Mixed Review

Use the figure to the right to determine whether each statement is true or false.

1. If $\overline{AE} \cong \overline{EC}$ and $\overline{DE} \cong \overline{EB}$, then $\triangle AED \cong \triangle CEB$.
2. If $ABCD$ is a rectangle, then $\triangle ACD \cong \triangle BDC$.
3. If $\triangle AED \cong \triangle CEB$, then $ABCD$ must be a rectangle.
4. If $\overline{DB}$ and $\overline{AC}$ bisect each other, then $ABCD$ must be a rhombus.
5. If $ABCD$ is a parallelogram, then $\triangle AED$ cannot be congruent to $\triangle AEB$.
6. $ABCD$ is a rectangle if and only if $\triangle AEB \cong \triangle CED$.

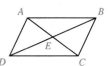

Enrichment

Mirrors

When you see an object in a mirror, you are witnessing a type of
line reflection. Light reflected off an object strikes the mirror and
is reflected back to the eye so that the *angle of incidence* equals
the *angle of reflection*. The brain then perceives the reflected
image as far behind the mirror as the object is in front of the
mirror. Such an image behind a mirror is called a *virtual image*.

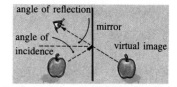

angle of reflection

mirror

angle of
incidence

virtual image

Exercises

1. If the apple in the above drawing lies 3 ft in front of the mirror, find the
distance between the apple and its virtual image.
2. Light from an object on the ground strikes a vertical mirror with an
angle of incidence of 30°. If the object lies 2 m in front of the mirror
and the viewer is standing directly over the object, how far is the virtual
image from the viewer's eye?

OBJECTIVE: *Find the image of a figure under a translation.*

13-2 Translations and Translational Symmetry

An object on a conveyor belt moves a certain distance in one direction as it moves from one robot to the next. This type of motion is a model for the transformation called a **translation.**

■ DEFINITION

A **translation** PP' is a transformation that slides all points of the plane a fixed distance in a given direction. If A is mapped to A', then $AA' = PP'$ and $AP = A'P'$.

The distance and direction for the translation PP' are given by a **directed segment** $\overline{PP'}$ showing the relationship between a point P and its **translation image** P'.

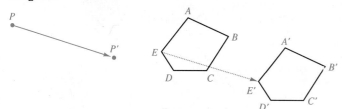

The translation image of point A is A' since the directed segment $\overline{AA'}$ has the same length and direction as $\overline{PP'}$. Similarly, the translation image of B is B' and of C is C'. We also say that the translation image of figure $ABCDE$ is $A'B'C'D'E'$.

Example 1

For the translation XY, find the translation image of each of the following.

a. A b. $\overline{UV}$ c. $\overline{CB}$

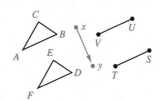

Solution

a. F b. $\overline{ST}$ c. $\overline{ED}$

Try This

Find the translation image of $\overline{AB}$ and $\triangle ABC$.

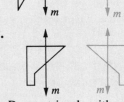

This figure illustrates how the translation image of a point can be described in terms of the original coordinates of the point. The translation XY creates a horizontal shift of 4 units and a vertical shift of 2 units. Consequently, the translation image of $A(1, 1)$ is $A'(1 + 4, 1 + 2)$ or $(5, 3)$. The image of $B(3, -1)$ under the translation XY is $B'(7, 1)$.

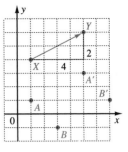

Example 2

The translation RS is defined by points $R(3, 4)$ and $S(7, 9)$. Find the translation image under RS for each point.

a. $C(3, 2)$ **b.** $D(-1, 3)$ **c.** $M(x, y)$

> **Solution**
> **a.** $C'(7, 7)$ **b.** $D'(3, 8)$ *The translation RS creates a horizontal shift*
> **c.** $M'(x + 4, y + 5)$ *of 4 units and a vertical shift of 5 units.*

Try This

Find the translation image under RS for each point.

a. $(-2, 4)$ **b.** $(5, -7)$

A figure has **translational symmetry** if there is a translation that maps the figure onto itself. For example, if we assume that the figure in the box below is repeated indefinitely to the right and to the left, then the resulting pattern has translational symmetry since the translation that maps X to Y maps the entire pattern onto itself. Trace the pattern and then slide the tracing from X to Y to verify the translational symmetry.

Example 3

Imagine that the figure in the box below is repeated indefinitely to the right and to the left to form the pattern shown. This pattern has translational symmetry. If the translation image of point A is __?__ the pattern maps onto itself.

> **Solution**
> Point C

Try This

Complete this statement in two ways.
If the translation image of point B is ____ the pattern maps onto itself.

Class Exercises

Short Answer

For translation *XY*, find the image of each of the following.

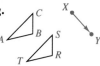

1. point *C*
2. $\overline{BC}$
3. $\triangle ABC$

For the translation *UV*, find the image of each of the following.

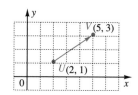

4. point (1, 3)
5. point (3, −1)
6. point (*x*, *y*)
7. the segment with endpoints (0, 4) and (1, 2)

Sample Exercises

Consider the translation *AB* from *A*(2, 1) to *B*(3, 4). Find the translation image of each point.

8. *X*(3, 1)   9. *Y*(−2, 3)
10. *D*(5, 4)   11. *F*(1, 6)

12. For the translation described by the directed segment *XY*, find the translation image of point *X*.

Discussion

Use tracing paper and/or ruler to determine whether each statement is true or false. If true, give a convincing argument. If false, give a counterexample.

13. If lines *p* and *q* are perpendicular, then their translation images are also perpendicular.
14. If the translation image of line *p* is line *q*, then lines *p* and *q* are parallel.
15. If the translation image of *X* is *Y* and if the translation image of line *p* is line *q*, then *XY* is the distance between lines *p* and *q*.

Exercises

A

Consider translation *RT*. Find the image of each of the following.

1. point *B*   2. point *C*
3. point *F*   4. $\overline{AC}$
5. $\overline{FG}$ 6. ∠*BAC*
7. $\triangle ABC$ 8. ∠*BCA*

For translation *AB* from *A*(1, 3) to *B*(4, 5), find the image of each point.

9. *X*(2, 1)   10. *Z*(−2, 3)
11. *Y*(4, −2)   12. *P*(*x*, 4)
13. *Q*(5, *y*)   14. *R*(*x*, *y*)

Assignment Guide
Minimum: 1–27 e/o, 34–36, MR
Regular: 1–36 e/o, MR
Advanced: 6–27 e/o, 28–36, MR

Applications
Exercise 33
Coordinate Geometry
Class Exercises 4–11
Exercises 9–18, 20–26, 28–29, 31, 34, 36
Algebra
Class Exercise 6
Exercises 12–14, 18, 28, 29, 34

Lesson Closure
Review the definition of a translation and ways of finding the image of a point under a translation.

Teacher's Resource Materials
Enrichment Using Manipulatives 77
Practice Master 91
Transparency 59

For translation CD from $C(3, 2)$ to $D(-1, -3)$, find the image of each point.

15. $U(1, 4)$ 16. $V(5, 2)$ 17. $P(3, 7)$ 18. $A(x, y)$

19. Assume that the figure in the box below is extended indefinitely to the
right and to the left. The resulting pattern has translational symmetry.
Complete this statement in three different ways.
The translation that maps ＿ to ＿ maps the pattern onto itself.

B

Consider the translation that maps (x, y) to $(x + 2, y + 3)$.

20. What is the translation image of $(1, 4)$?
21. What is the translation image of $(-3, 5)$?
22. What point has $(2, 3)$ for its image?
23. What point has $(3, 4)$ for its image?
24. Suppose that ℓ is the line through $(-1, 3)$ and $(3, 2)$. Find the slope of ℓ.
Find the slope of its translation image.
25. Suppose that m is a line with slope $\frac{3}{2}$. Find the translation image of m.
26. Suppose the translation image of the point (x, y) is the point
$(x + 1, y + 2)$. If ℓ is the line through the points $(1, 2)$ and $(3, 5)$,
explain why the translation image of ℓ is a line parallel to ℓ.
27. If the translation image of A is A' and of B is B', explain why points A, A',
B, and B' are either collinear or are the vertices of a parallelogram.

C

28. Suppose that the translation image of $(2, 3)$ is $(4, 7)$. For this translation,
write the equation of the translation image of the line $y = 2x + 3$.
29. Suppose that the translation image of $(0, 0)$ is $(2, b)$, and of the line
$y = 3x - 4$ is the line itself. Find b.
30. Suppose that line ℓ is parallel to line m and perpendicular to line n. If m
is translated in a direction parallel to line n, what can you say about
points on ℓ and the translation images of points on m?
31. Suppose that the translation image of (x, y) is $(x + a, y + b)$ where a
and b are constants. Use the distance formula to show that the distance
between any two points P and Q is equal to distance between the
translation images of these two points.
32. A student claimed that for the five parallelograms he tried, the
translation images were again parallelograms. Does this prove that
the translation images of all parallelograms are parallelograms?
Explain.
33. A key-cutting machine has a guide that slides along a key that is
being copied and a cutting wheel that cuts the new key. Explain
how this process might be viewed as an application of translations.

Critical Thinking

34. If the translation PP' is defined by the mapping that sends (x, y) to $(x + 3, y + 4)$, what is the image of the line $y = x$ under PP'?

35. Give a convincing argument that the translation image of a line is a parallel line or the same line.

36. Suppose that $A'(x, y)$ is the image of point A under the translation PP' which maps (x, y) to $(x - 7, y + 8)$. Find the coordinates of the point A in terms of the coordinates of A'.

Mixed Review

Find the volume of each solid.

1. a right rectangular prism with length 9, width 7, and height 4
2. a right cylinder with radius 3 and height 5
3. a sphere with radius 2
4. a regular square pyramid with base edges of length 20 and slant height 26
5. a right cone with diameter 6 and height 10

34. $y = x + 1$ **35.** The slope of the translation image of a line is the same as the slope of the line. **36.** $(x + 7, y - 8)$

Mixed Review Answers

1. 252 **2.** 45π
3. $\frac{32}{3}\pi$ **4.** 3200 **5.** 30π

Connections Answers

1. $f(x, y) = (x + 4, y + 1)$
2. $f(x, y) = (x, y + 1)$
3. $f(x, y) = (x, -y)$
4. $f(x, y) = (y, x)$

CONNECTIONS

Transformations and Functional Notation

Recall that a *function* is a mapping that assigns to each member of the *domain* exactly one member of the *range*. The domain is the set of all possible inputs and the range is the set of all possible outputs.

Transformations can be thought of as functions. In this chapter, we are concerned primarily with transformations whose domain and range are the plane. The notation of functions can be used to describe transformations in a compact way.

For example, consider the translation AB defined by the points $A(1, 1)$ and $B(3, 4)$. This transformation creates a horizontal shift of 2 units and a vertical shift of 3 units. Thus, the translation image of the point $(3, -1)$ is $(3 + 2, -1 + 3)$ or $(5, 2)$. If this translation is considered a function f, you can write $f(3, -1) = (5, 2)$. More generally, the transformation is described by the notation $f(x, y) = (x + 2, y + 3)$.

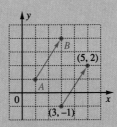

Exercises

Write the functional notation that describes each of the following transformations.

1. the translation CD defined by points $C(5, 8)$ and $D(9, 9)$
2. the translation RS defined by the points $R(-2, 4)$ and $S(-2, 5)$
3. the reflection in the x-axis
4. the reflection in the line $y = x$

13-2 Translations and Translational Symmetry **587**

(Quiz on previous lesson)

1. Find the image under the translation *XY*.

2. If a translation maps the origin to *A*(6, 2), where does it map *B*(4, 4)? (10, 6)
3. If the image of *A*(−2, 4) under a translation is *A′*(4, 7), what is the image of *B*(2, 5)?
B′(8, 8)

Lesson Opener

Use the Explore as an introductory activity to the third type of transformation—rotations.

Key Questions

1. How does a rotation differ from a reflection?
2. How does a rotation differ from a translation?
3. Is distance preserved by a rotation?
4. Identify other properties that are preserved by a rotation.

Materials

student notebooks
tracing paper
investigative software

Key Terms

rotation image
center of rotation
angle of rotation
half-turn
rotational symmetry

OBJECTIVE: *Find the rotation image of a figure.*

13-3 Rotations and Rotational Symmetry

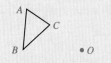

EXPLORE

How could you use tracing paper to find the image of △*ABC* when it is rotated clockwise 40° about point *O*? How does this transformation of a triangle differ from a reflection? a translation?

Rotations of objects such as gears, records, windmills, or carnival rides are common occurrences in the world around us. These motions can be studied through mappings.

▨ **DEFINITION**

A **rotation about a point *O* through an angle of *x*°** is a transformation that associates each point *P* of the plane with a point *P′*, called the **rotation image** of *P*. *P′* is a point in the plane such that *m*∠*POP′* = *x* and *OP* = *OP′*. Point *O* is called the **center of the rotation** and *x*° is called the **angle of rotation.**

In the figure to the right, the 45° (clockwise) rotation image of *A* about point *O* is the point *A′*. Point *B′* is the 45° clockwise rotation image of *B* about point *O*. It can also be said that *A* is the 45° (counterclockwise) rotation image of *A′*. Sometimes this is simply referred to as a rotation of 45°. When no direction is specified, a positive angle measure refers to the counterclockwise direction and a negative angle measure refers to the clockwise direction.

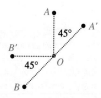

Often, the angle of rotation is allowed to exceed the 0 to 180 degree bounds we have ordinarily placed on angle measures. An angle of 270° refers to a $\frac{3}{4}$ turn in the counterclockwise direction. An angle of −300° refers to $\frac{5}{6}$ of a turn in the clockwise direction.

588　*Chapter 13　Transformations*

Example 1

Pictured are two squares with point O the intersection of the diagonals of both squares. Find the 90° clockwise rotation image about O of each of the following.

a. point D **b.** point G **c.** $\overline{BG}$

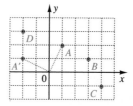

Solution

a. point A $m\angle DOA = 90°$ and $OD = OA$
b. point H $m\angle GOH = 90°$ and $OG = OH$
c. $\overline{CH}$

Try This

Find each of the following.

a. the 90° clockwise rotation image of A
b. the 180° rotation image of E
c. the 90° counterclockwise rotation image of F

A rotation can be described in terms of coordinates with the origin as the point of rotation. For example, the 90° counterclockwise rotation image of point $A(1, 2)$ is point $A'(-2, 1)$. Notice that this rotation maps the point (x, y) to the point $(-y, x)$. This pattern always holds for the 90° counterclockwise rotation. Similar patterns exist for the 90° clockwise rotation and for the 180° rotation. A rotation of 180° is often referred to as a **half-turn**.

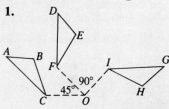

Example 2

Find the image of each point under a 90° counterclockwise rotation about the origin.

a. $B(3, 1)$ **b.** $C(4, -1)$ **c.** $D(-2, 3)$

Solution

a. $B'(-1, 3)$
b. $C'(1, 4)$
c. $D'(-3, -2)$

Try This

Find the image of each point under a 90° counterclockwise rotation about the origin.

a. $(2, -3)$ **b.** $(-1, -3)$

If a figure or pattern can be rotated $x°$ about a point so that the pattern appears identical to its original position, then the pattern has $x°$ **rotational symmetry**. For example, this quilt has 90°, 180°, and 270° rotational symmetry. It also has 360° rotational symmetry. However, since *any* figure can be rotated 360° onto itself, 360° rotational symmetry is usually not mentioned.

13-3 *Rotations and Rotational Symmetry*   **589**

Teaching Notes

Point out that the direction of a rotation can be either clockwise or counterclockwise. A clockwise rotation is considered negative, whereas a counterclockwise rotation is positive.

Remind students that a 450° counterclockwise rotation about a point is the same as a 90° counterclockwise rotation. Also, a 90° counterclockwise rotation is equal to a 270° clockwise rotation. Ask students to name other equivalent rotations.

Using coordinates, a 90° counterclockwise rotation maps (x, y) to $(-y, x)$; a 90° clockwise rotation maps (x, y) to $(y, -x)$; a 180° (half-turn) rotation maps (x, y) to $(-x, -y)$.

Guided Practice

Chalkboard Examples

1.

Pictured are three triangles with point O the center of rotation.
a. What is the 45° clockwise rotation image of B? E
b. What is the 90° counterclockwise rotation image of H? E

Answer to **Try This** a. B
b. G c. E

2. a. Find the 90° clockwise rotation image of $C(4, -1)$.
$(-1, -4)$
b. Find the half-turn rotation image of $D(-2, 3)$. $(2, -3)$

Answer to **Try This** a. $(3, 2)$
b. $(3, -1)$

Class Exercise Answers

1. A 2. G 3. H
4. B 5. $\overline{HE}$ 6. $\overline{BC}$
7. (−1, 1) 8. (−1, −2)
9. (1, 1) 10. B
11. △AOB 12. trapezoid FCBA 13. rhombus FEOA 14. (−5, 4)
15. (2, −3)
16. 90° + 270° = 360°
17. true 18. false, ∠BCA ≢ ∠DEF

Assignment Guide

Minimum: 1–49 e/o, 57, AR
Regular: 10–59 e/o, AR
Advanced: 20–39 e/o, 40–59, AR

Coordinate Geometry
Class Exercises 7–9, 14–15
Exercises 21–26, 43–45

Algebra
Exercises 43–45, AR

Lesson Closure

Review the definitions of rotation and rotational symmetry and the methods of finding the rotation image of a point or set of points.

Teacher's Resource Materials

Enrichment Using Manipulatives 78
Practice Master 92
Transparency 60

Exercise Answers

1. A′ 2. B′ 3. $\overline{A'B'}$
4. A 5. B 6. $\overline{AB}$
7. B 8. A 9. E
10. G 11. $\overline{CD}$ 12. $\overline{CF}$
13. $\overline{DH}$ 14. $\overline{GD}$

Class Exercises

Short Answer

Find the 90° clockwise rotation image about O of each point.

1. D 2. F 3. G 4. A

Find the 90° counterclockwise rotation image about O of each segment.

5. $\overline{EF}$ 6. $\overline{CD}$

Find the 90° counterclockwise rotation image about (0, 0) of each point.

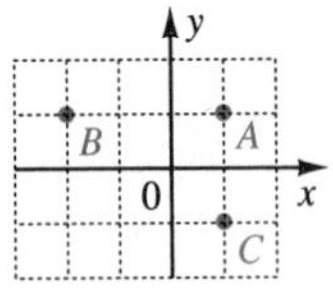

7. $A(1, 1)$ 8. $B(-2, 1)$ 9. $C(1, -1)$

Sample Exercises

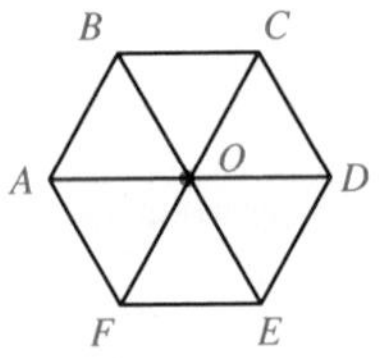

Find the 60° rotation image about O of each of the following.

10. point C
11. $\triangle BOC$
12. trapezoid $ADCB$
13. rhombus $AFOB$

14. Find the 90° counterclockwise rotation image of point (4, 5) about the origin.
15. Find the 90° clockwise rotation image of point (3, 2) about the origin.

Discussion

16. Explain why a 90° clockwise rotation results in the same image as a 270° counterclockwise rotation.

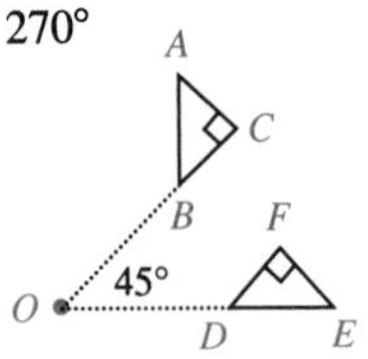

OD = OB **Determine whether each statement is true or false. Explain your answers.**

17. The 45° counterclockwise rotation image about O of D is B.
18. The 45° clockwise rotation image about O of $\triangle ABC$ is $\triangle DEF$.

Exercises

A

Find the 90° clockwise rotation image about O of each of the following.

1. point A 2. point B 3. $\overline{AB}$

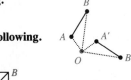

Find the 90° counterclockwise rotation image about O of each of the following.

4. point A' 5. point B' 6. $\overline{A'B'}$

***ABCD* and *EFGH* are squares. Find the 90° clockwise rotation image about O of each of the following.**

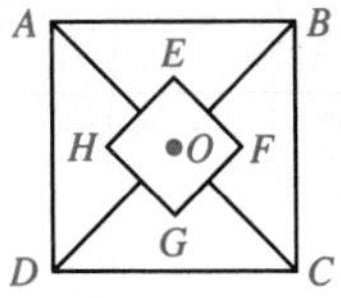

7. point A 8. point D
9. point H 10. point F
11. $\overline{BC}$ 12. $\overline{BE}$
13. $\overline{CG}$ 14. $\overline{FC}$

590 *Chapter 13 Transformations*

This pattern of five squares is centered at O. Find the 90° counterclockwise rotation image about O of each of the following.

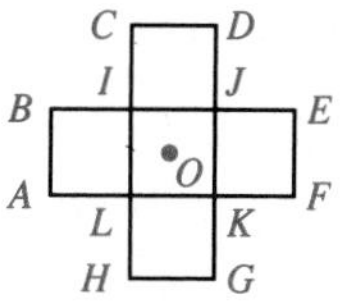

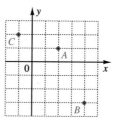

15. point A
16. square $ABIL$
17. rectangle $ABEF$
18. rectangle $CDKL$
19. square $IJKL$
20. $\overline{AE}$

Find the 90° counterclockwise rotation image about (0, 0) of each point.

21. $A(2, 1)$ 22. $B(4, -3)$ 23. $C(-1, 2)$

Find the 90° clockwise rotation image about (0, 0) of each point.

24. $A(2, 1)$ 25. $B(4, -3)$ 26. $C(-1, 2)$

Trace the figure and determine whether each statement is true or false. Explain your reasoning.

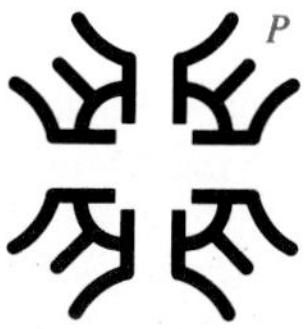

27. If P' is the half-turn image of point P, then P is the half-turn image of P'.
28. The figure has 45° rotational symmetry.
29. The figure has 90° rotational symmetry.
30. The figure has 270° rotational symmetry.

Trace the figure and use the tracing to answer each question.

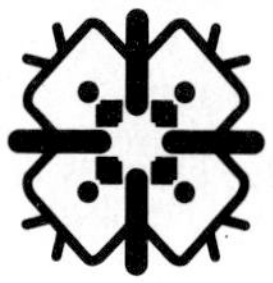

31. Does the figure have 90° rotational symmetry?
32. Does the figure have 45° rotational symmetry?
33. Does the figure have 270° rotational symmetry?
34. Does the figure have 60° rotational symmetry?
35. Does the figure have reflectional symmetry?

Trace the figure and use the tracing to answer each question.

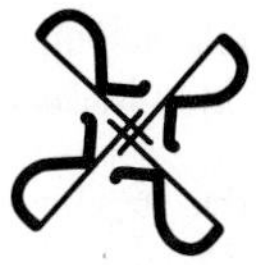

36. Does the figure have 180° rotational symmetry?
37. Does the figure have 135° rotational symmetry?
38. Does the figure have 90° rotational symmetry?
39. Does the figure have reflectional symmetry?

B

40. If $\overline{R'S'}$ is the rotation image of $\overline{RS}$ for a rotation with center O, name an angle that could be measured to find the angle of the rotation.

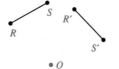

The points in the figure show the results of various rotations about point O. Use a protractor to find the measure of the rotation angle that mapped

41. point A to point A'.
42. point B to point B'.

15. G **16.** square $GHLK$
17. rectangle $GHCD$
18. rectangle $ABJK$
19. square $LIJK$
20. $\overline{GC}$ **21.** $(-1, 2)$
22. $(3, 4)$ **23.** $(-2, -1)$
24. $(1, -2)$
25. $(-3, -4)$ **26.** $(2, 1)$
27. true **28.** false
29. true **30.** true
31. yes **32.** no **33.** yes
34. no **35.** yes **36.** yes
37. no **38.** yes **39.** no
40. $\angle ROR'$ or $\angle SOS'$
41. approx. 120°
42. approx. 35° **43.** $(-y, x)$
44. $(y, -x)$ **45.** a. $(-4, -3)$ b. $(2, -3)$ c. $(-x, -y)$
46. 90° clockwise about O
47. 90° clockwise about O (45° counterclockwise about F)
48. 90° counterclockwise about O **49.** The rotation images of line ℓ intersect to form a square centered about O. $\overline{OA} \cong \overline{OA'} \cong \overline{OA''} \cong \overline{OA'''}$, and $\overline{AA''}$ and $\overline{A'A'''}$ are ⊥ bis. of each other, intersecting at O.
50. If the half-turn image of A about O is A', and of B is B', then O is on $\overline{AA'}$ and $\overline{BB'}$, so (a) if O is not on $\overline{AB}$, then $\angle AOB \cong \angle A'OB'$ (Vert. ∠ Th.) and $\overline{AO} \cong \overline{A'O}$, $\overline{BO} \cong \overline{B'O}$ (Def. of rotation about O). So $\triangle AOB \cong \triangle A'OB'$ (SAS Post.), so $\angle OAB \cong \angle OA'B'$ (Corr. parts of $\cong$ △s are $\cong$.) Finally, $\overline{AB} \parallel \overline{A'B'}$, since the lines are cut by a trans. such that alt. int. ∠s are $\cong$. (b) If O is on $\overline{AB}$, then so are A' and B'. $\overline{AB}$ and $\overline{A'B'}$ are the same line.

13-3 Rotations and Rotational Symmetry 591

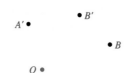

51. The diagonals of a □ are bis. of each other, so $\overline{AO} \cong \overline{OC}$ and $\overline{BO} \cong \overline{OD}$. Since $m\angle AOC = m\angle BOD = 180$, it follows that C is the half-turn image of A about O; D is the half-turn image of B about O; A is the half-turn image of C about O; B is the half-turn image of D about O.   **52.** Given ℓ and O not on ℓ, draw m through $O \perp \ell$ and label the intersection point X. Draw rays p and q from O at 45° angles to $\overline{OX}$. Label points Y and Z where these rays intersect ℓ. Finally, label W on $\overleftrightarrow{OY}$ such that $OW = OY$.

First, $m\angle OYX = m\angle XZO = 45$ and $m\angle YOZ = m\angle ZOW = 90$. $\triangle YOZ$ is isos. rt. $\triangle$, so $OY = OZ$. Since $OW = OY$, you have $OW = OZ$, and Z is the 90° rotation image about O of Y, and W is the 90° rotation image about O of Z. So the 90° rotation image of ℓ is $\overleftrightarrow{WZ}$. Now $\triangle OYZ$ is $\cong$ to $\triangle OZW$ (SAS Post.) so $m\angle OZW = 45$ and $\angle WZY$ is a right $\angle$. Thus $\overline{WZ} \perp \ell$.   **53.** Find the $\perp$ bis. of $\overline{XX'}$ and $\overline{YY'}$. These lines either intersect or are identical. If they intersect, the center of rotation is at their intersection point. If they are identical, then draw $\overleftrightarrow{XY}$ and $\overleftrightarrow{X'Y'}$. These lines will intersect at the center of rotation which will be on the common $\perp$ bis. of $\overline{XX'}$ and $\overline{YY'}$.

54. A, D, or F **55.** A, B, C, D, or F **56.** $m\angle AOA' = x$, $m\angle BOB' = x$ (Def. of $x°$ rotation) So $m\angle AOA' = m\angle BOB'$. (Substitution) $\overline{AO} \cong \overline{A'O}$ and $\overline{BO} \cong \overline{B'O}$ (Def. of rotation) Therefore, $\triangle AOB \cong \triangle A'OB'$ (SAS Post.) and $\overline{AB} \cong \overline{A'B'}$ (Corr. parts of $\cong \triangle$s are $\cong$.)

---

43. Find the 90° counterclockwise rotation image about $(0, 0)$ of $P(x, y)$.

44. Find the 90° clockwise rotation image about $(0, 0)$ of $P(x, y)$.

45. Find the 180° (half-turn) rotation image about $(0, 0)$ of each point.

   a. $A(4, 3)$ **b.** $B(-2, 3)$ **c.** $C(x, y)$

Copy $\triangle ABC$ and $\triangle DEF$ onto a piece of paper. Use tracing paper to answer each question.

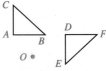

46. What rotation maps A to D?

47. What rotation maps B to E?

48. What rotation maps $\overline{EF}$ to $\overline{BC}$?

49. Consider a 90°, 180°, and 270° rotation of a line ℓ about point O. What does the resulting figure look like? What can you say about $\overrightarrow{OA}$, $\overrightarrow{OA'}$, $\overrightarrow{OA''}$, and $\overrightarrow{OA'''}$?

c

Assume that the rotation image of a line is a line.

50. Prove that the half-turn image of line AB is a line $A'B'$ parallel to $\overleftrightarrow{AB}$.

51. Suppose that O is the intersection of the diagonals of a parallelogram. Prove that a 180° rotation about O maps parallelogram $ABCD$ to parallelogram $CDAB$.

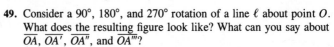

52. If O is a point not on line ℓ, prove that the 90° rotation image about O of line ℓ is a line perpendicular to ℓ.

53. If a rotation image of X is X' and of Y is Y', explain how you can find the center of the rotation.

Imagine that the entire plane is covered with this repeating pattern. Complete each statement and answer the question.

54. A 90° rotation about point ___ will map the entire pattern onto itself.
Can you complete this statement any other way?

55. A 180° rotation about point ___ will map the entire pattern onto itself.
Can you complete this statement any other way?

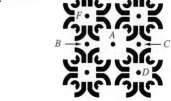

56. Suppose that A' and B' are the $x°$ rotation images about O of points A and B. Use the SAS Postulate to prove that $\overline{AB} \cong \overline{A'B'}$.

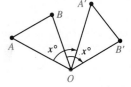

Critical Thinking

57. Consider the arcs swept out by points A and B in the rotation of the line segment OA. Explain why the lengths of the arcs are different, while the angle of rotation is the same.

58. Give a convincing argument that the lower figure to the right is not the rotation image about O of the upper figure.

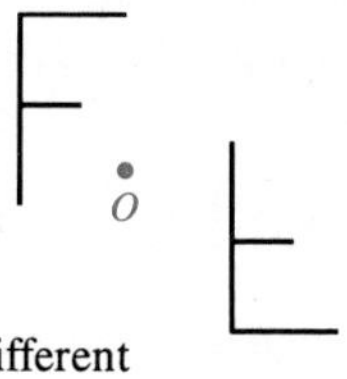

59. Give a convincing argument that a regular n-gon has $n - 1$ different rotations that map the figure onto itself.

Algebra Review

Determine whether each pair of lines are parallel, perpendicular, or neither.

1. $4x + y = 6$
   $4x + y = 8$
2. $3x - y = 6$
   $3x + y = 8$
3. $x + 4y = 8$
   $x = -4y - 10$
4. $2x - 5y = -3$
   $5x + 2y = 6$
5. $8x - 4y = 16$
   $5y - 10x = 3$
6. $2x + 6y = -3$
   $12y = 4x + 20$

Computer Activity

Given a point in the coordinate plane, how could you find its image under a rotation of, for example, 37°? The BASIC program below allows you to input the coordinates of any point and the degree measure of a counterclockwise rotation. It outputs the coordinates of the rotation image of the point.

Notice that the program converts degrees to radians (180° equals π radians) and that the trigonometric ratios SIN and COS are used. Although we have defined these ratios only for angles between 0° and 90°, it is possible to input any degree measure for the rotation.

```
10 PRINT "ENTER THE X-COORDINATE"
20 INPUT X
30 PRINT "ENTER THE Y-COORDINATE"
40 INPUT Y
50 PRINT "ENTER THE AMOUNT OF ROTATION IN DEGREES"
60 INPUT A
70 LET U = X * COS (3.14159 * A/180) - Y * SIN (3.14159 * A/180)
80 LET V = X * SIN (3.14159 * A/180) + Y * COS (3.14159 * A/180)
90 PRINT "THE ROTATION IMAGE IS ("; U; ", "; V; ")"
100 END
```

Exercises

1. Run the program several times with various points and a rotation of 90°. What pattern do you see?
2. Use the program to find the rotation image of (3, 5) under a 70° rotation.
3. Modify the program so that it allows the user to find the rotation image of the point under as many different rotations as desired.

---

57. From Theorem 10.9, arc length equals $\frac{2\pi rm}{360}$. For both arcs, m ($\angle$ of rotation) is the same, but r is different, so the arc lengths are different.
58. A rotation about O of the upper figure will always be F-shaped. The lower figure is a backward F.   **59.** The figure has n sides, and one side may be rotated to any of the $n - 1$ other sides in exactly one way.

Algebra Review Answers

1. parallel   2. neither
3. parallel
4. perpendicular
5. parallel   6. neither

Computer Activity Answers

1. 90° rotation maps (x, y) to $(-y, x)$
2. $(-3.6724, 4.5292)$
3. Add the following lines.
91 PRINT "ENTER 1 IF YOU WISH TO ROTATE ("; X; ", "; Y; ") THROUGH ANOTHER ANGLE"
92 INPUT B
93 IF B = 1, GOTO 50

(Quiz on previous lesson)
Use the figure to identify each
mapping as a reflection, translation, rotation, or half-turn.

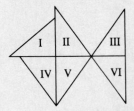

1. triangle I → triangle IV
rotation
2. triangle V → triangle VI
reflection
3. triangle II → triangle IV
half-turn
4. triangle IV → triangle VI
translation
5. triangle IV → triangle V
reflection

Lesson Opener

This lesson can be presented
after the first three lessons of
the chapter (13-1, 13-2, 13-3)
or with each section when
applicable.

Materials

student notebooks
investigative software

Key Terms

composition

OBJECTIVE: *Find the image of a figure under a composition of
transformations.*

13-4 Compositions of Mappings

When one transformation is performed after another, the result is called the
composition of the two transformations. For example, consider the points A
and B and the lines ℓ and m. The reflection of $\overline{AB}$ in line ℓ followed by the
reflection of $\overline{A'B'}$ in line m gives the result $\overline{A''B''}$. This appears to be
equivalent to a translation of $\overline{AB}$ to $\overline{A''B''}$.

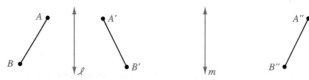

Another example of a composition of transformations is when region A is
rotated 90° clockwise about O followed by another 45° clockwise rotation
about O. The result is equivalent to a 135° clockwise rotation about O that
maps region A to region C.

The result of this composition is summarized in the following theorem.

◆ **THEOREM 13.1**

The composition of two rotations about the same center point O is a
rotation about center O with an angle of rotation equal in measure to the
sum of the measures of the angles of rotation of the two rotations.

Example 1

Complete each statement.

a. The composition of a 54° clockwise rotation about O and a 95°
clockwise rotation about O is a ____ rotation about ____.
b. The composition of these two rotations maps A to ____ and D to ____.

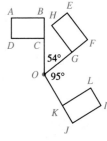

Solution
a. 149° clockwise rotation about O **b.** A to I and D to L

Try This

Complete this statement.
The composition of these two clockwise rotations
maps B to ____ and C to ____.

The composition of the translation AE and the
translation EI maps rectangle $ABCD$ to rectangle $IJKL$.
The composition is the translation AI. This example
suggests the following theorem.

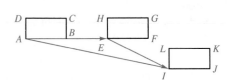

594 *Chapter 13 Transformations*

◆ **THEOREM 13.2**

The composition of two translations is a translation. If translation PR is followed by translation RQ, then the composition translation is the translation PQ.

Example 2

Complete each statement.

a. The composition of the translation AE followed by the translation EI is the translation ___ .

b. Under the composition of the translation AE followed by the translation EI the image of A is ___ .

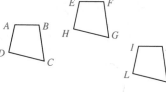

Solution

   a. *AI*   b. *I*

Try This

The composition of the translation DL followed by the translation LH is the translation __?__ .

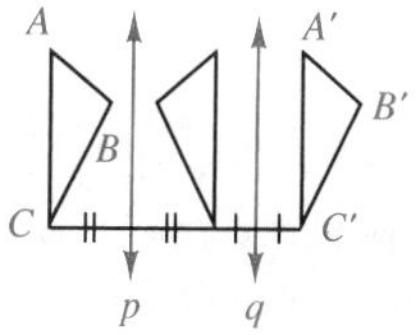

We next consider the composition of two line reflections in parallel lines. Suppose that lines p and q are parallel. The reflection of $\triangle ABC$ in line p and the reflection of its image in line q results in $\triangle A'B'C'$. Notice that this composition results in a translation that maps A to A', B to B', and C to C'. Also, $\overline{AA'} \perp p$ and AA' is twice the distance between lines p and q.

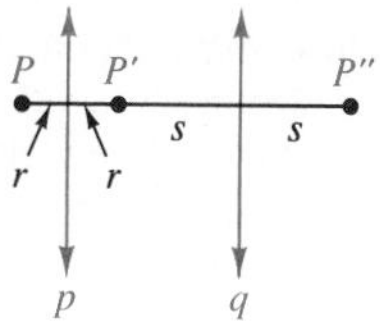

In general, suppose P is a point reflected in line p to P' where the distance PP' is $2r$. Then, suppose P' is reflected in line q to P'' where the distance $P'P''$ is $2s$. The distance PP'' is $2r + 2s$ or twice the distance, $r + s$, between p and q. The same would be true for any other point P in the plane. This argument suggests the following theorem.

◆ **THEOREM 13.3**

The composition of two line reflections in parallel lines p and q is a translation in a direction perpendicular to p and q having a length equal to twice the distance between p and q.

Example 3

$p \parallel q$ **Complete each statement.**

a. The composition of the reflection in p followed by the reflection in q is the translation ___ .

b. The length of $\overline{DH}$ is ___ .

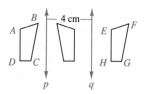

Solution

   a. *AE, BF, DH,* or *CG*   b. 8 cm

Try This

The composition of the reflection in p followed by the reflection in q is the translation that maps D to __?__ and $\overline{BC}$ to __?__ .

Teaching Notes

Emphasize that the composition of two successive reflections in two parallel lines is a translation. This is illustrated in the figure on page 595.

Stress that the number of reflections and the relationship of the lines of reflection are key factors in determining the final transformation.

Key Points

1. The composition of two rotations about the same center is a rotation. (Theorem 13.1)
2. The composition of two translations is a translation. (Theorem 13.2)
3. The composition of two reflections in parallel lines is a translation. (Theorem 13.3)
4. The composition of two reflections in intersecting lines is a rotation. (Theorem 13.4)

Guided Practice

Chalkboard Examples

1. Complete the statement. The composition of the two rotations maps B to ___, A to ___, ___ to K, and $\overline{DC}$ to ___ .
J, I, C, $\overline{LK}$.

Answer to **Try This** J, K

2. Complete the statement. The composition of the translation AE and the translation EI maps A to ___, B to ___, C to ___, and D to ___ . *I, J, K, L*

Answer to **Try This** DH

3. Complete the statement. The composition of the reflection in p followed by the reflection in q is the translation that maps C to ___, $\overline{DC}$ to ___, ___ to H, and ___ to $\overline{EH}$.
G, $\overline{HG}$*, D,* $\overline{AD}$

Answer to **Try This** H, $\overline{FG}$

Class Exercise Answers

1. true **2.** false **3.** true
4. true **5.** false **6.** false
7. $\triangle EDH$, $\triangle JKL$ **8.** $\triangle JIM$
9. Yes; it would have the same effect. Both compositions result in translation WY. **10.** It is never the same, as may be seen from the final image of O. When the rotation is done first, O does not move under the rotation, and then is mapped to O', its translation image. When the translation is done first, O is mapped to O' which is then rotated to a different point O''.

Assignment Guide

Minimum: 1–36 e/o, 4i, 43, AR
Regular: 1–44 e/o, AR
Advanced: 1–16 e/o, 17–44, AR

Coordinate Geometry
Exercises 27–34

Algebra
Algebra Review

Lesson Closure

Make a table to summarize Theorems 13.1 through 13.4.

Teacher's Resource Materials

Enrichment Using
   Manipulatives 79
Practice Master 93
Quiz 25

Suppose that lines p and q intersect at point O. The reflection of $\triangle ABC$ in line p and the reflection of its image in line q results in a rotation centered at O that maps A to G, B to H, and C to I. The angle of rotation is twice the angle formed by line p and line q. That is, $m\angle AOG = 2m\angle WOT$.

This example suggests the following theorem.

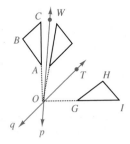

◆ **THEOREM 13.4**

The composition of two line reflections in lines intersecting at O is a rotation with center O and angle of rotation twice the angle from the first line to the second line.

Class Exercises

Short Answer

Determine whether each statement is true or false.

1. The composition of a 45° clockwise rotation about O followed by a 30° clockwise rotation about O is a 75° clockwise rotation about O.
2. The composition of a 35° counterclockwise rotation about O followed by a 45° clockwise rotation about O is a 75° rotation.
3. The composition of a 35° counterclockwise rotation about O followed by a 45° clockwise rotation about O is a 10° clockwise rotation.
4. The composition of a translation and a translation is again a translation.
5. The composition of a line reflection and a line reflection is always a line reflection.
6. If the distance between two points A and B on two intersecting lines p and q is 8 cm, then the composition of successive line reflections in these two lines is a translation that moves points 16 m.

Sample Exercises

Complete each statement.

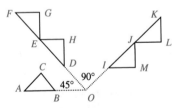

7. The 45° clockwise rotation about O maps $\triangle ABC$ onto ____ and the 90° clockwise rotation about O maps $\triangle EFG$ onto ____ .
8. The composition of the 45° rotation followed by the 90° rotation maps $\triangle ABC$ onto ____ .

Discussion

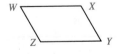

9. After looking at parallelogram $WXYZ$, Raoul said that he thought the translation WX followed by the translation XY would have the same result as the translation WZ followed by the translation ZY. Do you agree? Explain why or why not.
10. Is the image of a rotation about O followed by a translation always, sometimes, or never the same as the translation followed by the rotation about O? Explain the reasoning behind your answer.

Exercises

A

Draw pictures as necessary to help complete each statement.

1. The composition of a 45° clockwise rotation about O and a 90° clockwise rotation about O is a ____ rotation about ____ .
2. The composition of a 90° clockwise rotation about O and a 45° counterclockwise rotation about O is a ____ rotation about ____ .
3. The composition of a ____ clockwise rotation about O and a 45° clockwise rotation about O is a 135° clockwise rotation about O.
4. The composition of a 135° counterclockwise rotation about O and a 45° clockwise rotation about O is a ____ rotation about O.

Complete each statement about the composition of a 45° clockwise rotation about O and a 90° clockwise rotation about O.

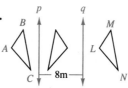

5. ____ maps A to ____ and F to ____
6. ____ maps B to ____ and D to ____
7. ____ maps ____ to C and ____ to D
8. ____ maps ____ to A and ____ to F

Complete each statement about the composition of the translation AE followed by the translation EI.

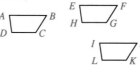

9. ____ maps A to ____
10. ____ maps D to ____
11. ____ maps C to ____
12. ____ maps B to ____

Consider the composition of the reflection in line p followed by the reflection in line q. Complete each statement about this translation.

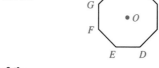

13. ____ maps A to ____   14. ____ maps B to ____
15. ____ maps ____ to N 16. AL = ____

B

Complete each statement about the reflection in line q followed by the reflection in line s.

17. ____ maps A to ____   18. ____ maps L to ____
19. ____ maps O to ____   20. ____ maps N to ____

Complete each statement about the reflection in line p followed by the reflection in line q.

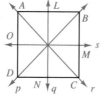

21. ____ maps A to ____   22. ____ maps B to ____
23. ____ maps D to ____   24. ____ maps L to ____
25. ____ maps C to ____   26. ____ maps M to ____

One translation, PQ, maps (x, y) to $(x + 3, y + 1)$ and a second translation, RS, maps (x, y) to $(x + 2, y - 1)$. Complete each statement about the composition of PQ followed by RS.

27. ____ maps $(1, 1)$ to ____   28. ____ maps $(-2, 3)$ to ____
29. ____ maps $(2, -1)$ to ____   30. ____ maps $(-3, -5)$ to ____

31. (3, 4) **32.** (5, 4)
33. (2, 9) **34.** (6, 9)
35.

36. r

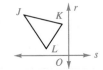

37. O lies on q and q is the ⊥
bis. of $\overline{PP'}$. (Def. of reflection in
q) So $\overline{OP} \cong \overline{OP'}$ because points
on ⊥ bis. of a seg. are equidist.
from the endpoints of the seg.
38. $\overline{OP} \cong \overline{OP'}$ and $\overline{OP'} \cong \overline{OP''}$
(See Exercise 37). Let X be the
intersection point of $\overline{PP'}$ and q.
Let Y be the intersection point
of $\overline{P'P''}$ and p. $\overline{OX} \cong \overline{OX}$ and
$\overline{OY} \cong \overline{OY}$ (Reflex. Prop. of ≅)
$\overline{PX} \cong \overline{P'X}$ and $\overline{P'Y} \cong \overline{P''Y}$ (Def.
of reflection) So △OPX ≅
△OP'X and △OP'Y ≅ △OP''Y
(SSS Post.) Therefore,
∠POX ≅ ∠P'OX and
∠P'OY ≅ ∠P''OY. Finally, by
the ∠ Addition Post., m∠POP'' =
m∠POP' + m∠P'OP'' =
m∠POX + m∠P'OX +
m∠P'OY + m∠P''OY. So, by
substitution, m∠POP'' =
m∠P'OX + m∠P'OX +
m∠P'OY + m∠P'OY =
2(m∠P'OX + m∠P'OY). Since
m∠XOY = m∠P'OX + m∠P'OY
(∠ Addition Post.), m∠POP'' =
2m∠XOY by substitution.
39. $\overline{AA'}$ is ⊥ to p and $\overline{A'A''}$
is ⊥ to q. (Def. of reflection)
Two distinct lines ⊥ to ∥ lines
are ∥. $\overline{A'A''}$ is not ∥ $\overline{AA'}$ because
they share point A'. Therefore,
the two lines must not be dis-
tinct; that is, A' is on $\overleftrightarrow{AA''}$, so
$\overline{AA''}$ is ⊥ to p.

**Complete each statement about the composition of the reflection in the
line y = 3 followed by the reflection in the line x = 2.**

31. maps (1, 2) to ___ **32.** maps (−1, 2) to ___
33. maps (2, −3) to ___ **34.** maps (−2, −3) to ___

**Trace the figures for Exercises 35 and 36 and use tracing paper to help
find the results of the compositions described.**

35. Lines p and q are parallel. Draw the image of △ABC
after a reflection in line p, followed by a 90° clockwise
rotation about D, then followed by a reflection in line q.

36. Lines r and s are perpendicular. Draw the image of △JKL after a
reflection in line r, followed by a reflection in line s, followed by a
counterclockwise rotation about O of 90°.

C

**Lines p and q intersect at O. P″ is the image of P after
reflection in line q followed by reflection in line p.**

37. Prove $\overline{OP} \cong \overline{OP'}$.
38. Prove $m\angle POP'' = 2m\angle x$.

39. Given: Lines p and q are parallel.
    A′ is the reflection image in p of A.
    A″ is the reflection image in q of A′.
  Prove: $\overline{AA''}$ is perpendicular to p.

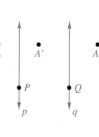

40. Given: Lines p and q are parallel.
    A′ is the reflection image in p of A.
    A″ is the reflection image in q of A′.
    $\overline{PQ}$ is perpendicular to p.
  Prove: AA″ = 2PQ

Critical Thinking

41. One square is a 180° rotation about O of the other. Do
you think that one cube is a 180° rotation about O′ of
the other? Use a drawing, if desired, to explain your
answer.

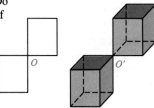

598 *Chapter 13 Transformations*

42. Plane *RST* is a plane of reflectional symmetry for the cube *ABCDEFGH*. Find eight other planes of symmetry for the cube.

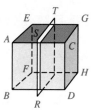

43. Consider a sphere with center *O* and radius *r*. How many planes of symmetry does the sphere have?

44. A line ℓ is an axis of symmetry of a cube if a rotation of the cube in space about the line maps the cube to itself. How many different lines of symmetry can you find for *ABCDEFGH*?

Algebra Review

Solve each inequality.

1. $3x > 9x + 6$ **2.** $4y + 3 \leq 5y - 8$ **3.** $7n - 10 < 5 + 2n$
4. $-3z < -5z + 24$ **5.** $10x \geq 4x$ **6.** $8 - 5y \leq 5y - 12$

Quiz

Complete each statement.

1. The reflection image in *t* of point *B* is ___ .
2. The reflection image in *t* of $\overline{HG}$ is ___ .
3. The reflection image in *t* of ___ is point *C*.

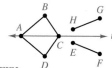

State the number of lines of reflectional symmetry for each figure.

4. equilateral triangle **5.** square

Determine whether each statement is true or false for the translation *LM* defined by *L*(−3, 5) and *M*(2, 6).

6. The image of (3, 4) is (8, 5).
7. The image of (0, 0) is (2, 6).
8. The image of (x, y) is (x + 2, y + 6).

9. Find the 90° clockwise rotation image about *T* of *A*.
10. Find the half-turn image about *T* of *D*.
11. Does the figure have 270° rotational symmetry?

Complete each statement about the composition of a 30° clockwise rotation about *O* followed by a 60° clockwise rotation about *O*.

12. maps $\overline{AB}$ to ___ **13.** maps *C* to ___
14. maps ___ to $\overline{HI}$ **15.** maps ___ to *G*

40. From Exercise 39, *A′* is on $\overleftrightarrow{AA''}$, so by Seg. Add. Post., $AA'' = AA' + A'A''$. Let *X* be the intersection point of $\overleftrightarrow{AA'}$ and *p*. Let *Y* be the intersection point of $\overline{A'A''}$ and *q*. From Exercise 39, $\overleftrightarrow{XY} \perp p$, so $\overleftrightarrow{XY} \parallel \overline{PQ}$ (In a plane, 2 lines $\perp$ to the same line are $\parallel$.) and $XY = PQ$ ($\parallel$ lines are equidist. at all points; opp. sides of a $\square$ are $\cong$.) Also $AX = A'X$ and $A'Y = A''Y$ by def. of reflection, so $AA' = AX + A'X = 2(A'X)$ and $A'A'' = A'Y + A''Y = 2(A'Y)$ (Seg. Add. Post. and Substitution) Now $AA'' = AA' + A'A'' = 2(A'X) + 2(A'Y) = 2(A'X + A'Y) = 2(XY) = 2(PQ)$. **41.** Many 180° rotations about *O′* are possible. Only some of these rotate one cube to the other.

42. *AEDH, BFCG, BDEG, ACFH, ABGH, EFCD*, and two other planes like *RST* **43.** infinitely many **44.** 13; 4 lines like ℓ, 6 lines connecting the midpoints of opposite edges, 3 lines connecting the centers of opposite faces

Algebra Review Answers

1. $x < -1$ **2.** $y \geq 11$
3. $n < 3$ **4.** $z < 12$
5. $x \geq 0$ **6.** $y \geq 2$

Quiz Answers

1. *D* **2.** $\overline{EF}$ **3.** *C*
4. 3 **5.** 4 **6.** true
7. false **8.** false
9. *B* **10.** *B* **11.** yes
12. $\overline{GH}$ **13.** *I* **14.** $\overline{BC}$
15. *A*

OBJECTIVE: *Use properties of isometries.*

13-5 Isometries and Congruence

In Chapter 4 you studied the concept of congruence as it applies to triangles. This concept of congruence can be extended to apply to polygons and to figures which are not polygons, such as semicircles. The concept of **isometry** is the basis for generalizing the concept of congruence to figures that are not polygons. Reflections, translations, and rotations have the common property that the distance between any two points and the distance between their images are equal. Transformations with this property are called isometries.

■ DEFINITION

An **isometry** is a transformation that satisfies the following property. If P and Q are any two points and P' and Q' are the transformation images of P and Q, then $PQ = P'Q'$.

Example 1

Suppose that an isometry maps A to A', B to B', C to C', and D to D'. Find each length.

a. $A'D'$ **b.** $B'C'$

Solution

a. $A'D' = 4$ *By the definition of isometry,*
b. $B'C' = 5$ $AD = A'D'$ and $BC = B'C'$.

Try This

Find each length.

a. $C'D'$ **b.** $A'B'$

◆ THEOREM 13.5

A line reflection is an isometry.

Given: Line ℓ and any two points P and Q
P' and Q' are the reflection images of P and Q.

Prove: $PQ = P'Q'$

Plan   Use the definition of line reflection to show that $PXYA$ and $P'XYB$ are rectangles and that $QA = Q'B$. Use SAS congruence to show that $\triangle APQ \cong \triangle BP'Q'$ and conclude that $PQ = P'Q'$. A similar argument works when P and Q are not on the same side of ℓ.

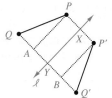

Example 2

Suppose that *GHIJKM* is the reflection image in line of *ABCDEF*. Find each length.

a. *KJ* b. *IH* c. *GH*

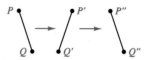

Solution

a. 7 b. 4 c. 2

Try This

Find *IJ* and *KM*.

If one isometry maps *PQ* to *P'Q'* and another isometry maps *P'Q'* to *P"Q"*, then *PQ* = *P'Q'* and *P'Q' = P"Q"*.

This observation is the basis of the proof of the following theorem.

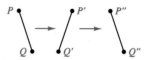

◆ THEOREM 13.6

The composition of two isometries is an isometry.

In Lesson 13-4, you saw that a composition of reflections is either a translation or a rotation. The converse is also true. That is, every translation and every rotation can be expressed in terms of a composition of reflections. Since reflections are isometries, the following are consequences of Theorem 13.6.

▶ COROLLARY 13.6a

A translation is an isometry.

▶ COROLLARY 13.6b

A rotation is an isometry.

■ DEFINITION

A figure *F* is **congruent** to figure *F'* if there is an isometry such that *F'* is the image of *F*.

Example 3

Suppose *p* is a line of symmetry for *ABCDEFGH*. Explain why quadrilaterals *ABCD* and *HGFE* are congruent.

Solution

HGFE is the reflection image of *ABCD*. Since a line reflection is an isometry, these two quadrilaterals are congruent.

Try This

Explain why pentagons *ABCDO* and *HGFEO* are congruent.

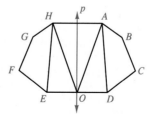

13-5 *Isometries and Congruence* **601**

Teaching Notes

Encourage students to name the vertices of the image of a figure in the same order as the vertices of the preimage.

Guided Practice

Chalkboard Examples

1. Suppose an isometry maps *A* to *D*, *B* to *E*, and *C* to *F*.

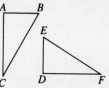

Complete each statement.
a. *AC* = *DF*
b. △*ABC* ≅ △*DEF*

Answer to **Try This**
a. *C'D'* = 6 b. *A'B'* = 8

2.

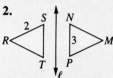

Suppose △*RST* is the reflection image in line *ℓ* of △*MNP*. Find *MN* and *TS*. 2, 3

Answer to **Try This** *IJ* = 5, *KM* = 13

3.

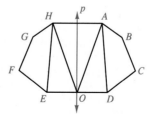

Suppose *q* is a line of symmetry for *IJKLMNOP*. Explain why △*OJM* is isosceles. *JM* is the reflection image of *JO*. Since reflection is an isometry, *JM* ≅ *JO* and △*OJM* is isosceles.

Answer to **Try This** *HGFEO* is the reflection image of *ABCDO*. Since a line reflection is an isometry, the pentagons are congruent.

The fact that congruent figures are mapped under isometries into congruent figures provides a basis for another theorem which characterizes isometries.

◆ THEOREM 13.7

If figure F' is the image of figure F under an isometry, then the areas of F and F' are equal.

Class Exercises

Short Answer

Determine whether each statement is true or false.

1. A line reflection is an isometry.
2. An isometry is a line reflection.
3. If a figure F' is the image of a figure F under an isometry, then F and F' are congruent.
4. A translation is an isometry.
5. An isometry is a mapping that preserves congruence.
6. If the image of a figure is congruent to the original figure, then the mapping is an isometry.

Sample Exercises

Suppose that lines p and q are both lines of symmetry for quadrilateral $ABCD$. Find each length.

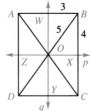

7. AO 8. CY 9. DY 10. AZ
11. Explain why you can conclude that $AX = DX$.
12. Explain why you can conclude that $WX = YX$.
13. Explain why you can conclude that $WX = YZ$.

Discussion

14. Is there a composition of two line reflections that maps the figure on the left to the figure on the right? Explain.

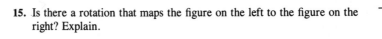

15. Is there a rotation that maps the figure on the left to the figure on the right? Explain.

16. Make a drawing of a $\triangle ABC$ and two parallel lines p and q. Consider the reflection of the triangle in p followed by the reflection of the image in q. Then repeat the process, first reflecting in q and then in p. Were the two final images the same? Do you think that the composition of reflections in parallel lines is commutative? Give another example to illustrate your conclusion.

602   *Chapter 13   Transformations*

Exercises

A

Suppose that $A'B'C'D'$ is the image of parallelogram $ABCD$ under an isometry. Find each length.

1. $A'B'$ 2. $A'D'$
3. BC 4. $B'C'$
5. CD 6. $C'D'$

7. Explain how you know that $AC = A'C'$.
8. Explain how you know that $A'B'C'D'$ is a parallelogram.

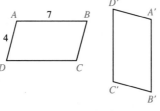

Given that lines p and q are lines of symmetry of $ABCDEF$, complete each statement.

9. The reflection image in line p of A is ___ .
10. The reflection image in line q of C is ___ .
11. $BC = $ ___   12. $FE = $ ___   13. $DE = $ ___
14. $XD = $ ___   15. $FY = $ ___   16. $AY = $ ___

B

Given that lines p and q are lines of symmetry, answer the following.

17. Why is $ACDF$ a rectangle?
18. The reflection in which line explains why $AE = FB$?
19. The reflection in which line explains why $FB = BD$?
20. Why are quadrilaterals $ABCX$ and $FEDX$ congruent?
21. Why are pentagons $AFEDX$ and $FABCX$ congruent?
22. **Given:** Lines p and q are lines of symmetry of $ABCDEF$.
    Prove: $ABDE$ is a parallelogram.

C

23. If an isometry maps A to A', B to B', and C to C' prove that $\triangle A'B'C'$ is congruent to $\triangle ABC$ assuming that A, B, and C are noncollinear points.
24. Prove that if $\angle A'B'C'$ is the reflection image of a line of $\angle ABC$ then $m\angle ABC = m\angle A'B'C'$.

The composition of the translation described by AB followed by the reflection in line ℓ maps the red region below onto the blue region. This composition of isometries is called a **glide reflection** with glide line ℓ.

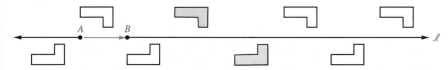

25. If point P is above ℓ where is its glide reflection image?
26. If point P is below ℓ where is its glide reflection image?
27. If point P is on ℓ where is its glide reflection image?

Exercise Answers

1. 7   2. 4   3. 4
4. 4   5. 7
6. 7   7. The distance between points is preserved under isometries.   8. Opposite sides of $A'B'C'D'$ are the images of opposite sides of $ABCD$ under an isometry, hence are congruent. So $A'B'C'D'$ is a parallelogram.   9. C
10. D 11. 8   12. 8
13. 8   14. 3
15. 3   16. 3   17. Answers may vary. Diagonals are congruent and bisect each other by reflection.   18. reflection in q
19. reflection in p
20. $FEDX$ is the reflection image of $ABCX$ in q. Since line reflection is an isometry, $ABCX$ and $FEDX$ are congruent.
21. $FABCX$ is the reflection of $AFEDX$ in line q. Since line reflection is an isometry, $AFEDX$ and $FABCX$ are congruent.
22. $\overline{AE}$ is the reflection image of $\overline{CE}$ in line p. $\overline{CE}$ is the reflection image of $\overline{BD}$ in line q. $\overline{AB}$ is the reflection image of $\overline{CB}$ in line p. $\overline{CB}$ is the reflection image of $\overline{ED}$ in line q. So, since line reflections are isometries, $\overline{AE} \cong \overline{CE} \cong \overline{BD}$, and $\overline{AB} \cong \overline{CB} \cong \overline{ED}$. Therefore, opposite sides of $ABDE$ are congruent, so $ABDE$ is a parallelogram.
23. $\overline{AB} \cong \overline{A'B'}$, $\overline{AC} \cong \overline{A'C'}$, and $\overline{BC} \cong \overline{B'C'}$ because isometries preserve distances. So $\triangle ABC \cong \triangle A'B'C'$ by the SSS Post.
24. If $\triangle A'B'C'$ is the reflection image in a line of $\triangle ABC$, then $\overline{AB} \cong \overline{A'B'}$, $\overline{AC} \cong \overline{A'C'}$, and $\overline{BC} \cong \overline{B'C'}$. So, by the SSS Post., $\triangle ABC \cong \triangle A'B'C'$ and $\angle ABC \cong \angle A'B'C'$. (Corr. parts of $\cong \triangle$s are $\cong$.)   25. below ℓ
26. above ℓ 27. on ℓ

28. *KJFB* is the reflection image of *ABFJ* in line *q*. Since line reflection is an isometry, the lines are congruent.   **29.** The figure in quadrant I is the reflection image of the figure in quadrant II in line *q*. The figure in quadrant II is the reflection image of the figure in quadrant III in line *p*. Therefore, the figure in quadrant I is the image of the figure in quadrant III under reflection in line *p* followed by reflection in line *q*. Since the composition of reflections is an isometry, the figure in quadrant I is congruent to the figure in quadrant III.   **30.** Rotate △*ABB′* 60° about *A*. Since △*ABC′* is equilateral, *m*∠*BAC′* = 60 and *BA* = *C′A*. Similarly, since △*AB′C* is equilateral, *m*∠*B′AC* = 60 and *B′A* = *CA*. So, the rotation image of *B* is *C′*, and the rotation image of *B′* is *C*. Thus *BB′* = *CC′*, since rotations are isometries.

31. Corresponding parts of the figures are congruent since they are mapped to each other by an isometry. Corresponding perimeters, circumferences, etc. are equal.   **32.** If *A*, *B*, and *C* are the respective images of *R*, *S*, and *T*, then $\overline{AB} \cong \overline{RS}$, $\overline{AC} \cong \overline{RT}$, $\overline{BC} \cong \overline{ST}$, so △*ABC* ≅ △*RST*. Thus ∠*ABC* ≅ ∠*RST* since corr. parts of ≅ △s are ≅.

Mixed Review Answers

1. 72   **2.** 35   **3.** 28
4. 6   **5.** 8   **6.** 5

Suppose that lines *p* and *q* are lines of symmetry of the figure.

28. Prove that quadrilateral *ABFJ* and quadrilateral *KJFB* are congruent.

29. Prove that the figure "S" in quadrant I and the figure "S" in quadrant III are congruent.

Critical Thinking

30. In △*ABC*, *m*∠*A* = 20. If △*ABC′* and △*AB′C* are equilateral triangles, explain how a 60° rotation of one triangle in this figure would allow you to make a comparison between *BB′* and *CC′*.

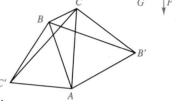

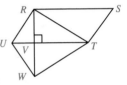

31. If *R* is an isometry that maps figure *A* to figure *B*, what can you say about the relationship of the borders (perimeters, circumferences, . . .) of figures *A* and *B*?

32. If ∠*ABC* is the image of ∠*RST* under an isometry *M*, give a convincing argument why ∠*ABC* ≅ ∠*RST*.

Mixed Review

RSTU is a parallelogram.

1. *RS* = 12, *RV* = 6   Find the area of ▱*RSTU*.
2. *RW* = 7, *UT* = 10   Find the area of quadrilateral *URTW*.
3. *RV* = 4, *RS* = 8, *VT* = 6   Find the area of trapezoid *RSTV*.
4. If the area of ▱*RSTU* is 48 cm and *UT* = 8, find *RV*.
5. If *URTW* is a kite with area 64 and *UT* = 16, find *RW*.
6. Find the height of trapezoid *RSTV* if its area is 30, *RS* = 7, and *VT* = 5.

Biographical Note

Sophie Germain (1776–1831)

Sophie Germain, one of the most prominent women mathematicians of the nineteenth century, was largely self-taught. Her interests included acoustics, higher arithmetic, and the theory of elasticity.

Germain was influenced by a work of the great mathematician Gauss and wrote to him some of her own arithmetical observations. Concerned that Gauss would be prejudiced against a female mathematician, she used a man's name. Gauss was very impressed with Germain's work and eventually discovered that his correspondent was a woman. Realizing the prejudices and difficulties a woman in science must have encountered, he wrote that Germain possessed "the noblest courage, quite extraordinary talents, and a superior genius."

OBJECTIVE: *Find the image of a figure under a dilation.*

13-6 Dilations

A magnifying glass or a microscope can be used to enlarge your view of an object or figure. The shape of the object stays the same but the size is allowed to vary. The same effect is produced by a transformation called a **dilation.** It preserves the *shape* of a figure, but allows the *size* to change.

■ DEFINITION

A **dilation** with center O is a transformation that associates with a point P, the unique point P' on ray OP such that $\frac{OP'}{OP} = k$. We say that the **dilation image** of point P is point P'. The dilation image of O is O itself. The number k is called the **scale factor** of the dilation.

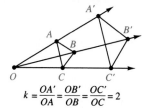

The scale factor of a dilation, like the scale factor for similarity, can be any positive real number. In the figure to the right, the scale factor is 2. The points A', B', and C' are the dilation images of points A, B, and C for the dilation with center O and scale factor 2.

$$k = \frac{OA'}{OA} = \frac{OB'}{OB} = \frac{OC'}{OC} = 2$$

Example 1

Complete each statement for the dilation with center O and scale factor 3.

a. The image of B is ___ .
b. The image of $ABCD$ is ___ .

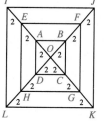

Solution

a. J since $\frac{OJ}{OB} = \frac{6}{2} = 3$
b. $IJKL$

Try This

a. If the image of F is J for the dilation with center O and scale factor k, find the value of k.
b. If the image of $EFGH$ is $ABCD$ for the dilation with center O and scale factor k, find the value of k.

Notice that if $k > 1$ the image figure is an enlargement, and if $0 < k < 1$, the image figure is a reduction. Consequently, we call the dilation an **enlargement** if $k > 1$ and a **reduction** if $0 < k < 1$. If $k = 1$, then the dilation is the **identity mapping** (the mapping that leaves all points unchanged).

13-6 Dilations   **605**

13-6 Dilations   **605**

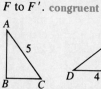

Chalkboard Examples

1.

If the image of P is Q for the dilation with center O and scale factor k, find the value of k. **2**

Answer to **Try This** a. 1.5 b. 0.5

2. If the scale factor of a dilation centered at the origin is 7, find the image of $(-2, 3)$ $(-14, 21)$

Answer to **Try This** a. $(1, 3)$
b. $(-0.5, 0.75)$

Class Exercise Answers

1. E **2.** A **3.** I
4. $\triangle GHI$ **5–6.** Check students' drawings.   **7.** $(6, -2)$
8. $(2, 3)$ **9.** $(16, 8)$
10. lines through O or all lines if scale factor is 1.   **11.** scale factor 1   **12.** all values

Assignment Guide

Minimum: 1–21 e/o, 28–29, MR
Regular: 1–29 e/o, MR
Advanced: 8–15 e/o, 16–29, MR

Coordinate Geometry

Class Exercises 7–9
Exercises 12–17, 23–28

Algebra

Exercise 26

Lesson Closure

Summarize by asking students to define dilation and scale factor.

Teacher's Resource Materials

Practice Master 95
Technology: Calculator 20

Using a coordinate system, it is possible to describe a dilation with scale factor k and center at the origin as a mapping from (x, y) to (kx, ky). The following example illustrates this.

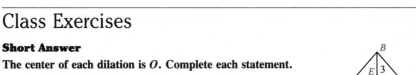

Example 2

If the scale factor of a dilation centered at the origin is 2, find the image of each point.

a. $(3, 3)$ **b.** $(-1, -2)$

    <u>Solution</u>
    a. $(6, 6)$ **b.** $(-2, -4)$ *Multiply each coordinate by 2.*

Try This

If the scale factor of a dilation centered at the origin is $\frac{1}{4}$, find the image of each point.

a. $(4, 12)$ **b.** $(-2, 3)$

Class Exercises

Short Answer

The center of each dilation is O. Complete each statement.

1. For scale factor of 2, the dilation image of H is ____ .
2. For scale factor of 3, the dilation image of G is ____ .
3. For scale factor of $\frac{1}{3}$, the dilation image of C is ____ .
4. For scale factor of $\frac{1}{2}$, the dilation image of $\triangle DEF$ is ____ .

Sample Exercises

Trace $\overline{AB}$ and O as shown to the right. Draw the image of $\overline{AB}$ for each dilation.

5. the dilation with center O and scale factor 2
6. the dilation with center O and scale factor $\frac{1}{2}$

Complete each statement.

7. The image of $(3, -1)$ under the dilation with center $(0, 0)$ and scale factor 2 is ____ .
8. The image of $(6, 9)$ under the dilation with center $(0, 0)$ and scale factor $\frac{1}{3}$ is ____ .
9. The image of ____ under the dilation with center $(0, 0)$ and scale factor $\frac{1}{2}$ is $(8, 4)$.

Discussion

10. For which lines ℓ is the dilation image of ℓ with center O the line ℓ itself?
11. For what value of the scale factor is the dilation image of a figure a figure of the same size and shape?
12. For what values of the scale factor is the dilation image of a figure a figure of the same shape?

Exercises

A

Trace the figure to the right. Draw the image of △ABC under each.

1. the dilation with center O and scale factor 2
2. the dilation with center A and scale factor 3

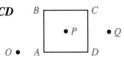

Trace the figure to the right. Draw the image of square $ABCD$ under each.

3. the dilation with center O and scale factor 2
4. the dilation with center P and scale factor 3
5. the dilation with center Q and scale factor $\frac{1}{2}$

The center of each dilation is O. Complete each statement.

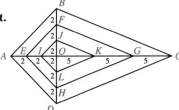

6. For a scale factor of 2, the image of K is ___ .
7. For a scale factor of 2, the image of $IJKL$ is ___ .
8. For a scale factor of 3, the image of $IJKL$ is ___ .
9. For a scale factor of $\frac{1}{2}$, the image of H is ___ .
10. For a scale factor of $\frac{1}{2}$, the image of $EFGH$ is ___ .
11. For a scale factor of $\frac{1}{3}$, the image of $ABCD$ is ___ .

Consider dilations with center (0, 0) in a rectangular coordinate system. Complete each statement.

12. The dilation image with scale factor 3 of (3, 5) is ___ .
13. The dilation image with scale factor 2 of (−2, 1) is ___ .
14. The dilation image with scale factor $\frac{1}{2}$ of (−4, 3) is ___ .
15. The dilation image with scale factor $\frac{1}{5}$ of (10, 7) is ___ .

B

16. If the dilation image of (1, 2) is (4, 8) under a dilation centered at the origin, find the scale factor. Using the same scale factor, find the coordinates of the dilation images of points A (2, 3), B (−1, 4), and C (3, 5).
17. If (3, 5) is the dilation image with scale factor 2 of point A, find the coordinates of point A.
18. Suppose that △$A'B'C'$ is the dilation image of △ABC under the dilation with center O and scale factor k. Prove that $A'B' = kAB$.
19. Suppose that △$A'B'C'$ is the dilation image of △ABC under the dilation with center O and scale factor k. Prove that $BC = \frac{1}{k}B'C'$.
20. If $A'B'C'D'$ is the image of square $ABCD$ under the dilation with center P and scale factor 4, and if the length of one side of $ABCD$ is 5, find the perimeter of square $A'B'C'D'$.
21. If $A'B'C'D'$ is the image of square $ABCD$ under the dilation with center P and scale factor 4, and if the area of $ABCD$ is 4, find the area of square $A'B'C'D'$.

C

22. If line ℓ' is the dilation image of line ℓ under a dilation with center O and scale factor k, prove that $\ell \parallel \ell'$ or ℓ and ℓ' are the same line.

Exercise Answers

1.–5. Check students' drawings.
6. G **7.** *EFGH*   **8.** *ABCD*
9. L **10.** *IJKL*   **11.** *IJKL*
12. (9, 15)   **13.** (−4, 2)
14. (−2, 1.5)   **15.** (2, 1.4)
16. scale factor 4, images of A, B, C are, respectively, (8, 12), (−4, 16), (12, 20)
17. (1.5, 2.5)   **18.** If O is on $\overleftrightarrow{AB}$, then, since $kOA = OA'$ and $kOB = OB'$ (i) if O is between A and B, $A'B' = A'O + OB' = kAO + kBO = k(AO + BO) = kAB$; (ii) if A is between O and B, then A' is between O and B' and $A'B' = OB' − OA' = kOB − kOA = k(OB − OA) = kAB$; (iii) if B is between O and A, then B' is between O and A' and $A'B' = OA' − OB' = kOA − kOB = k(OA − OB) = kAB$.
If O is *not* on $\overleftrightarrow{AB}$, then $OA' = kOA$, $OB' = kOB$, $\frac{OA'}{OA} = \frac{OB'}{OB}$. And since $\angle AOB \cong \angle A'OB'$, △$ABO$ is similar to △$A'B'O$ by the SAS Similarity Theorem, so $\frac{A'B'}{AB} = \frac{OA'}{OA} = k$; i.e., $A'B' = kAB$.   **19.** As in Exercise 18, $B'C' = kBC$, so $BC = \frac{1}{k}B'C'$.   **20.** 80
21. 64   **22.** First, if O is on ℓ, then every point on ℓ is mapped to another point on ℓ; i.e., ℓ' is the same line as ℓ. If O is *not* on ℓ, consider any two points X and Y on ℓ and their dilation images X' and Y' on ℓ'. $kOX = OX'$ and $kOY = OY'$, so $\frac{OX}{OX'} = \frac{OY}{OY'}$. Also $\angle XOY \cong \angle X'OY'$, so △$XOY$ is similar to △$X'OY'$ by the SAS Similarity Theorem. This means $\angle OXY \cong \angle OX'Y'$, and since two lines cut by a transversal such that a pair of corresponding angles are $\cong$ are $\parallel$, $\ell \parallel \ell'$.
23. The dilation image of (1, 5) is (2, 10). The dilation image of (3, 2) is (6, 4). Slope of ℓ = $\frac{5-2}{1-3} = \frac{-3}{2}$, slope of ℓ' = $\frac{10-4}{2-6} = \frac{-3}{2}$, $\ell \parallel \ell'$

23. Suppose that ℓ is the line through the points $(1, 5)$ and $(3, 2)$. If line ℓ' is the image of line ℓ under the dilation with center $(0, 0)$ and scale factor 2, calculate the slopes of both ℓ and ℓ'. What do you conclude?

24. Suppose that A' and B' are the images of $A(2, 3)$ and $B(4, 7)$ under the dilation with center $(0, 0)$ and scale factor k. Show that $A'B' = kAB$.

25. $\triangle A'B'C'$ is the image of $\triangle ABC$ under the dilation with center $(0, 0)$ and scale factor 2. Given $A(-1, 2)$, $B(2, 4)$, and $C(5, 2)$, how does the area of $\triangle ABC$ compare to the area of $\triangle A'B'C'$?

26. Suppose that ℓ is the line through points $A(x_1, y_1)$ and $B(x_2, y_2)$ and that ℓ' is the line through A' and B'. A' and B' are the dilation images of A and B under the dilation with center $(0, 0)$ and scale factor k. Show that ℓ and ℓ' have equal slopes.

27. $\triangle A'B'C'$ is the dilation image with center $(0, 0)$ and scale factor $\frac{1}{3}$ of $\triangle ABC$. Given $A(-3, 5)$, $B(3, 6)$, and $C(5, -2)$, find the coordinates of A', B', and C'.

Critical Thinking

28. Draw on graph paper polygon $ABCDEF$ and its dilation image $A'B'C'D'E'F'$ under the dilation with center $(0, 0)$ and scale factor 2. Estimate how many times greater the area of $A'B'C'D'E'F'$ is than the area of $ABCDEF$. Calculate the area of each to check your guess. State a generalization about the effect a dilation with scale factor k has on the area of a polygon.

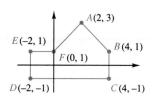

29. The figure to the right shows the result of a dilation in space which maps a smaller cube into a larger cube. If the dilation is centered at O and the scale factor is 2, what is the ratio of the surface areas of the cubes? the volumes of the cubes?

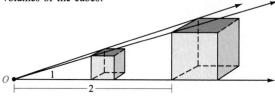

Mixed Review

Give the center and radius of each circle.

1. $x^2 + y^2 = 64$ **2.** $(x - 1)^2 + (y - 2)^2 = 1$
3. $(x + 4)^2 + (y - 5)^2 = 10$ **4.** $(x + 1)^2 + y^2 = 40$

Given each center and radius, write the equation of the circle in the form shown in Exercises 1–4.

5. center $(0, 0)$; radius 6   **6.** center $(1, 4)$; radius 9
7. center $(-1, 0)$; radius $\sqrt{5}$ **8.** center $(-2, -3)$; radius $2\sqrt{7}$

DISCRETE MATH

Fitting a Line to a Set of Data

Researchers and businesspeople who use mathematics often need to fit a line to a set of data. Such a line represents the set of data and can be used to predict trends from the data. The line *m* on the graph below fits or describes the relationships between the length of a video game and points scored.

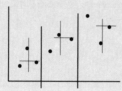

Video Game Points per Min

Example

What score would you predict for a 12-min game?

Solution

Using line *m* as a model, a score of 1450 points seems reasonable, as the point (12,1450) appears to be on the line.

Try This

What score would you predict for an 8-min game? Lines can be fit to a set of data in several ways. One way is shown below.

1. Divide the set of points into thirds, moving from left to right. If the number is not divisible by three, put the leftover points in the middle portion.

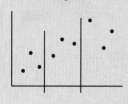

2. Find the point in each portion that has half the points to its left and half to its right. Draw a vertical line through each. Find the point in each portion that has half the points below it and half above it. Draw a horizontal line through each.

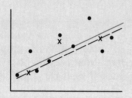

3. Draw a line connecting the intersections of the two lines in the first and third portions. Then slide the line one third of the way to the point of intersection of the lines in the middle third.

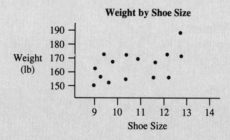

Exercise

Find a line of fit for the data below to predict the weight of an adult male from his shoe size. What weight would you expect for a person with a size 13 shoe?

Weight by Shoe Size

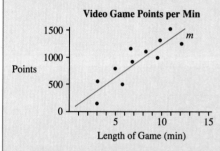

Discrete Math

Fitting a Line to a Set of Data

Begin by discussing examples of data that can be represented as an ordered pair—time of day and temperature, age of a person and height, price of a car and the number of cars sold, etc.

Points from this type of data rarely lie on a straight line. However, it is often useful to find a line that approximates the data points as closely as possible. The line can then be used to predict values of the data for points not previously given.

Answer to **Try This** 970

Exercise Answer
about 170 lb

1. Find the image of $A(-6, -4)$ under the dilation centered at the origin with scale factor 3. $(-18, -12)$

2. Find the image of $B(3, -2)$ under the dilation centered at the origin with scale factor $\frac{1}{2}$. $(\frac{3}{2}, -1)$

3. If the dilation image of $(1, 2)$ is $(4, 8)$ under a dilation centered at the origin, find the scale factor. 4

4. If the image of K is G for the dilation with center O, find the scale factor. $\frac{5}{2}$

5. If the image of H is L for the dilation with center O, find the scale factor. $\frac{2}{5}$

Lesson Opener

It may be helpful to review properties of similarity and ways of proving triangles similar (AA Similarity Postulate, SAS and SSS Similarity Theorems) before discussing this lesson with students.

Tell students that dilations are sometimes called *similarity transformations* since preimages and images under dilations are similar.

Materials

student notebooks
compasses
straightedges
investigative software

OBJECTIVE: *Use dilations to draw conclusions about figures.*

13-7 Dilations and Similarity

In the figure to the right, $\triangle DEF$ is the image of $\triangle ABC$ under the dilation with center O and scale factor 2. It is also evident that the lengths of the sides of $\triangle ABC$ have been multiplied by 2 and that the two triangles are similar. These facts are the subject of the theorems in this lesson.

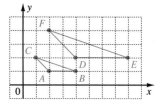

◆ **THEOREM 13.8**

If A' and B' are the images of A and B under the dilation with center O and scale factor k, then $A'B' = kAB$.

Given: points A and B and their images A' and B' under the dilation with center O and scale factor k

Prove: $A'B' = kAB$

Plan By the definition of the dilation with center O and scale factor k, you know that $k = \frac{OA'}{OA} = \frac{OB'}{OB}$. With this proportion and the SAS Similarity Theorem, you can show that $\triangle AOB \sim \triangle A'OB'$. Since corresponding sides of similar triangles are proportional, conclude that $A'B' = kAB$.

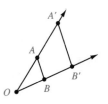

The following example shows how Theorem 13.8 may be used when one figure is the dilation image of another.

Example 1

Suppose that *GHIJKL* is the image of *ABCDEF* under the dilation with center O and scale factor 2. Find each length.

a. GH **b.** JK **c.** FE

   Solution

   a. $GH = 2AB = 2 \cdot 12 = 24$
   b. $JK = 2DE = 2 \cdot 4 = 8$
   c. $KL = 2FE$ $16 = 2FE$ $FE = 8$

Try This

Complete each statement.

a. If $BC = 8$, then $HI = $ ___ .
b. If $GL = 8$, then $AF = $ ___ .
c. If ___ $= 5$, then $GL = 10$.

The next theorem describes the relationship between dilations and the concept of similarity.

610   *Chapter 13   Transformations*

◆ THEOREM 13.9

If $\triangle A'B'C'$ is the image of $\triangle ABC$ under the dilation with center O and scale factor k, then $\triangle A'B'C'$ is similar to $\triangle ABC$.

Given: $\triangle A'B'C'$ is the image of $\triangle ABC$ under the dilation with center O and scale factor k.

Prove: $\triangle A'B'C'$ is similar to $\triangle ABC$.

Plan Use Theorem 13.8 to conclude that $A'B' = kAB$, $A'C' = kAC$, and $B'C' = kBC$. Use the SSS Similarity Theorem to conclude that $\triangle A'B'C'$ is similar to $\triangle ABC$.

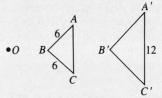

The concept of similarity of figures is quite general. It centers on the fact that two figures are similar if and only if you can "size" one figure and then "move" the sized figure to match the other. This idea is used in the following definition of similarity.

■ DEFINITION

A figure F is similar to a figure F' if there is a dilation and an isometry such that the composition of the dilation and the isometry maps F onto F'.

Note that in the above definition, the dilation and the isometry may be composed in either.

In Example 2, two figures are shown to be similar by showing that one is the image of the other under a composition of a dilation and an isometry.

Example 2

Show that figures $MNKL$ and $PNSQ$, each made up of a square and semicircle, are similar.

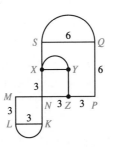

Solution

The $180°$ rotation about N maps M to Z, K to X, and L to Y. The dilation with center N and scale factor 2 maps Z to P, Y to Q, and X to S. Therefore, the composition maps square $MNKL$ to $PNSQ$ and semicircle LK to semicircle SQ. You can conclude that figure $MNKL$ is similar to $PNSQ$.

Try This

Use the above definition to show that figures $ABCDEF$ and $TUVWXY$ below are similar.

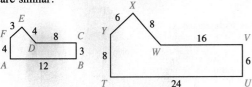

Teaching Notes

Point out that in the first figure on page 610, $\triangle ABC \sim \triangle DEF$ by the SSS Similarity Theorem. Using the Distance Formula, show the following.

1. $DE:AB = 4:2$ or $2:1$, $DE:AC = 2\sqrt{2}:1\sqrt{2}$ or $2:1$, $FE:BC = 2\sqrt{10}:1\sqrt{10}$ or $2:1$
2. The product of the length of any side of $\triangle ABC$ and the scale factor 2 yields the length of the corresponding side of $\triangle DEF$.

Guided Practice

Chalkboard Examples

1. This figure shows a dilation of $\triangle ABC$ having center O and scale factor $\frac{3}{2}$. Find each length.

a. $A'B'$ 9 **b.** AC 8

Answer to **Try This** a. 16 b. 4 c. AF

2.

Suppose $\triangle ABC$ and $\triangle DEC$ are equilateral triangles. Use a composition of an isometry and a dilation to show that $\triangle ABC \sim \triangle DEC$.

The $60°$ clockwise rotation about C followed by the dilation with center C and scale factor 2 maps $\triangle ABC$ to $\triangle DEC$.

Answer to **Try This**
Translation AT followed by the dilation with center T and scale factor 2 maps $ABCDEF$ to $TUVWXY$.

Class Exercises

Short Answer

$AB = 1$, $AC = \sqrt{5}$, $BC = 2\sqrt{2}$ $\triangle DEF$ is the image of $\triangle ABC$ under the dilation with center O and scale factor 2 and $\triangle GHI$ is the image of $\triangle DEF$ under the dilation with center O' and scale factor $\frac{3}{2}$. Find each length.

1. DE
2. EF
3. DF
4. GH
5. GI
6. HI

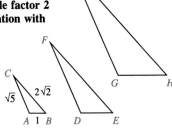

Sample Exercises

Complete each statement.

7. If $\triangle ABC$ is the dilation image of $\triangle DEF$, then the scale factor $k = $ ___ .
8. If $\triangle ABC$ is the dilation image of $\triangle GHI$, then the scale factor $k = $ ___ .
9. If $\triangle GHI$ is the dilation image of $\triangle ABC$, then the scale factor $k = $ ___ .
10. If $\triangle ABC$ is the dilation image of $\triangle DEF$, then $\triangle ABC$ is similar to ___ .

Discussion

11. If circle C_1 has radius r_1 and circle C_2 has radius r_2, how would you prove that C_1 and C_2 are similar figures in each case?

  a. if the circles have the same center
  b. if the circles have different centers

Exercises

A

$\triangle DEF$ is the image of $\triangle ABC$ under the dilation with center O and scale factor 2. Find each length.

1. DE **2.** DF **3.** BC

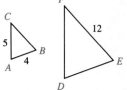

$EFGH$ is the image of $ABCD$ under a dilation with scale factor $\frac{5}{3}$. Find each length.

4. EF **5.** FG
6. GH **7.** EH

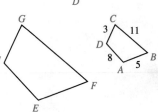

$\triangle XYZ$ is the image of $\triangle ABC$ under a dilation with scale factor 4. Complete each statement.

8. If $AB = 25$, then $XY = $ ___ .   **9.** If $AC = 30$, then $XZ = $ ___ .
10. If $YZ = 32$, then $BC = $ ___ .   **11.** If $XY = 14$, then $AB = $ ___ .
12. If $BC = $ ___ , then $YZ = 4$.   **13.** If ___ = 12, then $XZ = 48$.

14. Use a dilation to show that figures *BODF* and *AOEG* are similar if $\frac{OF}{OG} = \frac{1}{2}$ and the arcs are parts of circles tangent at *O*.

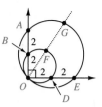

15. Explain why polygon *ABFGE* is similar to polygon *HBDJI*. Angles which appear congruent may be assumed congruent.

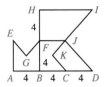

B

Suppose that △*A′B′C′* is the dilation image of △*ABC* with scale factor $\frac{1}{2}$ and △*A″B″C″* is the dilation image of △*A′B′C′* with scale factor 3. Complete each statement.

16. If *AB* = 20, then *A″B″* = ___ .

17. If *A″C″* = 36, then *AC* = ___ .

18. If *A′B′* = 14, then *AB* = ___ .

19. If *A″B″* = 12, then *AB* = ___ .

20. If *B″C″* = ___ , then *BC* = 10.

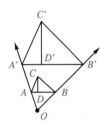

A dilation with center *O* and scale factor 3 maps *A* to *A′*, *B* to *B′*, *C* to *C′*, and *D* to *D′*.

21. Prove that if $\overline{CD}$ is an altitude of △*ABC*, then $\overline{C′D′}$ is an altitude of △*A′B′C′*.

22. Find the ratio of the area of △*A′B′C′* to the area of △*ABC*.

C

The larger cube below is the image of the smaller cube under a three-dimensional dilation with scale factor 3.

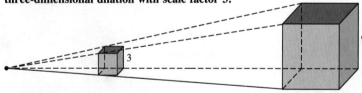

23. Find the surface area of the larger cube.

24. Find the volume of the larger cube.

25. Find the ratio of the surface area of the larger cube to the surface area of the smaller cube? Find the ratio of the volumes.

26. Given that the dilation image of circle *C* is circle *C′* and that the scale factor of the dilation is 2, what can you conclude about the relationship between the circumference of circle *C′* and the circumference of circle *C*? Prove that your conjecture is true.

14. Use the dilation with scale factor 2 and center O. Since the dilation image of a circle is a circle, and since three points determine a circle, and this dilation maps *B* to *A*, *D* to *E*, *O* to *O*, and *F* to *G*, the dilation image of *BODF* is *AOEG*.

15. Rotate *ABFGE* −90° about *B*. Follow this with the dilation of scale factor 2 and center *B*.

16. 30   **17.** 24   **18.** 28

19. 8   **20.** 15

21. By Theorem 13.10, dilations take triangles to similar triangles. So △*ACD* is similar to △*A′C′D′*, hence, ∠*CDA* ≅ ∠*C′D′A′*. Since $\overline{CD}$ is an altitude of △*ABC*, ∠*CDA* is a right angle, so ∠*C′D′A′* is a right angle, so $\overline{C′D′}$ is an altitude of △*A′B′C′*.   **22.** 9 to 1

23. 486   **24.** 729

25. 9 to 1, 27 to 1

26. Circumference ratio is 2 to 1. If radius of circle *C* is *r*, and center is point *X*, then points on *C′* are distance 2*r* away from the dilation image of *X*. Therefore, the radius of *C′* is 2*r*. The circumference of *C* is 2*πr*. The circumference of *C′* is $2\pi(2r) = 4\pi r$.

$\frac{\text{circumference of } C′}{\text{circumference of } C} = \frac{4\pi r}{2\pi r} = \frac{2}{1}$

Algebra Review Answers

1. $-10, 3$ **2.** -4 **3.** ± 7
4. $-2, 12$ **5.** $\frac{1}{2}, 3$
6. $-1, \frac{1}{3}$

Quiz Answers

1. true   **2.** false
3. true   **4.** 6   **5.** $\overline{DE}$
6. 24 cm²   **7.** 18   **8.** 6
9. true   **10.** $(-18, 27)$

27. Explain why the letters C and U and letters I and H as shown below are similar or are not similar.

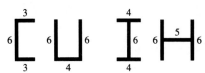

Critical Thinking

28. Suppose that figure F_1 is similar but not congruent to F_2 and F_2 is similar but not congruent to F_3. Must it be true that F_1 is similar but not congruent to F_3? Explain.

29. A point G is called a **fixed point** of a transformation if the point is its own image under the transformation. A given transformation may have a number of fixed points. For each of the following transformations, describe the fixed points in the plane under the transformation.
   a. reflection   **b.** rotation   **c.** translation
   d. dilation   **e.** composition of rotation and dilation (same center)

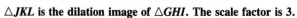

Algebra Review

Solve each equation.

1. $x^2 + 7x - 30 = 0$ **2.** $x^2 + 8x + 16 = 0$ **3.** $y^2 - 49 = 0$
4. $a^2 - 10a - 24 = 0$ **5.** $2x^2 - 7x + 3 = 0$ **6.** $3x^2 + 2x - 1 = 0$

Quiz

Determine whether each statement is true or false.

1. Every translation is an isometry.
2. Every dilation is an isometry.
3. Two figures are similar if there is a dilation and an isometry whose composition maps one figure onto the other.

***RSTUVW* is the image of *ABCDEF* under an isometry.**

4. If $BC = 6$, find ST.
5. If $UV = 2$, what other segment must also have length 2?
6. If the area of *ABCDEF* is 24 cm², find the area of *RSTUVW*.

△*JKL* is the dilation image of △*GHI*. The scale factor is 3.

7. If $HI = 6$, find KL.   **8.** If $JL = 18$, find GI.
9. True or false: $\triangle GHI \sim \triangle JKL$?

10. Find the image of $(-6, 9)$ under the dilation with center $(0, 0)$ and scale factor 3.

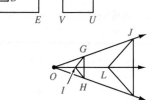

CRITICAL THINKING

Making and Supporting Decisions

Many critical thinking problems require the use of visual reasoning. Use these skills to develop a solution for the following situation.

In a certain two-person game, the players take turns placing a penny on a circular table top with a green tablecloth. The pennies may touch, but are not allowed to rest upon one another. Furthermore, they must be completely on the table—not hanging out over the edge. Once a penny is placed on the table it cannot be moved. The last player to place a penny on the table is the winner.

If each player makes an optimal move on his or her turn, will the player who went first or second be the winner?

Answer the questions in each step below to use the process of critical thinking.

1. Understand the Situation

  a. What is the situation about?

  b. What conclusion, decision, or solution is required?

  c. Are there any questions you could ask to clarify the problem?

2. Deal with the Data/Evidence/Assumptions

  a. Make a list of the most important rules and data. Is other information needed?

  b. Which data given in the situation is not relevant?

  c. What assumptions are made? What other assumptions could be made?

3. Go Beyond the Data/Evidence/Assumptions

  a. Try this problem with very small tables.

  b. Consider a table whose diameter is the width of a certain number of pennies.

  c. Does it make a difference if the diameter is a certain number of pennies long?

4. State and Support your Conclusion/Decision/Solution

Write a paragraph, with an accompanying diagram, describing your solution to this situation.

5. Apply the Conclusion/Decision/Solution

A similar situation involved a square table. What modifications, if any, would need to be made in the solution strategy to answer the same question about the game played on this table?

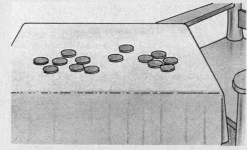

Exercise

Use the above process for the following situation.

Lucille found four sections of a bracelet. Each piece consisted of three links of gold. She wanted to have the four pieces joined to form one loop. A jeweler told her it would cost one dollar for each link that was opened and welded shut again. When the jeweler wrote a bill for $4, Lucille said she thought the loop could be made with less than four links being cut. Do you agree?

The first player will always win the game whether it is played on a round table or a square table.

Exercise Answer

The loop can be made for $3 by cutting apart all three links of one section and using them to join the remaining three sections.

CHAPTER SUMMARY

Vocabulary

angle of rotation (13-3)	identity mapping (13-6)	reflection (13-1)
composition (13-4)	image (13-1)	reflectional symmetry (13-1)
dilation (13-6)	isometry (13-5)	rotation (13-3)
directed segment (13-2)	line of symmetry (13-1)	rotational symmetry (13-3)
enlargement (13-6)	mapping (13-1)	transformation (13-1)
fixed point (13-7)	preimage (13-1)	translation (13-2)
glide reflection (13-5)	reduction (13-6)	translational symmetry (13-2)
half-turn (13-3)		

Key Ideas

1. A mapping which establishes a one-to-one correspondence between points in the plane is called a transformation.
2. When one transformation is performed after another, the result is called the composition of the transformations.
3. An isometry is a transformation that preserves distance. Reflections, rotations, and translations are all isometries.
4. The composition of two isometries is an isometry.
5. A dilation with center O and scale factor k is a transformation that associates with each point P a point P' such that P' is on $\overrightarrow{OP}$ and $\frac{OP'}{OP} = k$.
6. A dilation with scale factor k and center at the origin is a mapping from (x, y) to (kx, ky).
7. A figure F is congruent to a figure F' if there is an isometry so that F' is the image of F.
8. A figure F is similar to a figure F' if there is a dilation and an isometry such that the composition of the dilation and the isometry maps F onto F'.

CHAPTER REVIEW

13-1

Complete each statement.

1. The reflection image in ℓ of A is ___ .
2. The reflection image in ℓ of B is ___ .
3. The reflection image in ℓ of $\overline{GH}$ is ___ .
4. The reflection image in ℓ of ___ is $\overline{AB}$.

5. Give the number of lines of reflectional symmetry for the letter H.

13-2

For translation RS from $R(-2, 3)$ to $S(2, 4)$, find the translation image of each point.

6. $(4, 6)$ 7. $(0, -1)$ 8. (x, y)

Complete each statement.

9. The image of point A under translation CG is ___.
10. The image of point ___ under translation JB is point C.
11. The image of $\overline{EF}$ under translation HL is ___.
12. The image of $ABCD$ under translation AE is ___.

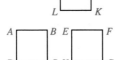

13-3

$LMNOPQ$ is a regular hexagon. Consider rotations about R.

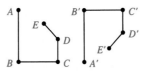

13. Name the 60° clockwise rotation image of L.
14. Name the half-turn image of $\overline{NO}$.
15. Does the figure have 90° rotational symmetry?
16. Does the figure have 120° rotational symmetry?

13-4

Determine whether each statement is true or false.

17. The composition of a 90° clockwise rotation about O followed by a 45° clockwise rotation about O is a 135° clockwise rotation about O.
18. The composition of two line reflections is always a line reflection.
19. Translation AB followed by translation BC is translation CA.

13-5

$A'B'C'D'E'$ is the image of $ABCDE$ under an isometry.

20. If $AB = 6$, find the length of $\overline{A'B'}$.
21. If $D'E' = 12$, find the length of $\overline{DE}$.
22. Can you conclude that $ABCDE$ is congruent to $A'B'C'D'E'$?

13-6

Complete each statement.

23. The dilation with center $(0, 0)$ and scale factor 5 maps $(10, -5)$ to ___.
24. The dilation with center O and scale factor 3 maps point R to ___.
25. The dilation with center O and scale factor $\frac{1}{2}$ maps point W to ___.

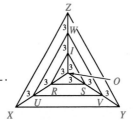

13-7

26. If LMN is the image of IJK under a dilation with scale factor 2 and $LM = 6$, find IJ.
27. Show that rectangle $AEBF$ is similar to rectangle $GCBD$.

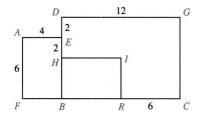

CHAPTER TEST

Determine whether each statement is true or false.

1. If $\triangle RST$ is the dilation image of $\triangle ABC$ and the scale factor is 2, then $AB = 2RS$.
2. The composition of two isometries is always an isometry.
3. Figure G is congruent to figure G' if there is an isometry that maps G to G'.
4. Two figures are similar only if there is a dilation that maps one figure onto the other.
5. Every line reflection is an isometry.

Complete each statement.

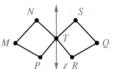

6. The reflection image in line ℓ of $\overline{MN}$ is ___ .
7. The reflection image in line ℓ of ___ is point T.
8. The letter I has ___ lines of reflectional symmetry.
9. The image of C under translation FJ is ___ .
10. The image of ___ under translation HL is M.
11. The image of $\overline{CE}$ under translation FN is ___ .

$\triangle TUV$ is an equilateral triangle. Consider rotations about O.

12. Find the 120° clockwise rotation image of $\overline{TO}$.
13. Find the 240° counterclockwise rotation image of $\overline{UV}$.
14. Does the figure have 90° rotational symmetry?

Complete each statement.

15. The composition of a 37° clockwise rotation about O and a 92° clockwise rotation about O is a ___ rotation about O.
16. The composition of translation QR followed by translation RS is ___ .
17. The composition of the reflection in line p followed by the reflection in line q is a translation if p and q are ___ .

18. Suppose $AE = 6$ and $EO = 2$. Find the scale factor of the dilation with center O that maps point E to point A.
19. If B is the image of F under the dilation with center O and scale factor 3 and $OF = 5$, find FB.
20. Find the image of (8, 10) under the dilation with center (0, 0) and scale factor $\frac{1}{2}$.
21. Show that $\triangle HOI$ is similar to $\triangle LOM$.

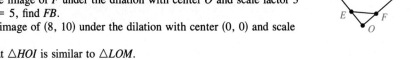

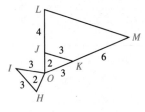

PROBLEM SOLVING

Choosing a Strategy

The problems below give you practice in choosing among the various strategies presented in the book.

Problem-Solving Strategies	
Draw a Diagram	Simplify the Problem
Make a Table	Make an Accurate Drawing
Look for a Pattern	Guess, Check, Revise
Work Backward	

Problems

Choose a strategy and solve each problem.

1. A painter had $48 to buy brushes. The two types of brushes available cost $4 and $6. In how many different ways could the painter spend all of her money buying these brushes?

2. Edie needed to think of a four-digit code for her automatic teller. She was allowed to use the numbers 0, 1, 2, 3, and 4 in any order and as often as she wished. How many different codes could Edie create?

3. A biologist has a mixture of two types of cells, type A and type B. Every two hours, each B cell produces one A cell and one B cell. Type A cells do not produce additional cells. Assume that there was one cell of each type to start. How many cells of each type would there be after one day?

4. It takes four equilateral triangles with sides of length 1 to make an equilateral triangle with sides of length 2. How many equilateral triangles with sides of length 1 does it take to make an equilateral triangle with sides of length 10?

5. A large circular park is to have six straight walking paths through it. The architect has been told to design the park so that there will be a maximum number of flower and garden areas inside the park and around the paths. What is the greatest number of flower and garden areas possible with six straight paths through the park?

6. What should be the dimensions of the bottom row of a pyramid that continues to build like the one below if there are 100 blocks to work with and as many blocks as possible are to be used?

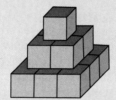

7. A certain game has two possible scoring plays—a three-point play and an eight-point play. How many different total scores for one player are not possible in this game?

8. A math exam had 20 items. Students received two points for each correct answer and lost one point for each incorrect or missing answer. Mari had a score of 16. How many items were correctly answered on her test?

9. A computer access-code number was designated in a special way. It was a four-digit number between 1000 and 2000. Also, it was the smallest integer in this range that can be written as the sum of two positive cubes in two different ways. What was the code number?

10. A basketball series between the Aces and the Falcons is determined when one team wins three games. In how many ways can the Falcons win the series?

11. Grant always carries a lot of change in quarters, dimes, nickels, and pennies. Beth needed change for a dollar. It turned out that Grant had the most change he could possibly have had without having change for a dollar. How much money did Grant have in change?

Encourage students to consider all the problem-solving strategies introduced in the book. Remind them that more than one strategy may be suitable for a problem and that a combination of strategies is often useful.

Problem Answers
1. 5   **2.** 625   **3.** 4096 of each type   **4.** 100   **5.** 22
6. 6 × 6 (91 blocks used)
7. 7 scores (1, 2, 4, 5, 7, 10, 13)
8. 12   **9.** 1729 =
1728 + 1 = 1000 + 729
10. 10   **11.** $1.19

CUMULATIVE REVIEW

Chapters 1–13

1. The inverse of "If an angle has measure 90, then it is a right angle" is ___ .

   a. If an angle is a right angle, then it has measure 90.
   b. If an angle does not have measure 90, then it is a right angle.
   c. If an angle does not have measure 90, then it is not a right angle.
   d. If an angle has measure 90, then it is not a right angle.

2. An angle that forms a linear pair with an interior angle of a triangle is called a(n)

   a. remote interior angle. b. exterior angle.
   c. corresponding angle. d. obtuse angle.

3. $\overline{AD} \cong \overline{BD} \cong \overline{BC}$, $m\angle 1 = 40$ Find $m\angle C$.

   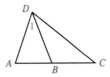

   a. 35 b. 40 c. 70 d. 110

4. In $\triangle RST$, U and V are midpoints of $\overline{RT}$ and $\overline{RS}$. If $\overline{UV} \| \overline{TS}$, which of the following statements is true?

   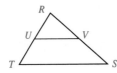

   a. $\overline{RU} \cong \overline{RV}$ b. $\overline{UV}$ is a median of $\triangle RST$.
   c. $TS = \frac{1}{2}UV$ d. $UV = \frac{1}{2}TS$

5. Which proportion is not equivalent to $\frac{a}{b} = \frac{x}{y}$?

   a. $\frac{a+b}{b} = \frac{x+y}{y}$ b. $\frac{y}{b} = \frac{x}{a}$
   c. $\frac{a}{y} = \frac{x}{b}$ d. $\frac{b}{a} = \frac{y}{x}$

6. The hypotenuse in a 45°–45°–90° triangle has length 12. Find the length of each leg.
   a. 6 b. $4\sqrt{3}$ c. $6\sqrt{2}$ d. $6\sqrt{3}$

7. Find x in the triangle below.

   a. $2\sqrt{3}$ b. $\sqrt{74}$ c. 8 d. $2\sqrt{37}$

8. In a circle with radius 5 in., find the length of a chord that is located 4 in. from the center.

   a. 3 in. b. 6 in.
   c. $\sqrt{41}$ in. d. $2\sqrt{41}$ in.

9. In space, what is the locus of points equidistant from two parallel lines?

   a. a point b. a line
   c. a sphere d. a plane

10. Find the area of a circle if the circumference is 10π.
    a. 20π b. 25π c. 50π d. 100π

11. Find the area of a trapezoid with height 3 and bases 10 and 12.
    a. 33 b. 66 c. 11 d. 45

12. $\square ABCD$, $AB = 8$, $AD = 6$, $m\angle A = 60$
    Find the area of the parallelogram.
    a. $24\sqrt{3}$ b. 24 c. $12\sqrt{3}$ d. 48

13. Find the area of a regular hexagon if its perimeter is 48.
    a. $144\sqrt{3}$ b. 96 c. $96\sqrt{3}$ d. $192\sqrt{3}$

14. The areas of two similar polygons are in the ratio 16:25. If the radius of the smaller polygon is $4\sqrt{2}$, find the radius of the larger polygon.
    a. $5\sqrt{2}$ b. 5 c. $\frac{5\sqrt{2}}{2}$ d. 50

15. Which formula could you use to find the lateral area of a right pentagonal prism?
    a. $\frac{1}{3}Bh$ b. ph c. ℓwh d. $\frac{1}{2}p\ell$

16. A pyramid has a base with an area of 49 cm² and a height of 12 cm. Find the volume of the pyramid.

   a. 294 cm³   **b.** 588 cm³
   c. 84 cm³   **d.** 196 cm³

17. Find the volume of a right cylinder with base radius 4 and height 5.

   a. 40π **b.** 72π
   c. 80π **d.** 144π

18. Find the surface area of a sphere with diameter 12.

   a. 36π **b.** 48π
   c. 144π **d.** 288π

19. Find the volume of the cone below.

   a. 48π **b.** 192π **c.** 24π **d.** 576π

20. Find the midpoint of $\overline{AB}$ for $A(-3, 6)$ and $B(5, -2)$.

   a. $(2, 4)$ **b.** $(-1, 4)$
   c. $(1, -2)$ **d.** $(1, 2)$

21. Find the slope of a line that is perpendicular to the line $2x + 3y = 6$.

   a. $\frac{3}{2}$ **b.** $\frac{-3}{2}$ **c.** 2 **d.** $\frac{-2}{3}$

22. Find the slope of a line that is parallel to the line $7x - 14y = 3$.

   a. $\frac{1}{2}$ **b.** 2 **c.** -2 **d.** $\frac{-1}{2}$

23. Find the equation of the line containing $(-6, 5)$ and having slope $\frac{2}{3}$.

   a. $y = \frac{2}{3}x - 1$
   b. $y = \frac{2}{3}x + 9$
   c. $y = \frac{2}{3}x + 11$
   d. $y = \frac{2}{3}x$

24. Find the equation of a circle with center $(-3, 4)$ and radius 9.

   a. $(x + 3)^2 + (y - 4)^2 = 9$
   b. $(x - 3)^2 + (y + 4)^2 = 9$
   c. $(x + 3)^2 + (y - 4)^2 = 81$
   d. $(x - 3)^2 + (y + 4)^2 = 81$

25. Which of the following figures has no lines of reflectional symmetry?

   a. parallelogram   **b.** square
   c. circle   **d.** isosceles triangle

26. Which transformation is not always an isometry?

   a. translation   **b.** reflection
   c. rotation   **d.** dilation

27. If $(-6, 15)$ is the dilation image of point X with scale factor 3 and center $(0, 0)$, find the coordinates of point X.

   a. $(2, -5)$ **b.** $(-2, 5)$
   c. $(6, -15)$ **d.** $(-18, 45)$

28. What is the composition of two reflections in parallel lines?

   a. a translation   **b.** a reflection
   c. a rotation   **d.** a dilation

29. Find the image of point P under the translation ST followed by the translation TU.

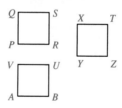

   a. point A **b.** point Y
   c. point V **d.** point B

30. Find the image of $(2, -4)$ under the dilation with center $(0, 0)$ and scale factor 2.

   a. $(4, -2)$ **b.** $(1, -2)$
   c. $(4, -8)$ **d.** $(-4, 8)$

Algebra Review

Algebraic Properties and Integer Operations

Algebra Review

Algebraic Properties and Integer Operations

	Properties of Addition	Properties of Multiplication
Commutative Property	$a + b = b + a$	$a \cdot b = b \cdot a$
Associative Property	$(a + b) + c = a + (b + c)$	$(a \cdot b) \cdot c = a \cdot (b \cdot c)$
Identity Property	$a + 0 = a$	$a \cdot 1 = a$
Inverse Property	$a + (-a) = 0$	$a \cdot \frac{1}{a} = 1 \ (a \neq 0)$

Property of Zero for Multiplication $a \cdot 0 = 0$

Distributive Property of Multiplication over Addition $a \cdot (b + c) = a \cdot b + a \cdot c$

Exercises
Which property is illustrated by each equation?

1. $62 + 87 = 87 + 62$
2. $3a + 0 = 3a$
3. $17 \cdot 0 = 0$
4. $(3b + 1) \cdot 1 = 3b + 1$
5. $7 \cdot (x + b) = 7x + 7b$
6. $450 + (-450) = 0$
7. $(22 \cdot x) \cdot z = 22 \cdot (x \cdot z)$
8. $3y \cdot \frac{1}{3y} = 1$
9. $y \cdot z = z \cdot y$

Use the commutative and associative properties to write three equivalent expressions.

10. $(x + y) + 5$ 11. $(a \cdot b) \cdot 5$ 12. $4 + (c + d)$

Operations with Integers

Example 1
Simplify $-2(8 - 3 + 4)$.

Solution

$$-2(8 - 3 + 4) = -2 \cdot 8 + -2(-3) + -2(4)$$
$$= -16 + 6 - 8$$
$$= -18$$

Example 2
Simplify $x(13 + 8) - 3(x - 7)$.

Solution

$$x(13 + 8) - 3(x - 7) = 13x + 8x - 3x - (-21)$$
$$= 18x + 21$$

Exercises
Simplify.

13. $-4 + 3$
14. $-4 - 7$
15. $2 - 3 + 4 - 5 + 6$
16. $267 - 378$
17. $-486 - 715$
18. $-1764 - (-1765)$
19. $-3(7 + 2 - 3)$
20. $4(x + 3 + 7)$
21. $(3x + 4)(-3) + 5x$
22. $6 + 3(m - 4)$
23. $7 \cdot 5y + 3(2y - 6)$
24. $3(t + 7) - 7(t - 13)$
25. $(3a + 5)4 + (2a + 8)6$
26. $12y - 12x + 3y - 3x$
27. $(-7)(-3) - 8(-2)$

Algebra Review

Solving Linear Equations

Example 1

Solve $3x + 4 = 13$.

Solution

$$3x + 4 = 13$$
$$3x + 4 - 4 = 13 - 4 \qquad \textit{Add } -4 \textit{ to each side of the equation.}$$
$$3x = 9 \qquad \textit{Combine like terms.}$$
$$\tfrac{1}{3} \cdot 3x = \tfrac{1}{3} \cdot 9 \qquad \textit{Multiply each side of the equation by } \tfrac{1}{3}.$$
$$x = 3$$

Example 2

Solve $15x - 3x = 8x - 12$.

Solution

$$15x - 3x = 8x - 12$$
$$12x = 8x - 12 \qquad \textit{Subtract } 3x \textit{ from } 15x.$$
$$12x - 8x = 8x - 12 - 8x \qquad \textit{Add } -8x \textit{ to each side of the equation.}$$
$$4x = -12 \qquad \textit{Combine like terms.}$$
$$\tfrac{1}{4} \cdot 4x = \tfrac{1}{4}(-12) \qquad \textit{Multiply each side of the equation by } \tfrac{1}{4}.$$
$$x = -3$$

Solve.

1. $5x + 6 = 31$
2. $3x + 6 = 30$
3. $4x - 6 = 34$
4. $z - (-16) = 36$
5. $75 = p + 8$
6. $x - 3 = 2x + 10$
7. $5(3x - 2) = 35$
8. $3(2y - 3) = 27$
9. $-5a + 4(2 + 2a) = -1$
10. $\frac{x}{5} + 3 = 88$
11. $\frac{y + 6}{3} = 12$
12. $2(a + 4) = a + 10$
13. $7y - 2 = 3(3y + 3)$
14. $\frac{4b - 3}{5} = 6$
15. $-10(z + 3) = -25$
16. $5x + 9 = 8x$
17. $7(n + 8) = 3(n + 12)$
18. $3.2x - 1.7(x + 6) = 15$
19. $-25 = -\frac{4x}{5} + 3x$
20. $\frac{3}{4}x + \frac{1}{4} = 8$
21. $\frac{1}{2}(4x - 6) = 6x + 5$

Solve for the underlined variable.

22. $a\underline{y} - b = c$
23. $3(2\underline{x} + a) = b$
24. $P = 2\ell + 2\underline{w}$
25. $A = \underline{b}h$
26. $a(2b + 2\underline{c}) = d$
27. $C = 2\pi\underline{r}$

Translate to an equation and solve.

28. Eight more than a number is 57. Find the number.
29. A number decreased by 14 is -51. Find the number.
30. Eighteen times a number is -1134. Find the number.
31. A rectangle has a length 4 times its width. Find the length and width of the rectangle if the perimeter is 36 in.
32. A linear pair of angles have measures of $(x + 50)$ and $(x + 30)$. Find the measure of each angle.

Exercise Answers

1. 5
2. 8
3. 10
4. 20
5. 67
6. -13
7. 3
8. 6
9. -3
10. 425
11. 30
12. 2
13. $-5\frac{1}{2}$
14. $8\frac{1}{4}$
15. $-\frac{1}{2}$
16. 3
17. -5
18. 16.8
19. $-11\frac{4}{11}$
20. $10\frac{1}{3}$
21. -2
22. $\frac{c + b}{a}$
23. $\frac{b}{6} - \frac{a}{2}$
24. $\frac{P}{2} - \ell$
25. $\frac{A}{h}$
26. $\frac{d}{2a} - b$
27. $\frac{C}{2\pi}$
28. 49
29. -37
30. 63
31. 14.4 in., 3.6 in.
32. 100, 80

Algebra Review

Fractional Equations and Absolute Value

Example 1

Solve $\frac{4b}{12} + \frac{8}{4} = \frac{3b}{3}$.

Solution

$$\frac{4b}{12} + \frac{8}{4} = \frac{3b}{3}$$

$\dfrac{4b}{4 \cdot 3} + \dfrac{8}{4} = \dfrac{3b}{3}$ *Factor the denominators to find the LCD.*

$4 \cdot 3 \left(\dfrac{4b}{4 \cdot 3} + \dfrac{8}{4} \right) = 4 \cdot 3 \dfrac{3b}{3}$ *Multiply each side by the LCD.*

$4 \cdot 3 \dfrac{4b}{4 \cdot 3} + 4 \cdot 3 \cdot \dfrac{8}{4} = 4 \cdot 3 \cdot \dfrac{3b}{3}$ *Use the distributive property and multiply.*

$4b + 24 = 12b$

$24 = 8b$

$3 = b$

Exercises

Solve.

1. $\frac{x}{2} + \frac{3}{4} = \frac{x}{8}$ **2.** $\frac{3a}{8} + \frac{2}{4} = \frac{5a}{2}$ **3.** $\frac{3a-5}{5} - \frac{3}{2} = \frac{a}{10}$

4. $\frac{5}{x} + \frac{5}{4} = \frac{5}{2}$ **5.** $\frac{3x+4}{4} + \frac{5}{2} = \frac{2x-4}{8}$ **6.** $\frac{4}{3x} - \frac{3}{2} = \frac{7}{3x}$

Example 2

$|x + 3| = 4$

Solution

$|x + 3| = 4$

$x + 3 = 4$ or $-(x + 3) = 4$

$x = 1$ or $x = -7$

Example 3

$-2|x| + 6 = 0$

Solution

$-2|x| + 6 = 0$

$-2|x| = -6$

$2|x| = 6$

$|x| = 3$

$x = 3$ or $x = -3$

Exercises

Find all values of x.

7. $|x| = 7$ **8.** $|x| = -7$ **9.** $|-x| = 7$

10. $x = |7|$ **11.** $2|x| = 7$ **12.** $x = |-7|$

13. $|x| + 1 = 7$ **14.** $|x| + |-1| = 7$ **15.** $x - |-1| = 7$

16. $-2|x| = -14$ **17.** $|2x + 1| = 14$ **18.** $|x - 1| - 1 = 7$

Algebra Review

Solving Inequalities

Example 1
Find the solution set of $-8x + 4 < -5x - 2$.

Solution

$$-8x + 4 < -5x - 2$$

$-8x < -5x - 6$	*Add -4 to both sides.*
$-3x < -6$	*Add $5x$ to both sides.*
$-x < -2$	*Multiply both sides by $\frac{1}{3}$.*
$x > 2$	*Multiply both sides by -1, reversing the inequality.*

Example 2
Find the solution set of $-12 \leq 3 - 2x < 11$.

Solution

$$-12 \leq 3 - 2x < 11$$

$-15 \leq -2x < 8$	*Add -3 to each component.*
$-7.5 \leq -x < 4$	*Multiply through by $\frac{1}{2}$.*
$7.5 \geq x > -4$	*Multiply each side by -1, reversing the inequalities.*
$-4 < x \leq 7.5$	*Write the solution in least-to-greatest form.*

Exercises

Solve each inequality.

1. $-x < 9$
2. $y + 3 > 7$
3. $2y + 4 < y - 3$
4. $\frac{2a}{3} > 15$
5. $18 - 2b < b$
6. $2x + 5 > x - 2$
7. $3x + 6 > 15$
8. $2 + 3x > -6$
9. $5x + 6 > -24$
10. $-7 + 6a < 7a + 2$
11. $9d - 4 > 10d + (-12)$
12. $\frac{3y}{4} < 9$
13. $\frac{4y - 6}{3} > 3y + 2$
14. $\frac{3x}{4} - \frac{5}{8} < 0$
15. $x - 6 \geq 3x + 2$
16. $3(y + 6) < 2y + 12$
17. $\frac{8 - 3b}{5} \leq -8$
18. $2(y + 5) > y + 15$
19. $5(n + 6) < 3n - 6$
20. $\frac{3x - 4}{2} \geq \frac{2x}{4}$
21. $\frac{4x}{3} + \frac{2}{5} > 0$
22. $6(w - 2) < 5(2 - w)$
23. $\frac{s}{6} + \frac{1}{7} \geq \frac{s - 30}{21}$
24. $\frac{2}{v} < 1$
25. $17 - 2p \leq 17$
26. $3q + 2 \geq -5(q + 1)$
27. $\frac{3m - 1}{6} < \frac{4m - 1}{7}$
28. $\frac{t + 1}{31} < \frac{t}{30}$
29. $15 - s < 15s - 1$
30. $\frac{s + 100}{2} \geq s + \frac{100}{2}$
31. $5m + 1 > 13 - m$
32. $57 - 6b < 3 + 3b$
33. $3x - 1 \geq 4x - 3$
34. $5k - 7 > 6(k - 7)$
35. $\frac{p + 10}{7} < \frac{7p - 6}{10}$
36. $\frac{2a}{3} + 5 < \frac{2a}{5} + 3$

37. A rectangular field is 3 times as long as it is wide. If the width were increased by 10 m and the length were decreased by 25 m, the perimeter would be greater than 210 m. What is the minimum width of the original field?

38. The sum of two integers is greater than 50, but less than 60. One of the integers is one less than four times the other. Find all possible values for the integers.

Exercise Answers

1. $x > -9$
2. $y > 4$
3. $y < -7$
4. $a > \frac{45}{2}$
5. $b > 6$
6. $x > -7$
7. $x > 3$
8. $x > -\frac{8}{3}$
9. $x > -6$
10. $a > -9$
11. $d < 8$
12. $y < 12$
13. $y < -\frac{12}{5}$
14. $x < \frac{5}{6}$
15. $x \leq -4$
16. $y < -6$
17. $b \geq 16$
18. $y > 5$
19. $n < -18$
20. $x \geq 2$
21. $x > -\frac{3}{10}$
22. $w < 2$
23. $s \geq -\frac{66}{5}$
24. $v > 2$
25. $p \geq 0$
26. $q \geq -\frac{7}{8}$
27. $m > -\frac{1}{3}$
28. $t > 30$
29. $s > 1$
30. $s \leq 0$
31. $m > 2$
32. $b > 6$
33. $x \leq 2$
34. $k < 35$
35. $p > \frac{142}{39}$
36. $a < -\frac{15}{2}$
37. 30 m
38. 12, 47; 11, 43

Algebra Review

Solving Systems of Equations

Example 1 *Substitution Method*

Solve. $3x + 4y = 14$
$x - 3y = -17$

Solution

$x - 3y = -17$

$x = 3y - 17$ *Solve for x in one equation.*

$3x + 4y = 14$

$3(3y - 17) + 4y = 14$ *Substitute for x in the other equation.*

$y = 5$

$x - 3y = -17$

$x - 3(5) = -17$ *Substitute for y in either equation.*

$x - 15 = -17$

$x = -2$

The solution is $x = -2, y = 5$.

Example 2 *Addition Method*

Solve. $8a - 6b = 10$
$4a - 5b = 3$

Solution

$5(8a - 6b) = 5 \cdot 10$ *Multiply each equation so that, when added,*
$-6(4a - 5b) = -6 \cdot 3$ *the result will be an equation in one variable.*

$40a - 30b = 50$
$\underline{-24a + 30b = -18}$ *Add.*
$16a = 32$
$a = 2$

$8a - 6b = 10$

$8(2) - 6b = 10$ *Substitute for a in one equation.*

$b = 1$

The solution is $a = 2$ and $b = 1$.

Exercises

Solve each system of equations using either method.

1. $a = 3b - 5$ **2.** $2x + 5y = 7$ **3.** $2a + b = 14$
$b = -2a - 10$ $x = \frac{-3}{2}$ $3a + b = 4$

4. $2m - 4n = 30$ **5.** $3p - 2q = 2$ **6.** $5a + 8b = 1$
$3m + 2n = -3$ $5p + 2q = 14$ $2a - 7b = -20$

7. $-2a + 5b = -3$ **8.** $4s - 3t = 14$ **9.** $2a = -9b + 24$
$2a + 3b = 11$ $5s = -3t + 31$ $-9b + 4a = -6$

10. $3x - 2y = 5$ **11.** $5p + 4q = 29$ **12.** $2(r - 2) + s = -18$
$2x = 5y - 4$ $3p = 13 + 2q$ $3r + 2(s - 1) = -26$

13. $8d + 5 = 7t$ **14.** $2z + w = 7$ **15.** $u = \frac{2}{3}v + 7$
$-9t + 2d = -23$ $4w - z = 37$ $2u = 3v - 6$

Algebra Review

Factoring Polynomials

Example 1

Factor $4x^4 - 20x^3 + 24x^2$ completely.

Solution

$$4x^4 - 20x^3 + 24x^2 = 4x^2(x^2 - 5x + 6) \qquad \textit{Factor out } 4x^2.$$
$$= 4x^2(x - 3)(x - 2) \qquad \textit{Factor } x^2 - 5x + 6 \textit{ into}$$
$$\textit{two binomial factors.}$$

Example 2

Factor $16x^2 - 64$.

Solution

$$16x^2 - 64 = 16(x^2 - 4) \qquad \textit{Factor out the GCF.}$$
$$= 16(x + 2)(x - 2) \qquad x^2 - 4 \textit{ is the difference of two squares.}$$

Example 3

Factor completely.
$x^4 + 6x^3 + 5x^2 - x^2y^2 - 6xy^2 - 5y^2$

Solution

$$x^4 + 6x^3 + 5x^2 - x^2y^2 - 6xy^2 - 5y^2 = x^2(x^2 + 6x + 5) - y^2(x^2 + 6x + 5)$$
$$= (x^2 - y^2)(x^2 + 6x + 5)$$
$$= (x + y)(x - y)(x + 1)(x + 5)$$

Exercises

Factor completely.

1. $m^2 - 25$
2. $x^2 - 14x + 49$
3. $4y^2 - 12y + 9$
4. $x^2 + 2x - 15$
5. $4y^2 - 25$
6. $9a^2 - 81$
7. $10x^2 + 25x + 15$
8. $3y^2 - 3y - 168$
9. $8b^2 - 10b + 3$
10. $14y^2 - 49y - 28$
11. $9x^3 - 30x^2 - 75x$
12. $5c^3 - 55c^2 + 150c$
13. $cd^2 + 2c^2d + c^3$
14. $5t^2 + 5ts - 10s^2$
15. $100m^2 - 100m - 375$
16. $15z^3 + 36z^2 - 27z$
17. $9r^2 - 16p^2$
18. $81x^4 - y^4$
19. $5a^2 + 9ab - 2b^2$
20. $-150f^2 + 455fg - 294g^2$
21. $16x^3y^4 + 14x^2y^2z + 3xz^2$
22. $20u^2v^2 - 5w^4$
23. $63d^2 - 116dr^2 + 45r^4$
24. $16c(c^2 + dc) - 25d(dc + d^2)$
25. $14s^2 - 167st - 12t^2$
26. $p^4 + 2p^3q - 2pq^3 - q^4$
27. $81x^4 - 72x^2y^2 + 16y^4$
28. $500m^6n^3 - 20m^4n^4 - 39m^2n^5$
29. $(4a^2 + 12ab + 9b^2)(b + c) - 24ab(b + c)$
30. $11r^4 + 90r^3s + 16r^2s^2 + (12r - 13s)(11r^2s + 90rs^2 + 16s^3)$

Solve.

31. The product of a number increased by 1 and the number decreased by 2 is 10. Find the number.
32. The product of a number and the number increased by 2 is 35. Find the number.
33. A number squared is equal to 110 less than 21 times the number. Find the number.

Algebra Review **627**

Simplifying Radicals

Example 1

Simplify $-3x^2y\sqrt{54x^3y^4}$. Assume x and y are positive.

Solution

$$-3x^2y\sqrt{54x^3y^4} = -3x^2y\sqrt{9\cdot6\cdot x^2\cdot x^1\cdot y^4}$$
$$= -3x^2y\sqrt{9x^2y^4}\cdot\sqrt{6x}$$
$$= -3x^2y(3xy^2)\sqrt{6x}$$
$$= -9x^3y^3\sqrt{6x}$$

Find the greatest perfect square factor of $54x^3y^4$.

Rationalizing the denominator means writing the fraction without a radical in the denominator.

Example 2

Rationalize the denominator of $\frac{3x\sqrt{24x^2}}{\sqrt{3}}$. Assume x is positive.

Solution

$$\frac{3x\sqrt{24x^2}}{\sqrt{3}} = \frac{3x\sqrt{24x^2}}{\sqrt{3}}\cdot\frac{\sqrt{3}}{\sqrt{3}}$$
$$= \frac{3x\sqrt{72x^2}}{3}$$
$$= \frac{3x\sqrt{36\cdot2\cdot x^2}}{3}$$
$$= 6x^2\sqrt{2}$$

Make the denominator a perfect square.

Exercises

Simplify. Assume all variables are positive.

1. $\sqrt{8a^2}$
2. $\sqrt{120}$
3. $-\sqrt{144x}$
4. $\sqrt{27}+\sqrt{3}$
5. $\sqrt{75}-\sqrt{12}$
6. $\sqrt{\frac{4y^2}{9y^2}}$
7. $\sqrt{18}-\frac{\sqrt{8}}{4}$
8. $\sqrt{z^6}$
9. $\sqrt{45x^3y}$
10. $\sqrt{1600r^3}$
11. $\frac{2}{3}\sqrt{24x^2y^2}$
12. $\sqrt{\frac{81x^2}{36y^4}}$
13. $\frac{\sqrt{36x^3}}{\sqrt{2y}}$
14. $\frac{4\sqrt{8}}{\sqrt{5}}$
15. $-7x\sqrt{48x^3y^2}$
16. $6xy\sqrt{18x^3y^7z^4}$
17. $-6c^3d\sqrt{27cd^3}$
18. $\sqrt{\frac{5ab}{15a^3b^2}}$
19. $4\sqrt{3x}\cdot6\sqrt{8x}$
20. $-7x^2\sqrt{2x^3}\cdot5\sqrt{8x}$
21. $\frac{4}{5}x^2\sqrt{32x^3y^5}$
22. $-2x\sqrt{108x^3y^4}$
23. $6pq\sqrt{8q^5}\cdot-3p\sqrt{3p^3q^2}$
24. $\sqrt{56x^2y^3z}$
25. $\sqrt{p^2-4pq+4q^2}$
26. $\sqrt{18pq^3}+\sqrt{50p^3q}$
27. $\frac{\sqrt{pq}}{\sqrt{p}+\sqrt{q}}$
28. $\sqrt{\frac{36s^3t^2}{2m}}$
29. $\frac{7}{\sqrt{3}-5}$
30. $\sqrt{\frac{68y^2}{45a^3b^5}}\cdot\frac{a^2}{\sqrt{5b}}$
31. $\frac{\sqrt{m^2+6m-7}}{\sqrt{m^2-4m+3}}$
32. $\frac{\sqrt{70a}+\sqrt{56b}}{\sqrt{28a^4b^3}}$
33. $\frac{\sqrt{2xz}}{\sqrt{3xyz}}\cdot\sqrt{3z}$
34. $\frac{\sqrt{(h-k)(h+k)}}{\sqrt{h^2+3hk+2k^2}}(\sqrt{h-k})^3$
35. $\frac{\sqrt{3}+\sqrt{5}}{\sqrt{3}-\sqrt{5}}$
36. $(\sqrt{12xy^3z})^5$

Sidebar

Algebra Review

Simplifying Radicals

Exercise Answers

1. $2\sqrt{2a}$
2. $2\sqrt{30}$
3. $-12\sqrt{x}$
4. $4\sqrt{3}$
5. $3\sqrt{3}$
6. $\frac{2}{3}$
7. $\frac{5\sqrt{2}}{2}$
8. z^3
9. $3\sqrt{5}x\sqrt{xy}$
10. $40r\sqrt{r}$
11. $\frac{4\sqrt{6}}{3}xy$
12. $\frac{3x}{2y^2}$
13. $\frac{3x\sqrt{2xy}}{y}$
14. $\frac{8\sqrt{10}}{5}$
15. $-28yx^2\sqrt{3x}$
16. $18\sqrt{2}x^2\sqrt{xy^3}\sqrt{yz^2}$
17. $-18\sqrt{3}c^3\sqrt{cd^2}\sqrt{d}$
18. $\frac{\sqrt{3b}}{3ab}$
19. $48\sqrt{6x}$
20. $-140x^4$
21. $\frac{16\sqrt{2}}{5}x^3\sqrt{xy^2}\sqrt{y}$
22. $-12\sqrt{3}x^2\sqrt{xy^2}$
23. $-36\sqrt{6}p^3q^4\sqrt{pq}$
24. $2\sqrt{14}xy\sqrt{yz}$
25. $p-2q$
26. $(3q+5p)\sqrt{2pq}$
27. $\frac{p\sqrt{q}-q\sqrt{p}}{p-q}$
28. $\frac{3\sqrt{2}s\sqrt{st}\sqrt{m}}{m}$
29. $\frac{7\sqrt{3}+35}{-22}$
30. $\frac{2\sqrt{17}ya^2\sqrt{a}}{15a^2b^3}$
31. $\frac{\sqrt{(m+7)(m-3)}}{m-3}$
32. $\frac{\sqrt{10}\sqrt{ab}+2\sqrt{2}b}{2a^2b^2}$
33. $\frac{\sqrt{2yz}}{y}$
34. $\frac{(h-k)^2\sqrt{h+2k}}{h+2k}$
35. $-4-\sqrt{15}$
36. $288\sqrt{3}x^2y^7z^2\sqrt{xyz}$

Algebra Review

Exponents

Example 1

Simplify $(8a^2)(6a^3)$.

Solution

$$(8a^2)(6a^3) = (8 \cdot 6)(a^2 a^3) \quad \text{To multiply, add exponents.}$$
$$= 48a^{2+3}$$
$$= 48a^5$$

Example 2

Simplify $(3x^2)(7x^{-5})$.

Solution

$$(3x^2)(7x^{-5}) = (3 \cdot 7)(x^2 x^{-5}) \quad \text{Add exponents.}$$
$$= 21x^{2+(-5)}$$
$$= 21x^{-3} \text{ or } 21\frac{1}{x^3}$$

Example 3

Simplify $\frac{55y^{-6}}{5y^{-8}}$.

Solution

$$\frac{55y^{-6}}{5y^{-8}} = \frac{55}{5}\frac{y^{-6}}{y^{-8}} \quad \text{To divide, subtract exponents.}$$
$$= 11y^{-6-(-8)}$$
$$= 11y^2$$

Example 4

Simplify $(6m^2n^2p^4)^3$.

Solution

$$(6m^2n^3p^4)^3 = (6m^2n^3p^4)(6m^2n^3p^4)(6m^2n^3p^4)$$
$$= 6^3 m^{2 \cdot 3} n^{3 \cdot 3} p^{4 \cdot 3} \quad \text{To find a power, multiply exponents.}$$
$$= 216m^6n^9p^{12}$$

Exercises

Simplify.

1. $3^2 \cdot 3^4$
2. $10^5 \cdot 10^3$
3. $5^6 \cdot 5^{-4}$
4. $\frac{8^4}{8^5}$
5. $x^6 x^{-3}$
6. $3x^5 x^{-5}$
7. $\frac{3a^2}{4a^6}$
8. $(3x^2)^2$
9. $(4a^3)(7a^7)$
10. $(4y^2)^4$
11. $(-8m^6n^2)^2$
12. $(-5p^2q^3)(3p^3q)$
13. $\frac{12m^3n^{-4}}{3m^{-5}n^2}$
14. $(2a^{25})^4$
15. $\frac{-6a^2b^3}{2ab^2}$
16. $\frac{-18m^3p^6}{3m^3p^6}$
17. $(-6q^3r^2)^4$
18. $\frac{7a^3b^6c^4}{2a^3b^{-1}c^4}$
19. $(3r^2)(5r^3)(2r^{-1})$
20. $(5p^2q)^2(2p^{-1}q)$
21. $\frac{36a^2b^2c}{(3a^2b)(2ac)}$
22. $((2s^2)^3)^2$
23. $\frac{(13z)(10y^2x)}{(2xyz)^2}$
24. $30mn\left(\frac{24mn^3}{16m^2n}\right)$

Algebra Review

Exponents

Exercise Answers

1. 729
2. 100,000,000
3. 25
4. $\frac{1}{8}$
5. x^3
6. 3
7. $\frac{3}{4a^4}$
8. $9x^4$
9. $28a^{10}$
10. $256y^8$
11. $64m^{12}n^4$
12. $-15p^5q^4$
13. $\frac{4m^8}{n^6}$
14. $16a^{100}$
15. $-3ab$
16. -6
17. $1296q^{12}r^8$
18. $\frac{7}{2}b^7$
19. $30r^4$
20. $50p^3q^3$
21. $\frac{6b}{a}$
22. $64s^{12}$
23. $\frac{65}{2xz}$
24. $45n^3$

Algebra Review

Functions

Example 1

What is the range of the function $f(x) = x^2 − 3x + 4$ given the domain, or
possible *x*-values, $D = \{2, 3, 5, 7, 11\}$?

> **Solution**
>
> For $x = 2, f(2) = 2^2 − 3(2) + 4 = 2$ *The range is the set of function values for the domain.*
> The values for 3, 5, 7, and 11 are also found by substitution.
> The range is {2, 4, 14, 32, 92}.

Example 2

The range of $f(t) = t^2$ is {0, 9, 36}. What is its largest possible domain?

> **Solution**
>
> $\{−6, −3, 0, 3, 6\}$

Example 3

Given $f(x) = 3x^2$ and $g(x) = −2x^2$, find $f(2), g(2), f(2) + g(2)$, and $f(g(x))$.

> **Solution**
>
> $f(2) = 3(2)^2 = 12$ $g(2) = −2(2)^2 = −8$
> $f(2) + g(2) = 12 + −8 = 4$
> $f(g(x)) = f(−2x^2) = 3(−2x^2)^2 = 3 \cdot 4x^4 = 12x^4$

Exercises

State the range of each function.

1. $h(k) = 3k^2$ $D = \{−1, 0, 1, 2\}$
2. $f(u) = u + 1$ $D = \{0, 1, 99\}$
3. $f(x) = \frac{x^3}{x^2}$ $D = \{−2, −1, 1, 2\}$
4. $g(x) = \frac{−x^3}{x^2}$ $D = \{−2, −1, 1, 2\}$
5. $f(z) = \frac{z − 5}{10} + \frac{5 − z}{10}$ $D = \{$all real numbers$\}$
6. $p(r) = r + 2$ $D = \{$all real numbers$\}$

Given $f(m)$ and $g(n)$, find $f(1), g(1), f(1) + g(1), f(g(1))$, and $g(f(1))$.

7. $f(m) = m^2 − 1, g(n) = (n − 1)^2$
8. $f(m) = m + 2, g(n) = 2n$
9. $f(m) = −m, g(n) = n$
10. $f(m) = \frac{2}{m}, g(n) = \frac{1}{n}$
11. $f(m) = 3m + 9, g(n) = \frac{n}{3} − 3$
12. $f(m) = 1, g(n) = 2n^2$

13. The length of your shadow is a function of your height. If, at a certain
time, the length of your shadow is $f(h) = 0.9h + 63$, find the length of
your shadow if you are 175 cm tall.
14. The length of a fun house mirror image is $f(h) = h − 2\sqrt{h}$, where *h* is
your height. Find the height of your image if you are 169 cm tall.
15. The area of a circle as a function of its circumference *c* is $A(c) = \frac{c^2}{4\pi}$.
What is the area of a circle with circumference 10π cm?
16. Find the perimeter of the following polygons as a function of their area.
    a. square   **b.** equilateral triangle   **c.** regular hexagon

630   *Algebra Review*

Statistics

Frequency Distributions

The branch of mathematics that deals with the collection, organization, display, and interpretation of data is called statistics. Statistics is used to help solve problems and make decisions.

When a set of data is collected, it is often disorganized. Data can be organized using charts or tables like the frequency distribution below.

Example

Here is a set of temperatures, in degrees Fahrenheit, for the month of April.

49, 50, 49, 50, 50, 51, 49, 49, 51, 52, 51, 56, 53, 54, 50
49, 53, 53, 55, 54, 50, 57, 49, 55, 56, 58, 54, 59, 55, 54

Construct a frequency distribution.

Solution

The temperatures range from a low of 49 to a high of 59.

Temperature	Tally	Frequency
49	ΝΙ Ι	6
50	ΝΙ	5
51	ΙΙΙ	3
52	Ι	1
53	ΙΙΙ	3
54	ΙΙΙΙ	4
55	ΙΙΙ	3
56	ΙΙ	2
57	Ι	1
58	Ι	1
59	Ι	1

Exercises

Construct a frequency distribution for each set of data.

1. Scores on a quiz:

    9, 10, 8, 10, 6, 9, 8, 7, 5, 10, 8, 8, 7,
    0, 2, 6, 5, 7, 6, 7, 9, 8, 7, 8, 6

2. Golf scores:

    86, 79, 68, 74, 78, 87, 83, 81, 76, 80, 88, 79,
    86, 90, 86, 75, 78, 79, 80, 87, 78, 74, 87, 80, 79

3. Heights of players on high school basketball team (centimeters):

172	168	183	201	203	178	183	196
198	196	201	198	196	178		

4. Distances jumped by members of high school track team (centimeters):

177	180	172	168	172	165	159	165	176
181	166	174	168	170	174	165	179	180

Exercise Answers

NOTE: Values for which the frequency is 0 have been omitted.

1.

Score	Tally	Frequency
10	ΙΙΙ	3
9	ΙΙΙ	3
8	ΝΙ Ι	6
7	ΝΙ	5
6	ΙΙΙΙ	4
5	ΙΙ	2
2	Ι	1
0	Ι	1

2.

Score	Tally	Frequency
90	Ι	1
88	Ι	1
87	ΙΙΙ	3
86	ΙΙΙ	3
83	Ι	1
81	Ι	1
80	ΙΙΙ	3
79	ΙΙΙΙ	4
78	ΙΙΙ	3
76	Ι	1
75	Ι	1
74	ΙΙ	2
68	Ι	1

3.

Height (cm)	Tally	Frequency
203	Ι	1
201	ΙΙ	2
198	ΙΙ	2
196	ΙΙΙ	3
183	ΙΙ	2
178	ΙΙ	2
172	Ι	1
168	Ι	1

4.

Dist. (cm)	Tally	Frequency
181	Ι	1
180	ΙΙ	2
179	Ι	1
177	Ι	1
176	Ι	1
174	ΙΙ	2
172	ΙΙ	2
170	Ι	1
168	ΙΙ	2
166	Ι	1
165	ΙΙΙ	3
159	Ι	1

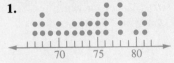
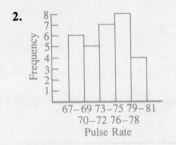
Statistics

Line Plots and Histograms

To construct a *line plot*, draw a portion of a number line and place a dot above the line for each occurrence of a value.

Example 1

Construct a line plot for this set of morning temperatures, in degrees Celsius, for the month of March in a northwestern town.
5, 7, 4, 5, 3, 2, 0, 3, 2, 4, 5, 5, 4, 5, 6, 4, 7, 7, 9, 10, 9, 11, 12, 11, 13, 11, 10, 9, 10, 11, 13

Solution

Temperature in Degrees Celsius

A bar graph called a *histogram* is useful for comparing data and can be constructed from a frequency distribution.

Example 2

Construct a histogram from this frequency distribution of heights, in centimeters, of players on a high-school basketball team.

Height	Frequency
160–169	1
170–179	2
180–189	4
190–199	5
200–210	3

Solution

Let the horizontal scale represent heights and the vertical scale represent frequency.

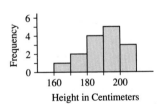

Height in Centimeters

Exercises

1. Construct a line plot for this set of pulse rates of 30 patients.
   76, 78, 68, 73, 80, 78, 67, 76, 75, 78, 74, 75, 81, 75, 72,
   73, 81, 67, 68, 72, 70, 78, 76, 81, 69, 71, 68, 70, 74, 76
2. Use appropriate intervals to construct a histogram for the data in Exercise 1.

Statistics

Mean, Median, and Mode

Example 1

Find the mean, median, and mode for this set of test scores from a geometry class.
75, 89, 82, 95, 63, 100, 81, 94, 92, 60, 55, 73, 82, 83, 82

Solution

There are 15 values. To find the mean (average), add the values and divide by 15.
The sum is 1206. The mean is $\frac{1206}{15} = 80.4$.
To find the median, arrange the values in order from least to greatest and choose the middle value.
55, 60, 63, 73, 75, 81, 82, 82, 82, 83, 89, 92, 94, 95, 100
The 8th number, 82, is the middle value so the median is 82.
The mode, the value which occurs most frequently, is 82.

Example 2

Inge's scores on four biology tests are 85, 90, 84, and 92. What must she score on her next exam to have an average of exactly 90?

Solution

Let x = the score on the fifth exam.
$$\frac{85 + 90 + 84 + 92 + x}{5} = 90$$
$$\frac{351 + x}{5} = 90$$
$$x = 99$$

She must score 99 to have an average of 90.

Exercises

Find the mean, median, and mode for each set of data.

1. The number of students in English classes at Washington High School:
   18, 22, 19, 25, 22, 17, 20, 21, 19, 22
2. A gymnast's scores on the parallel bars at nine gymnastics meets:
   8.7, 9.3, 9.0, 9.3, 9.3, 9.3, 9.0, 8.8, 9.0
3. Games won by the Comets in successive seasons:
   14, 12, 12, 8, 13, 5, 7, 10, 10, 12, 4, 8, 10, 11, 14, 12, 9, 9
4. The depths, in meters, of certain points of the oceans and seas of the world:
   10918, 9219, 7455, 5625, 4632, 5016, 4773, 3787, 3658, 2782, 3742, 3777, 660, 2211, 421, 6946, 183
5. Glenn's scores on five chemistry tests are 75, 85, 86, 79 and 84. What must he score on the sixth test to have an average of exactly 83?
6. The maximum score possible on algebra quizzes is 25. If Rochelle has scores of 20, 22, 21, 17, and 15 on the first five quizzes, is it possible for her to have an average of at least 21 after seven quizzes? Why or why not?

Exercise Answers

1. mean = 20.5, median = 20.5, mode = 22   **2.** mean ≈ 9.08, median = 9, mode = 9.3
3. mean = 10, median = 10, mode = 12
4. mean ≈ 4459 m, median = 3787, no mode   **5.** 89
6. No. She would need a total of at least 52 points on the last two tests to have an average of 21 after 7 tests. This is more than the maximum possible score.

Computer Exploration 1

Angle Measures of a Triangle

Objective
Determine the sum of the measures of the angles of a triangle.

Investigation
Construct a triangle. Measure its interior angles and record the data. Find the sum of the angle measures. Repeat for other types of triangles.

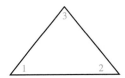

	$m\angle 1$	$m\angle 2$	$m\angle 3$	Sum
Acute				
Acute				
Obtuse				
Obtuse				
Right				
Right				
Isosceles				
Isosceles				
Equilateral				
Equilateral				

Conjectures

1. Make a conjecture about the sum of the measures of the angles of a triangle.
2. Make a conjecture about the angles of an equilateral triangle.
3. Make a conjecture about the acute angles of a right triangle.

Computer Exploration 2

Exterior Angles of a Triangle

Objectives

Determine the sum of the measures of the exterior angles of a triangle.
Determine the relationship between an exterior angle and its two remote interior angles.

Investigation

Construct a triangle and extend each side as shown in the figure. Measure the exterior angles and the interior angles. Record the data. Repeat for the different triangles shown in the charts.

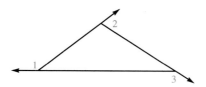

	$m\angle 1$	$m\angle 2$	$m\angle 3$	Sum
Equilateral				
Isosceles				
Right				
Obtuse				
Acute				

	$m\angle 1$	Remote $\angle$s	$m\angle 2$	Remote $\angle$s	$m\angle 3$	Remote $\angle$s
Equilateral						
Isosceles						
Right						
Obtuse						
Acute						

Conjectures

1. Using your data from the first chart, make a conjecture about the sum of the measures of the exterior angles of a triangle.
2. Using your data from the second chart, make a conjecture about the measure of an exterior angle of a triangle and the measures of its two remote interior angles.

Computer Exploration 2

Exterior Angles of a Triangle

Use before Lesson 3-5.

You may need to introduce the terms *exterior angle* and *remote interior angle* before students begin the exploration.

This activity may be used in place of the Explore on page 129. Make sure that students extend only one triangle side at each vertex, as shown in the figure. All three sides are to be extended, each from a different vertex. Conjecture 1 involves these three exterior angles. To encourage experimentation and discovery by students, the charts do not have columns for the sums of remote angles. If students have trouble making Conjecture 2 (Theorem 3.11), suggest that they try finding sums of various angle measures.

Conjectures

1. The sum of the measures of the exterior angles of a triangle (one at each vertex) is 360.
2. The measure of an exterior angle of a triangle is equal to the sum of the measures of the two remote exterior angles. (Theorem 3.11)

Computer Exploration 3

Isosceles Triangles

Use before Lesson 4-6 or 4-7.

This activity may be used in conjunction with Exercise 20, page 187. Review terminology for isosceles triangles (page 177), noting that in this activity the altitudes must be drawn from base angles. Be sure students construct at least one triangle for which the intersection point of the altitudes lies outside the triangle.

Discuss how the data for the non-isosceles triangles differs from that for isosceles triangles. Also discuss why results would differ if one of the altitudes in an isosceles triangle were drawn from the vertex angle.

Conjecture

1. The triangle formed by the base of an isosceles triangle and the altitudes drawn from the base angles to the congruent sides is an isosceles triangle.

Isosceles Triangles

Objective

Determine the type of triangle formed by the base of an isosceles triangle and the altitudes drawn from the base angles to the congruent sides.

Investigation

Construct an isosceles triangle. Draw the altitudes from the base angles. Label the intersection of the altitudes as shown. Measure segments AF and BF. Record the data. Repeat for the different triangles shown in the chart.

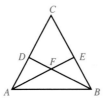

	AF	BF
Isosceles (three acute angles)		
Isosceles (one obtuse angle)		
Equilateral		
Another Isosceles		
Non-isosceles		

Conjecture

1. Make a conjecture about the type of triangle that is formed by the base of an isosceles triangle and the altitudes drawn from the base angles to the congruent sides.

Computer Exploration 4

Diagonals of a Parallelogram

Objective
Investigate the properties of the diagonals of a parallelogram.

Investigation
Draw a parallelogram and its two diagonals. Label the point of intersection of the diagonals. Measure the lengths of the four segments formed by the diagonals.

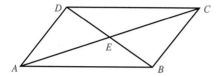

	AE	CE	BE	DE
Parallelogram 1				
Parallelogram 2				
Parallelogram 3				
Parallelogram 4				

Conjecture
1. Make a conjecture about the diagonals of a parallelogram.

Diagonals of a Parallelogram

Use before Lesson 5-1.

Students may already be familiar with some of the properties of parallelograms. The conjecture involves Theorem 5.3.

Conjecture

1. The diagonals of a parallelogram bisect each other. (Theorem 5.3)

Diagonals of a Quadrilateral

Use with Lessons 5-2 and 5-3.

This activity is related to the Computer Activity on page 212 and to the Critical Thinking Exercises on page 218. It should be used after defining special quadrilaterals, but before the introduction of the theorems in Lesson 5-3.

Conjecture 1 involves Theorem 5.8. Conjectures 2 and 3 are related to Theorems 5.10 and 5.9, respectively. To collect data for Conjectures 2 and 3, students must experiment with diagonal lengths and intersection angles. Make sure they make the diagonals bisect each other and that they try equal diagonal lengths, unequal diagonal lengths, right angles, and non-right angles in various combinations.

Conjectures

1. If the diagonals of a quadrilateral bisect each other, then the quadrilateral is a parallelogram. (Theorem 5.8)
2. If the diagonals of a quadrilateral bisect each other and are perpendicular, then the quadrilateral is a rhombus.
3. If the diagonals of a quadrilateral bisect each other and are congruent, then the quadrilateral is a rectangle.

Diagonals of a Quadrilateral

Objective
Determine the type of quadrilateral formed by diagonals that bisect each other.

Investigation
Construct a quadrilateral by drawing diagonal segments that bisect each other. Measure the angles and segments listed in the chart. Record the data. Construct other quadrilaterals as needed to make your conjectures.

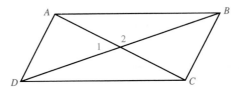

	$m\angle 1$	$m\angle 2$	AC	BD	Type of Quadrilateral
Quadrilateral 1					
Quadrilateral 2					
Quadrilateral 3					
Quadrilateral 4					

Conjectures
1. Make a conjecture about the type of quadrilateral that is formed by diagonals that bisect each other.
2. Make a conjecture about how the angle of the intersection of the diagonals affects the type of quadrilateral that is formed.
3. Make a conjecture about how the lengths of the diagonals affect the type of quadrilateral that is formed.

Computer Exploration 6

Diagonals of a Rhombus

Objective

Investigate the properties of the diagonals of a rhombus.

Investigation

Draw a rhombus and its two diagonals. Measure the angles formed by the diagonals. Measure the angles formed by the diagonals and the sides of the rhombus.

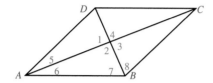

	$m\angle 1$	$m\angle 2$	$m\angle 3$	$m\angle 4$	$m\angle 5$	$m\angle 6$	$m\angle 7$	$m\angle 8$
Rhombus 1								
Rhombus 2								
Rhombus 3								
Rhombus 4								

Conjectures

1. Make a conjecture about the angles formed by the diagonals of a rhombus.
2. Make a conjecture about the pair of angles formed by a diagonal and the consecutive sides of a rhombus.

Conjecture 1 involves Theorem 5.10. Conjecture 2 involves Theorem 5.11, which is proved in Exercise 43, page 218.

Conjectures

1. The diagonals of a rhombus are perpendicular. (Theorem 5.10)
2. Each diagonal of a rhombus bisects a pair of opposite angles. (Theorem 5.11)

Median of a Trapezoid

Use before Lesson 5-4.

Both conjectures involve Theorem 5.16, which is proved in Exercise 23, page 223. Students need to know that a trapezoid's parallel sides are its bases. Discuss why the measures of angles 1 and 2 imply that the median is parallel to the bases.

Conjectures

1. The length of the median of a trapezoid is one-half the sum of the lengths of the bases. (Theorem 5.16)
2. The median of a trapezoid is parallel to the bases of the trapezoid. (Theorem 5.16)

Computer Exploration 7

Median of a Trapezoid

Objective
Investigate relationships between the median and the two bases of a trapezoid.

Investigation
Draw a trapezoid and its median. Measure the length of the bases and the median. Measure the angles indicated.

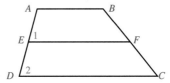

	AB	CD	EF	m∠1	m∠2
Trapezoid 1					
Trapezoid 2					
Trapezoid 3					
Trapezoid 4					

Conjectures
1. Make a conjecture about the lengths of a trapezoid's median and its two bases.
2. Make a conjecture about the position of a trapezoid's median in relation to its bases.

Computer Exploration 8

Midpoints of a Quadrilateral

Objective
Determine the type of quadrilateral formed by joining the midpoints of consecutive sides of a quadrilateral.

Investigation
Draw a quadrilateral. Label the midpoints of each side of the quadrilateral. Draw the segments joining the midpoints of consecutive sides of the quadrilateral. Measure the lengths of the sides and the angles of the newly formed quadrilateral.

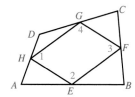

	EF	FG	GH	HE	$m\angle 1$	$m\angle 2$	$m\angle 3$	$m\angle 4$
Quadrilateral 1								
Quadrilateral 2								
Quadrilateral 3								
Quadrilateral 4								

Conjecture
1. Make a conjecture about the type of quadrilateral that is formed by joining the midpoints of consecutive sides of a quadrilateral.

Computer Exploration 8

Midpoints of a Quadrilateral

Use before Lesson 5-5.

Students may need to be reminded of the conditions that determine a parallelogram before making the conjecture (Theorem 5.18). Students may save the sequence of commands they use in this construction for use in Computer Exploration 9.

Conjecture

1. The quadrilateral formed by joining the midpoints of the consecutive sides of another quadrilateral is a parallelogram. (Theorem 5.18)

This activity can be used in conjunction with Critical Thinking Exercise 36, page 228. Students need to know the conditions that determine a rhombus.

Conjecture

1. The quadrilateral formed by joining the midpoints of the consecutive sides of an isosceles trapezoid is a rhombus.

Computer Exploration 9

Midpoints of an Isosceles Trapezoid

Objective

Determine the type of quadrilateral formed by joining the midpoints of consecutive sides of an isosceles trapezoid.

Investigation

Draw an isosceles trapezoid and label the midpoints of each side. Draw the segments joining the midpoints of consecutive sides of the isosceles trapezoid. Measure the lengths of the sides and the angles of the newly formed quadrilateral.

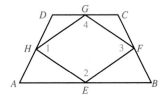

	EF	FG	GH	HE	$m\angle 1$	$m\angle 2$	$m\angle 3$	$m\angle 4$
Isosceles Trapezoid 1								
Isosceles Trapezoid 2								
Isosceles Trapezoid 3								
Isosceles Trapezoid 4								

Conjecture

1. Make a conjecture about the type of quadrilateral formed by joining the midpoints of consecutive sides of an isosceles trapezoid.

Computer Exploration 10

Triangle Midsegments

Objective
Determine special relationships between a midsegment of a triangle and the side that does not contain the endpoints of the midsegment.

Investigation
Construct a triangle and a midsegment as shown. Measure the midsegment and the side of the triangle that does not contain the midsegment's endpoints. Measure angles 1 and 2. Record the data. Repeat for the different triangles shown in the chart.

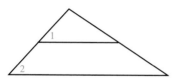

	Length of Midsegment	Length of Side	$m \angle 1$	$m \angle 2$
Equilateral				
Isosceles				
Right				
Obtuse				
Acute				

Conjectures
1. Make a conjecture about the length of the midsegment and the length of the side of a triangle not containing the endpoints of the midsegment.
2. Will the line containing the midsegment intersect the side of the triangle that does not contain the midsegment's endpoints? How do you know?

Triangle Midsegments
Use before Lesson 5-5.

Both conjectures involve Theorem 5.17. The "length of side" column in the chart refers to the triangle side that is parallel to the midsegment. For Conjecture 1, if students do not see the relationship, suggest that they look for ratios. For Conjecture 2, students should know that the lines cannot intersect because they are parallel. See Exercise 31, page 228, in which Theorem 5.17 is proved.

Conjectures
1. The segment that joins the midpoints of two sides of a triangle has a length equal to half the length of the third side. (Theorem 5.17)
2. No, they will not intersect, because they are parallel. (Angles 1 and 2 are congruent corresponding angles.) The segment that joins the midpoints of two sides of a triangle is parallel to the third side. (Theorem 5.17)

Use before Lesson 5-7.

The conjecture involves Theorem 5.21. If students have trouble making a conjecture, ask, "How does the measure of the angle opposite the longest side compare to the measures of the other angles?"

Conjecture

1. If one side of a triangle is longer than a second side, then the measure of the angle opposite the longer side is greater than the measure of the angle opposite the shorter side. (Theorem 5.21)

Computer Exploration 11

Triangle Side Lengths and Angle Measures

Objective
Determine the relationship between the lengths of the sides of a triangle and the measures of the angles of the triangle.

Investigation
Draw a triangle having the side lengths given in the chart for Triangle 1. Measure the angles of the triangle and the lengths of the sides of the triangle. Record your data. Repeat for the other triangles in the chart.

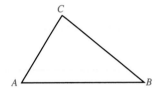

	AB	AC	BC	$m\angle C$	$m\angle B$	$m\angle A$
Triangle 1	10	12	14			
Triangle 2	21	17	25			
Triangle 3	17	20	14			
Triangle 4	18	20	19			
Triangle 5	25	15	20			
Triangle 6	20	18	16			

Conjecture
1. For each triangle, compare the measures of each side and the angle opposite that side. Make a conjecture about the relationship between the measures of the angles of a triangle and the lengths of the sides of the triangle.

Computer Exploration 12

Lines Parallel to a Side of a Triangle

Objective
Determine ratios of the lengths of segments produced by a line that is parallel to one side of a triangle and intersects the triangle's other two sides.

Investigation
Construct a triangle and label a point on a side. Draw a line through the point that is parallel to one of the other sides and intersects the third side. Measure the segments formed. Record the data. Find the ratios shown in the charts. Repeat for different types of triangles.

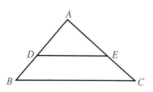

	AD	DB	AE	EC	DE	AB	AC	BC
Acute								
Obtuse								
Isosceles								
Equilateral								

	AD:DB	AE:EC	AD:AB	AE:AC	DE:BC
Acute					
Obtuse					
Isosceles					
Equilateral					

Conjectures

1. Make a conjecture about the ratios of the lengths of the segments formed by a line that is parallel to a side of a triangle and that intersects the other two sides.

2. Make a conjecture about the relationships between the ratio of the lengths of the two parallel line segments in your investigation and the ratios of the lengths of the other segments in the triangle

3. Make a conjecture about the relationship between a triangle and the triangle formed by a line that is parallel to one of its sides and that intersects the other two sides.

Lines Parallel to a Side of a Triangle

Use before Lesson 6-6.

The three conjectures involve Theorem 6.6 and its proof on page 281. Students should select a software option that places a point on a side of the triangle. Because of decimal approximations of exact real numbers, measurements of some segments created with random points may not be accurate enough to illustrate equal ratios. If decimal approximations prove problematic, or just to vary the activity, have students try subdividing a triangle side into a fixed number of parts. They can then draw several parallel lines using the same triangle.

If the software allows the same construction sequence to be repeated for new triangles, students should be aware that the new triangle may not be oriented in the same way as the previous triangle.

Conjectures

1. If a line parallel to a side of a triangle intersects the other two sides, then it divides the two sides proportionally. (Theorem 6.6)

2. If a line parallel to a side of a triangle intersects the other two sides, then it divides the two sides so that the lengths of corresponding segments are proportional to the lengths of the intersected sides.

3. The triangle formed by a line that is parallel to one side of a triangle and intersects the other two sides is similar to the original triangle.

Angle Bisector Segments
Use before or during Lesson 6-6.

This activity can be used mid-lesson, but before the introduction of Theorem 6.9, since Conjecture 1 involves that theorem. In the construction, students should make the angle bisector intersect the opposite side.

Special ratios exist for equilateral and isosceles triangles. If students have difficulty with Conjecture 2, have them focus on data for those triangle types.

Conjectures

1. If a ray bisects an angle of a triangle, then it divides the opposite side into two segments whose lengths are proportional to the lengths of the other two sides. (Theorem 6.9)

2. Yes. If a ray bisects the vertex angle of an isosceles triangle, then the bisector divides the base into two congruent segments. The ratio of the lengths of these segments is the same as the ratio of the lengths of the legs. In both cases the ratios are equal to one.

Computer Exploration 13

Angle Bisector Segments

Objective
Determine relationships between the segments formed by an angle bisector of a triangle and the other two sides of the triangle.

Investigation
Construct a triangle. Construct an angle bisector that intersects the opposite side. Measure segments and record your data. Compare segment ratios as shown in the chart. Repeat for the different types of triangles shown in the chart.

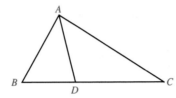

	AB	AC	BD	DC	AB:AC	BD:DC
Acute						
Obtuse						
Isosceles						
Equilateral						
Right						

Conjectures
1. Make a conjecture about the segments formed by an angle bisector of a triangle and the other two sides of the triangle.

2. Does any class of triangles have special segment ratios? If so, what data supports your conclusion?

Computer Exploration 14

Angle Bisectors of Similar Triangles

Objective
For similar triangles, determine relationships between the lengths of
corresponding angle bisectors and the lengths of corresponding sides.

Investigation
Construct a triangle. Construct an angle
bisector that intersects the opposite side.
Measure segments and record your data.
Then draw a triangle similar to the first by
giving it a different size (scale), and
construct a corresponding angle bisector.
Find the segment ratios indicated in the
second chart. Repeat for other pairs of
triangles.

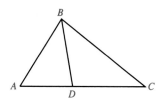

	First Triangle				Scaled Triangle			
	AB	*BC*	*AC*	*BD*	*A'B'*	*B'C'*	*A'C'*	*B'D'*
Acute								
Acute								
Obtuse								
Obtuse								

	AB:A'B'	*BC:B'C'*	*AC:A'C'*	*BD:B'D'*
Acute				
Acute				
Obtuse				
Obtuse				

Conjecture
1. Make a conjecture about the relationship between corresponding sides and
   angle bisectors of similar triangles.

**Angle Bisectors of
Similar Triangles**
Use before or during Lesson
6-6.

This activity can be used in
mid-lesson, but should be
completed before the introduction of Theorem 6.10.

Conjecture
1. The lengths of bisectors of
corresponding angles of two
similar triangles are in the
same ratio as the lengths of
corresponding sides. (Theorem
6.10)

Computer Exploration 15

Altitude to Hypotenuse
Use before Lesson 7-1.

For each construction of a right triangle and altitude, data is to be entered in all three charts. "Right Triangle 1" refers to the first construction, "Right Triangle 2" to the second construction, and so on. The conjecture involves Theorem 7.1. The similarity of the three triangles can also be proved by measuring sides and comparing side-length ratios.

Conjecture

1. The altitude to the hypotenuse of a right triangle forms two triangles that are similar to each other and to the original triangle. (Theorem 7.1)

Computer Exploration 15

Altitude to Hypotenuse

Objective
Determine relationships among a right triangle and the two triangles that are formed by the altitude to the hypotenuse.

Investigation
Construct a right triangle. Construct the altitude to the hypotenuse. Measure the angles indicated in the three charts. Record your data in the rows for Right Triangle 1. Repeat for other right triangles.

Triangle *ABC*	$m\angle BCA$	$m\angle CAB$	$m\angle ABC$
Right Triangle 1			
Right Triangle 2			
Right Triangle 3			

Triangle *BCD*	$m\angle CDB$	$m\angle BCD$	$m\angle DBC$
Right Triangle 1			
Right Triangle 2			
Right Triangle 3			

Triangle *CAD*	$m\angle ADC$	$m\angle CAD$	$m\angle DCA$
Right Triangle 1			
Right Triangle 2			
Right Triangle 3			

Conjecture
1. Make a conjecture about the relationships among a right triangle and the two triangles that are formed by the altitude to the hypotenuse.

Computer Exploration 16

Length of Altitude to Hypotenuse

Objective
Determine the relationship between the length of the altitude to the hypotenuse of a right triangle and the length of the two segments on the hypotenuse.

Investigation
Construct a right triangle. Construct the altitude to the hypotenuse. Measure the segments. Record your data. Repeat for other right triangles.

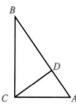

	BD	DA	CD	BD·DA
Right Triangle 1				
Right Triangle 2				
Right Triangle 3				
Right Triangle 4				

Conjecture
1. Make a conjecture about the relationship between the length of the altitude to the hypotenuse of a right triangle and the length of the two segments on the hypotenuse.

Length of Altitude to Hypotenuse

Use before Lesson 7-1.

If students do not find the relationship (Theorem 7.2), suggest that they try squaring segment lengths. This should help them discover that the altitude squared equals the product of the two segments on the hypotenuse.

Conjecture

1. In a right triangle, the length of the altitude to the hypotenuse is the geometric mean between the lengths of the two segments on the hypotenuse. (Theorem 7.2)

Use with Lesson 7-1.

This activity may be used at any point in the lesson. If students do not find the relationship, suggest that they try multiplying segment lengths and comparing them to the other data. The conjecture is proved in Exercise 49, page 299.

Conjecture

1. In a right triangle with an altitude to the hypotenuse, the product of the length of the altitude and the length of the hypotenuse is equal to the product of the lengths of the legs of the triangle.

Computer Exploration 17

Hypotenuse, Legs, and Altitude

Objective
Determine the relationship among the legs, altitude, and hypotenuse of a right triangle.

Investigation
Construct a right triangle. Construct the altitude to the hypotenuse. Measure segments and record your data. Repeat for other right triangles.

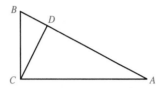

	AC	BC	AB	CD	$AB \cdot CD$
Right Triangle 1					
Right Triangle 2					
Right Triangle 3					
Right Triangle 4					

Conjecture
1. Make a conjecture about the relationship between a right triangle's hypotenuse and altitude, and its two legs.

Computer Exploration 18

Hypotenuse, Hypotenuse Segments, and Legs

Objective
Given an altitude to the hypotenuse of a right triangle, determine the relationship among the hypotenuse, a leg, and a segment on the hypotenuse.

Investigation
Construct a right triangle. Construct the altitude to the hypotenuse. Measure the segments. Record your data. Find the products listed in the chart. Repeat for other right triangles.

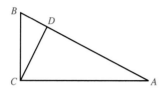

	AC	BC	AB	BD	AD	BD · AB	AD · AB
Right Triangle 1							
Right Triangle 2							
Right Triangle 3							
Right Triangle 4							

Conjecture
1. Make a conjecture about the relationship among the hypotenuse of a right triangle, the two segments formed by the altitude to the hypotenuse, and the legs.

Computer Exploration 18

Hypotenuse, Hypotenuse Segments, and Legs

Use before Lesson 7-1.

If students do not find the relationship (Theorem 7.3), suggest that they try squaring leg lengths and comparing them to the other data.

Conjecture

1. In a right triangle with an altitude to the hypotenuse, each leg is the geometric mean between the length of the hypotenuse and the length of the segment of the hypotenuse adjacent to that leg. (Theorem 7.3)

Use before Lesson 7-3.

Allow students to experiment with various triangles. Since this activity leads to discovery of the converse of the Pythagorean Theorem (Theorem 7.5) and to Theorem 7.6, triangle types are not given in the chart; students are to derive the types from their measurements and calculations. Make sure that for right triangles, students compare the squared hypotenuse length with the squared leg lengths.

It is important to note that AC and BC represent the two shorter sides of the triangle and that AB represents the longest side. The last column of the table, $AC^2 + BC^2$, represents the sum of the squares of the lengths of the two shorter sides of the triangle.

Conjectures

1. If the sum of the squares of the lengths of the two shorter sides of a triangle equals the square of the length of the longest side, then the triangle is a right triangle. (Theorem 7.5)
2. If the sum of the squares of the lengths of the two shorter sides of a triangle is less than the square of the length of the longest side, then the triangle is an obtuse triangle. (Theorem 7.6)
3. If the sum of the squares of the lengths of the two shorter sides of a triangle is greater than the square of the length of the longer side, then the triangle is an acute triangle. (Theorem 7.6)

Computer Exploration 19

Triangles and Side Lengths

Objectives
Find special relationships of side lengths in triangles, and find the type of triangle determined by certain side-length relationships.

Investigation
Construct triangles with sides of different lengths. Label the longest side AB. Measure the lengths of the sides. Record your data. Make the calculations required to complete the chart.

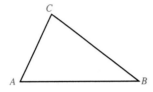

Type of Triangle	AC	BC	AB	AC^2	BC^2	AB^2	$AC^2 + BC^2$

Conjectures
1. For what type of triangle does AC^2 plus BC^2 equal AB^2?
2. For what type of triangle is $AC^2 + BC^2$ less than AB^2?
3. For what type of triangle is $AC^2 + BC^2$ greater than AB^2?

Computer Exploration 20

45°–45°–90° Triangles

Objective
Determine the relationship between the length of the hypotenuse of a 45°–45°–90° triangle and the length of a leg.

Investigation
Construct a 45°–45°–90° triangle. Measure the lengths of the sides. Record your data. Calculate the ratio shown in the chart. Repeat for other 45°–45°–90° triangles.

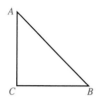

	AC	CB	AB	AB:CB
45°–45°–90° Triangle 1				
45°–45°–90° Triangle 2				
45°–45°–90° Triangle 3				
45°–45°–90° Triangle 4				

Conjecture
1. Make a conjecture about the relationship between the length of the hypotenuse of a 45°–45°–90° triangle and the length of a leg. Express your conjecture in terms of an exact real number.

45°–45°–90° Triangles
Use before Lesson 7-4.

The conjecture involves Theorem 7.7. Since collected data will be in decimal form, remind students that decimal representations of exact real numbers may be approximate. The order in which ratios are expressed can reveal or hide the exact real number. Some time may need to be spent looking at decimal approximations of real numbers (e.g., $\sqrt{2}$, $\sqrt{3}$, $\frac{1}{\sqrt{2}}$, etc).

Students should recognize that certain decimal numbers are approximations of exact real numbers.

Conjecture

1. The length of the hypotenuse of a 45°–45°–90° triangle is $\sqrt{2}$ times the length of a leg. (Theorem 7.7)

30°–60°–90° Triangles

Use before Lesson 7-4.

Both conjectures involve Theorem 7.8. Again note the decimal representations of exact real numbers may be approximate.

Conjectures

1. The length of the hypotenuse of a 30°–60°–90° triangle is 2 times the length of the shorter leg. (Theorem 7.8)
2. The length of the longer leg of a 30°–60°–90° triangle is √3 times the length of the shorter leg. (Theorem 7.8)

Computer Exploration 21

30°–60°–90° Triangles

Objective

Given a 30°–60°–90° triangle, determine the relationship between the lengths of the hypotenuse and the shorter leg, and the relationship between the lengths of the longer leg and the shorter leg.

Investigation

Construct a 30°–60°–90° triangle. Measure the lengths of the sides. Record your data. Calculate the ratios shown in the chart. Repeat for other 30°–60°–90° triangles.

	AC	AB	BC	AC:BC	AB:BC
30°–60°–90° Triangle 1					
30°–60°–90° Triangle 2					
30°–60°–90° Triangle 3					
30°–60°–90° Triangle 4					

Conjectures

1. Make a conjecture about the relationship between the length of the hypotenuse of a 30°–60°–90° triangle and the length of the shorter leg.
2. Make a conjecture about the relationship between the lengths of the legs of a 30°–60°–90° triangle. Express your conjecture in terms of an exact real number.

Computer Exploration 22

The Tangent Ratio

Objective

Investigate the ratio of the lengths of the two legs of similar right triangles.

Investigation

Draw a right triangle. Measure the lengths of the two legs and calculate the ratio of their lengths. Draw a triangle similar to the original one by giving it a different size (scale). Record the data. Repeat for two more similar triangles.

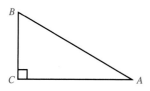

	BC	AC	BC:AC
Right Triangle			
1st Similar Triangle			
2nd Similar Triangle			
3rd Similar Triangle			

Conjecture

1. Make a conjecture about the ratio of the lengths of the legs of similar right triangles.

The Tangent Ratio

Use before Lesson 7-5.

A similar activity could be used for the sine and cosine ratios. After this activity, point out that the ratio students have been considering is known as the tangent of $\angle A$.

Conjecture

1. The ratio of the length of the leg opposite an acute angle of a right triangle to the length of the leg adjacent to the angle is constant for all similar right triangles.

**Perpendicular
Bisectors of the Sides
of a Triangle, I**

Use before Lesson 9-5.

This activity is related to the Explore and figures on page 410. No data collection is required. Students need to observe the positions of the bisectors for acute, right, and obtuse triangles. If they have difficulty making conjectures, ask, "Do the bisectors always have a point in common? Where is the point of inter-section—inside the triangle, outside the triangle, or on a side? If it is on a side, which side is it on?"

Students can proceed directly to Computer Exploration 24, or can save the construction sequence they used here for use in that activity.

Conjectures

1. The perpendicular bisectors of the sides of a triangle have one point in common (i.e., they are concurrent).

2. The point of intersection lies in the interior of the triangle if the triangle is acute. The point of intersection lies in the exterior of the triangle if the triangle is obtuse. The point of intersection lies on the hypotenuse if the triangle is a right triangle.

Computer Exploration 23

Perpendicular Bisectors of the Sides of a Triangle, I

Objective
Investigate the properties of the perpendicular bisectors of the sides of a triangle.

Investigation
Draw a triangle and the perpendicular bisector of each side. Be sure each bisector intersects one of the other sides of the triangle. Do this construction for acute, right, and obtuse triangles.

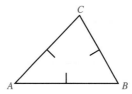

Conjectures
1. Make a conjecture about the three perpendicular bisectors of the sides of a triangle.
2. Make specific conjectures about the perpendicular bisectors of acute, right, and obtuse triangles.

Computer Exploration 24

Perpendicular Bisectors of the Sides of a Triangle, II

Objective

Investigate the properties of the perpendicular bisectors of the sides of a triangle.

Investigation

Draw a triangle and the perpendicular bisector of each side of the triangle. Label the intersection of the perpendicular bisectors. Draw a line segment from the intersection of the perpendicular bisectors to the vertices. Measure each segment. Repeat the construction for the other triangles in the chart.

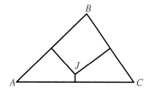

	AJ	BJ	CJ
Acute Triangle			
Obtuse Triangle			
Right Triangle			

Conjecture

1. Make a conjecture about the distance from each vertex of a triangle to the point of intersection of the perpendicular bisectors.

Perpendicular Bisectors of the Sides of a Triangle, II

Use before Lesson 9-5.

The conjecture involves Theorem 9.1. Students may use the same construction sequence they used in Computer Exploration 23.

Conjecture

1. The point of intersection of the perpendicular bisectors of the sides of a triangle is equidistant from the three vertices of the triangle. (Theorem 9.1)

Ask students whether they think the three angle bisectors of a triangle are always concurrent. Have them try the construction for acute, right, and obtuse triangles before deciding.

The conjecture involves Theorem 9.2. To measure the distance from the point of intersection to each side, students must create a perpendicular from that point to each side. Make sure they understand that (using the figure as an example) $\overline{GF}$ is not the shortest distance from point G to $\overline{AB}$, unless $\overline{GF}$ is perpendicular to $\overline{AB}$.

Conjecture

1. The angle bisectors of the angles of a triangle are concurrent in a point that is equidistant from the three sides of the triangle. (Theorem 9.2)

Computer Exploration 25

Angle Bisectors of a Triangle

Objective

Investigate the properties of the bisectors of the angles of a triangle.

Investigation

Draw a triangle. Draw the bisector of each of its angles. Be sure each bisector intersects a side of the triangle. Measure the perpendicular distance from the point of intersection of the angle bisectors to each of the sides of the triangle. Repeat for other triangles.

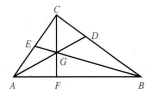

	Distance from G to:		
	$\overline{AB}$	$\overline{BC}$	$\overline{CA}$
Triangle 1			
Triangle 2			
Triangle 3			
Triangle 4			

Conjecture

1. The angle bisectors of a triangle intersect at a point. Make a conjecture about the distance from the point of intersection of the angle bisectors to each of the sides.

Computer Exploration 26

Medians of a Triangle

Objective

Investigate the properties of the medians of a triangle.

Investigation

Draw a triangle and its three medians. Label the point of intersection of the medians. Measure the length of the segments formed by the medians.

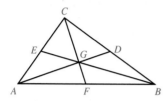

	AG	GD	BG	GE	CG	GF
Triangle 1						
Triangle 2						
Triangle 3						
Triangle 4						

Conjecture

1. The three medians of a triangle intersect at a point. This point divides each median into two segments. Make a conjecture about the relationship between the two segments of each median.

Medians of a Triangle
Use before Lesson 9-5.

Ask students whether they think the three medians of a triangle are always concurrent. Make sure they try the construction with acute, right, and obtuse triangles before deciding.

If students need additional help in making a conjecture, suggest that they focus on ratios of segments.

Conjecture

1. The point of concurrency of the medians of a triangle divides each median into two segments whose lengths have a ratio of 2:1. (Theorem 9.3)

Use before Lesson 10-5.

The conjecture involves Theorem 10.6.

Conjecture

1. The ratio of the perimeters of similar triangles equals the ratio of the lengths of any pair of corresponding sides. (Theorem 10.6)

Computer Exploration 27

Similar Triangles and Perimeter

Objective

Determine the relationship between the perimeter and the corresponding sides of similar triangles.

Investigation

Construct a triangle. Measure the sides and calculate the perimeter. Record your data. Construct another triangle similar to the first one by giving it a different size (scale). Measure and record its side lengths and perimeter. Find the ratios indicated in the chart. Repeat for other pairs of triangles.

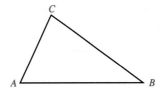

	First Triangle				Scaled Triangle			
	AB	BC	AC	Perimeter	$A'B'$	$B'C'$	$A'C'$	Perimeter
Acute								
Obtuse								
Isosceles								
Right								

	$AB{:}A'B'$	$BC{:}B'C'$	$AC{:}A'C'$	Perimeter of $\triangle ABC$: Perimeter of $\triangle A'B'C'$
Acute				
Obtuse				
Isosceles				
Right				

Conjecture

1. Make a conjecture about the ratio of two similar triangles' perimeters and the ratio of their corresponding side lengths.

Computer Exploration 28

Similar Triangles and Area

Objective

Determine the relationship between the area and the corresponding sides of similar triangles.

If students have trouble finding the relationship (Theorem 10.7), suggest that they try squaring a side-length ratio. (Since corresponding side lengths are proportional, the product of two side-length ratios is also equal to the area ratio.)

Investigation

Construct a triangle. Measure the sides and find the area. Record your data. Construct another triangle similar to the first one by giving it a different size (scale). Measure and record the side lengths and area. Find the ratios indicated in the chart. Repeat for other pairs of triangles.

Conjecture

1. The ratio of the areas of similar triangles equals the square of the ratio of the lengths of any pair of corresponding sides. (Theorem 10.7)

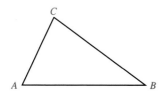

	First Triangle				Scaled Triangle			
	AB	*BC*	*AC*	Area	*A'B'*	*B'C'*	*A'C'*	Area
Acute								
Obtuse								
Isosceles								
Right								

	AB:A'B'	*BC:B'C'*	*AC:A'C'*	Area of △*ABC*: Area of △*A'B'C'*
Acute				
Obtuse				
Isosceles				
Right				

Conjecture

1. Make a conjecture about the ratio of two similar triangles' areas and the ratio of their corresponding side lengths.

Computer Exploration   **661**

Milestones in Mathematics

Gauss called mathematics the Queen of the sciences. Clearly then, mathematicians are her courtiers. To fully enjoy mathematics, you need a sense of its development and of the people of genius who have devoted their lives to its exploration. **Milestones in Mathematics** is a partial list of important events in mathematical history. You may want to find additional information in the library to learn more about these and other mathematicians and their contributions to the field of mathematics.

Milestones in Mathematics

c. 30,000+ BC	The knucklebones of animals were used as dice in games of chance.
c. 20,000+ BC	A wolfbone with 55 notches in two rows divided into groups of five was used for counting (discovered at Vestonice in Czechoslovakia).
c. 8,000 BC	First evidence of recorded counting.
c. 2,000 BC	The Egyptians had arrived at the value for pi of $\pi = 4(8/9)^2$.
c. 1,900 BC	Babylonian scholars used cuneiform numerals to the base 60 in the oldest-known written numeration for place value.
c. 1,700 BC	Sumerian notation was used to solve quadratic equations by the equivalent of the formula we use today.
c. 800 BC	Queen Dido founded the great city of Carthage by solving the geometric "Problem of Dido." A rigorous proof of this problem—what closed curve of specified length will enclose a maximum area—did not come until the nineteenth century.
c. 700 BC	Zero appeared in the Seleucid mathematical tables.
c. 550 BC	Pythagoras developed a logical, deductive proof of the Pythagorean theorem.
c. 300 BC	Euclid wrote the first geometry text, *Elements*.
c. 250 BC	Archimedes wrote *On Mechanical Theorems, Method* for his friend Eratosthenes.
c. 250 AD	An initial-letter shorthand for algebraic equations was developed.
c. 300 AD	Pappus of Alexandria discussed the areas of figures with the same perimeter in the *Mathematical Collection*.
c. 375 AD	Earliest known Mayan Initial Series inscriptions for expressing dates and periods of time.
c. 400 AD	Hypatia, the foremost mathematician in Alexandria, lectured on Diophantine algebra.
595	Date of an Indian deed on copper plate showing the oldest known use of the nine numerals according to the place value principle: the first written decimal numeration with the structure used today.

825   A treatise on linear and quadratic equations was published by Mohammed Al-Khwarizmi.

850   Mahavira contributed to the development of algebra in India.

1202   Leonardo of Pisa, also called Fibonacci, wrote *Liber abaci*, introducing Arabic numbers to Europe. This book contains his "rabbit problem" involving the numbers we now call Fibonacci.

1261   Yang Hui of China wrote on the properties of the binomial coefficients.

1557   The equal sign ($=$) came into general use during the 16th century, A.D. (The twin lines as an equal sign were used by the English physician and mathematician Robert Recorde with the explanation that "noe .2. thynges, can be moare equalle.")

1614   John Napier invented logarithms.

1639   René Descartes published his treatise on the application of algebra to geometry (analytic geometry).

1654   Blaise Pascal described the properties of the triangle we now call Pascal's triangle.

1657   Major contributions to number theory were made by Pierre de Fermat including his formulation of the "Pell" equation.

1670   G. Mouton devised a decimal-based measuring system.

1688   The calculus was published by Isaac Newton in *Principia Mathematica*.

1735   Graph theory was originated by Leonard Euler in his paper on the problem, "The Seven Bridges of Konigsberg."

1784   Maria Agnesi developed new ways to deal with problems involving infinite quantities in her book, *Analytical Institutions*.

1799   The fundamental theorem of algebra was delineated by Carl Friederich Gauss, who also developed rigorous proof as the requirement of mathematics.

1816   Sophie Germain published equations which stated the law for vibrating elastic surfaces.

1832   Evariste Galois wrote the theorem stating the conditions under which an equation can be solved.

1854   George Boole developed the postulates of "Boolean Algebra" in *Laws of Thought*.

1854   Mary Fairfax Somerville wrote books to popularize mathematics and extend the influence of the work of mathematicians.

1859   George F. B. Reimann published his work on the distribution of primes; "Reimann's Hypothesis" became one of the famous unsolved problems of mathematics.

1886   Modern combinatorial topology was created by Henri Poincare.

1888   Sonya Kovalesvskaya was awarded the Prix Bordin for her paper "On the Rotation of a Solid Body About a Fixed Point."

1897   David Hilbert published his monumental work on the theory of number fields and later clarified the foundations of geometry.

1906   Grace Chisholm Young and William Young published the first text on set theory.

1914   Srinivasa Ramanujan went to England to collaborate with G. H. Hardy on analytic number theory.

1925   Hermann Weyl published fundamental papers on group theory.

1931   Gödel showed that there must be undecidable propositions in any formal system and that one of those undecidable propositions is consistency.

1932   A completely general theory of ideal numbers was built up, on an axiomatic basis, by Emmy Noether.

1936   The minimax principle in probability and statistics was developed by Abraham Wald.

1937   Goldbach's conjecture that every even number is the sum of two primes ($12 = 5 + 7$, $100 = 3 + 97$) was established by I. M. Vinogradov for every sufficiently large even number that is the sum of, at most, four primes.

1938   Claude E. Shannon discovered the analogy between the truth values of propositions and the states of switches and relays in an electric circuit.

1942   Jacqueline Ferrand created the concept of preholomorphic functions, using these to produce a new methodology for mathematical proofs.

1951   Elizabeth Scott, Jerzy Newyman, and C. D. Shane applied statistical theories to deduce the existence of clusters of galaxies.

1953   Maria Pastori extended the usefulness of the tensor calculus in the pure mathematical investigation of generalized spaces.

1960   Advances in the application of probability and statistics were made by Florence Nightingale David.

1976   Four color problem proved using electronic computing in concert with human deduction.

1985   A new algorithm for factoring large numbers by using elliptic curves was developed by Hendrik W. Lenstra, Jr.

1985   David Hoffman discovered a fourth minimal surface, the first new minimal surface discovered since the 1700s.

????   "Fermat's Last Theorem" on the impossibility of separating any power above the second into two powers of the same degree is proved.

Symbols

$\pm$	positive or negative		$\triangle ABC$	triangle ABC
$=$	is equal to		$\square ABCD$	parallelogram $ABCD$
$\neq$	is not equal to		$\odot O$	circle O
$\approx$	is approximately equal to		$\overarc{AB}$	minor arc determined by A and B
$<$	is less than		$\overarc{ACB}$	major arc determined by A and B
$\leq$	is less than or equal to		$m\overarc{AB}$	measure of $\overarc{AB}$
$>$	is greater than		$\cong$	is congruent to
$\geq$	is greater than or equal to		$\ncong$	is not congruent to
$\lvert x \rvert$	absolute value of x		$\parallel$	is parallel to
$\sqrt{x}$	principal square root of x		$\nparallel$	is not parallel to
(x, y)	ordered pair		$\perp$	is perpendicular to
$^\circ$	degrees		$\sim$	is similar to
$\overleftrightarrow{AB}$	line AB		$\leftrightarrow$	corresponds to
$\overline{AB}$	segment AB		$p \rightarrow q$	p implies q (if p, then q)
$\overrightarrow{AB}$	ray AB		$\sim p$	not p
$\overrightarrow{AB}$	vector AB		$\sin A$	sine of $\angle A$
$\overline{AB}$	length of AB		$\cos A$	cosine of $\angle A$
$\angle ABC$	angle ABC		$\tan A$	tangent of $\angle A$
$m\angle ABC$	measure of $\angle ABC$		π	pi, approximately 3.14

Formulas

Rectangle	**Square**	**Parallelogram**
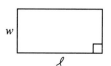		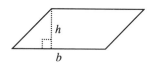
Area: $A = \ell w$ Perimeter: $p = 2\ell + 2w$	Area: $A = s^2$ Perimeter: $p = 4s$	Area: $A = bh$

Triangle	**Trapezoid**	**Regular Polygon**
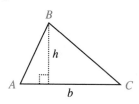	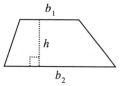	
Area: $A = \frac{1}{2} bh$ $m \angle A + m \angle B + m \angle C = 180$	Area: $A = \frac{1}{2} h(b_1 + b_2)$	Area: $A = \frac{1}{2} ap$

Circle	**Right Prism**	**Regular Pyramid**
		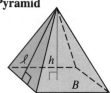
Area: $A = \pi r^2$ Circumference $= C = \pi d = 2\pi r$	Volume: $V = Bh$ Lateral Area: $LA = ph$ Surface Area: $SA = ph + 2B$	Volume: $V = \frac{1}{3} Bh$ Lateral Area: $\frac{1}{2} p\ell$ Surface Area: $SA = \frac{1}{2} p\ell + B$

Right Cylinder	**Right Cone**	**Sphere**
Volume: $V = \pi r^2 h$ Lateral Area: $LA = 2\pi rh$ Surface Area: $SA = 2\pi rh + 2\pi r^2$	Volume: $V = \frac{1}{3} \pi r^2 h$ Lateral Area: $LA = \pi r \ell$ Surface Area: $SA = \pi r \ell + \pi r^2$	Volume: $V = \frac{4}{3} \pi r^3$ Surface Area: $SA = 4\pi r^2$

Values of Trigonometric Functions

Degrees	Sin	Cos	Tan	Degrees	Sin	Cos	Tan
0°	0.0000	1.0000	0.0000				
1°	0.0175	0.9998	0.0175	46°	0.7193	0.6947	1.0355
2°	0.0349	0.9994	0.0349	47°	0.7314	0.6820	1.0724
3°	0.0523	0.9986	0.0524	48°	0.7431	0.6691	1.1106
4°	0.0698	0.9976	0.0699	49°	0.7547	0.6561	1.1504
5°	0.0872	0.9962	0.0875	50°	0.7660	0.6428	1.1918
6°	0.1045	0.9945	0.1051	51°	0.7771	0.6293	1.2349
7°	0.1219	0.9925	0.1228	52°	0.7880	0.6157	1.2799
8°	0.1392	0.9903	0.1405	53°	0.7986	0.6018	1.3270
9°	0.1564	0.9877	0.1584	54°	0.8090	0.5878	1.3764
10°	0.1736	0.9848	0.1763	55°	0.8192	0.5736	1.4281
11°	0.1908	0.9816	0.1944	56°	0.8290	0.5592	1.4826
12°	0.2079	0.9781	0.2126	57°	0.8387	0.5446	1.5399
13°	0.2250	0.9744	0.2309	58°	0.8480	0.5299	1.6003
14°	0.2419	0.9703	0.2493	59°	0.8572	0.5150	1.6643
15°	0.2588	0.9659	0.2679	60°	0.8660	0.5000	1.7321
16°	0.2756	0.9613	0.2867	61°	0.8746	0.4848	1.8040
17°	0.2924	0.9563	0.3057	62°	0.8829	0.4695	1.8807
18°	0.3090	0.9511	0.3249	63°	0.8910	0.4540	1.9626
19°	0.3256	0.9455	0.3443	64°	0.8988	0.4384	2.0503
20°	0.3420	0.9397	0.3640	65°	0.9063	0.4226	2.1445
21°	0.3584	0.9336	0.3839	66°	0.9135	0.4067	2.2460
22°	0.3746	0.9272	0.4040	67°	0.9205	0.3907	2.3559
23°	0.3907	0.9205	0.4245	68°	0.9272	0.3746	2.4751
24°	0.4067	0.9135	0.4452	69°	0.9336	0.3584	2.6051
25°	0.4226	0.9063	0.4663	70°	0.9397	0.3420	2.7475
26°	0.4384	0.8988	0.4877	71°	0.9455	0.3256	2.9042
27°	0.4540	0.8910	0.5095	72°	0.9511	0.3090	3.0777
28°	0.4695	0.8829	0.5317	73°	0.9563	0.2924	3.2709
29°	0.4848	0.8746	0.5543	74°	0.9613	0.2756	3.4874
30°	0.5000	0.8660	0.5774	75°	0.9659	0.2588	3.7321
31°	0.5150	0.8572	0.6009	76°	0.9703	0.2419	4.0108
32°	0.5299	0.8480	0.6249	77°	0.9744	0.2250	4.3315
33°	0.5446	0.8387	0.6494	78°	0.9781	0.2079	4.7046
34°	0.5592	0.8290	0.6745	79°	0.9816	0.1908	5.1446
35°	0.5736	0.8192	0.7002	80°	0.9848	0.1736	5.6713
36°	0.5878	0.8090	0.7265	81°	0.9877	0.1564	6.3138
37°	0.6018	0.7986	0.7536	82°	0.9903	0.1392	7.1154
38°	0.6157	0.7880	0.7813	83°	0.9925	0.1219	8.1443
39°	0.6293	0.7771	0.8098	84°	0.9945	0.1045	9.5144
40°	0.6428	0.7660	0.8391	85°	0.9962	0.0872	11.4301
41°	0.6561	0.7547	0.8693	86°	0.9976	0.0698	14.3007
42°	0.6691	0.7431	0.9004	87°	0.9986	0.0523	19.0811
43°	0.6820	0.7314	0.9325	88°	0.9994	0.0349	28.6363
44°	0.6947	0.7193	0.9657	89°	0.9998	0.0175	57.2900
45°	0.7071	0.7071	1.0000	90°	1.0000	0.0000	

Squares and Square Roots

N	N²	√N	N	N²	√N
1	1	1	51	2,601	7.141
2	4	1.414	52	2,704	7.211
3	9	1.732	53	2,809	7.280
4	16	2	54	2,916	7.348
5	25	2.236	55	3,025	7.416
6	36	2.449	56	3,136	7.483
7	49	2.646	57	3,249	7.550
8	64	2.828	58	3,364	7.616
9	81	3	59	3,481	7.681
10	100	3.162	60	3,600	7.746
11	121	3.317	61	3,721	7.810
12	144	3.464	62	3,844	7.874
13	169	3.606	63	3,969	7.937
14	196	3.742	64	4,096	8
15	225	3.873	65	4,225	8.062
16	256	4	66	4,356	8.124
17	289	4.123	67	4,489	8.185
18	324	4.243	68	4,624	8.246
19	361	4.359	69	4,761	8.307
20	400	4.472	70	4,900	8.367
21	441	4.583	71	5,041	8.426
22	484	4.690	72	5,184	8.485
23	529	4.796	73	5,329	8.544
24	576	4.899	74	5,476	8.602
25	625	5	75	5,625	8.660
26	676	5.099	76	5,776	8.718
27	729	5.196	77	5,929	8.775
28	784	5.292	78	6,084	8.832
29	841	5.385	79	6,241	8.888
30	900	5.477	80	6,400	8.944
31	961	5.568	81	6,561	9
32	1,024	5.657	82	6,724	9.055
33	1,089	5.745	83	6,889	9.110
34	1,156	5.831	84	7,056	9.165
35	1,225	5.916	85	7,225	9.220
36	1,296	6	86	7,396	9.274
37	1,369	6.083	87	7,569	9.327
38	1,444	6.164	88	7,744	9.381
39	1,521	6.245	89	7,921	9.434
40	1,600	6.325	90	8,100	9.487
41	1,681	6.403	91	8,281	9.539
42	1,764	6.481	92	8,464	9.592
43	1,849	6.557	93	8,649	9.644
44	1,936	6.633	94	8,836	9.695
45	2,025	6.708	95	9,025	9.747
46	2,116	6.782	96	9,216	9.798
47	2,209	6.856	97	9,409	9.849
48	2,304	6.928	98	9,604	9.899
49	2,401	7	99	9,801	9.950
50	2,500	7.071	100	10,000	10

Postulates

Postulate 1	A line, a plane, and space each contain an infinite number of points. Some points in a plane are noncollinear. Some points in space are noncoplanar. [1.1]
Postulate 2	For any two points, there is exactly one line containing them. [1.1]
Postulate 3	For any three noncollinear points, there is exactly one plane containing them. [1.1]
Postulate 4	If two points are in a plane, then the line containing them is in the plane. [1.1]
Postulate 5	If two planes intersect, then they intersect in exactly one line. [1.1]
Postulate 6	Ruler Postulate: The points on a line can be matched one-to-one with real-number coordinates so that **a.** for any two points there corresponds a unique positive number, called the distance between the two points, **b.** the distance between any two points is the absolute value of the difference of their coordinates. [1.2]
Postulate 7	Segment Addition Postulate: If Q is between P and R, then $PQ + QR = PR$. [1.2]
Postulate 8	Protractor Postulate: Given any line AB with point O between A and B; $\overrightarrow{OA}$, $\overrightarrow{OB}$, and all the rays from point O on one side of $\overleftrightarrow{AB}$ can be matched one-to-one with the real numbers from 0 through 180 so that **a.** $\overrightarrow{OA}$ is matched with 0 **b.** $\overrightarrow{OB}$ is matched with 180 **c.** if $\overrightarrow{OR}$ is matched with r and $\overrightarrow{OS}$ is matched with s, then $m\angle ROS = |r - s| = |s - r|$. [1.3]
Postulate 9	Angle Addition Postulate: If F is in the interior of $\angle CDE$, then $m\angle CDF + m\angle FDE = m\angle CDE$. [1.3]
Postulate 10	Midpoint Postulate: A segment has exactly one midpoint. [1.4]
Postulate 11	Angle Bisector Postulate: An angle has exactly one bisector. [1.4]
Postulate 12	Linear Pair Postulate: Two angles that form a linear pair are supplementary. [2.2]
Postulate 13	If two parallel lines are cut by a transversal, then corresponding angles are congruent. [3.2]
Postulate 14	If two lines are cut by a transversal and a pair of corresponding angles are congruent, then the lines are parallel. [3.3]
Postulate 15	Given a line ℓ and a point P not on ℓ, there exists one and only one line through P parallel to ℓ. [3.4]
Postulate 16	SSS Postulate: If each of the three sides of one triangle are congruent respectively to corresponding sides of another triangle, then the two triangles are congruent. [4.2]
Postulate 17	ASA Postulate: If two angles and the included side of one triangle are congruent to two angles and the included side of another triangle, then the two triangles are congruent. [4.2]
Postulate 18	SAS Postulate: If two sides and the included angle of one triangle are congruent to two sides and the included angle of another triangle, then the triangles are congruent. [4.2]
Postulate 19	AA Similarity Postulate: If two angles of one triangle are congruent respectively to two angles of another triangle, then the two triangles are similar. [6.4]
Postulate 20	Arc Addition Postulate: The measure of adjacent nonoverlapping arcs is the sum of the measures of the two arcs. [8.4]
Postulate 21	Every closed region has an area, which is a unique positive number. [10.1]
Postulate 22	The area A of a rectangle is the product of its length ℓ times its width w. $A = \ell w$ [10.1]

Postulate 23   If two closed figures are congruent, then they have equal areas. [10.1]

Postulate 24   The area of a region is the sum of the areas of all its nonoverlapping parts. [10.1]

Postulate 25   Cavalieri's Principle: Let S and T be two solids and let X be a plane. If every plane parallel to X that intersects S and T intersects both S and T in a cross section having the same area, then volume of S = volume of T. [11.3]

Theorems

Theorem 1.1   Congruence of segments and angles is reflexive, symmetric, and transitive. [1.8]

Theorem 1.2   If two segments are congruent to the same segment, then they are congruent to each other. [1.8]

Theorem 1.3   If two angles are congruent to the same angle, then they are congruent to each other. [1.8]

Theorem 2.1   The sum of the measures of the angles in a linear pair is 180. [2.2]

Theorem 2.2   Vertical Angle Theorem: If two angles are vertical angles, then they are congruent. [2.2]

Theorem 2.3   Through a given point on a line, there is exactly one line in the plane perpendicular to the given line. [2.3]

Theorem 2.4   All right angles are congruent. [2.5]

Theorem 2.5   Midpoint Theorem: The midpoint M of $\overline{AB}$ divides $\overline{AB}$ so that $AM = \frac{1}{2}AB$. [2.5]

Theorem 2.6   Angle Bisector Theorem: If $\overrightarrow{BD}$ is the bisector of $\angle ABC$, then $m\angle ABD = \frac{1}{2}m\angle ABC$. [2.5]

Theorem 2.7   Common Segment Theorem
1. If $\overline{AB} \cong \overline{CD}$, then $\overline{AC} \cong \overline{BD}$.
2. If $\overline{AC} \cong \overline{BD}$, then $\overline{AB} \cong \overline{CD}$. [2.6]

Theorem 2.8   If two lines form congruent adjacent angles, then they are perpendicular. [2.6]

Theorem 2.9   Only one perpendicular can be drawn from a point to a line. [2-6]

Theorem 2.10   Common Angle Theorem
1. If $\angle AOB \cong \angle COD$, then $\angle AOC \cong \angle BOD$.
2. If $\angle AOC \cong \angle BOD$, then $\angle AOB \cong \angle COD$. [2.7]

Theorem 2.11   If two lines are perpendicular, then they form congruent adjacent angles. [2.7]

Theorem 2.12   Congruent Complements Theorem: Two angles that are complementary to the same angle (or to congruent angles) are congruent. [2.7]

Theorem 2.13   Congruent Supplements Theorem: Two angles that are supplementary to the same angle (or to congruent angles) are congruent. [2.7]

Theorem 2.14   If one angle of a linear pair is a right angle, then the other angle is also a right angle. [2.7]

Theorem 3.1   If two parallel planes are cut by a third plane, the lines of intersection are parallel. [3.1]

Theorem 3.2   If two parallel lines are cut by a transversal, then alternate interior angles are congruent. [3.2]

Theorem 3.3   If two parallel lines are cut by a transversal, then alternate exterior angles are congruent. [3.2]

Theorem 3.4   If two parallel lines are cut by a transversal, then same-side interior angles are supplementary. [3.2]

Theorem 3.5   If two lines are cut by a transversal and a pair of alternate interior angles are congruent, then the lines are parallel. [3.3]

Theorem 3.6   If two lines are cut by a transversal and a pair of alternate exterior angles are congruent, then the lines are parallel. [3.3]

Theorem 3.7	If two lines are cut by a transversal and a pair of same-side interior angles are supplementary, then the lines are parallel. [3.3]
Theorem 3.8	In a plane, two coplanar lines perpendicular to the same line are parallel. [3.3]
Theorem 3.9	Two lines parallel to a third line are parallel to each other. [3.3]
Theorem 3.10	Angle Sum Theorem for Triangles: The sum of the measures of the angles of a triangle is 180. [3.4]
Corollary 3.10a	The angles of an equiangular triangle each have a measure of 60. [3.4]
Corollary 3.10b	The acute angles of a right triangle are complementary. [3.4]
Theorem 3.11	The Exterior Angle Theorem: The measure of an exterior angle of a triangle is equal to the sum of the measures of its two remote interior angles. [3.5]
Theorem 3.12	If two angles of one triangle are congruent to two angles of another triangle, then the third angles are congruent. [3.5]
Theorem 3.13	The sum of the measures of the angles of a convex polygon of n sides is $(n-2)180$. [3.6]
Corollary 3.13a	The measure of each angle of a regular polygon of n sides is $\frac{(n-2)180}{n}$. [3.6]
Theorem 3.14	The sum of the measures of the exterior angles of a convex polygon is 360. [3.6]
Theorem 4.1	Isosceles Triangle Theorem: If two sides of a triangle are congruent then the angles opposite those sides are congruent. [4.6]
Corollary 4.1a	If a triangle is equilateral then it is equiangular. [4.6]
Corollary 4.1b	The segment from the vertex of an isosceles triangle to the midpoint of the base bisects the vertex angle. [4.6]
Theorem 4.2	If two angles of a triangle are congruent, then the sides opposite them are congruent. [4.6]
Corollary 4.2a	If a triangle is equiangular, then the triangle is equilateral. [4.6]
Theorem 4.3	AAS Congruence: If two angles and a side opposite one of them in one triangle are congruent to the corresponding parts in another triangle, then the two triangles are congruent. [4.7]
Theorem 4.4	HA Congruence: If the hypotenuse and one acute angle of a right triangle are congruent to the hypotenuse and one acute angle of another right triangle, then the triangles are congruent. [4.7]
Theorem 4.5	HL Congruence: If the hypotenuse and a leg of one right triangle are congruent to the corresponding parts of a second right triangle, then the triangles are congruent. [4.7]
Theorem 4.6	In an isosceles triangle, the altitude to the base bisects the base and bisects the vertex angle. [4.8]
Theorem 4.7	If a point is equidistant from the endpoints of a segment, then it is on the perpendicular bisector of the segment. [4.8]
Theorem 4.8	If a point is on the perpendicular bisector of a segment, then it is equidistant from the endpoints of the segment. [4.8]
Theorem 4.9	If a point is equidistant from the sides of an angle, then it is on the angle bisector. [4.8]
Theorem 4.10	If a point is on an angle bisector, then it is equidistant from the sides of the angle. [4.8]
Theorem 5.1	Opposite sides of a parallelogram are congruent. [5.1]
Corollary 5.1a	Two parallel lines are equidistant at all points. [5.1]
Theorem 5.2	Opposite angles of a parallelogram are congruent. [5.1]
Corollary 5.2a	Consecutive angles of a parallelogram are supplementary. [5.1]
Theorem 5.3	The diagonals of a parallelogram bisect each other. [5.1]

Theorem 5.4	If both pairs of opposite sides of a quadrilateral are congruent, then the quadrilateral is a parallelogram. [5.2]
Theorem 5.5	If one pair of opposite sides of a quadrilateral are both parallel and congruent, then it is a parallelogram. [5.2]
Theorem 5.6	If both pairs of opposite angles of a quadrilateral are congruent, then the quadrilateral is a parallelogram. [5.2]
Theorem 5.7	If the consecutive angles of a quadrilateral are supplementary, then the quadrilateral is a parallelogram. [5.2]
Theorem 5.8	If the diagonals of a quadrilateral bisect each other, then the quadrilateral is a parallelogram. [5.2]
Theorem 5.9	The diagonals of a rectangle are congruent. [5.3]
Theorem 5.10	The diagonals of a rhombus are perpendicular. [5.3]
Theorem 5.11	Each diagonal of a rhombus bisects a pair of opposite angles. [5.3]
Theorem 5.12	If a parallelogram has a right angle, then it is a rectangle. [5.3]
Theorem 5.13	If a parallelogram has two adjacent sides congruent, then it is a rhombus. [5.3]
Theorem 5.14	Each pair of base angles of an isosceles trapezoid are congruent. [5.4]
Theorem 5.15	The diagonals of an isosceles trapezoid are congruent. [5.4]
Theorem 5.16	The median of a trapezoid is parallel to the bases and has a length equal to half the sum of the lengths of the bases. That is, $PQ = \frac{1}{2}(XY + WZ)$. [5.4]
Theorem 5.17	Midsegment Theorem: The segment that joins the midpoints of two sides of a triangle is parallel to the third side and has length equal to half the length of the third side. [5.5]
Theorem 5.18	The quadrilateral formed by joining the midpoints of the consecutive sides of another quadrilateral is a parallelogram. [5.5]
Theorem 5.19	If three or more parallel lines cut off congruent segments on one transversal, then they will cut off congruent segments on every transversal. [5.5]
Corollary 5.19a	A line that contains the midpoint of one side of a triangle and is parallel to another side bisects the third side. [5.5]
Theorem 5.20	Exterior Angle Inequality Theorem: The measure of an exterior angle of a triangle is greater than the measure of either remote interior angle. [5.7]
Theorem 5.21	If one side of a triangle is longer than a second side, then the measure of the angle opposite the longer side is greater than the measure of the angle opposite the shorter side. [5.7]
Theorem 5.22	If one angle of a triangle is larger than another angle, then the side opposite the larger angle is longer than the side opposite the smaller angle. [5.7]
Corollary 5.22a	The perpendicular segment from a point to a line is the shortest segment from the point to the line. [5.7]
Theorem 5.23	Triangle Inequality Theorem: The sum of the lengths of any two sides of a triangle is greater than the length of the third side. [5.7]
Theorem 5.24	SAS Inequality Theorem: If two sides of one triangle are congruent to two sides of a second triangle and the included angle of the first triangle is larger than the included angle of the second triangle, then the third side of the first triangle is longer then the third side of the second triangle. [5.8]
Theorem 5.25	SSS Inequality Theorem: If two sides of one triangle are congruent to two sides of a second triangle and the third side of the first triangle is longer than the third side of the second triangle, then the angle opposite the third side of the first triangle is larger then the angle opposite the third side of the second triangle. [5.8]

Theorem 6.1	Means-Extremes Products Theorem: In a proportion, the product of the means equals the product of the extremes. [6.1]
Theorem 6.2	Properties of Proportions: [If $\frac{a}{b} = \frac{c}{d}$, and a, b, c, and $d \neq 0$, then each of the following is true.

a. $\frac{a}{c} = \frac{b}{d}$

b. $\frac{d}{b} = \frac{c}{a}$

c. $\frac{b}{a} = \frac{d}{c}$

d. $\frac{a + b}{b} = \frac{c + d}{d}$

e. $\frac{a - b}{b} = \frac{c - d}{d}$ [6.2]

Theorem 6.3	Right Triangle Similarity: If an acute angle of one right triangle is congruent to an acute angle of another right triangle, then the triangles are similar. [6.4]
Theorem 6.4	SAS Similarity Theorem: If an angle of one triangle is congruent to an angle of another triangle and if the lengths of the sides including these angles are proportional, then the triangles are similar. [6.5]
Theorem 6.5	SSS Similarity Theorem: If corresponding sides of two triangles are proportional, then the two triangles are similar. [6.5]
Theorem 6.6	Triangle Proportional Segment Theorem: If a line parallel to one side of a triangle intersects the other two sides, then it divides the two sides proportionally. [6.6]
Theorem 6.7	If a line divides two sides of a triangle proportionally, then the line is parallel to the third side. [6.6]
Theorem 6.8	Parallels Proportional Segment Theorem: If three parallel lines intersect two transversals, then they divide the transversals proportionally. [6.6]
Theorem 6.9	Triangle Angle Bisector Theorem: If a ray bisects an angle of a triangle, then it divides the opposite side into two segments whose lengths are proportional to the lengths of the other two sides. [6.6]
Theorem 6.10	The lengths of bisectors of corresponding angles of two similar triangles are in the same ratio as the lengths of corresponding sides. [6.6]
Theorem 6.11	The lengths of altitudes from corresponding vertices of similar triangles are in the same ratio as the lengths of corresponding sides. [6.6]
Theorem 6.12	The lengths of medians from corresponding vertices of similar triangles are in the same ratio as the lengths of corresponding sides. [6.6]
Theorem 7.1	The altitude to the hypotenuse of a right triangle forms two triangles that are similar to each other and to the original triangle. [7.1]
Theorem 7.2	In a right triangle, the length of the altitude to the hypotenuse is the geometric mean between the lengths of the two segments on the hypotenuse. [7.1]
Theorem 7.3	In a right triangle with an altitude to the hypotenuse, each leg is the geometric mean between the length of the hypotenuse and the length of the segment of the hypotenuse adjacent to that leg. [7.1]
Theorem 7.4	Pythagorean Theorem: In a right triangle, the square of the length of the hypotenuse equals the sum of the squares of the lengths of the legs. [7.2]
Theorem 7.5	Converse of the Pythagorean Theorem: If a triangle has side lengths a, b, and c, and $a^2 + b^2 = c^2$, then the triangle is a right triangle with the right angle opposite the side with length c. [7.3]
Theorem 7.6	If $a < b < c$ are lengths of the sides of a triangle and **a.** $a^2 + b^2 < c^2$, then the triangle is an obtuse triangle. **b.** $a^2 + b^2 > c^2$, then the triangle is an acute triangle. [7.3]

Theorem 7.7	45°–45°–90° Triangle Theorem: The length of the hypotenuse of a 45°–45°–90° triangle is $\sqrt{2}$ times the length of the leg. [7.4]
Theorem 7.8	30°–60°–90° Theorem: In a 30°–60°–90° triangle the length of the hypotenuse is 2 times the length of the shorter leg and the length of the longer leg is $\sqrt{3}$ times the length of the shorter leg. [7.4]
Theorem 8.1	If a line is perpendicular to a radius of a circle at a point on the circle, then the line is tangent to the circle. [8.2]
Theorem 8.2	If a line is tangent to a circle, then it is perpendicular to the radius at the point of tangency. [8.2]
Theorem 8.3	The two tangent segments from an exterior point of a circle are congruent. [8.2]
Corollary 8.3a	The line through an external point and the center of a circle bisects the angle formed by the two tangents from the external point. [8.2]
Theorem 8.4	In a circle or in congruent circles congruent chords have congruent minor arcs. [8.4]
Theorem 8.5	In a circle or in congruent circles congruent minor arcs have congruent chords and congruent central angles. [8.4]
Theorem 8.6	If a diameter is perpendicular to a chord, then it bisects the chord and its minor and major arcs. [8.5]
Theorem 8.7	If a diameter bisects a chord that is not a diameter, then it is perpendicular to the chord and bisects its major and minor arcs. [8.5]
Theorem 8.8	The perpendicular bisector of a chord contains the center of the circle. [8.5]
Theorem 8.9	In the same circle or in congruent circles congruent chords are equidistant from the center. [8.5]
Theorem 8.10	In the same circle or in congruent circles, chords equidistant from the center are congruent. [8.5]
Theorem 8.11	Inscribed Angle Measure: The measure of an inscribed angle is half the measure of its intercepted arc. [8.6]
Corollary 8.11a	If two inscribed angles intercept the same arc, then the angles are congruent. [8.6]
Corollary 8.11b	If a quadrilateral is inscribed in a circle, then its opposite angles are supplementary. [8.6]
Corollary 8.11c	An angle inscribed in a semicircle is a right angle. Also, if an inscribed angle is a right angle its intercepted arc is a semicircle. [8.6]
Theorem 8.12	The measure of a tangent-chord angle is half the measure of its intercepted arc. [8.6]
Theorem 8.13	The measure of an angle formed by two chords intersecting inside a circle is one half the sum of the intercepted arcs. [8.7]
Theorem 8.14	The measure of an angle formed by two secants, two tangents, or a secant and a tangent drawn from a point on the exterior of a circle is equal to half the difference of the measures of the intercepted arcs. [8.7]
Theorem 8.15	If two chords intersect in a circle, then the product of the lengths of the segments of one chord equals the product of the lengths of the segments of the second chord. [8.8]
Theorem 8.16	If two secant segments are drawn to a circle from an exterior point, then the product of the lengths of one secant segment and its external segment equals the product of the lengths of the other secant segment and its external segment. [8.8]
Theorem 8.17	If a tangent segment and a secant segment are drawn to a circle from an exterior point, then the square of the length of the tangent segment equals the product of the lengths of the secant segment and its external secant segment. [8.8]
Theorem 9.1	The perpendicular bisectors of the sides of a triangle are concurrent in a point that is equidistant from the three vertices of the triangle. [9.5]
Theorem 9.2	The bisectors of the angles of a triangle are concurrent in a point that is equidistant from the three sides of the triangle. [9.5]

Theorem 9.3	The medians of a triangle are concurrent in a point that is two thirds of the distance from each vertex to the midpoint of the opposite side. [9.5]
Theorem 9.4	The lines that contain the altitudes of a triangle are concurrent. [9.5]
Theorem 10.1	The area of a parallelogram equals the product of the base b and the height h. $A = bh$ [10.2]
Theorem 10.2	The area of a triangle equals one half the product of the base b and the altitude h. $A = \frac{1}{2}bh$ [10.2]
Theorem 10.3	The area of a trapezoid equals one half the product of the height h and the sum of the bases b_1 and b_2. $A = \frac{1}{2}h(b_1 + b_2)$ [10.3]
Theorem 10.4	The area of any quadrilateral with perpendicular diagonals, d_1 and d_2, is half the product of the lengths of its diagonals. $A = \frac{1}{2}d_1d_2$ [10.3]
Theorem 10.5	The area of a regular polygon equals one half the product of its apothem a and its perimeter p. $A = \frac{1}{2}ap$ [10.4]
Theorem 10.6	If two polygons are similar, then the ratio of their perimeters equals the ratio of the lengths of any pair of corresponding segments. [10.5]
Theorem 10.7	If two polygons are similar, then the ratio of their areas equals the square of the ratio of the lengths of any pair of corresponding segments. [10.5]
Theorem 10.8	The ratio $\frac{C}{d}$ of the circumference C to the diameter d is the same for all circles. [10.6]
Theorem 10.9	The ratio of the length of an arc of a circle ℓ, to the circumference C equals the ratio of the degree measure of the arc, m, to 360. $\frac{\ell}{C} = \frac{m}{360}$ or $\frac{\ell}{2\pi r} = \frac{m}{360}$ [10.6]
Theorem 10.10	The area of a circle with radius r is given by the formula $A = \pi r^2$. [10.7]
Theorem 10.11	The area of a sector, with arc degree measure m, of a circle with radius r is given by the formula $A = \frac{m}{360}(\pi r^2)$. [10.7]
Theorem 11.1	The lateral area of a right prism is equal to the perimeter p of a base times the height h of the prism. $LA = ph$ The surface area is the sum of the lateral area and twice the area of a base B. $SA = ph + 2B$ [11.1]
Theorem 11.2	The lateral area of a regular pyramid is equal to one half the product of the perimeter of the base p and the slant height ℓ. $LA = \frac{1}{2}pl$ The surface area of a regular pyramid is the sum of the lateral area and the area of the base B. $SA = \frac{1}{2}p\ell + B$ [11.2]
Theorem 11.3	The volume of any prism is the product of its height and the area of its base B. $V = Bh$ [11.3]
Corollary 11.3a	The volume of a right rectangular prism is the product of its length ℓ, its width w, and its height. That is: $V = \ell wh$ [11.3]
Theorem 11.4	The volume of a pyramid is one third the product of the area of the base B and the length of the altitude h. $V = \frac{1}{3}Bh$ [11.4]
Theorem 11.5	The lateral area of a right cylinder is equal to the circumference of the base $(2\pi r)$ times the height h. $LA = 2\pi rh$
	The surface area of a right cylinder is equal to the lateral area $(2\pi rh)$ plus the area of the two bases $(2\pi r^2)$ $SA = 2\pi rh + 2\pi r^2$ [11.5]
Theorem 11.6	The volume of a right cylinder is the product of π, the radius r squared, and the height h. $V = \pi r^2h$ [11.5]
Theorem 11.7	The lateral area of a right cone is equal to the product of π, the radius r and the slant height ℓ. $LA = \pi r \ell$
	The surface area of a right cone is equal to the sum of the lateral area $(\pi r \ell)$ and the area of the base (πr^2). $SA = \pi r \ell + \pi r^2$ [11.6]

Theorem 11.8	The volume of a right cone is one third the product of π, the radius r squared, and the height h. $V = \frac{1}{3}\pi r^2 h$. [11.6]
Theorem 11.9	The volume of a sphere is $\frac{4}{3}$ the product of π and the radius r cubed. $V = \frac{4}{3}\pi r^3$ The surface area of a sphere is four times the product of π and the radius r squared. $S = 4\pi r^2$ [11.7]
Theorem 11.10	If the lengths of two corresponding parts of two similar solids are in a ratio of $a : b$, then **a.** the ratio of any corresponding lengths is $a : b$, **b.** the ratio of corresponding surface areas is $a^2 : b^2$, **c.** the ratio of corresponding volumes is $a^3 : b^3$. [11.8]
Theorem 12.1	If the coordinates of the endpoints of the segment P_1P_2 are $P_1(x_1, y_1)$ and $P_2(x_2, y_2)$, then the coordinates of the midpoint of $\overline{P_1P_2}$ are $(\frac{x_1 + x_2}{2}, \frac{y_1 + y_2}{2})$. [12.1]
Theorem 12.2	Two nonvertical lines are parallel if and only if their slopes are equal. [12.3]
Theorem 12.3	Two nonvertical lines are perpendicular if and only if the product of their slopes is -1. [12.3]
Theorem 12.4	An equation of the line that has slope m and y-intercept b is $y = mx + b$. [12.4]
Theorem 12.5	Point-Slope Form: An equation of the line that passes through point (x_1, y_1) and has slope m is $y - y_1 = m(x - x_1)$.
Theorem 12.6	Distance Formula: The distance d between points $P_1(x_1, y_1)$ and $P_2(x_2, y_2)$ is given by the formula $d = \sqrt{(x_2 - x_1)^2 + (y_2 - y_1)^2}$. [12.5]
Theorem 12.7	An equation of a circle with center (h, k) and radius r is $(x - h)^2 + (y - k)^2 = r^2$. [12.6]
Theorem 13.1	The composition of two rotations about the same center point O is a rotation about center O with an angle of rotation equal in measure to the sum of the measures of the angles of rotation of the two rotations. [13.4]
Theorem 13.2	The composition of two translations is a translation. If translation PR is followed by translation RQ, then the composition translation is the translation PQ. [13.4]
Theorem 13.3	The composition of two line reflections in parallel lines p and q is a translation in a direction perpendicular to p and q having a length equal to twice the distance between p and q. [13.4]
Theorem 13.4	The composition of two line reflections intersecting at O is a rotation with center O and angle of rotation twice the angle from the first line to the second line. [13.4]
Theorem 13.5	A line reflection is an isometry. [13.5]
Theorem 13.6	The composition of two isometries is an isometry. [13.5]
Corollary 13.6a	A translation is an isometry. [13.5]
Corollary 13.6b	A rotation is an isometry. [13.5]
Theorem 13.7	If figure F' is the image of figure F under an isometry, then the areas of F and F' are equal. [13.5]
Theorem 13.8	If A' and B' are the images of A and B under the dilation with center O and scale factor k, then $A'B' = kAB$. [13.7]
Theorem 13.9	If $\triangle A'B'C'$ is the image of $\triangle ABC$ for the dilation with center O and scale factor k, then $\triangle A'B'C'$ is similar to $\triangle ABC$. [13.7]

Glossary

Abscissa (p. 533) The first number in an ordered pair, the x-coordinate

Acute (p. 14) An angle that measures betweeen 0 and 90 degrees

Acute triangle (p. 26) A triangle having all acute angles

Adjacent angles (p. 64) Two angles that have the same vertex and a common side, but that have no common interior points

Alternate exterior angles (p. 106) Two nonadjacent exterior angles on opposite sides of the transversal

Alternate interior angles (p. 106) Two nonadjacent interior angles on opposite sides of the transversal

Altitude (p. 189) A segment from a vertex of a triangle to the line containing the opposite side perpendicular to that side (p. 441) Of a parallelogram, a segment perpendicular to a pair of opposite sides and having endpoints on those sides (p. 485) Of a prism, a segment perpendicular to both bases with endpoints in the planes of the bases

Angle (p. 13) A figure consisting of two noncollinear rays with a common endpoint

Angle of depression (p.331) The angle made by the line of sight with the horizontal when an observer sights downward

Angle of elevation (p. 331) The angle made by the line of sight with the horizontal when an observer sights upward

Angle of rotation (p. 588) The angle through which a transformation is rotated about a point

Apothem (p. 455) In a regular polygon, the distance from the center to a side

Arc (p. 355) Two points and a continuous part of a circle between the points

Area of a region (p. 437) The number of square units contained in the region

Auxiliary line (p. 123) A line added to a figure, often used to help prove a proof

Base (p. 177) In an isosceles triangle, the third side, in addition to the congruent pair (p. 443) Any side of a parallelogram (p. 484) In a prism, one of a pair of identical, parallel faces (p. 491) In a pyramid, the face that does not contain the vertex

Base angles (p. 177) The angles opposite the congruent pair of sides in an isosceles triangle or (p. 220) the pairs of angles formed by a base and the legs in a trapezoid

Base of a parallelogram (p. 441) Any side of a parallelogram may be called a base

Bases of a trapezoid (p. 220) In a trapezoid, the parallel sides

Biconditional (p. 33) When a conditional and its converse are both true and are combined into one statement using the phrase "if and only if"

Bisector (p. 20) Any point, line, part of a line, or plane that divides the segment into two congruent segments

Boundary (p. 437) The points that make up the sides of a figure

Center (p. 341) A given point in the interior of a circle that is equidistant from all points on the circle

Center of a regular polygon (p. 455) The center of its inscribed circle

Central angle (p. 355) For a circle, an angle whose vertex is the center of the circle

Centroid (p. 411) The point of intersection of the medians of a triangle

Chord (p. 341) A segment that joins two points on a circle

Circle (p. 341) The set of all points in a plane that are a given distance from a given point in the plane called the center

Circumcenter (p. 410) The point that is equidistant from the vertices of a triangle

Circumference (p. 467) In a circle, the length of the boundary

Circumscribed polygon (p. 341) A polygon with each of its sides tangent to a circle

Collinear (p. 4) Points all in one line

Common tangent (p. 351) A line that is tangent to two coplanar circles

Complementary angles (p. 63) Two angles whose measures have a sum of 90

Composition (p. 594) Two transformations performed one after another

Concentric circles (p. 341) Two circles in the same plane with the same center

Conclusion (p. 32) In an if-then statement, the part following "then" that tells the result of the statement

Concurrent lines (p. 410) Three or more coplanar lines that have a point in common

Conditional (p. 32) An if-then statement consisting of a hypothesis *(if)* and a conclusion *(then)*

Cone (p. 511) A solid figure with a vertex and a circular base

Congruent (p. 20) Describes angles or segments that have the same measure or length

Congruent arcs (p. 355) Arcs with equal measure that lie in the same circle or in congruent circles

Congruent circles (p. 341) Circles that have congruent radii

Congruent triangles (p. 149) Triangles having a correspondence between the vertices such that each pair of corresponding sides and each pair of corresponding angles are congruent

Construction (p. 391) A geometric figure produced by using only a compass and straightedge

Contradiction (p. 230) A statement involving conflicting elements

Contrapositive (p. 34) Formed by interchanging the hypothesis and the conclusion of a conditional statement and negating both

Converse (p. 33) Formed by interchanging the hypothesis and the conclusion of a conditional statement

Convex polygon (p. 135) A polygon whose exterior angles measure 360 and whose diagonals all lie in the interior of the polygon

Coordinate(s) (p. 9) An ordered pair of numbers (x, y) that can be used to describe the location of a point on a plane

Coordinate plane (p. 533) The plane containing a rectangular coordinate system

Coplanar (p. 4) Points or lines all in one plane

Corollary (p. 178) A theorem that follows directly from another theorem

Correspondence (p. 149) The matching up of similar parts of two triangles, including the measure of angles and length of sides

Corresponding angles (p. 106) Two nonadjacent angles on the same side of the transversal such that one is an exterior angle and the other is an interior angle

Cosine ratio (p. 325) For a given acute angle in a right triangle, the ratio of the length of the adjacent leg to the length of the hypotenuse

Counterexample (p. 33) A single example that shows a general conditional statement to be false

Cylinder (p. 506) A solid figure having congruent circular bases in a pair of parallel planes

Deductive reasoning (p. 45) A process in which conclusions are drawn logically from given information

Degree (p. 13) A unit of measure for angles

Diagonal of a polygon (p. 135) A segment joining two nonconsecutive vertices

Diagram (p. 58) A figure that shows the given information, a key element in a two-column proof

Diameter (p. 341) A chord through the center of a circle

Dilation (p. 605) A transformation that preserves the shape of a figure, but allows the size to change

Directed segment (p. 583) A segment showing the distance and direction for a translation by showing the relationship between a point P and its translation image P'

Distance (p. 8) The absolute value of the difference of the coordinates for any two points on a number line

Edges (p. 485) The sides of the faces of polyhedrons

Enlargement (p. 605) A dilation with a scale factor greater than one

Equiangular (p. 26) Having all angles congruent

Equidistant (p. 189) The condition of a point P lying between two points A and B such that $PA = PB$

Equilateral (p. 27) Having all sides congruent

Exterior of an angle (p. 14) Those points on a plane separated by an angle which lie outside the angle

Exterior angle of a triangle (p. 129) Forms a linear pair with the adjacent interior angle of the triangle

Extremes (p. 255) In the proportion $\frac{a}{b} = \frac{c}{d}$, the first and fourth terms, or a and d

Faces (p. 485) Polygonal regions that make up a polyhedron

45°–45°–90° triangle (p. 312) A triangle whose angles measure 45°, 45°, and 90°

Geometric mean (p. 295) When a, b, and x are positive numbers and $\frac{a}{x} = \frac{x}{b}$, x is the geometric mean between a and b

Given (p. 58) A statement of facts given to be true, a key element in a two-column proof

Half-turn (p. 589) A rotation of 180°

Height (p. 443) The length of an altitude

Hypotenuse (p. 26) In a right triangle, the side opposite the right angle

Hypothesis (p. 32) In an if-then statement, the part following "if" that states the conditions necessary for the result to be true

Identity mapping (p. 605) A dilation with a scale factor of one

Incenter (p. 411) The point of concurrency of the angle bisectors of a triangle and the center of the inscribed circle of the triangle

Included (p. 153) Either an angle or a side of a triangle, lying between either two sides or two angles, respectively

Indirect proof (p. 230) A proof in which, after first assuming the negation of what is to be proved, a contradiction is reached through logical reasoning

Inscribed angle (p. 366) An angle with vertex on a circle and sides that contain chords of the circle

Inscribed polygon (p. 341) A polygon with all of its vertices on a circle

Interior of an angle (p. 14) Those points on a plane separated by an angle which lie inside the angle

Intersection (p.4) With two figures, the set of points both figures have in common

Inverse (p. 34) Formed when both the hypothesis and the conclusion in a conditional statement are negated

Isometry (p. 600) A concept used as the basis for generalizing the concept of congruence to figures that are not polygons; reflections, translations, or rotations having the common property that the distance between any two points and the distance between their images are equal

Isosceles triangle (p. 177) A triangle with a pair of congruent sides

Isosceles trapezoid (p. 220) A trapezoid with congruent nonparallel sides

Kite (p. 450) A quadrilateral with two distinct pairs of congruent adjacent sides

Lateral area (p. 486) The sum of the areas of the lateral faces of a prism

Lateral edge (p. 485) The common edge shared by adjacent lateral faces of a prism

Lateral face (p. 485) Of a prism, a parallelogram-shaped region formed by joining the vertices of the bases of the prism (p. 491) Of a pyramid, one of the faces containing the vertex of a pyramid

Legs (p. 26) In a right triangle, the sides not opposite the hypotenuse or (p. 177) the congruent sides of an isosceles triangle. Also (p. 220) the nonparallel sides of a trapezoid

Length of an arc (page 466) In a circle, the fractional part of the circumference subtended by the arc

Linear pair (p. 64) A pair of adjacent angles with two noncommon sides on the same line. Two angles that form a linear pair are supplementary

Line of symmetry (p. 578) A line in which a figure coincides with its reflection image

Locus (pl. loci) (p. 415) A set of points and only those points that satisfy one or more conditions

Major arc (p. 355) The arc in the exterior of the central angle of a circle

Mapping (p. 577) A correspondence between points of a plane

Means (p. 255) In the proportion $\frac{a}{b} = \frac{c}{d}$, the second and third terms, or b and c

Median (p. 189) A segment from a vertex of a triangle to the midpoint of the opposite side or (p. 221) the segment joining the midpoint of the legs of a trapezoid

Midpoint (p. 20) The midpoint of a segment is the point that divides the segment into two congruent segments

Midsegment (p. 224) The segment that joins the midpoints of two sides of a triangle

Minor arc (p. 355) The endpoints and all the points on both the circle and the interior of the central angle of the circle

Negation of a statement (p. 230) A statement having opposite meaning

Noncollinear (p. 4) Points that are not in one line

Noncoplanar (p. 4) Points or lines that are not in the same plane

Oblique cone (p. 511) A cone in which the axis is not perpendicular to the base

Oblique cylinder (p. 506) A cylinder in which the axis is not perpendicular to the bases

Oblique prism (p. 485) A prism with lateral edges not perpendicular to the bases

Obtuse (p. 14) An angle that measures between 90° and 180°

Obtuse triangle (p. 26) A triangle having one obtuse angle

Opposite angle (p. 153) In triangle ABC, angle B is opposite $\overline{AC}$, angle C is opposite $\overline{AB}$

Ordinate (p. 533) The second number in an ordered pair, the y-coordinate

Origin (p. 533) In a coordinate system, the intersection of the x-axis and the y-axis

Orthocenter (p. 412) The point of intersection of the lines containing the altitudes of a triangle

Parallel lines (p. 105) Coplanar lines that do not intersect

Parallelogram (p. 201) A quadrilateral with two pairs of parallel sides

Parallel planes (p. 105) Planes that do not intersect

Perimeter of a polygon (p. 437) The sum of the lengths of its sides

Perpendicular (p. 69) At a right angle to a given line or plane

Perpendicular bisector (p. 70) A line, segment, ray, or plane that is perpendicular to a segment and bisects it

Perpendicular lines (p. 69) Two lines that intersect at right angles

Point of tangency (p. 341) The point at which a line in the plane of a circle intersects that circle

Point-slope form (p. 547) One form of linear equation; for a line having slope m and passing through point (x_1, y_1), $y - y_1 = m(x - x_1)$

Polyhedron (p. 485) A three-dimensional solid made up of polygonal regions called faces

Postulate (p. 4) A statement that is accepted as true without proof

Prism (p. 485) A polyhedron with a pair of identical faces, called bases, that lie in parallel planes

Proof (p. 46) A valid argument which shows that a mathematical statement, called a theorem, is true

Proportion (p. 255) An equation stating that two ratios are equal

Protractor (p. 13) A tool marked in degree units that can be used to find the measure of an angle

Prove (p. 58) A statement of the conclusion to be established, a key element in a two-column proof

Pyramid (p. 491) A polyhedron in which all faces but one have a vertex in common

Pythagorean Triple (p. 308) Any three whole numbers a, b, and c for which $a^2 + b^2 = c^2$

Quadrants (p. 533) In a coordinate plane, the four regions formed by the intersecting axes

Radius of a circle (p. 341) In a circle, a segment with one endpoint the center and the other endpoint on the circle; the length of this segment

Radius of a regular polygon (p. 455) The distance from the center to a vertex

Ratio (p. 255) For any two numbers, x and y, the quotient obtained by dividing x and y

Ray (p. 13) A ray, $\overrightarrow{AB}$, is the part of $\overleftrightarrow{AB}$ that contains the point A and all the points on the same side of A as B

Reasons (p. 58) Numbered reasons in the right column of a proof, such as definitions, postulates (including properties of algebra), and previously proven theorems

Rectangle (p. 213) A quadrilateral with four right angles

Rectangular coordinate system (p. 533) A horizontal number line and a vertical number line intersecting at a point called the origin

Reduction (p. 605) A dilation with a scale factor less than one but greater than zero

Reflection (p. 577) A transformation that maps every point P of the plane to a point P' such that if point P is on ℓ then it is mapped to itself, or if point P is not on ℓ then ℓ is the perpendicular bisector of PP'

Reflectional symmetry (p. 578) Symmetry in which a figure coincides with its reflection image in ℓ

Region of a figure (p. 437) The figure and its interior

Regular polygon (p. 136) A polygon that is both equilateral and equiangular

Regular pyramid (p. 491) A pyramid with a regular polygon as the base and all lateral edges congruent

Remote interior angles (p. 129) The two angles of the triangle that are not adjacent to the exterior angle

Rhombus (p. 213) A quadrilateral with four congruent sides

Right angle (p. 14) An angle that measures $90°$

Right cone (p. 511) A cone in which the axis is perpendicular to the base

Right cylinder (p. 506) A cylinder in which the axis is perpendicular to the bases

Right prism (p. 485) A prism in which the lateral edges are perpendicular to the bases

Right triangle (p. 26) A triangle having one right angle

Rotation (p. 588) A transformation about a point O through an angle of $x°$ that associates each point P of the plane with a point P'

Rotational symmetry (p. 589) Symmetry such that a figure or pattern can be rotated $x°$ about a point so that the pattern appears identical to its original position

Same-side interior angles (p. 106) Two interior angles on the same side of the transversal

Scalene (p. 27) Having no sides congruent

Secant (p. 341) A line that contains a chord of a circle

Sector of a circle (page 473) A region formed by two radii and an arc of a circle

Segment (p. 9) A set of points consisting of two points, called endpoints, and all the points between these points

Segment of a circle (p. 474) A region formed by an arc and its chord

Semicircle (p. 355) One of two arcs formed when the endpoints of the arcs are the endpoints of the diameter of a circle

Side (p. 13) The two rays with a common vertex that form an angle

Similar polygons (p. 264) Two polygons that have the same shape

Sine ratio (p. 325) For a given acute angle in a right triangle, the ratio of the length of the opposite leg to the length of the hypotenuse

Skew lines (p. 105) Lines that are not coplanar and do not intersect

Slant height (p. 491) The height of any one of the lateral faces of a regular pyramid or the distance from the vertex to the base along the surface of a right cone

Slope (p. 538) The degree of steepness of a line, determined by the change in the vertical distance divided by the change in the horizontal distance

Slope-intercept form (p. 547) One form of linear equation; for slope m and y-intercept b, $y = mx + b$

Space (p. 3) The set of all points

Sphere (p. 342) The set of all points in space a given distance from a point called the center of the sphere

Square (p. 213) A quadrilateral with four right angles and four congruent sides

Standard form (p. 547) An equation of a line written in the form $Ax + By = C$, where A and B are both not zero

Statements (p. 58) Numbered statements in the left column of a proof that must be shown to be true in order to prove the conclusion

Supplementary angles (p. 63) Two angles whose measures have a sum of 180

Surface area (p. 485) The area of the surfaces enclosing a polyhedron

Tangent (p. 341) A line in the plane of a circle that intersects the circle in exactly one point, the point of tangency

Tangent-chord angle (p. 368) An angle that has its vertex on a circle with one side tangent to the circle at the vertex and the other side containing a chord

Tangent ratio (p. 319) For a given acute angle in a right triangle, the ratio of the length of the opposite leg to the length of the adjacent leg

Theorem (p. 46) A mathematical statement that must be proven before being accepted

30°–60°–90° triangle (p. 313) A triangle whose three angles measure $30°$, $60°$, and $90°$

Transformation (p. 577) A mapping that establishes a one-to-one correspondence between points in the plane

Translation (p. 583) A transformation that slides all points of the plane a fixed distance in a given direction

Translational symmetry (p. 584) Symmetry in which a translation maps a figure onto itself

Transversal (p. 106) A line that intersects two coplanar lines in two different points

Trapezoid (p. 220) A quadrilateral with exactly one pair of parallel sides

Triangle (p. 26) A figure formed by three segments joining three noncollinear points

Trigonometric ratio (p. 319) A ratio of the lengths of two sides of a right triangle

Trigonometry (p. 319) The study of the relationships between the sides and the angles of triangles

Two-column proof (p. 57) A style of proof in which statements that lead to the desired conclusion are listed in the left column and a reason for each statement is listed in the right column

Vertex (pl. vertices) (p. 13) The common endpoint at which two noncollinear rays meet, forming an angle

Vertex angle (p. 177) The angle opposite the base in an isosceles triangle

Vertical angles (p. 64) Two nonadjacent angles formed by a pair of intersecting lines

Volume (p. 496) The number of cubic units contained in a solid

x-axis (p. 533) The horizontal number line in the coordinate system

x-coordinate (p. 533) The first number in an ordered pair

y-axis (p. 533) The vertical number line in the coordinate system

y-coordinate (p. 533) The second number in an ordered pair

Selected Answers

CHAPTER 1

Lesson 1-1 Try This
Point E

Exercise Set 1-1
1. $\overleftrightarrow{AB}$ **3.** $\overleftrightarrow{AB}$, $\overrightarrow{AC}$ **5.** E

7.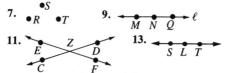

9.

11. **13.**

15. true **17.** false **19.** $\overrightarrow{TU}$ **21.** Post. 2 **23.** Post. 4
25. Post. 2 **27.** false

29. true **31.** true **33.** Post. 2 **35.** Post. 4
37. a. **b.** not possible **c.**

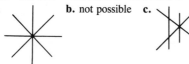

d. **e.** **f.** **39.** 10

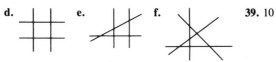

Algebra Review
1. 3 **3.** 7.5 **5.** 0 **7.** 5 **9.** 7 **11.** 2

Lesson 1-2 Try This
1. 3 **2.** 16, $PQ + QR = 14 + 16 = 30 = PR$
3. $E(1, -4)$, $F(3, -2)$ (2, 3) is between E and F.

Exercise Set 1-2
1. 9 **3.** 12 **5.** 9 **7.** 36 **9.** 36 **11.** 3 **13.** 21 **15.** 8
17. 31 **19.** $14\frac{1}{4}$ **21.** 6, 12 **23.** 8, 38 **25.** 6, 8
27. 15 in. **29.** 17 **31.** 15 **33.** A **35.** 3 **37.** 4, 24
39. 5, 30 **41.** ±4 **43.** 5, 9, 7, 8
45. They are reflections of each other.

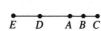

Algebra Review
1. 7 **3.** 13

Lesson 1-3 Try This
1. 85°, acute **2.** 91 **3.** 72, 32

Exercise Set 1-3
1. 10 **3.** 85 **5.** 80 **7.** $\angle 5$, $\angle JKL$, $\angle LKJ$, $\angle K$
9. right, 90 **11.** obtuse, 140 **13.** acute, 55 **15.** 19
17. 24, 48 **19.** 48, 26
21. false
23. true
25. false
27. 70 **29.** 20 **31.** 160 **33.** 56 **35.** 50 **37.** 36

39. 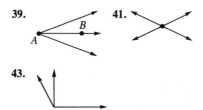 **41.**

43.

45. Sometimes; true when C is in the interior of $\angle ABD$.
47. never, different vertices
49. always **51.** 120, 130

Mixed Review
1. D **3.** collinear **5.** 13

Lesson 1-4 Try This
1. 16 **2.** 64

Exercise Set 1-4
1. $\overline{DE} \cong \overline{EF}$, $\overline{EH} \cong \overline{HJ}$, $\overline{GH} \cong \overline{HI}$ **3.** $\overline{GS} \cong \overline{SH}$ **5.** $\overline{AB}$
and $\overline{CD}$, $\overline{BC}$ and $\overline{DE}$; $\overline{AB} \cong \overline{CD}$, $\overline{BC} \cong \overline{DE}$ **7.** -2 **9.** 30,
30, 60 **11.** 9, 9, 18 **13.** 45 **15.** 45 **17.** 90 **19.** 54,
27, 27 **21.** 144, 72, 72 **23.** 10 ft **25.** true, def. of $\cong$
seg. **27.** true, Post. 11 **29.** no **31.** no **33.** no
35. true **37.** false **39.** true **41.** 32 **43.** 45 **45.** 15
47. $D(2.5, 4.5)$, $E(5, 4.5)$; $AB = 5$, $DE = \frac{1}{2}AB$; yes
49. $\frac{a+b}{2}$ **51.** The pitcher's mound is on the $\angle$ bis. of the $\angle$
formed by third base, home plate (vertex), and first base. It
is near the midpt. of the seg. joining first base and third
base.

Algebra Review
1. 5 **3.** $\sqrt{29}$ **5.** $\sqrt{37}$

Lesson 1-5 Try This
1. $\triangle PRS$, $\triangle STQ$ **2.** $\triangle TUV$, $\overline{UV} \cong \overline{TV} \cong \overline{TU}$ **3.** $\sqrt{13}$;
$\triangle ABC$ is isos. since $\overline{AB} \cong \overline{AC}$.

Exercise Set 1-5
1. $\triangle AEC$, $\triangle CED$, $\triangle BED$, $\triangle AEB$ **3.** $\overline{BE}$, $\overline{ED}$, $\overline{DB}$
5. $\triangle AEB$ **7.** $\triangle BED$ **9.** $\triangle AEB$ **11.** equilateral
13. isos. **15.** acute **17.** obtuse **19.** isos.
21. equilateral **23.** obtuse **25.** 4, $2\sqrt{5}$, $2\sqrt{5}$; isos.
27. sometimes **29.** always **31.** sometimes **33.** 30
35. 56, 34 **37.** 72 **39.** 5, 6, 5; isos. **41.** Constructions
may vary. **43.**

Mixed Review
1. 75 **3.** 30

Lesson 1-6 Try This

1. If all ∠s of △KLM have measure <90, then △KLM is acute. **2.** If 2 lines intersect, then they form rt. ∠s. $\overleftrightarrow{AB}$ and $\overleftrightarrow{CD}$ intersect, but do not form rt. ∠s. **3.** If M is between A and B, then M is the midpt. of $\overline{AB}$. (not true) **4.** I: If △EFG is not an obtuse △, then it does not contain an obtuse ∠. C: If △EFG does not contain an obtuse ∠, then it is not an obtuse △.

Exercise Set 1-6

1. H: You are funny. C: You will make people laugh. **3.** H: A pt. is in the int. of an ∠. C: It cannot be in the ext. of the ∠. **5.** H: ∠A ≅ ∠B, C: $m∠A = m∠B$ **7.** H: △JKL has 3 acute ∠s. C: △JKL is acute. **9.** If a man lives in Houston, then he lives in Texas. **11.** If 4 pts. are all in one plane, then the pts. are coplanar. **13.** If R is between S and U, and T is between R and U, then T is between S and U. **15.** If a line bisects a seg., then it contains the midpt. of the seg. (T) **17.** If pts. lie on the same line, then they are collinear. (T) **19.** If you go to law school, then you will become a judge. (F) **21.** If a △ is equilateral, then it is also an isos. △. (T) **23.** If 2 ∠s are ≅, then they have the same measure. **25.** If 2 ∠s are ≅, then the 2 ∠s each measure 30. **27.** If 2 lines are intersecting lines, then the 2 lines have a common pt. **29.** If △ABC is isos., then △ABC is equilateral. **31.** (25) I: If 2 ∠s do not each measure 30, then they are not ≅. C: If 2 ∠s are not ≅, then they do not each measure 30. (26) I: If you are not 21 years old or older, then you cannot legally vote. C: If you cannot legally vote, then you are not 21 years old or older. **33.** If 2 ∠s are ≅, then they have the same measure. If 2 ∠s have the same measure, then they are ≅. **35.** If $\overrightarrow{BD}$ is the bis. of ∠ABC, then D is in the interior of the ∠ and ∠ABD ≅ ∠DBC. If D is in the interior of ∠ABC and ∠ABD ≅ ∠DBC, then $\overrightarrow{BD}$ is the bis. of ∠ABC. **37.** H: Jim may vote. C: He is at least 18 years old. **39.** H: A number ends in 5. C: It is odd. **41.** H: ∠s have the same measure. C: The ∠s are ≅. **43.** If $\overrightarrow{GJ}$ bisects ∠HGI, then ∠HGJ ≅ ∠JGI. Converse is true. **45.** If 2 sides of a △ are ≅, then it is isos. Converse is true. **47.** A △ is acute if and only if all of its ∠s are acute. A △ is obtuse if and only if one of its ∠s is obtuse. A △ is a rt. △ if and only if one of its ∠s is a rt. ∠. A △ is equiangular if and only if all of its ∠s are ≅. **49.** Inverse: If a △ is not equilat., then it is not isos. Contrapositive of inverse: If a △ is not not isos. then the △ is not not equilat. (same as converse)

51.

Conditional			Contrapositive		
p	q	$p → q$	$\sim q$	$\sim p$	$\sim q → \sim p$
T	T	T	F	F	T
T	F	F	F	T	T
F	T	T	T	F	F
F	F	T	T	T	T

A conditional and its contrapositive are equivalent. The converse and inverse are equivalent to each other, but not to the original conditional.

Mixed Review

1. right **3.** equiangular

Lesson 1-7 Try This

1. No; if an ∠ is obtuse, then it is >90°. **2.** $\overline{SW} ≅ \overline{WT}$; if a line bisects a seg., then it divides the seg. into 2 ≅ seg.

Exercise Set 1-7

1. $\overline{LM} ≅ \overline{MN} ≅ \overline{NL}$ **3.** △GEF is a rt. △. **5.** If an ∠ is a rt. ∠, then the ∠ measures 90. **7.** If a △ has at least 2 ≅ sides, then it is isos. **9.** If a ray in the interior of an ∠ divides it into 2 ≅ ∠s, then it bisects the ∠. **11.** If a pt. divides a line seg. into 2 ≅ seg., then it is the midpt. of the seg. **13.** The conditional has the wrong hypothesis. **15.** Conditional: If a ray is an ∠ bis., then it divides the ∠ into 2 ≅ ∠s. **17.** Conditional: If a △ is scalene, then it has no ≅ sides. Conclusion: △ABC has no ≅ sides. **19.** Conditional: If 2 ∠s have = measure, then they are ≅. Conclusion: ∠PQR ≅ ∠STW **21.** Conditional: If N is in the interior of ∠KLM, then $m∠KLN + m∠NLM = m∠KLM$. Conclusion: $m∠KLM = 90$. **23.** (1) If a line bisects a seg., then it divides it into 2 ≅ seg. (2) If a line bisects a seg., then it contains the seg.'s midpt. **25.** (1) If N is between S and T, then $SN + NT = ST$. (2) If a pt. is between 2 other pts., then the 3 pts. are collinear. **27.** △KML is isos. (Def. of isos. △) **29.** ∠S ≅ ∠T (Def. of ≅ ∠s) **31.** $\overline{GT} ≅ \overline{TH}$ **33.** Jerome earned an A. **35.** $\overleftrightarrow{AB}$ is not the bis. of ∠CAD. **37.** If a line is a bis. of a seg., then it contains the midpt. of the seg.

Algebra Review

1. commutative **3.** associative

Lesson 1-8 Try This

1. Add. Prop. **2.** Since $3(x - 2) = 9$, $3x - 6 = 9$ (Dist. Prop.). Also, $3x = 15$ (Add. Prop.), and so $x = 5$ (Div. Prop.). **3.** $m∠E = m∠E$ (Reflex. Prop.) so ∠E ≅ ∠E (def. ≅). **4.** Suppose ∠A ≅ ∠C and ∠B ≅ ∠C. From symmetry of congruence (Th. 1.1), ∠C ≅ ∠B. But then ∠A ≅ ∠C and ∠C ≅ ∠B, so trans. of congruence (Th. 1.1) allows the conclusion that ∠A ≅ ∠B.

Exercise Set 1-8

1. $RS = PQ$ **3.** $JK = PQ$ **5.** $m∠T = m∠T$ **7.** $AB + EF = CD + GH$ **9.** $PQ · TU = RS · VW$ **11.** $ST = 90 + 60$ **13.** Seg. congruence is symmetric. **15.** ∠ congruence is symmetric. **17.** Seg. congruence is trans. **19.** If $15p + 4 = 64$, then $15p = 60$ (Sub. Prop.). and $p = 4$ (Div. Prop.). **21.** If $3(n + 1) = 99$, then $n + 1 = 33$ (Div. Prop.) and $n = 32$ (Sub. Prop.). **23.** $AB + CD = GH$ **25.** $m∠RST$ **27.** $m∠1 = m∠2$ **29.** $m∠JKL = 37$ **31.** $\overline{AB} ≅ \overline{EF}$, $\overline{AC} ≅ \overline{BD}$, $\overline{AC} ≅ \overline{CE}$, $\overline{AD} ≅ \overline{CF}$, $\overline{BD} ≅ \overline{CE}$, $\overline{BD} ≅ \overline{DF}$, $\overline{AE} ≅ \overline{BF}$, $\overline{BC} ≅ \overline{DE}$ **33.** Since GH is a real number, $GH = GH$ by the reflex. prop. of real numbers. Thus, $\overline{GH} ≅ \overline{GH}$ by the def. ≅ seg. **35. a.** no **b.** yes **c.** yes **d.** no

Mixed Review

1. B, C, D **3.** B **5.** 55   **7.** $\angle EBA \cong \angle ABC$, $\overline{BC} \cong \overline{CD}$

Chapter Review

1. true   **2.** true   **3.** false   **4.** 17   **5.** 17   **6.** C **7.** 57
8. $\angle ACF \cong \angle FCB$ **9.** 8   **10.** $\triangle KLM$ **11.** $\triangle KMN$
12. 10   **13.** H: A number is positive. C: It is > 0.   **14.** If Mr. Wong lives in Ohio, then he lives in the U.S.   **15.** If the sides of a $\triangle$ are $\cong$, then it is equilat.   **16.** $EF = GH$
17. If the measure of an $\angle$ is 90, then it is a rt. $\angle$.
18. $AB = CD$ **19.** symmetric

CHAPTER 2

Exercise Set 2-1

1. 1. c, 2. c, 3. a, 4. b   **3.** 1.g, 2.e   **5.** 1. g, 2. b
7. 1. g, 2. g, 3. c, 4. d   **9.** 1. Given 2. Given 3. Def. equiang. $\triangle$ 4. Th. 1.3   **11.** 1. Q is between P and R. (Given) 2. Seg. Add. Post. 4. Sub. Prop. 5. $PQ = PR - QR$
13. 1. Given 2. $\angle$ Add. Post. 3. $\angle$ Add. Post. 4. $m\angle LKP = m\angle 1 + m\angle 2 + m\angle 3$.   **15.** Conclusion: $GI = IJ$ 1. G, H, I, J are collinear. (Given) 2. $GH + HI = GI$ (Seg. Add. Post.) 3. $GH + HI = IJ$ (Given) 4. $GI = IJ$ (Subst.)

Mixed Review

1. $\overline{DE} \cong \overline{EF}$ **3.** 50

Lesson 2-2 Try This

1. $m\angle EFH = 144$, $m\angle HFG = 36$ **2.** $m\angle 3 = 50$, $m\angle 4 = 130$

Exercise Set 2-2

1. $\angle GCA, \angle ACD$ **3.** $\angle GCB, \angle ECD$ **5.** $\angle ACE, \angle GCB$
7. 30   **9.** 150   **11.** 70   **13.** $m\angle AXG = 60$, $m\angle GXF = 30$ **15.** 45 and 45   **17.** 1. Given 2. Given 3. Th. 2.2 4. Th. 1.3   **19.** 30, 60   **21.** 25
23. always   **25.** never (sum of measures >90)

27. Comp: 22.5, supp: 112.5   **29.** comp: $60 + 2x$, supp: $150 + 2x$ **31.** $m\angle DEB = 57$, $m\angle FED = 33$
33. $m\angle DEF = 28$, $m\angle DEB = 62$ **35.** 50 and 130
37. 54, 36   **39.** 72   **41.** 1. $\angle 1$ is supp. to $\angle 2$. $\angle 4$ is supp. to $\angle 3$. (Given) 2. $m\angle 1 + m\angle 2 = 180$, $m\angle 4 + m\angle 3 = 180$ (Def. supp. $\angle$s) 3. $\angle 2 \cong \angle 3$ (Given) 4. $m\angle 2 = m\angle 3$ (Def. $\cong \angle$s) 5. $m\angle 1 + m\angle 2 = m\angle 4 + m\angle 3$ (Subst.) 6. $m\angle 1 = m\angle 4$ (Sub. Prop.) 7. $\angle 1 \cong \angle 4$ (Def. $\cong \angle$s)   **43.** Let the measures of the $\angle$s be x. Then $x + x = 180$, so $x = 90$ and the $\angle$s are rt. $\angle$s.
45. Let the measure of $\angle$ be x. $x + 2(90 - x) = x + 180 - 2x = 180 - x =$ measure of the supp.

Algebra Review

1. 25   **3.** 0

Lesson 2-3 Try This

1. 72   **2.** $\overline{PS} \cong \overline{SQ}$, $\overline{PR} \perp \overline{RQ}$, S is the midpt. of $\overline{PQ}$.

Exercise Set 2-3

1. b   **3.** d   **5.** $m\angle 1 = m\angle 2 = m\angle 3 = m\angle 4 = 90$
7. $\angle TXS, \angle SXR$ **9.** 63   **11.** 60   **13.** 36   **15.** 1. Given 2. Given 3. Def. $\perp$ 4. Def. $\perp$ bis.   **17.** 1. Given 2. Def. comp. $\angle$s 3. $\angle$ Add. Post. 4. $m\angle QPR = 90$ 5. Def. rt. $\angle$ 6. $\overline{PQ} \perp \overline{PR}$ (Def. $\perp$)
19.   **21.**

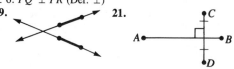

23. $\frac{YC}{AC} = \frac{1}{4}, \frac{YC}{XC} = \frac{1}{2}, \frac{AX}{YC} = 2$ **25.** sometimes **27.** never
29. $180 - x$ **31.** 90, 90 **33.** 1. $\angle 1$ is comp. to $\angle 2$
(Given) 2. $m\angle 1 + m\angle 2 = 90$ (Def. comp.) 3. $m\angle 1 +$
$m\angle 2 = m\angle JKL$ ($\angle$ Add. Post.) 4. $m\angle JKL = 90$ (Subst.)
5. $\angle JKL$ is a rt. $\angle$. (Def. rt. $\angle$) 6. $\overline{JK} \perp \overline{KL}$ (Def. $\perp$)
35. false

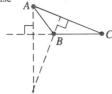

37. Put compass tip on P and make an arc that forms a seg.
on l. Construct the $\perp$ bis. to this seg.

Mixed Review

1. H: A $\triangle$ is isos. C: It has 2 $\cong$ sides. **3.** If a $\triangle$ has
2 $\cong$ sides, then it is isos. **5.** $m\angle B = m\angle D$

Lesson 2-4 Try This

1. A is in the interior of $\angle BEF$ **2.**

Exercise Set 2-4

1. no **3.** no **5.** yes **7.** yes **9.** no **11.** yes
13. no **15.** yes
17.

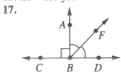

19.

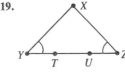

21.

23.

25.

27.

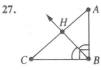

29.

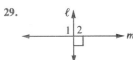

1. Given 2. Def. $\perp$
3. $m\angle 1 = 90$, $m\angle 2 = 90$
4. $m\angle 1 = m\angle 2$

31.

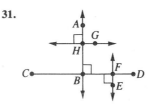

33.

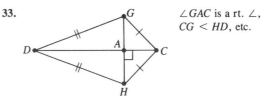

$\angle GAC$ is a rt. $\angle$,
$CG < HD$, etc.

35. The sum of these distances is the same no matter what
pt. is chosen. (The sum is = to the alt. of the $\triangle$.) To test
this, pick any pt., measure the distances, find the sum, and
then try this with other pt.

Algebra Review

1. $(x + 2)(x + 1)$ **3.** $(m - 3)(m - 2)$
5. $(n - 7)(n + 3)$ **7.** $(2y + 1)(y - 2)$
9. $(3x - 1)(2x + 3)$

Exercise Set 2-5

1. If 2 intersecting lines form $\cong$ adj. $\angle$s, then they are $\perp$.
3.

5. If 2 $\angle$s are $\cong$ and supp., then they are rt. $\angle$s.

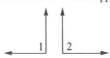

Given: $\angle 1 \cong \angle 2$, $\angle 1$ and $\angle 2$ are supp.
Prove: $\angle 1$ and $\angle 2$ are rt. $\angle$s.
7. If 2 $\angle$s are vert. $\angle$s, then they are $\cong$.

Given: $\angle 1$ and $\angle 2$ are vert. $\angle$s.
Prove: $\angle 1 \cong \angle 2$ **9.** $\angle ABD \cong \angle DBC$ **11.** $m\angle JKL =$
90 **13.** $\overline{SX} \perp \overline{WY}$ **15.** 1. $\angle 1 \cong \angle 2$, $\angle 3 \cong \angle 4$ (Given)
2. $\angle 2 \cong \angle 3$ (Th. 2.2) 3. $\angle 1 \cong \angle 3$ (Th. 1.1) 4. $\angle 1 \cong \angle 4$
(Th. 1.1) **17.** 1. $\overline{RT} \perp \overline{PQ}$, $\overline{WY} \perp \overline{PQ}$ (Given) 2. $\angle 1$ and
$\angle 3$ are rt. $\angle$s. (Def. rt. $\angle$) 3. $\angle 1 \cong \angle 3$ (Th. 2.4)
19.

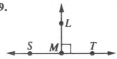

1. $\overline{LM} \perp \overline{ST}$ (Given) 2. $\angle LMS$ is a rt. $\angle$. (Def. $\perp$) 3.
$m\angle LMS = 90$ (Def. rt. $\angle$)

21.

1. $m\angle KLM = 90$ (Given) 2. $\angle KLM$ is a rt. $\angle$. (Def. rt. $\angle$) 3. $\overline{KL} \perp \overline{LM}$ (Def. $\perp$)

23.

1. $\overline{AB} \perp \overline{BC}$, $\overline{DC} \perp \overline{BC}$ (Given) 2. $\angle ABC$ is a rt. $\angle$. $\angle DCB$ is a rt. $\angle$. (Def. $\perp$) 3. $\angle ABC \cong \angle DCB$ (Th. 2.4) **25.** 1. O is the midpt. of $\overline{BC}$. $\triangle AOB$ is isos. with $\overline{OA} \cong \overline{OB}$. (Given) 2. $CO \cong OB$ (Def. midpt.) 3. $\overline{OA} \cong \overline{CO}$ (Th. 1.2) 4. $\triangle AOC$ is isos. (Def. isos. $\triangle$) **27.** 1. B is between A and C. E is between D and F. (Given) 2. $AB + BC = AC$, $DE + EF = DF$ (Seg. Add. Post.) 3. $AC = DF$, $BC = EF$ (Given) 4. $AB + EF = DF$ (Subst.) 5. $AB + EF = DE + EF$ (Subst.) 6. $AB = DE$ (Sub. Prop.)

Mixed Review

1. equilateral **3.** $\triangle BCG$ **5.** $\sqrt{10}$

Lesson 2-6 Try This

1. $GI = HJ$, Common Seg. Th. **2.** $\overleftrightarrow{AC}$ is the $\perp$ bis. of $\overline{DB}$.

Exercise Set 2-6

1. $\overline{MP} \cong \overline{NQ}$ **3.** $\overline{IE} \cong \overline{KA}$ **5.** 8 **7.** 18 **9.** $\overline{QR} \cong \overline{RS}$ **11.** $\overline{QR} \cong \overline{RS}$ **13.** $\overline{FH} \perp \overline{EG}$ **15.** false **17.** false **19.** 1. $\angle 1$ and $\angle 2$ are comp. (Given) 2. $m\angle 1 + m\angle 2 = 90$ (Def. comp. $\angle$s) 3. $m\angle 1 + m\angle 2 = m\angle UTW$ ($\angle$ Add. Post.) 4. $m\angle UTW = 90$ (Subst.) 5. $\angle UTW$ is a rt. $\angle$. (Def. rt. $\angle$) 6. $\triangle UTW$ is a rt. $\triangle$. (Def. rt. $\triangle$) **21.** 1. $\overline{AB} \cong \overline{BD}$, $\overline{BC} \cong \overline{DE}$ (Given) 2. $\overline{BD} \cong \overline{CE}$ (Common Seg. Th.) 3. $\overline{AB} \cong \overline{CE}$ (Th. 1.1) **23.** $\overline{RS} \cong \overline{MN}$ and $\overline{TU} \cong \overline{MN}$. **25.** Yes; $AB = CD$ by the Common Seg. Th. **27.** 1. $\overline{GI} \cong \overline{HJ}$, $\overline{IK} \cong \overline{JL}$ (Given) 2. $\overline{GH} \cong \overline{IJ}$, $\overline{IJ} \cong \overline{KL}$ (Common Seg. Th.) 3. $\overline{GH} \cong \overline{KL}$ (Th. 1.1) **29.** 1. $\overline{AC} \cong \overline{BD}$ (Given) 2. $AC = BD$ (Def. $\cong$ seg.) 3. $BC = BC$ (Reflex. prop.) 4. $AC - BC = BD - BC$ (Sub. Prop.) 5. $AB = CD$ (Seg. Add. Post.) 6. $\overline{AB} \cong \overline{CD}$ (Def. $\cong$ seg.) **31.** always **33.** never **35.** 1. $\angle 1$ and $\angle 3$ are comp. (Given) 2. $m\angle 1 + m\angle 3 = 90$ (Def. comp. $\angle$s) 3. $m\angle 2 + m\angle 3 = m\angle ADC$ ($\angle$ Add. Post.) 4. $m\angle 1 + m\angle ADC = 180$ (Th. 2.1) 5. $m\angle 1 + m\angle 2 + m\angle 3 = 180$ (Subst.) 6. $m\angle 2 + 90 = 180$ (Subst.) 7. $m\angle 2 = 90$ (Sub. Prop.) 8. $\angle 2$ is a rt. $\angle$. (Def. rt. $\angle$) 9. $\overline{AD} \perp \overline{DB}$ (Def. $\perp$) **37.** Incorrect Reasoning: There is no common seg. in the fig. Proof: 1. $\overline{AB} \cong \overline{DE}$, $\overline{AC} \cong \overline{DF}$ (Given) 2. $AB = DE$, $AC = DF$ (Def. $\cong$ seg.) 3. $AB + BC = AC$, $DE + EF = DF$ (Seg. Add. Post.) 4. $DE + BC = DF$ (Subst.) 5. $EF = DF - DE$, $BC = DF - DE$ (Sub. Prop.) 6. $EF = BC$ (Subst.) 7. $\overline{EF} \cong \overline{BC}$ (Def. $\cong$ seg.)

Algebra Review

1. $x > 7$ **3.** $x < 0$ **5.** $x > -3$

1. $\angle XTW \cong \angle UTV$ **2.** $\angle MRT \cong \angle QRT$ **3.** $\angle 3 \cong \angle 5$

Exercise Set 2-7

1. $\angle PTQ \cong \angle RTS$ **3.** $\angle CBE \cong \angle DBF$ **5.** $\angle ABF \cong \angle EBG$ (Common $\angle$ Th.) **7.** $\angle 2 \cong \angle EBC$ ($\cong$ Supp. Th.) **9.** $\angle 3 \cong \angle 4$ (Th. 2.11) **11.** $\angle EBG \cong \angle BFG$ (Th. 2.1) **13.** $m\angle 4 = 55$ ($\cong$ Supp. Th., Vert. $\angle$ Th.) **15.** 76 **17.** false **19.** true **21.** 1. $\angle LMQ \cong \angle PMN$ (Given) 2. $\angle LMP \cong \angle QMN$ (Common $\angle$ Th.) **23.** 1. $\angle 2 \cong \angle 3$, $\overline{HP} \perp \overline{PQ}$, $\overline{JQ} \perp \overline{PQ}$ (Given) 2. $\angle HPQ$, $\angle JQP$ are rt. $\angle$s. (Def. $\perp$ lines) 3. $m\angle HPQ = m\angle JQP = 90$ (Def. rt. $\angle$) 4. $m\angle 1 + m\angle 2 = 90$, $m\angle 3 + m\angle 4 = 90$ ($\angle$ Add. Post.) 5. $\angle 1$ is comp. to $\angle 2$. $\angle 4$ is comp. to $\angle 3$. (Def. comp. $\angle$s) 6. $\angle 1 \cong \angle 4$ ($\cong$ Comp. Th.) **25.** 1. $\overrightarrow{QT}$ bisects $\angle SQU$. (Given) 2. $\overline{TQ} \perp \overline{PR}$ (Given) 3. $\angle 6 \cong \angle 7$ (Def. $\angle$ bis.) 4. $\angle PQT$ and $\angle RQT$ are rt. $\angle$s. (Def. $\perp$) 5. $m\angle PQT = m\angle RQT = 90$ (Def. rt. $\angle$) 6. $m\angle 5 + m\angle 6 = 90$, $m\angle 7 + m\angle 8 = 90$ ($\angle$ Add. Post.) 7. $\angle 5$ is comp. to $\angle 6$. $\angle 8$ is comp. to $\angle 7$. (Def. comp. $\angle$s) 8. $\angle 5 \cong \angle 8$ ($\cong$ Comp. Th.) **27.** 1. $\angle 1 \cong \angle 2$, $\angle 3 \cong \angle 4$ (Given) 2. $\angle 2 \cong \angle 4$ (Vert. $\angle$ Th.) 3. $\angle 1 \cong \angle 4$ (Th. 1.1) 4. $\angle 1 \cong \angle 3$ (Th. 1.3) **29.** 1. $\angle BFE \cong \angle ECA$, $\angle CFD \cong \angle ECA$ (Given) 2. $\angle BFE \cong \angle CFD$ (Th. 1.3) 3. $\angle BFD \cong \angle CFE$ (Common $\angle$ Th.) **31.** 1. $\overline{RS} \perp \overline{XY}$ (Given) 2. $\angle RSX$ and $\angle RSY$ are rt. $\angle$s. (Def. $\perp$ lines) 3. $\angle RSX \cong \angle RSY$ (Th. 2.4) **33.** 1. $\angle A$ and $\angle C$ are supp., $\angle B$ and $\angle C$ are supp. (Given) 2. $m\angle B + m\angle C = 180$, $m\angle B + m\angle C = 180$ (Def. supp. $\angle$s) 3. $m\angle A + m\angle C = m\angle B + m\angle C$ (Subst.) 4. $m\angle A = m\angle B$ (Sub. Prop.) 5. $\angle A \cong \angle B$ (Def. $\cong \angle$s) **35.** The formula holds for all acute $\angle$s.

Mixed Review

1. $\angle KGL$ **3.** $\angle JGK$ **5.** 48 **7.** $m\angle NGM$

Chapter Review

1. 1. b 2. b 3. a 4. c **2.** 40 **3.** $\angle AFB$, $\angle EFD$ **4.** 20 **5.** 90 **6.** $\overline{FD}$ **7.** yes **8.** no **9.** yes **10.** If a $\triangle$ is an equilat. $\triangle$, then it is an isos. $\triangle$. Given: $\triangle IJK$ is equilat. Prove: $\triangle IJK$ is isos.

11. 1. $\angle 1 \cong \angle 2$ (Vert. $\angle$ Th.) 2. $\angle 2 \cong \angle 3$ (Given) 3. $\angle 1 \cong \angle 3$ (Th. 1.1) 4. $\angle 3 \cong \angle 4$ (Vert. $\angle$ Th.) 5. $\angle 1 \cong \angle 4$ (Th. 1.1) **12.** $\overline{PR} \cong \overline{QS}$ **13.** 5 **14.** $\angle PTQ \cong \angle RTS$ **15.** 1. $\angle 3$ is supp. to $\angle 1$. (Given) 2. $m\angle 1 + m\angle 2 = 180$ (Given) 3. $\angle 2$ is supp. to $\angle 1$. (Def. supp. $\angle$s) 4. $\angle 2 \cong \angle 3$ ($\cong$ Supp. Th.)

CHAPTER 3

Lesson 3-1 Try This

1. Answers may vary.   **2.** $\angle ADB$ and $\angle DBC$, $\angle DAC$ and $\angle ACB$

Exercise Set 3-1

1. plane $EDJK$ **3.** plane $FEKL$ **5.** Answers may vary:
plane $ABCDEF \parallel$ plane $GHIJKL$, plane $ABHG \parallel$ plane $EDJK$,
plane $BCIH \parallel$ plane $FEKL$, plane $CDJI \parallel$ plane $AFLG$
7. $\overline{AG}$, $\overline{FL}$ **9.** $\overline{GH}$, $\overline{JK}$ **11.** $\angle 3$ and $\angle 7$, $\angle 2$ and $\angle 6$
13. $\angle 2$ and $\angle 3$, $\angle 7$ and $\angle 6$ **15.** $\angle 8$ and $\angle 6$ **17.** corr.
19. alt. ext.   **21.** alt. int.   **23.** alt. ext.   **25.** $\angle 1$ and $\angle 6$,
$\angle 5$ and $\angle 4$ **27.** $\angle DCA$ **29.** always   **31.** sometimes
33. sometimes   **35.** always   **37.** never   **39.** $\parallel$ lines   **41.** $\parallel$
lines   **43.** $\parallel$ lines   **45.** $\parallel$ and intersecting lines   **47.** $\overline{DF}$
49. none   **51.** Answers may vary: $\overline{BE}$, $\overline{CE}$, $\overline{BF}$, $\overline{CF}$ **53.** 12
55. $\parallel$ lines CD and EF cut by trans. $\overleftrightarrow{AK}$ **57.** $A(-4, -1)$,
$B(-2, 0)$, $D(2, 2)$, $E(4, 3)$; $F(6, 4)$, $G(8, 5)$, $H(-1, -2)$,
$I(1, -1)$, $K(5, 1)$, $L(7, 2)$ **59.** $\parallel$ lines in a coord. plane
have $=$ ratios of $\frac{y}{x}$.   **61.** 18 (3 groups of 6 $\parallel$ lines)
63–65. Answers may vary.   **67.** not always true

Mixed Review

1. $\angle PUQ$ and $\angle TUS$ **3.** $\angle PUQ$ and $\angle QUR$ **5.** $\angle TUR$

Lesson 3-2 Try This

1. 60   **2.** 42.5

Exercise Set 3-2

1. 115   **3.** 115   **5.** 65   **7.** 110   **9.** 28   **11.** 70   **13.** 70
15. 42   **17.** $\angle ACD$ **19.** None have names.   **21.** 7
23. 6   **25.** $x = 53$, $y = 62$ **27.** $x = 30$, $y = 90$
29. $m\angle CEF = 75$, $m\angle CGH = 75$ **31.** 1. $a \parallel b$ (Given)
2. $\angle 2 \cong \angle 3$ (If $\parallel$ lines are cut by a trans., alt. int. $\angle$s
are $\cong$.) 3. $m\angle 1 + m\angle 3 = 180$ (Def. linear pair)
4. $m\angle 1 + m\angle 2 = 180$ (Subst.) 5. $\angle 1$ and $\angle 2$ are supp.
(Def. supp. $\angle$s)   **33.** 28   **35.** 56   **37.** 1. $p \parallel q$ (Given)
2. $\angle 1 \cong \angle 6$ (If $\parallel$ lines are cut by a trans., alt. int. $\angle$s are
$\cong$.) 3. $s \parallel t$ (Given) 4. $\angle 6 \cong \angle 7$ (If $\parallel$ lines are cut by a
trans., alt. int. $\angle$s are $\cong$.) 5. $\angle 1 \cong \angle 7$ (Trans. Prop.)
39. 1. $\overline{AD} \parallel \overline{BE}$ (Given) 2. $\angle DAB$ and $\angle EBA$ are supp.
(If $\parallel$ lines are cut by a trans., same-side int. $\angle$s are $\cong$.)
3. $m\angle DAB + m\angle EBA = 180$ (Def. supp.) 4. $\overrightarrow{CA}$ bisects
$\angle DAB$. (Given) 5. $m\angle 1 = \frac{1}{2}m\angle DAB$ (Def. $\angle$ bis.)
6. $2m\angle 1 = m\angle DAB$ (Mult. Prop.) 7. $m\angle 2 + m\angle EBC =$
$m\angle EBA$ ($\angle$ Add. Post.) 8. $2m\angle 1 + m\angle 2 + m\angle EBC =$
180 (Subst.) 9. $\angle 1$ and $\angle 2$ are comp. (Given) 10. $m\angle 1 +$
$m\angle 2 = 90$ (Def. comp.) 11. $m\angle 1 + m\angle EBC = 90$ (Add.
Prop.) 12. $m\angle EBC = m\angle 2$ (Subst.) 13. $\overrightarrow{BC}$ bisects $\angle ABE$
(Def. $\angle$ bis.)   **41.** 1. $\overline{AM} \parallel \overline{BD}$ (Given) 2. $\angle AMB \cong$
$\angle CBD$ (If $\parallel$ lines are cut by a trans., corr. $\angle$s are $\cong$.)
3. $\overrightarrow{BD}$ bisects $\angle ABC$. (Given) 4. $\angle CBD \cong \angle ABD$ (Def. $\angle$
bis.) 5. $\angle ABD \cong \angle AMB$ (Trans. Prop.)   **43.** (Refer to fig-
ure for Class Exercises 1–6.) Given: $a \parallel b$ Prove: $\angle 1 \cong \angle 5$
1. $a \parallel b$ (Given) 2. $\angle 2$ and $\angle 3$ are supp. (If $\parallel$ lines are cut
by a trans., same-side int. $\angle$s are supp.) 3. $\angle 1$ and $\angle 3$ are
supp. (Def. linear pair) 4. $\angle 1 \cong \angle 5$ (2 $\angle$s supp. to the
same $\angle$ are $\cong$.)

Algebra Review

1. $x = 1$, $y = 9$ **3.** $x = 5\frac{2}{3}$, $y = \frac{2}{3}$

Lesson 3-3 Try This

1. $m\angle 4 + m\angle 5 = 180$ **2.** 11

Exercise Set 3-3

1. $a \parallel c$ (If 2 lines are cut by a trans. and corr. $\angle$s are $\cong$,
the lines are $\parallel$.)   **3.** $c \parallel b$ (If 2 lines are cut by a trans. and
same-side int. $\angle$s are supp., the lines are $\parallel$.)   **5.** $b \parallel c$ (If 2
lines are cut by a trans. and corr. $\angle$s are $\cong$, the lines are $\parallel$.)
7. yes (If 2 lines are cut by a trans. and same-side int. $\angle$s
are supp., the lines are $\parallel$.)   **9.** $\angle 3$ and $\angle 7$, $\angle 1$ and $\angle 8$
11. yes   **13.** no   **15.** 15   **17.** 12   **19.** 8   **21.** $x = 118$,
$y = 0$ **23.** $x = 15$, $y = -12$ **25.** $\angle 1$ and $\angle 3$ are supp.
(Given) 2. $\angle 1$ and $\angle 2$ are supp. (Def. linear pair) 3. $\angle 3 \cong$
$\angle 2$ (Subst.) 4. $p \parallel q$ (If 2 lines are cut by a trans. and alt.
int. $\angle$s are $\cong$, the lines are $\parallel$.)   **27.** 65   **29.** 1. $m \perp p$,
$n \perp p$ (Given) 2. $\angle 1$ and $\angle 2$ are rt. $\angle$s. (Def. $\perp$)
3. $\angle 1 \cong \angle 2$ (Rt. $\angle$s are $\cong$.) 4. $m \parallel n$ (If 2 lines are cut
by a trans. and corr. $\angle$s are $\cong$, the lines are $\parallel$.)
31. 1. $\angle BCD \cong \angle CDE$; $m\angle B + m\angle D = 180$ (Given)
2. $m\angle B + m\angle C = 180$ (Subst.) 3. $\overline{AB} \parallel \overline{CD}$ (If 2 lines
are cut by a trans. and same-side int. $\angle$s are supp., the
lines are $\parallel$.)   **33. a.** reflex: no, symmetric: yes, trans: no
b. reflex: no, symmetric: yes, trans: no

Mixed Review

1. acute   **3.** obtuse

Lesson 3-4 Try This

1. 40   **2.** acute

Exercise Set 3-4

1.   **3.** not possible   **5.**   **7.**

9. 70   **11.** 55   **13.** 50   **15.** 50   **17.** 104   **19.** 20, 60, 100;
obtuse   **21.** 80, 80, 20   **23.** Given: $\triangle ABC$ is equiang.
Prove: $m\angle A = m\angle B = m\angle C = 60$ 1. $\triangle ABC$ is equiang.
(Given) 2. $m\angle A = m\angle B = m\angle C$ (Def. equiang.)
3. $m\angle A + m\angle B + m\angle C = 180$ (Sum of measures of $\angle$s
of a $\triangle$ is 180.) 4. $3(m\angle A) = 180$ (Subst.) 5. $m\angle A = 60$
(Mult. Prop.) 6. $m\angle A = m\angle B = m\angle C = 60$ (Subst.)
25. 18, 18, 144   **27.** 31, 31, 118   **29.** 130   **31.** 40
33. 54   **35.** Extend $\overline{BA}$ to form a $\triangle CBF$. 1. $\overline{AB} \parallel \overline{DE}$
(Given) 2. $\angle D \cong \angle BFC$ (If $\parallel$ lines are cut by a trans., corr.
$\angle$s are $\cong$.) 3. $m\angle B + m\angle C + m\angle BFC = 180$ (Sum of measures of $\angle$s of a $\triangle$ is 180.) 4. $m\angle B + m\angle C + m\angle D =$
180 (Subst.)
37. $\angle$s labeled 1 are $\cong$ (corr. $\angle$s);
$\angle$s labeled 2 are $\cong$ (alt. int. $\angle$s);
$m\angle 1 + m\angle 2 + m\angle 3 = 180$
39. 80

Mixed Review

1. 45, 135

Lesson 3-5 Try This

1. 45 **2.** 100 **3.** ∠WYZ ≅ ∠WYX (All rt. ∠s are ≅.), ∠XWY ≅ ∠ZWY (An ∠ bis. forms 2 ≅ ∠s.), ∠WXY ≅ ∠WZY (If 2 ∠s of 1 △ are ≅ to 2 ∠s of another △, then the third ∠s are ≅.)

Exercise Set 3-5

1. 35 **3.** 105 **5.** 40 **7.** 170 **9.** 60 **11.** 78
13. 3. Rt. ∠s are ≅. 4. Reflex. Prop. 5. If 2 ∠s of one △ are ≅ to 2 ∠s of another △, the third ∠s are ≅.
15. 1. $\overline{AB} \perp \overline{BD}$, $\overline{CD} \perp \overline{BD}$ (Given) 2. ∠ABE is a rt. ∠. ∠CDE is a rt. ∠. (Def. ⊥) 3. ∠ABE ≅ ∠CDE (Rt. ∠s are ≅.) 4. ∠1 ≅ ∠2 (Given) 5. ∠A ≅ ∠C (If 2 ∠s of one △ are ≅ to 2 ∠s of another △, the third ∠s are ≅.)
17. 20 **19.** 52 **21.** 27 **23.** 65 and 25 **25.** m∠FAD = 120, m∠DEF = 105, m∠ADE = 60, m∠AFE = 75
27. 1. $\overline{CE}$ bisects ∠BCD. (Given) 2. ∠DCE ≅ ∠ECB (Def. ∠ bis.) 3. m∠DCE = m∠ECB (Def. ≅ ∠s) 4. m∠DCE + m∠ECB = m∠DCB (∠Add. Post.) 5. 2m∠DCE = m∠DCB (Subst.) 6. m∠DCB = m∠A + m∠B (Ext. ∠ Th.) 7. 2(m∠DCE) = m∠A + m∠B (Subst.) 8. ∠A ≅ ∠B (Given) 9. m∠A = m∠B (Def. ≅ ∠s) 10. 2(m∠DCE) = 2(m∠A) (Subst.) 11. m∠DCE = m∠A (Mult. Prop.) 12. ∠DCE ≅ ∠A (Def. ≅ ∠s) 13. $\overline{CE} \parallel \overline{AB}$ (If 2 lines are cut by a trans.and corr. ∠s are ≅, the lines are ∥.)
29. 1. Label E on line $\overline{AB}$ so that A is between E and B. Draw auxiliary $\overline{AC}$. (2 pt. determine a line.) 2. m∠EAC = m∠B + m∠BCA (Ext. ∠ Th.) 3. m∠EAC = m∠1 + m∠DAC (∠ Add. Post.) 4. m∠1 + m∠DAC = m∠B + m∠BCA (Subst.) 5. m∠2 = m∠DAC + m∠DCA (Ext. ∠ Th.) 6. m∠1 + m∠DAC + m∠2 = m∠B + m∠BCA + m∠2 (Add. Prop.) 7. m∠1 + m∠DAC + m∠2 = m∠B + m∠BCA + m∠DAC + m∠DCA (Subst.) 8. m∠1 + m∠2 = m∠B + m∠BCA + m∠DCA (Add. Prop.) 9. m∠BCA + m∠DCA = m∠C (∠ Add. Post.) 10. m∠1 + m∠2 = m∠B + m∠C (Subst.) **31.** 1. Draw auxiliary $\overline{DB}$, label E so that B is between E and D. (2 pt. determine a line.) 2. m∠ABE = m∠2 + m∠ADB (Ext. ∠ Th.) 3. m∠EBC = m∠BDC + m∠4 (Ext. ∠ Th.) 4. m∠1 = m∠ABE + m∠EBC (∠ Add. Post.) 5. m∠3 = m∠ADB + m∠BDC (∠ Add. Post.) 6. m∠ABE + m∠EBC = m∠2 + m∠3 + m∠4 (Subst.) 7. m∠1 = m∠2 + m∠3 + m∠4 (Subst.)

Algebra Review

1. 9 and 17

Lesson 3-6 Try This

1. 11 **2.** 9 **3.** 60

Exercise Set 3-6

1. 1080 **3.** 2160 **5.** $(p - 2)180$ **7.** 13 **9.** 12
11. $128\frac{4}{7}$ **13.** $147\frac{3}{11}$ **15.** $158\frac{14}{17}$ **17.** $51\frac{3}{7}$ **19.** 20
21. m∠1 = m∠2 = 135 **23.** 24

25.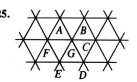

m∠AGB + m∠BGD = 180 so m∠AGB + m∠BGC + m∠CGD = 180 and similarly m∠AGF + m∠FGE + m∠EGD = 180. Thus, the sum of the measures of the 6 ∠s is 360. **27.** m∠1 = 90, m∠2 = 135, m∠3 = 135, 90 + 135 + 135 = 360 **29.** 108 + 108 + 144 = 360
31. 6 **33.** 18 **35.** 90 **37.** 360 **39.** sum of ∠s = $(n - 4)180$ **41.** 35; $d = \frac{n(n-3)}{2}$

Mixed Review

1. $\overline{ST} \cong \overline{VT}$ **3.** ∠ABC ≅ ∠CBD

Chapter Review

1. ∠2 and ∠7, ∠3 and ∠6 **2.** ∠2 and ∠3, ∠6 and ∠7
3. ∠1 and ∠8, ∠5 and ∠4 **4.** ∠1 and ∠3, ∠2 and ∠4, ∠5 and ∠7, ∠6 and ∠8 **5.** Alt. int. ∠s are ≅.
6. Same-side int. ∠s are supp. **7.** Corr. ∠s are ≅.
8. Alt. ext. ∠s are ≅. **9.** 157 **10.** $\overline{ST} \parallel \overline{RU}$ (If alt. int. ∠s are ≅, the lines are ∥.) **11.** $\overline{SR} \parallel \overline{TU}$ (If same-side int. ∠s are sup., the lines are ∥.) **12.** $\overline{SR} \parallel \overline{TU}$ (If corr. ∠s are ≅, the lines are ∥.) **13.** $\overline{ST} \parallel \overline{RU}$ (If, in a plane, 2 lines are ⊥ to the same line, the lines are ∥.) **14.** x = 2 **15.** x = 2
16. x = 160 **17.** 1. $\overline{AB} \parallel \overline{CD}$, ∠1 ≅ ∠2 (Given) 2. ∠1 ≅ ∠ABC (Th. 3.2) 3. ∠2 ≅ ∠ABC (Subst.) 4. $\overline{AD} \parallel \overline{BC}$ (Post. 14) **18.** 92 **19.** 50 **20.** 10
21. ∠UST **22.** 55 **23.** 85 **24.** ∠SUT, ∠2, ∠T
25. 1440 **26.** 25 **27.** 120 **28.** 45

CHAPTER 4

Lesson 4-1 Try This

1. $\overline{VU}$, $\angle W$ **2.** 73, 14

Exercise Set 4-1

1. $\overline{DE}$ **3.** $\angle E$ **5.** $\angle C$ **7.** $\triangle CBA$ **9.** 17 **11.** 95
13. $\angle A \cong \angle F$, $\angle B \cong \angle E$, $\angle C \cong \angle D$, $\overline{AB} \cong \overline{FE}$,
$\overline{AC} \cong \overline{FD}$, $\overline{BC} \cong \overline{ED}$ **15.** $\angle K \cong \angle L$, $\angle J \cong \angle M$,
$\angle H \cong \angle N$, $\overline{KJ} \cong \overline{LM}$, $\overline{JH} \cong \overline{MN}$, $\overline{KH} \cong \overline{LN}$ **17.** 17
19. 68 **21.** 27 **23.** $\angle T$ **25.** $\overline{AT}$ **27.** $\overline{MA}$ **29.** 50
31. 130 **33.** 20 **35.** 25 **37.** 70 **39.** 3 **41.** yes
43. no **45.** $\overline{AB}$, $\overline{AC}$, and $\overline{AD}$ or $\overline{BE}$, $\overline{CE}$, and $\overline{DE}$ **47.** $\angle L$
49. $\overline{JK}$ **51. a.** 4 **b.** 2 The $\triangle$s are $\cong$ if either $\triangle ABC \cong$
$\triangle XYZ$ or $\triangle ABC \cong \triangle YXZ$.

Mixed Review

1. 16 **3.** 97 **5.** obtuse

Lesson 4-2 Try This

1. ASA **2.** SAS **3.** SSS

Exercise Set 4-2

1. $\triangle ABC \cong \triangle DFE$, SAS **3.** $\triangle ABC \cong \triangle FDE$, SSS
5. No conclusion can be made. **7.** $\overline{AC} \cong \overline{EF}$ **9.** $\overline{WX} \cong$
$\overline{YZ}$ **11.** $\angle 2$ **13.** $\angle BCD$, $\overline{CD}$, or $\angle 1$, $\overline{BD}$ **15.** SAS
17. $\triangle DCE$ **19.** $\overline{BE} \cong \overline{CE}$ by Corr. parts of $\cong \triangle$s
are $\cong$. **21.** Place through the midpt. of $\overline{AD}$ and $\overline{BC}$.
$\overline{AF} \cong \overline{FD}$, $\overline{BF} \cong \overline{FC}$, $\angle AFB \cong \angle CFD$ (Vert. $\angle$s are $\cong$.);
$\triangle AFB \cong \triangle DFC$ by SAS. $\overline{AB} \cong \overline{DC}$ by Corr. parts of $\cong$
$\triangle$s are $\cong$. **23.** $9x - 48 = 6x - 15$, $3x = 33$, $x = 11$,
$AB = 16$, $DE = 16$, $AC = 10$, $DF = 10$, $\overline{AB} \cong \overline{DE}$, $\overline{AC} \cong$
$\overline{DF}$. By SAS, $\triangle ABC \cong \triangle DEF$. **25.** 79 **27.** $(-4, 4)$ or
$(-4, -2)$ **29.** $(2, 3)$ or $(6, 3)$ **31.** $\triangle FAB \cong \triangle FED$,
$\triangle FAC \cong \triangle FEC$, $\triangle FAD \cong \triangle FEB$, $\triangle FBC \cong \triangle FDC$
33. ASA, $m\angle A = 61 = m\angle D$, $AC = 14 + BC = BD$,
$m\angle ECA = 29 = m\angle FBD$ **35.** $AD = DC = DB$,
$m\angle ADC = m\angle ADB = m\angle CDB = 90$. By SAS,
$\triangle ADC \cong \triangle BDC$, $\triangle ADC \cong \triangle ADB$, and $\triangle BDC \cong$
$\triangle ADB$. **37.** Answers may vary.

Mixed Review

1. 45 **3.** 45 **5.** 60 **7.** $\triangle GFH \cong \triangle JKL$, SAS
9. $\triangle XYW \cong \triangle DEC$, SSS

Exercise Set 4-3

1. 1. Given 2. Given 3. Given 4. ASA **3.** 1. Given 2. Def.
$\angle$ bisector 3. Reflex. Prop. 4. Given 5. $\triangle RTQ \cong \triangle RTS$
5. 1. $\overline{DE} \cong \overline{DF}$ (Given) 2. $\overline{DH}$ bisects $\overline{EF}$. (Given)
3. $\overline{EH} \cong \overline{FH}$ (Def. seg. bis.) 4. $\overline{DH} \cong \overline{DH}$ (Reflex. Prop.)
5. $\triangle DHE \cong \triangle DHF$ (SSS) **7.** 1. $\overline{AB} \cong \overline{CD}$ (Given)
2. $\angle 1 \cong \angle 4$ (Given) 3. $\overline{AC} \cong \overline{CA}$ (Reflex. Prop.)
4. $\triangle ABC \cong \triangle CDA$ (SSS) **9.** 1. $\overline{HI} \cong \overline{KI}$ (Given)
2. $\angle 1 \cong \angle 2$ (Given) 3. $\overline{JI} \cong \overline{IL}$ (Given) 4. $\triangle HIJ \cong \triangle KIL$
(SAS) **11.** $\triangle ABC \cong \triangle ADC$ by SSS **13.** $\triangle ABC \cong$
$\triangle ADC$ by SAS **15.** $\triangle EFI \cong \triangle GFH$ by SAS
17. 1. $\overline{BD} \perp$ plane M (Given) 2. $\overline{BD} \perp \overline{AB}$, $\overline{BD} \perp \overline{CB}$
(If a line is $\perp$ to a plane at B, it is $\perp$ to all lines in the plane
that contain B.) 3. $\angle ABD$, $\angle CDB$ are rt. $\angle$s ($\perp$ seg. form
rt. $\angle$s.) 4. $\angle ABD \cong \angle CBD$ (All rt. $\angle$s are $\cong$.) 5. $\overline{AB} \cong$

$\overline{BC}$ (Given) 6. $\overline{BD} \cong \overline{BD}$ (Reflex. Prop.) 7. $\triangle ABD \cong$
$\triangle CBD$ (SAS) **19.** 1. $\overline{AI}$ bisects $\angle BAC$ (Given) 2. $\angle BAI \cong$
$\angle CAI$ (Def. $\angle$ bisector) 3. $\overline{AB} \cong \overline{AC}$ (Given) 4. $\overline{AI} \cong \overline{AI}$
(Reflex. Prop.) 5. $\triangle ABI \cong \triangle ACI$ (SAS) **21.** The SSS
Post. implies that a $\triangle$ of fixed side length has a unique
shape, hence it is less likely to collapse. **23.** $BD = CD$, so
$9x - 2 = 4x + 3$, $5x = 5$, $x = 1$. $AB = 12$, $AC = 12$, so
$\overline{AB} \cong \overline{AC}$. $\overline{AD} \cong \overline{AD}$ (Reflex. Prop.) so $\triangle ABD \cong \triangle ACD$
by SSS. **25.** By the Vert. $\angle$ Th., $m\angle AOD = m\angle BOC$. So
$2x + 9 = 3x + 5$, $x = 4$. $AO = 14$, $OB = 14$, $OC = 15$,
$DO = 15$, so $\overline{AB}$ and $\overline{CD}$ bisect each other. **27.** sometimes
true **29.** always true; If $\overline{AB} \cong \overline{AC}$ and $\overline{BD} \cong \overline{DC}$ then by
Reflex. Prop., $\overline{AD} \cong \overline{AD}$ and SSS, $\triangle ADB \cong \triangle ADC$, so
$\angle BAD \cong \angle CAD$.

Mixed Review

1. skew or $\parallel$ **3.** interior **5.** lies in the same plane also

Exercise Set 4-4

1. AB **3.** $m\angle C$ **5.** 1. Given 2. Given 3. An $\angle$ bis. forms
$2 \cong \angle$s. 4. $\overline{BD} \cong \overline{BD}$ 5. SAS 6. Corr. parts of $\cong \triangle$s are
$\cong$. **7.** 1. $\overline{AC}$ bisects $\overline{BD}$, $\overline{BD}$ bisects $\overline{AC}$ (Given) 2. $\overline{BO} \cong$
$\overline{DO}$, $\overline{CO} \cong \overline{AO}$ (A seg. bis. forms $2 \cong$ seg.) 3. $\angle 1 \cong \angle 2$
(Vert. $\angle$.) 4. $\triangle BOC \cong \triangle DOA$ (SAS) 5. $\overline{CB} \cong \overline{AD}$ (Corr.
parts of $\cong \triangle$s are $\cong$.) **9.** 1. D bisects $\overline{CE}$. (Given)
2. $\overline{CD} \cong \overline{ED}$ (A seg. bis. forms $2 \cong$ seg.) 3. $\angle 1 \cong \angle 2$,
$\angle C \cong \angle E$ (Given) 4. $\triangle BCD \cong \triangle FED$ (ASA) 5. $\overline{BD} \cong$
$\overline{FD}$ (Corr. parts of $\cong \triangle$s are $\cong$.) **11.** 1. O is the midpt. of
$\overline{AB}$ and $\overline{CD}$. (Given) 2. $\overline{AO} \cong \overline{BO}$, $\overline{DO} \cong \overline{CO}$ (A seg. midpt.
forms $2 \cong$ seg.) 3. $\angle AOD \cong \angle BOC$ (Vert. $\angle$ Th.)
4. $\triangle AOD \cong \triangle BOC$ (SAS) 5. $\angle A \cong \angle B$ (Corr. parts
of $\cong \triangle$s are $\cong$.) 6. $\overline{AD} \parallel \overline{BC}$ (If 2 lines are cut by a trans.
and a pair of alt. int. $\angle$s are $\cong$, the lines are $\parallel$.)
13. Since $AP = DP$, $BP = CP$, and $\angle APB = \angle CPD$
(Vert. $\angle$ Th.), $\triangle APB \cong \triangle DPC$ by SAS. Therefore $AB =$
CD, as corr. parts of $\cong \triangle$s are $\cong$. **15.** 1. $AB \cong DC$,
$\angle A \cong \angle D$ (Given) 2. $\overline{AD} \cong \overline{AD}$ (Reflex. Prop.)
3. $\triangle ABD \cong \triangle DCA$ (SAS) 4. $\overline{BD} \cong \overline{AC}$ (Corr. parts
of $\cong \triangle$s are $\cong$.) 5. $\overline{BC} \cong \overline{BC}$ (Reflex. Prop.) 6. $\triangle ABC \cong$
$\triangle DCB$ (SSS) 7. $\angle B \cong \angle C$ (Corr. parts of $\cong \triangle$s are $\cong$.)
17. 26 **19.** Given: $m\angle BGC = m\angle DGC = 65$, $\overline{BG} \cong \overline{DG}$
Prove: $\overline{BF} \cong \overline{DF}$ 1. $m\angle BGC = m\angle DGC$ (Given)
2. $\angle BGC \cong \angle DGC$ ($\angle$s of $=$ measure are $\cong$.)
3. $\angle BGF \cong \angle DGF$ ($\cong$ Supp. Th.) 4. $\overline{BG} \cong \overline{DG}$ (Given)
5. $\overline{GF} \cong \overline{GF}$ (Reflex. Prop.) 6. $\triangle BGF \cong \triangle DGF$ (SAS)
7. $\overline{BF} \cong \overline{DF}$ (Corr. parts of $\cong \triangle$s are $\cong$.) **21.** Given: $\angle A$
and $\angle B$ are rt. $\angle$s. $m\angle CAB = m\angle DBA = 32$ Prove:
$\angle D \cong \angle C$ 1. $\angle A$ and $\angle B$ are rt. $\angle$s. (Given) 2. $\angle A \cong$
$\angle B$ (All rt. $\angle$s are $\cong$.) 3. $\angle CAB \cong \angle DBA$ (Given)
4. $\angle D \cong \angle C$ (If 2 $\angle$s of a $\triangle$ are $\cong$ to 2 $\angle$s of another $\triangle$,
then the third $\angle$s are $\cong$.) **23.** $AC = \sqrt{13}$, $DF = \sqrt{13}$
25. $\triangle ABC \cong \triangle DEF$ by SSS. So $\angle A \cong \angle D$, as corr.
parts of $\cong \triangle$s are $\cong$. **27.** 1. $AB \cong CF$, $\angle 1 \cong \angle 2$,
$\overline{AF} \perp \overline{AB}$, $\overline{BG} \perp \overline{CF}$ (Given) 2. $\angle IAB$ and $\angle IGF$ are rt.
$\angle$s. ($\perp$ lines meet to form rt. $\angle$s.) 3. $\angle IAB \cong \angle IGF$ (All
rt. $\angle$s are $\cong$.) 4. $\triangle ABI \cong \triangle GFI$ (ASA) 5. $\overline{AI} \cong \overline{GI}$ (Corr.
parts of $\cong \triangle$s are $\cong$.) 6. $\overline{IH} \cong \overline{IH}$ (Reflex. Prop.)
7. $\triangle AHI \cong \triangle GHI$ (SSS) **29.** Draw auxiliary line AC. 1.
$\overline{AD} \cong \overline{AB}$, $\overline{CD} \cong \overline{CB}$ (Given) 2. $\overline{AC} \cong \overline{AC}$ (Reflex. Prop.)

3. $\triangle ACD \cong \triangle ACB$ (SSS) 4. $\angle D \cong \angle B$ (Corr. parts of $\cong \triangle$s are $\cong$.) **31.** Each face is identical, so the distance from a vertex to an opp. midpt. will be the same for each face ($AB = AC = DC = DE$), and the distance between 2 adj. midpt. will be the same for each face ($BC = CE$). The 2 $\triangle$s are then $\cong$ by SSS.

Algebra Review

1. 46, 52, 82 **3.** 98, 27, 55

Lesson 4-5 Try This

1. You can prove $\triangle BAE \cong \triangle BCD$ by SAS. Then $\angle 3 \cong \angle 4$ by corr. parts of $\cong \triangle$s. **3.** 1. Given 2. $\triangle ABE \cong \triangle CBD$, SAS 3. Corr. parts of $\cong \triangle$s are $\cong$., 4. $\angle 2 \cong \angle 5$, Supp. of $\cong \angle$s are $\cong$.

Exercise Set 4-5

1. $\triangle ABC$, $\triangle DCB$ **3.** $\triangle ADC$, $\triangle BCD$ or $\triangle ACB$, $\triangle BDA$ **5.** $\triangle ACB$, $\triangle BDA$ or $\triangle ADC$, $\triangle BCD$ **7.** $\overline{BC}$ **9.** $\angle CAF$ **11.** 1. $\angle ADC \cong \angle ACD$ (Given) 2. $\angle 1 \cong \angle 2$ (Given) 3. $\overline{CD} \cong \overline{CD}$ (Reflex. Prop.) 4. $\triangle BCD \cong \triangle EDC$ (ASA) 5. $\overline{BC} \cong \overline{ED}$ (Corr. parts of $\cong \triangle$s are $\cong$.) **13.** 1. $\angle 1 \cong \angle 2$ (Given) 2. $\overline{PQ} \cong \overline{RQ}$ (Given) 3. $\angle Q \cong \angle Q$ (Reflex. Prop.) 4. $\triangle PQV \cong \triangle RQT$ (ASA) 5. $\overline{QT} \cong \overline{QV}$ (Corr. parts of $\cong \triangle$s are $\cong$.) **15.** $AB = CD = 19$ **17.** 11 **19.** 1. $\overline{ST} \cong \overline{VW}$, $\angle S \cong \angle V$, $\angle STR \cong \angle VWU$ (Given) 2. $\triangle RST \cong \triangle UVW$ (ASA) 3. $\angle R \cong \angle U$ (Corr. parts of $\cong \triangle$s are $\cong$.) 4. $\overline{RS} \parallel \overline{UV}$ (If 2 lines are cut by a trans. and alt. int. $\angle$s are $\cong$, the lines are $\parallel$.) **21.** 1. $\angle 1 \cong \angle 2$ (Given) 2. $\angle EDB \cong \angle CDA$ (Common $\angle$ Th.) 3. $\overline{BD} \cong \overline{AD}$ (Given) 4. $\overline{ED} \cong \overline{CD}$ (Given) 5. $\triangle EDB \cong \triangle CDA$ (SAS) 6. $\angle 5 \cong \angle 6$ (Corr. parts of $\cong \triangle$s are $\cong$.) **23.** 1. $\overline{AE} \cong \overline{DF}$, $\angle E \cong \angle F$, $\overline{EC} \cong \overline{FB}$ (Given) 2. $\triangle AEC \cong \triangle DFB$ (SAS) 3. $\overline{AC} \cong \overline{DB}$ (Corr. parts of $\cong \triangle$s are $\cong$.) 4. $\overline{AB} \cong \overline{CD}$ (Common Seg. Th.) **25.** 1. $\angle ADC \cong \angle ACD$ (Given) 2. $\overline{CD} \cong \overline{CD}$ (Reflex. Prop.) 3. $\triangle ADC \cong \triangle ACD$ (ASA) 4. $\overline{AC} \cong \overline{AD}$ (Corr. parts. of $\cong \triangle$s are $\cong$.) 5. $\overline{BC} \cong \overline{ED}$ (Given) 6. $\overline{AB} \cong \overline{AE}$ (Seg. Add. Post.) **27.** A—36 B—24 C—8

Algebra Review

1. 4 **3.** 108 or 84

Lesson 4-6 Try This

$BA = BD = 14$ by Th. 4.2. $BD = DC = 14$, so $\angle DBC \cong \angle DCB$ by Th. 4.1.

Exercise Set 4-6

1. $\overline{BD} \cong \overline{CD}$ (Th. 4.2) **3.** $\angle 1 \cong \angle 2$ (Th. 4.1) **5.** $\angle ABC \cong \angle ACB$ (Th. 4.1) **7.** 14 **9.** 14 **11.** 59 **13.** 3 **15.** 9 **17.** 9 **19.** 1. Given 2. Base $\angle$s of an isos. $\triangle$ are $\cong$. 3. Given 4. ASA 5. Corr. parts of $\cong \triangle$s are $\cong$. 7. Sides opp. $\cong \angle$s are $\cong$. 8. Def. isos. $\triangle$. **21.** $4x = 6x - 15$, $2x = 15$, $x = 30$, $AB = BC = 30$ **23.** By Th. 4.1, $m\angle X = m\angle Z$, so $4x + 60 = 14x + 30$. $30 = 10x$, $x = 3$, $m\angle X = m\angle Z = 72$, $m\angle Y = 2x + 30 = 36$. **25.** 1. $\triangle ADC$ is isos. with vertex A (Given) 2. $\overline{AC} \cong \overline{AD}$ (Def. isos. $\triangle$) 3. $\angle ACD \cong \angle ADC$ (Isos. $\triangle$ Th.) 4. $\overline{BC} \cong \overline{ED}$ (Given) 5. $\overline{BD} \cong \overline{EC}$ (Common Seg. Th.) 6. $\triangle AEC \cong \triangle ABD$ (SAS) 7. $\overline{AE} \cong \overline{AB}$ (Corr. parts of $\cong \triangle$s are $\cong$.) 8. $\triangle ABE$ is isos. (Def. isos. $\triangle$)

27. 1. $\overline{AB} \cong \overline{AC}$ (Given) 2. $\angle ABC \cong \angle ACB$ (Isos. $\triangle$ Th.) 3. $\overline{BE}$ bisects $\angle ABC$, $\overline{CD}$ bisects $\angle ACB$. (Given) 4. $m\angle ABE = \frac{1}{2}m\angle ABC$, $m\angle ACD = \frac{1}{2}m\angle ACB$ ($\angle$ Bis. Th.) 5. $\angle ABE \cong \angle ACD$ (Trans. Prop.) 6. $\angle A \cong \angle A$ (Reflex. Prop.) 7. $\triangle ABE \cong \triangle ACD$ (ASA) 8. $\overline{AD} \cong \overline{AE}$ (Corr. parts of $\cong \triangle$s are $\cong$.) **29.** $m\angle ABC = m\angle BAC + m\angle BCA$, by the Ext. $\angle$ Th. If $m\angle DBC = 2m\angle DAC$, then $m\angle DAC = m\angle BCA$, so by Th. 4.2 $AB = BC$. **31.** Given: $\triangle ABC$ is isos. with base $\overline{BC}$. D is midpt. of $\overline{BC}$. Prove: $\overline{AD}$ bisects $\angle BAC$ 1. $\triangle ABC$ is isos. with base $\overline{BC}$. (Given) 2. D is midpt. of BC. (Given) 3. $\overline{BD} \cong \overline{CD}$ (A midpt. forms 2 $\cong$ seg.) 4. $\overline{AB} \cong \overline{AC}$ (Def. of isos. $\triangle$) 5. $\overline{AD} \cong \overline{AD}$ (Reflex. Prop.) 6. $\triangle ABD \cong \triangle ACD$ (SSS) 7. $\angle BAD \cong \angle CAD$ (Corr. parts of $\cong \triangle$s are $\cong$.) 8. $\overline{AD}$ bisects $\angle BAC$. (Def. $\angle$ bisector) **33.** $\angle ABE$ and $\angle CDE$ are $\cong$. $\angle ABE$ and $\angle CDE$ are rt. $\angle$s. $\overline{BE} \cong \overline{DE}$, so by Th. 4.1 $\angle EBD \cong \angle EDB$. $m\angle ABE + m\angle EBD = m\angle CDE + m\angle EDB$, so, by the $\angle$ Add. Post. $\angle ABD \cong \angle CDB$. **35.** 1. $\overline{AB} \cong \overline{FE}$, $\angle A \cong \angle F$ (Given) 2. $\overline{AD} \cong \overline{FC}$ (Given) 3. $\overline{AC} \cong \overline{FD}$ (Common Seg. Th.) 4. $\triangle ABC \cong \triangle FED$ (SAS) 5. $\angle ACB \cong \angle FDE$ (Corr. parts of $\cong \triangle$s are $\cong$.) 6. $\overline{GD} \cong \overline{GC}$ (If 2 $\angle$s of a $\triangle$ are $\cong$, then the sides opp. them are $\cong$.) 7. $\triangle CDG$ is isos. (Def. isos. $\triangle$) **37.** 1. $\angle B \cong \angle C$ (Given) 2. $\overline{BC} \cong \overline{CB}$ (Reflex. Prop.) 3. $\triangle ABC \cong \triangle ACB$ (ASA: $\angle B \cong \angle C$, $\overline{BC} \cong \overline{CB}$, $\angle C \cong \angle B$) 4. $\overline{AB} \cong \overline{AC}$ (Corr. parts of $\cong \triangle$s are $\cong$.) **39.** No; it assumes that A, B, C, D are collinear and that $\angle 3$ and $\angle 4$ are ext. $\angle$s of $\triangle EBC$. **41.** Answers may vary; e.g., if $m\angle DCB = m\angle DBC$ and $m\angle DAC = m\angle DCA$.

Mixed Review

1. 52, 60, 68; acute **3.** 5

Exercise Set 4-7

1. $\angle CAB \cong \angle DAB$ or $\angle ABC \cong \angle ABD$ **3.** $\angle CAB \cong \angle DAB$ or $\angle ABC \cong \angle ABD$ **5.** $\angle CAB \cong \angle DAB$ and $\angle ABC \cong \angle ABD$, or $\angle CAB \cong \angle DAB$ and $\overline{AC} \cong \overline{AD}$, or $\angle ABC \cong \angle ABD$ and $\overline{CB} \cong \overline{DB}$ **7.** $\angle BCA \cong \angle EDF$ or $\angle A \cong \angle F$ **9.** $\overline{AB} \cong \overline{EF}$ or $\overline{BC} \cong \overline{ED}$ **11.** 1. $\angle B$ and $\angle D$ are rt. $\angle$s. (Given) 2. $\triangle ABC$ and $\triangle CDA$ are rt. $\triangle$s. (Def. rt. $\triangle$) 3. $\overline{AB} \cong \overline{CD}$ (Given) 4. $\overline{AC} \cong \overline{AC}$ (Reflex. Prop.) 5. $\triangle ABC \cong \triangle CDA$ (HL Th.) **13.** 1. $\angle A$ and $\angle B$ are rt. $\angle$s. (Given) 2. $\triangle AOD$ and $\triangle BOC$ are rt. $\triangle$s. (Def. rt. $\triangle$) 3. $\overline{OD} \cong \overline{OC}$ (Given) 4. O is midpt. of $\overline{AB}$. (Given) 5. $\overline{AO} \cong \overline{OB}$ (A midpt. forms 2 $\cong$ seg.) 6. $\triangle AOD \cong \triangle BOC$ (HL Th.) **15.** 1. $\angle A$ and $\angle B$ are rt. $\angle$s. (Given) 2. $\angle A \cong \angle B$ (All rt. $\angle$s are $\cong$.) 3. O is midpt. of $\overline{AB}$. (Given) 4. $\overline{AO} \cong \overline{OB}$ (A midpt. forms 2 $\cong$ seg.) 5. $\angle AOD \cong \angle BOC$ (Given) 6. $\triangle AOD \cong \triangle BOC$ (ASA) **17.** $\overline{DE} \perp \overline{AC}$, $\overline{BF} \perp \overline{AC}$ (Given) 2. $\angle DEC$ and $\angle BFA$ are rt. $\angle$s. ($\perp$ seg. form rt. $\angle$s.) 3. $\triangle DEC$ and $\triangle BFA$ are rt. $\triangle$s. (Def. rt. $\triangle$) 4. $\overline{DE} \cong \overline{BF}$ (Given) 5. $\overline{CD} \cong \overline{AB}$ (Given) 6. $\triangle DEC \cong \triangle BFA$ (HL Theorem) 7. $\angle 1 \cong \angle 2$ (Corr. parts of $\cong \triangle$s are $\cong$.) **19.** 1. $\overline{DE} \perp \overline{AC}$, $\overline{BF} \perp \overline{AC}$ (Given) 2. $\angle DEC$ and $\angle BFA$ are rt. $\angle$s. ($\perp$ seg. form rt. $\angle$s.) 3. $\triangle DEC$ and $\triangle BFA$ are rt. $\triangle$s. (Def. rt. $\triangle$) 4. $\overline{DE} \cong \overline{BF}$ (Given) 5. $\overline{CD} \cong \overline{AB}$ (Given) 6. $\triangle DEC \cong \triangle BFA$ (HL Theorem) 7. $\overline{AF} \cong \overline{CE}$ (Corr. parts of $\triangle$s are $\cong$.) 8. $\overline{AE} \cong \overline{CF}$ (Common Seg. Th.) **21.** 1. $\overline{CD} \perp \overline{AB}$, $\overline{BE} \perp \overline{AC}$ (Given) 2. $\angle CDB$ and $\angle BEC$ are rt. $\angle$s. ($\perp$ seg. form rt.

∠s.) 3. △CDB and △BEC are rt. △s. (Def. rt. △) 4. $\overline{BE} \cong$ $\overline{CD}$ (Given) 5. $\overline{BC} \cong \overline{BC}$ (Reflex. Prop.) 6. △BEC ≅ △CDB (HL Th.) 7. ∠ECB ≅ ∠DBC (Corr. parts of ≅ △s are ≅.) 8. $\overline{AB} \cong \overline{AC}$ (Converse of Isos. △ Th.) 9. △ABC is isos. (Def. isos. △)   **23.** 26.   **25.** △APD, △BPD, △CPD are all rt. △s since $\overline{DP}$ is ⊥ to the roof and $\overline{AP}, \overline{BP}, \overline{CP}$ are all in the plane of the roof. It is given that $\overline{AD} \cong \overline{BD} \cong \overline{CD}$ and by the Reflex. Prop. $\overline{DP} \cong \overline{DP}$, so △APD ≅ △BPD ≅ △CPD by the HL Th. Then $\overline{AP} \cong \overline{BP} \cong \overline{CP}$ since they are corr. parts of ≅ △s, so $AP = BP = CP$.
27. Given: rt. △ABC and rt. △DEF, $\overline{AC} \cong \overline{DF}$, ∠A ≅ ∠D, ∠B and ∠E are rt. ∠s. Prove: △ABC ≅ △DEF 1. ∠B and ∠E are rt. ∠s. (Given) 2. ∠B ≅ ∠E (Rt. ∠s are ≅.) 3. ∠A ≅ ∠D (Given) 4. $\overline{AC} \cong \overline{DF}$ (Given) 5. △ABC ≅ △DEF (AAS)
29. Given: isos. △ABC with D the midpt. of base $\overline{BC}$, $\overline{DE} \perp \overline{BA}, \overline{DF} \perp \overline{AC}$ Prove: $\overline{DE} \cong \overline{DF}$ 1. $\overline{DE} \perp \overline{BA}$, $\overline{DF} \perp \overline{AC}$ (Given) 2. ∠DEB and ∠DFC are rt. ∠s. (⊥ lines form rt. ∠s.) 3. △DEB and △DFC are rt. △s. (Def. rt. △) 4. D is midpt. of $\overline{BC}$. (Given) 5. $\overline{BD} \cong \overline{DC}$ (A midpt. forms 2 ≅ seg.) 6. △ABC is isos. (Given) 7. ∠B ≅ ∠C (Isos. △ Th.) 8. △DBE ≅ △DCF (HA Theorem) 9. $\overline{DE} \cong \overline{DF}$ (Corr. parts of ≅ △s are ≅.)   **31.** If 2 sides and the not included ∠ of a △ are ≅ respectively to 2 sides and the not included ∠ of another △, the △s are ≅.

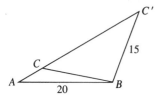

SSA should not be a post. because the measure of the included ∠ may vary.

Algebra Review
1. $y^3 - 2y^2 + 3y$ 3. $y - 5$ 5. $y - 4$

Lesson 4-8 Try This
1. a. median   b. alt.   2. E is on the ⊥ bis. of $\overline{BD}$.

Exercise Set 4-8
1. an alt.   3. an alt., a median, a ⊥ bis.   5. $\overline{AD}$ is a median for △ACE and a ⊥ bis. of $\overline{EC}$, △AEC is isos, ∠1 ≅ ∠2, $\overline{BG} \cong \overline{GF}$.   7. $\overline{AD}$ is an ∠ bis. of ∠BAF, $\overline{AC} \cong \overline{AE}$, $\overline{BG} \cong \overline{FG}$, △AEC is isos.   9. △ABG   11. Th. 4.6   13. 9   15. Th. 4.7   17. an ∠ bis.   19. 8   21. By Th. 4.9, P lies on the ∠ bis. As 2 pt. determine only 1 line (Post. 2), $\overline{BP}$ is the ∠ bis. of ∠B.   23. yes   25. $AC = \sqrt{3^2 + 4^2} = \sqrt{25} = 5$ $AB = \sqrt{0^2 + 5^2} = \sqrt{25} = 5$, so $AB = AC$ and △ABC is isos. with base $\overline{BC}$. In an isos. △, the median to the base is the alt. to the base (by Th. 4.6). As $\overline{AD}$ is the median to the base, it is also an alt.   27. By Ex. 25, $\overline{AD}$ is an alt. to the base of the isos. △ABC. By Th. 4.6, $\overline{AD}$ bisects ∠CAB. By Th. 4.10, D is equidistant from $\overline{AC}$ and $\overline{AB}$.   29. The transmitter station must be built on the ∠ bis. of the ∠ formed by q and p, but not within the city.   31. Given: q is the ⊥ bis. of $\overline{AB}$ and P is on q. Prove:

$\overline{PA} \cong \overline{PB}$ 1. q is the ⊥ bis. of $\overline{AB}$ (Given) 2. C is the midpt. of $\overline{AB}$, ∠PCA and ∠PCB are rt. ∠s. (Def. ⊥ bis.) 3. ∠PCA ≅ ∠PCB (All rt. ∠s are ≅.) 4. $\overline{AC} \cong \overline{BC}$ (A midpt. forms 2 ≅ seg.) 5. $\overline{PC} \cong \overline{PC}$ (Reflex. Prop.) 6. △PCA ≅ △PCB (SAS) 7. $\overline{PA} \cong \overline{PB}$ (Corr. parts of ≅ △s are ≅.)
33. Given: P is on the ∠ bis. $\overline{BP}$. Prove: $\overline{PA} \cong \overline{PC}$ 1. ∠PAB and ∠PCB are rt. ∠s. (⊥ seg. form rt. ∠s.) 2. △PAB and △PCB are rt. ∠s. (Def. rt. △) 3. $\overline{BP}$ is ∠ bis. for ∠ABC. (Given) 4. ∠PBA ≅ ∠PBC (∠ bis. forms 2 ≅ ∠s.) 5. $\overline{PB} \cong \overline{PB}$ (Reflex. Prop.) 6. △PAB ≅ △PCB (HA Th.) 7. $\overline{PA} \cong \overline{PC}$ (Corr. parts of ≅ △s are ≅.)   **35.** Given: isos. △ABC, base $\overline{BC}$, $\overline{AD}$ is an alt. Prove: $\overline{AD}$ is a median and ⊥ bis. of △ABC. 1. $\overline{AD}$ is an alt. to the base of isos. △ABC. (Given) 2. $\overline{AD}$ bisects $\overline{BC}$. (Th. 4.6) 3. $\overline{AD} \perp \overline{BC}$ (Alt. is ⊥ to base.) 4. D is the midpt. of $\overline{BC}$ (Def. bis.) 5. $\overline{AD}$ is a median of △ABC. (Def. median) 6. $\overline{AD}$ is ⊥ bis. of $\overline{BC}$. (Def. ⊥ bisector)   **37.** False. For a counterexample, take any isos. △ with the ∠ opp. the base > 90°. By Th. 4.6, the alt. from the base bisects the vertex ∠.

Algebra Review
1. $(7y^2 - 9)(7y^2 + 9)$ 3. $(3y - 8)(3y + 8)$
5. $-1(x + 9)(x - 8)$

Chapter Review
1. ∠S   2. $\overline{RS}$ 3. ∠BAC   4. 10   5. 6   6. △STR
7. △SRU ≅ △STU, SAS   8. △EAB ≅ △EDC, ASA
9. No conclusion can be made.   10. △DAB ≅ △DCB, SSS   11. △DAB ≅ △DCB, SAS   12. 1. E is the midpt. of $\overline{DC}$. (Given) 2. $\overline{ED} \cong \overline{EC}$ (Def. midpt.) 3. ∠1 ≅ ∠2 (Given) 4. $\overline{BE} \cong \overline{BE}$ (Reflex. Prop.) 5. △DEB ≅ △CEB (SAS)   13. 1. G bisects $\overline{DF}$. (Given) 2. $\overline{GD} \cong \overline{GF}$ (Def. bis.) 3. ∠1 ≅ ∠2 (Given) 4. $\overline{EG} \cong \overline{EG}$ (Reflex. Prop.) 5. △EDG ≅ △EFG (SAS)   14. 1. ∠1 is a rt. ∠. (Given) 2. $m\angle 1 = 90$ (Def. rt. ∠) 3. $m\angle 1 + m\angle 2 = 180$ (Def. linear pair) 4. $m\angle 2 = 90$ (Sub. Prop.) 5. $m\angle 1 = m\angle 2$ (Trans. Prop.) 6. ∠1 ≅ ∠2 (Def. ≅ ∠s) 7. $\overline{EG} \cong \overline{EG}$ (Reflex. Prop.) 8. ∠3 ≅ ∠4 (Given) 9. △EDG ≅ △EFG (ASA) 10. $\overline{DE} \cong \overline{EF}$ (Corr. parts of ≅ △s are ≅.)
15. $\overline{WT}$ 16. ∠TAS   17. 1. $\overline{QA} \cong \overline{TA}$ (Given) 2. ∠QAS ≅ ∠TAW (Given) 3. $\overline{AW} \cong \overline{AS}$ (Given) 4. △QAS ≅ △TAW (SAS) 5. ∠1 ≅ ∠2 (Corr. parts of ≅ △s are ≅.)
18. $\overline{JE} \cong \overline{JG}$ 19. ∠2 ≅ ∠8   20. ∠1 ≅ ∠2 (Corr. parts of ≅ △s are ≅.)   21. $\overline{FC} \cong \overline{EB}$, ∠F ≅ ∠E, or ∠FCA ≅ ∠EBD   22. ∠FCA ≅ ∠EBD   23. $\overline{FC} \cong \overline{EB}$ 24. 1. ∠1 ≅ ∠2 (Given) 2. $\overline{AB} \cong \overline{BC}$ (Given) 3. ∠BAC ≅ ∠BCA (Isos. △ Th.) 4. $\overline{AC} \cong \overline{AC}$ (Reflex. Prop.) 5. △AEC ≅ △CDA (AAS)   25. true   26. false   27. false   28. true

CHAPTER 5

Lesson 5-1 Try This

1. $AD = BC = 54$ **2.** $m\angle T = m\angle R = 38$, $m\angle S = m\angle U = 142$

Exercise Set 5-1

1. Opp. $\angle$s of a $\square$ are $\cong$. **3.** Opp. sides of a $\square$ are $\cong$.
5. 20 **7.** 11 **9.** 105 **11.** 16 **13.** 15 **15.** 132 **17.** 125
19. 3 **21.** 79 **23.** 120 **25.** 85 **27.** $AB = CD = 58$, $BC = AD = 36$ **29.** 1. $ABCD$ is $\square$, $AECF$ is $\square$. (Given)
2. $\angle D \cong \angle B$ (Opp. $\angle$s of $\square$ are $\cong$.) 3. $\overline{CD} \cong \overline{AB}$, $\overline{AD} \cong \overline{CB}$, $\overline{AF} \cong \overline{CE}$ (Opp. sides of $\square$ are $\cong$.) 4. $AD = CB$, $AF = CE$ (Def. $\cong$ seg.) 5. $AD = AF + FD$, $CD = CE + EB$ (Seg. Add. Post.) 6. $AF + FD = CE + EB$ (Subst.) 7. $FD = ED$ (Add. Prop.) 8. $\overline{FD} \cong \overline{EB}$ (Def. $\cong$ seg.) 9. $\triangle CDF \cong \triangle ABE$ (SAS) **31.** 1. $ABCD$ is $\square$. (Given) 2. $\overline{AB} \cong \overline{CD}$ (Opp. sides of $\square$ are $\cong$.)
3. $CD = AB$ (Def. $\cong$) 4. A, F, E, C are collinear. (Given)
5. $\angle DCA \cong \angle BAC$ ($\parallel$ lines cut by trans., alt. int. $\angle$s are $\cong$.) 6. $\overline{AF} \cong \overline{CE}$ (Given) 7. $\triangle DEC \cong \triangle BFA$ (SAS)
8. $\angle AFB \cong \angle CED$ (Corr. parts of $\cong$ $\triangle$s are $\cong$.)
9. $\overline{DE} \parallel \overline{BF}$ (Lines cut by a trans. and alt. int. $\angle$s are $\cong$, lines are $\parallel$.) **33.** 120 **35.** 120 **37.** 120 **39.** 1. $\square ABCD$, $\overline{DE} \cong \overline{FB}$ (Given) 2. $\overline{DA} \cong \overline{CB}$ (Opp. sides of $\square$ are $\cong$.)
3. $DA = CB$ (Def. $\cong$) 4. $DE + EA = FB + CF$ (Seg. Add. Post.) 5. $DE + EA = DE + CF$ (Subst.) 6. $EA = CF$ (Add. Prop.) 7. $\overline{EA} \cong \overline{CF}$ (Def. $\cong$) 8. $\angle EXA \cong \angle FXC$ (Vert. $\angle$s)
9. $\overline{AD} \parallel \overline{BC}$ (Def. $\square$). 10. $\angle EAX \cong \angle FCX$ ($\parallel$ lines cut by a trans., alt. int. $\angle$s are $\cong$.) 11. $\triangle XAE \cong \triangle XCF$ (AAS)
12. $\overline{EX} \cong \overline{XF}$ (corr. parts of $\cong$ $\triangle$s) 13. X bisects $\overline{EF}$. (Def. seg. bis.) **41.** 1. $\triangle ABC$; $\overline{PF} \parallel \overline{AB}$, $\overline{PE} \parallel \overline{AC}$ (Given) 2. $AFPE$ is a $\square$. (Def. $\square$) 3. $\overline{EP} \cong \overline{AF}$, $\overline{EA} \cong \overline{PF}$ (Opp. sides of $\square$ are $\cong$.) 4. $\angle ACB \cong \angle EPB$, $\angle ABC \cong \angle FPC$ (Lines cut by trans., alt. int. $\angle$s are $\cong$.) 5. $\overline{AB} \cong \overline{AC}$ (Given)
6. $\angle ABC \cong \angle ACB$ (If $\angle$s of a $\triangle$ are $\cong$, sides opp. are $\cong$.)
7. $\angle ABC \cong \angle EPB \cong \angle FPC \cong \angle ACB$ (Trans. Prop.)
8. $\overline{EB} \cong \overline{EP}$, $\overline{FP} \cong \overline{FC}$ (If $\angle$s of a $\triangle$ are $\cong$, sides opp. are $\cong$.) 9. $AB = AE + EB$, $AC = AF + FC$ (Seg. Add. Post.)
10. $AB + AC = AE + EB + AF + FC$ (Add. Post.)
11. $AB + AC = AE + EP + AF + FP$ (Subst.)
43. 2 planes are equidistant at all pt. In order for a ceiling to be $\parallel$ to floor, studs in wall joining them must be same length.

Mixed Review

1. $\triangle BDA \cong \triangle BDC$ (SAS) **3.** $\triangle BDA \cong \triangle BDC$ (HL)
5. $p \parallel q$ (If alt. int. $\angle$s are $\cong$, the lines are $\parallel$.) **7.** $p \parallel q$ (If corr. $\angle$s are $\cong$, the lines are $\parallel$.) **9.** $p \parallel q$ (If alt. ext. $\angle$s are $\cong$, the lines are $\parallel$.)

Lesson 5-2 Try This

$x = 16$, $y = 16$

Exercise Set 5-2

1. If both pairs of opp. sides of quad. are $\cong$, it is a $\square$.
3. no **5.** If diag. of quad. bisect each other, it is a $\square$.
7. If both pairs of opp. sides of a quad. are $\cong$, it is a $\square$.
9. $x = 70$, $y = 10$ **11.** $x = 36$, $y = 23$ **13.** $x = 6$, $y = 12$ **15.** yes **17.** no **19.** no **21.** 1. $\triangle ABC \cong \triangle CDA$ (Given) 2. $\overline{AB} \cong \overline{DC}$, $\overline{AD} \cong \overline{BC}$ (Corr. parts of $\cong$ $\triangle$s) 3. $ABCD$ is a $\square$. (If both pairs of opp. sides of quad. are $\cong$, it is a $\square$.) **23.** 4 poles are bolted together

at pt. A, B, and C so that $\overline{AB} \cong \overline{CD}$ and $\overline{AD} \cong \overline{BC}$. If opp. sides are $\cong$, as the swing moves, $ABCD$ is always a $\square$, and $\overline{CD} \parallel$ to $\overline{AB}$. **25.** X_1X_2 and Y_1Y_2 are $\cong$ and $\parallel$. $X_1X_2Y_2Y_1$ is a $\square$. $X_1Y_1 \parallel X_2Y_2$. **27.** $x = 81\frac{2}{3}$, $y = 8$ **29.** $x = 5$, $y = 1$
31. 1. $\overline{AD} \parallel \overline{BC}$, $\overline{EF} \parallel \overline{BC}$, $\overline{AD} \parallel \overline{FE}$ (Def. $\square$) 2. $\overline{AD} \cong \overline{BC}$, $\overline{FE} \cong \overline{BC}$, $\overline{AD} \cong \overline{FE}$ (If 2 lines are $\parallel$ to a third line, they are $\parallel$ to each other.) 3. $ADEF$ is a $\square$. (If 1 pair of opp. sides of quad. are both $\parallel$ and $\cong$, it is a $\square$.) **33.** 1. $\angle A \cong \angle C$, $\angle B \cong \angle D$ (Given) 2. $m\angle A + m\angle B + m\angle C + m\angle D = 360$ (Sum of $\angle$s of quad. = 360.) 3. $m\angle A = m\angle C$, $m\angle B = m\angle D$ (Def. $\cong$) 4. $m\angle A + m\angle B + m\angle A + m\angle B = 360$ (Substitution) 5. $2(m\angle A + m\angle B) = 360$ (Distr. Prop.) 6. $m\angle A + m\angle B = 180$ (Division)
7. $\angle A$ and $\angle B$ are supp. (Def. supp. $\angle$s) 8. $\overline{AD} \parallel \overline{BC}$ (If 2 lines are cut by a trans. and same-side int. $\angle$s are supp. the lines are $\parallel$.) 9. $\overline{AB} \parallel \overline{DC}$ (As in 1–8.) 10. $ABCD$ is a $\square$. (Def. $\square$) **35.** 1. $ABCD$ is $\square$. (Given) 2. $\overline{CD} \cong \overline{AB}$, $\overline{AD} \cong \overline{BC}$ (If quad. is $\square$, opp. sides are $\cong$.) 3. $\overline{AB} \parallel \overline{CD}$, $\overline{AD} \parallel \overline{BC}$ (Def. $\square$) 4. $\angle ACD \cong \angle CAB$, $\angle ACB \cong \angle CAD$ ($\parallel$ lines cut by trans., alt. int. $\angle$s are $\cong$.) 5. $\triangle BCF \cong \triangle DAE$ (SAS) 6. $\overline{DE} \cong \overline{FB}$ (Corr. parts of $\cong$ $\triangle$s) 7. $\triangle DCF \cong \triangle BAE$ (SAS) 8. $\overline{BE} \cong \overline{DF}$ (Corr. parts of $\cong$ $\triangle$s) 9. $BFDE$ is $\square$. (If opp. sides of quad. are $\cong$, it is a $\square$.) **37.** 1. $\overline{AB} \cong \overline{BC} \cong \overline{CD} \cong \overline{DE} \cong \overline{EF} \cong \overline{FA}$ (Def. reg. poly.) 2. $\angle BAF \cong \angle CDE$ (Def. reg. poly.) 3. $\triangle FAB \cong \triangle CDE$ (SAS) 4. $\overline{BF} \cong \overline{CE}$ (Corr. parts of $\cong$ $\triangle$s) 5. $BCEF$ is $\square$. (If quad. has opp. sides $\cong$, it is $\square$.) **39.** 1. $\overline{AB} \parallel \overline{CD}$, $\overline{AD} \parallel \overline{BC}$ (Given) 2. $\angle ADB \cong \angle DBC$, $\angle ABD \cong \angle CDB$ ($\parallel$ lines cut by trans., alt. int. $\angle$s are $\cong$.) 3. $\overline{DB} \cong \overline{DB}$ (Reflex. Prop.) 4. $\triangle DAB \cong \triangle BCD$ (ASA) 5. $\overline{AD} \cong \overline{BC}$, $\overline{AB} \cong \overline{DC}$ (Corr. parts of $\cong$ $\triangle$s are $\cong$.) 6. $ABCD$ is $\square$. (Def. $\square$)

Lesson 5-3 Try This

1. 22 **2.** -15

Exercise Set 5-3

1. $\cong$ diag., diag. bisect each other, diag. bisect opp. $\angle$s
3. rhombus **5.** 6 **7.** 70 **9.** 43 **11.** 45 **13.** true
15. false **17.** false **19.** All sides are $\cong$, all $\angle$s are rt. $\angle$s. **21.** 1. $ABCD$ is $\square$, $m\angle 3 + m\angle 4 = 90$ (Given) 2. $m\angle DAB + m\angle 3 + m\angle 4 = 180$ ($\angle$ Sum Th.) 3. $m\angle DAB + 90 = 180$ (Subst.) 4. $m\angle DAB = 90$ (Add. Prop.) 5. $ABCD$ is rect. (If $\square$ has rt. $\angle$, it is rect.)
23.   **25.**

27. $AB = DC = AD = 34$ **29.** $AC = \sqrt{41}$ and $BD = \sqrt{41}$, therefore $\overline{AC} \cong \overline{BD}$ (Def. $\cong$ seg.) **31.** $(-2, -2)$
33. $(-1, -5)$ **35.** 1. $\overline{WX} \cong \overline{ZY}$, $\overline{WZ} \cong \overline{XY}$ (Given)
2. $WXYZ$ is $\square$. (Def. $\square$) 3. $\overline{WY} \cong \overline{ZX}$ (Given) 4. $WXYZ$ is rect. (If diag. of $\square$ are $\cong$, $\square$ is rect.) **37.** 1. $WXYZ$ is rhombus. (Given) 2. $\overline{ZX}$ bisects $\overline{XY}$. (Diag. of $\square$ bisect each other.) 3. $\overline{WV} \cong \overline{VY}$ (Def. seg. bis.) 4. $WV = VY$ (Def. $\cong$ seg.) 5. $WV = WR + RS$, $VY = VT + TY$ (Seg. Add. Post.) 6. R is midpt. of $\overline{WV}$. T is midpt. of $\overline{VY}$. (Given) 7. $\overline{WR} \cong \overline{RV}$, $\overline{VT} \cong \overline{TY}$ (Def. seg. bis.) 8. $WR = RV$, $VT = TY$ (Def. $\cong$ seg.) 9. $WV = 2RV$, $VY = 2VT$ (Subst.)

10. $2RV = 2VT$ (Subst.) 11. $RV = VT$ (Mult. Prop.)
12. $\overline{RV} \cong \overline{VT}$ (Def. $\cong$ seg.) 13. $\overline{WY} \perp \overline{ZX}$ (Diag. of rhom.
are $\perp$.) 14. $\angle SVR \cong \angle SVT$ (Def. $\perp$ lines) 15. $\overline{SV} \cong \overline{SV}$
(Reflex. Prop.) 16. $\triangle SVR \cong \triangle SVT$ (SAS) 17. $\overline{SR} \cong \overline{ST}$
(Corr. parts of $\cong$ $\triangle$s) 18. $\triangle RST$ is isos. (Def. isos. $\triangle$)
39. 1. $ABCD$ is square. (Given) 2. $\angle ADE$, $\angle CBA$, $\angle C$ and
$\angle A$ are rt. $\angle$s. (Def. square) 3. $m\angle ADE = 90$ (Def. rt. $\angle$)
4. $\overline{DB}$ bisects $\angle ADE$. (Diag. of rhom. bisect opp. $\angle$s.)
5. $m\angle EDF = \frac{1}{2}m\angle ADE$ (Def. $\angle$ bis.) 6. $m\angle EDF = $
$\frac{1}{2}(90) = 45$ (Subst.) 7. $\overline{EF} \perp \overline{BD}$ (Given) 8. $\angle DFE$ is a rt.
$\angle$. (Def. $\perp$ lines) 9. $m\angle DFE = 90$ (Def. rt. $\angle$)
10. $m\angle DFE + m\angle FED + m\angle EDF = 180$ ($\angle$ Sum Th.)
11. $90 + m\angle FED + 45 = 180$ (Subst.) 12. $m\angle FED = 45$
(Add. Prop.) 13. $\angle FED \cong \angle EDF$ (Def . $= \angle$s) 14. $\overline{DF} \cong$
$\overline{FE}$ (If $\angle$s of a $\triangle$ are $\cong$, sides opp. are $\cong$.) 15. Draw $\overline{EB}$.
(2 pt. determine a line.) 16. $\overline{EB} \cong \overline{EB}$ (Reflex. Prop.)
17. $\overline{FB} \cong \overline{BC}$ (Given) 18. $\triangle EFB \cong \triangle ECB$ (HL Th.)
19. $\overline{FE} \cong \overline{EC}$ (Corr. parts of $\cong$ $\triangle$s) 20. $DF = FE = EC$
(Trans. Prop.) **41.** A cube is made up of $\cong$ squares and a
square has all sides $\cong$, so $\overline{AE} \cong \overline{CG}$, $\overline{FE} \cong \overline{FG}$, and
$\overline{AB} \cong \overline{BC}$. A square is a rect., so all $\angle$s are rt. $\angle$s. Therefore, $\angle EFG \cong \angle ABC$ and $\overline{AC} \cong \overline{EG}$ by corr. parts of $\cong$
$\triangle$s. Thus, $ACGE$ is a rect.
43. 1. $ABCD$ is rhom. (Given) 2. $\overline{AB} \cong \overline{BC} \cong \overline{CD} \cong \overline{AD}$
(Def. rhom.) 3. $\overline{AC}$ and $\overline{BD}$ bisect each other. (Diag. of a
rhom. bisect each other.) 4. E is midpt. of $\overline{AC}$ and $\overline{BD}$. (Def.
seg. bis.) 5. $\overline{AE} \cong \overline{EC}$, $\overline{BE} \cong \overline{ED}$ (Def. midpt.) 6. $\triangle BEA \cong$
$\triangle BEC \cong \triangle DEC \cong \triangle DEA$ (SSS) 7. $\angle EAB \cong \angle EAD$,
$\angle ABE \cong \angle EBC$, $\angle BCE \cong ECD$, $\angle EDC \cong \angle EDA$ (Corr.
parts of $\cong$ $\triangle$s) 8. $\overline{AC}$ bisects $\angle BAD$ and $\angle BCD$, $\overline{BD}$ bisects
$\angle ABC$ and $\angle CDA$. (Def. $\angle$ bis.) **45.** 1. $ABCD$ is $\square$.
(Given) 2. $\overline{AB} \cong \overline{DC}$, $\overline{AD} \cong \overline{BC}$ (If quad. is $\square$ opp. sides
are $\cong$.) 3. $\overline{AB} \cong \overline{BC}$ (Given) 4. $\overline{AB} \cong \overline{BC} \cong \overline{DC} \cong \overline{AD}$
(Trans. Prop.) 5. $ABCD$ is a rhom. (Def. rhom.) **47.** yes: a,
b, c, e, f; no: d **49.** yes: a, c, e; no: b, d, f

Algebra Review
1. $x = \pm\sqrt{15}$ **3.** $y = \pm\frac{2}{3}$

Lesson 5-4 Try This
1. $m\angle F = m\angle G = 60$, $m\angle E = m\angle H = 120$ **2.** 27

Exercise Set 5-4
1. 33.5 **3.** 17.15 **5.** 5 **7.-9.** always **11.** never
13. 16, 64 **15.** 6 cm **17.** 1. $\overline{AB} \parallel \overline{CD}$, $\overline{AP}$ bisects $\angle A$.
(Given) 2. $\angle DAP \cong \angle PAB$ (Def. $\angle$ bis.) 3. $\angle PAB \cong$
$\angle DPA$ (If 2 $\parallel$ lines are cut by a trans., alt. int. $\angle$s
are $\cong$.) 4. $\angle DAP \cong \angle DPA$ (Trans. Prop.) 5. $\overline{DA} \cong \overline{DP}$
(Th. 4.2) 6. $\triangle APD$ is isos. (Def. isos. $\triangle$)
19. 1. $\triangle ABC$ is isos. with base $\overline{BC}$. (Given) 2. $\angle B \cong \angle C$
(Base $\angle$s of isos. $\triangle$ are $\cong$.) 3. $\angle AED \cong \angle B$ (Given)
4. $\overline{BC} \parallel \overline{ED}$ (Lines cut by a trans. and corr. $\angle$s are $\cong$, lines
are $\parallel$.) 5. $\angle C \cong \angle ADE$ (Lines cut by a trans., corr. $\angle$s
are $\cong$.) 6. $\angle AED \cong \angle ADE$ (Trans. Prop.) 7. $\overline{AE} \cong \overline{AD}$
(If $\angle$s of an isos. $\triangle$ are $\cong$, sides opp. are $\cong$.) 8. $AE =$
AD, $AB = AC$ (Def. $\cong$ seg.) 9. $AB = AE + EB$, $AC =$
$AD + DC$ (Seg. Add. Post.) 10. $AE + EB = AD + DC$
(Subst.) 11. $EB = DC$ (Add. Prop.) 12. $\overline{EB} \cong \overline{DC}$
(Def. $\cong$ seg.) 13. $BEDC$ is an isos. trap. with $\overline{BE} \cong \overline{CD}$.

(Def. isos. trap.) **21.** not isos. **23. a.** 1. Trap. $ABCD$
(Given) 2. $\overline{AD} \parallel \overline{BC}$ (Def. of trap.) 3. Draw $\overline{FE}$ through
$N \parallel$ to $\overline{AB}$. (Through a pt. not on a line, there exists 1 and
only 1 line $\parallel$ to the given line.) 4. $AFEB$ is a $\square$. (Def of $\square$)
5. $\angle FDN \cong \angle ECN$ (Alt. int. $\angle$s are $\cong$.) 6. N is midpt. of
$\overline{DC}$. (Given) 7. $\overline{DN} \cong \overline{CN}$ (A midpt. forms 2 $\cong$ seg.)
8. $\angle DNF \cong \angle CNE$ (Vert. $\angle$s.) 9. $\triangle DNF \cong \triangle CNE$ (ASA
Post.) 10. $\overline{DF} \cong \overline{CE}$, $\overline{FN} \cong \overline{EN}$ (CPCTC) 11. N is midpt. of
$\overline{FE}$. (Def. of midpt.) 12. $\overline{AF} \cong \overline{BE}$, $\overline{AB} \cong \overline{FE}$ (Opp. sides of
a $\square$ are $\cong$.) 13. M is midpt. of $\overline{AB}$. (Given) 14. $AM = \frac{1}{2}AB$,
$FN = \frac{1}{2}FE$; $MB = \frac{1}{2}AB$; $NE = \frac{1}{2}FE$ (Midpt. Th.) 15.
$AB = FE$ (Def. of $\cong$ seg.) 16. $\frac{1}{2}AB = \frac{1}{2}FE$ (Mult. Prop.)
17. $AM = FN$, $MB = NE$ (Subst.) 18. $\overline{AM} \cong \overline{FN}$,
$\overline{MB} \cong \overline{NE}$ (Def. of $\cong$.) 19. $AMNF$ and $MBEN$ are $\square$. (If one
pair of opp. sides of a quad. are both $\parallel$ and $\cong$, then it is a
$\square$.) 20. $\overline{MN} \parallel \overline{AD}$, $\overline{MN} \parallel \overline{BC}$ (Def. of $\square$) **b.** (Repeat steps
1–19.) 20. $\overline{AF} \cong \overline{MN}$, $\overline{BE} \cong \overline{MN}$ (Opp. sides of a $\square$ are
$\cong$.) 21. $MN = AF$, $MN = BE$, $DF = EC$ (Def. of $\cong$ seg.)
22. $2MN = AF + BE$ (Add. Prop.) 23. $MN = \frac{1}{2}(AF + BE)$
(Div. Prop.) 24. $MN = \frac{1}{2}(AD + DF + BE)$ (Seg. Add.
Post.) 25. $MN = \frac{1}{2}(AD + EC + BE)$ (Subst.) 26. $MN =$
$\frac{1}{2}(AD + BC)$ (Seg. Add. Post.) **25.** 1. Draw $\overline{DE} \parallel \overline{AB}$. (2 pt.
determine a line.) 2. $ABCD$ is trap. (Given) 3. $\overline{AD} \parallel \overline{BE}$ (Def.
trap.) 4. $ABED$ is $\square$. (Def. $\square$) 5. $m\angle B + m\angle DEC = 180$
(Consec. $\angle$s of a $\square$ are supp.) 6. $m\angle BED + m\angle DEC =$
180 (Linear Post.) 7. $\angle B \cong \angle DEC$ (Def. $\cong$ $\angle$s) 8. $\angle B \cong$
$\angle C$ (Given) 9. $\angle DEC \cong \angle C$ (Trans. Prop.) 10. $\overline{DE} \cong \overline{DC}$
(If $\angle$s of $\triangle$ are $\cong$, sides opp. are $\cong$.) 12. $\overline{DC} \cong \overline{AB}$ (Trans.
Prop.) 13. $ABCD$ is isos. trap. (Def. isos. trap.) **27.** 3; P
must be equidistant from A, B, and C.

Mixed Review
1. 720 **2.** 120 **3.** 60

Lesson 5-5 Try This
1. 24, 12 **2.** 15

Exercise Set 5-5
1. 20 **3.** 16 **5.** 32 **7.** 16 **9.** 16 **11.** no **13.** 40
15. 13 **17.** $a = 3.5$ **19.** Th. 5.20; if 3 or more $\parallel$ lines
cut off $\cong$ seg. on 1 trans., they will cut off $\cong$ seg. on every
trans. **21.** $X = (0, 3)$, $Y = (-4, 5)$, $XY = \sqrt{20} =$
$2\sqrt{5}$, $BC = \sqrt{80} = 4\sqrt{5}$, $2\sqrt{5} = \frac{1}{2}(4\sqrt{5})$ **23.** Locate
midpt. of XZ and YZ, then find the distance between those 2
midpt. Apply the Midseg. Th. to find XY, which is twice the
distance between the midpt. of XZ and YZ. **25.** $MN = 5$,
$AB = 10$ **27.** $EC = 11\frac{1}{5}$ **29.** 1. $\overline{AB} \cong \overline{AC}$ (Given) 2. E is
midpt. of $\overline{AB}$. D is midpt. of $\overline{CB}$. (Given) 3. $\overline{AC} \parallel \overline{DE}$ (Midseg. Th.) 4. $2DE = AC$ (Midseg. Th.) 5. $2EB = AB$ (Def.
midpt.) 6. $2DE = 2EB$ (Trans. Prop.) 7. $DE = EB$ (Mult.
Prop.) 8. $\overline{DE} \cong \overline{EB}$ (Def. $\cong$ seg.) 9. $\triangle BDE$ is isos. (Def.
isos. $\triangle$) **31.** 1. D is midpt. of $\overline{AB}$. E is midpt of $\overline{AC}$.
(Given) 2. Draw $\overline{DF}$ so $DE = EF$. (Ruler Post.) 3. $AE = CE$
(Def. midpt.) 4. $ADCF$ is $\square$. (Th. 5.8) 5. $\overline{AD} \cong \overline{FC}$
(Th. 5.1) 6. $AD = FC$ (Def. $\cong$) 7. $AD = DB$ (Def. midpt.)
8. $FC = DB$ (Subst.) 9. $\overline{BD} \parallel \overline{CF}$ (Def. $\square$) 10. $DBCF$ is $\square$.
(Th. 5.8) 11. $\overline{DE} \parallel \overline{BC}$ (Def. $\square$) 12. $DE + EF = DF$ (Seg.
Add. Post.) 13. $2DE = DF$ (Subst.) 14. $\overline{DF} \cong \overline{BC}$ (Th. 5.1)
15. $DF = BC$ (Def. $\cong$) 16. $2DE = BC$ (Trans. Prop.)

17. $DE = \frac{1}{2}BC$ (Div.) **33.** 6 **35.** 1. $\overrightarrow{AD} \parallel \overrightarrow{BE} \parallel \overrightarrow{CF}$
(Given) 2. Draw $\overrightarrow{DX} \parallel \overline{AB}$ with X on $\overline{BE}$ and $\overrightarrow{EY} \parallel \overrightarrow{AC}$ with Y
on $\overline{CF}$. (Post. 15) 3. $ABXD$, $BCYE$ are $\square$s. (Def. $\square$)
4. $\overline{AB} \cong \overline{DX}$, $\overline{BC} \cong \overline{EY}$ (Th. 5.1) 5. $\overline{AB} \cong \overline{BC}$ (Given)
6. $\overline{DX} \cong \overline{EY}$ (Subst.) 7. $\angle DEX \cong \angle EFY$ (Post. 13)
8. $\angle DAB \cong \angle EBC$ (Post. 13) 9. $\angle DAB \cong \angle EBC$,
$\angle EBC \cong \angle EYC$ (Th. 5.2) 10. $\angle DXB \cong \angle EYC$ (Subst.)
11. $\angle DXE \cong \angle EYF$ ($\cong$ Supp. Th.) 12. $\triangle DXE \cong \triangle EYF$
(AAS $\cong$) 13. $\overline{DE} \cong \overline{EF}$ (CPCTC) **37.** yes

Lesson 5-6 Try This

1. $\overline{AB}$ does not intersect $\overline{CD}$. **2.** b and c

Exercise Set 5-6

1. $\angle A$ is not supp. to $\angle B$. **3.** $\angle A$ and $\angle B$ are vert. $\angle$s.
5. $\triangle ABC$ is an equilat. $\triangle$. **7.** yes **9.** yes **11.** yes **13.** It
follows that $AC \cong AB$ by corr. parts of $\cong \triangle$s. This contradicts the fact that $AC \ne AB$. The assumption $\overline{AD} \perp \overline{BC}$ must
be false. Therefore, $\overline{AD} \perp \overline{BC}$. **15.** Assume $\angle 3 \cong \angle 5$.
Then $a \parallel b$ since corr. $\angle$s are $\cong$. This contradicts the fact
that $a \nparallel b$. The assumption must be false. Therefore,
$\angle 3 \ncong \angle 5$. **17.** Assume $\overline{BC} \cong \overline{CD}$. Since it is given that
$\overline{AB} \cong \overline{AD}$ and $\overline{AC} \cong \overline{AC}$, by Reflex. Prop. conclude
$\triangle ABC \cong \triangle ADC$. Then $\angle 1 \cong \angle 2$ because corr. parts
of $\cong \triangle$s. This contradicts fact $\angle 1 \ncong \angle 2$. The assumption
$\overline{BC} \cong \overline{CD}$ is false. Therefore, $\overline{BC} \ncong \overline{CD}$. **19.** Assume
$\overline{AC} \perp \overline{BD}$. Then $\angle ACB \cong \angle ACD$. Since $\overline{AC}$ is a median,
$\overline{BC} \cong \overline{CD}$ because a median of a $\triangle$ divides base into
2 $\cong$ seg. $\overline{AC} \cong \overline{AC}$ by Reflex. Prop. Conclude $\triangle ACB \cong$
$\triangle ACD$ by SAS. Then $\overline{AB} \cong \overline{AD}$ by corr. parts of $\cong \triangle$s.
This contradicts fact $\triangle ABD$ is scalene. The assumption
$\overline{AC} \perp \overline{BC}$ must be false. Therefore, $\overline{AC} \perp \overline{BD}$. **21.** Assume
$\overline{MN} \cong \overline{QP}$. Since $\overline{MN} \perp \overline{NP}$ and $\overline{QP} \perp \overline{NP}$, $\angle MNP$ and
$\angle QPN$ are rt. $\angle$s. $\angle MNP \cong \angle QPN$ because all rt. $\angle$s are
$\cong$. $\overline{NP} \cong \overline{NP}$ by the Reflex. Prop. Then $\triangle MNP \cong \triangle QPN$
by SAS. $\angle M \cong \angle Q$ since corr. parts of $\cong \triangle$s are $\cong$. This
contradicts fact $\angle M \ncong \angle Q$. The assumption $\overline{MN} \cong \overline{QP}$
must be false. Therefore, $\overline{MN} \ncong \overline{QP}$. **23.** Assume $\angle BAC \cong$
$\angle DAC$. Since $\overline{AC} \perp M$, $\overline{AC} \perp \overline{BC}$ and $\overline{AC} \perp \overline{CD}$ because a
line $\perp$ to a plane is $\perp$ to every line in the plane. Then
$\angle ACB$ and $\angle ACD$ are rt. $\angle$s and $\cong$ since all rt. $\angle$s are $\cong$.
$\overline{AC} \cong \overline{AC}$ by Reflex. Prop. $\triangle ACB \cong \triangle ACD$ by ASA. Then
$\angle B \cong \angle D$ by corr. parts of $\cong \triangle$s. This contradicts
fact $\angle B \ncong \angle D$. The assumption $\angle BAC \cong \angle DAC$
must be false. Therefore, $\angle BAC \ncong \angle DAC$.
25. Given: $\overline{BC} \perp \overline{AD}$, $\overline{AB}$ and $\overline{AD}$ are sides of $\angle BAD$.
Prove: $\overline{BC} \not\perp \overline{AB}$. Proof: Assume $\overline{BC} \perp \overline{AB}$. Since
$\overline{BC} \perp \overline{AD}$, $\overline{AB} \parallel \overline{AD}$ by Th. 3.8. This contradicts the given
information, so the assumption must be false. Therefore,
$\overline{BC} \not\perp \overline{AB}$. **27.** Given: $\triangle ABC$ in plane M, D not in plane
M Prove: $\overline{BD}$ is skew to $\overline{AC}$. Proof: Assume $\overline{BD}$ is not skew
to $\overline{AC}$. Then $\overline{BD}$ and $\overline{AC}$ are coplanar. Therefore, D would be
in same plane as ABC. This contradicts fact that D is not in
plane M. Therefore, $\overline{BD}$ is skew to $\overline{AC}$.

Mixed Review

1. 125 **3.** 80

5. sometimes true  yes   no

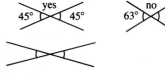
Lesson 5-7 Try This

1. $\angle C$ **2.** $\overline{CD}$ **3.** a and c

Exercise Set 5-7

1. $\overline{AB}$, $\overline{BC}$, $\overline{AC}$ **3.** $\overline{MQ}$, $\overline{QP}$, $\overline{NP}$, $\overline{MN}$ **5.** $\overline{BC}$, $\overline{AC}$, $\overline{AB}$
7. $\overline{BC}$, $\overline{AC}$, $\overline{AB}$ **9.** $\angle C$, $\angle B$, $\angle A$ **11.** $\overline{AC}$, $\overline{BA}$, $\overline{BC}$, $\overline{BD}$,
$\overline{DC}$, $\overline{DE}$, $\overline{CE}$ **13.** yes **15.** no **17.** no **19.** 6
21. $m\angle 6 > m\angle 1$ **23.** $m\angle 2 > m\angle 4$ **25.** a possible, no;
b possible, no; c possible, yes; d not possible; e not possible
27. $< x$ and $> 10 - x$ **29.** 1. $m\angle 1 > m\angle EDC$ (Ext. $\angle$
Inequal. Th.) 2. $m\angle EDC > m\angle 2$ (Ext. $\angle$ Inequal. Th.)
3. $m\angle 1 > m\angle 2$ (Trans. Prop.) **31.** 1. Draw $\overline{AC}$.
(2 pt. determine a line.) 2. $AB + BC > AC$ ($\triangle$ Inequal. Th.)
3. $AB + BC + CD > AC + CD$ (Add. Prop.) 4. $AC +$
$CD > AD$ ($\triangle$ Inequal. Th.) 5. $AB + BC + CD > AD$
(Trans. Prop.) **33.** 1. Suppose $\overline{PQ}$ is not shortest seg. from
P to ℓ. (Indirect proof assumption) 2. Choose N on ℓ such
that $PN < PQ$. ($\overline{PQ}$ is not shortest seg. to ℓ.) 3. $\overline{PQ} \perp \ell$
(Given) 4. $\angle PQN$ is a rt. $\angle$. (Def. $\perp$) 5. $m\angle PQN = 90$
(Def. rt. $\angle$.) 6. $m\angle P + m\angle PNQ + m\angle PQN = 180$
($\angle$ Sum Th.) 7. $m\angle P + m\angle PNQ = 90$ (Add. Prop.)
8. $m\angle PNQ < 90$ (Def. $<$) 10. $PQ < PN$ (If 1 $\angle$ of $\triangle$ is
larger than a second $\angle$, the side opp. larger $\angle$ is $>$ than side
opp. smaller $\angle$.) 11. $\overline{PQ}$ is shortest segment from P to ℓ.
(Indirect logic) **35.** $138 + 46\sqrt{3}$ km; the intersection of
$\overline{AC}$ and $\overline{BD}$. **37.** $\angle A$ **39.** $\angle B$ **41.** Assume 1 side, $\overline{BC}$, is
longer than, or at least as long as, the other 2 sides, $\overline{AC}$ and
$\overline{AB}$. Then statements 1 and 2 are true. Draw $\overline{AD} \perp \overline{BC}$, using fact that from a pt. not on a line a $\perp$ be drawn to the
line. Since $\angle ADB$ and $\angle ADC$ are rt. $\angle$s, $AB > BD$ and
$AC > DC$. Thus $AB + AC > BD + DC$. Conclude $AB +$
$AC > BC$. **43.** 1. $\triangle ABC$; $\overline{AD}$, $\overline{BE}$, and $\overline{CF}$ are alt. (Given)
2. $\overline{AD} \perp \overline{CD}$, $\overline{CF} \perp \overline{AF}$, $\overline{BE} \perp \overline{AC}$ (Def. alt.) 3. $AB > AD$,
$BC > BE$, $AC > CF$ ($\perp$ seg. from pt. to line is shortest seg-
ment from pt. to line.) 4. $AB + BC + AC > AD + BE +$
CF (Add Prop.) **45.** 3, 4, 5; 2, 5, 5; 4, 4, 4

Algebra Review

1. $-7, 7$ **3.** $-7, 7$ **5.** $-\frac{7}{2}, \frac{7}{2}$ **7.** $-6, 6$ **9.** 8 **11.** $-7\frac{1}{2}$,
$6\frac{1}{2}$

Exercise Set 5-8

1. $AC > AB$ **3.** $m\angle 2 > m\angle 1$ **5.** never **7.** always
9. never **11.** 1. $\overline{AB} \cong \overline{CD}$ (Given) 2. $\overline{BC} \cong \overline{BC}$ (Reflex.
Prop.) 3. $m\angle ABC > m\angle BCD$ (Given) 4. $AC > BD$ (SAS
Inequal. Th.) **13.** 1. $\overline{AC}$ is a median. (Given) 2. $\overline{BC} \cong \overline{CD}$
(Def. median) 3. $m\angle 1 > m\angle 2$ (Given) 4. $\overline{AC} \cong \overline{AC}$
(Reflex. Prop.) 5. $AB > AD$ (SAS Inequal. Th.)

15. $\overline{CD} > \overline{BC}$, $m\angle B > m\angle D$ **17.** $m\angle A < m\angle D$
19. 1. $AC < BC$, $AE = BF$, D is midpt. of $\overline{AB}$. (Given)
2. $m\angle A > m\angle B$ (If 1 side of $\triangle$ is longer than second side, the measure of $\angle$ opp. longer side is $>$ measure of $\angle$ opp. shorter side.) 3. $BD = AD$ (Def. midpt.) 4. $DF < DE$ (SAS Inequal. Th.) **21.** 1. $RU > RT$, $\overline{VU} \cong \overline{ST}$ (Given)
2. $m\angle RTU > m\angle RUT$ (If 1 side of $\triangle$ is longer than second side, the measure of $\angle$ opp. longer side is $> \angle$ opp. shorter side.) 3. $\overline{TU} \cong \overline{TU}$ (Reflex. Prop.) 4. $SU > TV$ (SAS Inequal. Th.) **23.** 1. $m\angle MNQ > m\angle MNP$, $\overline{NP} \cong \overline{NQ}$ (Given) 2. $MN = MN$ (Reflex. Prop.) 3. $MQ > MP$ (If 1 $\angle$ of $\triangle$ is $>$ than second $\angle$, side opp. $> \angle$ is longer than side opp. $< \angle$.) 4. $m\angle MPQ > m\angle MQP$ (If 1 side of $\triangle$ is longer than second side, the measure of $\angle$ opp. longer side is $> \angle$ opp. shorter side. **25.** 1. $m\angle 1 = m\angle 2$ (Given) 2. $\overline{BE} \cong \overline{EC}$ (If $\angle$s of $\triangle$ are $\cong$, sides opp. are $\cong$.) 3. $\overline{AE} \cong \overline{AE}$ (Reflex. Prop.) 4. $m\angle 3 + m\angle AEB = m\angle 4 + m\angle AEC = 180$ (Def. linear pair) 5. $m\angle 3 + m\angle AEB = m\angle 4 + m\angle AEC$ (Trans. Prop.) 6. $m\angle 3 > m\angle 4$ (Given) 7. $m\angle AEB < m\angle AEC$ (Algebra) 8. $AC > AB$ (SAS Inequal. Th.)
27. 1. $\overleftrightarrow{AC} \perp$ plane N, $AD > AB$ (Given) 2. Let E be on $\overleftrightarrow{CD}$ so that $BC = CE$. (Construction) 3. $\overline{AC} \cong \overline{AC}$ (Reflex. Prop.) 4. $\angle ACB$ and $\angle ACE$ are rt. $\angle$s (Def. $\perp$) 5. $\angle ACB \cong \angle ACE$ (All rt. $\angle$s are $\cong$.) 6. $\triangle ACB \cong \triangle ACE$ (SAS) 7. $\overline{AB} \cong \overline{AE}$, $AB = AE$ (CPCTC, Def. $\cong$) 8. $AD > AE$ (Subst.) 9. $AC^2 = AD^2 - CD^2 = AE^2 - CE^2$ (Pythagorean Th.) 10. $AD^2 - AE^2 = CD^2 - CE^2$ (Add. Prop.) 11. $AD^2 - AE^2 > 0$ ($AD > AE$) 12. $CD^2 - CE^2 > 0$ (Subst.) 13. $CD > CE$ (Algebra) 14. $CD > BC$ (Subst.) **29.** Since $\triangle ABC$ is equilat., $\overline{AB} \cong \overline{BC} \cong \overline{CA}$. $\angle PAB$ and $\angle PAC$ are rt. $\angle$s since $\overline{PA} \perp \overline{AB}$ and $\overline{PA} \perp \overline{AC}$. In rt. $\triangle$, other 2 angles are acute, so $PB > PA$, $PB > AB$, $PC > BC$, and $PC > CA$, because side of $\triangle$ opp. $> \angle$ is longer than side opp. $< \angle$. Therefore, since $\angle PAB \cong \angle PAB$, the longest side is $\overline{PB}$ or $\overline{PC}$.

Algebra Review

1. 6 **3.** ± 8

Chapter Review

1. 32 **2.** 55, 125 **3.** RA **4.** 8 **5.** 65 **6.** Yes, if both pairs of opp. $\angle$s are $\cong$, then the quad is $\square$. **7.** Yes, if diag. bisect each other, then quad. is $\square$. **8.** Yes, 2 $\triangle$s are $\cong$ by SAS, so opp. sides are $\cong$ and quad. is $\square$. **9.** Yes, if both pairs of opp. sides are $\parallel$, then quad. is $\square$. **10.** always **11.** sometimes **12.** always **13.** sometimes **14.** bases **15.** 35 **16.** 10 **17.** 17 **18.** false **19.** true **20.** true **21.** false **22.** $\angle ABC$ is not an obtuse $\angle$. **23.** contradiction **24.** $\overline{ST}$, $\overline{RT}$, $\overline{RS}$ **25.** $\angle Y$ **26.** 4, 10 **27.** $EF = FG$ **28.** $DE < DG$ **29.** $DE > FG$

CHAPTER 6

Lesson 6-1 Try This
1. a. $\frac{3}{5}$ **b.** $\frac{10}{9}$ **2.** $\frac{15}{7}$ **3. a.** yes **b.** no **c.** yes **4. a.** 5 **b.** 3

Exercise Set 6-1
1. $\frac{5}{7}$ **3.** $\frac{16}{9}$ **5.** $\frac{y}{21}$ **7.** $\frac{3}{5}$ **9.** $\frac{5}{6}$ **11.** yes **13.** yes **15.** 12 **17.** $\frac{75}{8}$ **19.** $\frac{3}{2} = \frac{6}{4}$, $\frac{4}{2} = \frac{6}{3}$ **21.** $\frac{3}{4} = \frac{9}{12}$, $\frac{3}{2} = \frac{12}{4}$ **23.** $\frac{2}{3}$ **25.** 60, 120 **27.** $\frac{4}{9}$ **29.** $\frac{5}{2}$ **31.** $\frac{AD}{DB} = \frac{\sqrt{5}}{2\sqrt{5}} = \frac{AE}{EC} = \frac{\sqrt{2}}{2\sqrt{2}} = \frac{1}{2}$ **33.** Answers may vary. $\frac{AD}{AB} = \frac{DE}{BC} = \frac{\sqrt{5}}{3\sqrt{5}} = \frac{1}{3}$, $\frac{AB}{AC} = \frac{AD}{AE} = \frac{\sqrt{5}}{\sqrt{2}} = \frac{\sqrt{10}}{2}$ **35.** $\frac{1+x}{1} = \frac{1}{x}$, $x^2 + x = 1$, $x^2 + x - 1 = 0$, $x = 1 - x^2$ $x = (1-x)(1+x)$, $\frac{x}{1-x} = \frac{1+x}{1}$, $\frac{1+x}{1} = \frac{x}{1-x} = \frac{DF}{AD} = \frac{FH}{HC}$ **37.** You cannot draw a diag. from vert. to itself or to its 2 adjac. vert. So no. of diag. $= n - 3$. $\frac{n-3}{360} = \frac{2}{7}$, $7n - 21 = 720$, $7n = 741$, $n = \frac{741}{7}$, not a whole no. The proposition is contradictory since the poly. must have a whole no. for no. of sides.

Mixed Review
1. 56 **3.** 68 **5.** 56

Lesson 6-2 Try This
1. $\frac{3}{18} = \frac{7}{42}$, $\frac{42}{7} = \frac{18}{3}$, $\frac{7}{3} = \frac{42}{18}$, $\frac{10}{7} = \frac{60}{42}$, $-\frac{4}{7} = -\frac{24}{42}$ **2. a.** $\frac{13}{5}$ **b.** $\frac{y+8}{8}$ **3.** 1. $\frac{AB}{AD} = \frac{AC}{AE}$ (Given) 2. $\frac{AB - AD}{AD} = \frac{AC - AE}{AE}$ (Prop. of Propor.) 3. $\frac{BD}{AD} = \frac{CE}{AE}$ (Seg. Add. Post.)

Exercise Set 6-2
1. $\frac{7}{14} = \frac{8}{16}$, $\frac{16}{8} = \frac{14}{7}$, $\frac{8}{7} = \frac{16}{14}$, $\frac{15}{8} = \frac{30}{16}$, $-\frac{1}{8} = -\frac{2}{16}$ **3.** $\frac{5}{125} = \frac{3}{75}$, $\frac{75}{3} = \frac{5}{5}$, $\frac{8}{5} = \frac{75}{125}$, $\frac{8}{3} = \frac{200}{75}$, $\frac{2}{3} = \frac{50}{75}$ **5.** $\frac{u}{v} = \frac{8}{9}$, $\frac{9}{8} = \frac{v}{u}$, $\frac{8}{u} = \frac{9}{v}$, $\frac{u+8}{8} = \frac{v+9}{9}$, $\frac{u-8}{8} = \frac{v-9}{9}$ **7.** $\frac{4}{y}$ **9.** $\frac{x+y}{y}$ **11.** $\frac{4}{3}$ **13.** 1. $\frac{LQ}{QM} = \frac{LR}{RN}$ (Given) 2. $\frac{QM}{LQ} = \frac{RN}{LR}$ (Prop. of Propor.) **15.** 1. $\frac{LQ}{QM} = \frac{LR}{RN}$ (Given) 2. $\frac{QM}{LQ} = \frac{RN}{LR}$ (Prop. of Propor.) 3. $\frac{QM + LQ}{LQ} = \frac{RN + LR}{LR}$ (Prop. of Propor.) 4. $\frac{LM}{LQ} = \frac{LN}{LR}$ (Seg. Add. Post.) **17** 1. $\frac{LQ}{QM} = \frac{LR}{RN}$ (Given) 2. $\frac{QM}{LQ} = \frac{RN}{LR}$ (Prop. of Propor.) 3. $\frac{LQ + QM}{LQ} = \frac{RN + LR}{LR}$ (Prop. of Propor.) **19.** $\frac{b}{a}$ **21.** $\frac{u}{v}$ **23.** $\frac{u + 2v}{v}$ **25.** 5 **27.** $\frac{8}{5}$ **29.** 4, -1 **31.** 3, -3 **33.** 30, 21, 45 **35.** 14, 18, 39 **37.** 9, 12, 16 **39.** 28, 15, 27 **41.** 10, 16, 15 **43.** 1. $\frac{a}{b} = \frac{c}{d}$ (Given) 2. $ad = bc$ (Means/Extr.) 3. $\frac{a}{c} = \frac{b}{d}$ (Conv. of Means/Extr.) **45.** 1. $\frac{a}{b} = \frac{c}{d}$ (Given) 2. $bc = ad$ (Means/Extr.) 3. $\frac{b}{a} = \frac{d}{c}$ (Conv. of Means/Extr.) **47.** 1. $\frac{a}{b} = \frac{c}{d}$ (Given) 2. $ad = bc$ (Means/Extr.) 3. $ad - bd = bc - bd$ (Sub. Prop.) 4. $(a - b)d = b(c - d)$ (Dist. Prop.) 5. $\frac{a-b}{b} = \frac{c-d}{d}$ (Conv. of Means/Extr.) **49.** $7\frac{1}{2}$ in. by $12\frac{1}{2}$ in. **51.** 78 ft **53.** 3, 6, 4, 8 **55.** 12, 6, 6, 3 **57.** $\frac{a}{b} = \frac{a + c + e + g \ldots}{b + d + f + h \ldots}$ **59.** Sometimes true; only if terms are added within ratio itself and not across $=$ sign do new ratios form a propor.

Mixed Review
1. 34 **3.** 68 **5.** 118 **7.** 64 **9.** 46 **11.** 26 **13.** 1. $\triangle PQR$ is isos. (Given) 2. $\overline{PQ} \cong \overline{PR}$ (Def. isos. $\triangle$) 3. $\overline{PT}$ is an alt. (Given) 4. $\overline{PT}$ bisects $\angle QPR$. (In isos. $\triangle$ the alt. to the base bisects the vertex $\angle$.) 5. $\angle QPS \cong \angle RPS$ (An $\angle$ bis. forms 2 $\cong \angle$s.) 6. $\overline{PS} \cong \overline{PS}$ (Reflex. Prop.) 7. $\triangle PQS \cong \triangle PRS$ (SAS)

Lesson 6-3 Try This

8

Exercise Set 6-3

1. $\angle E$ 3. $\angle U$ 5. $\frac{6}{5}$ 7. $\frac{5}{6}$ 9. 30 11. $\angle C$ 13. $\frac{84}{5}$
15. $\frac{70}{3}$ 17. $\frac{5}{3}$ 19. $\frac{3}{5}$ 21. 32 23. $\angle P$ 25. 15 27. 8
29. (3, 2) or (3, 4) 31. $C'(-2, 1\frac{1}{2})$, $D'(-2, 3\frac{1}{2})$; $C'(-4, 1\frac{1}{2})$, $D'(-4, 3\frac{1}{2})$ 33. 18 35. 24 37. 52 39. $\frac{56}{9}$
41. 1. $\overline{AB} \parallel \overline{DE}$ (Given) 2. $\angle CDE \cong \angle A$, $\angle CED \cong \angle B$ (When $\parallel$ lines are cut by a trans., corr. $\angle$s are $\cong$.) 3. $\angle C \cong \angle C$ (Reflex. Prop.) 4. $CD + DA = CA = 9$, $CE + EB = CB = 12$ (Seg. Add.) 5. $\frac{6}{9} = \frac{8}{12} = \frac{12}{18}$ (Prop. of Propor.)
6. $\frac{CD}{CA} = \frac{CE}{CB} = \frac{DE}{AB}$ (Subst.) 7. $\triangle ABC \sim \triangle DEC$ (Def. $\sim \triangle$s) 43. x 45. $x\sqrt{2}$ 47. 1. $\triangle ACD$ and $\triangle ABC$ are rt. $\angle$s. $y = x\sqrt{2}$ (Given) 2. $\angle ADC \cong \angle ACB$ (All rt. $\angle$s are $\cong$.) 3. $\angle A \cong \angle A$ (Reflex. Prop.) 4. $\angle ACD \cong \angle ABC$ (If 2 $\angle$s of one $\triangle$ are $\cong$ to 2 $\angle$s of another $\triangle$, the third $\angle$s are $\cong$.) 5. $m\angle ACD = m\angle ABC = 45$ (Acute $\angle$s of rt. $\triangle$ are comp.) 6. $CD = x$, $CB = y = x\sqrt{2}$ (If 2 $\angle$s of $\triangle$ are $\cong$, sides opp. are $\cong$.) 7. $m\angle DCB = 45$ (Acute $\angle$s of rt. $\triangle$ are comp.) 8. $DB = x$ (If 2 $\angle$s of $\triangle$ are $\cong$, sides opp. are $\cong$.)
9. $AB = AD + DB = x + x = 2x$ (Seg. Add. Post.) 10. $\frac{AC}{CD} = \frac{CB}{CB} = \frac{AD}{AC} = \frac{1}{\sqrt{2}}$ (Subst.) 11. $\triangle ACD \sim \triangle ABC$ (Def. $\sim \triangle$s)
49. always true 51. sometimes true 53. a. 3, 5, 7, 9, 11 b. 4, 7, 10, 13, 16 c. 2, 7, 12, 17, 22

Algebra Review

1. $x + (x + 12) + (x + 24) = 180$; 48, 60, 72
3. $3x + 4x + 6x = 39$; 9, 12, 18
5. $2x + 4x + 7x + 11x = 360$; 30, 60, 105, 165

Lesson 6-4 Try This

1. 18, 15 2. $\frac{75}{8}$

Exercise Set 6-4

1. $\triangle AED$ 3. 8 5. 10 7. $\frac{20}{3}$, 9 9. $\triangle ABE \sim \triangle ACD$, 4, 5 11. $\triangle ZXY \sim \triangle WXZ \sim \triangle WZY$, $\frac{64}{15}$, $\frac{136}{15}$ 13. 1. $\angle ABC$ and $\angle BDC$ are rt. $\angle$s. (Given) 2. $\angle ABC \cong \angle BDC$ (All rt. $\angle$ are $\cong$.) 3. $\angle C \cong \angle C$ (Reflex. Prop.) 4. $\triangle ABC \sim \triangle BDC$ (Th. 6.3) 15. 1. $\angle ADB$, $\angle DEC$, and $\angle ABC$ are rt. $\angle$s. (Given) 2. $\triangle ABC$, $\triangle DEC$, $\triangle ADB$ are rt. $\triangle$s. (Def. rt. $\triangle$s) 3. $\angle A \cong \angle A$, $\angle C \cong \angle C$ (Reflex. Prop.) 4. $\triangle ABC \sim \triangle ADB$, $\triangle ABC \sim \triangle DEC$ (Th. 6.3) 5. $\triangle ADB \sim \triangle DEC$ (Trans. Prop.) 17. $134\frac{5}{14}$ ft 19. 75 m 21. 1. $\overline{AB} \parallel \overline{ED}$ (Given) 2. $\angle 3 \cong \angle 4$ ($\parallel$ lines cut by trans., alter. int. $\angle$s are $\cong$.) 3. $\angle 1 \cong \angle 2$ (Vert. $\angle$s are $\cong$.) 4. $\triangle ABC \sim \triangle EDC$ (AA) 5. $\frac{AB}{ED} = \frac{BC}{DC}$ (Def. $\sim \triangle$s) 23. $\triangle DFE \sim \triangle CFB$, $\frac{16}{3}$, $\frac{63}{4}$ 25. When diag. $\overline{OT}$ passes through M, then $\triangle OMN$ and $\triangle OTU$ are $\sim$ as they are both rt. $\triangle$s and share $\angle MON$.
27. similar 29. Given: $\overline{AB} \parallel \overline{A'B'}$ Prove: $\triangle LAB \sim \triangle LB'A'$ 1. $\overline{AB} \parallel \overline{A'B'}$ (Given) 2. $\angle B' \cong \angle A$, $\angle B \cong \angle A'$ ($\parallel$ lines cut by trans., alter. int. $\angle$s are $\cong$.) 3. $\triangle LAB \sim \triangle LB'A'$ (Post. 19) 31. $\frac{x}{20} = \frac{AB}{A'B'}$, $A'B' = \frac{20\,AB}{x}$
33. halved 35. 1. $\angle A$, $\angle C$ are rt. $\angle$s. (Given) 2. $\angle A \cong \angle C$ (All rt. $\angle$s are $\cong$.) 3. $\triangle AEB$ is isos. (Given)
4. $\angle EAB \cong \angle EBA$ (Isos. $\triangle$ Th.) 5. $\triangle DAB \sim \triangle FCA$ (Post. 19) 6. $\frac{AD}{CF} = \frac{BD}{AF}$ (Lengths of sides of $\sim \triangle$s are in propor.)
7. $AD \cdot AF = CF \cdot BD$ (Prop. of Propor.) 37. 1. $\overline{AB} \cong \overline{AC}$ (Given) 2. $\angle ABC \cong \angle C$ (Isos. $\triangle$ Th.) 3. $\angle A \cong \angle CBD$

(Given) 4. $\triangle ABC \sim \triangle BDC$ (Post. 19) 5. $\frac{AC}{BD} = \frac{BC}{CD}$
(Def. $\sim \triangle$s) 6. $AB = AC$ (Def. $\cong$ seg.) 7. $\frac{AB}{BD} = \frac{BC}{CD}$
(Subst.) 39. 12 41. 108°: $\angle ABC$, $\angle BCD$, $\angle CDE$, $\angle DEA$, $\angle EAB$, $\angle EJA$, $\angle AFB$, $\angle BGC$, $\angle CHD$, $\angle DIE$, $\angle DJB$, $\angle EFC$, $\angle AGD$, $\angle BHE$, $\angle CIA$; 36°: $\angle EAJ$, $\angle JAF$, $\angle FAB$, $\angle ABF$, $\angle FBG$, $\angle GBC$, $\angle BCG$, $\angle GCH$, $\angle HCD$, $\angle CDH$, $\angle HDI$, $\angle IDE$, $\angle DEI$, $\angle IEJ$, $\angle JEA$; 72°: $\angle AJB$, $\angle AFE$, $\angle BFC$, $\angle BGA$, $\angle CGD$, $\angle CHB$, $\angle DHE$, $\angle DIC$, $\angle EIA$, $\angle EJD$, $\angle EAC$, $\angle DAB$, $\angle ABD$, $\angle EBC$, $\angle BCE$, $\angle ACD$, $\angle CDA$, $\angle BDE$, $\angle DEB$, $\angle CEA$ 43. $\frac{EJ}{EF} = \frac{EF}{EB}$, $\frac{x}{1} = \frac{1}{1+x}$, $x + x^2 = 1$, $x^2 + x - 1 = 0$. By the quad. eq. $x = \frac{-1 \pm \sqrt{5}}{2}$. So that $x > 0$, $x = \frac{-1 + \sqrt{5}}{2}$.

Mixed Review

1. If 2 $\triangle$s are equilat., then they are $\sim$. 3. If 2 $\triangle$s are not $\sim$, then they are not equilat. 5. Any 2 $\sim \triangle$s with scale factor $\neq 1$ are $\not\cong$.

Lesson 6-5 Try This

1. $\frac{AB}{XY} = \frac{AC}{XZ}$ 2. $\frac{2}{1}$ 3. $x = 6 = AD = AE$, $BC = AC = 9$

Exercise Set 6-5

1. $\frac{126}{11}$ or $\frac{198}{7}$, SAS 3. $\frac{21}{5}$, SAS 5. $\frac{95}{4}$ or $\frac{76}{5}$, SAS 7. $\frac{25}{4}$, SAS 9. $\frac{14}{3}$, SAS or SSS 11. $\frac{UA}{RB} = \frac{UZ}{RN}$ 13. $\frac{XY}{UV} = \frac{YZ}{VW} = \frac{XZ}{UW}$ 15. no 17. 1. $\frac{AO}{CO} = \frac{BO}{DO}$ (Given) 2. $\angle 1 \cong \angle 2$ (Vert. $\angle$s are $\cong$.) 3. $\triangle AOB \sim \triangle COD$ (SAS) 4. $\angle B \cong \angle D$ (Def. $\sim \triangle$s) 19. $\frac{12}{5}$ 21. 2.1 m 23. $\frac{DC}{AC} = \frac{FC}{EC} = \frac{DF}{AE}$
25. Increase by ≈ 0.74 ft. 27. $\triangle ABF \sim \triangle ACE$
29. none 31. none 33. $WY = 3XZ$ since $\triangle WOY \sim \triangle XOZ$ by SAS and $\frac{WY}{XZ} = \frac{OW}{OX} = 3$. 35. $\frac{DE}{CB} = \frac{DF}{AC} = \frac{EF}{AB} = \frac{2}{1}$ so $\triangle ABC \sim \triangle FED$ and then $\angle DFE \cong \angle CAB$. 37. 1. $\angle A \cong \angle CBD$ (Given) 2. $\angle C \cong \angle C$ (Reflex. Prop.) 3. $\triangle ACB \sim \triangle BCD$ (AA) 4. $\frac{AC}{BC} = \frac{BC}{DC}$ (Lengths of corr. sides of $\sim \triangle$s are propor.) 5. $AC \cdot DC = BC \cdot BC$ (Prop. of Propor.) 39. $\frac{AB}{AC} = \frac{DE}{DF}$ (since $AB = DE$ and $AC = DF$) and $\angle B \cong \angle E$ but $\triangle$s are not $\sim$. 41. a. $AC_3 \cdot AC_4 = (AB_3)^2$, $AC_4 \cdot AC_5 = (AB_4)^2$ b. $AB_3 \cdot AB_4 = (AC_4)^2$, $AB_4 \cdot AB_5 = (AC_5)^2$

Algebra Review

1. 3, -3 3. 2, -2 5. -2, 2 7. 4, -4

Lesson 6-6 Try This

1. $\frac{10}{3}$ 2. 3, $\frac{15}{2}$ 3. $\frac{65}{17}$, $\frac{156}{17}$

Exercise Set 6-6

1. 9, $\triangle$ Propor. Seg. 3. 12, $\parallel$s Propor. Seg. 5. $\frac{81}{7}$, $\parallel$s Propor. Seg. 7. $\frac{3}{5}$ 9. $\frac{40}{3}$ 11. $\frac{21}{5}$ 13. 8 15. $\frac{11}{4}$ 17. Method works by $\triangle$ Propor. Seg. Th. 19. 6, 2, $\frac{21}{2}$, $\frac{7}{2}$ 21. 10
23. Plan: Extend lines CA and DB so they intersect at pt. E. $\triangle EAB \sim \triangle ECD$ by AA. ($\angle E \cong \angle E$ by Reflex. Prop., $\angle EAB \cong \angle ECD$ because corr. $\angle$s are $\cong$ when $\parallel$ lines are cut by a trans.) Draw $\overline{EX}$. Where it intersects $\overline{CD}$ is point Y. We know that $\frac{EA}{EC} = \frac{EB}{ED}$. Also $\frac{EA}{EC} = \frac{AX}{CY}$ and $\frac{EB}{ED} = \frac{XB}{YD}$. By subst., $\frac{AX}{CY} = \frac{XB}{YD}$. By a Prop. of Propor. (switching the means) $\frac{AX}{XB} = \frac{CY}{YD}$. 25. 1. Draw aux. seg. $\overline{BE} \parallel$ to $\overline{CD}$. Extend $\overline{AC}$ to E. (Through a pt. not on a given line, a line $\parallel$ to the given line may be drawn.) 2. $\angle 1 \cong \angle 2$ (Given) 3. $\angle 1 \cong \angle 4$ ($\parallel$ lines cut by trans., corr. $\angle$s are $\cong$.) 4. $\angle 2 \cong \angle 4$ (Th. 1.3) 5. $\angle 2 \cong \angle 3$ ($\parallel$ lines cut by trans., alter. int. $\angle$s are $\cong$.)

6. $\angle 3 \cong \angle 4$ (Th. 1.3) 7. $\overline{CE} \cong \overline{CB}$ (Sides opp. $\cong \angle$s are $\cong$.) 8. $\frac{AD}{DB} = \frac{AC}{CE}$ ($\triangle$Propor. Seg. Th.) 9. $\frac{AD}{DB} = \frac{AC}{CB}$ (Subst.)
27.

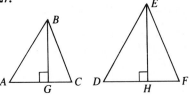

Given: $\triangle BAC \sim \triangle EDF$, $\overline{BG}$ and $\overline{EH}$ are alt.
Prove: $\frac{BG}{EH} = \frac{AB}{DE}$
Proof: $\angle A \cong \angle D$ (Def. $\sim \triangle$s), $\angle AGB \cong \angle DHE$
(All rt. $\angle$s are $\cong$.), $\triangle AGB \sim \triangle DHE$ (AA), so $\frac{BG}{EH} = \frac{AB}{DE}$
29. $\frac{12}{5}, \frac{18}{5}$ **31.** a. never b. $\overline{AX} \parallel \overline{BB'}$ (Th. 3.1), so $\frac{AB}{BC} = \frac{XB'}{B'C}$
(Th. 6.6). Also, $\overline{B'Y} \parallel \overline{CZ}$ so by Th. 6.6, $\frac{XB'}{B'C} = \frac{XY}{YZ}$. Put the
2 eq. together to get $\frac{AB}{BC} = \frac{XY}{YZ}$.

Mixed Review

1. 82.5 mi **3.** 10 mi **5.** scalene **7.** acute, isosceles

Chapter Review

1. $\frac{t}{5}$ **2.** $\frac{11}{3}$ **3.** $4y : 5$ **4.** $\frac{5x}{2y}$ **5.** $\frac{35}{3}$ **6.** 6 **7.** $30°, 150°$
8. 15, 27 **9.** $5y$ **10.** $\frac{w}{4}$ **11.** $\frac{x}{3}$ **12.** $\frac{4-w}{w}$ **13.** 17
14. 13 **15.** 19 **16.** 4 **17.** $-6, 2$ **18.** $-2, 3$ **19.** 3 mi
20. 60 yd x 40 yd **21.** 52 **22.** 23 **23.** 15 **24.** 8 **25.** $\frac{2}{3}$
26. $\triangle SWX$, AA **27.** 1. $\overline{RS} \parallel \overline{UT}$ (Given) 2. $\angle RSU \cong$
$\angle TUS$ ($\parallel$ lines cut by trans., alt. int. $\angle$s are $\cong$.)
3. $\angle WXS \cong \angle VXU$ (Vert. $\angle$s are $\cong$.) 4. $\triangle WXZ \sim \triangle VXU$
(AA) **28.** ≈ 25.5 ft **29.** $6\frac{3}{4}$ or 6 ft 9 in. **30.** yes, SAS
31. $\triangle$s not $\sim$ **32.** yes, SSS **33.** $\frac{RT}{GI} = \frac{ST}{HI}$ **34.** $\frac{WX}{DE} =$
$\frac{XY}{EF} = \frac{WY}{DF}$ **35.** 1. $\square DFGI$ (Given) 2. $\overline{DF} \parallel \overline{IG}$ (Def. $\square$)
3. $\angle FDG \cong \angle IGD$ ($\parallel$ lines cut by trans., alt. int. $\angle$s are
$\cong$.) 4. $\angle DJE \cong \angle GJH$ (Vert. $\angle$s are $\cong$.) 5. $\triangle DJE \sim$
$\triangle GJH$ (AA) 6. $\frac{DE}{GH} = \frac{EJ}{HJ}$ (Sides of $\sim \triangle$s are propor.)
7. $DE \cdot HJ = EJ \cdot GH$ (Means/Extr.) **36.** $\frac{20}{7}$ **37.** 6

CHAPTER 7

Lesson 7-1 Try This
1. $\frac{2\sqrt{5}}{5}$ **2.** 6 **3.** 20 **4.** 10

Exercise Set 7-1

1. $2\sqrt{2}$ **3.** $\frac{\sqrt{2}}{2}$ **5.** $\frac{2\sqrt{5}}{15}$ **7.** 12 **9.** $\sqrt[4]{15}$ **11.** 10,
$x = \sqrt{30}$ **13.** 3, $z = \sqrt{39}$ **15.** y, $y = \sqrt{130}$
17. $4\sqrt{3}$ **19.** 12 **21.** $GH = 6\sqrt{3}$, $HK = 6$ **23.** xy
25. xc **27.** 27 **29.** $\frac{32}{3}$ **31.** $\frac{8}{5}$ **33.** $4\sqrt{3}$ **35.** 2 or 8
37. $\frac{64}{5}$ **39.** $8\sqrt{2}$ **41.** $8\sqrt{3}$ km **43.** $16\sqrt{3}$ cm **45.** By
Th. 7.1, $\triangle ACB$, $\triangle ADC$, and $\triangle CDB$ are $\sim$. Because $\overline{DB}$
in $\triangle DCB$ corr. to $\overline{CB}$ in $\triangle ACB$ and $\overline{CB}$ in $\triangle DCB$ corr. to
$\overline{AB}$ in $\triangle ACB$, $\frac{DB}{CB} = \frac{CB}{AB}$, or $\frac{y}{a} = \frac{a}{c}$. Because $\overline{AD}$ in $\triangle ACD$
corr. to $\overline{AC}$ in $\triangle ACB$ and $\overline{AC}$ in $\triangle ACD$ corr. to $\overline{AB}$ in
$\triangle ACB$, $\frac{AD}{AC} = \frac{AC}{AD}$ or $\frac{x}{b} = \frac{b}{c}$. **47.** Given AB is the geo. mean
between BC and AC or $\frac{BC}{AB} = \frac{AB}{AC}$, prove $\frac{AB}{AC} = \frac{AC}{AD}$. If $CD =$
AB, then all propor. can be written in terms of AB and BC.
Given $\frac{BC}{AB} = \frac{AB}{AB + BC}$ prove $\frac{AB}{AB + BC} = \frac{AB + BC}{2AB + BC} \cdot \frac{BC}{AB} = \frac{AB}{AB + BC}$
is equiv. to $(BC)^2 + AB \cdot BC = AB^2$. Now add
$(AB)^2 + AB \cdot BC$ to both sides of the eq. to get $(BC)^2 +$
$2AB \cdot BC + (AB)^2 = 2(AB)^2 + AB \cdot BC$ or $(AC + BC)^2 =$
$AB(2AB + BC)$. $(AC + BC)^2 = AB(2AB + BC)$ is equiv.
to the propor. $\frac{AB}{AB + BC} = \frac{AB + BC}{2AB + BC}$.
49. Let $AD = x$ and $DC = d - x$. By Th. 7.2, $\frac{x}{c} = \frac{c}{d - x}$
or $x(d - x) = c^2$. By Th. 7.3, $\frac{x}{a} = \frac{a}{d}$ and $\frac{d - x}{b} = \frac{b}{d}$. Multiply the propor.: $\frac{x}{a} \cdot \frac{d - x}{b} = \frac{a}{d} \cdot \frac{b}{d}$ or $d^2 \cdot x(d - x) =$
$a^2 b^2 x(d - x) = c^2$, so $d^2 c^2 = a^2 b^2$, or $cd = ab$. Product of
length of alt. to hyp. and length of hyp. = product of lengths
of the two legs.

Algebra Review

1. 2 **3.** $4a$ **5.** $\frac{3}{4}$ **7.** $5a$ **9.** $\frac{\sqrt{3a}}{3}$ **11.** $\frac{2c\sqrt{5}}{5}$

Lesson 7-2 Try This

17

Exercise Set 7-2

1. 5 **3.** 8 **5.** $2\sqrt{6}$ **7.** 10 **9.** $2\sqrt{2}$ **11.** $\sqrt{5}$
13. $6\sqrt{2}$ **15.** ≈ 25 in. **17.** 10 **19.** $2\sqrt{2}$ **21.** $4\sqrt{2}$
23. Answers may vary. $d = \sqrt{2}s$ **25.** 20 **27.** $\sqrt{23}$
29. $\frac{3\sqrt{5}}{5}$ **31.** $8\sqrt{3}$ **33.** $a = 10$, $b = 2\sqrt{29}$ **35.** $x = 1$,
$y = 2\sqrt{2}$, $h = 3$ **37.** $10 + 2\sqrt{39}$ **39.** $4\sqrt{2}$ ft ≈ 5 ft
8 in. **41.** yes **43.** 24 **45.** $2\sqrt{6}$ **47.** $6 + 2\sqrt{5} +$
$2\sqrt{10} + 2\sqrt{2}$ **49.** Construct a rt. $\triangle$ with hyp. = the
length of seg. shown in text. **51.** $AB = \sqrt{2}$, $AC = \sqrt{3}$,
$AD = 2$, $AE = \sqrt{5}$ Construct seg. with lengths $\sqrt{6}$ and
$\sqrt{7}$. **53.** Draw a vert. line through point F, as shown.

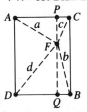

By the Pythag. Th., $PC^2 + x^2 = c^2$, $DQ^2 + y^2 = d^2$,
$AP^2 + x^2 = a^2$, and $QB^2 + y^2 = b^2$. Then, $a^2 + b^2 =$
$AP^2 + x^2 + QB^2 + y^2 = DQ^2 + x^2 + PC^2 + y^2 =$
$(PC^2 + x^2) + (DQ^2 + y^2) = c^2 + d^2$. NOTE: $PC = QB$ and
$AP = DQ$ **55.** $d = \sqrt{3}s$

Mixed Review

1. alt. int. **3.** 110 **5.** $180 - m\angle BEF$ **7.** 120

Lesson 7-3 Try This

1. no **2.** No; it is an acute $\triangle$.

Exercise Set 7-3

1. obtuse **3.** acute **5.** rt. **7.** acute **9.** acute **11.** rt.
13. obtuse **15.** yes, yes; $9^2 + 40^2 = 41^2$ and $18^2 + 80^2 = 81^2$ **17.** obtuse **19.** $x = 47$; 14, 48, 50 **21.** $90\sqrt{2}$
23. $ED^2 + DC^2 = EC^2$, so $25 + 576 = 601$. $EC = AC = \sqrt{601}$. If $\triangle ABC$ is rt. then $BC^2 + AB^2 = AC^2$. $144 + 529 = 673$, which is > 601. $\triangle ABC$ is acute. **25.** Using the Dist. Form., $AC = \sqrt{13}$, $BC = 5$, and $AB = 6$. By Th. 7.6, $AC^2 + BC^2 = AB^2$ if $\triangle ABC$ is rt. $13 + 25 > 36$, so $\triangle ABC$ is acute. **27.** $a^2 + b^2 = (2n + 1)^2 + (2n^2 + 2n)^2 = 4n^4 + 8n^3 + 8n^2 + 4n + 1$. $c^2 = (2n^2 + 2n + 1)^2 = 4n^4 + 8n^3 + 8n^2 + 4n + 1$ so $a^2 + b^2 = c^2$, and a, b, and c is a Pythag. Triple. **29.** $\triangle A'B'C'$ will be acute by Th. 7.6, if $(a + k)^2 + (b + k)^2 > (c + k)^2$. $a^2 + 2ak + k^2 + b^2 + 2bk + k^2 = c^2 + 2k^2 + 2k(a + b)$. By $\triangle$ Ineq. Th., $a + b \geq c$, so $c^2 + 2k^2 + 2k(a + b) > c^2 + 2ck + k^2$. $(a + k)^2 + (b + k)^2 = c^2 + 2k^2 + 2k(a + b) > c^2 + 2kc + k^2 = (c + k)^2$.

Algebra Review

1. 3 **3.** 5 **5.** -2 **7.** 2 **9.** $\frac{1}{3}$

Lesson 7-4 Try This

1. $12\sqrt{2}$ cm ≈ 17 cm **2.** length $= 5\sqrt{3}$, diag. length $= 10$

Exercise Set 7-4

1. 6, $6\sqrt{2}$ **3.** 2.5, $\frac{5\sqrt{2}}{2}$ **5.** 7, 7 **7.** $4\sqrt{3}$, 8 **9.** 3, $3\sqrt{3}$ **11.** 5, 10 **13.** 12 **15.** $12 + 12\sqrt{3}$ **17.** $5\sqrt{2}$ cm **19.** 6 **21.** 6 **23.** 60 **25.** 90 **27.** 45 **29.** 6 **31.** $6\sqrt{3}$ **33.** 12 **35.** $3\sqrt{3}$ m **37.** $26 + 8\sqrt{2} + 6\sqrt{3}$ **39.** $x = 3\sqrt{2}$, $y = \frac{3\sqrt{2}}{2}$, $z = \frac{3\sqrt{6}}{2}$ **41.** Construct $\triangle ACD$ such that $\triangle ACD \cong \triangle ACB$ and the rt. $\angle$s are adj.

$\triangle ABD$ is equiang., since $30° + 30° = 60°$. By Cor. 4.2a, $\triangle ABD$ is equilat. Therefore, $2a = c$. By Pythag. Th., $a^2 + b^2 = c^2$. Subst. $2a$ for c: $c = 2a$, $a^2 + b^2 = 4a^2$ or $b^2 = 3a^2$ and $b = \sqrt{3}a$. **43.** 15 **45.** $AG = 8$, $AF = 4\sqrt{3}$ **47.** Alt. $\overline{BD}$ divides $\triangle ABC$ into 2 smaller $30°$–$60°$–$90°$s, $\triangle ABD$ and $\triangle BCD$. By Th. 7.6, $h = \sqrt{3}x$ and $y = \sqrt{3}h$. Subst. for h, $y = \sqrt{3} \cdot \sqrt{3}x = 3x$, so y is 3 $\times$ as long as x.

Mixed Review

1. always **3.** never **5.** always **7.** never

Lesson 7-5 Try This

1. $\tan A = \frac{5}{12}$, $\tan B = \frac{12}{5}$ **2.** ≈ 8.15 **3.** ≈ 21

Exercise Set 7-5

1. $\tan A = \frac{12}{5}$, $\tan B = \frac{5}{12}$ **3.** $\tan A = \frac{8}{15}$, $\tan B = \frac{15}{8}$
5. 0.343 **7.** 62 **9.** 0.7002 **11.** 57.2900 **13.** 50°
15. 80° **17.** 45 **19.** 8.40 **21.** 50° **23.** 25 **25.** ≈ 24
27. ≈ 6.95 **29.** ≈ 35.75 **31.** ≈ 11.41 cm **33.** 53, 37
35. ≈ 10 **37.** 21.45 **39.** ≈ 77, ≈ 13 **41.** ≈ 326 m
43. Given a as the length of side opp. $\angle A$ and b as the length of side adj. to $\angle A$, then as $m\angle A$ increases, a remains the same and b decreases. So the ratio $\frac{a}{b}$, or $\tan A$, increases. yes, $\tan 89.43 \approx 100$

Mixed Review

1. ASA **3.** SAS

Lesson 7-6 Try This

1. ≈ 13.42 **2.** ≈ 64 **3.** ≈ 33.29

Exercise Set 7-6

1. $\sin \angle A = \cos \angle B = \frac{12}{13}$, $\cos \angle A = \sin \angle B = \frac{5}{13}$ **3.** $\sin \angle A = \cos \angle B = \frac{18}{17}$, $\cos \angle A = \sin \angle B = \frac{15}{17}$ **5.** 0.6561 **7.** 40 **9.** 85 **11.** $x \approx 23.93$, $y \approx 10.16$ **13.** a. $x = 35 \cdot \cos 37°$, $y = 35 \cdot \cos 53°$ b. $x = 26 \cdot \cos 23°$, $y = 26 \cdot \cos 67°$ c. $x = 75 \cos 74°$, $y = 75 \cos 16°$ **15.** $m\angle A \approx 62$, $m\angle B \approx 28$ **17.** 24.61 **19.** 57.96 **21.** $\sin 45° = \frac{\sqrt{2}}{2}$, $\sin 60° = \frac{\sqrt{3}}{2}$, $\cos 30° = \frac{\sqrt{3}}{2}$, $\cos 45° = \frac{\sqrt{2}}{2}$, $\cos 60° = \frac{1}{2}$, $\tan 30° = \frac{\sqrt{3}}{3}$, $\tan 45° = 1$, $\tan 60° = \sqrt{3}$ **23.** ≈ 14.83 cm **25.** $\frac{\sqrt{39}}{8}$ **27.** sometimes **29.** never **31.** 8, 60 **33.** ≈ 4.88, ≈ 11.13 **35.** 250.47 m **37.** $\sin A = 0.6$, $\cos A = 0.8$, $\sin B = 0.8$, $\cos B = 0.6$ **39.** 60 km east **41.** a. 1 b. 1 c. $(\sin x)^2 + (\cos x)^2 = 1$ d. $\frac{\sin x}{\cos x} = \tan x$ e. By Pythag. Th., $a^2 + b^2 = c^2$. Divide by c^2: $\left(\frac{a}{c}\right)^2 + \left(\frac{b}{c}\right)^2 = 1$. $\frac{a}{c} = \sin A$, $\frac{b}{c} = \cos A$, so $(\sin A)^2 + (\cos A)^2 = 1$. $\tan A = \frac{a}{b} = \frac{\frac{a}{c}}{\frac{b}{c}} = \frac{\sin A}{\cos A}$.

Algebra Review

1. $-5, 5$ **3.** $-4, 10$ **5.** $-1, 11$ **7.** $-17\frac{1}{2}, 16$

Lesson 7-7 Try This

1. ≈ 7.9 m **2.** ≈ 5.23 km

Exercise Set 7-7

1. ≈ 275.19 ft **3.** ≈ 4.20 km **5.** ≈ 158.60 ft **7.** ≈ 5.71 km **9.** ≈ 25.16 km **11.** ≈ 2.08 min **13.** ≈ 1145.43 m

Mixed Review

1. $\angle S$ **3.** $\overline{RT}$ **5.** 8 **7.** 3:2

Chapter Review

1. 9 **2.** $2\sqrt{6}$ **3.** 15 **4.** 18 **5.** $2\sqrt{13}$ **6.** 15
7. $2\sqrt{14}$ **8.** 8 in. **9.** obtuse **10.** rt. **11.** acute
12. $7\sqrt{2}$ **13.** $x = 5$, $y = 10$ **14.** $x = 4$, $y = 4\sqrt{3}$, $z = 4\sqrt{3}$ **15.** ≈ 0.4245 **16.** ≈ 2.4751 **17.** $\approx 37°$
18. ≈ 2.9713 **19.** ≈ 55 **20.** $\sin 32° = \frac{4}{x}$, ≈ 7.5483
21. $\cos 72° = \frac{x}{14}$, ≈ 4.3262 **22.** $\sin x = \frac{7}{12}$, $\approx 19°$
23. ≈ 240 ft

CHAPTER 8

Exercise Set 8-1

1. $\overline{PA}$, $\overline{PB}$, $\overline{PE}$, $\overline{PF}$; 8 **3.** 2 **5.** $\overline{EF}$ **7.** $\overline{PE} \cong \overline{PF}$ (radii of $\odot P$), $\overline{QE} \cong \overline{QF}$ (radii of $\odot Q$), $\overline{PQ} \cong \overline{PQ}$ (Reflex. Prop.), $\triangle PEQ \cong \triangle PFQ$ (SSS)
9. $\triangle ABC$ **11.** $\overleftrightarrow{AC}$, $\overleftrightarrow{BC}$, $\overrightarrow{AB}$; the larger circle **13.** 2
15. none
17. **19.** **21.**

23. never true **25.** always true **27.** 0.035 cm
29. 0.297 in. **31.** never **33.** always **35.** 2

Mixed Review

1. 105 **3.** 25 **5.** 50 **7.** 3.6 cm

Lesson 8-2 Try This

1. 13 **2.** $\sqrt{176}$ **3.** 86

Exercise Set 8-2

1. 24 **3.** 64 **5.** 142 **7.** 9 **9.** 2 **11.** 3 **13.** 24
15. 1. $\angle 1 \cong \angle 2 \cong \angle 3$ (Given) 2. $m\angle 1 = m\angle 2 = m\angle 3$ (Def. $\cong \angle$s) 3. $m\angle 1 + m\angle 2 + m\angle 3 = 360$ (No. of degrees in $\odot$) 4. $m\angle 1 = m\angle 2 = m\angle 3 = 120$ (Div. Prop.) 5. $m\angle ADH = m\angle CDH = m\angle CFH = m\angle BFH = m\angle BEH = m\angle AEH = 90$ (Line tan. to $\odot$ is $\perp$ to radius at point of tan.) 6. $m\angle A = m\angle B = m\angle C = 60$ (Sum of measures in quad. is 360.) 7. $\triangle ABC$ is equiang. and therefore equilat. **17.** Edges of board are line seg. If a line is $\perp$ a radius of $\odot$ at pt. on $\odot$, then line is tan. to $\odot$. 2 edges of board are tan. to $\odot$. **19.** 1. $\overline{PA}$ and $\overline{PB}$ are tan. to $\odot O$. (Given) 2. $\overline{PA} \cong \overline{PB}$ (Tan. seg. from ext. point of $\odot$ are $\cong$.) 3. $\overline{PO} \cong \overline{PO}$ (Reflex. Prop.) 4. $\overline{OA} \cong \overline{OB}$ (Radii of $\odot$ are $\cong$.) 5. $\triangle PAO \cong \triangle PBO$ (SSS) 6. $\angle OPA \cong \angle OPB$ (Corr. parts of $\cong \triangle$s) 7. $\overrightarrow{OP}$ bis. $\angle PBA$. (Def. $\angle$ bis.)
21.

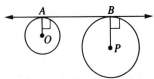

23. 1. $\overline{PA}$ and $\overline{PB}$ are tan. from ext. pt. P. (Given) 2. $\overline{PA} \cong \overline{PB}$ (Tan. seg. from ext. pt. of $\odot$ are $\cong$.) 3. $\triangle PAB$ is isos. (Def. isos. $\triangle$) 4. $\angle 3 \cong \angle 4$ (Base $\angle$s of isos. $\triangle$ are $\cong$.)
25. 19 **27.** 30 **29.** 1. $\overline{AB} \parallel \overline{DE}$ (Given) 2. $m\angle ABC + m\angle EDB = 180$ ($\parallel$ lines cut by a trans., same-side int. $\angle$s are supp.) 3. $m\angle ABC = 2m\angle OBC$, $m\angle EDB = 2m\angle BDO$ (Line through ext. pt. and center of $\odot$ bis. $\angle$ formed by tan. from ext. pt.) 4. $2m\angle OBC + 2m\angle BDO = 180$ (Subst.) 5. $2(m\angle OBC + m\angle BDO) = 180$ (Dist. Prop.) 6. $m\angle OBC + m\angle BDO = 90$ (Div. Prop.) 7. $m\angle OBC + m\angle BDO + m\angle BOD = 180$ (Sum of measures of $\angle$s of $\triangle$ is 180.) 8. $m\angle BOD = 90$ (Sub. Prop.) 9. $\angle BOD$ is a rt. $\angle$. (Def. rt. $\angle$) 10. $\overline{BO} \perp \overline{DO}$ ($\perp$ lines form rt. $\angle$s.)
31. 1. quad. $WXYZ$ circumscribed about a $\odot$ (Given) 2. $\overline{XM} \cong \overline{XN}$, $\overline{YN} \cong \overline{YO}$, $\overline{ZO} \cong \overline{ZP}$, $\overline{WP} \cong \overline{WM}$ (Tan. seg.

from ext. pt. of circle are $\cong$.) 3. $XM = XN = x$, $YN = YO = y$, $ZO = ZP = z$, $WP = WM = w$ (Def. $\cong$ seg.)
4. $WX = w + x$, $XY = x + y$, $YZ = y + z$, $WZ = w + z$ (Seg. Add. Post.) 5. $XY + WZ = (x + y) + (w + z)$, $WX + YZ = (w + x) + (y + z)$ (Add Prop.) 6. $XY + WZ = WX + YZ$ (Trans. Prop.) **33.** $P_1 P_2 \ldots P_n$ is reg. poly. of n sides. $\triangle A_1 O P_1 \cong \triangle A_2 O P_1 \cong A_2 O P_2 \cong \ldots$ by ASA so $\overline{A_1 P_1} \cong \overline{P_1 A_2} \cong \overline{A_2 P_2}$ by corr. parts of $\cong \triangle$s. Therefore, $\overline{P_1 P_2} \cong \overline{P_2 P_3} \cong \ldots$, so the poly. is reg.

Mixed Review

1. $\frac{u}{v} = \frac{7+y}{7}$ or $\frac{x+5}{5}$ **3.** $\frac{x}{y} = \frac{5}{7}$ **5.** $\frac{21}{5}$

Lesson 8-3 Try This

1. 50 **2.** $10\sqrt{2}$

Exercise Set 8-3

1. 24 **3.** 13 **5.** $ED = 10$; no, they are not. **7.** 40 **9.** 12
11. $6\sqrt{3}$ **13.** 9 **15.** $\frac{85}{8}$ or 10.625 **17.** 1. $m\angle CAP = m\angle DBP = 90$ (Line tan. to $\odot$, is $\perp$ to radius at pt. of tan.) 2. $\angle CAP \cong \angle DBP$ (Def. $\cong \angle$s) 3. $\angle CPA \cong \angle DPB$ (Vert. $\angle$s are $\cong$.) 4. $\triangle CAP \sim \triangle DPB$ (AA) 5. $\angle PCA \cong \angle PDB$ (Corr. $\angle$s of $\sim \triangle$s are $\cong$.) **19.** $8\sqrt{3}$ **21.** 1. $\overline{AB}$ and $\overline{CD}$ are common ext. tan. that intersect at P. (Given) 2. $\overline{PA} \cong \overline{PC}$, $\overline{PB} \cong \overline{PD}$ (Tan. seg. from ext. pt. of $\odot$ are $\cong$.) 3. $PA - PB = PC - PD$ (Sub. Prop.) 4. $AB = CD$ (Seg. Add. Post.) 5. $\overline{AB} \cong \overline{CD}$ (Def. $\cong$ seg.) **23.** 1. $\odot C$, $\odot D$ with common int. tan. $\overline{AB}$ (Given) 2. $m\angle CAB = m\angle DBA = 90$ (Line tan. to $\odot$ is $\perp$ to radius at pt. of tan.) 3. $\angle CAB \cong \angle DBA$ (Def. $\cong \angle$s) 4. $\overline{AC} \parallel \overline{DB}$ (If lines cut by a trans. and pair of alt. int. $\angle$s are $\cong$, lines are $\parallel$.) 5. $\angle ACD \cong \angle BDC$ (Lines are $\parallel$, alt. int. $\angle$s are $\cong$.) 6. $\overline{AC} \cong \overline{BD}$ (Radii of $\cong \odot$s are $\cong$.) 7. $\triangle CAP \cong \triangle DBP$ (ASA) 8. $\overline{CP} \cong \overline{DP}$, $\overline{AP} \cong \overline{BP}$ (Corr. parts of $\cong \triangle$s) 9. $\overline{AB}$ and $\overline{CD}$ bisect each other. (Def. seg. bis.) **25.** side length = 40, about 14.6 cm shorter
27.

29. 4, 8 total

Algebra Review

1. $5x - 10$ **3.** $-6y + 24$ **5.** $12x - 18y - 48z$
7. $-16x - 48y + 56$

Lesson 8-4 Try This

1. a. 90 **b.** 205 **2. a.** 162 **b.** $m\overarc{ED} = m\overarc{DC} = 42$

Exercise Set 8-4

1. 80 **3.** 258 **5.** 80 **7.** $\overarc{AEC}$ and $\overarc{BAE}$ or $\overarc{AB}$ and $\overarc{CE}$
9. 140 **11.** 90 **13.** 220 **15.** 52 **17.** 34 **19.** 83
21. 1. $\overarc{AB} \cong \overarc{CD}$ (Given) 2. $\overarc{BC} \cong \overarc{BC}$ (Reflex. Prop.)
3. $m\overarc{AB} + m\overarc{BC} = m\overarc{BC} + m\overarc{CD}$ (Arc Add. Post.) 4. $m\overarc{AC} = m\overarc{BD}$ (Arc Add. Post.) 5. $\overarc{AC} \cong \overarc{BD}$ (Def. $\cong$ arcs) **23.** 1. $\odot O$ with tan. $\overline{CA}$ and $\overline{CB}$ (Given) 2. $\overline{OA} \perp \overline{CA}$, $\overline{OB} \perp \overline{CB}$

(Line is tan. to $\odot$, then it is $\perp$ to radius at pt. of tan.) 3. $m\angle OAC = m\angle OBC = 90$ (Def. of $\perp$) 4. $m\angle OAC + m\angle ACB + m\angle OBC + m\angle AOB = 360$ (Sum of measures of $\angle$s of quad. $= 360$.) 5. $m\angle ACB = x$ (Given) 6. $90 + x + 90 + m\angle AOB = 360$ (Subst.) 7. $x + m\angle AOB = 180$ (Sub. Prop.) 8. $m\angle AOB = 180 - x$ (Sub. Prop.) 9. $m\overarc{AB} = 180 - x$ (Def. arc measure) 25. $(0, 2)$ 27. $(\sqrt{2}, \sqrt{2})$ 29. 1. Circumscribed $\triangle XYZ$, $m\angle X = x$, $m\angle Y = y$ (Given) 2. $m\angle AOB = 180 - x$, $m\angle BOC = 180 - y$ (See Ex. 24.) 3. $m\angle AOC = 360 - (180 - x) - (180 - y)$ (Arc Add. Post.) 4. $m\angle AOC = x + y$ (Add. Prop.) 5. $m\overarc{AC} = x + y$ (Def. arc measure) 31. 10 chords, $\frac{n(n-1)}{2}$, 20 arcs, $n(n-1)$

Mixed Review

1. 20 3. 105 5. 20

Lesson 8-5 Try This

1. 246 2. $z = 8$, $\overline{AB}$ and $\overline{BE}$ are equidist. from O and $\cong$ by Th. 8.10.

Exercise Set 8-5

1. 7 3. 148 5. 90 7. 138 9. 6 11. 3 13. 28 15. 13 17. 90 19. 70 21. $2\sqrt{2}$ 23. 31 25. 1. $\overline{AD} \perp \overline{BC}$, $\overline{AD}$ is a dia. (Given) 2. $\overline{AD}$ bisects $\overarc{BAC}$. (If dia. is $\perp$ to a chord, it bisects chord's major arc.) 3. $\overarc{BA} \cong \overarc{AC}$ (Def. bis.) 4. $\overline{BA} \cong \overline{AC}$ ($\cong$ arcs have $\cong$ chords.) 5. $\triangle ABC$ is isos. (Def. isos. $\triangle$) 27. 24 in. 29. 1. $\odot P$, dia. $\overline{CD}$ bisects $\overline{AB}$. (Given) 2. $\overline{AE} \cong \overline{BE}$ (Def. bis.) 3. $\overline{PA} \cong \overline{PB}$ (Radii $\cong$ in same $\odot$.) 4. $\overline{PE} \cong \overline{PE}$ (Reflex. Prop.) 5. $\triangle APE \cong \triangle BPE$ (SSS) 6. $\angle AEP \cong \angle BEP$ (Corr. parts of $\cong$ $\triangle$s) 7. $m\angle AEP + m\angle BEP = 180$ (Linear Pair Post.) 8. $m\angle AEP = m\angle BEP = 90$ (Div. Prop.) 9. $\overline{CD} \perp \overline{AB}$ (Def. $\perp$ lines) 10. $m\angle APD = m\angle BPD$ (Corr. parts of $\cong$ $\triangle$s) 11. $\overarc{AD} \cong \overarc{DB}$ (Def. arc measure) 12. $\angle APC \cong \angle BPC$ ($\angle$s supp. to $\cong$ $\angle$s are $\cong$.) 13. $\overarc{AC} \cong \overarc{BC}$ (Def. arc measure) 31. 1. $\overline{AB} \cong \overline{CD}$ (Given) 2. Draw $\overline{OT} \perp \overline{AB}$, $\overline{OS} \perp \overline{CD}$ (Through a given pt. not on line there is exactly 1 line in plane $\perp$ given line.) 3. $\angle ATO$, $\angle CSO$ are rt. $\angle$s. ($\perp$ lines form rt. $\angle$s.) 4. $\triangle ATO$ and $\triangle CSO$ are rt. $\triangle$s. (Def. rt. $\triangle$) 5. $\overline{OA} \cong \overline{OB} \cong \overline{OC} \cong \overline{OD}$ (Radii of same $\odot$ are $\cong$.) 6. $\overline{OT}$ and $\overline{OS}$ are on dia. (Def. dia.) 7. $\overline{AT} \cong \overline{BT}$, $\overline{CS} \cong \overline{DS}$ (If a dia. is $\perp$ chord, it bisects chord.) 8. $AT = \frac{1}{2}AB$, $CS = \frac{1}{2}CD$ (Def. seg. bis.) 9. $\overline{AT} \cong \overline{CS}$ (Subst.) 10. $\triangle CSO \cong \triangle ATO$ (HL Th.) 11. $\overline{OS} \cong \overline{OT}$ (Corr. parts of $\cong$ $\triangle$s) 12. $OS = OT$ (Def. $\cong$ seg.) 33. Locate A, B, and C on inner arc. Find $\perp$ bis. of $\overline{AB}$ and $\overline{BC}$. Their intersection is center O of circle. $\overline{OA}$ is radius. 35. 1. $AB = CD$, $\overline{OX} \perp \overline{AB}$, $\overline{OY} \perp \overline{CD}$ (Given) 2. $OX =$ dist. $\overline{AB}$ to O, $OY =$ dist. $\overline{CD}$ to O (Def. dist. from line to pt.) 3. $OX = OY$ (In same $\odot$, $\cong$ chords are equidist. from center.) 4. $\overline{OX} \cong \overline{OY}$ (Def. $\cong$ seg.) 5. $\angle 1 \cong \angle 2$ (Base $\angle$s of isos. $\triangle$ are $\cong$.) 6. $m\angle 1 = m\angle 2$ (Def. $\cong$ $\angle$s) 37. $C(-4, 3)$, $D(4, 3)$ 39. $x^2 + 3^2 = 25$, $x = \pm 4$; $C(-4, 3)$, $D(4, 3)$ 41. always

Algebra Review

1. 8 3. 6 5. $-\frac{1}{2}$ 7. -7

Lesson 8-6 Try This

1. 92, 46 2. 59, 112

Exercise Set 8-6

1. 31 3. 59 5. 110 7. 70 9. 48 11. 27 13. 40 15. 20 17. $m\angle A = 135$, $m\angle B = 90$, $m\angle C = 45$, $m\angle D = 90$ 19. 44 21. 1. inscribed trap. $ABCD$ with $\overline{AB} \parallel \overline{DC}$ (Given) 2. $\overarc{AD} \cong \overarc{BC}$ (See Class Ex. 16.) 3. $\angle ACD \cong \angle BDC$ (Def. arc measure) 4. $\overarc{AB} \cong \overarc{AB}$ (Reflex. Prop.) 5. $\overarc{DA} + \overarc{AB} = \overarc{CB} + \overarc{BA}$ (Add. Prop.) 6. $\overarc{DB} \cong \overarc{CA}$ (Seg. Add. Post.) 7. $\angle BCD \cong \angle ADC$ (Def. arc measure) 8. $\triangle ACD \cong \triangle BDC$ (ASA) 9. $\overline{BC} \cong \overline{AD}$ (Corr. parts of $\cong$ $\triangle$s) 10. $ABCD$ is isos. (Def. isos. trap.) 23. 1. $\overline{AB}$, $\overline{CB}$ are dia. $\odot X$ and $\odot Y$ are tan. at B. (Given) 2. $m\angle AEB = m\angle CDB = 90$ (An $\angle$ inscribed in a semicircle is a rt. $\angle$.) 3. $\angle AEB \cong \angle CDB$ (All rt. $\angle$s are $\cong$.) 4. $\angle ABE \cong \angle DBC$ (Vert. $\angle$s are $\cong$.) 5. $\triangle AEB \sim \triangle CDB$ (AA) 6. $\angle 1 \cong \angle 2$ (Corr. $\angle$s of $\sim$ $\triangle$s) 25. 1. inscribed $\angle BAC$ (Given) 2. $\overline{OA} \cong \overline{OB}$ (Radii in same $\odot$ $\cong$.) 3. $\angle BAC \cong \angle ABO$ (Isos. $\triangle$ Th.) 4. $m\angle BAC \cong m\angle ABO$ (Def. $\cong$ $\angle$s) 5. $m\overarc{BC} = m\angle BOC$ (Def. arc measure) 6. $m\angle BOC = m\angle BAC + m\angle ABO$ (Ext. $\angle$ Th.) 7. $m\overarc{BC} = m\angle BAC + m\angle ABO$ (Subst.) 8. $m\overarc{BC} = 2m\angle BAC$ (Subst.) 9. $m\angle BAC = \frac{1}{2}m\overarc{BC}$ (Div. Prop.) 27. 1. inscribed $\angle BAC$ (Given) 2. $m\angle BAD = \frac{1}{2}m\overarc{BD}$, $m\angle CAD = \frac{1}{2}m\overarc{CD}$ (Case 1) 3. $m\angle BAC = m\angle BAD - m\angle 2$ (Sub. Prop.) 4. $m\angle BAC = \frac{1}{2}m\overarc{BD} - \frac{1}{2}m\overarc{CD}$ (Subst.) 5. $m\angle BAC = \frac{1}{2}(m\overarc{BD} - m\overarc{CD})$ (Dist. Prop.) 6. $m\angle BAC = \frac{1}{2}m\overarc{BC}$ (Arc Add. Post.) 29. 1. inscribed quad. $ABCD$ (Given) 2. $m\angle A = \frac{1}{2}m\overarc{BCD}$, $m\angle C = \frac{1}{2}m\overarc{BAD}$ (Th. 8.11) 3. $m\angle A + m\angle C = \frac{1}{2}m\overarc{BCD} + \frac{1}{2}m\overarc{BAD}$ (Add. Prop.) 4. $m\angle A + m\angle C = \frac{1}{2}(m\overarc{BCD} + m\overarc{BAD})$ (Dist. Prop.) 5. $m\angle A + m\angle C = \frac{1}{2}(360) = 180$ (Arc Add. Post.) 6. $\angle A$, $\angle C$ are supp. (Def. supp. $\angle$s) 7. $m\angle B = \frac{1}{2}m\overarc{ADC}$, $m\angle D = \frac{1}{2}m\overarc{ABC}$ (Inscribed $\angle$ measure) 8. $m\angle B + m\angle D = \frac{1}{2}m\overarc{ADC} + \frac{1}{2}m\overarc{ABC}$ (Add. Prop.) 9. $m\angle B + m\angle D = \frac{1}{2}(m\overarc{ADC} + m\angle ABC)$ (Dist. Prop.) 10. $m\angle B + m\angle D = \frac{1}{2}(360) = 180$ (Arc Add. Post.) 11. $\angle B$ and $\angle D$ are supp. (Def. supp. $\angle$s) 31. 6 33. 1. $\odot O \cong \odot P$, chord $\overline{AB} \cong$ chord $\overline{DE}$, adj. $\angle A \cong$ adj. $\angle D$ (Given) 2. $\overarc{AB} \cong \overarc{DE}$ (In $\cong$ $\odot$s, $\cong$ chords have $\cong$ minor arcs.) 3. $m\overarc{AB} = m\overarc{DE}$ (Def. $\cong$ arcs) 4. $m\angle C = \frac{1}{2}m\overarc{AB}$, $m\angle F = \frac{1}{2}m\overarc{DE}$ (Measure of inscribed $\angle \frac{1}{2}$ measure of intercepted arc.) 5. $m\angle C = m\angle F$ (Subst.) 6. $\angle C \cong \angle F$ (Def. $\cong$ $\angle$s) 7. $\triangle ABC \cong \triangle DEF$ (AAS) 35. $6\frac{2}{3}$ 37. Always; the diag. bisect each other so quad. is a $\square$. Opp. $\angle$s are inscribed in semicircles and are rt. $\angle$s.

Algebra Review

1. a^2b^2 3. $x^2 - y^2$ 5. $24x^2y^3$ 7. $(x^2 + 16)(x - 2)$

Lesson 8-7 Try This

1. 92 2. 52 3. 100

Exercise Set 8-7

1. 83 3. 24 5. 62 7. 35 9. 38 11. 60 13. 51 15. $\frac{1}{2}(x - y)$ 17. 90 19. 135 21. 160 23. 52 25. 90 27. 1. secants $\overline{PA}$ and $\overline{PD}$ (Given) 2. Draw aux. line $\overline{BD}$. (2 pt. determine a line.) 3. $m\angle ABD = m\angle BDP +$

$m\angle P$ (Measure of ext. $\angle$ of $\triangle$ = sum of measures of 2 remote int. $\angle$s.) 4. $\frac{1}{2}m\widehat{AD} = \frac{1}{2}m\widehat{BC} + m\angle P$ (Measure of inscribed $\angle$ is $\frac{1}{2}$ measure of its intercepted arc.) 5. $m\angle P = \frac{1}{2}m\widehat{AD} - \frac{1}{2}m\widehat{BC}$ (Sub. Prop.) 6. $m\angle P = \frac{1}{2}(m\widehat{AD} - m\widehat{BC})$ (Dist. Prop.) **29.** 70 **31.** No. For $\overline{AD} \parallel \overline{PB}$, $\angle 1$ must be supp. to $\angle 2$. But $m\angle 1 + m\angle 2 = 187\frac{1}{2}$. **33.** 80 **35.** 48 **37.** 40 **39.** 50 **41.** 2

Mixed Review

1. $x = 58, y = 16$ **3.** $x = 43, y = 18$ **5.** $\approx 36°$

Lesson 8-8 Try This

1. $\frac{120}{7}$ **2.** $\frac{167}{7}$ **3.** $\frac{32}{3}$

Exercise Set 8-8

1. 3 **3.** 13 **5.** 4 **7.** $\frac{84}{11}$ **9.** $7\frac{4}{9}$ **11.** $\frac{7 + \sqrt{661}}{2}$ **13.** $AQ = 12, CQ = 3$ **15.** $u = 10, v = 12$ **17.** scalene **19.** $AB = 7, CD = 8$ **21.** ≈ 34.8 mi **23.** 40 **25.** $AP \cdot PB = PE^2, PD \cdot PC = PE^2$ (Th. 8.17), $AP \cdot PB = PD \cdot PC$ (Trans. Prop.), $DP \cdot PC = 15 \cdot 6 = 90$ **27.** $\frac{CG}{DG} = \frac{5}{7}, \frac{EG}{FG} = \frac{5}{7}$
29. 1. $\odot$s intersect at A and B. Chords $\overline{AF}$ and $\overline{BE}$ intersect at G. chords $\overline{HI}$ and $\overline{EF}$ (Given) 2. Draw aux. line $\overline{BA}$. (2 pt. determine a line.) 3. $m\angle BEF = m\angle BAF, m\angle BCI = m\angle BAF$ ($\angle$s intercepting same arc have same measure.) 4. $m\angle BEF = m\angle BCI$ (Trans. Prop.) 5. $\angle BEF \cong \angle BCI$ (Def. $\cong \angle$s) 6. $\overline{CD} \parallel \overline{EF}$ (Lines cut by trans. and corr. $\angle$s are $\cong$, lines are $\parallel$.) **31. a.** Always true by Th. 8.16. **b.** Sometimes true; true if $PC = PC'$. **c.** Always true; $PC \cdot PD = PC' \cdot PD', \frac{PC}{PC'} = \frac{PD'}{PD} \angle P \cong \angle P, \triangle PCC' \sim \triangle PD'D$ by SAS, $\triangle PCC' \sim \triangle PB'B, \triangle PD'D \sim \triangle PB'B, \triangle PB'B \sim \triangle PAA', \triangle PD'D \sim \triangle PAA', \frac{PD}{PA'} = \frac{PD'}{PA}, PD \cdot PA = PA' \cdot PD'.$

Algebra Review

1. $x^2 + 2x + 1$ **3.** $a^2 + 10a + 25$ **5.** $m^2 + m - 6$ **7.** $3s^2 + 5s - 12$

Chapter Review

1. true **2.** false **3.** false **4.** false **5.** 90 **6.** 10 **7.** 6 **8.** 2 **9.** 3 **10.**

11. 43 **12.** 127 **13.** 140 **14.** 48 **15.** $7\sqrt{2}$ **16.** $\sqrt{17}$ **17.** true **18.** false **19.** false **20.** 83 **21.** 164 **22.** 16 **23.** 97 **24.** 4 **25.** 4

CHAPTER 9

Lesson 9-1 Try This

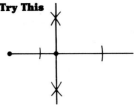

Exercise Set 9-1

1. **3.**

5. 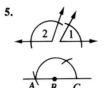 **7.**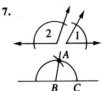

9.

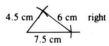

11.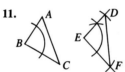

13. SAS Post.; because it is easier to construct $\cong$ seg. than $\cong \angle$s.

15. **17.**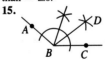

19.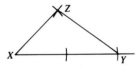

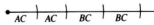

21. **23.**

25.

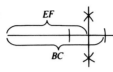

27.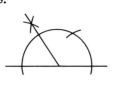

29.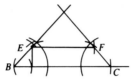

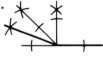

23.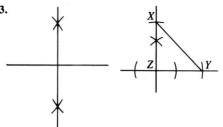

25. Have your work checked. **27.**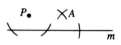

Mixed Review

1. 3 **3.** 2

Exercise Set 9-3

1. Const. 8 **3.** Const. 8 at A and also at B **5.** Const. 9 twice **7.** Const. 10 **9.**

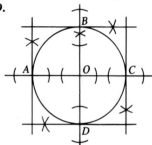

Algebra Review

1. $y < -6$ **3.** $y > \frac{9}{2}$ **5.** $x \geq \frac{4}{5}$

Lesson 9-2 Try This

Use Const. 5 to draw $90°\ \angle$. Use Const. 4 to draw $45°\ \angle$. Use Const. 4 to draw $22\frac{1}{2}°\ \angle$.

Exercise Set 9-2

1. Const. 6 **3.** Const. 6 **5.** Const. 5 **7.** Const. 7
9. Const. 7

11. 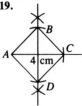 **13.**

15.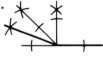

17. Draw a line $\overline{EF} = n$ using Const. 1. Use Const. 5 to construct $\perp$ lines at E and F and cut off line seg. $\overline{EH}$ and $\overline{FG}$ each $= n$ using Const. 1. Connect F and G to make sq. $EFGH$. **19.**

11. 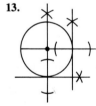 **13.**

15.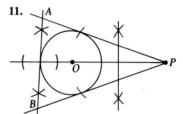

17. 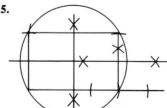 **19.**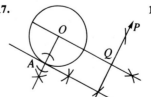

21. Answers may vary. Draw a line seg. ≈ 8 cm long. Bisect it to get 2 seg. each ≈ 4 cm. Bisect one of these to get a seg. ≈ 2 cm. Draw a line and cut off a seg. ≈ 2 cm (AB) using Const. 1. Construct a $\perp$ at $A\,(\overline{AD})$ using Const. 5 and cut off a seg. on $\overline{AD} \cong \overline{AB} \approx 2$ cm. Draw arcs ≈ 2 cm from B and D to intersect at C making sq. $ABCD$.

21. 1. Construct $\perp$ at P. 2. Find the length from vertex to P. 3. Mark off same length from vertex on other ray. 4. Label pt. *R*. **5.** Construct $\perp$ at *R*. **6.** Mark center of $\odot$ at intersection of both $\perp$s. **7.** Draw $\odot$.

23.

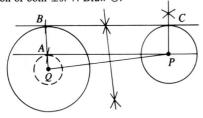

Mixed Review

1. $\frac{2}{x} = \frac{x}{3}$; $x = \sqrt{6}$ **2.** $\frac{5}{y} = \frac{y}{3}$; $y = \sqrt{15}$ **3.** $\frac{5}{z} = \frac{z}{2}$; $z = \sqrt{10}$ **4.** $\frac{2}{z} = \frac{z}{5}$; $z = \sqrt{10}$ **5.** $\frac{2}{x} = \frac{x}{3}$; $x = \sqrt{6}$ **6.** $\frac{3}{y} = \frac{y}{5}$; $y = \sqrt{15}$

Exercise Set 9-4

1.

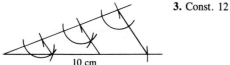

10 cm

3. Const. 12

5. Invert proportion and use Const. 12   **7.** Const. 13

9.

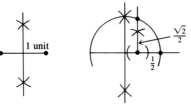

1 unit

$\frac{\sqrt{2}}{2}$

$\frac{1}{2}$

11. Const. 13 with seg. of length 1 and 8
13. Use Const. 11 to divide the seg. into 3 parts and put 2 of these together to make the longer seg.

15.

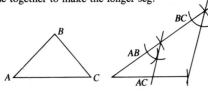

BC

AB

AC

17.

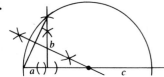

b

a

c

19. Const. 13 with seg. of length 2*a* and *b*

21.

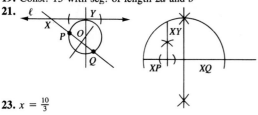

ℓ

X

Y

P

O

Q

XY

XP

XQ

23. $x = \frac{10}{3}$

Mixed Review

1. $\frac{x}{y} = \frac{3}{3}$, $\frac{x}{y} = \frac{6}{z}$

Lesson 9-5 Try This

2. 45

Exercise Set 9-5

1. Use Const. 3 to find the midpt. of each side, connect each midpt. to the opp. vertex.   **3.** Use Const. 6 to draw the 3 altitudes.   **5.** Use Const. 3 to draw the $\perp$ bis. of each side. Their intersection is the center of the circumscribed $\odot$.
7. rt. $\triangle$ on, obtuse $\triangle$ outside   **9.** acute $\triangle$ inside, rt. $\triangle$ inside, obtuse $\triangle$ inside   **11.** 6   **13.** 24   **15.** 8   **17.** $\frac{1}{2}x$
19. Given: isos. $\triangle ABC$, $\overline{AB} \cong \overline{AC}$, median $\overline{AD}$ Prove: $\overline{AD}$ bisects $\angle BAC$. **1.** $\overline{AB} \cong \overline{AC}$ (Given) **2.** $\angle B \cong \angle C$ (Isos. $\triangle$ Th.) **3.** $\overline{AD}$ is median. (Given) **4.** $\overline{BD} \cong \overline{CD}$ (Def. median) **5.** $\triangle ADB \cong ADC$ (SAS) **6.** $\angle BAD \cong \angle CAD$ (Corr. parts of $\cong \triangle$s) **7.** $\overline{AD}$ bisects $\angle BAC$. (Def. $\perp$ bis.)   **21.** $\frac{5\sqrt{3}}{6}$
23. 1. *r*, *s*, *t* $\perp$ bis. of sides of $\triangle ABC$ (Given) **2.** $\overline{WA} \cong \overline{WB}$, $\overline{XB} \cong \overline{XC}$, $\overline{YA} \cong \overline{YC}$ (Def. bis.) **3.** $\angle OWA$, $\angle OWB$, $\angle OXB$, $\angle OXC$, $\angle OYC$, $\angle OYA$ are rt. $\angle$s and are $\cong$. ($\perp$ lines form $\cong$ rt. $\angle$s.) **4.** $\overline{OW} \cong \overline{OW}$, $\overline{OX} \cong \overline{OX}$, $\overline{OY} \cong \overline{OY}$ (Reflex. Prop.) **5.** $\triangle OWA \cong \triangle OWB$, $\triangle OXB \cong \triangle OXC$, $\triangle OYC \cong \triangle OYA$ (SAS) **6.** $\overline{OA} \cong \overline{OB}$, $\overline{OB} \cong \overline{OC}$, $\overline{OA} \cong \overline{OC}$ (Corr. parts of $\cong \triangle$s) **7.** $\overline{OA} \cong \overline{OB} \cong \overline{OC}$ (Trans. Prop.)
25. 1. $\overline{DX}$, $\overline{EY}$, and $\overline{FZ}$ are medians. (Given) **2.** $\overline{EZ} \cong \overline{ZD}$, $\overline{DY} \cong \overline{YF}$, $\overline{EX} \cong \overline{XE}$ (Def. median) **3.** $\frac{EZ}{FZ} = 1$, $\frac{DY}{DY} = 1$, $\frac{FX}{FX} = 1$ (Algebra) **4.** $\frac{EZ}{ZD} = 1$, $\frac{DY}{YF} = 1$, $\frac{FX}{XE} = 1$ (Subst.)
5. $\frac{EZ}{ZD} \cdot \frac{DY}{FY} \cdot \frac{FX}{XE} = 1 \cdot 1 \cdot 1 = 1$ (Mult. Prop.) **6.** $\overline{DX}$, $\overline{EY}$, and $\overline{FZ}$ are concurrent. (Ceva's Th.)   **27. 1.** $\overline{DX}$, $\overline{EY}$, and $\overline{FZ}$ are alt. (Given) **2.** $\overline{FZ} \perp \overline{DE}$, $\overline{DX} \perp \overline{EF}$, $\overline{EY} \perp \overline{DF}$ (Def. alt.) **3.** $\angle EYF$, $\angle EYD$, $\angle FZD$, $\angle FZE$, $\angle DXE$, and $\angle DXF$ are rt. $\angle$s. (Def. $\perp$ lines) **4.** $\triangle EYF$, $\triangle DXF$, $\triangle DXE$, $\triangle FZE$, $\triangle FZD$, and $\triangle EYD$ are rt. $\triangle$s. (Def. rt. $\triangle$) **5.** $\triangle EYF \sim \triangle DXF$, $\triangle DXE \sim \triangle FZE$, $\triangle FZD \sim \triangle EYD$ (Rt. $\triangle \sim$)
6. $\frac{YF}{XF} = \frac{EF}{DF}$, $\frac{XE}{ZE} = \frac{DE}{FE}$, $\frac{ZD}{YD} = \frac{FD}{ED}$ (Def. $\sim \triangle$s) **7.** $\frac{YF}{XF} \cdot \frac{XE}{ZE} \cdot \frac{ZD}{YD} = \frac{EF}{DF} \cdot \frac{DE}{FE} \cdot \frac{FD}{ED}$ (Mult. Prop.) **8.** $\frac{YF}{XF} \cdot \frac{XE}{ZE} \cdot \frac{ZD}{YD} = 1$ (Algebra) **9.** $\overline{DX}$, $\overline{EY}$, and $\overline{FZ}$ are concurrent. (Ceva's Th.)

Algebra Review

1. $2a\sqrt{2}$ **3.** $-12\sqrt{x}$ **5.** $3\sqrt{3}$ **7.** z^3

Lesson 9-6 Try This

1. plane equidist. between *A* and *B*   **2.** sphere with radius 3 in.   **3.** cylinder with radius 1 cm

Exercise Set 9-6

1. 50-yd line   **3.** $\odot$ with dia. given hyp. and endpt. of dia. deleted   **5.** concentric $\odot$ with radius $\frac{1}{2}$ that of given $\odot$
7. 2. lines on either side of track $\parallel$, and 4 mi from, railroad track   **9.** bis. of $\angle ABC$ **11.** $\odot$ with radius $\frac{1}{2}$ the length of diag. with center at intersection of diag.   **13.** plane equidist. from and $\parallel$ given planes   **15.** plane $\perp$ line at given pt. **17.** line through *O* and *P*   **19.** line seg. $\parallel \overline{BC}$ connecting midpt. of $\overline{AB}$ and $\overline{AC}$ **21.** semicircle   **23.** $x = -1.5$ **25.** $y = x + 3$ **27.** arc from tan. to tan., which includes center of $\odot$ when chord is a dia.   **29.** major arcs of $\odot$

Mixed Review

1. obtuse **3.** obtuse **5.** obtuse

Lesson 9-7 Try This

2. 2 pt. equidist. between 2 ⊙s and 2 tang. **3.** a line ⊥ plane containing 2 ∥ lines and equidist. between 2 pt. and the 2 lines

Exercise Set 9-7

1. The ∠bis. of ∠APB, ∠APD, ∠DPC, and ∠CPB

3. 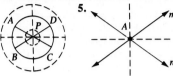 **5.**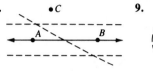

7. 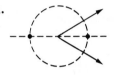 **9.**

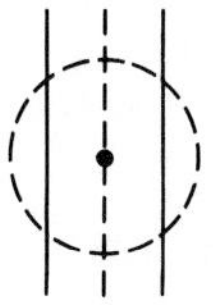

11. 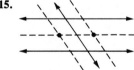 **13.**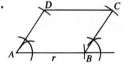

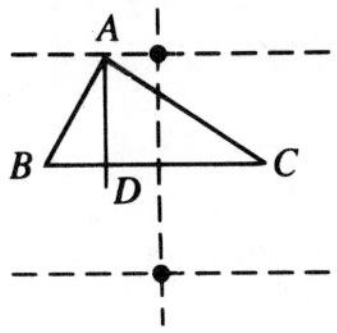

15.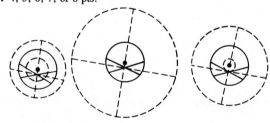

17. 4, 5, 6, 7, or 8 pts.

19. isos. **21.** $x > r$

23. 2 ⊙s 2 cm from plane containing P, where 2 planes ∥ plane containing P intersect sphere

25. 4 **27.** $y = 1, x = 0$

29.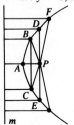

Algebra Review

1. $y < -6$ **3.** $n < -18$

Lesson 9-8 Try This

1. Copy $\overline{BC}$. Construct ⊥ at C. Using radius $\overline{AB}$ and center B, make an arc. Pt. of intersection with ⊥ is A. Draw $\overline{AB}$.

2.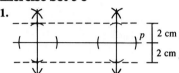

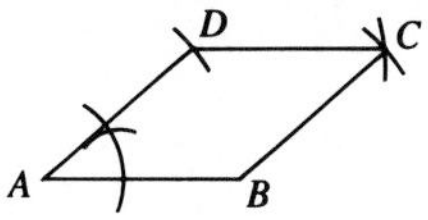

Exercise Set 9-8

1.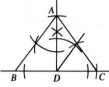

3. Construct 2 lines ∥ to, and 2 cm from, the sides of the ∠ in the interior of the ∠. Construct a ⊥$\overline{BC}$ from their pt. of intersection B to one of the sides of the ∠. Draw a circle with center B and radius $\overline{BC}$.

5. **7.**

9. 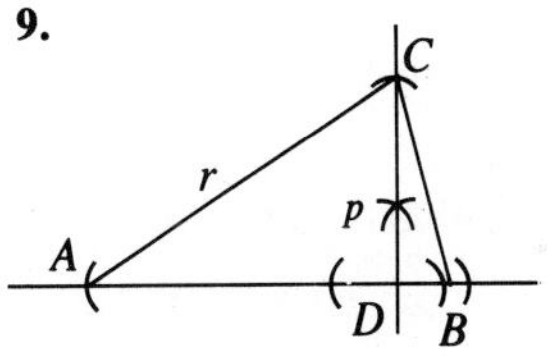 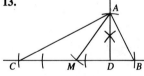 **11.**

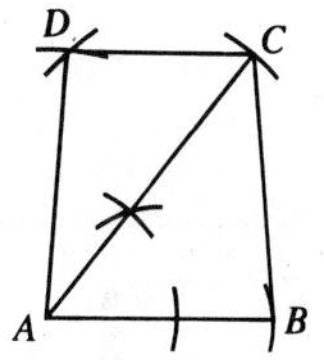

13. 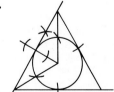 **15.**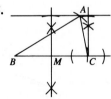

17. **19.**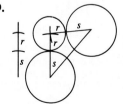

21.

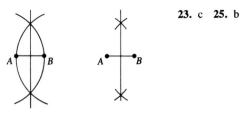

Collapsible compass   Rusty compass

23. c **25.** b

Mixed Review
1. 144° **3.** T **5.** T

Chapter Review
1. Const. 1 **2.** Const. 4 **3.** Const. 2
4.

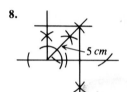

5. Const. 6 **6.** Const. 5 **7.** Const. 7

8.

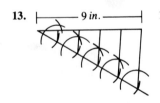

9.

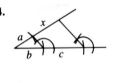

10. Const. 9 **11.** Const. 8 **12.** Const. 10

13.

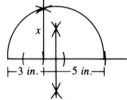

14.

15.

16. c **17.** b **18.** a **19.** 9 **20.** ⊙ with center T and radius 2 cm **21.** line ∥ $\overline{AB}$ and $\overline{CD}$ such that it is ⊥ bis. of $\overline{AD}$ and $\overline{BC}$ **22.** 4 pt.: pt. of intersection of lines ∥, and 3 cm to, line ℓ and of ⊙R with radius 4 cm **23.** 2 pt.: pt. of intersection of two ⊙s, X and Y, with centers 5 m apart and radii of 3 m

24.

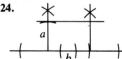

25.

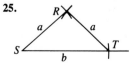

CHAPTER 10

Lesson 10-1 Try This
1. 44 **2.** 177 **3.** Let N be the intersection of $\overline{KJ}$ and $\overline{GH}$. Find area $GNKL = 8.68$ cm² and area $NHIJ = 42.78$ cm². Add both for area $GHIJKL$.

Exercise Set 10-1
1. $A = 117, p = 44$ **3.** $A = 30, p = 16\sqrt{2}$ **5.** $\ell = 18$, $A = 180$ **7.** $w = y - 5, p = 4y - 10$ **9.** 330
11. 96 **13.** 382 **15.** Post. 21 **17.** Post. 23 **19.** 240
21. $144\sqrt{3}$ **23.** always **25.** sometimes **27.** 56 m²
29. 224 **31.** 134.2 yd **33.** 32–4 × 8 ft plywood sheets
35. $BN = \frac{2}{3}BC$ **37.** The pen should be 16 ft by 16 ft sq.
39. 7 cm by 3 cm, 25 cm² **41.** Let $IF = y, EF = x$. $FG = W - Y, FH = L - x$, with L = length of large rect., W = width. $EFLD$ and $IFHB$ are ∼ to $ABCD$, so $\frac{X}{W-Y} = \frac{L}{W}$, and $\frac{Y}{L-x} = \frac{W}{L}$. Then $\frac{X}{W-Y}\frac{Y}{L-x} = \frac{L}{W}\frac{W}{L} = 1$, or $XY = (W - Y)(L - X)$, so region X has same area as region Y.

Mixed Review
1. 10 **3.** $\sqrt{69}$ **5.** 8 **7.** 10 **9.** $6\sqrt{6}$

Lesson 10-2 Try This
1. 75 **2.** 36

Exercise Set 10-2
1. 151.2 m² **3.** 6 cm **5.** $y^2 + 5y + 6$ **7.** 7 cm
9. $4x$ **11.** 72 **13.** 153.6 **15.** 16 **17.** 21,168 m²
19. $39\sqrt{3}$ **21.** $120\sqrt{2}$ **23.** $\frac{7}{4}$ **25.** Alt. to $\overline{AB}$ is $\frac{1}{2}$ alt. to $\overline{EF}$. **27.** Area is quadrupled. **29.** area of shaded region: $\frac{75}{2}$, area of unshaded region: $\frac{25}{2}$, ratio of shaded area of area of $\triangle RST$: $\frac{3}{4}$
31.

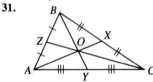

As in Ex. 30, the following pairs of △s have = areas: (i) $\triangle ABX$ and $\triangle ACX$, (ii) $\triangle ABY$ and $\triangle CBY$, (iii) $\triangle ACZ$ and $\triangle BCZ$, (iv) $\triangle OYA$ and $\triangle OYC$, (v) $\triangle OXB$ and $\triangle OXC$, (vi) $\triangle OZA$ and $\triangle OZB$. By (i) and (v), area $(\triangle AOB)$ = area $(\triangle ABX)$ − area $(\triangle OXB)$ = area $(\triangle ACX)$ − area $(\triangle OXC)$ = area $(\triangle AOC)$. Similarly, area $(\triangle AOB)$ = area $(\triangle BOC)$. Since area $(\triangle ABC)$ = area $(\triangle AOB)$ + area $(\triangle AOC)$ + area $(\triangle BOC)$, conclude area $(\triangle AOB)$ = area $(\triangle AOC)$ = area $(\triangle BOC)$ = $\frac{1}{3}$ area $(\triangle ABC)$. By (iv), (v), and (vi), conclude each of the small △s has area = $\frac{1}{6}$ area $(\triangle ABC)$. **33.** $32\sqrt{3}$
35. 20

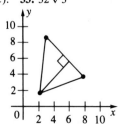

37. $\frac{k^2}{\sqrt{2}}$; about 15 ft   **39.** Let $b = AB = CD$ be base length of the $\square$, and let h_1, h_2 be the heights of the shaded $\triangle$s. area of shaded region $= \frac{1}{2}h_1b + \frac{1}{2}h_2b = \frac{1}{2}(h_1 \pm h_2)b = \frac{1}{2}$ (height of $\square$)$b = \frac{1}{2}$ (area of $\square$)   **41. a.** $BE = \sqrt{2}$, $BH = \sqrt{3}$ **b.** $\frac{\sqrt{3}}{2}$ **c.** $\sqrt{2}$ **d.** $\frac{\sqrt{2}}{4}$ **43.** Area of $\triangle LMN$ is sum of areas of $\triangle LFM$, $\triangle MFN$, and $\triangle NFL$. $\triangle LMN$ is equilat., so $LM = MN = LN$. Thus area $\triangle LMN = \frac{1}{2}a \cdot LM + \frac{1}{2}b \cdot MN + \frac{1}{2}c \cdot LN = \frac{a+b+c}{2} \cdot LM$. This means that no matter where pt. F is inside $\triangle LMN$, $a + b + c = \frac{2}{LM} \cdot$ area $\triangle LMN$.

Mixed Review

1. $5\sqrt{2}$ **3.** 8   **5.** $16\sqrt{2}$

Lesson 10-3 Try This

96.05

Exercise Set 10-3

1. 300   **3.** 59.85   **5.** 40   **7.** median 12, area 84   **9.** 38.4 **11.** 216   **13.** need AB **15.** 108   **17.** 7200 m^2 **19. a.** \$637.50   **b.** \$2437.50   **21.** $60\sqrt{2}$ **23.** 20 **25.** $2\sqrt{34} \approx 11.7$ cm   **27.** 24   **29.** 8   **31.** $95\sqrt{3} + 119$ **33.** $\triangle GHK$ and $\triangle KIJ$ have $=$ bases and alt., and so have $=$ areas. Area $GHIK =$ area $\triangle GHK +$ area $\triangle HIK$, area $HIJK =$ area $\triangle HIK +$ area $\triangle KIJ$. So, since area $\triangle KIJ =$ area $\triangle GHK$, the areas of the 2 quad. are $=$. **35.** $\frac{RS}{PQ + RS} = \frac{1}{1 + \frac{PQ}{RS}}$ **37.** $4\sqrt{5}$ **39.** 18,744 m^2

41. Let P be midpt. of base $\overline{AB}$, let Q be midpt. of base $\overline{DC}$. Heights of $APQD$ and $PBCQ$ are same. Area of $APQD = \frac{1}{2}(AP + DQ)h$ and area of $PBCQ = \frac{1}{2}(PB + QC)h$. Areas are $=$ since $AP = PB$ and $DQ = QC$.   **43.** Area $NLMP$ is 5 times area $\triangle LMO$. If $LM = x$, then area $NLMP = \frac{x + 4x}{2}h = \frac{5x}{2}h$ and area $\triangle LMO = \frac{x}{2}h$.   **45. a.** Draw a circle and an inscribed quad. Use a ruler to measure its sides.   **b.** Sides of quad. are 8, 6, $3\sqrt{10}$, and $\sqrt{10}$ so, area $= 39$. To check, note that diag. from $(-3, -4)$ to $(3, 4)$ is a dia. of $\odot$, hence by Cor. 8.11c, diag. divides quad. into 2 rt. $\triangle$s, with areas $\frac{1}{2}8 \cdot 6 = 24$, and $\frac{1}{2}(3\sqrt{10})(\sqrt{10}) = 15$. area of quad. $= 39$ **c.** Formula for area depends only on lengths of sides of quad. Side lengths of quad. can be preserved while changing its area. (Consider a sq. with side s and a rhom. with side s.) If formula were valid for all quad., it would assign same area to all quad. with $\cong$ sides, which is wrong. The restriction that quad. has its vertices on a $\odot$ removes all ambiguity.   **d.** If quad. is a rect., with a sq. as special case, then $c = a$ and $d = b$, and $s = a + b$. Formula then gives $A = \sqrt{baba} = \sqrt{b^2a^2} = ba$, which is area of rect. If $b = a$, $A = a^2$, area of square with side length a.

Mixed Review

1. 90   **3.** 5   **5.** AD **7.** 150   **9.** 5

Lesson 10-4 Try This

$3\sqrt{3}$ cm, $54\sqrt{3}$ cm^2

Exercise Set 10-4

1. $12\sqrt{3}$ **3.** 313.5   **5.** 696   **7.** 60, 30   **9.** 36, 54 **11.** 10, $30\sqrt{3}$, 5, $75\sqrt{3}$ **13.** $8\sqrt{2}$, 64, 8, 256   **15.** 10, $10\sqrt{2}$, $40\sqrt{2}$, 200   **17.** 18, 18, 108, $486\sqrt{3}$ **19.** true

21. true   **23.** true   **25.** $54\sqrt{3}$ **27.** $3\sqrt{2}$ cm, $2\sqrt{6}$ cm   **29.** $27\sqrt{3}$ **31.** 3, $2\sqrt{3}$ **33.** side ≈ 16, apothem ≈ 11 **35.** $(144\sqrt{2} + 72)$ ft^2 **37.** \$20.78 **39.** area of $\triangle = \frac{1}{2}\left(\frac{\sqrt{3}}{2}s\right)s = \frac{\sqrt{3}s^2}{4}$, area of hexagon $= \frac{1}{2}\left(\frac{\sqrt{3}}{2} \cdot \frac{s}{2}\right)3s = \frac{3\sqrt{3}s^2}{8}$, ratio of areas $= \frac{\frac{\sqrt{3}}{4}s^2}{\frac{3\sqrt{3}s^2}{8}} = \frac{2}{3}$ **41.** $1 + \sqrt{2}$ **43.** Area is multiplied by 4.   **45.** No; there is no pattern to justify such a chain of reasoning. On a 4×4 grid, an octagon has the most sides possible; on a 5×5, a nonagon.

Algebra Review

1. $2h$ **3.** at least 98

Lesson 10-5 Try This

1:2

Exercise Set 10-5

1. By Th. 10.6, the ratio of perimeters $= \frac{12}{8} = \frac{3}{2}$. By computation, the ratio $= \frac{12 \times 6}{8 \times 6} = \frac{72}{48} = \frac{3}{2}$.   **3.** 1:2, 1:4   **5.** $a:b$, $a^2:b^2$ **7.** 1:4, 1:16   **9.** 3:4, 3:4   **11.** $\sqrt{p}:\sqrt{q}$, $\sqrt{p}:\sqrt{q}$ **13.** 1:4   **15.** 169:400   **17.** All ratios are 5:6.   **19.** \$225 **21. a.** 4:1   **b.** 4:5   **23.** $\frac{80}{9}$, $\frac{100}{9}$ **25.** \$112,500   **27.** \$585 **29.** 7776 m^2 **31.** 1:16   **33.** 2:1   **35.** $\sqrt{2}:1$, 2:1 **37.** $12\sqrt{2}$ in.   **39.** Lines should intersect the altitude at $4\sqrt{6}$ and $4\sqrt{3}$ units from B.

Mixed Review

1. alt. int. or $\cong$ **3.** 180   **5.** 51   **7.** true

Lesson 10-6 Try This

1. 31.4 cm   **2.** 120

Exercise Set 10-6

1. 8, 8π **3.** 4, 8   **5.** 176 cm   **7.** 10 cm   **9.** 90   **11.** 18 **13.** 63π cm   **15.** $36 + 3\pi$ cm   **17.** $4\sqrt{3}\pi$ cm   **19.** 4 gal **21.** $32 + 4\pi$ ft   **23.** $\frac{12\pi}{5}$ **25.** $\frac{8\pi}{9}$, $\frac{16\pi}{9}$ **27. a.** $\ell = \frac{mC}{360}$ **b.** $m = 360\frac{\ell}{C}$ **29.** $\frac{\pi(\text{radius})}{2}$ **31.** $6\pi + 24$ in.

Algebra Review

1. $10x(x + 3)(x - 3)$ **3.** $8(t^2 + 1)(t + 1)(t - 1)$ **5.** $5(x - 3)(x + 1)$ **7.** $2(3 + x)(3 - x)$ **9.** $(2x - 3)(x + 4)$

Lesson 10-7 Try This

1. 8   **2.** $\frac{175\pi}{2}$ **3.** $\frac{45\pi}{2}$ **4.** $16\pi - 32$

Exercise Set 10-7

1. 16π **3.** 49π **5.** 5π **7.** $\frac{361\pi}{16}$ **9.** 8π **11.** 11   **13.** $2\sqrt{2}$ **15.** $0.4(\sqrt{10})$ **17.** 16π **19.** $\frac{100}{\pi}$ **21.** 4π cm^2 **23.** 8π cm^2 **25.** 13.08 cm^2 **27.** 21.37 cm^2 **29.** $12\pi - 9\sqrt{3}$ **31.** 36, $\frac{360}{n}$ **33.** 4:3   **35.** 90   **37.** $\frac{9}{2}\pi - 9$ **39.** $\frac{36}{25}$ times as much   **41.** $\frac{13\pi}{16}$ sq in.   **43.** $\frac{1}{3}$ **45.** Shaded area $=$ area of 2 semicircles on legs $-$ area of semicircle containing $\triangle ABC +$ area of $\triangle ABC = \frac{1}{2}\pi\left(\frac{AB}{2}\right)^2 + \frac{1}{2}\pi\left(\frac{BC}{2}\right)^2 - \frac{1}{2}\pi\left(\frac{AC}{2}\right)^2 + \frac{1}{2}(AB)(BC) = \frac{1}{8}\pi(AC)^2 - \frac{1}{8}\pi(AC)^2 + \frac{1}{2}(AB)(BC) = \frac{1}{2}(AB)(BC) =$ area $\triangle ABC$ where the Pythag. Th. has been used.   **47.** $\frac{(\sqrt{3} - \frac{\pi}{2})r^2}{\sqrt{3}r^2} = 1 - \frac{\sqrt{3}\pi}{6}$

49. $63 - 36\sqrt{3} \approx 0.646$ **51.** As long as ~ fig. are used, with 1 straight seg. of appropriate length, it will work for any fig.

Mixed Review

1. false **3.** false **5.** false

Chapter Review

1. 32 **2.** 48 **3.** 20.4 **4.** $p = 30 + 10\sqrt{3}$, $a = 50\sqrt{3}$
5. 33.6 **6.** $\frac{21}{2}$ **7.** 120 **8.** $9\sqrt{3}$ **9.** 4 cm **10.** 20
11. 6.2 cm **12.** $96\sqrt{3}$ **13.** 100 m² **14.** $150\sqrt{3}$
15. true **16.** false **17.** true **18.** 147 **19.** 12π
20. $6\sqrt{2}\pi$ **21.** $\frac{35\pi}{9}$ **22.** 8π **23.** $16\sqrt{3}$

CHAPTER 11

Lesson 11-1 Try This

1. $LA = 540$, $SA = 600$ **2.** $LA = 360$, $SA = 360 + 75\sqrt{3}$

Exercise Set 11-1

1. 112 **3.** 216 **5.** $LA = 96\frac{1}{3}$, $SA = 126\frac{1}{3}$ **7.** $LA = 108$,
$SA = 188$ **9.** $LA = 136x^2$, $SA = 276x^2$ **11.** $LA = 60 + 30\sqrt{2}$, $SA = 85 + 30\sqrt{2}$ **13.** never **15.** sometimes
17. sometimes **19.** 1136 **21.** 814 cm² **23.** $LA = 100$
cm², $SA = 150$ cm² **25.** 5.2 cm **27.** 4 cm **29.** $2\sqrt{3}$
cm **31.** Since $\overline{AD} \| \overline{GF}$ and $\overline{DG} \| \overline{AF}$, $ADGF$ is a $\square$. By Th.
5.3, $\overline{DF}$ bisects $\overline{AG}$. Midpt. of $\overline{AG}$ is O, so O is also midpt.
of $\overline{DF}$. **33.** $24\sqrt{2}$ ft **35.** 27 cm² **37.** Faces must be identical.

39. a. 42 sq units

b.
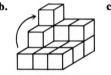
c.

Mixed Review

1. 9.58 **3.** 18° **5.** 9.14

Lesson 11-2 Try This

1. $LA = 60$, $SA = 96$ **2.** $LA = 80\sqrt{3}$ cm², $SA = 130\sqrt{3}$ cm²

Exercise Set 11-2

1. $LA = 80$, $SA = 105$ **3.** $LA = 72$, $SA = 72 + \frac{27\sqrt{3}}{2}$
5. $l = 25$, $LA = 700$, $SA = 896$ **7.** $LA = 260x^2$,
$SA = 360x^2$ **9.** $60 + \frac{25\sqrt{3}}{4}$ sq in. **11.** 9 cm **13.** 11 cm
15. $64\sqrt{3}$ cm² **17.** $108\sqrt{3}$ **19.** 16 cm² **21.** $\sqrt{3}x^2$
23. $LA = \frac{3s^2}{2}$, $SA = (\frac{3}{2} + \frac{\sqrt{3}}{2})s^2$

Algebra Review

1. $y = 4x - 3$ **3.** $y = 8$ **5.** $y = -\frac{3}{10}x - \frac{1}{5}$

Lesson 11-3 Try This

1. 18 ft³ **2.** $28\sqrt{3}$ cm³

Exercise Set 11-3

1. 280 cm³ **3.** 343 cm³ **5.** 90 **7.** $36\sqrt{3}$ cm³ **9.** 15 cu ft
11. Volume is mult. by 8. **13.** 270.2 cu yd **15.** 102 cm³
17. 3450 m³ **19.** 4 in., 4 in., $4\sqrt{2}$ in. **21.** $\sqrt[3]{18}$ cm
23. $7779.85 **25.** $\frac{\sqrt{3}}{4}s^3$ cu units

Mixed Review

1. 176 **3.** 24

Lesson 11-4 Try This

1. 216.75 cm³ **2.** $\frac{50\sqrt{3}}{3}$ cm³

Exercise Set 11-4

1. 8 **3.** 384 **5.** 4583 $\frac{1}{3}$ **7.** 3456$\sqrt{3}$ **9.** 108 cm³
11. 140 cm³ **13.** 12 **15.** 1280 cm³ **17.** $\frac{400\sqrt{3}}{9}$ cm
19. Vol. of taller pyramid is twice vol. of shorter pyramid.
21. 112 cm³ **23.** Heights of pyramids are in the ratio
$\frac{9}{10}$. **25.** $\frac{9}{2}$ cm³ **27.** $\frac{256\sqrt{2}}{3}$ cm³ **29.** Vol. of double pyramids
is $\frac{2}{3}$ vol. of hexagonal prism.

Algebra Review

1. $x = 1, y = 3$ **3.** $p = 1, q = -1$

Lesson 11-5 Try This

1. $LA = 64\pi$ cm², $SA = 96\pi$ cm² **2.** 5 cm

Exercise Set 11-5

1. $LA = 48\pi$, $SA = 80\pi$, $V = 96\pi$ **3.** $LA = 18\pi$ cm²,
$SA = 26\pi$ cm², $V = 18\pi$ cm³ **5.** $LA = 140\pi$, $SA = 340\pi$,
$V = 700\pi$ **7.** $r = 4$, $LA = 32\pi$, $SA = 64\pi$
9. 62.963π cu yd **11.** 130π cm² **13.** 324π cu ft
15. $SA = 920\pi$ sq in., $V = 3600\pi$ cu in. **17.** about 50
min **19.** $(1000 - 160\pi)$ cu in. **21.** No; if r is doubled, V
is quadrupled. **23.** $\frac{4}{7}$ **25.** $SA = (232 + 6\pi)$ cm²,
$V = (160 - 4\pi)$ cm³ **27.** If r and h are each doubled, then
SA is quadrupled. Vol. is multiplied by 8.

Algebra Review

1. $m = 7$ **3.** $m = -\frac{5}{6}$

5. $m = 2$ **7.** $m = -\frac{5}{4}$

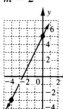 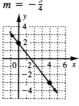

Lesson 11-6 Try This

1. 15 cm **2.** Vol. is doubled.

Exercise Set 11-6

1. $LA = 60\pi$, $SA = 96\pi$, $V = 96\pi$ **3.** $l = 10$,
$LA = 80\pi$, $SA = 144\pi$, $V = 128\pi$ **5.** $h = 5\sqrt{3}$, $l = 10$,
$SA = 75\pi$, $V = \frac{125\sqrt{3}}{3}\pi$ **7.** $\pi(\sqrt{2} + 1)36$ **9.** vol. of
cone = $3\pi h$ cu in., vol. of cylinder = $4\pi h$ cu in., vol of
cylindrical cup is >. **11.** 65π cm² **13.** Vol. is doubled.
15. 40π cm³ **17.** 448π cm³ **19.** $\frac{100\pi}{27}$ min
21. $V = \frac{970}{3}\sqrt{2}\pi$, $SA = (110\sqrt{2} + 146)\pi$

23. $\frac{\pi 6572}{3}$ cu units **25.** If a cone has $\frac{1}{3}$ vol. of a cylinder,
then it has same base diameter and height as the cylinder.
Converse is false. A counter example is a cylinder with base
diameter $2r$ and height h and a cone with base diameter r and
height $4h$. vol. of cylinder = $\pi r^2 h$, vol. of
cone = $\frac{1}{3}\pi\left(\frac{r}{2}\right)^2 4h = \frac{1}{3}\pi r^2 h$

Mixed Review

1. 10 cm **3.** 9

Lesson 11-7 Try This

1. $SA = 100\pi$ cm², $V = \frac{500\pi}{3}$ cm³ **2.** 324π cm²

Exercise Set 11-7

1. $SA = 196\pi$, $V = \frac{1372\pi}{3}$ **3.** $SA = 16\pi$, $V = \frac{32\pi}{3}$
5. $SA = 256\pi$, $V = \frac{2048\pi}{3}$ **7.** $r = 6$, $SA = 144\pi$
9. $\frac{9\pi}{2}$ cm³ **11.** 2 cm **13.** $\frac{352\sqrt{11}}{3}\pi$ cm³ **15.** 12π
17. $\frac{256\pi}{3}$ cm³ **19.** $1600\pi + \frac{4000}{3}\pi$ **21.** $\frac{5}{6}$ **23.** none of
these **25.** SA of sphere is equal to $4\pi r^2$. Lateral surface
area of cylinder is equal to $2\pi rh = 2\pi r \cdot 2r = 4\pi r^2$. Both
SA of sphere and lateral area of cylinder are $4\pi r^2$. **27.** $\frac{3}{2}$
29. It will remain as 1 solid. Holes do not join to form a cut.

Algebra Review

1. $3 < x < 7$

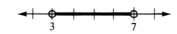

3. $x < -\frac{10}{3}$ or $x > 5$

5. $1 < x < 3$

7. $0 < x \le 6$

Lesson 11-8 Try This

1. 160π **2.** 297 cm²

Exercise Set 11-8

1. 8 to 5 **3.** 512 to 125 **5.** 125 cm³ **7.** 9 to 4
9. 225 cm² **11.** 64 to 1 **13.** 64 to 1 if walls are imagined
as having small width or 16 to 1 if width does not change
(i.e., walls treated as 2-dimensional) **15.** 3h **17.** Larger
tank has $(1.5)^3$ or 3.375 times vol. of smaller tank. Larger
tank has lower price per unit capacity, making it the better
buy. **19.** Particles 0.5 cm in dia. are more effective. Larger
particle has 4 times SA of one of smaller particles, but there
are 8 times as many of smaller particles per unit vol. Smaller
size has twice total SA of larger size. **21.** Weight increases
proportionally to vol. (or cube of factor). Strength increases
as sq. of factor.

Mixed Review

1. 6   **3.** 125   **5.** 90   **7.** 15   **9.** $4\sqrt{3}$

Chapter Review

1. 12 vert., 18 edges, 8 faces   **2.** $LA = 36 \text{ cm}^2$, $SA = 72 \text{ cm}^2$ **3.** $LA = 180$, $SA = 180 + 108\sqrt{3}$ **4.** $LA = 45$, $SA = 45 + \frac{25\sqrt{3}}{4}$ **5.** 6 cm   **6.** 210   **7.** 270   **8.** 96 sq in.   **9.** $160\sqrt{3}$ cu in.   **10.** 384   **11.** 9 cm   **12.** 400π **13.** $LA = 58.8\pi$, $SA = 156.8\pi$, $V = 205.8\pi$ **14.** 75π **15.** $LA = 255\pi$, $SA = 480\pi$, $V = 600\pi$ **16.** 21π **17.** $SA = 196\pi$ **18.** $V = \frac{32\pi}{3}$ **19.** 36π **20.** 3:4   **21.** 9:16   **22.** 3:4   **23.** 27:64   **24.** 135

Chapter 12

Lesson 12-1 Try This

1. a. (0, 2) **b.** (−2, 0)   **2.** (1, 2)   **3.** (−1, −1)

Exercise Set 12-1

1. (2, 1)   **3.** E **5.** I   **7.** II   **9.** II   **11.** $\left(\frac{5}{2}, \frac{1}{2}\right)$ **13.** $\left(\frac{1}{2}, -2\right)$ **15.** (2, 6)   **17.** (2, 1)   **19.** $\left(\frac{1}{2}, -\frac{1}{2}\right)$ **21.** $\left(\frac{a}{2}, \frac{b}{2}\right)$

23.

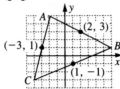

25. (−2, 8)   **27.** (4, −3)   **29.** (90, 45)

31. parallelogram

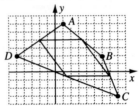

33. $\left(2, -\frac{5}{2}\right)$, which is the midpoint of $\overline{MP}$ **35.** $\left(-1, -\frac{3}{2}\right)$

37. $\left(\frac{x_1 + 2x_2}{3}, \frac{y_1 + 2y_2}{3}\right)$, $\left(\frac{2x_1 + x_2}{3}, \frac{2y_1 + y_2}{3}\right)$

Algebra Review

1. $9x^4y^2z^8$ **3.** n^{30} **5.** $\frac{3}{31}$

Lesson 12-2 Try This

$-\frac{1}{7}$, $-\frac{16}{7}$, 2

Exercise Set 12-2

1. −1; neg.   **3.** $-\frac{1}{4}$; neg.   **5.** 0; zero   **7.** $-\frac{5}{4}$; neg.   **9.** undef.   **11.** $-\frac{1}{2}$ **13.** $\frac{3}{10}$ **15.** $\frac{7}{2}$ **17.** 1   **19.** 1

21. slope of $\overline{RS} = -1$, of $\overline{ST} = 4$, of $\overline{UT} = -1$, and of $\overline{RU} = 4$; $RSTU$ is a parallelogram.   **23.** 0

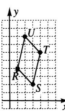

25. −3   **27.** 1   **29.** $6\frac{2}{3}$ ft   **31.** $\frac{1}{3}$ **33.** (0, 24)   **35.** $x = 2$ **37.** $x = 11$ **39.** Median from A has slope 2, from B slope $-\frac{1}{4}$, from C slope -16.   **41.** 1. Coord. of D, H, and L are (4, 0), (10, 0), (18, 0). (Given) 2. Let coord. of G, K, and P be (4, y_1), (10, y_2), (18, y_3). (Every pt. on a given line $\parallel$ y-axis has same x-coord.) 3. $\overline{AY}$ has a slope of $\frac{1}{2}$. (Given) 4. G, K, and P are on $\overline{AY}$ and have coord. G (4, 2), K (10, 5), P (18, 9). (Slope formula with A (0, 0) and coord. in 2) 5. DEFG, HIJK, and LMNP are squares. (Given)

6. $\overline{GF} \parallel \overline{DE}$, $\overline{JK} \parallel \overline{HI}$, $\overline{NP} \parallel \overline{LM}$ (Def. square) 7. $GD = GF$, $KH = KJ$, $PL = PN$ (Def. square) 8. $GD = 2$, $KH = 5$, $PL = 9$ (Diff. in y-coord.) 9. Coord. of E, I, and M are (6, 0), (15, 0), (27, 0). (Def. square) 10. Coord. of F, J, and N are (6, 2), (15, 5), (27, 9). (Same as 10 and every pt. on a given line $\parallel$ y-axis has same x-coord.) 11. Slope of $\overline{FJ}$ is $\frac{1}{3}$, slope of $\overline{JN}$ is $\frac{1}{3}$. (Def. slope) 12. F, J, and N are collinear. (Fact: Three pt. A, B, and C are collinear if the slope of $\overline{AB}$ = slope of $\overline{BC}$.)

Mixed Review
1. 65

Lesson 12-3 Try This
1. $-\frac{5}{2}$ 2. slope of $\overline{RS} = -3$, slope of $\overline{TS} = \frac{1}{3}$
Since $(-\frac{1}{3})(3) = -1$, $\overline{RS} \perp \overline{TS}$, so $\angle S$ is a rt. $\angle$.

Exercise Set 12-3
1. $\overline{AB} \parallel \overline{CD}$ 3. neither 5. slope from (3, 9) to (7, 5) is -1; slope from (7, 5) to (3, -3) is 2; slope from (3, -3) to (-1, 1) is -1; slope from (-1, 1) to (3, 9) is 2; opp. sides are $\parallel$ so the fig. is a $\square$. 7. Slope from (-3, -3) to (-1, 2) is $\frac{1}{2}$; slope from (-1, -2) to (1, -6) is -2; slope from (1, -6) to (-1, -7) is $\frac{1}{2}$; slope from (-1, -7) to (-3, -3) is -2; consecutive sides are $\perp$, so fig. is rect. 9. $y = -3$
11. $-\frac{4}{3}$ 13. slope of $\overline{RS} = 1$, of $\overline{ST} = -1$, of $\overline{RT} = -5$
15. (0, 3) or (0, -3) 17. $y = \frac{1}{3}$ 19. $b = -8$
21. $(\frac{12}{5}, 0)$ 23. (1, -1) 25. Slope of $\overline{AB} = 0$; of $\overline{BC} = \frac{e-b}{d}$; of $\overline{CD} = 0$; of $\overline{DA} = \frac{e-b}{d}$; opp. sides are $\parallel$, so $ABCD$ is a $\square$. 27. $-\frac{c}{d}$

Algebra Review
1. -4 3. 24 5. 41 7. -8 9. 18

Lesson 12-4 Try This
1. $y = -2x - 3$ 2. $\frac{5}{2}$, -5 3. $y + 5 = \frac{4}{3}(x - 2)$

4. $y = -\frac{6}{5}x + 4$
$y - 4 = -\frac{6}{5}x$ or
$y + 2 = -\frac{6}{5}(x - 5)$

Exercise Set 12-4
1. $y = 2x + 3$ 3. $y = -\frac{3}{4}x - \frac{1}{2}$ 5. $y = -2$
7. 1, 4 9. $-\frac{3}{2}$, 3 11. 0, -1

13. $-\frac{1}{2}$, 2 15. $-\frac{3}{2}$, $\frac{5}{2}$

17. $y = \frac{2}{3}x$ 19. $y = -3$ 21. $y - 4 = -\frac{5}{2}x$
23. $y = -2x$ 25. $y = \frac{3}{4}x$ or $y - 3 = \frac{3}{4}(x - 4)$ 27. $y = x$ or $y + 3 = x + 3$ 29. $y - 3 = x - 1$ or $y + 2 = x + 4$ 31. $y - 4 = 2(x - 2)$ or $y + 4 = 2(x + 2)$
33. $y = 0$ 35. a. 0.1 b. $5.50 37. $\frac{1}{2}$ 39. $-\frac{3}{2}$
41. $y - 2 = \frac{1}{2}(x - 4)$ 43. $y = -3x$ 45. (4, 1) 47. $\frac{25}{2}$
49. $\overline{AC}$: $y + 4 = -2(x - 6)$ or $y - 2 = -2(x - 3)$; $\overline{BD}$: $y - 2 = 2(x - 6)$ or $y + 4 = 2(x - 3)$ 51. $x = \frac{13}{4}$
53. $y + 7 = -\frac{1}{2}(x - 8)$ and $y + 7 = -3(x - 8)$
55. (5.4, 1.8) 57. Answers may vary.

Algebra Review
1. $4\sqrt{3}$ 3. $9\sqrt{3}$

Lesson 12-5 Try This
1. $\sqrt{145}$ 2. isos.

Exercise Set 12-5
1. 10 3. $7\sqrt{2}$ 5. $2\sqrt{13}$ 7. $\sqrt{74}$ 9. isos. 11. isos.
13. yes 15. slope, less multiplication with smaller numbers 17. no 19.

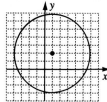

21. $3\sqrt{5}$ 23. 4 25. $\sqrt{130}$ 27. 20 29. $70\sqrt{17}$ ft
31. 65 yd 33. (2, 4) 35. $\frac{11}{5}\sqrt{5}$ 37. Answers may vary. Greatest % of error is $\approx 5.7\%$.

Mixed Review
1. 80 3. 70

Lesson 12-6 Try This
1. $(x - 4)^2 + (y + 1)^2 = 16$ 2. (-3, 7), $5\sqrt{2}$

Exercise Set 12-6
1. $x^2 + y^2 = 25$ 3. $(x + 5)^2 + y^2 = 16$ 5. $(x + 3)^2 + (y + 4)^2 = 16$ 7. $(x + 1)^2 + (y - 3)^2 = 12$

9. $(x - a)^2 + (y - b)^2 = c^2$ **11.** $(0, 0), 2\sqrt{5}$
13. $(-6, 0), 3\sqrt{5}$ **15.** $(a, b), 6$
17.

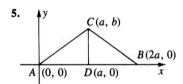

19. $(x + 4)^2 + y^2 = 16$ **21.** $(x - 4)^2 + (y + 2)^2 = 65$
23. $(x + 1)^2 + y^2 = 9$ **25.** $(x + 1)^2 + (y - 6)^2 = 16$
27. $y + 3 = -\frac{5}{9}(x - 5)$ or $y - 2 = -\frac{5}{9}(x + 4)$,
$5x + 9y + 2 = 0$ **29.** $(x + 4)^2 + (y - 3)^2 = 16$
31. neither **33.** secant **35.** secant **37.** neither
39. $(x - 4)^2 + y^2 = 16$, $(x + 4)^2 + y^2 = 16$,
$x^2 + (y - 4)^2 = 16$, $x^2 + (y + 4)^2 = 16$ **41.** 11π
43. $(x - 1)^2 + (y - 7)^2 = 10$ **45.** $x^2 + y^2 + z^2 = 48$
47. Ellipses; effect is to stretch or contract axis corresponding
to term with coefficient. Given $ax^2 + by^2 = 16$, if $a = 1$
and $b = 1$, the eq. is of a circle, but as a gets larger, the circle is compressed along x-axis. Similarly, as b gets larger,
fig. is compressed along y-axis. Resulting fig. are ellipses.

Mixed Review

1. 7900 sq yd

Lesson 12-7 Try This

1. $(\frac{a}{2}, \frac{a\sqrt{3}}{2})$ **2.**

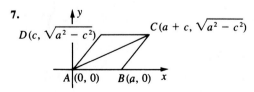

Exercise Set 12-7

1. $C(p + m, n)$
3.

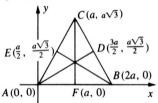

5.

7.

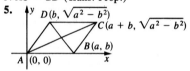

---

9. $C(0, \sqrt{3}a)$ **11.** $E(\frac{a + b}{2}, c)$
13. $GF = \sqrt{(b + e - (a + b))^2 + (c + f - c)^2} = $
$\sqrt{(e - a)^2 + f^2}$ $HE = \sqrt{(e - a)^2 + (f - 0)^2} = $
$\sqrt{(e - a)^2 + f^2}$ so $GE = HE$;
$HG = \sqrt{(b + e - e)^2 + (c + f - f)^2} = \sqrt{b^2 + c^2}$
$EF = \sqrt{(a + b - a)^2 + (c - 0)^2} = \sqrt{b^2 + c^2}$ so
$HG = EF$. $EFGH$ is $\square$, because opp. sides of $EFGH$ are $\cong$.
15. $B(\frac{a}{2}, \frac{\sqrt{3}a}{2})$; $D(-a, 0)$; $E(-\frac{a}{2}, -\frac{\sqrt{3}a}{2})$; slope of
$\overline{AB} = \frac{\frac{a\sqrt{3}}{2}}{\frac{a}{2} - a} = -\sqrt{3}$, slope of $\overline{DE} = \frac{-\frac{a\sqrt{3}}{2}}{-\frac{a}{2} + a} = -\sqrt{3}$

Algebra Review

1. $\frac{3}{4a^4}$ **3.** $-3ab$

Exercise Set 12-8

1. 1. $\triangle RST$ with coord. $R(0, 0), S(a, 0), T(b, c)$ (Given)
2. M is midpt. of $\overline{RT}$; N is midpt. of $\overline{ST}$. (Given) 3. M has
coord. $(\frac{b}{2}, \frac{c}{2})$; N has coord. $(\frac{a + b}{2}, \frac{c}{2})$. (Midpt. Th.)
4. $MN = \sqrt{(\frac{a + b}{2} - \frac{b}{2})^2 + (\frac{c}{2} - \frac{c}{2})^2} = \frac{a}{2}$, $RS = $
$\sqrt{(a - 0)^2 + (0 - 0)^2} = a$ (Dist. Form.) 5. $\frac{1}{2}RS = \frac{a}{2}$ (Mult.
Prop.) 6. $MN = \frac{1}{2}RS$ (Trans. Prop.) **3.** 1. isos. trap. $ABCD$
(Given) 2. $AC = \sqrt{(a - b)^2 + c^2}$; $BD = \sqrt{(b - a)^2 + c^2}$
(Dist. Form.) 3. $(a - b)^2 = (b - a)^2$ (Prop. of Real No.)
4. $\sqrt{(a - b)^2 + c^2} = \sqrt{(b - a)^2 + c^2}$ (Subst.)
5. $AC = BD$ (Trans. Prop.)
5.

1. rhom. $ABCD$ with coord. $A(0, 0), B(a, 0), C(a + b,$
$\sqrt{a^2 - b^2}), D(b, \sqrt{a^2 - b^2})$ (Given) 2. slope of
$\overline{AC} = \frac{\sqrt{a^2 - b^2}}{a + b}$; slope of $\overline{BD} = -\frac{\sqrt{a^2 - b^2}}{a - b}$ (Def. slope) 3.
(slope of $\overline{AC}$)(slope of $\overline{BD}$) $= \frac{\sqrt{a^2 - b^2} \cdot -\sqrt{a^2 - b^2}}{(a + b)(a - b)}$ (Subst.)
4. $\frac{\sqrt{a^2 - b^2} \cdot -\sqrt{a^2 - b^2}}{(a + b)(a - b)} = \frac{-(a^2 - b^2)}{a^2 - b^2}$ (Prop. of Real No.)
5. (slope of $\overline{AC}$)(slope of $\overline{BD}$) $= -1$ (Trans. Prop.)
6. $\overline{AC} \perp \overline{BD}$ (2 nonvert. lines are $\perp$ if product of their
slopes is -1.)
7.

1. trap. $ABCD$ with coord. $A(0, 0), B(a, 0), C(d, c) D(b, c)$
and $\overline{EF}$ median (Given) 2. E is midpt. of $\overline{AD}$. F is midpt. of
$\overline{BC}$. (Def. median) 3. E has coord. $(\frac{b}{2}, \frac{c}{2})$
(Midpt. Th.) 4. $AB = \sqrt{a^2 + 0^2} = a$; $DC = $
$\sqrt{(d - b)^2 + (c - c)^2} = d - b$; $EF = $
$\sqrt{(\frac{a + d}{2} - \frac{b}{2})^2 + (\frac{c}{2} - \frac{c}{2})^2} = \frac{a + d - b}{2}$ (Dist. Form.)
5. $\frac{a + d - b}{2} = \frac{1}{2}[a + (d - b)]$ (Prop. of Real No.)
6. $EF = \frac{1}{2}(AB + DC)$ (Subst.)

9.

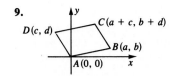

1. $\square ABCD$ with coordinates $A(0, 0)$, $B(a, b)$, $C(a + c, b + d)$, $D(c, d)$; $\overline{AC} \cong \overline{BD}$ (Given) 2. $AC = \sqrt{(a + c)^2 + (b + d)^2}$; $BD = \sqrt{(a - c)^2 + (b - d)^2}$ (Dist. Form.) 3. $\sqrt{(a + c)^2 + (b + d)^2} = \sqrt{(a - c)^2 + (b - d)^2}$ (Subst.) 4. $(a + c)^2 + (b + d)^2 = (a - c)^2 + (b - d)^2$ (Prop. of Real No.) 5. $(a + c)^2 - (a - c)^2 = (b - d)^2 - (b + d)^2$ (Add. Prop.) 6. $(2a)(2c) = 2b(-2d)$ (Prop. of Real No.) 7. $-1 = \frac{b}{a} \cdot \frac{d}{c}$ (Mult. Prop) 8. slope of $\overline{AB} = \frac{b}{a}$, slope of $\overline{AD} = \frac{d}{c}$ (Def. slope) 9. (slope of $\overline{AB}$)(slope of $\overline{AD}$) $= -1$ (Subst.) 10. $\overline{AB} \perp \overline{AD}$ (2 nonvert. lines are $\perp$ if product of slopes is -1.) 11. $ABCD$ is a rect. (If 2 sides of a $\square$ are $\perp$, the $\square$ is a rect.)

11.

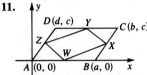

1. Quad. $ABCD$ with midpt. W, X, Y, and Z, and coord. $A(0, 0)$, $B(a, 0)$, $C(b, c)$, $D(d, c)$ (Given) 2. W has coord. $(\frac{a}{2}, 0)$; X has coord. $(\frac{a + b}{2}, \frac{c}{2})$; Y has coord. $(\frac{b + d}{2}, \frac{c + e}{2})$; Z has coord. $(\frac{d}{2}, \frac{e}{2})$ (Midpt. Th.) 3. slope of $\overline{WX} = \frac{\frac{c}{2}}{\frac{a + b}{2} - \frac{a}{2}} = \frac{c}{b}$, slope of $\overline{XY} = \frac{\frac{c + e}{2} - \frac{c}{2}}{\frac{b + d}{2} - \frac{a + b}{2}} = \frac{e}{d - a}$; slope of $\overline{YZ} = \frac{\frac{c + e}{2} - \frac{e}{2}}{\frac{b + d}{2} - \frac{d}{2}} = \frac{c}{b}$; slope of $\overline{ZW} = \frac{\frac{e}{2}}{\frac{d}{2} - \frac{a}{2}} = \frac{e}{d - a}$ (Def. slope) 4. $\overline{WX} \parallel \overline{YZ}$, $\overline{XY} \parallel \overline{ZW}$ (2 lines with same slope are $\parallel$). 5. $WXYZ$ is a $\square$. (Def. $\square$) **13.** If O is at the origin, $\overline{OD}$ on x-axis, $\overline{OC}$ on y-axis, and $\overline{OE}$ on z-axis; coord. of vert. of cube of side length a are: $O(0, 0, 0)$, $D(a, 0, 0)$, $C(0, a, 0)$, $E(0, 0, a)$, $A(a, a, 0)$, $B(0, a, a)$,
$OA = \sqrt{(a - 0)^2 + (a - 0)^2 + (0 - 0)^2} = a\sqrt{2}$;
$OB = \sqrt{(0 - 0)^2 + (a - 0)^2 + (0 - a)^2} = a\sqrt{2}$;
$AB = \sqrt{(a - 0)^2 + (a - a)^2 + (0 - a)^2} = a\sqrt{2}$ so $\triangle OAB$ is equilat. **15.** Answers may vary. Coordinate method uses simple algebra but has several variables. Method using $\triangle$s formed by diag. does not need many steps.

Mixed Review
1. 96 cm², 64 cm²

Chapter Review
1.–4.

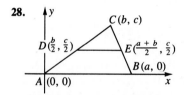

---

5. $(-4, 3)$ **6.** $(-10, 13)$ **7.** $-\frac{3}{5}$ **8.** 0 **9.** -3 **10.** 7 **11.** $\perp$ **12.** $\parallel$ **13.** $-\frac{1}{4}$ **14.** $-\frac{3}{2}, 5$ **15.** $0, -2$

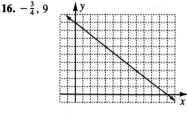

16. $-\frac{3}{4}, 9$

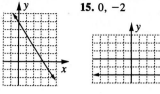

17. $y = \frac{1}{6}x + \frac{9}{2}$ **18.** $y = 3x - 9$ **19.** 4 **20.** $5\sqrt{2}$ **21.** isos., $AB = BC$ **22.** $C(-2, 4)$, $r = 4$ **23.** $C(1, 0)$, $r = 2\sqrt{5}$ **24.** $(x + 3)^2 + (y - 2)^2 = 81$ **25.** $(x - 4)^2 + (y - 7)^2 = 20$ **26.** $A(0, k)$, $B(h, 0)$

27.

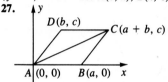

28.

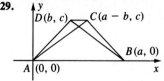

1. $\triangle ABC$ with coord. $A(0, 0)$, $B(a, 0)$, $C(b, c)$ (Given) 2. D is midpt. of $\overline{AC}$, E is midpt. of $\overline{CB}$. (Given) 3. D has coord. $(\frac{b}{2}, \frac{c}{2})$; E has coord. $(\frac{a + b}{2}, \frac{c}{2})$. (Midpt. Th.) 4. slope of $\overline{DE} = 0$, slope of $\overline{AB} = 0$ (Def. slope) 5. $\overline{DE} \parallel \overline{AB}$ (2 nonvert. lines are $\parallel$ if slopes are $=$.)

29.

1. $ABCD$ is isos. trap. with coord. $A(0, 0)$, $B(a, 0)$, $C(a - b, c)$, $D(b, c)$ and diag. $\overline{AC}$ and $\overline{BD}$. (Given) 2. $AC = \sqrt{(a - b)^2 + c^2}$, $BD = \sqrt{(b - a)^2 + c^2}$ (Dist. Form.) 3. $(a - b)^2 = (b - a)^2$ (Prop. of Real No.) 4. $\sqrt{(a - b)^2 + c^2} = \sqrt{(b - a)^2 + c^2}$ (Subst.) 5. $AC = BD$ (Subst. Prop.) 6. $\overline{AC} \cong \overline{BD}$ (Def. $\cong$ seg.)

Chapter 13

Lesson 13-1 Try This

1. a. U' **b.** V **c.** $\overline{T'W}$ **2.** in x-axis $(1, 1)$; in y-axis $(-1, -1)$ **3. a.**

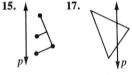

Exercise Set 13-1

1. H **3.** $\overline{CB}$ **5.** $\overline{XW}$ **7.** $\overline{TS}$ **9.** $(-1, 2)$ **11.** $(-2, -1)$
13. $(-3, 1)$, $(-4, 2)$
15.   **17.**   **19.** no lines of symmetry

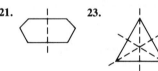

21.   **23.**

25.   **27.**

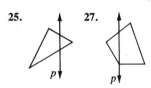

29. Answers may vary.   **31.** $(2, 4)$ **33.** $(1, 1)$ **35.** $(-1, -1)$ **37.** 1. L' is reflection image of L in line p. (Given) 2. line p is $\perp$ bis. of LL'. (Def. reflection image) 3. M is on line p. (Given) 4. $\overline{LM} \cong \overline{L'M}$ (Pt. on $\perp$ bis. of seg. are equidist. from endpt.)   **39.** $y = -x$ **41.** Reflect 1 city about line formed by river. Draw line connecting reflection image to other city. Bridge should be built where line intersects river.   **43.** Reflect I about south shoreline and reflect that reflection image about north shoreline. Draw line connecting A to new reflection image. Intersection of line with north shoreline is point B. Draw line connecting B to original reflection image of I. Intersection of line with south shoreline is C.   **45.** If $A'B'C'D'$ is a rhombus, then $ABCD$ is a $\square$. Converse is true. Original implication is not.

Mixed Review

1. true   **3.** false   **5.** false

Lesson 13-2 Try This

1. $\overline{FD}$ and $\triangle FDE$ **2. a.** $(2, 9)$ **b.** $(9, -2)$ **3.** E or G

Exercise Set 13-2

1. point Y **3.** point H **5.** $\overline{HI}$ **7.** $\triangle XYZ$ **9.** $(5, 3)$
11. $(7, 0)$ **13.** $(8, y + 2)$ **15.** $(-3, -1)$ **17.** $(-1, 2)$
19. $A, D; A, F; D, F; B, G; C, E$ **21.** $(-1, 8)$ **23.** $(1, 1)$
25. line with slope $\frac{3}{2}$ **27.** If A' is on $\overrightarrow{AB}$; then, since $\overrightarrow{BB}'$ is in same direction as $\overrightarrow{AA}'$, B is also on $\overrightarrow{AB}$. If A' is not on $\overrightarrow{AB}$; then, since $\overrightarrow{BB}'$ is in same direction and of same length as $\overrightarrow{AA}'$, $\overline{AA}' \parallel \overline{BB}'$ and $\overline{AA}' \cong \overline{BB}'$, and by Theorem 5.5 $ABB'A'$ is a $\square$.   **29.** 6   **31.** $P(p_1, p_2)$, $Q(q_1, q_2)$,

$P'(p_1 + a, p_2 + b)$, $Q'(q_1 + a, q_2 + b)$ $PQ = \sqrt{(p_1 - q_1)^2 + (p_2 - q_2)^2} = P'Q'$ **33.** As original key is slid along guide, it is "translated" to copy.   **35.** Slope of translation image of line is same as slope of the line.

Mixed Review

1. 252   **3.** $\frac{32}{3}\pi$ **5.** 30π

Lesson 13-3 Try This

1. a. B **b.** G **c.** E **2. a.** $(3, 2)$ **b.** $(3, -1)$

Exercise Set 13-3

1. A' **3.** $\overline{A'B'}$ **5.** B **7.** B **9.** E **11.** $\overline{CD}$ **13.** $\overline{DH}$
15. G **17.** rectangle $GHCD$ **19.** Square $LIJK$
21. $(-1, 2)$ **23.** $(-2, -1)$ **25.** $(-3, -4)$ **27.** true
29. true   **31.** yes   **33.** yes   **35.** yes   **37.** no   **39.** no
41. approx. $120°$ **43.** $(-y, x)$ **45. a.** $(-4, -3)$ **b.** $(2, -3)$
c. $(-x, -y)$ **47.** $90°$ clockwise about O ($45°$ counterclockwise about F)   **49.** The rotation images of line ℓ intersect to form a sq. centered about O. $\overline{OA} \cong \overline{OA'} \cong \overline{OA''} \cong \overline{OA'''}$, and $\overline{AA''}$ and $\overline{A'A'''}$ are bis. of each other, intersecting at O.
51. The diag. of a $\square$ are bis. of each other, so $\overline{AO} \cong \overline{OC}$ and $\overline{BO} \cong \overline{OD}$. Since $m\angle AOC = m\angle BOD = 180$; it follows that C is the half-turn image of A about O, D is the half-turn image of B about O, A is the half-turn image of C about O, B is the half-turn image of D about O.
53. Find $\perp$ bis. of $\overline{XX'}$ and $\overline{YY'}$. These lines either intersect or are identical. If they intersect, center of rotation is at their intersection pt. If they are identical, then draw $\overleftrightarrow{XY}$ and $\overleftrightarrow{X'Y'}$. These lines will intersect at center of rotation which will be on the common $\perp$ bis. of $\overline{XX'}$ and $\overline{YY'}$.   **55.** A, B, C, D, or F **57.** From Th. 10.9, arc length equals $\frac{2\pi r m}{360}$. For both arcs, $m(\angle$ of rotation$)$ is the same, but r is different, so arc lengths are different.   **59.** Figure has n sides, and 1 side may be rotated to any of the $n - 1$ other sides in exactly 1 way.

Algebra Review

1. $\parallel$ **3.** $\parallel$ **5.** $\parallel$

Lesson 13-4 Try This

1. J, K **2.** DH **3.** $H, \overline{FG}$

Exercise Set 13-4

1. $135°$ clockwise, O **3.** $90°$ clockwise   **5.** D, A **7.** H, A **9.** I **11.** K **13.** L **15.** C **17.** C **19.** M **21.** D
23. C **25.** B **27.** $(6, 1)$ **29.** $(7, -1)$ **31.** $(3, 4)$
33. $(2, 9)$ **35.**

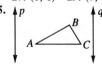

37. O lies on q and q is the $\perp$ bis. of $\overline{PP'}$. (Def. reflection in q) So $\overline{OP} \cong \overline{OP'}$ because pt. on $\perp$ bis. of seg. are equidist. from endpt. of seg.   **39.** $\overline{AA'} \perp p$, $\overline{A'A''} \perp q$ (Def. reflection) Two distinct lines $\perp$ to $\parallel$ lines are $\parallel$. $\overline{A'A''}$ is not $\parallel \overline{AA'}$ because they share point A'. Therefore, the 2 lines must not be distinct, that is A' is on $\overleftrightarrow{AA''}$, so $\overline{AA''} \perp p$.   **41.** Many $180°$ rotations about O' are possible. Only some of these rotate 1 cube to other.   **43.** infinitely many

Algebra Review

1. $x < -1$ **3.** $n < 3$ **5.** $x \geq 0$

Lesson 13-5 Try This

1. a. $C'D' = 6$ **b.** $A'B' = 8$ **2. a.** $IJ = 5$ **b.** $KM = 13$
3. *HGFEO* is reflection image of *ABCDO*. Since a line reflection is an isometry, the pentagons are $\cong$.

Exercise Set 13-5

1. 7 **3.** 4 **5.** 7 **7.** Distance between points is preserved under isometries. **9.** *C* **11.** 8 **13.** 8 **15.** 3 **17.** Answers may vary. Diag. are $\cong$ and bisect each other by reflection.
19. reflection in *p* **21.** *FABCX* is reflection of *AFEDX* in line *q*. Since line reflection is an isometry, *AFEDX* and *FABCX* are $\cong$. **23.** $\overline{AB} \cong \overline{A'B'}$, $\overline{AC} \cong \overline{A'C'}$, and $\overline{BC} \cong \overline{B'C'}$ because isometries preserve distances. So $\triangle ABC \cong \triangle A'B'C'$ by SSS. **25.** below ℓ **27.** on ℓ
29. Fig. in quad. I is reflection image of fig. in quad. II in line *q*. Fig. in quad. II is the reflection image of fig. in quad. III in line *p*. Therefore, fig. in quad. I is image of fig. in quad. III under reflection in line *p* followed by reflection in line *q*. Since composition of reflections is an isometry, fig. in quad. I is $\cong$ to fig. in quad. III. **31.** Corr. parts of the fig. are $\cong$ since they are mapped to each other by an isometry. Corr. perimeters, circumferences, etc. are $=$.

Mixed Review

1. 72 **3.** 28 **5.** 8

Lesson 13-6 Try This

1. a. 1.5 **b.** 0.5 **2. a.** (1, 3) **b.** (−0.5, 0.75)

Exercise Set 13-6

7. *EFGH* **9.** *L* **11.** *IJKL* **13.** $\overleftrightarrow{(-4.2)}$ **15.** (2, 1.4)
17. (1.5, 2.5) **19.** If *O* is on $\overline{BC}$, then since $kOB = OB'$ and $kOC = OC'$ (i) if *O* is between *B* and *C*, $B'C' = B'O + OC' = kBO + kCO = k(BO + CO) = kBC$; (ii) if *B* is between *O* and *C*, then *B'* is between *O* and *C'* and $B'C' = OC' - OB' = kOC - kOB = k(OC - OB) = kBC$; (iii) if *C* is between *O* and *B*, then *C'* is between *O* and *B'* and $B'C' = OB' - OC' = kOB - kOC = k(OB - OC) = kBC$. If *O* is not on *BC*, then since $OB' = kOB$, $OC' = kOC$, $\frac{OB'}{OB} = \frac{OC'}{OC}$. And since $\angle BOC \cong \angle B'OC'$, $\triangle BCO$ is $\sim$ to $\triangle B'C'O$ by the SAS $\sim$ Th., so $\frac{B'C'}{BC} = \frac{OB'}{OB} = k$, i.e. $B'C' = kBC$, so $BC = \frac{1}{k}B'C'$. **21.** 64
23. Dilation image of (1, 5) is (2, 10). Dilation image of (3, 2) is (6, 4). slope of $\ell = \frac{5-2}{1-3} = \frac{-3}{2}$, slope of $\ell' = \frac{10-4}{2-6} = \frac{-3}{2}$, $\ell \| \ell'$ **25.** *A'* is (−2, 4), *B'* is (4, 8), *C'* is (10, 4). Area of $\triangle ABC = \frac{1}{2}(6 \times 2) = 6$, area of $\triangle A'B'C' = \frac{1}{2}(12 \times 4) = 24$, area of $\triangle A'B'C' = 4 \times$ area of $\triangle ABC$ **27.** $A'(-1, 1\frac{2}{3})$, $B'(1, 2)$, $C'\left(1\frac{2}{3}, \frac{-2}{3}\right)$ **29.** *SA*: 4 to 1, vol.: 8 to 1

Mixed Review

1. center (0, 0), radius 8 **3.** center (−4, 5), radius $\sqrt{10}$
5. $x^2 + y^2 = 36$ **7.** $(x - 1)^2 + y^2 = 5$

Lesson 13-7 Try This

1. a. 16 **b.** 4 **c.** *AF* **2.** Translation *AT* followed by dilation with center *T* and scale factor 2 maps *ABCDEF* to *TUVWXY*.

Exercise Set 13-7

1. 8 **3.** 6 **5.** $18\frac{1}{3}$ **7.** $13\frac{1}{3}$ **9.** 120 **11.** $3\frac{1}{2}$ **13.** *AC*
15. Rotate *ABFGE* − 90° about *B*. Follow this with dilation of scale factor 2 and center *B*. **17.** 24 **19.** 8 **21.** By Th. 13.10, dilations take $\triangle$s to $\sim$ $\triangle$s. So $\triangle ACD \sim \triangle A'C'D'$, hence $\angle CDA \cong \angle C'D'A'$. Since $\overline{CD}$ is an alt. of $\triangle ABC$, $\angle CDA$ is a rt. $\angle$, so $\angle C'D'A'$ is a rt. $\angle$, so $\overline{C'D'}$ is an alt. of $\triangle A'B'C'$. **23.** 486 **25.** 9 to 1, 27 to 1 **27. a.** Not $\sim$; no isometry composed with a dilation will map one to the other. **b.** Not $\sim$; no isometry composed with a dilation will map one to the other. **29. a.** line of reflection **b.** center of rotation **c.** none **d.** center of dilation **e.** common center

Algebra Review

1. −10, 3 **3.** ±7 **5.** $\frac{1}{2}$, 3

Chapter Review

1. *E* **2.** *F* **3.** $\overline{CD}$ **4.** $\overline{EF}$ **5.** 2 **6.** (8, 7) **7.** (4, 0)
8. $(x + 4, y + 1)$ **9.** *E* **10.** *K* **11.** $\overline{IJ}$ **12.** *EFGH*
13. *M* **14.** $\overline{QL}$ **15.** no **16.** yes **17.** true **18.** false
19. false **20.** 6 **21.** 12 **22.** yes **23.** (50, −25)
24. *X* **25.** *I* **26.** 3 **27.** 90° clockwise rotation about *B* followed by dilation with scale factor 2 and center *B* maps *AEBF* to *GCBD*.

ACKNOWLEDGEMENTS

page	credit
2	Craig Aurness/Woodfin Camp & Associates
3	Wayland Lee*/Addison-Wesley Publishing Company
5	Gary Withey/Bruce Coleman Inc.
6 B	Janice Sheldon*
6 T	Wayland Lee*/Addison-Wesley Publishing Company
11	Janice Sheldon*
13	Wayland Lee*/Addison-Wesley Publishing Company
17	Wayland Lee*/Addison-Wesley Publishing Company
18	Wayland Lee*/Addison-Wesley Publishing Company
19	Greg Vaughn/Tom Stack & Associates
25	Peter Tenzer/Wheeler Pictures
26	Dan McCoy/Rainbow
29	Eric Carle/Stock, Boston
30	Janice Sheldon*
35	Janice Sheldon*
51 BR	Wayland Lee*/Addison-Wesley Publishing Company
51 TL	Patrick Vielcanet/Allsport-USA/Vandystadt
56	Gary Milburn/Tom Stack & Associates
58	Janice Sheldon*
62	The Bettman Archive, Inc.
63	David Madison/Bruce Coleman Inc.
78	Greg Vaughn/Tom Stack & Associates
82	Janice Sheldon*
92	Ann Duncan/Tom Stack & Associates
96	Scott Blackman/Tom Stack & Associates
104	Craig Aurness/Woodfin Camp & Associates
105	Cameron Davidson/Bruce Coleman Inc.
109	Stephen Frisch*
110	Wayland Lee*/Addison-Wesley Publishing Company
122	Rick Stewart/Allsport-USA
135	Wayland Lee*/Addison-Wesley Publishing Company
139 B, C, T	Wayland Lee*/Addison-Wesley Publishing Company
141	Bob Winsett/Tom Stack & Associates
145	Wayland Lee*/Addison-Wesley Publishing Company
148	Harald Sund
149	Leif Skoogfors/Woodfin Camp & Associates
159	Janice Sheldon*
164	Paul Solomon/Wheeler Pictures
166	R. S. Uzzell/Woodfin Camp & Associates
183	Declan Haun/Black Star
200	Chuck O'Rear/Woodfin Camp & Associates
210	Wayland Lee*/Addison-Wesley Publishing Company
222	Peter L. Cole/Bruce Coleman Inc.
227	Cary Wolinsky/Stock, Boston
229 C	Collection Haags Gemeentemuseum - The Hague M. C. Escher, Drawing (frogs)
229 L	Collection Haag Gemeentemuseum - The Hague M. C. Escher, 1946 (horsemen)
229 R	Timothy Egan/Woodfin Camp & Associates
235	Janice Sheldon*
239	Janice Sheldon*
254	Janice Sheldon*
260	Wayland Lee*/Addison-Wesley Publishing Company
261 B	Kevin Schafer/Tom Stack & Associates
261 R	Art Resource/Scala
261 T	Judy Canty/Stock, Boston
262	Janice Sheldon*
265	Janice Sheldon*
273	Wayland Lee*/Addison-Wesley Publishing Company
274	Wayland Lee*/Addison-Wesley Publishing Company
285	Janice Sheldon*
294	Hal Clasun/Tom Stack & Associates

page	credit
300 B	Pete Saloutos/The Stock Market
300 T	Bill Gallery/Stock, Boston
303	Rob Nelson/Stock, Boston
319	Brownie Harris/The Stock Market
323	Brian Parker/Tom Stack & Associates
325	Bob Straus/Woodfin Camp & Associates
333	Roy Morsch/The Stock Market
339	Billy Stickland/Allsport USA
340	Jose Azel/Contact Press/Woodfin Camp & Associates
350	Greg Davis/Black Star
351	Wayland Lee*/Addison-Wesley Publishing Company
360	Wayland Lee*/Addison-Wesley Publishing Company
361	Wayland Lee*/Addison-Wesley Publishing Company
390	Michael C. Radigan /The Stock Market
391	G. Contorakes/The Stock Market
400	Janice Sheldon*
415	Claudia Parks/The Stock Market
418 B, C	Wayland Lee*/Addison-Wesley Publishing Company
418 T	Alan Schwartz/Allsport USA
420	Greg Vaughn/Tom Stack & Associates
423	Wayland Lee*/Addison-Wesley Publishing Company
428 B	Budd Symes/Allsport USA
428 T	Janice Sheldon*
433 B	James Sugar/Black Star
433 T	Janice Sheldon*
436	David Madison/Bruce Coleman Inc.
437	William Waterfall/The Stock Market
442	The Bettmann Archive, Inc.
447	David Austen/Stock, Boston
451	John Flannery/Bruce Coleman Inc.
460 BL	Keith Gunnar/Bruce Coleman Inc.
460 BR	Wendy Neefus/Earth Scenes
460 T	Joan Saxe/Bruce Coleman Inc.
467	Doug Wechsler/Earth Scenes
473	George Gardner/Stock, Boston
484	Frank E. Pedrick/Light Images
490	E. R. Degginger/Earth Scenes
491	C. Benjamin/Tom Stack & Associates
498	Janice Sheldon*
499	Christopher Morris/Black Star
506	Wayland Lee*/Addison-Wesley Publishing Company
510	Dan McCoy/Rainbow
517	Stephen Frisch*
522	Charles Feil/Stock, Boston
525	Robert Essel/The Stock Market
525	Wayland Lee*/Addison-Wesley Publishing Company
532	Chris Sorensen/The Stock Market
537	The Bettmann Archive, Inc.
538 C	Tom Stack/Tom Stack & Associates
538 L	Donald Dietz/Stock, Boston
538 R	Janice Sheldon*
540	Matt Bradley/Tom Stack & Associates
557	Wayland Lee*/Addison-Wesley Publishing Company
575	Harald Sund
583	Dick Durrance/Woodfin Camp & Associates
586	Janice Sheldon*
588 L	Thomas Braise/The Stock Market
588 R	Charles Gupton/Stock, Boston
589	Dan McCoy/Rainbow
605	George Dritsas/Light Images
Cover:	© Ken Graham/AllStock

*Photographs provided expressly for the publisher

Index

SSS Inequality Theorem, 243
SSS Postulate, 153
SSS Similarity Theorem, 276
Standard form of a linear equation, 547
Statement (See also if-then statement.)
    biconditional, 33
    conclusion, 32
    conditional, 32–34
    contradictory, 230–31
    contrapositive, 34
    converse, 33
    equivalent, 38
    hypothesis, 32
    if-then, 32
    inverse, 34
    negation of, 230
    truth of, 195
Statistics
    average, 633
    coordinate geometry and, 556
    frequency distributions, 631
    histograms, 632
    line plots, 632
    mean, 633
    median, 633
    mode, 632
Straightedge, 391
Study Skills, 7, 85, 152, 206, 400
Substitution property, 45
Subtraction property, 45
    of equality, 45
Supplementary angles, 63
Surface, lateral, 511
Surface area
    of a cone, 511–12
    of a cylinder, 506–7
    of a prism, 485–86
    of a pyramid, 491–92
    of a solid, 485
    of similar solids, 522–23
    of a sphere, 517–18
Surveyor, 19, 166
Symbolic logic, 44
Symbols, 3, 44, 666
Symmetric property, 45
Symmetry
    line, 577–78
    metric properties and, 318
    reflectional, 578
    rotational, 588–89
    translational, 583–84
Synthetic approach, 194, 219

Tables
    list of symbols, 666
    square roots, 669
    trigonometric, 668
    truth, 33
Tangency, point of, 341, 345
Tangent
    angles of, 374
    circle, 351–52
    common, 351–52

external, 351
internal, 351
line, 345–46
plane, 342
ratio, 319–20
segments of, 380–81
to a circle, 341
to a sphere, 342
Tangent-chord angle, 368
Technical illustrator, 235
Terms, undefined, 3
Tessellation, 229
Theorem, 46
    Angle Bisector, 82
    Angle Sum, 123
    Common Angle, 92
    Common Segment, 86, 173
    Concurrency, 410–12
    Congruent Complements, 93
    Congruent Supplements, 93
    Corollary, 124
    Exterior Angle, 129
    Exterior Angle Inequality, 236
    Isosceles Triangle, 177
    meaning of, 46
    Means-Extremes Product, 256
    Midpoint, 81
    Midsegment, 224–25
    Parallels Proportional Segment, 282
    proving, 567
    Pythagorean, 301–2, 306, 307–8
    SAS Inequality, 243
    SAS Similarity, 275–76
    SSS Inequality, 243
    SSS Similarity, 276
    Triangle Angle Bisector, 283
    Triangle Inequality, 237, 242
    Triangle Proportional Segment, 281
    Vertical Angle, 65
Tolerance, levels of, 505
Translations, 583–84
Transformation, 31, 188, 274, 577
    compositions of, 594–96
    congruence, 600–1
    dilation, 605–6
    functional notation and, 587
    glide reflection, 603
    identity, 605
    isometry, 600–2
    line reflection, 577–78
    reflection, 577–78
    rotation, 588–89
    similarity, 610–11
    translation, 583–84
Transitive property, 45
Translation, 31, 583–84
Translation image, 583
Transversal, 106, 110
    parallel lines and, 117–19
    properties of, 112, 119
    proportional segments, 281
Trapezoid
    area of, 449–50
    bases of, 220
    bases angles of, 220
    definition, 220

height of, 449
isosceles, 220
legs of, 220
median of, 221
Tree diagram, 428
Triangle Inequality Theorem, 237, 242
Triangle, 26–28 (See also Right triangle.)
    acute, 26
    altitude of, 189
    angle measures, sum of, 123
    angles of, 26, 123–24
    angle bisector of, 283
    area of, 444–45
    base of, 177
    centroid of, 411
    circumcenter of, 410
    circumscribed, 343
    classification of, 26–27
    concurrency theorems for, 410–12
    congruent, 149
    corresponding parts of, 149
    dividing sides proportionally, 281
    equiangular, 26, 178
    equilateral, 27, 178
    exterior angle of, 129
    incenter of, 411
    included angle, 26
    included side, 26
    inequalities in, 236–37, 243–44
    inscribed in circle, 343
    isosceles, 27, 177–78, 189
    legs of, 26, 177
    median of, 189
    naming, 26
    obtuse, 26
    opposite angle, 26
    opposite side, 26
    orthocenter of, 412
    overlapping, 172–73
    perimeter of, 394
    perpendicuar bisector of, 189
    proportional parts, 281
    Pythagorean Theorem, 301–2
    remote interior angle of, 129
    right, 26
    scalene, 27
    sides of, 26
    similar, 269–70, 275–76
    special, 312–13
    theorems of, 177–78
    vertices of, 26
Triangle Angle Bisector Theorem, 283
Triangle Angle Sum Theorem, 123
Triangle Inequality Theorem, 237, 242
Triangle Proportional Segment Theorem, 281
Triangle ratios, 404
Triangular
    prism, 486
    region, 447
Trigonometric ratios, 319–20, 325–26
    using calculators, 324
    table, 668
Trigonometry, 319